The Holt Science Program

SCIENCE, *A Story of Observation and Experiment*, by Davis, Burnett, and Gross

SCIENCE, *A Story of Experiment and Discovery*, by Davis, Burnett, and Gross

SCIENCE, *A Story of Discovery and Progress*, by Davis, Burnett, and Gross

MODERN BIOLOGY, by Moon, Mann, and Otto
MODERN CHEMISTRY, by Dull, Brooks, and Metcalfe
MODERN PHYSICS, by Dull, Metcalfe, and Brooks
MODERN HEALTH, by Otto, Julian, and Tether

LIVING THINGS, by Fitzpatrick and Bain
MODERN PHYSICAL SCIENCE, by Brooks and Tracy
APPLIED CHEMISTRY, by Wilson and Mullins

HENRY HOLT AND COMPANY · NEW YORK

MODERN PHYSICS

Charles E. Dull

H. Clark Metcalfe

William O. Brooks

The authors of MODERN PHYSICS

H. CLARK METCALFE is a teacher in the Science Department in Shaler High School, Glenshaw, Pennsylvania ...... WILLIAM O. BROOKS was a teacher in the Science Department in Technical High School, Springfield, Massachusetts ..... Mr. Dull was head of the Science Department in West Side High School, Newark, New Jersey and supervisor of science for the Junior and Senior High Schools of that city.

Preface...

MODERN PHYSICS is designed to meet the varying needs in the standard high-school course in physics. Classroom developed from the first edition, this revision of the book carries forward the sound idea of classroom testing. Many teachers have given us practical ideas and suggestions for its improvement. Great textbooks are built only in this way. In its various editions over a long period of years, teachers have found it highly teachable and thoroughly successful in meeting the wide variations in student ability and course objectives.

The objective in MODERN PHYSICS has always been to present the science of physics with a directness and a simplicity that will enable every student to achieve maximum understanding. A real understanding of science is always its own best motivation. The directness of presenting physics as a science, the balance in content, and the thoroughness with which each topic is developed, are basic qualities which have contributed to the success of previous editions.

The authors and editors, ever mindful of the need to retain all the fine qualities of previous editions, have zealously kept each of these qualities. The step-by-step inductive approach has proved especially to be one of the greatest keys to understanding for beginners.

In preparing this 1955 revision of MODERN PHYSICS, certain overall changes were necessarily made. We felt that it was necessary to alter somewhat the method of presentation of physical theory so as to conform to the most acceptable college-preparatory practice. To give the book more focus for the general student, we have placed a star (★) before the optional sections of the text. Thus, the teacher may omit these sections if he so wishes and use the book in classes of general students without any loss of continuity. We have changed the formulas and abbreviations so as to conform in every case to the recommendations of the American Association of Physics Teachers. We have particularly stressed units of measurement in the Meter-Kilogram-Second system. We have also continually emphasized throughout the text the relation between mass and energy. Lastly, we have added separate, new chapters on atmosphere and weather, fluids in motion, magnetic effects of electricity, chemical effects of electricity, heating and lighting effects of electricity, alternating current, electronics, and radio and television.

A particularly ingenious feature of this book is the use of the Trans-Vision insert. By means of this device, we have been able to illustrate the application of simple machines to a complex mechanism such as the power shovel. This Trans-Vision method presents the material more graphically and clearly than has ever been done before in a physics textbook.

This revision of MODERN PHYSICS abounds in instructional aids which are helpful to both the teacher and the student. Each unit has a short preview consisting of a motivating text and a photograph to point up the subject matter content. Each chapter contains a *Vocabulary* which defines and pronounces the essential scientific words or terms used in that chapter. This is a practical aid for the student in mastering the language of physics. As an additional aid to his understanding, whenever a new scientific word or term occurs in the text it is again defined and pronounced the first time it appears. Following the presentation of a topic involving a mathematical relationship, one or two sample problems and solutions are given in detail. These are set off from the text in rectangles and show the method and each stage in solving that particular problem. To further facilitate problem solving, we have included a *Mathematics Refresher* section following Chapter 35. Constant reference is made to this in the text proper where it will be helpful to the student in solving a given set of problems.

At the end of each chapter there is a summary and a list of terms to be defined. Included also as a part of the end matter of each chapter are two sets of *Questions* and two sets of *Problems,* graded and differentiated as *Group A* and *Group B.* The materials in the *A* sets are planned as basic material for all students. Those in the *B* sets are more difficult, so as to provide for individual or group differentiation, with special emphasis for the college-preparatory student. Very difficult, or honor, problems are marked with a bullet (●). Several suggestions for individual or group projects entitled *Things to Do* appear at the end of most chapters. A complete *Glossary* includes the definitions of all words or terms used in the text and the pronunciation of the more difficult ones. The *Appendix* contains all the formulas used in the text and also a set of tables with the various data which are essential for working any problems.

MODERN PHYSICS has always been respected for the quantity and excellence of its line drawings. The authors and editors believe that nothing can quite take the place of a well-executed line drawing in a science textbook. Therefore, great care has been taken to use color in the diagrams wherever it will aid understanding and have meaning, to label each part clearly, and to employ three-dimensional effects where pertinent.

The following persons have been very helpful in offering many suggestions which we have been pleased to incorporate in this revision: Mr. Leo A. Armagost, Curriculum Consultant for Science, Erie Public Schools, Erie, Pennsylvania; Mr. Werner Peterson, San Diego High School, San Diego, California; Mr. Justin Ricker, Warren Harding High School, Bridgeport, Connecticut; Mr. Albert Thorndike, Milton Academy, Milton, Massachusetts; Mr. Donald H. Westin, Mt. Hermon School, Mt. Hermon, Massachusetts; and Mr. C. L. Shellenberger, Gallatin County High School, Bozeman, Montana. To them we extend our sincere thanks.

The entire manuscript has been critically read and evaluated by Mr. Raymond Agren, Physics Instructor, Cody High School, Detroit, Michigan, and by Fr. Richard D. Spohn, S.J., Physics Instructor, St. Ignatius High School, San Francisco, California. Their comments and suggestions have been most helpful, and we wish to express our sincere thanks to them.

Contents...

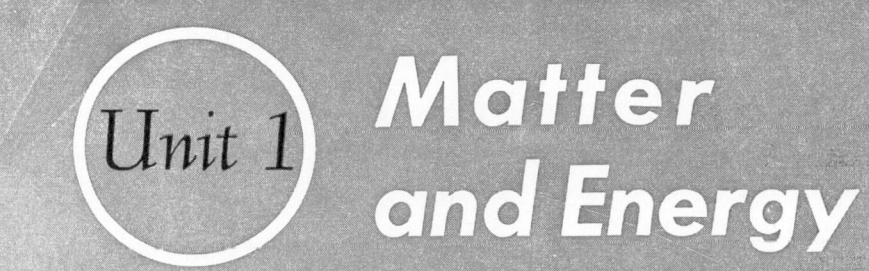

Unit 1 — Matter and Energy

For many centuries men believed that the materials which make up our world and the different forms of energy, such as heat and light, were unrelated. About fifty years ago scientists realized that there must be a connection between matter and energy. Yet, it is only now that we are making practical use of the conversion of matter into energy.

The photograph shows the explosion of a powerful hydrogen bomb. Its great destructive energy is the result of the conversion of a very small quantity of matter into energy. Similar changes, which take place more slowly and under control, can be used to generate electricity. Radioactive materials for medicine and research are also produced by nuclear reactions.

In this unit we shall study the composition and properties of matter. We shall also learn how matter and energy are related.

Chapter 1

Matter and Energy

1. New discoveries change our world. Scientific discoveries are rapidly changing our world. Today, in jet and rocket airplanes men travel faster and higher than ever before. By means of television, audiences see events as they actually happen, and sometimes in full color, too! Magnetic tapes which have been used for several years to record radio broadcasts now record both sight and sound for television.

Nuclear energy comes into the headlines when more destructive weapons are developed. But on the constructive side, nuclear power plants generate electricity and produce valuable chemicals for research and the treatment of disease. The isolation of the polio virus, and the development by Dr. Jonas E. Salk of a vaccine to combat it, offer great promise for the eventual disappearance of this dread disease.

The science of electronics continually offers improvements in communication and control. Electronic computers — sometimes called " electronic brains " — solve complex problems at lightning speed. They also can control the operations in an entire manufacturing plant. Transistors, which are metal crystals with peculiar properties, are being used more and more in place of vacuum tubes. They are used in radio and television sets, telephone circuits, hearing aids, and in other electronic devices.

These are some of the results of research in physics, and the application

Vocabulary

ATOM. The smallest particle of a chemical element.

CHEMICAL CHANGE. A change which alters the composition of the molecules of a substance. New substances with new properties are produced.

CHEMICAL ELEMENT. A simple kind of matter.

ELECTRON. A negatively charged particle which revolves about the nucleus of an atom.

ENERGY. The ability to do work.

MATTER. Anything which occupies space and has weight.

MOLECULE. The smallest particle into which matter may be divided without destroying its characteristic properties.

NEUTRON. A neutral particle found in the nucleus of an atom.

NUCLEAR CHANGE. A change which alters the identity of atoms.

NUCLEUS. The central part of an atom.

PHYSICAL CHANGE. A change which does not alter the composition of the molecules of a substance.

PROTON. A positively charged particle found in the nucleus of an atom.

Fig. 1-1. In rocket airplanes such as this Douglas D-558 II Skyrocket, men are flying faster and at greater altitudes than has ever before been possible.   This is one of the achievements produced by modern physicists and engineers.

of physics to the fields of engineering, medicine, communication, and entertainment.   Your study of physics may someday enable you to have part in a discovery which will change the world!

2. What is physics? PHYSICS *is the science which deals with matter and energy and with physical changes in matter.*   Words like " matter," " energy," and " physical changes " have particular meanings.   We must understand these meanings before we begin our study of physics.   These terms will be explained briefly in this chapter.   More detailed explanations will be given as we go along.   We can get some idea of what physics is about from the names of the major units in physics.   These are *mechanics, heat, sound, light, electricity,* and *nuclear physics.*   We shall study these topics in that order.

3. What is matter?   The best way to illustrate what we mean by matter is to give some examples.   Wood, iron, copper, gold, and salt are typical examples of matter.   Also, liquids like water, alcohol, gasoline, and turpentine are matter.   Gases like the oxygen we breathe and the acetylene in a cutting torch are matter, too.   All of these materials take up space.   They all have weight.   Tentatively we may define *matter as anything which occupies space and has weight.*   After we have studied nuclear physics we will be able to understand more about the nature of matter.

4. What is energy?   We did not include heat, light, and electrical waves in our examples of matter.   They do not fit our definition because they don't take up space.   We would find it extremely difficult to weigh them.   These

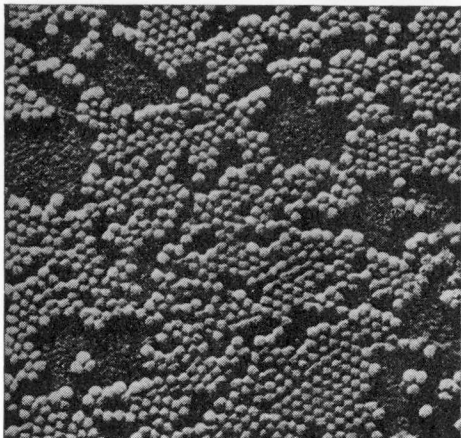

Fig. 1-2. Very large molecules, like these poliomyelitis virus molecules, can be seen with the help of an electron microscope.

are forms of energy. In turn, *energy may be defined as the ability to do work*. We put heat energy to work in a steam turbine. Electrical energy works for us in refrigerators, clocks, and washing machines. A photographer uses light energy when he exposes a photographic plate.

5. Matter is made up of molecules. Suppose, in imagination, we take a crystal of sugar and break it into two pieces. Next we break one of these pieces in two, and then break one of the resulting pieces in two. We might expect to continue this process indefinitely, getting smaller and smaller fragments each time. However, ultimately we would reach a limit. We would get two particles of sugar which, if further divided, would yield smaller particles that no longer had the properties of sugar. Other kinds of matter would give us the same results. We reach a point in our dividing beyond which the identity and properties of that matter change. *The smallest particle into which matter can be divided without destroying its characteristic properties is called a **molecule**.*

Ordinary molecules have never been seen. They are far too small to be revealed by even the best microscope. However, certain very large virus molecules have been photographed with the powerful electron microscope. See Fig. 1-2. Several examples will give us some idea of the size of molecules. For instance, if a drop of water were magnified until it was the size of the earth, its molecules would be only about three feet in diameter. An " empty " quart milk bottle, which is actually full of air, is estimated to contain about 27,000,000,000,000,000,-000,000 (27 sextillion) molecules. If you inhale very deeply, you may draw in three or four times that number of molecules with each breath.

When we inflate an automobile tire to a pressure of 25 pounds per square inch, we are simply pumping gas molecules from the air into the tire. If the tire were strong enough, we might pump into it twice as many molecules, or even ten times as many as it originally contained. By so doing, we would be crowding the molecules more closely together. This would reduce the spaces between them. If, in spite of the enormous number of molecules originally in the tire, we yet can add ten times that number, we must realize that, at ordinary pressures, gas molecules are quite far apart.

6. Molecules are composed of atoms. We now are ready to continue with the division of our molecule of sugar. We know that this molecule is the smallest particle which still retains the properties of sugar. When we divide the molecule we find that it is made

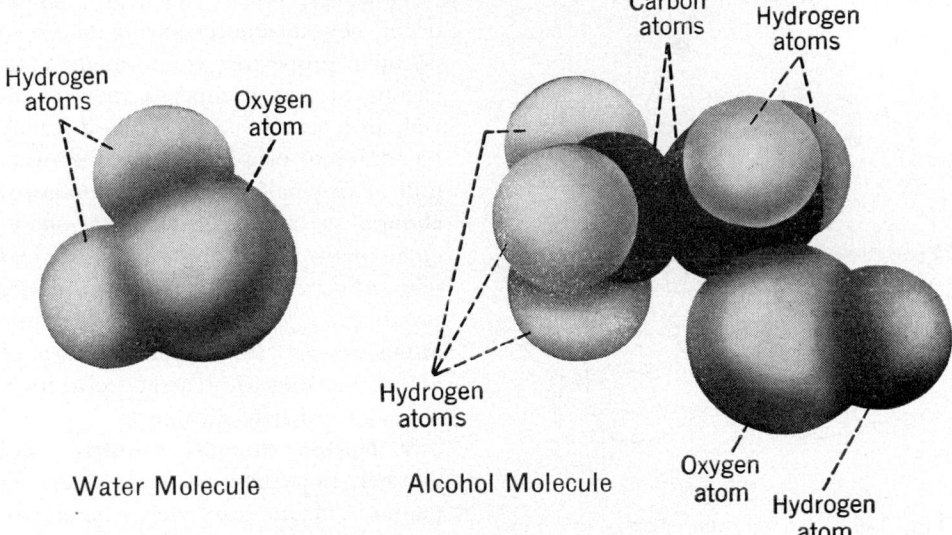

Fig. 1-3. The water molecule, at the left, is composed of atoms of hydrogen and oxygen. A molecule of ethyl alcohol, shown at the right, is made up of atoms of carbon, hydrogen, and oxygen.

of three different kinds of matter. The simple kinds of matter of which molecules are composed are the **chemical elements.** The three chemical elements in sugar are carbon, hydrogen, and oxygen. The particles of the elements, carbon, hydrogen, and oxygen, which make up a molecule of sugar are called atoms. The **atom** *is the smallest particle of certain kinds of matter called chemical elements.*

Scientists have learned a great deal about the way in which atoms are arranged in some molecules. For example, they have reason to believe that the atoms of hydrogen and oxygen are arranged in a water molecule as shown in Fig. 1-3 at the left. At the right, in the same figure, is shown a molecule of ethyl alcohol composed of carbon, oxygen, and hydrogen atoms.

7. The structure of the atom. The atoms of the 100 known chemical elements are complex. For the present, however, a fairly simple picture of an atom will do. The central part of an atom is called the **nucleus.** It contains some electrically charged particles called **protons.** The charge on a proton is a *positive charge.* Along with the protons in the nucleus are some other particles. These have about the same weight as the protons, but have no electrical charge. They are called **neutrons.** Surrounding the nucleus, and probably moving around it in a cloud-like formation similar to the swarming of honeybees about a hive, are more particles. These are called **electrons.** Each electron has a *negative charge* of electricity. The arrangement of protons, neutrons, and electrons in an atom of oxygen is shown in Fig. 1-4.

These particles all have different weights. A proton is 1836 times as

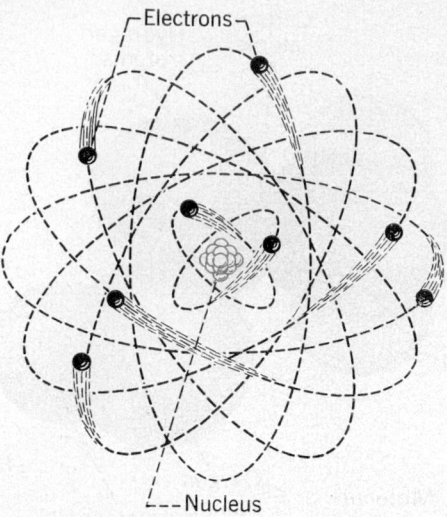

Fig. 1-4. An oxygen atom. The central nucleus contains 8 protons and 8 neutrons. Eight electrons revolve about the nucleus.

heavy as an electron. A neutron is 1838.5 times as heavy as an electron. The lightest atoms are those of the element, hydrogen. These atoms have the same weight as 1837 electrons.

8. Physical and chemical changes in matter are taking place all the time. For example, iron rusts; water freezes; sugar dissolves in water; milk sours. These are just some of the changes which occur daily. Changes in matter are of three kinds: (1) *physical;* (2) *chemical;* and (3) *nuclear.*

When a physical change occurs the identity of the substance is not lost. When water freezes and forms ice, its composition is not changed. If we heat the ice, it changes back into water. Dissolving sugar in water is another physical change. If the water evaporates, the sugar remains behind. *In a physical change the composition of the molecules of the substance is not changed.*

However, when chemical changes occur, new substances having their own peculiar properties are formed. The rusting of iron produces a new material, iron oxide. Sour milk certainly has different properties from the sweet milk it originally was. *In a chemical change the composition of the molecules of the substance is changed, and new substances with new properties are produced.* We still have the same atoms, as well as the same number of atoms, but they are rearranged to form molecules of new substances.

9. Nuclear changes in matter. Still another important change occurs in matter. A *nuclear change* is like a chemical change because new substances with new properties are formed. In a chemical change the new materials were formed by a rearrangement of the atoms of the original materials. *In a nuclear change, however, the new materials are formed by changes in the identity of the atoms themselves.* In nature some of these changes take place spontaneously. An example is the gradual change of radium atoms into lead atoms. Under man's direction, more important nuclear changes are being brought about. Atomic bombs owe their destructive force to nuclear changes. The creative results of nuclear changes include the improved treatment of disease, new understanding of plant and animal life, and the production of atomic power.

10. The relation of matter and energy. By studying nuclear experiments, scientists have discovered that matter and energy are related. Albert Einstein (1879–   ) predicted this relationship about 50 years ago. According to Einstein's theory, matter and energy are related by the equation

Fig. 1-5. The *chemical change* of exploding dynamite in the quarry at the left produced the *physical change* of the broken rock at the right.

$E = mc^2$. E represents the amount of energy, m is the amount of matter, and c is the velocity of light. In the last 20 years a variety of experiments have proved this relationship to be true.

In the most violent *chemical* reactions the amount of matter changed into large quantities of energy is unbelievably small. Suppose we burn 6 tons of carbon with 16 tons of oxygen. All of the energy released as heat and light during this burning will make the products of combustion 0.00007 ounce lighter than the 22 tons of material with which we started. Only in nuclear reactions like the explosion of a hydrogen bomb does the amount of matter which is transformed into energy become significant.

For many years scientists believed that matter could neither be created nor destroyed. This belief was called the Law of Conservation of Matter. During that time, no loss of material could be detected in any chemical changes produced, even with the most sensitive measuring devices. From our example of burning carbon, we can see why this was so. The instruments used in earlier times were just not sensitive enough. It also was believed that en-ergy could neither be created nor destroyed. This belief was called the Law of Conservation of Energy. The most sensitive devices for detecting energy showed no loss of energy when one form was changed to another. Thus, at that time, matter and energy

Fig. 1-6. Albert Einstein (1879–   ), the world's foremost theoretical physicist. About fifty years ago Einstein predicted the relationship between matter and energy. It is only in the last twenty years that his prediction has been proved to be true.

were considered to be separate ideas.

Now we know that matter and energy are related — that they are not separate and distinct. Consequently we must combine the Law of Conservation of Matter and the Law of Conservation of Energy into one new law. This one states that *matter and energy are interchangeable;* and that *the total amount of energy and matter in the universe is constant.* If energy appears, some matter must have disappeared. If energy disappears, matter must always appear in its place.

Summary

Physics is the science which deals with matter and energy, and with physical changes in matter. The major units in physics are mechanics, heat, sound, light, electricity, and nuclear physics.

Matter is anything which occupies space and has weight. Energy is the ability to do work.

The smallest particle into which matter can be divided without destroying its characteristic properties is called a molecule. Molecules are composed of atoms, which are the smallest particles of chemical elements.

Atoms contain three types of particles: protons, neutrons, and electrons. The protons and neutrons are found in the nucleus of an atom. Electrons revolve about the nucleus.

Changes in matter may be physical, chemical, or nuclear. A physical change is one which does not change the composition of the molecules of a substance. A chemical change produces new substances with new properties. New molecules have been formed from the atoms present in the original materials. A nuclear change produces new materials by changing the identity of atoms themselves.

Matter and energy are related by the equation $E = mc^2$. The energy of chemical changes results from almost infinitesimal changes in the quantity of matter. Significant amounts of matter are converted into energy in powerful nuclear explosions. Matter and energy are interchangeable. The total amount of energy and matter in the universe is constant.

Terms to Define...

Atom	Electron	Nuclear change
Chemical change	Energy	Nucleus
Conservation of matter and energy	Matter	Physical change
	Molecule	Physics
$E = mc^2$	Neutron	Proton

Questions

GROUP A

1. What is physics? Explain any scientific terms used in your definition.

2. What is matter? What is energy?

3. Give three examples of matter.

4. What is a physical change? Give five examples of physical changes.

5. What is a chemical change? Give five examples of chemical changes.

6. What is a nuclear change? How does it differ from a chemical change?

7. What are molecules? Give an illustration which indicates their approximate size.

8. What is an atom? In what way does an atom differ from a molecule?

9. What kinds of particles are found in atoms? How do they differ in weight and in electrical charge? In which part of the atom is each particle found?

10. What are some of the main topics studied in physics?

GROUP B

11. Name three forms of energy. What changes in matter may they produce?

12. Explain how a chemical change may produce a physical change.

13. What are some constructive applications of nuclear changes?

14. List a few of the more recent discoveries which physics has made possible.

15. Why do we no longer learn the Law of Conservation of Matter and the Law of Conservation of Energy separately? What statement reveals our present belief about matter and energy?

16. Who developed the idea that matter and energy are related? How are matter and energy related?

17. What are we really putting into a balloon when we blow the balloon up?

18. Why did early scientists believe that the Law of Conservation of Matter was an exact statement of the behavior of matter in the known universe?

Things to Do

1. Make a collection of newspaper and magazine clippings which tell about new scientific discoveries made possible by physics.

2. Investigate and report to the class on such scientific advances as (1) rockets and rocket airplanes; (2) constructive applications of nuclear energy; (3) electronic computers; (4) uses of transistors; (5) color television.

3. Using a set of atom models, such as the Fisher-Hirschfelder-Taylor type, assemble a molecule of sugar. You first will need to find out how the atoms are arranged in such a molecule. Your instructor or school librarian can help you get this information.

4. Construct a model of an atom. Use beads of various colors for the protons, neutrons, and electrons. They may be kept in place with stiff wire, such as the wire from coat hangers.

Chapter 2

The Properties and Measurement of Matter

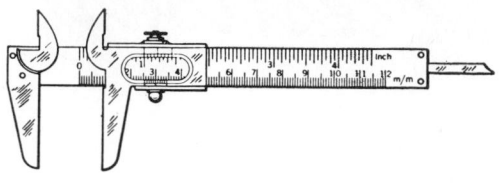

1. GENERAL PROPERTIES OF MATTER

1. What are the general properties of matter? All kinds of matter have certain properties in common. From the definition of matter we know that two of these properties are weight and volume. All forms of matter have several other common properties which we shall learn about in this chapter. These common properties are called the *general properties* of matter.

There are properties which are shown only by certain substances. These properties, such as hardness or brittleness, are used to identify substances. They are *special properties* of matter. Since they are the result of different molecular arrangements in various kinds of matter, we shall study

such properties when we take up the behavior of molecules in Chapter 6.

2. The three phases of matter. Matter exists in three phases, or states: (1) *solid,* (2) *liquid,* and (3) *gaseous.* In solids the molecules have such strong attractive force for one another that they do not change their relative positions easily. Consequently, **solids** *have a definite shape and a definite volume.* Heating a solid causes the molecules to vibrate more rapidly. When they vibrate fast enough to break away from their positions, the substance they make up becomes a liquid. This is what happens to ice at 32° F when it melts. Because the molecules of a liquid are not so strongly attracted to

Vocabulary

DENSITY. Weight per unit volume.

FLUID. A liquid or a gas.

GAS. The phase of matter which has neither a definite shape nor a definite volume.

IMPENETRABILITY. The property of matter by virtue of which two objects can not occupy the same space at the same time.

LIQUID. The phase of matter which has a definite volume but takes the shape of its container.

MASS. The measure of the quantity of matter.

POROSITY. The property of having small openings or spaces between the particles.

SOLID. The phase of matter which has a definite shape and a definite volume.

VISCOSITY. The internal resistance of a fluid which tends to prevent it from flowing.

VOLUME. The space taken up by matter.

WEIGHT. The measure of the earth's attraction for a body.

one another as those of a solid, liquid molecules can slide over one another easily. Liquids change their shape unless they have sidewise support. The walls of a drinking glass, for example, furnish such support. **Liquids** *have a definite volume, but they take the shape of their container.* The addition of heat to a liquid will likewise increase the vibration of its molecules. Finally, some of the molecules will vibrate so violently that they escape from the liquid and become gas molecules. Water molecules do this when they change from water into steam at 212° F. Gas molecules move rapidly. Usually there is very little attraction between them. **Gases** *have neither a definite shape nor a definite volume.* They not only take the shape of their container, but they also expand and fill it, no matter what its volume.

Both liquids and gases are called **fluids** *because they flow freely. A liquid,* such as water, *that flows easily has a small* **viscosity.** A substance, such as tar, which flows slowly has a much larger viscosity. Because heat causes molecules to move faster, an increase in temperature lowers the viscosity of a liquid. Motor oils that have a large viscosity in cold weather may have too small a viscosity in summer for proper lubrication.

3. What is volume? If matter occupies space, it has **volume,** *which means that it has length, width, and thickness.* When you studied arithmetic, you learned how to find the volume of rectangular solids directly by obtaining the product of their length, width, and thickness. In the laboratory we can use an *indirect* method to find the volume of any solid, no matter how irregular it may be. Liquids

Fig. 2-1. The standard of mass for the United States is this very carefully protected platinum-iridium cylinder. The mass of this cylinder is one kilogram. It is preserved at the Bureau of Standards in Washington, D.C.

and gases also occupy space, and therefore have the property of volume.

4. What is mass? Suppose we have a solid rubber ball which has a diameter of 3 inches. The rubber ball contains a definite quantity of matter. We might compress it and thereby reduce its volume, but the quantity of matter remains the same. We might take the ball up on a high mountain, or even to the moon if it were possible, and we would find that the quantity of matter in the ball remains the same. *The measure of the quantity of matter which a body contains is called its* **mass.** The mass of a body does not vary.

In the United States the standard of mass is the platinum-iridium cylinder shown in Fig. 2-1. It is about 1½ inches high and about 1½ inches in di-

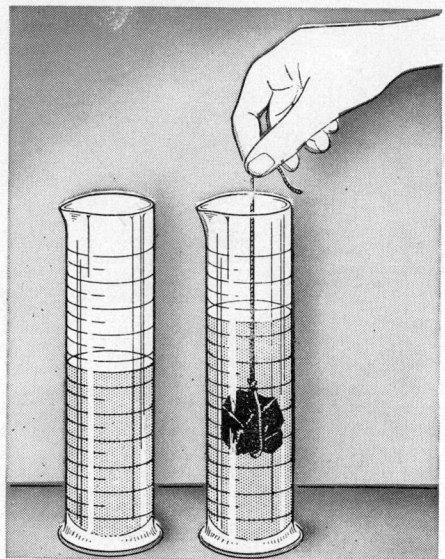

Fig. 2-2. The displacement method for finding the volume of an irregular solid depends on the general property of impenetrability.

ameter.   The mass of this very precisely made cylinder is one kilogram.

5. What is weight?   If we drop the same rubber ball we were using in Section 4, it will fall to the ground.   We say that it is attracted to the earth by gravity.   When we find the weight of an object, we are measuring the attraction of the earth for that object.

The weight of an object depends on two things: (1) the mass or quantity of matter that it contains, and (2) the amount of gravitational attraction the earth has for it.   The mass of the object does not vary.   It will contain the same quantity of matter anywhere.   However, the second factor can vary.   The attraction of the earth for the object will be less on a mountain than in a valley.   The rubber ball will weigh less 100 miles above the surface of the earth than it will at the surface.

Weight is defined as the measure of the earth's attraction for a body.

Mass and weight are such important concepts in physics that we shall explain them more fully after we study the gravity of the earth.   We shall learn more about them in Chapter 8.

6. The impenetrability of matter. When two drivers attempt to get their automobiles into the same space at the same time, the result may be dented fenders or actually a terrible accident. We can not pour water into a bottle through a narrow opening unless we allow air inside the bottle to escape. When we drive a nail into a piece of wood, the nail must push the wood fibers aside.   From examples such as these we conclude that *two objects can not occupy the same space at the same time*.   This property of matter is called *impenetrability.*

We make use of this property to find the volume of an irregularly shaped solid, such as a lump of coal.   To do this, we first put enough water into a graduated cylinder to be able to cover the coal.   Then we read the volume of water from the graduations marked on the cylinder.   Next we lower the coal into the water, as shown in Fig. 2-2. The water level rises because the coal takes the place of some of the water originally at the bottom of the cylinder. The difference between this new water level and the original level equals the volume of the lump of coal.   This method enables us to find the volume of any insoluble, non-porous solid.

7. Matter is porous, too.   We have little trouble seeing the *minute openings, or pores,* of a sponge.   However, the porous nature of a cement block is less obvious.   Water nevertheless will seep through a cement block foundation unless the exterior of the cement is waterproofed. Iron and silver have still smaller pores, but water under tremendous pressure can be forced through them. When one quart of water is mixed with one quart of alcohol, we get slightly less than two quarts of

the resulting mixture. This happens because both liquids are slightly porous. Some of the alcohol molecules occupy spaces between the water molecules, and some of the water molecules occupy spaces between the alcohol molecules.

2. MEASUREMENT

8. Systems of measurement. Science would not be the precise study it is today if it did not have some system for measurement. In almost every experiment in physics it is important to be able to measure accurately the quantities of materials, the amounts of energy, and the passage of time. In order to simplify the relationship between different kinds of measurements, scientists have adopted several systems.

9. The English system. This is the system which we use in our daily life. For units of length we use inches (in), feet (ft), yards (yd), or miles (mi). Area is usually measured in square inches (in^2), or in square feet (ft^2). Our common volume units are cubic

inches (in^3), cubic feet (ft^3), quarts (qt), and gallons (gal). The weight units include ounces (oz), pounds (lb), and tons (tn). See the Sample Problem at the bottom. Table 1, Appendix B, gives the relationship between the various units in the English system.

10. The metric system. This system of measurement was developed in France near the end of the eighteenth century. It is a decimal system similar to the table for United States money. Today the metric system is used almost exclusively in all civilized countries except Great Britain and the United States. In scientific work it is used throughout the world.

The metric system is not difficult to

SAMPLE PROBLEM

A box is 24 in long, 18 in wide, and 8 in deep. What is its volume in cubic feet?

SOLUTION

In order to find the volume of the box, we must multiply length × width × depth. But since the volume is desired in cubic feet and our dimensions are given in inches, it will be easier to change the dimensions to feet, and then multiply.

24 in = 2 ft; 18 in = 1.5 ft; 8 in = 0.67 ft.

Multiplying, 2 × 1.5 × 0.67 = 2 ft^3, the volume of the box.

learn. There are only three basic words and three prefixes which are necessary. The *meter* is a unit of *length;* the *liter* (*lee*-ter) is a unit of *volume;* and the *gram* is a unit of *mass.* The common subdivisions of each of these units are formed by the use of the prefixes *centi-,* $\frac{1}{100}$; and *milli-,* $\frac{1}{1000}$. The most common multiple for each of the units in the metric system is formed by using the prefix *kilo-,* 1000.

11. Units of length in the metric system. All of the units in the metric system originally were intended to be based upon natural standards. The meter was to be exactly $\frac{1}{10,000,000}$ of the distance from the earth's equator to either pole. However, because of a slight error, the meter only approximates this distance.

By definition, the *standard meter* is the distance, measured at 0° C, between two parallel lines scratched on a platinum-iridium bar kept at the International Bureau of Weights and Measures at Sèvres, near Paris, France. From this standard many copies have been made. The United States standard meter bar is kept at the Bureau of Standards in Washington, D.C.

Keep the following table in mind. You will find it useful in your study of physics.

$\frac{3600}{3937}$ of a meter. *One inch equals 2.54 centimeters.* One centimeter is approximately 0.4 inch. This last is a small unit, as you can see from Fig. 2-3.

12. Metric units for area and volume. For measuring areas of surfaces, the *square meter* (m^2) or the *square centimeter* (cm^2) is generally used. A floor 3 meters long and 2 meters wide has an area of 6 square meters. A comparison between a square centimeter and a square inch is shown in Fig. 2-4.

One type of volume unit in the metric system is the *cubic meter* (m^3), or the *cubic centimeter* (cm^3). A box 2 meters long, 1 meter wide, and 1.5 meters deep has a volume of 3 cubic meters. A cubic inch and a cubic centimeter are compared in Fig. 2-5. Liquids may be measured in cubic centimeters.

The other type of volume unit is derived from the length units as follows. If we construct a cubical box whose inside dimensions are 10 cm on each side, that box will hold exactly one *liter* (l). In the United States we use a *dry quart* measure for measuring berries and vegetables, and a *liquid quart* for measuring milk or motor oil. The dry quart is about 10 in³ bigger than

---

10 *millimeters* (mm) = 1 *centimeter* (cm)
100 *centimeters* = 1 *meter* (m)
1000 *meters* = 1 *kilometer* (km)

Because there are two systems, you should know how the metric units compare with the English units. *A meter equals 39.37 inches.* A yard is

the liquid quart. The liter is smaller than our dry quart, but a little larger than our liquid quart, as shown in Fig. 2-6. *The liter is equivalent to 1000*

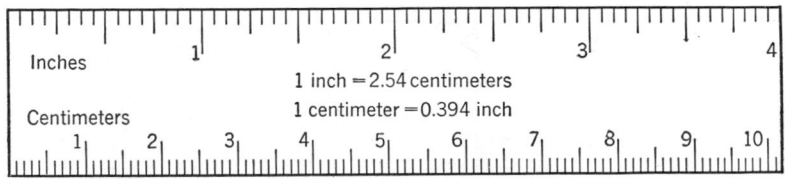

Fig. 2-3. A centimeter is about 0.4 inch. One inch equals 2.54 centimeters.

cm^3. So $\frac{1}{10000}$ of a liter, or a *milliliter* (ml), equals 1 cm^3.

13. Some units of mass and weight in the metric system. You recall that in Section 4 we described the standard kilogram for the United States. Like our standard meter, it is a copy of the *standard kilogram* kept at the International Bureau of Weights and Measures.

Let us once again use the cubical box with which we defined the liter. If we fill this box with distilled water at 4° C (approximately 39° F), the water it then contains will have a mass of *one kilogram* (kg). We see that one liter, or 1000 cm^3, of water has a mass of one kilogram. Therefore, *one milliliter or one cubic centimeter of water has a mass of one gram* (g). The gram is a very small unit. A new five-cent piece has a mass of almost exactly 5 grams. A very large mass unit, the metric ton, equals 1000 kilograms.

You will notice that the kilogram and the gram are *units of mass*. It is sometimes very convenient to use the weight of a kilogram mass and the weight of a gram mass as *units of weight*. Remember that weight is the measure of the earth's attraction for an object. These weight units should properly be called the kilogram-weight (kg-wt) and the gram-weight (g-wt). Sometimes they are just designated as kilogram and gram. It will be necessary for us to use these as metric weight units in this book until we are ready to define and understand other metric units of weight. The kilogram-weight equals 2.2046 pounds. See Fig. 2-7.

14. How do we measure time? In both the English and the metric system the *second* (sec) is the unit of time. There are 60 seconds in a *minute* (min) and 60 minutes in an *hour* (hr).

15. What systems of measurement do we use in physics? Three systems of measurement are now commonly

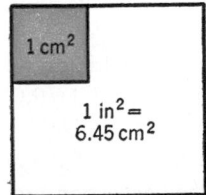

Fig. 2-4. Comparison of one square centimeter and one square inch.

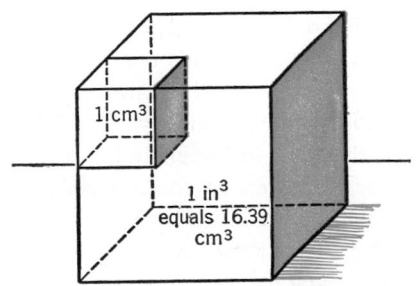

Fig. 2-5. Comparison of one cubic centimeter and one cubic inch.

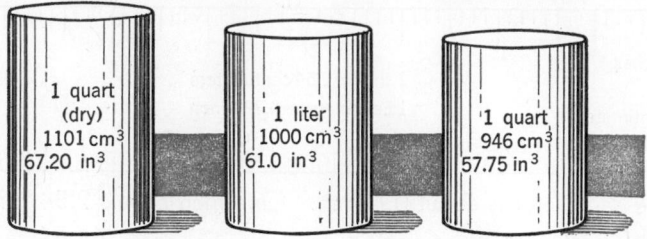

Fig. 2-6. The U.S. *dry* quart measure is larger than the liter, but our *liquid* quart is slightly smaller.

used by physicists in the United States. The first of these is an adaptation of the English system, called the *English*

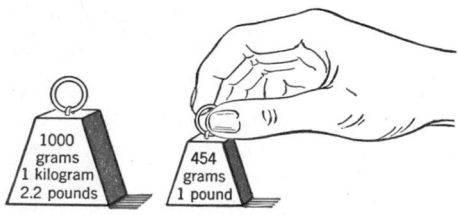

Fig. 2-7. The weight of a kilogram mass is more than twice that of the avoirdupois pound.

gravitational system. The second is the *meter-kilogram-second,* or *MKS system.* This system is gaining in importance and popularity because of its application not only to mechanics but to electricity as well. The third system is the *centimeter-gram-second,* or *CGS system.* This is still used somewhat in mechanics, but finds a wider application in heat. The last two systems are variations of the metric system. They differ in the units used as basic units. We shall use these three systems wherever applicable in our study of physics.

SAMPLE PROBLEM

How many inches are there in 2.5 meters?

SOLUTION

This problem is a typical one in converting from a measurement in one system to the equivalent measurement in another system. The following method should be used in solving all such problems.

From Table 2, Appendix B, we find that 1 m = 39.37 in, or that there are 39.37 in/m. This is our *conversion factor.* We multiply our known measurement, 2.5 m, by the conversion factor.

2.5 m × 39.37 in/m = 98.43 in.

If the table in Appendix B had given 1 in = 0.0254 m, we could have used this for a conversion factor also. The factor would have been 1 in/0.0254 m. Multiplying, 2.5 m × 1 in/0.0254 m = 98.43 in, as before. Note that *the unit of the numerator of the conversion factor must be the unit of the measurement you are seeking; the unit in the denominator of the conversion factor must be the unit of the measurement you already know.*

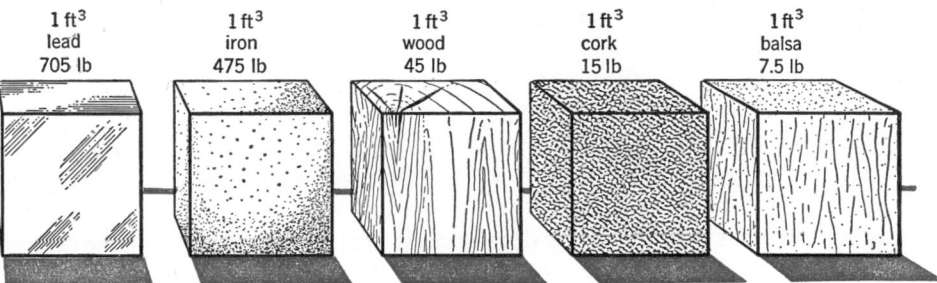

1 ft³
lead
705 lb

1 ft³
iron
475 lb

1 ft³
wood
45 lb

1 ft³
cork
15 lb

1 ft³
balsa
7.5 lb

Fig. 2-8. The weights of equal volumes of various materials are decidedly different. These materials all have different densities.

3. DENSITY

16. What do we mean by density? People say that lead is heavy or that cork is light. These statements don't really mean much. A *cubic foot* of cork is heavier than a *cubic inch* of lead. However, one cubic inch of lead is heavier than one cubic inch of cork. In order to make a comparison of the two materials, we must use equal volumes. Then the proper way to state our results would be to say, "Lead is *denser* than cork."

Suppose we have blocks of each of these materials: lead, iron, wood, cork, and balsa. Each block has a volume of exactly one cubic foot. If we weigh them, we find that the weights of these equal volumes are decidedly different, as shown in Fig. 2-8. *The weight of a unit volume of a substance is called its weight* **density.** In the English system this is expressed in pounds per cubic foot, which is abbreviated lb/ft³. In the metric system we find the weight of one cubic centimeter of each substance. Then density is expressed in grams

---

SAMPLE PROBLEM

A block of wood weighs 180 g. It is 10 cm long, 6 cm wide, and 4 cm thick. What is its density?

SOLUTION

We know already the weight of the block, 180 g. We need to find the volume by multiplying the length × width × thickness.
$10 \times 6 \times 4 = 240$ cm³.
Dividing to find the weight of one cubic centimeter,
$\frac{180}{240} = 0.75$ g/cm³, the density of the block.

(actually gram-weights) per cubic centimeter, abbreviated g/cm³.

To find experimentally the density of any substance, we first determine its weight. Then we find its volume, either directly or indirectly. Next we divide its weight by its volume to get the weight per unit volume, or its density, as shown on page 17.

We shall use the density of water many times in our problems. Memorize these densities: *In the metric system, the density of water is one gram per cubic centimeter, or 1 g/cm³. In the English system, the density of water is 62.4 pounds per cubic foot, or 62.4 lb/ft³.*

★ We may derive a formula to use in solving density problems. If we let the letter D represent the weight density, the letter w represent the weight, and the letter V represent the volume, then we have the formula,

$$D = \frac{w}{V}.$$

★ SAMPLE PROBLEM

A gold block is 15 cm long, 10 cm wide, and 5 cm thick. If gold has a density of 19.3 g/cm³, calculate the weight of the block.

SOLUTION

First we must find the volume of the block by multiplying length × width × thickness.

$15 \times 10 \times 5 = 750$ cm³, the volume.

Substituting the volume and the density in the formula $D = \frac{w}{V}$, we have,

$19.3 = \frac{w}{750}$. Multiply both sides of this equation by 750, and we get

$750 \times 19.3 = w$.

Solving, $w = 14{,}475$ g, the weight.

Summary

The properties shown by all kinds and phases of matter are called general properties. Some of these are weight, volume, mass, impenetrability, and porosity. Properties shown only by certain substances are called special properties.

The three phases of matter are solid, liquid, and gas. Solids have a definite shape and a definite volume. Liquids have a definite volume, but they take the shape of their container. Gases have neither a definite shape nor a definite volume. Both liquids and gases are called fluids. Viscosity is a general property of fluids.

The measure of the quantity of matter which a body contains is called its mass. Weight is the measure of the earth's attraction for a body.

The basic units in the English gravitational system of measurement are the foot, which is the unit of length, and the pound, which is the unit of weight.

The basic units in the MKS system are the meter, the unit of length, and the kilogram, the unit of mass. The basic units in the CGS system are the centimeter, the unit of length, and the gram, the unit of mass. For the unit of time, all three systems use the second.

The weight per unit volume of a substance is called its density. The density of water is 1 g/cm³ or 62.4 lb/ft³.

Terms to Define...

CGS system	Gram	Porosity
Centi-	Impenetrability	62.4 lb /ft³
Conversion factor	Indirect method for	Solid
Density	measuring volume	Special property
Direct method for	Liquid	of matter
measuring volume	Liter	Standard kilogram
English gravitational	MKS system	Standard meter
system	Mass	Units of mass
Fluid	Meter	Units of weight
Gas	Milli-	Viscosity
General property of	1 g /cm³	Volume
matter	Phase of matter	Weight

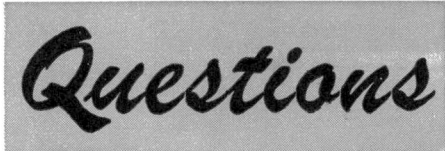

Questions

GROUP A

1. What are general properties of matter? What are special properties of matter? Name five general properties of matter.

2. What are the three phases of matter? What are the characteristics of each phase? List five examples of each phase of matter.

3. Does the mass of an object depend on its location? Does the weight of an object depend on its location? Explain.

4. Name the three systems of measurement most frequently used by physicists. What are the basic units of length, mass or weight, and time in each system?

5. A cubical box has a capacity of one liter. What is the volume of the box in cubic centimeters? What mass of water will the box hold?

6. What are the three common prefixes in the metric system? What does each mean? Give an example which shows how each is used.

7. How does a liter compare in volume with the dry quart and the liquid quart in the United States?

8. What is the standard meter? The standard kilogram? Where are the international standards maintained? Where are the United States standards kept?

GROUP B

9. How does the viscosity of molasses compare with that of water?

10. How would you proceed to find the volume of an irregular piece of granite?

11. What properties must be possessed by a waterproofing paint for concrete blocks?

12. Suppose you are to fasten a coat hook to the inside of a closet door with screws. Why should you first drill a small hole into the wood where each screw is to be inserted?

13. Motor oil is rated as 30, 20, 10, 10W, and so on. What property of the oil is indicated by these ratings?

14. What name is given to the weight of a gram mass? To the weight of a kilogram mass?

15. If three ounces of wood occupy the same volume as one ounce of cork, how does the density of the wood compare with that of the cork?

Problems

(Before starting to solve each set of problems, you should review the Sample Problems which are given in the preceding sections.

For this set of problems you will find Sections 3, 10, 13, and 16 in the Mathematics Refresher, helpful.

Additional data needed for the following problems will be found in Tables 1 and 2, Appendix B.)

GROUP A

1. A block of wood is 3 in long, 1.5 in wide, and 0.5 in thick. What is its volume in cubic inches?

2. The level of the water in a graduated cylinder stands at the 50 ml mark. When a piece of limestone is dropped into the cylinder, the water level rises to the 84 ml mark. What is the volume of the piece of limestone?

3. An aquarium is 12 in long, and 8 in wide. It is filled with water to a depth of 6 in. How many gallons of water does the aquarium contain?

4. The wooden handle of a rake is 6 ft long. What is its length in centimeters? In meters?

5. The maximum speed limit on the highways of some states is 65 mi/hr. What is this speed in ft/sec?

6. A metal rod is 12.5 cm long. What is its length in inches?

7. What is the density of a piece of rock which has a volume of 150 cm³ if its weight is 420 g?

8. What will be the weight, in grams, of 5 lb of sugar?

9. The density of wood is 45 lb/ft³. What will be the weight of a block 12 in long, 4 in wide, and 4 in thick?

10. If you purchase 10 kg of flour instead of 10 lb of flour, how many additional pounds of flour did you buy?

11. A train runs from Chicago to San Francisco in $51\frac{1}{3}$ hr. The distance is 2532 mi. What is the average speed in mi/hr?

12. The density of brass is 8.4 g/cm³. What volume of brass will be needed to make a 500-g brass weight?

GROUP B

13. Which is the greater distance, a kilometer or a mile? What is the difference in length, in meters, between them?

14. Mercury is 13.6 times as dense as water. How many cubic inches will 5 lb of mercury occupy?

15. A swimming pool is 25 m long, 10 m wide, and is filled to an average depth of 1.5 m. How many kilograms of water does it contain?

16. John pours 35 ml of water into a graduated cylinder. When he lowers an irregularly shaped piece of metal weighing 125 g into the water, the water level rises to the 60-ml mark. What is the density of the metal?

● **17.** A sample of a metal alloy weighs 500 g. Its volume is 75 cm³. What is the density of this metal in lb/ft³?

● **18.** A family uses 12 tons of coal to heat their home during the winter. What is the weight of this coal in metric tons?

● **19.** A cylindrical tank for gasoline is 10 ft long and 4 ft in diameter. The density of gasoline is $\frac{7}{10}$ that of water. How many pounds of gasoline will the tank hold?

20. A bar of silver is 6 cm long, 2 cm wide, and 1.5 cm thick. If the density of silver is 10.5 g/cm³, what will this bar of silver weigh?

Things to Do

1. As a class experiment, or as a demonstration, find the volume of an irregular solid by the water displacement method.

2. Place some ice cubes directly from the refrigerator tray into a beaker. Put the beaker on a wire gauze on a tripod. Heat gently with a burner. Note the changes in phase which take place. How are the differences between these phases explained in terms of molecular freedom?

3. Report to the class on the history of the origin of the metric system.

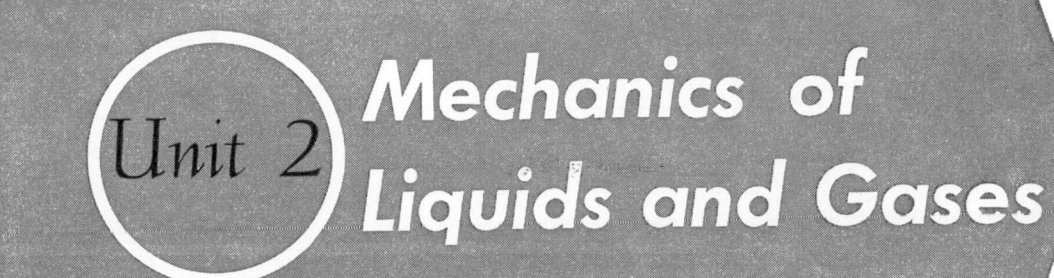

Unit 2 — Mechanics of Liquids and Gases

The oddly shaped device in this photograph is a bathyscaphe (*bath-iss-kayf*). It was devised by a Swiss scientist, Auguste Piccard, for deep sea diving. In this bathyscaphe, Piccard made the deepest dive ever attempted by man, descending to a depth of 10,330 feet in the Mediterranean Sea. He controlled his descent by varying the buoyancy of the bathyscaphe in the water.

In this unit you are going to learn about liquids and gases. You will find that because they have weight, gases and liquids exert pressure and force. They also can transmit pressure. Gases and liquids exert an upward, or buoyant force on objects placed in them. This principle was discovered many centuries ago by a famous Greek scientist, Archimedes.

Chapter 3

Mechanics of Liquids

1. LIQUID PRESSURE AND TOTAL FORCE

1. What are force and pressure? If we push against a refrigerator, we are using force. If we pull a heavy table into place, we also are using force. *Force may be defined as a push or a pull.* We measure force in weight units. In the English system, force is measured in pounds. In the metric system, it is measured in gram-weights or kilogram-weights. In this chapter we shall use the terms gram and kilogram to indicate the *weight* of a gram-mass and of a kilogram-mass.

Pressure is the force applied to a unit area. The units in which pressure may be measured are pounds per square inch (lb/in^2), pounds per square foot (lb/ft^2), grams per square centimeter (g/cm^2), or kilograms per square meter (kg/m^2).

Total force is measured in pounds, grams, or kilograms. **Total force** *is the force acting against the total area of a particular surface.*

2. Liquids exert pressure in all directions. Suppose we have a large

---

Vocabulary

ABSCISSA (ab-*sis*-uh). The horizontal line on a graph; the X axis.

ABSTRACT NUMBER. A number representing a measurement, but having no units associated with it.

BUOYANT (*boy*-unt) **FORCE.** The upward force which a fluid exerts on a body placed in it. It equals the weight of the fluid displaced by the body.

CONCRETE NUMBER. A number together with a unit of measurement.

DIRECT PROPORTION. The relation that exists between two quantities when an increase or decrease in one of them produces a corresponding increase or decrease in the other.

FORCE. A push or a pull.

INVERSE PROPORTION. The relation that exists between two quantities when an increase in one of them produces a corresponding decrease in the other.

MECHANICAL ADVANTAGE. The ratio of the weight supported to the force applied in any mechanical device.

ORDINATE. The vertical line on a graph; the Y axis.

PRESSURE. Force per unit area.

SPECIFIC GRAVITY. The ratio of the density of a substance to the density of a standard substance, such as water.

TOTAL FORCE. Force acting against the entire area of a surface.

WATER HEAD. Pressure caused by a difference in water level in connecting pipes.

metal barrel filled with water or some other liquid. If we bore a hole in the bottom of the barrel the liquid will flow out. This proves that liquids push *downward* upon the bottoms of their containers. Because they have weight, liquids exert a downward pressure. If we drill a hole in one side of the barrel, as shown in Fig. 3-1, the liquid will flow out through this opening, too. This shows that liquids exert pressure in a *sidewise* direction. If we push a cork down into water in a tumbler, the cork will rise to the surface as soon as we release it. See Fig. 3-2. We must use force to keep it beneath the surface of the water. The force we exert counteracts the *upward* push of the water on the cork. From these examples, we learn that *liquids exert pressure in all directions.*

3. Liquid pressure is proportional to the depth. A block lying on a table presses down upon the table. Similarly, water or any other liquid poured

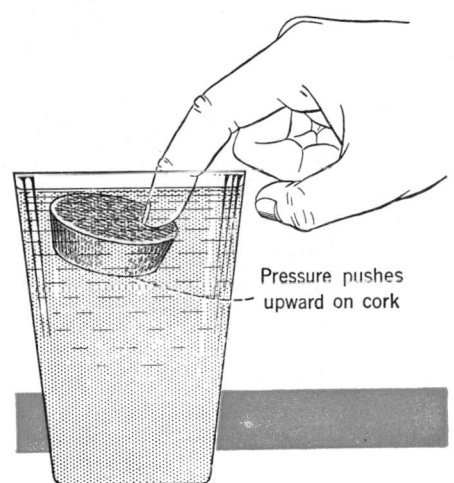

Pressure pushes upward on cork

Fig. 3-2. When we attempt to push downward on this cork, we find that the water exerts an upward pressure.

into a large glass jar exerts force, or pressure, on the bottom of the jar. The weight of the liquid causes this force. When we pile several blocks on one another, as in Fig. 3-3, the pressure on the table increases over the pressure exerted originally by just one block. Likewise, when we increase the depth of liquid in the jar, the pressure on the bottom is increased. *The pressure exerted by a liquid is directly proportional to the depth.*

Let us suppose that the unit area pressed upon in Fig. 3-3 is one square centimeter. The weight of one cubic centimeter of water is one gram. Then, water one centimeter deep exerts a pressure of one gram per square centimeter. The pressure at a depth of two centimeters is two grams per square centimeter. For each centimeter increase in depth, the increase in pressure is one gram per square centimeter. If the unit area pressed on is one square foot, water one foot deep will exert a pressure of 62.4 pounds per square

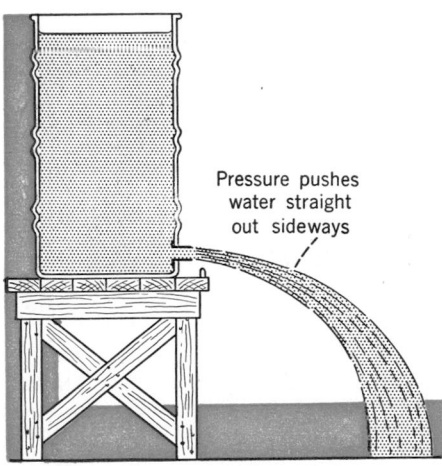

Pressure pushes water straight out sideways

Fig. 3-1. The sidewise pressure of the water against the walls of this metal barrel becomes apparent when we drill a hole in the side of the drum.

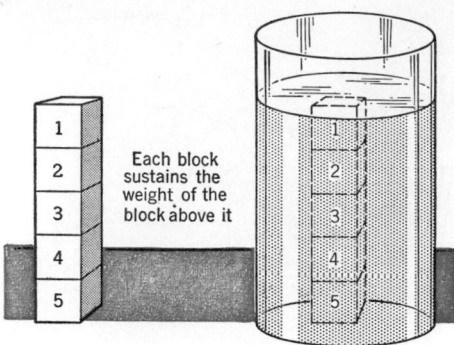

Fig. 3-3. Just as the pressure on the table caused by the pile of blocks depends on the number of blocks in the pile, the pressure exerted by a liquid against the bottom of its container depends on the depth of the liquid.

foot, which is the weight of one cubic foot of water. The water pressure on each square inch will be $\frac{1}{144}$ of 62.4

pounds each square foot, or *0.433 pound per square inch for each foot in depth.* This may be written as 0.433 lb/ft-in², and used as a convenient value for the density of water.

4. Liquid pressure is proportional to density. Liquids vary in density. Mercury is a dense liquid which weighs 13.6 times as much as an equal volume of water. Because the pressure exerted by liquids is due to the weight of the liquid, mercury exerts a much greater pressure than water of the same depth. *The pressure exerted by a liquid is directly proportional to its density.* We know that water 10 centimeters deep exerts a pressure of 10 grams per square centimeter. Therefore, mercury 10 centimeters deep exerts a pressure of 136 grams per square centimeter, or 13.6 times as

SAMPLE PROBLEM

A diver descends to a depth of 50 m in sea water, which has a density of 1.025 g/cm³. What is the pressure on each square centimeter of his body?

SOLUTION

The depth h is given as 50 m. However, since our answer is to be in g/cm², we must change 50 m to centimeters.
50 m × 100 cm/m = 5000 cm. The density D is 1.025 g/cm³.
Substituting these values in the formula, $p = hD$, $p = 5000 \times 1.025$.
Solving, $p = 5125$ g/cm², the pressure.

SAMPLE PROBLEM

The water pressure in a certain city is 150 lb/in². How high must a reservoir be above the city to supply this pressure?

SOLUTION

In this problem we shall use 0.433 lb/ft-in² as the density of water. The pressure is given as 150 lb/in².
Substituting in the formula $p = hD$, $150 = h \times 0.433$.
Solving, $h = 346.2$ ft, the height of the reservoir above the city.
(Note that the use of 0.433 lb/ft-in² as the density of water enables us to find the height in *feet* directly when the pressure is in lb/in².)

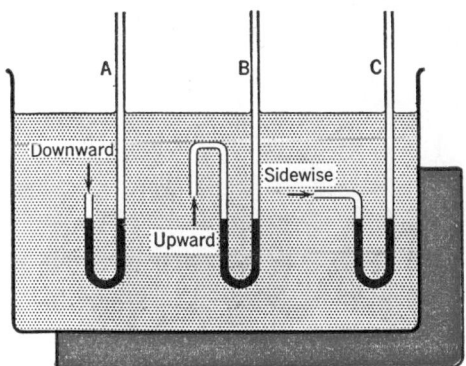

Fig. 3-4. The pressure exerted by a liquid at a given depth is independent of direction.

great. Gasoline has a density of 0.7 grams per cubic centimeter. The pressure exerted at a depth of 10 centimeters in gasoline is 7 grams per square centimeter (10 × 0.7 = 7). See Sample Problems, page 24. In equation form,

pressure = depth × density.

Using the letter *p* for pressure, *h* for depth, and *D* for weight density, the equation becomes

$$p = hD.$$

5. Is liquid pressure affected by direction? A pile of blocks resting on a table exerts pressure in a downward direction only. It does this because the blocks are solid and their molecules do not move freely. However, the molecules of a liquid move over one another so easily that a liquid takes the shape of its container. For this reason liquids exert both a downward and an outward, or sidewise, pressure. Our experience with floating objects showed us that liquids push upward also.

In order to find the pressure exerted at a particular depth by a liquid in these three directions we shall use the apparatus shown in Fig. 3-4. Three tubes of the same diameter contain the same amount of mercury. We lower the tubes into water so that all the open ends are at the same depth. The water pressure causes the mercury to rise in the long arm of each tube. At *A* the water presses *downward;* at *B* the water presses *upward;* at *C* the water presses *sidewise.* The mercury stands at the same level in the long

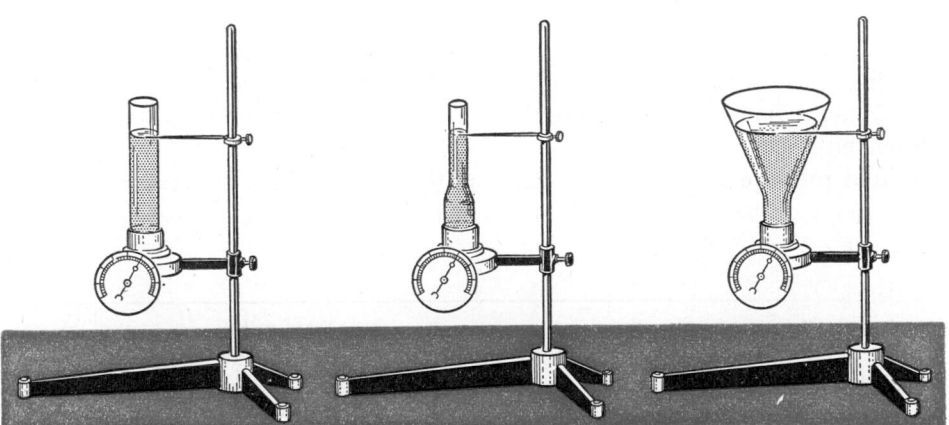

Fig. 3-5. The gauges show that the pressure caused by *equal depths of water* is the same at the bottom of each vase, even though the *volume of water* in the vases is different.

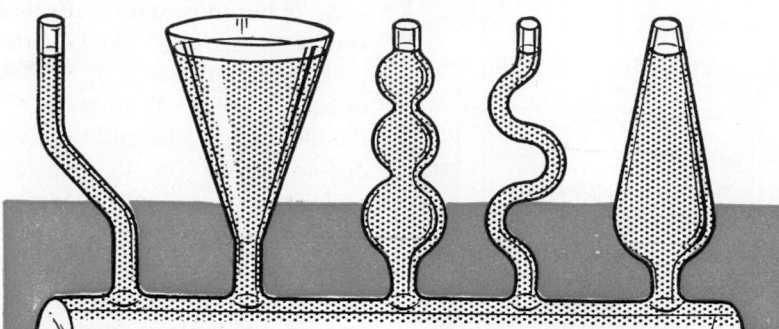

Fig. 3-6. Liquids in connecting vessels stand at the same height.

arm of each tube. These mercury columns indicate that all the pressures are equal, and that *the pressure exerted by a liquid is independent of direction.*

6. Does the area or shape of the container affect liquid pressure? Since pressure is measured in terms of a unit area, such as pounds per square inch or grams per square centimeter, we do not consider the *total area* when solving liquid pressure problems. The area of the liquid surface inside the main part of a teakettle is much greater than the area of the liquid surface in the spout. But in both cases the pressure of the water is the same. If the pressure increased with the area, water would always flow out of the spout of the teakettle.

Liquid pressure also is independent of the *shape* of the container. We can use *Pascal's* (*Pass-*kuls) *vases* and the apparatus shown in Fig. 3-5 to demonstrate this fact. The area of the diaphragm at the bottom of each vase is the same. We use it as our unit area for measuring pressure. The pointer, which shows the increase in pressure as water is poured into these vases, indicates the same pressure for each vase. The pressure at the bottom of each vase is the same even though the shapes are different and the amount of water in each one is different. For this reason liquids stand at the same height in connecting containers, regardless of their shape. See Fig. 3-6. Therefore, *liquid pressure is independent of the shape and area of the container.*

★ **7. Direct and inverse proportion.** The terms *direct proportion* and *in-*

SUMMARY OF LIQUID PRESSURE

(1) *Liquid pressure is directly proportional to the depth of the liquid.*

(2) *Liquid pressure is directly proportional to the density of the liquid.*

(3) *Liquid pressure is independent of the area or shape of the container; it also is independent of direction.*

verse proportion are used frequently in physics. *Two quantities are **directly proportional** when an increase or decrease in one of them produces a corresponding increase or decrease in the other.* In the formula for liquid pressure, $p = hD$, an increase in the depth of the liquid increases the pressure. An increase in the density of the liquid also increases the pressure. We say that the pressure exerted by a liquid is directly proportional to both the depth and the density of the liquid.

Let us plot a graph to show direct proportion. We shall use the following data:

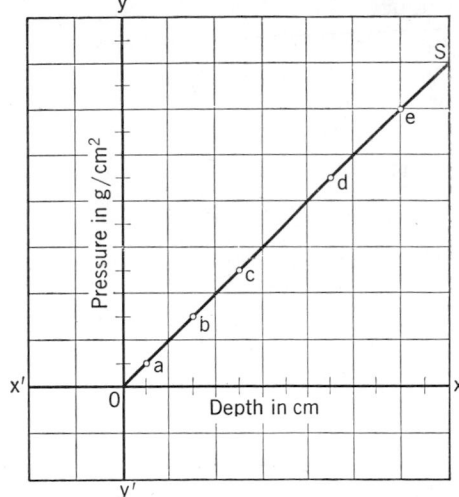

Fig. 3-7. The pressure exerted by a liquid is directly proportional to the depth of the liquid. The graph of two quantities which are directly proportional is a straight line.

Depth	Pressure
1 cm	1 g/cm²
3 cm	3 g/cm²
5 cm	5 g/cm²
9 cm	9 g/cm²
12 cm	12 g/cm²

We shall use point *O*, Fig. 3-7, as the origin of the graph. *The horizontal line through O, x'x, is called the X axis, or **abscissa*** (ab-*sis*-uh). On it we measure off distances equivalent to the various depths. For convenience we shall use one small space to represent 1 cm. *The vertical line through O, yy', is called the Y axis, or **ordinate**.* On it we measure off distances equivalent to the various pressures. We shall use one small space to represent 1 g/cm². Point *a* on the graph represents a pressure of 1 g/cm² at a depth of 1 cm; point *b* represents a pressure of 3 g/cm² at a depth of 3 cm. In a similar manner we can plot the points *c*, *d*, and *e*. Finally we draw a line through these points. We find that

this graph is a straight line, *OS*. *Therefore, when two quantities are in direct proportion, their graph is a straight line.*

*Two quantities are **inversely proportional** when an increase in one of them produces a corresponding decrease in the other.* For example, let us use the formula for weight density, $D = w/V$. If w is increased without any change in V, D will increase. The density of a material is directly proportional to its weight. However, if V is increased without any change in w, D will be decreased. The density of a material is inversely proportional to its volume. When we study the properties of gases, we shall plot a graph showing inverse proportion.

8. How do we find the total force on the bottom of a container? The pressure which a liquid exerts on the bottom of its container equals the product of the depth and the density. However, pressure is the force acting on a unit area. In order to find the total force acting on the bottom of a container, we multiply the pressure by the entire area. In equation form,

total force = area × pressure, or
total force = area × depth × density.

By using *F* to represent total force, *A* the area, *h* the depth, and *D* the density, the formula becomes,

$$F = AhD.$$

See the Sample Problem below and the one on page 29.

9. How can we find the total force against the side of a container, or against a dam? We know that a liquid exerts a force against the sides of its container. We must be able to calculate the sidewise force in order to know how strong to make tanks for large quantities of liquids, like gasoline or alcohol. In building a dam, engineers must calculate the total force which the water will exert against the dam. To calculate total force, we always use the entire area pressed upon. We know, too, that the pressure at a particular depth is the same in all directions. But the question is, what depth shall we use?

Imagine that the classroom in which you are sitting is full of water, as shown in Fig. 3-8. The width of the room is 12 feet; its length is 40 feet; and each wall is 8 feet high. The area of the front wall equals the width, 12 feet, multiplied by the height of the wall, 8 feet. The *area pressed upon* is 96 square feet. At the floor, the water is 8 feet deep; at the ceiling, the water is 0 feet deep. The depth varies. Three feet from the floor, the water is 5 feet

SAMPLE PROBLEM

A tank 10 ft long, 8 ft wide, and 6 ft deep is full of water. What is the total force on the bottom of the tank?

SOLUTION

Since the problem asks for the total force, we first must obtain the quantities we need for the formula, $F = AhD$. The area pressed upon, A, is 10 ft × 8 ft or 80 ft². The depth of the water, h, is 6 ft. The density of the water, D, is 62.4 lb/ft³.

Substituting these quantities in the formula, $F = 80 \times 6 \times 62.4$.

Solving, $F = 29,952$ lb, the total force on the bottom of the tank.

★ Special Note

In physics problems the units may be treated as algebraic symbols. In this problem we may write the expression for the answer, including all the units, as follows: $F = 80 \text{ ft}^2 \times 6 \text{ ft} \times \dfrac{62.4 \text{ lb}}{\text{ft}^3}$. The ft² of the area times the ft in depth give us ft³ in the numerator. This will completely cancel the ft³ in the denominator of the density: $F = 80 \cancel{\text{ft}^2} \times 6 \cancel{\text{ft}} \times \dfrac{62.4 \text{ lb}}{\cancel{\text{ft}^3}}$. The unit for our answer will be *lb*, because that is the product of the units.

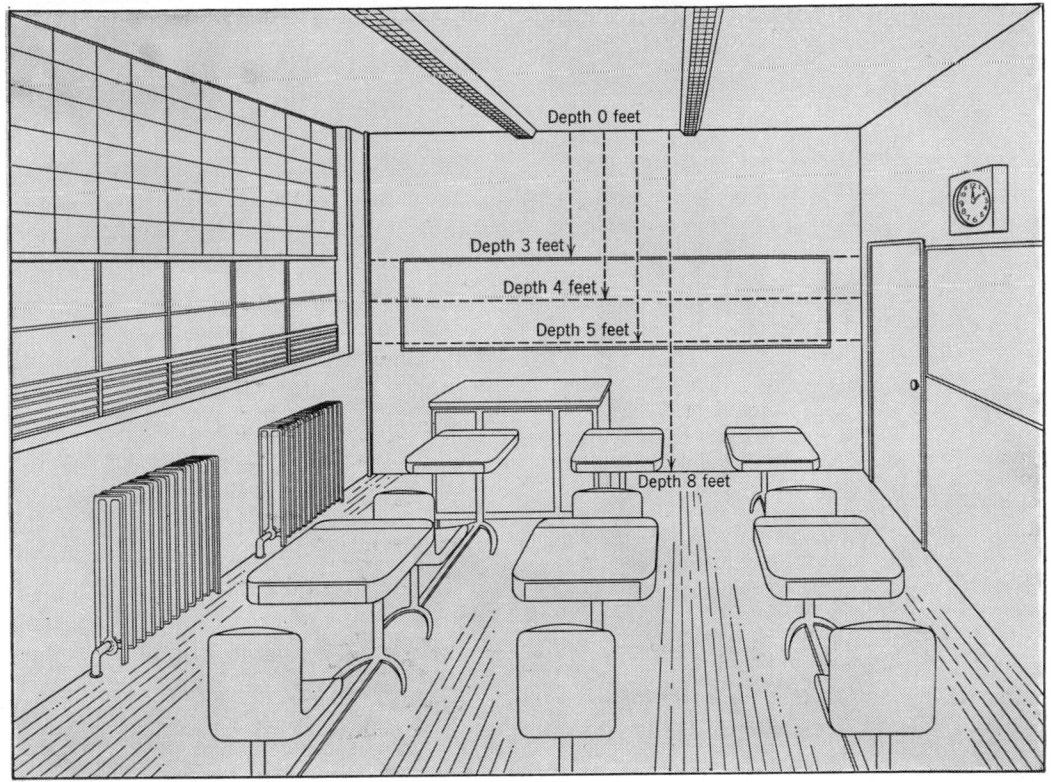

Fig. 3-8. In imagination, let us fill this classroom with water. Since the distance from the ceiling to the floor is 8 feet, the average depth of the water pressing against the front wall of the room is 4 feet.

SAMPLE PROBLEM

Find the total force on the bottom of a box 3 m long, 2 m wide, and 1 m deep when the box is full of water.

SOLUTION

Since the density of water in the metric system is 1 g/cm³, we shall find the problem easier if we change the dimensions of the box to centimeters. 3 m = 300 cm; 2 m = 200 cm; 1 m = 100 cm. The area of the bottom of the box is 300 cm × 200 cm = 60,000 cm². The depth is 100 cm.
Substituting in the formula, $F = 60,000 \times 100 \times 1$.
Solving, $F = 6,000,000$ g, or 6000 kg.

★ Special Note

We may treat the units in this problem as algebraic symbols in the following manner: $F = 60,000 \text{ cm}^2 \times 100 \text{ cm} \times \dfrac{1 \text{ g}}{\text{cm}^3}$. The unit for our answer will be g.

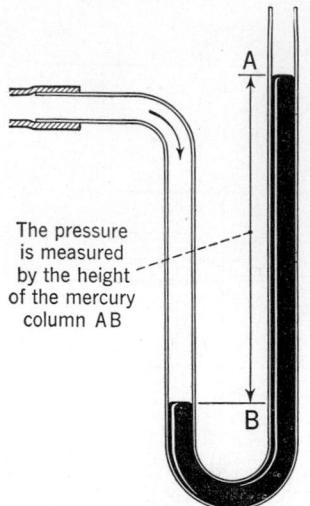

The pressure is measured by the height of the mercury column A B

Fig. 3-9. An open manometer is used to measure pressure.

deep; and 3 feet from the ceiling, the water is 3 feet deep. Halfway up the wall, the water is 4 feet deep. The *average depth,* therefore, is 4 feet. Since the depth of a vertical surface varies, we must use the *average depth* when we calculate total force. The total force on the wall of the room = 96 ft² (area) × 4 ft (average depth) × $\dfrac{62.4\ \text{lb}}{\text{ft}^3}$ (density). Solving, we find that the force is 23,961.6 lb.

Total force *always equals the area of the surface pressed upon times the average depth times the density.* For horizontal surfaces the depth is uniform. The formula is $F = AhD$. For vertical surfaces, the average depth is usually equal to *half* the depth. The formula for finding the total *sidewise* force against a surface is

$$F = A \times \frac{h}{2} \times D, \text{ or } F = \frac{AhD}{2}.$$

10. Measuring water pressure. The pressure in the mains of a water

supply system must be great enough to provide an adequate flow to all the users. The pressure must also be great enough to meet emergency needs, such as for fire fighting. Consequently, we must be able to measure water pressure conveniently. An *open manometer* (muh-*nom*-uh-ter), shown in Fig. 3-9, is one device which may be used. It shows the water pressure balanced against a column of mercury. The manometer, which is partially filled with mercury, is attached to the faucet. When the water is turned on, the pressure of the water is measured by the height reached by the mercury column *AB*. If the tube has a cross-sectional area of 1 square inch, the weight of the mercury column in pounds equals the water pressure in pounds per square inch.

A more convenient type of pressure gauge is the *Bourdon* (*boor*-dun) *gauge,* shown in Fig. 3-10. The pressure of the water tends to straighten out the flat, curved tube. The motion of the end of the tube is transmitted to a shaft by means of a lever and gear mechanism. The pointer on the shaft then moves across the dial, which is calibrated to read pressure directly in pounds per square inch.

The expression, *head of water,* or *water head,* is frequently used by engi-

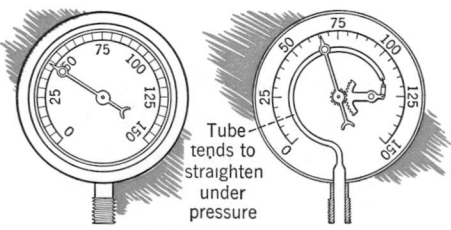

Tube tends to straighten under pressure

Fig. 3-10. The Bourdon pressure gauge. The internal mechanism is shown at the right.

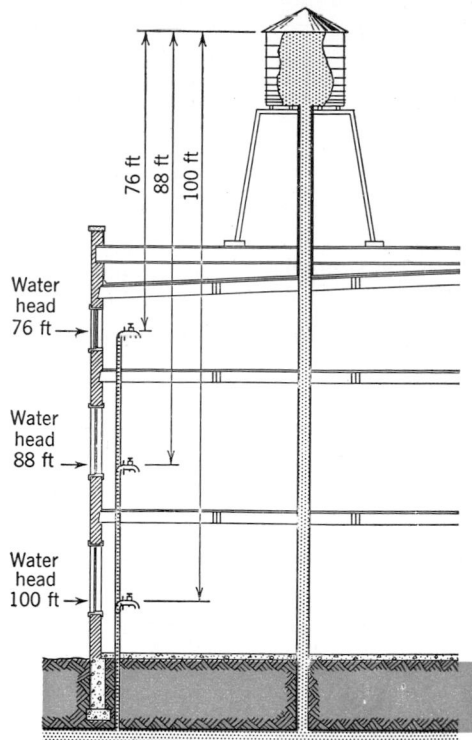

Fig. 3-11. The water head is greatest on the lowest floor. The effective pressure is least at the faucet on the top floor.

neers. If *the difference between the water levels in connecting pipes is 144 feet, the water head is said to be 144 feet*. This head of water produces a pressure of 62.4 lb/in², because a column of water 1 square inch in cross-sectional area and 144 feet high has a volume of 1 cubic foot. In Fig. 3-11 we can see why the water head on different floors of the same building is not the same.

11. The importance of water pressure. (1) *Water reaches its level.* Water stands at the same height in connecting containers regardless of their shape or relative area. The water in the spout of a teakettle is at the same level as the water inside the main part of the kettle. We can better understand why water reaches its level by

studying Fig. 3-12. This diagram shows at a particular instant the shape of the water surface in a tank after the water has been disturbed. The sidewise pressure at *A* and *B* causes the water to flow in the directions shown by the arrows until the surface is level. The water-gauge on a steam boiler is shown in Fig. 3-13. The water level in the glass gauge shows the water level inside the boiler.

The supply of water for some cities is stored in reservoirs that are located higher than any point in the city. From these reservoirs the water flows through mains. Since water reaches its own level, the water piped from the main into a house will rise in the house to all the faucets. But suppose that part of a tall building is higher than the surface of the water in the reservoir. The upper floors of the building will, therefore, be without water unless it is provided in some other way. Such a building may have a tank on the roof into which water may be pumped from the mains by a special pump. Or a pump may be used to provide increased water pressure in the pipes throughout the building, so that water will reach the top floors. Some-

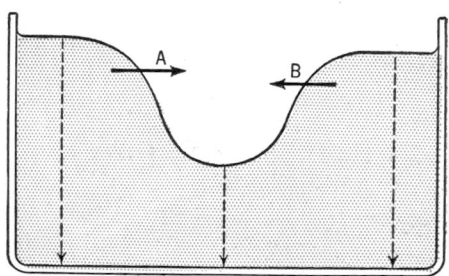

Fig. 3-12. The sidewise pressure at *A* and *B* causes the water at the sides of the tank to flow toward the center until the surface becomes level.

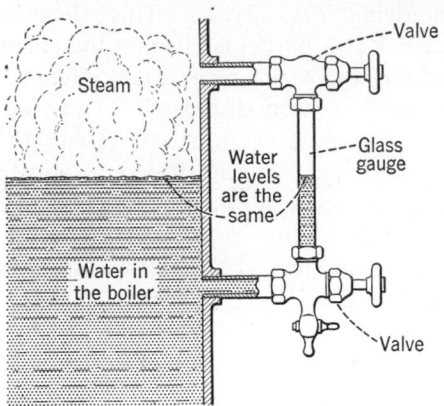

Fig. 3-13. Since water stands at the same height in connecting containers, the level of the water in the glass gauge of a steam boiler shows the level of the water inside the boiler.

times it is impossible or undesirable to use the natural flow of water from reservoirs. Then, large pumps force water into standpipes, where it is stored, or directly maintain the necessary pressure in the water mains. See Fig 3-14.

The *artesian* (ar-*tee*-zhun) *well* is another example of water reaching its level. In Fig. 3-15 we see that an artesian well consists of a layer of water-saturated gravel between two layers of non-porous rock. The water levels at *A* and *B* are higher than the level at *W*. Consequently, when we drill through the top rock layer water gushes out to form a flowing well, or fountain, at *W*.

(2) *Submerged objects must withstand pressure.* The base of the foundation walls of your home is probably four feet below the water level in the soil outside when snow and ice are melting in the spring. The water from them exerts a pressure of 4 ft × 0.433 lb/ft-in² = 1.73 lb/in² at the base of your cellar walls. This pressure may be sufficient to push water through the pores of the concrete wall and into the basement. The seepage can be prevented either by coating the outside of the foundation walls with waterproofing material, or by using special waterproofing paints on the inside walls.

We know that the deeper an object sinks in a liquid, the greater the pressure becomes. Therefore, the walls of a submarine must be very strong to withstand the increasing water pressure the submarine meets at cruising depths. The usual maximum depth

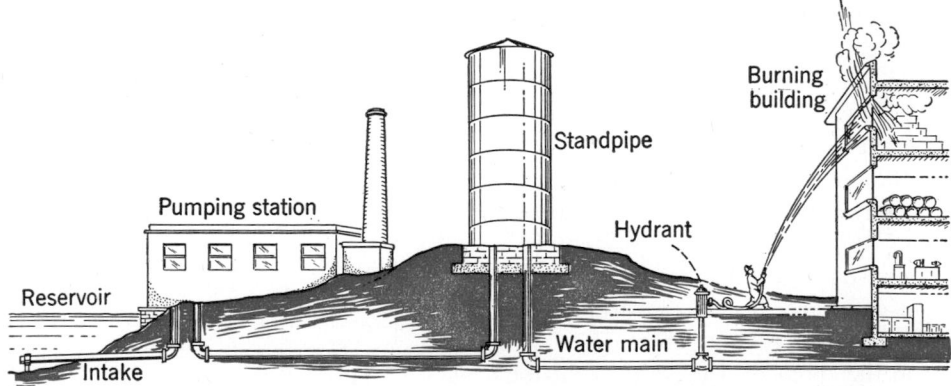

Fig. 3-14. The pumping station forces water from the reservoir into the standpipe. The height of the water in the standpipe provides sufficient water pressure for fire fighting.

for submarines is 200 feet below the surface. At this depth the total force on the hull of an 800-ton submarine is 40,000 tons. The hull of an ocean vessel may extend about 30 feet beneath the surface of the sea. The hull must be strong enough to resist the pressure at this depth.

If a diver goes to a depth of 10 feet, the water pressure on his body is more than 4 pounds per square inch. At 100 feet the pressure increases to more than 40 pounds per square inch. And yet deep-sea divers have descended to a depth of more than 500 feet, where the pressure is many times greater.

(3) *Construction work and total force.* Before building tanks, standpipes, dams, and canal locks, engineers must compute the pressure, or the total force, which these structures

Fig. 3-16. In order to prevent the seepage of water through the concrete block foundations of these houses, the outside of the foundation has been coated with an asphaltic waterproof coating.

will have to withstand. An enormous amount of material is used in constructing dams for storage reservoirs. The highest dam in the world is Hoover Dam, located on the Colorado River where it forms the boundary between Arizona and Nevada. Fig. 3-18 is a diagram of the cross-section of the dam, while Fig. 3-19 is a photograph of the dam itself. The dam is 726 feet high, and the length of its crest is 1200 feet. At the top, the dam is 45 feet wide. The base of the dam is 650 feet thick. In the actual construction of the dam, 3,400,000 cubic yards of concrete were used by the contractors.

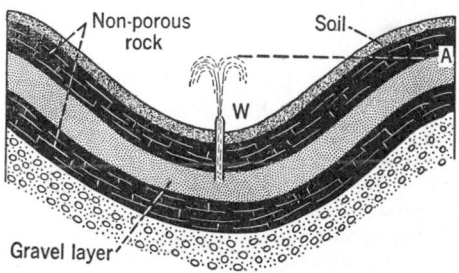

Fig. 3-15. The pressure of the water trapped in the gravel layer between two non-porous rock layers forces the water out the pipe at W.

QUESTIONS

GROUP A

1. What is force? In what units do we measure force in the English system? In the metric system?
2. What is pressure? In what units is it measured?
3. What is total force? In what units is it measured?

4. What specific examples show that liquids exert pressure in downward, upward, and sidewise directions?
5. The pressure exerted by a liquid depends upon two factors. What are they? How does the pressure vary with each of these factors?
6. What experiment shows that liquid pressure is independent of direction?
7. Upon what factors does the total force

Fig. 3-17. A Great Lakes freighter, used for carrying iron ore, in a dry dock undergoing repairs. Notice how much of the hull of the freighter is under water when the ship is afloat. The hull must be made strong enough to withstand the water pressure at the depth to which it is submerged.

exerted by the water against the side wall of a swimming pool depend? How do we calculate average depth?

8. What two devices are commonly used to measure liquid pressure? Explain each.

9. What is meant by the expression "head of water"?

10. Why must a large dam like Hoover Dam be so much thicker at the base than at the top? See Fig. 3-18.

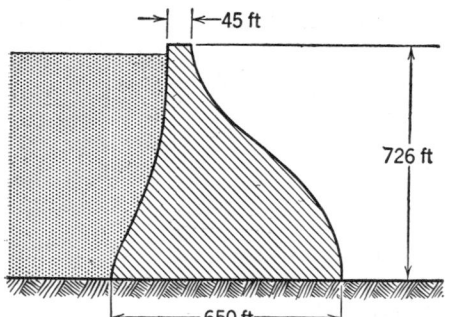

Fig. 3-18. Cross-section of Hoover Dam. Notice how rapidly the thickness of the dam increases so that it can withstand the increase of water pressure with depth.

GROUP B

11. What is a gram-weight? A kilogram-weight? How do they differ from a gram? A kilogram?

12. Why is pressure measured in a unit like pounds per square inch while total force is measured in pounds?

13. Explain why 0.433 lb/ft-in² is a value for the density of water.

14. Why is the total force on the diaphragm of each of Pascal's vases the same, Fig. 3-5, even though the weight of water in each vase is different?

15. Give examples to show how units may be treated as algebraic symbols in the formulas for density, pressure, and total force.

16. Why does a liquid stand at the same height in connecting containers?

★ **17.** What do we mean by direct proportion? By inverse proportion? Give five examples of quantities in physics which are directly proportional. Give at least one example of two quantities in physics which are inversely proportional.

★ **18.** What is the ordinate? The abscissa? What is the shape of the graph of two quantities which are in direct proportion?

PROBLEMS

(In the Mathematics Refresher, refer to Sections 10, 12, and 16.)

GROUP A

1. What pressure, in grams per square centimeter, will be exerted by a column of water 50 cm high?

2. The water level in a large storage tank is 35 ft above the ground. What pressure, in pounds per square foot, is exerted by this water at ground level?

3. What pressure is exerted by a column of mercury 72 cm high if the density of mercury is 13.6 g/cm³?

4. On a certain day the pressure of the atmosphere was 14.5 lb/in². What must be the height of a column of mercury to produce this same pressure? The density of mercury is 0.48 lb/in³.

5. If you are swimming at a depth of 5 ft under water, what is the pressure exerted by the water on each square inch of your body?

6. To what depth, in meters, must we descend in sea water to encounter a pressure of 15,000 g/cm²? Density of sea water, 1.03 g/cm³.

7. What pressure, in pounds per square inch, is exerted by a water head of 125 ft?

8. The difference between the mercury levels in the arms of a manometer is 15 cm. What is the indicated pressure?

9. A swimming pool is 50 ft long and 20 ft wide. If the water is 8 ft deep, what is the total force on the bottom of the pool?

10. Calculate the total force acting against one end of the pool mentioned in Problem 9.

11. What is the total force acting against one of the sides of the pool mentioned in Problem 9?

12. A tank is 5 m long and 3 m wide. If it is filled with alcohol to a depth of 2 m, what is the total force, in kilograms, on the bottom of the tank? What is the total force on each side? What is the total force on each end? The density of alcohol is 0.80 g/cm³.

13. The surface of Lake Mead, formed behind Hoover Dam, is 530 ft above the base of the dam. What is the pressure at the base of the dam?

Fig. 3-19. Hoover Dam, on the Arizona-Nevada border, impounds the water of the Colorado River for controlling floods, providing water for irrigation, and generating vast quantities of electricity. Lake Mead, formed behind the dam, is the largest artificial lake in the world. It is 115 miles long and an average of two miles wide.

GROUP B

14. What will be the pressure exerted by a column of gasoline 250 cm high? Gasoline is 0.70 as dense as water.

15. What pressure, in pounds per square inch, is exerted on the body of a deep-sea diver at the depth of 500 feet in sea water? You will need to know that sea water is 1.03 times as dense as fresh water.

16. Calculate the pressure at the bottom of a vertical glass tube 1 m long which is filled with mercury.

17. If the cross-sectional area of the tube of Problem 16 is 0.5 cm², what is the total force at the bottom of the tube?

18. A cylindrical tank 8 ft long, with a radius of 2.5 ft, is buried on its side in the ground. If the tank is full of gasoline, the density of which is 44 lb/ft³, what is the pressure against the lowest part of the tank?

● **19.** What is the total force against one of the circular ends of the tank mentioned in Problem 18?

● **20.** What was the pressure on the walls on Piccard's bathyscaphe at a depth of 10,330 ft in sea water?

21. A rectangular can containing turpentine is 25 cm long, 15 cm wide, and 75 cm high. Calculate the total force against the bottom of the can. The density of turpentine is 0.87 g/cm³.

22. What is the force against each side of the can mentioned in Problem 21?

2. PRESSURE APPLIED TO LIQUIDS

12. Pressure is transmitted by liquids. Suppose you put one end of a meter stick against the floor and push down on the other end. The stick *transmits your pressure* to the floor. But since the stick is rigid, it transmits pressure only in one direction — in this case, downward. Now put a stopper in one end of an iron pipe and completely fill the pipe with water. As you push a second stopper into the open end of the pipe, the first stopper is pushed out. The liquid in the pipe transmits the pressure exerted on the second stopper to the first stopper. Liquids are not easily compressed, and therefore readily transmit pressure.

Drill several small holes in the pipe and repeat the experiment. As the second stopper is pushed into the pipe, the liquid squirts out through the holes that were drilled. This shows that *the pressure applied to a confined liquid is transmitted in all directions.* Liquids transmit pressure in all directions because their molecules move freely and slide over one another readily.

Liquids are so extremely difficult to compress that we consider them almost incompressible. Water, for example, must be subjected to a pressure of 180,000 lb/in² to reduce its volume by 20%. Ocean water at a depth of 10,000 feet, where the pressure is 4500 lb/in², is only slightly more dense than the water near the surface.

13. What happens when external pressure is applied to confined liquids? There is an old story of the farm boy who took a jug to the well. After filling the jug with water, he inserted the stopper and then hit it sharply with the palm of his hand. He was astonished when the bottom fell out of the jug!

We can understand what really happened if we look at Fig. 3-21. This represents the jug filled with water. As the stopper is driven into the jug by the force of the blow, *the pressure of the stopper upon the confined liquid is*

Fig. 3-20. The uniform pattern of spray from the entire length of this perforated hose is proof of Pascal's principle that pressure is transmitted undiminished in all directions through a confined fluid.

transmitted equally in all directions. For convenience, let us assume that the neck of the jug has an area of exactly 1 square inch. Suppose the farm boy used 10 pounds of force in driving the stopper into the jug. Then *every square inch of the inside surface of the jug had a force of 10 pounds exerted on it in addition to the force caused by the weight of the liquid.* If the area of the bottom of the jug was 40 square inches, the total force on it was at least 400 pounds! The bottom of the jug was not strong enough to withstand such a force and broke away.

14. What is Pascal's principle? Blaise Pascal (1623–1662) was the French physicist who devised the vases we used in Section 6. These vases showed that the weight pressure of liquids is directly proportional to their depths, while independent of the shape

of the container. Pascal also devised an experiment to study the transmission of pressure by liquids when pressure from outside is applied to their

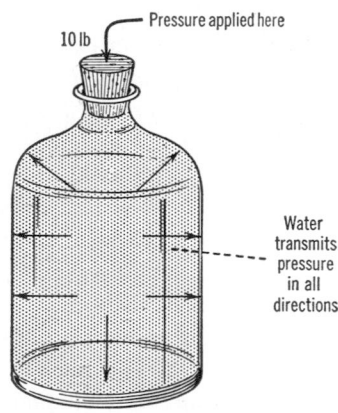

Fig. 3-21. When the farm boy struck the stopper of the jug, the water transmitted the pressure equally in all directions.

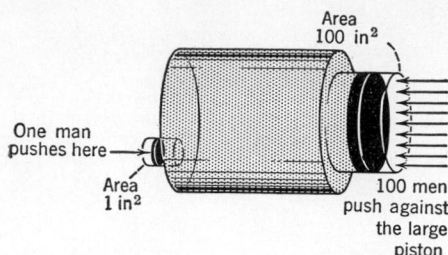

Fig. 3-22. Pascal discovered that a container like this, filled with water, was actually a machine for multiplying force.

surfaces. As shown in Fig. 3-22, he fitted pistons in openings in a box filled with water. One opening had an area 100 times as large as the other. The pistons fitted these openings tightly. Pascal observed that *one man,* pushing against the small piston, could hold it against the force of *100 men* pushing against the larger piston. Such an apparatus is actually *a machine which multiplies force.*

Pascal realized that the transmission of pressure by the water produced the results he noted. This principle of mechanics bears his name today. PAS-CAL'S PRINCIPLE may be stated as follows: *Pressure applied anywhere on a confined fluid is transmitted undiminished in every direction. The force thus exerted by the confined liquid acts at right angles to every portion of the surface of the container, and is equal upon equal areas.* Note that fluids may be either liquids or gases. Pascal's principle applies to both.

15. Using liquid pressure to multiply force. Fig. 3-23 is similar to Fig. 3-22, which we have just studied, except that the pistons are arranged so that they can move up or down. Assume that A, Fig. 3-23, has an area of 1 in^2 and B has an area of 100 in^2.

Then a weight of 1 lb on piston C will just balance a weight of 100 lb on piston D. The *pressure* produced by the weight on piston C is 1 lb/in^2. According to Pascal's principle, this pressure is transmitted undiminished through the liquid and is exerted on the lower surface of the large piston D. This piston has an area of 100 in^2. Consequently, the total force which acts upward on the large piston is 100 in^2 × 1 lb/in^2 = 100 lb. This force supports the 100-lb weight on piston D. A force *slightly* in excess of 1 lb acting downward on the small piston would lift the weight of 100 lb on the large piston. We can see from this example how it is possible to construct a mechanical device to multiply force. If we make the large piston 1000 times the area of the small one, the force on the small piston is multiplied by 1000.

It may seem at first as though we are getting something for nothing in this machine. We must remember, however, that as we multiply force by the use of any mechanical device, we

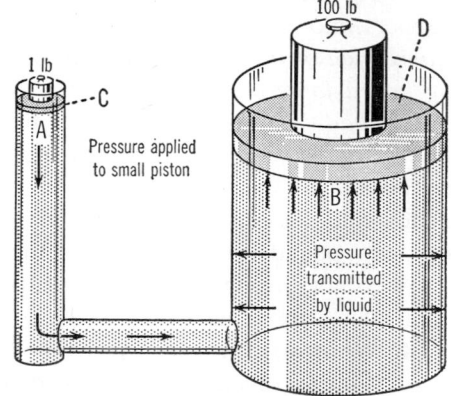

Fig. 3-23. A 1-lb weight placed on the small piston can balance a 100-lb weight placed on the large piston since the large piston has an area 100 times that of the small piston.

decrease correspondingly the distance and speed of the load. Suppose we push piston C down 10 in. Then 10 in³ of water will be forced from A into B. These 10 in³ of water must spread over an area of 100 in². Therefore they raise the water level and lift the large piston 10 in³ ÷ 100 in², or 0.1 in. When C moves 10 in, D moves only 0.1 in, $\frac{1}{100}$ as far as C. The force of 1 lb is multiplied 100 times by this device. But the object to be lifted on the large piston moves only $\frac{1}{100}$ as fast as the small piston. In all mechanical devices, *the product of the acting force multiplied by the distance through which it moves equals the product of the resisting force multiplied by the distance through which it moves.* In this particular case, 1 lb moving 10 in is equivalent to 100 lb moving 0.1 in.

16. How does a hydraulic press work? The commercial *hydraulic* (hy-*draw*-lik) *press* is an application of Pascal's principle. Fig. 3-24 shows a simplified diagram of a hydraulic press. It consists of two cylinders: a small and a large one. In each there is a piston which fits tightly, so that the liquid can not be forced past either piston. A lever is attached to the small piston. As the small piston is pushed down, some of the oil or water from the small cylinder A is forced into the large cylinder B. This lifts the large piston a small amount. As the lever is worked up and down, it pumps the liquid from the reservoir and forces it into the cylinder B. When the pressure is to be released, a valve (not shown in the diagram) is opened to let the liquid flow from B back into the reservoir.

A hydraulic press is used for baling cotton, squeezing the juice from apples

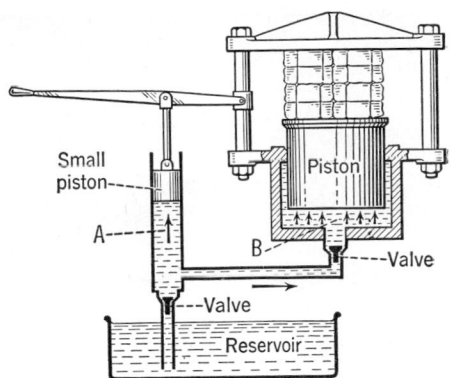

Fig. 3-24. The hydraulic press is an application of Pascal's principle.

and other fruits, punching holes in steel plates, shaping metal body parts for automobiles, and for lifting enormous weights.

17. What is mechanical advantage? We often use machines to multiply the force that we can exert. These machines give us an advantage. Suppose we have a frictionless machine in which a *force* of 1 pound can exactly counterbalance a *weight* of 5 pounds. We say the mechanical advantage of this machine is 5 because the weight supported is five times as great as the force applied. Let us call the weight supported, w, and the force applied, F. Then the *mechanical advantage equals weight supported divided by the force applied in any mechanical device,* or

$$\text{mechanical advantage} = \frac{w}{F}.$$

The mechanical advantage of any machine may also be found by measuring the distance the force moves and the distance the weight moves in the same time. Then,

mechanical advantage =

$$\frac{\text{distance weight moves}}{\text{distance force moves}}.$$

Fig. 3-25. Metal parts for automobile bodies are stamped from flat steel sheets by this huge hydraulic press.

Neglecting the advantage of the lever, the mechanical advantage of a hydraulic press is equal to the area A of the large piston divided by the area a of the small piston. From geometry, we learned that *the areas of two circles are proportional to the squares of their diameters*. Formulas for the mechanical advantage of a hydraulic press are:

$$\text{mechanical advantage} = \frac{A}{a}, \text{ or}$$

$$\text{mechanical advantage} = \frac{D^2}{d^2}.$$

We may also use the proportions:

$$\frac{w}{F} = \frac{A}{a}, \text{ or } \frac{w}{F} = \frac{D^2}{d^2}.$$

See the Sample Problem, page 41.

18. How do hydraulic brakes work? The hydraulic brakes on automobiles are applications of Pascal's principle. The force applied to the brake pedal acts upon a piston in the master cylinder. From the master cylinder the pressure is transmitted through oil in strong tubes to each brake cylinder. See Fig. 3-26. The pressure of the liquid in the brake cylinder pushes two pistons outward. These pistons are attached to brake shoes and push the shoes against the brake drum. The friction of the brake lining on the drum, which is attached to the wheel, slows down the automobile. When the pressure in the brake cylinder is lowered by releasing

SAMPLE PROBLEM

A force of 500 lb is applied to the small piston of a hydraulic press. Its diameter is 2 in. What weight can be supported by the large piston, which has a diameter of 40 in?

SOLUTION NO. 1

The mechanical advantage is $\dfrac{D^2}{d^2}$, or $\dfrac{(40)^2}{(2)^2}$, which equals 400. This means that the machine multiplies the applied force by 400.

Since the applied force is 500 lb, the weight which can be supported by the large piston is 400 × 500 lb = 200,000 lb.

SOLUTION NO. 2

We may also use the formula $\dfrac{w}{F} = \dfrac{D^2}{d^2}$.

Substituting the given values in this formula, $\dfrac{w}{500} = \dfrac{(40)^2}{(2)^2}$.

Solving, w = 200,000 lb.

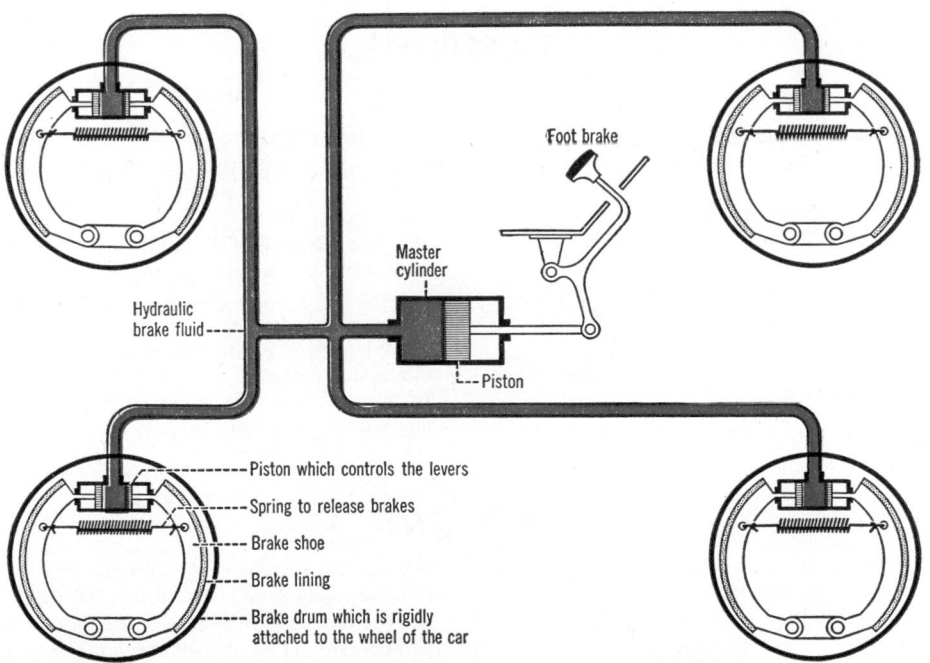

Foot brake

Master cylinder

Hydraulic brake fluid ----

---Piston

------Piston which controls the levers

----Spring to release brakes

----Brake shoe

----Brake lining

-----Brake drum which is rigidly attached to the wheel of the car

Fig. 3-26. The pressure on the foot brake is transmitted equally by the brake fluid to the brake shoes on all four wheels.

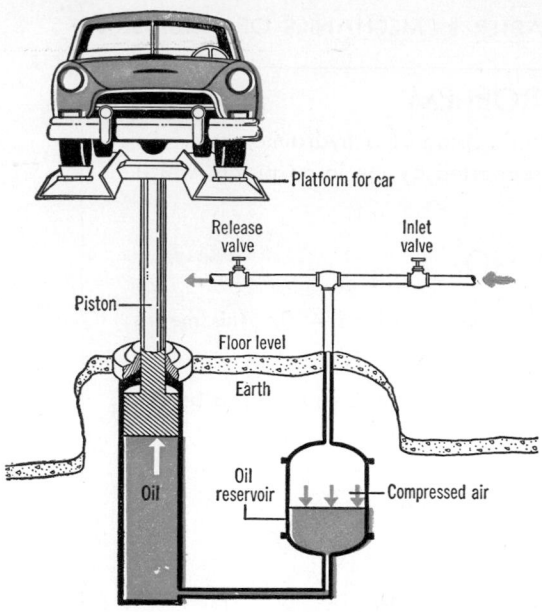

Piston —

Release valve

Inlet valve

— Platform for car

Floor level

Earth

Oil

Oil reservoir

— Compressed air

Fig. 3-27. The hydraulic lift is an application of Pascal's principle. The pressure of the compressed air is transmitted by the oil to the lower end of the piston of the lift.

the brake pedal, a spring pulls the shoes together again. The shoes are no longer in contact with the brake drum.

19. Other applications of Pascal's principle. Dentists' and barbers' chairs usually are lifted by hydraulic pressure. A hydraulic jack can be used for lifting very heavy loads through a short distance. The hydraulic lift found in service stations and garages, Fig. 3-27, is an application of Pascal's principle. Air pressure applied to the surface of oil in a reservoir is transmitted by the oil to the lower end of the piston of the lift. An automobile weighing one or two tons can be raised easily in order to get under it for lubricating parts and draining oil from the crankcase.

We also use another common application of Pascal's principle when we inflate an automobile tire.

QUESTIONS

GROUP A

1. Why can liquids be used to transmit pressure? Why do they transmit pressure in all directions?

2. What is Pascal's principle? To what phases of matter does it apply? Why will it not apply to solids?

3. List several uses for a hydraulic press.

4. Give two definitions for mechanical advantage.

5. Explain how the hydraulic brakes on an automobile operate.

6. Using Fig. 3-27, explain the operation of a hydraulic lift.

GROUP B

7. When you pour cold milk into a Thermos bottle, why do you think it is a good idea to allow some air to remain in the bottle below the stopper?

8. How could Pascal's apparatus, described in Section 14, be used to multiply speed or distance? Can you give a practical application of such a device?

9. What law is theoretically true for all mechanical devices?

10. Explain how a hydraulic press operates. Use Fig. 3-24 to help in your explanation of the principle.

PROBLEMS

(In the Mathematics Refresher, refer to Sections 8, 10, 12, and 16.)

GROUP A

1. A pressure of 50 lb/in² is applied to one portion of a confined liquid. What additional

total force is thereby exerted on one wall of its container if the area of the wall is 300 in²?

2. The cross-sectional area of the mouth of a jug is 5 cm². The area of the bottom of the jug is 200 cm². The jug is filled with water. What additional total force will be exerted on the bottom of the jug if 10 lb of force are applied to a stopper fitted into the mouth of the jug?

3. In a hydraulic press the area of the small piston is 10 cm² and the area of the large piston is 500 cm². What is the mechanical advantage of this press?

4. Calculate the mechanical advantage of a hydraulic press in which the large piston moves 0.01 inch when the small piston moves 5 inches.

5. A hydraulic press has a mechanical advantage of 100. What force must be applied to the small piston to produce a force of 2.5 tons on the large piston?

6. The areas of the two pistons of a hydraulic press are 2 cm² and 25 cm² respectively. What is the mechanical advantage of the press? What weight can be raised if a force of 15 kg is applied to the small piston? How far does the large piston move if the small piston is moved 10 cm?

7. The large piston of a hydraulic press has a diameter 20 times that of the small piston. What is the mechanical advantage?

GROUP B

8. The mechanical advantage of a hydraulic press is 300. If the large piston is to be moved through a distance of 0.5 ft, how far must the small piston be moved? If each stroke of the small piston is 6 in, how many strokes will be required?

9. The diameter of the small piston of a hydraulic press is 2 in and the diameter of the large piston is 30 in. What is the mechanical advantage of this press? What effort, in pounds, must be exerted to produce a force of 15 tons?

● **10.** The pistons of a hydraulic press have radii of 1 in and 7 in respectively. If the large piston moves 0.05 ft/sec, what must be the speed of the small piston? What force is exerted when an effort of 125 lb is applied to the small piston?

● **11.** The inlet pipe of a hydraulic lift is 1 inch in diameter. The piston is 15 inches in diameter. What air pressure, in pounds per square inch, must be used to raise an automobile weighing 2 tons?

3. ARCHIMEDES' PRINCIPLE

20. The buoyant force of liquids. Cork and wood float on water. If you fill your lungs with air, it is usually possible for you to float on water. These examples show that water exerts an upward force upon objects placed in it. An object will float if the upward force of the water is greater than the weight of the object itself. Objects denser than water, even though they sink readily, appear to lose a part of their weight when submerged. A man can lift a larger stone under water than he can possibly lift in air. The upward force of the water lifts part of the weight for him. *The upward force which any liquid exerts upon a body placed in it is called the* **buoyant** (*boy*-unt) **force.**

21. Archimedes' principle. Let us perform the following experiment. The overflow can shown in Fig. 3-29 is filled with water up to the spout. A heavy metal cylinder which will sink in water is weighed in air. It is then weighed while completey immersed in water. The difference between the two weights is the bouyant force of the water. Next, we lower the cylinder into the overflow can and catch all the water which overflows. The volume of water which overflows will equal the volume of the cylinder. If we do our work carefully, we find that the weight of the water displaced by the metal cylinder exactly equals the bouyant force of the water.

Experiments similar to this one were

Fig. 3-28. Archimedes (287–212 B.C.) was a famous Greek physicist and mathematician. He found that the buoyant force on objects placed in a fluid equals the weight of the fluid displaced.

performed by Archimedes (ark-ih-*mee*-deez) (287–212 B.C.). As a result of his experiments he discovered that *the buoyant force which a fluid*

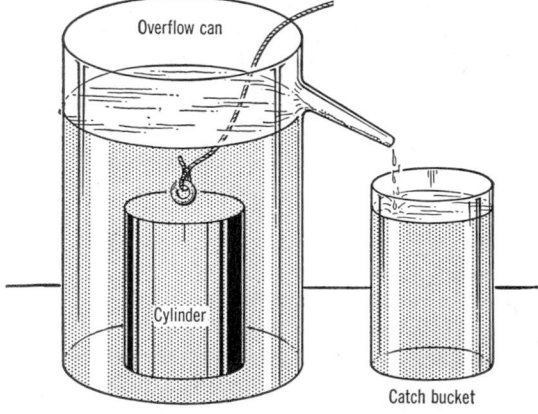

Fig. 3-29. The weight of the water in the catch bucket equals the buoyant force of the water on the cylinder.

exerts upon a submerged body is equal to the weight of the fluid the body displaces. Today we call this statement ARCHIMEDES' PRINCIPLE.

★ **22. How can we test Archimedes' principle?** Suppose we submerge a cubical block, 10 cm on a side, in water so that its upper surface A is just 10 cm below the surface of the water. We have shown this in Fig. 3-30. The total *downward* force on the upper surface of the block equals 1000 g. (Area, 100 cm², × depth, 10 cm, × density, 1 g/cm³, = total force, 1000g.) The total *upward* force on the lower surface B is 2000 g. (The surface B is 20 cm below the surface of the water. Verify this value for the upward force.) The upward force at B exceeds the downward force at A by 1000 g. Thus the buoyant force of the water on the block is 1000 g.

The volume of a cubical block 10 cm on a side is 1000 cm³. Since two materials can not occupy the same space at the same time, the block must displace 1000 cm³ of water. We know that 1 cm³ of water weighs 1 g. Therefore, the block displaced 1000 g of water. But we have seen that the buoyant force of the water on the block was also 1000 g. The facts about total force in liquids prove Archimedes' principle.

To check your understanding, calculate the buoyant force when the *upper* surface of the block is 20 cm below the surface of the water.

23. How can we tell whether an object will float or sink in a liquid? Archimedes' principle tells us that the buoyant force on a submerged object is exactly equal to the weight of the liquid displaced. If the submerged object weighs more than the liquid it displaces, it will sink. Suppose the block used in Section 22 weighs 1200 g. The buoyant force of the water is only 1000 g. Therefore an additional upward force of 200 g must be used to keep the block from sinking. The block loses 1000 g of its weight in water, but 200 g of its weight are still unbalanced.

Suppose, however, that the block weighs only 800 g in air. The buoyant force when the block is completely submerged is 1000 g. This block, if pushed under water and then released, rises to the surface. The upward force of the water is 1000 g but the downward force caused by the weight of the block is only 800 g. To keep the block submerged, we must use an additional force of 200 g.

Let us take one more example. A person whose volume is just 2 ft³ weighs 130 lb. If he jumps into sea water, which weighs 64 lb/ft³, he will sink. The 2 ft³ of water he displaces will buoy him up with a force of 128 lb. But his weight is 130 lb. Two pounds of force are needed to keep him from sinking. Suppose he uses 1 ft³ of cork as a life preserver. One cubic foot of cork weighs 15 lb. The combined volume of his body and the cork now equals 3 ft³. If this volume is completely submerged, it displaces 192 lb of water. But the total weight of his

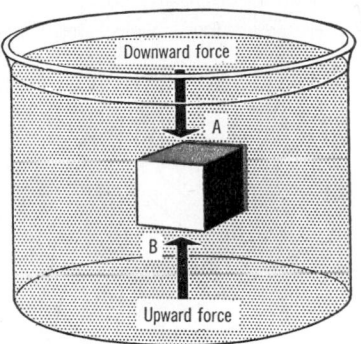

Fig. 3-30. The buoyant force equals the difference between the upward force and the downward force.

body and the cork is only 145 lb. An additional force of 47 lb would be needed to push him under water.

24. How do floating objects behave? Let us place blocks of different kinds of low density material on water, as shown in Fig. 3-31. As they float, some sink deeper than others. Suppose we select cubical blocks 10 cm on a side. The volume of each block is 1000 cm³. Block *A* represents a piece of balsa wood. It is only about one-eighth as dense as water, 0.12 g/cm³. The weight of block *A* is 120 g. Therefore it displaces 120 g or 120 cm³ of water as it floats. This means that 120 cm³ of the block of balsa are beneath the surface of the water. The part of the total volume of the block that is

To summarize what we have learned about floating and sinking objects:

(1) *A body sinks in a fluid, if the weight of the fluid it displaces is less than the weight of the body.*

(2) *A submerged body remains in equilibrium, neither rising nor sinking,* *if the weight of the fluid it displaces exactly equals its own weight.*

(3) *If a body when submerged displaces a weight of fluid greater than its own weight, the body will rise and float with part of its volume above the surface. A floating body displaces its own weight of liquid.*

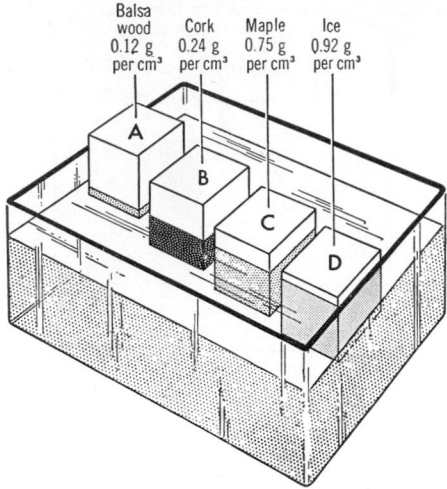

Fig. 3-31. The fractional part of these materials which is submerged in water is numerically equal to their density in grams per cubic centimeter.

submerged is 120 cm³ ÷ 1000 cm³ = 0.12. This is numerically equal to its density. Block *B* represents a piece of cork, density 0.24 g/cm³. Its weight is

240 g. It must displace 240 g or 240 cm³ of water in order to float. When this block is placed on the surface of the water, it sinks until 240 cm³ are submerged. This equals 0.24 of its volume, the same numerical value as the density. Block *C* has a density of 0.75 g/cm³. Since its weight is 750 g, it will sink in water until 750 cm³ of its volume are submerged. The fractional part submerged is 0.75, numerically the same as the density. *D* represents a block of ice, which has a density of 0.92 g/cm³. This block weighs 920 g and will sink into the water until it displaces 920 cm³ of water. When ice floats in water 0.92 of its volume is beneath the surface. Icebergs endanger ocean vessels because of the large fraction of their total volume which is hidden beneath the surface of the ocean. See Fig. 3-32.

Suppose we lower block *B* into gasoline, which has a density of only 0.7 g/cm³. It will sink deeper into the

Fig. 3-32. Icebergs such as this one are hazards to navigation because they drift southward into the shipping lanes. An iceberg floats with about *nine-tenths of its volume* beneath the surface of the water.

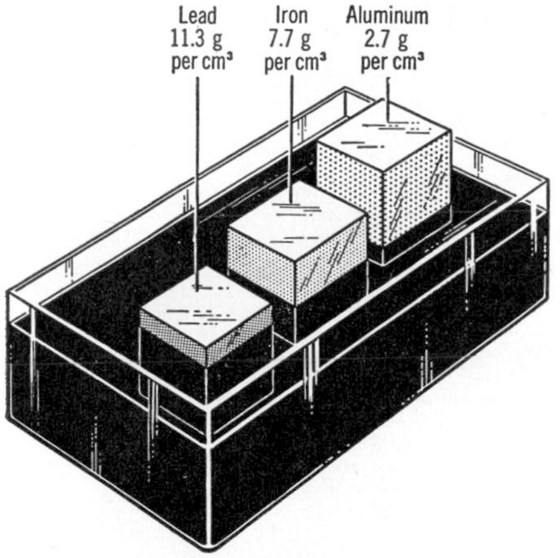

Lead	Iron	Aluminum
11.3 g	7.7 g	2.7 g
per cm³	per cm³	per cm³

Fig. 3-33. The depth to which a metal sinks in mercury depends on the ratio of its density to that of mercury.

gasoline than in water before it displaces an amount of liquid equal to its own weight. 240 g ÷ 0.7 g/cm³ = 343 cm³, the volume of gasoline which weighs 240 g. Consequently, 0.343 of the volume, or approximately $\frac{1}{3}$, is submerged when cork floats on gasoline.

Aluminum, iron, and lead will float, as shown in Fig. 3-33, in a very dense liquid like mercury. The fractional part submerged equals the ratio of the density of the metal to the density of mercury.

25. Applications of Archimedes' principle. The science of shipbuilding depends on Archimedes' principle. A ship that weighs 4000 tons and carries a cargo of 8000 tons must be so proportioned in length, breadth, and depth that it will displace 12,000 tons of water. The fastest ocean liner in the world, the *United States*, is 990 feet long and 101.5 feet wide. It must displace a volume of water having the same weight as its gross tonnage, 53,290 tons.

While on the surface, a submarine floats with about one-fourth of its volume exposed. Its density then is about 0.75 g/cm³. For submerging, its density must be increased to about 1 g/cm³. This is done by filling large ballast tanks aboard the subma-

Fig. 3-34. The *United States*, shown here leaving New York harbor, is the fastest ocean liner in the world. On its maiden voyage from New York to Southampton, England, in July of 1952, the *United States* traveled at a record speed of 35.59 knots, which is approximately 41 land miles per hour.

Fig. 3-35. This peculiar vehicle is a marsh buggy, and is used chiefly by petroleum prospectors. Its large balloon tires, when only slightly submerged, displace a weight of water equal to the weight of the marsh buggy. Thus it can travel equally well over swampy areas or dry land.

rine with sea water. The depth to which the submarine submerges is then controlled by the diving rudders. In order to dive quickly, its floating density must be maintained at a particular value. Separate ballast tanks are provided which can be filled with water to compensate for loss of weight due to the fuel used, the consumption of food and water by the crew, and the firing of shells. If these adjustments are made carefully, filling the main ballast tanks with water will increase the density of the submarine until it just equals that of the sea water. The ship sinks into the water. The propellers drive it forward, and the diving rudders are set

to keep the ship under water. To bring the submarine to the surface again, the diving rudders are set to push the bow of the ship upward. Compressed air then forces the water out of the ballast tanks. This reduces the density, so that the submarine again floats on the surface.

Other applications of Archimedes' principle are the pontoon bridge, the floating drydock, and various types of ocean buoys. In addition, the supply of gasoline to the carburetor of an automobile engine is controlled by a float. A floating ball closes the valve which shuts off the water supply in the tank of a toilet.

QUESTIONS

GROUP A

1. What is the buoyant force? In what direction does the buoyant force act?

2. How great is the buoyant force on a completely submerged object?

3. What is Archimedes' principle?

4. What conditions must be met in order that an object will float on a liquid? Will a brass weight float on mercury? Will a piece of solid gold float on mercury?

5. What conditions must be met in order that a submerged body remains in equilibrium in a liquid, neither rising nor sinking?

6. What weight of fluid is displaced by a floating object?

7. How does the fraction of the volume of a floating body which is beneath the surface of the water compare with the density of the body in grams per cubic centimeter?

8. Why is it possible for a person to float more readily in the Great Salt Lake than in Lake Erie?

GROUP B

9. How does the density of a "floating" soap compare with that of other soaps?

10. Why does a fish suddenly become heavier as it is pulled out of the water?

11. Why are icebergs hazards to navigation across the North Atlantic Ocean during certain months of the year?

12. Why is it important to keep the weight of a submarine as nearly constant as possible despite the consumption of food and fuel? How is this done?

13. If an object is floated in a liquid other than water, what does the fractional part submerged indicate about the density of the object?

14. Describe an experiment which proves that the buoyant force of water on a lead cylinder equals the weight of water displaced by the cylinder.

15. A fisherman ties a piece of lead to his line near the hook, and a cork to the line a foot or two up from the hook. Why?

PROBLEMS

(In the Mathematics Refresher, refer to Sections 10 and 16.)

GROUP A

1. A block of wood has a volume of 100 cm^3 and weighs 85 g. Will it float on water? On gasoline, density 0.70 g/cm^3?

2. A certain object has a volume of 0.75 ft^3. It weighs 50 lb. Will it float or sink in water?

3. An aluminum cylinder has a volume of 50 cm^3. What buoyant force will be exerted on the cylinder when it is immersed in water? When in alcohol, density 0.80 g/cm^3?

4. A 1 lb iron weight has a volume of 3.7 in^3. What buoyant force is exerted on it if it is submerged in water?

5. A wood rod 12 inches long is weighted so that it floats vertically in water with 2 inches above the surface. What is the density of the rod in g/cm^3? In lb/ft^3?

6. A rod 25 cm long floats vertically in carbon tetrachloride with 15 cm submerged. The density of carbon tetrachloride is 1.60 g/cm^3. What is the density of the rod?

7. A glass cylinder contains alcohol, density 0.80 g/cm^3. How much of a wooden rod, 15 cm long, with an average density of 0.65 g/cm^3, will be submerged if the rod is floated vertically in the alcohol?

8. What is the density, in pounds per cubic foot, of an 18 in rod which floats vertically in water with 6 in remaining above the water?

9. A block of iron weighs 150 g. Its density is 7.5 g/cm^3. What volume of water will it displace when immersed? What will be the buoyant force on it?

10. A cube of copper weighs 500 lb. If the density of copper is 8.9 times that of water, what is the volume of the block? If it is immersed in water, what volume of water will it displace? What buoyant force is exerted on it? What will be its apparent weight in water?

11. A hollow glass block has a volume of 100 in^3 and weighs 5 lb. If immersed in water, what volume of water will it displace? What buoyant force is exerted on it? What will be the apparent weight in water?

12. In a laboratory experiment, a brass cylinder weighing 150 g in air was immersed in water. If it displaced 18 cm^3 of water, what was its apparent weight in water?

GROUP B

13. A flat-bottomed river barge is 20 ft wide and 75 ft long. It is floating empty in a river. How much deeper will it sink into the water if a load of 250 tons of sand is placed in it?

14. What volume of sea water, density 64 lb/ft³, will be displaced by the liner *United States?* Assume the gross tonnage to be 53,300 tons.

15. A block of wood 50 cm long, 10 cm wide, and 5 mm thick floats on water. Its density is 0.75 g/cm³. How much does the block weigh in air? How many cubic centimeters of water does it displace? What is its apparent weight in water?

★**16.** Give a mathematical proof of Archimedes' principle. (1) Calculate the forces on the upper and lower surfaces of a submerged cubical block 5 inches on a side, whose upper surface is 10 inches below the surface of gaso-line in a large tank. (2) Compare the difference in these forces with the weight of gasoline displaced. Density of gasoline, 44 lb/ft³.

17. The density of the human body is about 1.07 times as great as the density of water. Using your own weight, and the density just given, calculate the volume of your body in cubic feet. What volume of water will you displace if you are completely submerged? Suppose you are kept afloat by a cork life preserver which is totally submerged. The volume of the life preserver is 1 ft³ and it weighs 15 lb. What fraction of your body will be kept out of water?

18. A piece of pine, density 0.5 g/cm³, has a piece of silver, density 10.5 g/cm³ imbedded in it. When immersed, it displaces 1000 cm³ of water, and has an apparent weight of 250 g. What are the weight and volume of the piece of pine and of the silver imbedded in it?

---

4. WEIGHT DENSITY AND SPECIFIC GRAVITY

26. What is specific gravity? In our study of the mechanics of liquids we used the weight densities of various substances several times. Frequently, it is helpful to compare the density of one substance with that of another. However, in order to make our comparisons meaningful, we need a standard. *Water is the standard* which physicists have chosen for comparing the densities of all *solids* and *liquids*. *The density of a solid or liquid divided by the density of water is called its* **specific gravity**. Since we are comparing the density of any substance with the density of a standard substance, we might use the term " relative density." This might be easier to understand. But physicists use the term " specific gravity," therefore we use it, too.

27. How are density and specific gravity related in the three systems of measurement? By experiment we find that 1 cm³ of copper weighs 8.9 g. We know that 1 cm³ of water weighs 1 g. In the metric system, the density of copper is 8.9 g/cm³, and the density of water is 1 g/cm³. Copper is thus 8.9 times as dense as water. This *abstract number,* 8.9, which tells how many times denser copper is than water, is called the specific gravity of copper. The density of copper is a **concrete number,** 8.9 g/cm³, because it *is an actual measurement of physical quantities.* The specific gravity of copper is an **abstract number,** 8.9, because it is only *the ratio of two density measurements; that is, the number represents a measurement but has no units.* Density and specific gravity are *numerically* the same in the CGS system.

If we weigh 1 ft³ of copper, we find that its weight is 555.36 lb. One cubic foot of water weighs 62.4 lb. By dividing 555.36 by 62.4 we get the specific gravity, 8.9.

Equal volumes of copper and water will have the same relative weights, whether they are both weighed in pounds, grams, or kilograms. In Appendix B you will find tables showing the specific gravities of various substances. To find the density of any substance from the table, *multiply its specific gravity by 1 g/cm³ if you use the CGS system. You multiply its specific gravity by 1000 kg/m³ if you use the MKS system. Multiply its specific gravity by 62.4 lb/ft³ if you use the English system.*

28. How can specific gravity be found? We can find the specific gravity of a substance experimentally by finding its density and dividing that number by the density of water:

$$\text{Sp. gr.} = \frac{\text{density of substance}}{\text{density of water}}.$$

It is easier to use a different formula:

$$\text{Sp. gr.} = \frac{\text{weight of substance}}{\text{weight of an equal volume of water}}.$$

By using Archimedes' principle, we easily can find the *weight of an equal volume of water,* since a body submerged in water is buoyed up by a force equal to the weight of the water displaced. In general, when we wish to find the specific gravity of a body: (1) we find its weight in air; (2) we find the weight of an equal volume of water by determining the buoyant force of the water on the body; (3) we divide the weight of the body in air by the weight of an equal volume of water.

29. How can we find the specific gravity of solids? Case (1) *Solids denser than water.* If the solid is insoluble, we first weigh it in air and then weigh it in water. The difference between the two weights is the buoyant force of the water, or the weight of an equal volume of water. Then,

$$\text{Sp. gr.} = \frac{\text{weight in air}}{\text{buoyant force of water}}.$$

See the Sample Problem below.

★ Case (2) *Solids less dense than water.* The buoyant force equals the weight of a floating object before it can be completely submerged. Consequently, it is more difficult to find its volume, or the weight of an equal volume of water. However, we can do it

---

SAMPLE PROBLEM

A stone weighs 30 g in air, and 20 g in water. What is its specific gravity?

SOLUTION

The difference between the weight in air and the weight in water is the buoyant force of the water. The buoyant force in this case is 30 g − 20 g = 10 g.

By substitution in the formula given above, 30 g ÷ 10 g = 3, the specific gravity. (Since the buoyant force on the stone was 10 g, the stone must have displaced 10 g of water. These 10 g of water occupy 10 cm³. Consequently the volume of the stone must have been 10 cm³.)

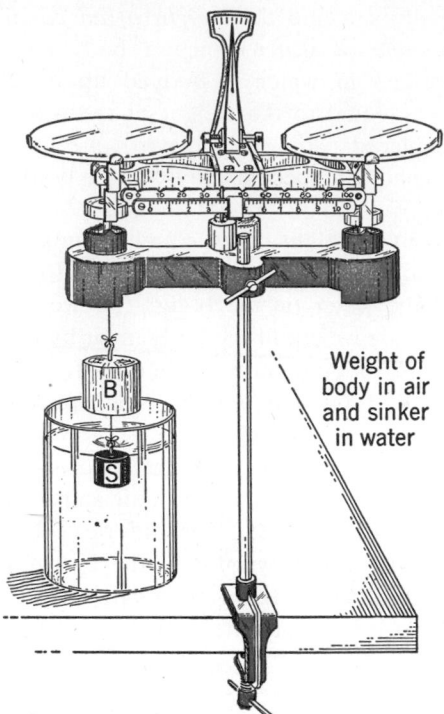

Fig. 3-36. The second step in the method of finding the specific gravity of a solid less dense than water, weighing the solid in air and the sinker in water.

Weight of body in air and sinker in water

if we use a dense sinker. We find the buoyant force acting on the sinker, and then the buoyant force acting on the low density solid with the sinker attached. See Fig. 3-36. Then the difference is the buoyant force on the low density solid. The steps are:

(1) We weigh the solid in air and call its weight w.

(2) We find the combined weight of the solid in air and the sinker in water and call this weight w'.

(3) We then find the combined weight of both the solid and the sinker in water and call this weight w''.

The difference between w' and w''

equals the buoyant force on the low density solid alone, or the weight of an equal volume of water. The formula then becomes:

$$\text{Sp. gr.} = \frac{w}{w' - w''}.$$

See Sample Problem on top of page 53.

30. How can we find the specific gravity of liquids? There are several methods for comparing the weight of a liquid with the weight of an equal volume of water. Three methods are:

(1) *The bottle method.* A small bottle, like that shown in Fig. 3-37, is first weighed. Then it is filled with water and weighed again. Next it is emptied of the water and filled with the liquid of unknown specific gravity. The bottle is weighed a third time. By subtracting the weight of the empty bottle from each of the other two weighings, we find the weight of water that the bottle can hold and the weight of the liquid of unknown specific gravity

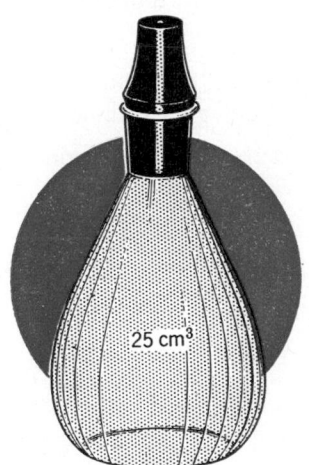

25 cm³

Fig. 3-37. A pycnometer is a small bottle which holds the precise quantity of the liquids needed for the bottle method of determining the specific gravity of a liquid.

★ SAMPLE PROBLEM

A piece of cork weighs 50 g. A sinker immersed in water weighs 210 g. The combined weight of the cork and sinker when both are submerged is 10 g. What is the specific gravity of the cork?

SOLUTION

The weight of the cork, 50 g, is w. The combined weight of the cork in air and the sinker in water, 50 g + 210 g, is w'. The combined weight of both the cork and sinker in water, 10 g, is w''.

Substituting in the formula,

$$\text{sp. gr.} = \frac{w}{w' - w''}, \text{ we obtain, sp. gr.} = \frac{50 \text{ g}}{(50 \text{ g} + 210 \text{ g}) - 10 \text{ g}}.$$

Solving, sp. gr. = 0.2, the specific gravity of the cork.

---

that it can hold. Then,

$$\text{Sp. gr.} = \frac{\text{weight of liquid}}{\text{weight of water}}.$$

The bottle shown in Fig. 3-37 is called *a pycnometer* (pik-*nom*-eh-ter). The tiny hole through the stopper makes it easy to fill the pycnometer with exactly the same volume of liquid each time. See the Sample Problem below.

★ (2) *Loss-of-weight methods,* or *bulb method.* The denser a liquid is, the greater is the buoyant force it can exert. We can find the relative weights of two liquids by comparing their buoyant forces upon the same solid. A glass bulb or a platinum ball is most

often used. First we weigh the bulb in air, then we weigh it in water, and finally we weigh it in the liquid of unknown specific gravity. The bulb displaces the same volume of each liquid. If the buoyant force of the unknown liquid is twice that of water, the unknown liquid must be twice as dense as water. The formula is:

$$\text{Sp. gr.} = \frac{\text{buoyant force of liquid}}{\text{buoyant force of water}}.$$

See Sample Problem on page 54.

(3) *The hydrometer method.* A wooden rod, loaded at one end so that it will float vertically, sinks in water until the weight of the water it dis-

---

SAMPLE PROBLEM

A pycnometer weighs 22 g. When filled with water it weighs 72 g. When filled with alcohol, it weighs 62 g. Find the specific gravity of the alcohol.

SOLUTION

The weight of water in the bottle is 72 g − 22 g, or 50 g. The weight of alcohol in the bottle is 62 g − 22 g, or 40 g.

Substituting in the formula given for the bottle method, sp. gr. = $\frac{40 \text{ g}}{50 \text{ g}}$.

Solving, sp. gr. = 0.8, the specific gravity of alcohol.

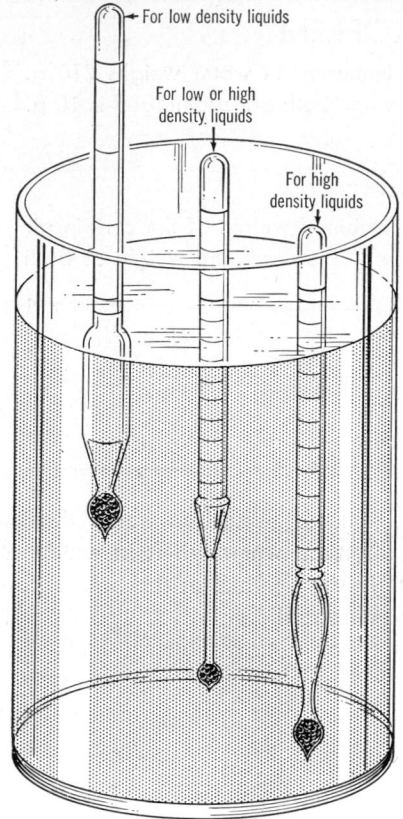

For low density liquids

For low or high density liquids

For high density liquids

Fig. 3-38. Different types of hydrometers.

places exactly equals its own weight. If it is placed in a liquid of unknown specific gravity, it sinks until it displaces a weight of the unknown liquid equal to its own weight. If the rod is uniform, the densities of the liquids displaced will be inversely proportional to the depths to which the rod sinks. For example, if the rod sinks 10 cm in water and to a depth of 8 cm in the unknown liquid, then the unknown liquid is $\frac{10}{8}$, or 1.25 times as dense as water.

$$\text{Sp. gr.} = \frac{\text{depth rod sinks in water}}{\text{depth rod sinks in liquid}}.$$

The commercial *hydrometer* (hy-*drom*-uh-ter), Fig. 3-38, has a scale graduated in such a way that the specific gravity of the liquid in which it floats may be read directly. The purpose of the upper bulb is to increase the volume of the hydrometer. The lower bulb is filled with shot or mercury so that the hydrometer will float in a vertical position. Some hydrometers are so designed as to weight and volume that they are suitable for determining the specific gravity of liquids less dense than water. Other hydrometers are designed for use with liquids of greater density.

31. How do we use our knowledge of specific gravity? Specific gravity determinations help us to identify rocks and minerals. The specific gravity of a liquid helps us to judge its purity. In an automobile storage battery, the spe-

---

★SAMPLE PROBLEM

A ball weighs 40 g in air, 32 g in water, and 28 g in a liquid of unknown specific gravity. Find the specific gravity of the liquid.

SOLUTION

The buoyant force of the unknown liquid is 40 g − 28 g = 12 g. The buoyant force of the water is 40 g − 32 g = 8 g.

Substituting in the formula given above for the bulb method, sp. gr. = $\dfrac{12 \text{ g}}{8 \text{ g}}$.

Solving. sp. gr. = 1.5, the specific gravity of the unknown liquid.

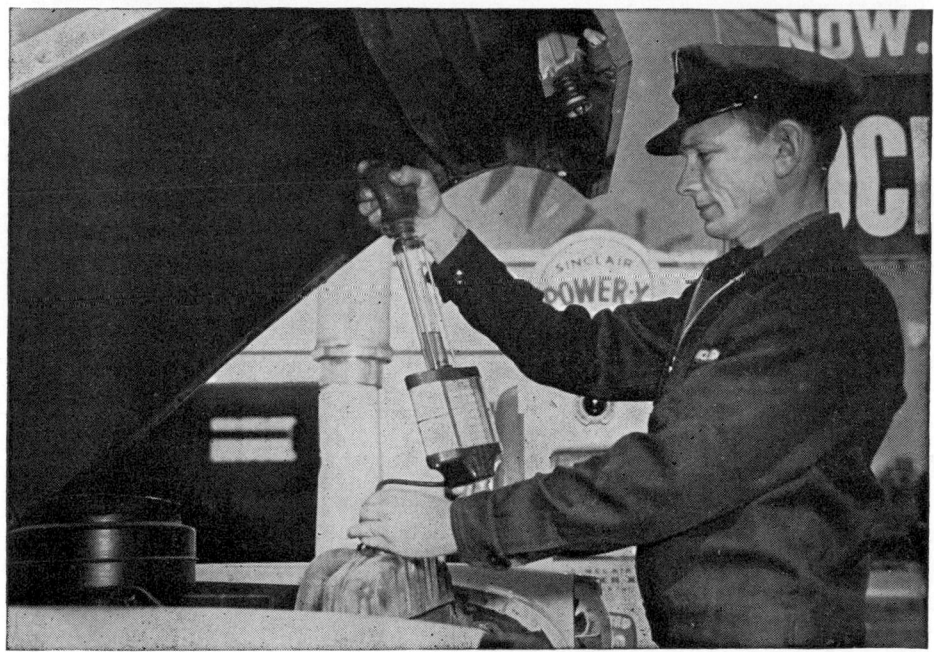

Fig. 3-39. The commercial hydrometer is an application of specific gravity determinations. Here a service station attendant uses a hydrometer to find out whether there is sufficient antifreeze in the car radiator.

cific gravity of the liquid indicates how fully the battery is charged. The liquid in a fully charged battery has a higher specific gravity than that in a battery which has lost most of its charge. Some special hydrometers, called *acidimeters* (ass-ih-*dim*-eh-ters), are used in testing the concentration of acids. The *alcoholometer* (al-kuh-hol-*om*-eh-ter) is a special hydrometer for measuring the amount of alcohol in various alcohol-water mixtures. A special hydrometer, called a *lactometer* (lak-*tom*-eh-ter), is used to indicate the specific gravity of milk. A service station attendant estimates the freezing point of the mixture of antifreeze and water in an automobile radiator by using a special hydrometer to check the specific gravity of the mixture.

Summary

Liquids have weight. As a result, they exert pressure on the bottom and sides of a containing vessel. Liquid pressure is directly proportional to the depth and density of the liquid and is independent of direction. The total force exerted upon any surface by a liquid equals the product of the area times the average depth times the density.

Pressure applied to any part of a confined fluid is transmitted with undiminished force in every direction.   Such pressure acts with equal force upon equal areas.   This is known as Pascal's principle.

Pascal's principle is applied in the hydraulic press, hydraulic brake, hydraulic lift, and various other devices.   By sacrificing speed, a small force may be used to overcome a great resistance.   In all frictionless machines, acting force times the distance the acting force moves equals resisting force times the distance the resisting force moves.

The upward force a fluid exerts on a body placed in it is called the buoyant force.   Archimedes found that this buoyant force just equals the weight of the fluid displaced.   If the buoyant force on a solid placed in water is greater than its weight, then the solid will rise to the surface and float with only part of its volume submerged.   If the buoyant force on a solid placed in water is exactly equal to its weight, the solid remains in equilibrium in the liquid.   If the buoyant force on a solid placed in water is less than its weight, the object sinks.

The weight density of a substance is its weight per unit volume.   Specific gravity is the density of a certain substance divided by the density of water. Specific gravity is found by dividing the weight of a body by the weight of an equal volume of water.   The weight of an equal volume of water is numerically equal to the loss of weight of the body in water.   The specific gravity of a liquid may be determined easily with a hydrometer.

SUMMARY OF LIQUID PRESSURE

(1) *Liquid pressure is directly proportional to the depth of the liquid.*
(2) *Liquid pressure is directly proportional to the density of the liquid.*
(3) *Liquid pressure is independent of the area or shape of the container; it also is independent of direction.*

Terms to Define...

Abscissa	Direct proportion	Pascal's vases
Abstract number	Entire area	Pressure
Acting force	Force	Pycnometer
Archimedes' principle	Hydraulic brakes	Relation between specific
Artesian well	Hydraulic press	gravity and density
Average depth	Hydrometer method	Resisting force
Bottle method	Inverse proportion	Specific gravity
Bourdon gauge	Manometer	Total force
Bulb method	Mechanical advantage	Unit area
Buoyant force	Ordinate	Water head
Concrete number	Pascal's principle	Weight density

Questions

GROUP A

1. What do we mean by specific gravity?

2. Why is it necessary to have a standard substance for specific gravity?

3. What is an abstract number? A concrete number?

4. How do we convert specific gravity to density in the CGS system?

5. How do we convert specific gravity to density in the MKS system?

6. How do we convert specific gravity to density in the English system?

7. How can we determine the buoyant force on an object placed in a liquid?

8. How do we calculate the specific gravity of a solid if we know its weight and the buoyant force exerted on it when it is placed in water?

9. How do we determine specific gravity by the bottle method?

10. What is a hydrometer? How do hydrometers which are used for different ranges of specific gravity differ in design?

11. Explain how a hydrometer can be used to indicate the freezing point of the antifreeze and water mixture in an automobile radiator.

12. The specific gravity of the liquid in a storage battery varies from 1.150 when the cell is discharged to 1.300 when fully charged. How can you use a hydrometer to determine the state of charge of a storage battery?

GROUP B

13. Given the following liquids which will not dissolve in one another: mercury, water, and carbon tetrachloride. If all three are placed in a graduated cylinder, which liquid will come to the top, which will be in the middle, and which will sink to the bottom?

14. If pieces of brass, gold, bituminous coal, and paraffin are placed with the liquids in Question 13, at what level will they float, or will they sink to the bottom?

15. What factors in the design of a pycnometer make it possible for us to fill the pycnometer each time with precisely the same volume of liquid, provided the temperature does not change?

★ 16. In the loss-of-weight method for determining specific gravity, we first weigh the bulb in air. Then we weigh the bulb in water. What do we do next? What calculations must be made?

★ 17. How may we determine the specific gravity of a solid which is less dense than water?

Problems

(Refer to the tables of specific gravities in Appendix B. In the Mathematics Refresher, refer to Section 3, 10, and 16.)

GROUP A

1. What is the specific gravity of magnesium? Its density is 1.74 g/cm³.

2. The specific gravity of gold is 19.3. What is its density in the MKS system?

3. What is the specific gravity of silver if it weighs 655.2 lb/ft³?

4. In a specific gravity experiment, Joseph found that the pycnometer held 25.0 g of water and 31.5 g of glycerin. What is the specific gravity of glycerin?

5. A block of copper weighs 100 g in air, and 88.8 g in water. What is its specific gravity?

6. A wooden stick hydrometer sinks to a depth of 10 inches in gasoline and to 7 inches in water. What is the specific gravity of the gasoline?

7. What will be the weight in pounds of 5 ft³ of sulfur?

8. A large lump of coal weighs 25 lb in air and 7.2 lb in water. What is the specific gravity of the coal? What is its volume?

★ 9. A glass bulb loses 35 g when immersed in water, and 52.5 g when immersed in chloroform. What is the specific gravity of chloroform?

10. A small flask weighs 30 g. When filled with water, it weighs 80 g. When filled with kerosene, it weighs 70 g. When filled with castor oil, it weighs 78 g. Calculate (1) the specific gravity of kerosene, (2) the specific gravity of castor oil.

11. John places a wooden stick hydrometer in water and finds that it sinks to a depth of 20 cm. When he transfers it to a cylinder of carbon disulfide, it sinks to a depth of only 15.7 cm. Calculate the specific gravity of carbon disulfide.

12. What volume in cubic meters will be occupied by 5000 kg of marble?

13. How much weight will 25 cm³ of tungsten lose in water? How much weight will 25 cm³ of magnesium lose in water?

14. How much weight will 25 g of tungsten lose in water? How much weight will 25 g of magnesium lose in water?

GROUP B

15. A piece of brick weighs 3 kg. When immersed in water, its apparent weight is 1.25 kg. What is its specific gravity? Volume?

16. The specific gravity of sterling silver is 10.38. What will be the buoyant force on 750 g of sterling silver if it is immersed in alcohol? The specific gravity of alcohol is 0.79.

17. An empty pycnometer weighs 23.2 g. When filled with water, it weighs 58.3 g. When filled with olive oil, it weighs 55.4 g. When filled with linseed oil, it weighs 56.2 g. Calculate the specific gravity of olive oil and of linseed oil.

★ **18.** A glass bulb weighs 50.2 g in air and 27.2 g in water. When immersed in nitric acid its apparent weight is 17.6 g. What is the specific gravity of nitric acid?

19. A hydrometer sinks to a depth of 6 inches in water. To what depth will it sink in a salt solution, the specific gravity of which is 1.09?

20. A block of maple is 15 inches long, 10 inches wide, and 2 inches thick. It weighs 7.6 lb. Calculate its density in lb/ft³ and its specific gravity.

21. The specific gravity of a piece of Bakelite

plastic is 1.50. What will be the weight of a piece of Bakelite 4 inches long, 2 inches wide, and ⅛ inch thick?

22. Paul found that a pycnometer weighed 24.7 g. When he filled it with water, the combined weight was 49.8 g. What will be the combined weight after the pycnometer is emptied of water and then filled with mercury?

★ **23.** When a piece of brass is weighed in water it weighs 1.977 lb. If it is weighed in glycerin its weight is 1.971 lb. The specific gravity of glycerin is 1.26. How much does the brass weigh in air?

● **24.** Scientists have estimated that the density of some stars is so great that one cubic inch weighs a ton. What would be the specific gravity of such heavy material?

● **25.** A hydrometer weighs 100 g. If the cross-sectional area of the tube containing the hydrometer scale is 5 cm², how much deeper will it sink into alcohol, density 0.8 g/cm³, than into water? If the hydrometer is graduated in fiftieths of a specific gravity unit, how far apart are these divisions on the scale?

★ **26.** A block of wood weighs 100 g in air, a sinker weighs 75 g in water, and the combined weight of block and sinker in water is 50 g. What is the specific gravity of the block?

★ **27.** A piece of maple weighs 175 g in air. The maple in air and the sinker in water have a combined weight of 350 g. When both are immersed in water, their weight is 60 g. Find the specific gravity of the maple.

★ **28.** Roger weighed a piece of cork in air and found the cork weighed 0.5 lb. He used a sinker weighing 2.2 lb in water. The weight of both cork and sinker in water was 0.6 lb. What was the specific gravity of the cork?

★ **29.** A block of oak weighs 14 oz in air. The combined weight of the block in air and a sinker in water is 29 oz. When both block and sinker are weighed in water they weigh 13.5 oz. Calculate the specific gravity of the oak block.

Things to Do

1. Construct a manometer and use it to measure the pressure produced by a head of five to ten feet of water.

2. Visit an artesian well. What can you tell about the lower rock formations from the surface?

3. Have a service station attendant explain the operation of the hydraulic lift he uses when raising automobiles in order to lubricate them.

4. Look up the legend surrounding the discovery of Archimedes' principle.

Chapter 4

The Atmosphere and Weather

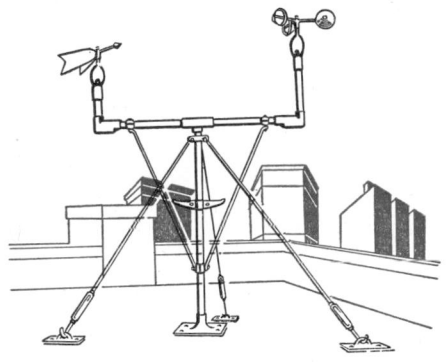

1. THE ATMOSPHERE

1. Man's conquest of the atmosphere. In our daily life, we are not usually too conscious of *the layer of gases which surrounds the earth and which make up the **atmosphere.*** We do not notice its pressure, and we move through it with little effort. We breathe it automatically. However, we become more conscious of the atmosphere on a rainy or snowy day. It is also brought to our attention when strong winds damage buildings and property. But, generally speaking, the atmosphere receives little notice.

As we move from one altitude to another on the surface of the earth, we become aware of differences in the atmosphere. We notice a change of pressure on our eardrums when we drive rapidly up a long hill, or descend from the top of a tall building in a fast elevator. Persons who normally live at

Vocabulary

ALTIMETER (al-*tim*-uh-ter). An aneroid barometer graduated to read altitude directly.

ANEROID (*an*-er-oid). Without liquid.

ATMOSPHERE. The layer of gases surrounding the earth.

BAROMETER (buh-*rom*-uh-ter). A device used to measure the pressure of the atmosphere.

CHEMOSPHERE (*kem*-uh-sfihr). The region of the atmosphere from 20 to 50 miles above the earth where ultraviolet rays are filtered out.

EXOSPHERE (*eks*-uh-sfihr). The region of the atmosphere from about 250 miles above the earth to the outer edge of the atmosphere.

FRONT. The boundary between two different air masses.

IONOSPHERE (eye-*on*-uh-sfihr). Region of atmosphere from 50 to 250 miles above the earth from which radio waves are reflected.

ISOBAR (*eye*-suh-bar). A line drawn on a weather map through places of equal barometric pressure.

STATION MODEL. A system of recording on a weather map by symbols the observations made at the various weather stations.

STRATOSPHERE (*strat*-uh-sfihr). The region of the atmosphere from 10 to 20 miles above the earth characterized by almost uniform temperature.

TROPOPAUSE (*troh*-puh-pawz). The upper edge of the troposphere.

TROPOSPHERE (*troh*-puh-sfihr). The lowest layer of the atmosphere.

Fig. 4-1. Edmond Hillary, right, followed by Tenzing Norkey, at an altitude of 25,000 feet during their climb of Mount Everest. They are both equipped with masks supplied with oxygen from the tanks across their shoulders. Note the flags wrapped around Tenzing's ice axe. They later were flown from the top of Mount Everest.

much lower elevations have difficulty breathing if they exercise strenuously at places like Denver, Colorado, or at the rim of the Grand Canyon in Arizona. Here the elevations are between 5000 and 7000 feet. The pressure of the atmosphere is less at such altitudes. Consequently there is not so much oxygen to breathe. If you are driving along U.S. Route 34 through Rocky Mountain National Park in Colorado, and get out of your car at the Continental Divide, 12,183 feet, you may experience a shortness of breath, and feel slightly dizzy. However, by living several weeks or months at such an al-

titude, your body would become adjusted to the change in the atmosphere.

During May, 1953, the highest mountain on earth was scaled by man for the first time. Edmond Hillary, a New Zealander, and Tenzing Norkey, a Nepalese tribesman, reached the top of Mount Everest, 29,002 feet high. Even though they had lived at high altitudes for several months in order to get adjusted to the rarefied atmosphere, the final climb of 1,100 feet had to be made using special oxygen masks.

The commercial airlines in the United States usually fly at altitudes of about 10,000 feet. However, in crossing the Rockies on flights from Chicago to the West Coast, planes may ascend to altitudes of 20,000 feet. The cabins of the planes which make these flights are pressurized so that the passengers do not feel the effects of the lowered pressure outside, or the decreased supply of oxygen.

The atmosphere is estimated to be from 500 to 5000 miles thick. Man slowly is reaching out toward the edge of it. The highest balloon ascent ever made by man was carried out by Anderson and Stevens on November 11, 1935. A huge balloon lifted them to an altitude of 72,395 feet, or over 13.7 miles. The highest reported altitude reached by a pilot flying an experimental rocket airplane is about 20 miles. Rockets have been fired to an altitude of about 250 miles.

2. What are the layers of the atmosphere? We live in the layer of the atmosphere called the **troposphere** (*troh*-puh-sfihr). *It extends upward from the earth's surface to a height of from 6 to 10 miles.* It contains about 75% of the weight of the atmosphere. The temperature of the air in the troposphere decreases as we get farther from the earth's surface, reaching −65° F at the top of this layer. The density of the atmosphere decreases rapidly, too. At an altitude of 6 miles there is not enough air for respiration. At 12 miles there is not enough oxygen to burn the fuel in a jet airplane engine. Airplanes which go this high or higher must be of the rocket type, which carry their oxygen supply with them. Nearly all of our clouds and storms are produced in the troposphere. *The upper*

Fig. 4-2. In crossing high mountain ranges, commercial airlines fly at altitudes as high as 20,000 feet. Inside the pressurized cabin, the passengers are not aware of the lower atmospheric pressure and decreased supply of oxygen at this altitude.

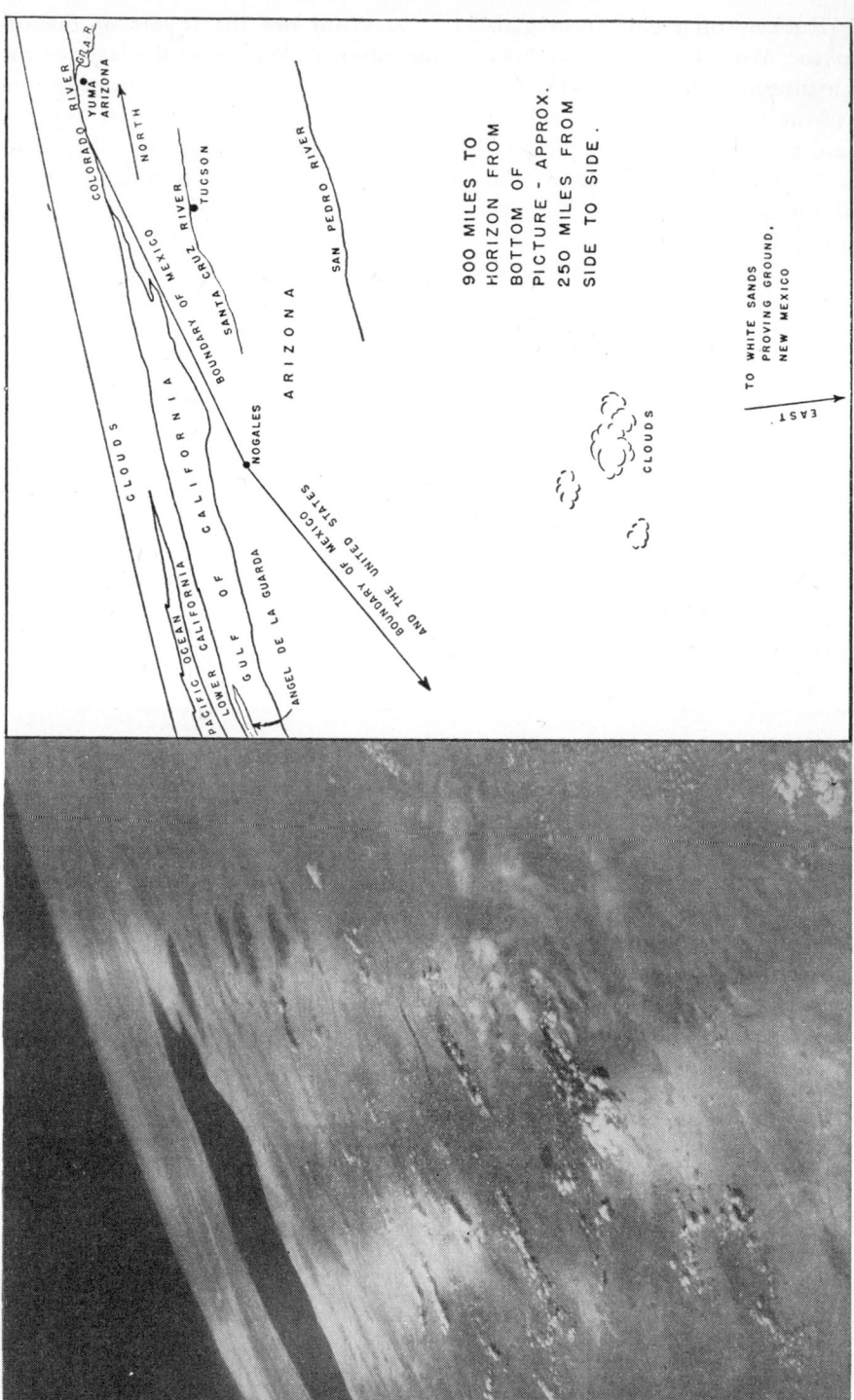

Fig. 4-3. The photograph at the left was taken by a camera on a V–2 rocket at an altitude of 100 miles above the earth. The diagram at the right will help you identify the important landmarks in the photograph.

edge of the troposphere is called the **tropopause** (*troh*-puh-pawz).

Above the troposphere is the **stratosphere** (*strat*-uh-sfihr). *This region of the atmosphere extends from about 10 miles to 20 miles above the earth.* It is in the lower part of the stratosphere that we find the highest clouds. This entire region has an almost uniform temperature of about −80° F. At the top of the stratosphere the atmosphere loses its light-scattering ability. If we were there, the sky would look black to us except for the spots of light made by the sun, moon, and stars.

The **chemosphere** (*kem*-uh-sfihr) is *the layer between 20 and 50 miles up.* This is as close as most meteors get to the earth before they burn out. At the lower edge of this layer most of the ultraviolet rays from the sun are filtered out. Only a small amount of ultraviolet rays reach the surface of the earth. It is in the chemosphere that we find the lowest examples of sky glow, or *auroras* (uh-*ror*-uhz). The temperature of the chemosphere is not uniform. It rises from −65° F at the top of the stratosphere to about 0° F at 30 miles. It then drops down to about −120° F at an altitude of 50 miles.

Above the chemosphere is the **ionosphere** (eye-*on*-uh-sfihr). *This region stretches upward from 50 miles to about 250 miles.* The temperature increases rapidly up through the ionosphere. It is here that the aurora borealis is observed. In a volume of air which contains a million molecules at sea level, there is only one molecule at the lower edge of the ionosphere. At sea level a molecule moves only about 0.000004 inch before it bumps into another molecule. At an altitude of 60 miles it may travel about 1 inch be-

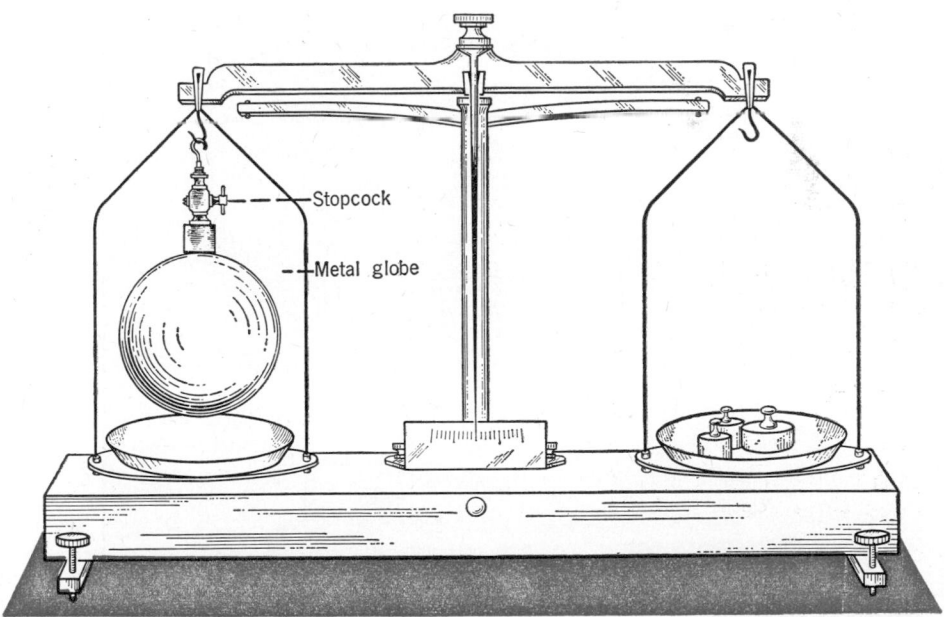

Fig. 4-4. When the baroscope globe has been evacuated, it weighs less than it does when it contains air.

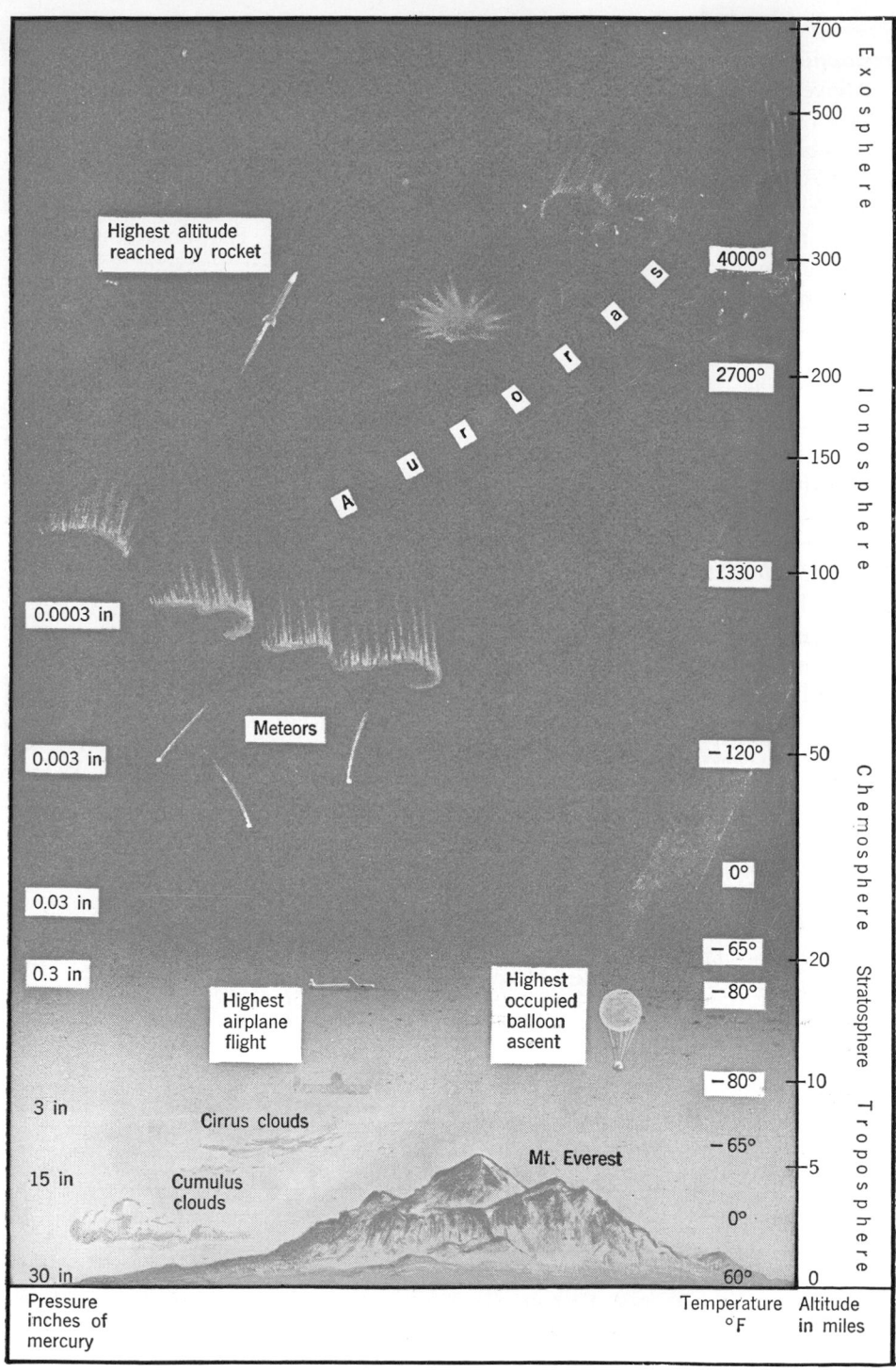

Fig. 4-5. The layers of the atmosphere.

fore it collides. The ionosphere is important for radio broadcasting. It reflects radio waves back to the earth and makes long-range short-wave transmission possible. *From an altitude of 250 miles to the outer edge of the atmosphere stretches the* **exosphere** (*eks*-uh-sfihr). There is very little air in the exosphere.

3. The density of air. We are not usually conscious of the fact that air has weight since we move so easily through it. However, in the laboratory, we may weigh a given volume of air and find its density. For this experiment we use a metal globe, like that shown in Fig. 4-4. First, we weigh the globe when it is full of air. Then we pump out the air and weigh the globe again. We find that now it weighs less than it did the first time. The difference in weight is the weight of the air removed. If we open the stopcock, air rushes in. If we now weigh the globe, we find its weight is the same as at first. This experiment proves that air takes up space and that it has weight. *One liter of dry air at a temperature of 0° C and a pressure of 760 millimeters of mercury weighs 1.293 g.* 0° C is the temperature at which water freezes. 760 millimeters of mercury is the average pressure of the atmosphere at sea level. One liter of air is about $\frac{1}{773}$ as heavy as one liter of water.

Although the density of air is very low compared to that of water, the weight of the air in a large room is surprisingly large. At sea level *1 ft³ of air weighs about 1.30 oz,* and 1 yd³ weighs slightly over 2 lb. The air in a schoolroom 45 ft long × 24 ft wide and with a 14 ft ceiling weighs more than 1200 lb.

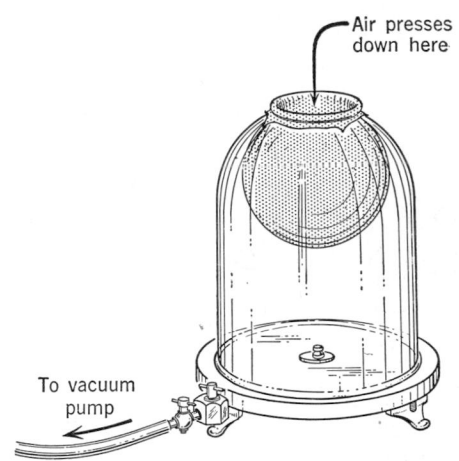

Fig. 4-6. As air is pumped out of the bell jar, the higher air pressure outside pushes the membrane down into the jar.

Air commonly is used as the standard for determining the specific gravity of gases. Hydrogen, the gas of lowest density, is also accepted by scientists as a standard. When hydrogen is used, no gas has a specific gravity that is less than one. Several gases are less dense than air. These include nitrogen, ammonia, and carbon monoxide. However, many gases are more dense than air.

4. Does air exert pressure? Since air has weight, it must exert pressure. Suppose we tie a thin, rubber membrane over the open top of a bell jar, as shown in Fig. 4-6. We put the bell jar on a pump plate, connect it to a vacuum pump, and begin to remove the air. The rubber membrane is pressed farther and farther down into the jar as we gradually pump out the air. Finally, the membrane may burst. As we removed air from the inside of the bell jar, we decreased the *upward force* which the air inside exerted. The *unbalanced downward force* finally burst the membrane.

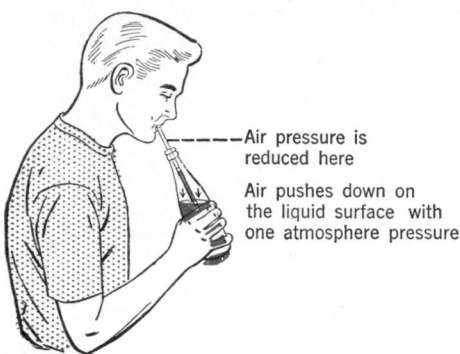

Air pressure is reduced here

Air pushes down on the liquid surface with one atmosphere pressure

Fig. 4-7. When you reduce the air pressure within the straw by the action of your cheeks and lips, the higher air pressure outside pushes the soft drink up through the straw into your mouth.

We may also use an empty varnish can to show air pressure. Let us take a can of one-half gallon capacity and put a small amount of water into it. Next we heat the water until it boils. The steam that forms drives all the air out of the can. Now we stopper the can tightly and cool it by holding it under running water. As the steam condenses and reduces the pressure inside, the unbalanced force of the air outside crushes the can. These experiments show that since air has weight, it exerts pressure.

Although we live at the bottom of a layer of air hundreds of miles deep, we do not feel the pressure which it exerts. This is because the pressure is nearly equal from all directions. However, we notice the enormous force the air can exert when we see wind breaking the limbs of trees, uprooting trees bodily, or damaging buildings.

Gases and liquids are both fluids, and they show some similar properties. Gases transmit pressure in accordance with Pascal's principle. In accordance with Archimedes' principle, gases also

exert a buoyant force on objects placed in them. However, it is not easy to calculate the pressure exerted by any great depth of a gas, since the density is not constant. The viscosity of a gas is very small.

5. Why do liquids rise in exhausted tubes? Every time we suck a soft drink through a straw we show that a liquid rises in an exhausted tube. We now realize that the soft drink rises in the straw because it is pushed up by the greater pressure of the atmosphere. We reduce the air pressure on the surface of the liquid within the straw by the action of our lips and cheeks. See Fig. 4-7. Fundamental experiments on the pressure of the atmosphere were performed by Evangelista Torricelli (toh-ree-*chel*-ee) (1608–1647), an Italian physicist. About the middle of the seventeenth-century men were trying to find out why water from deep wells would not rise more than 32 feet in the tubes of the pumps they were using. Torricelli knew that air had weight, and he suspected that it was the pressure of the surrounding air that pushed the water up the tube of a pump. If this were so, mercury, which is 13.6 times as dense as water, would be pushed up only $\frac{1}{13.6}$ times as high in an exhausted tube. Torricelli took a glass tube about 3 feet long and, after closing one end, filled the tube with mercury. Placing his finger over the open end of the tube, he then inverted the tube in a bowl of mercury, as shown in Fig. 4-8. When he removed his finger from the opening, only a little of the mercury flowed out from the tube. The mercury column, *AB*, stood at a height of about 30 inches above the level of the mercury in the bowl. Torricelli thus proved that the atmospheric pressure at sea level just counterbalances a column of mercury 30 inches high. It is not strictly correct to say that liquids " rise " in exhausted tubes; they are *pushed up* by the pressure of the air on the surface of the liquid outside the tube.

Torricelli's belief in the pressure of the atmosphere was confirmed by Pascal. Pascal reasoned that if the mercury column in a Torricellian tube was actually sustained by the pressure of the atmosphere, the height of the column would be less at higher altitudes. Pascal arranged to have a Torricellian apparatus carried to the top of a 3000 foot high mountain in central France. When the apparatus was assembled at the top of the mountain, the mercury column was found to be about 3 inches shorter than it was at the base of the mountain.

We know that water pressure increases with the depth. Consequently, we expect to find that the pressure of the atmosphere in a valley is greater than it is on the top of a nearby mountain. Air is so compressible, however, that its density varies greatly at different altitudes.

6. The pressure of the atmosphere.
The experiments of Torricelli and Pascal proved conclusively that the height to which a liquid will rise in an exhausted tube depends upon the pressure of the air on the surface of the liquid outside the tube. The air at sea level exerts a pressure which counterbalances a mercury column 76 cm high, which is about 30 in. We know how to calculate liquid pressure, so we can find the pressure exerted by the atmosphere. Liquid pressure equals depth times density. So we multiply 76 cm by 13.6 g/cm³. This gives us a

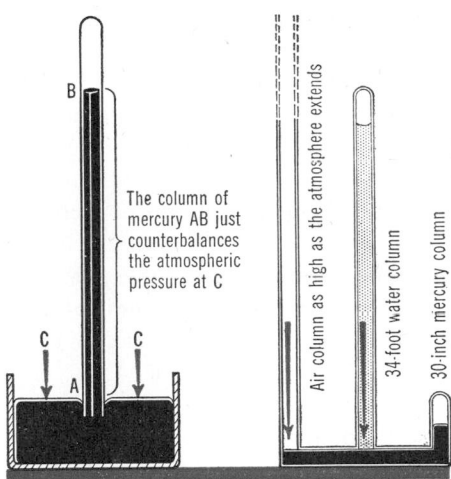

Fig. 4-8. Left. The air at sea level exerts a pressure which may be counterbalanced by a column of mercury 76 centimeters, or about 30 inches, high.
Fig. 4-9. Right. Pressure exerted by a column of air as high as the atmosphere is the same as that exerted by a 34-ft water column or a 30-in mercury column.

pressure of 1033.6 g/cm² at the base of the mercury column. This equals the pressure of the atmosphere at sea level.

In the English system the height of the mercury column is 30 in, or 2.5 ft. The density of mercury is 62.4 lb/ft³ × 13.6 (its specific gravity), or 848.6 lb/ft³. Then,

$$p = \frac{2.5 \text{ ft} \times 848.6 \text{ lb/ft}^3}{144 \text{ in}^2/\text{ft}^2}.$$

Solving, we find the pressure is 14.7 lb/in². This is known as a " pressure of one atmosphere." " Two atmospheres pressure " is twice that, or 29.4 lb/in².

If we make a Torricellian tube that will be filled with water, it must be 13.6 times as long as one filled with mercury. 13.6 × 30 in = 408 in or 34 ft. If the atmospheric pressure at sea level can support a column of water only 34 ft high we can understand why seventeenth-century pumps would not lift water more than 32 ft. No pump produces a perfect vacuum. Fig. 4-9 shows three tubes which represent the relative heights of columns of mercury, water, and the atmosphere, which produce the same pressure.

7. The Magdeburg hemispheres. About 1650 Otto von Guericke (*gay-rih-kuh*) (1602–1686), of Magdeburg, Germany, invented the first air pump which could be used to produce a vacuum. It is believed that, at the time, von Guericke knew nothing of the work of Torricelli and Pascal. He was anxious to observe what happened in a space from which the air had been removed.

Von Guericke devised a very striking experiment to show the enormous force that the atmosphere exerts upon a container from which the air has been pumped. He made two hollow hemispheres about 22 inches in diam-

eter. The edges were ground so perfectly smooth that when they were coated with heavy grease they fitted together airtight. He then pumped the air out of the hemispheres and closed the stopcock. It took 16 horses, eight on each side, to pull the hemispheres apart. See Fig. 4-10. Small hemispheres of this type, fitted together and evacuated of air, even though they are only 3 or 4 inches in diameter, can not be pulled apart by two strong boys.

8. The mercurial barometer. *A* **barometer** (buh-*rom*-uh-ter) *is used to measure the pressure of the atmosphere.* A mercurial barometer is simply a Torricellian apparatus mounted in a frame and having a device for measuring the height of the mercury column. Sometimes the tube and bowl are attached to a board upon which a scale is mounted. In Fig. 4-11, a metal tube is used as a frame to support the glass tube and bowl and to protect them from breakage. The scale, in inches or centimeters, is

Fig. 4-10. Otto von Guericke's experiment illustrating the tremendous force exerted by the atmosphere on two hemispheres which had been placed together and the air inside them evacuated.

etched on the metal tube. The tube has a vertical slot cut in it near the top, as shown in Fig. 4-12 (top right), so the level of the mercury in the glass tube can be seen and measured.

If the air pressure decreases, some of the mercury will flow out of the tube into the bowl. If the air pressure increases, the mercury will flow back into the tube. These changes in the level of the mercury in the bowl will produce an error in the measurements of the height of the mercury column to be read from the fixed scale. Consequently, each barometer has a fixed point, usually an ivory peg, from which to measure the height of the column. This peg is mounted on the frame of the barometer and just inside the bowl. The point of the peg is used as the zero mark of the scale. By means of a flexible membrane and a thumb-screw, as shown in Fig. 4-13 (bottom right), the surface of the mercury in the bowl can be adjusted to coincide with the tip of the ivory peg. This should be done before taking any readings.

Mercury is a suitable liquid for use in a barometer because it has a high specific gravity and does not freeze readily. However, mercury does expand with an increase in temperature. Consequently, readings taken with a mercurial barometer must be corrected for changes in temperature.

9. The aneroid barometer. Since a mercurial barometer is at least 3 feet in length and contains a liquid, it is awkward to handle. Also, it is inconvenient to carry a mercurial barometer from one place to another. In fact, extreme care must be used when one is moved. Furthermore, a mercurial barometer must be mounted in a vertical position.

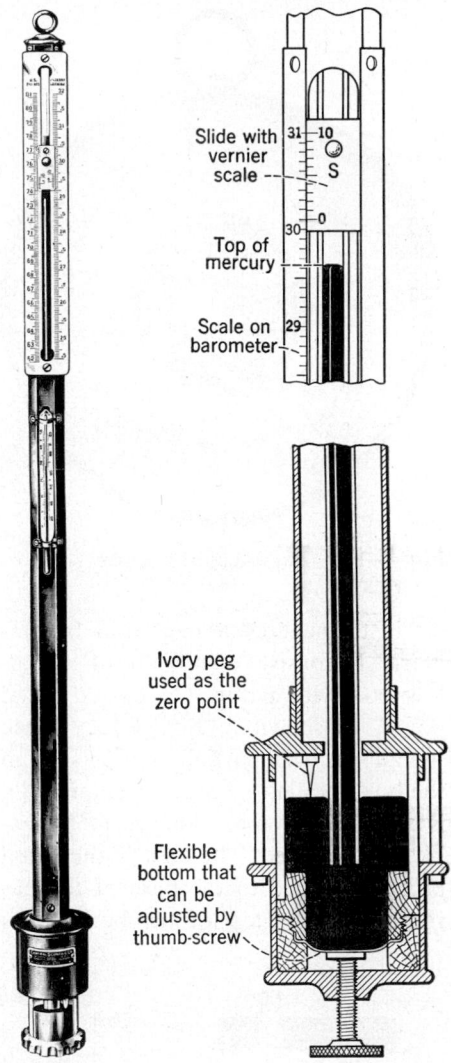

Fig. 4-11. Left. A mercurial barometer.

Fig. 4-12. Top right. A vernier scale is used to enable us to read a barometer more accurately.

Fig. 4-13. Bottom right. The mercury level in the bowl of a barometer must be adjusted to the zero point before each reading is taken.

An **aneroid** (*an*-er-oid) **barometer,** like that shown in Fig. 4-14, overcomes these difficulties since it *does not contain a liquid*. But it is not as accurate

Fig. 4-14. An aneroid barometer.

up or down in response to pressure changes. This motion is communicated by a system of levers and a chain to a shaft with a pointer that moves across a graduated scale. This system of levers multiplies the small movement of the diaphragm so that it may be measured on the scale. See Fig. 4-16. This scale is graduated by comparison with a standard mercurial barometer.

An aneroid barometer may be made in practically any size. Some are small enough to be carried in a pocket, like a watch. Many of them have a dial the size of an ordinary clock face. A good aneroid barometer is so sensitive that it shows a change of pressure when lowered from a table to the floor. ★ *A self-recording aneroid barometer is called a barograph* (*bair*-uh-graf). One type of barograph is shown in Fig. 4-17. It has a long pointer with an ink pen at one end. As the pointer moves up and down with variations in atmospheric pressure, the pen traces a continuous record in ink. Sheets of graph paper are marked with horizontal lines to indicate pressures and vertical lines to show the days and hours of the week. These sheets are fastened to a cylinder which makes a

an instrument as a mercurial barometer. It consists essentially of a shallow box with a thin, corrugated metal cover, as shown in Fig. 4-15. Since the air has been partially removed from the box, the elastic cover, or diaphragm, is very sensitive to changes in atmospheric pressure. The base of the metal box is fastened to the base of the barometer. The top of the box moves

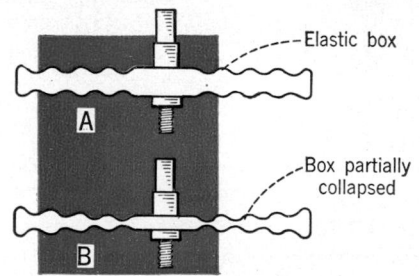

Fig. 4-15. The top figure, A, shows the partially evacuated metal box which is the essential part of an aneroid barometer. The lower figure, B, shows how the box collapses when the atmospheric pressure becomes greater.

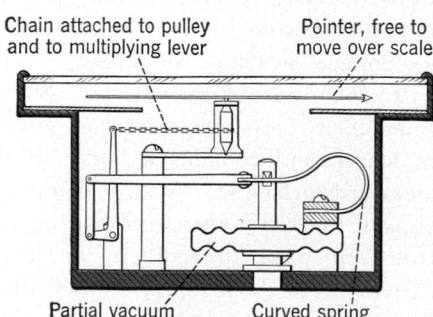

Fig. 4-16. Cross-section of an aneroid barometer showing the working parts.

Fig. 4-17. A barograph, or self-recording barometer. Variations in the atmospheric pressure produce slight movements in the cover of the partially evacuated corrugated metal box at the lower right of the instrument. A series of levers magnifies this movement and transmits it to the long arm, which is equipped with an ink pen. The variations in atmospheric pressure are then recorded as a wavy line on the graph paper mounted on the rotating cylinder at the left. The cylinder makes one complete revolution in seven days.

complete revolution in one week. As the paper turns on the cylinder, the pen in the pointer traces a continuous line that shows the pressure for any time during the week. Sheets of this kind may be filed as a permanent record of the atmospheric pressure. Fig. 4-18 shows such a record made at Newark, New Jersey, for the period of September 20–25, 1938.

10. A barometer may be used to measure altitude. Barometers have been used for many years to measure altitudes. The special type of aneroid barometer used in airplanes *is graduated to read altitudes directly*. It is called an **altimeter** (al-*tim*-uh-ter). This is one of the most important instruments used by airplane pilots. It can be adjusted easily to compensate for variations in atmospheric pressure caused by weather conditions encountered during a flight. Consequently, it gives the pilot a continuous, as well as a very reliable, indication of his altitude above sea level.

For comparatively small elevations the barometer falls 0.1 inch for every

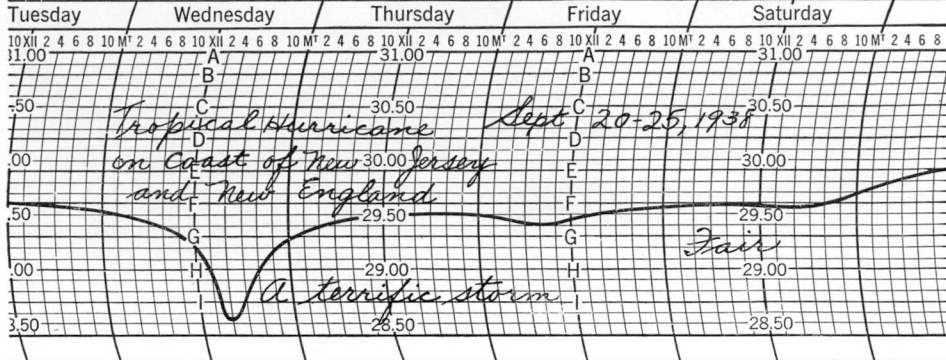

Fig. 4-18. Record of the barometric pressure during a very severe hurricane which swept up the coast of New Jersey and through New England during September, 1938. Notice the very low barometric pressure at the height of the storm between Wednesday noon and midnight.

90 feet of ascent. The fall is not so regular above a few hundred feet. At the top of Mt. Whitney in California,

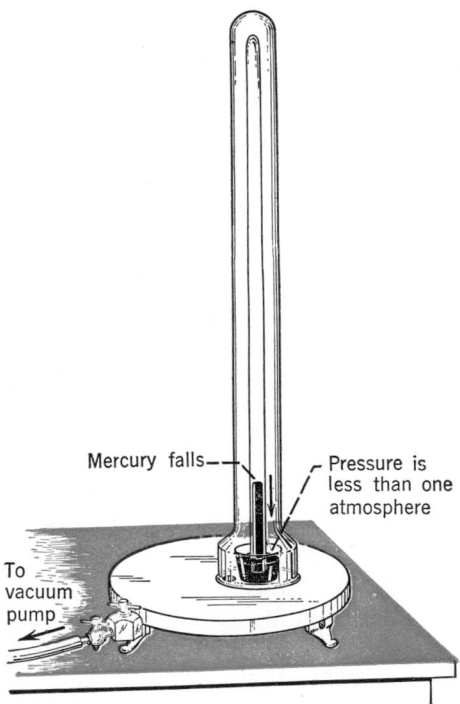

Fig. 4-19. As the pressure inside the tall bell jar is reduced, the mercury level in the barometer falls.

which is 14,495 feet above sea level, the barometer reading there is a little over half the reading at sea level. At the top of the highest mountain in the world, Mt. Everest in the Himalayas, which is 29,002 feet above sea level, the barometer reading is less than 10 inches.

Let us put a Torricellian apparatus under a bell jar so that the air pressure may be reduced by means of a vacuum pump, as shown in Fig. 4-19. Now we can easily see what happens to the mercury column as we pump the air from the bell jar. Without the necessity of carrying a barometer to the top of the mountain, we are able to observe what is happening to the mercury column in a barometer as the air pressure is being lowered.

As the air pressure is reduced, the mercury falls in the tube. The completeness with which we remove the air is shown by how nearly the level of the mercury in the tube reaches the mercury level in the bowl. When air is readmitted at atmospheric pressure, the mercury rises to its original height.

QUESTIONS

GROUP A

1. How can you sometimes detect whether you are ascending or descending through the atmosphere? Give some examples which illustrate how you may experience these effects in your own locality.

2. In which layer of the atmosphere do we live? What are its prominent characteristics? What is the upper edge of this layer called?

3. Where is the stratosphere located? What are its prominent characteristics?

4. What name is given to the layer of the atmosphere in which the ultraviolet rays of the sun are filtered out? What are some other characteristics of this layer?

5. Why is the ionosphere an important layer of the atmosphere?

6. What is the weight of one liter of air? What is the weight of one cubic foot of air?

7. Water is used as a standard for determining the specific gravity of solids and liquids. What is used as a standard for determining the specific gravity of gases?

8. Why do we not feel the pressure exerted by the atmosphere?

9. What is the pressure of the atmosphere in grams per square centimeter? In pounds per square foot?

10. What are the advantages of a mercurial barometer? What are its disadvantages?

11. What are the advantages of an aneroid barometer? What are its disadvantages?

★ **12.** What is a barograph? For what is it used?

GROUP B

13. How are the changes in atmospheric pressure experienced in airplane flight partially reduced in the cabins of large passenger airplanes?

14. Describe an experiment by which we may determine the density of the air.

15. Describe an experiment which proves that air exerts pressure.

16. Suppose you open a bottle of soft drink. Insert in the bottle a glass tube which has been passed through a stopper which fits the mouth of the bottle tightly. When you suck on the glass tube, are you able to obtain any soft drink? Why?

17. In what way did Pascal confirm Torricelli's belief that the pressure of the atmosphere supported the column of mercury in a closed glass tube?

18. What is a vernier? How is it used to measure fractions of a scale division on a barometer?

19. Describe in detail how you would make a reading of a mercurial barometer.

20. Does the diameter of a barometer tube have any effect on the height of the mercury column?

21. Why is mercury considered to be a more satisfactory liquid to use in a barometer than is water?

22. If a mercurial barometer is not hung vertically, will it give a true reading? What specific distance must be measured in order to get a true reading?

PROBLEMS

(In the Mathematics Refresher, refer to Sections 10, 12, 14, and 16.)

GROUP A

1. What will be the weight in grams of a cubic meter of air?

2. A physics laboratory is 45 ft long and 22 ft wide and has a ceiling 12-ft high. What is the weight, in pounds, of the air in this particular room?

3. The density of carbon monoxide gas is 1.250 g/l at 0° C and 760 mm of mercury pressure. Find its specific gravity, air standard.

4. The barometer at the bottom of a hill reads 29.8 inches. At the top of the hill, it reads 29.5 inches. What is the height of the hill?

5. What is the pressure in lb/in² of a pressure of three atmospheres? Of a pressure of 50 atmospheres? Of a pressure of 600 atmospheres?

6. The specific gravity of neon gas, which is used in some illuminated signs, is 0.696, air standard. Calculate the weight of a cubic foot of this gas.

7. If the barometer stands at 735 mm, what is the atmospheric pressure in g/cm²?

8. If the average pressure is 15 lb/in², calculate the total force on the six faces of an evacuated, oblong can 6 inches long, 4 inches wide, and 8 inches tall.

GROUP B

9. If a mercury barometer were sunk 15 ft below the surface of a lake when the air pressure was 29.5 inches of mercury, what would the reading of the barometer be?

10. Calculate the combined pressure of the air and water on an object immersed in 30 meters of water at the bottom of the lake.

11. The original Magdeburg hemispheres used by Otto von Guericke were 22 inches in diameter. What force was needed to separate them? (Hint: Calculate the pressure on a circle 22 inches in diameter. Why?)

12. The specific gravity of sulfur dioxide is 2.264, air standard. Calculate the weight of 5 liters of this gas. What will 1500 ft³ of sulfur dioxide weigh?

13. What will be the total pressure of air and sea water on the body of a diver who has descended 150 ft below the surface of the ocean?

14. Ordinary laboratory Magdeburg hemispheres have a diameter of 12.5 cm. If they are completely evacuated, how many gram-weights of force are needed to separate them?

15. On a certain day the mercury barometer stands at 760 mm. At what height would a water barometer stand? If the specific gravity of alcohol is 0.80, at what height would an alcohol barometer stand?

16. A high school gymnasium is 30 meters long, 20 meters wide, and 7 meters high. Calculate the weight, in kilograms, of the air in this gymnasium.

17. The diameter of a spherical baroscope globe is 4 inches. What weight of air does it hold at atmospheric pressure? (See the Mathematics Refresher for the formula for finding the volume of a sphere.)

★ 2. WEATHER

★ **11. Making a weather map.** Forecasts of the weather to be expected in your locality during the next 24 to 48 hours are made periodically by the United States Weather Bureau. These forecasts are based on the information compiled on weather maps. About 750 weather offices in North America, the West Indies, and in the adjacent ocean areas send reports to the Weather Bureau. These reports are made four times daily: at 1:30 A.M. and P.M. and at 7:30 A.M. and P.M., Eastern Standard Time. They come in by telephone, telegraph, radio, and teletypewriter. As the reports are received, the data they contain are entered on an outline map at the location corresponding to each station. The completed map then gives a picture of weather conditions over the entire area.

★ **12. What observations are made?** Many separate observations are made by the personnel of each weather station. They estimate the fraction of the sky covered by clouds, and classify the type of cloud. They read the barometer, and correct the reading to the corresponding value at sea level. By making this correction, the barometric readings from all the stations may be directly compared. The personnel of the weather station find the direction and speed of the winds. They measure the amount of rainfall or snowfall, if any. They record the present temperature, as well as the highest and lowest temperature since the last observation. They calculate the humidity, that is, the amount of moisture in the air. They report any other weather conditions, such as thunderstorms, fog, or smoke.

They code the data from these observations and transmit them to the collection center. At the receiving office, their messages are decoded and entered on a blank weather map. On this map there is a circle for each reporting station. *Around this circle the data are written on the map in a definite pattern using standardized weather symbols.* This arrangement is called a **station model.**

The forecaster records all the data on a weather map and *connects points of equal barometric pressure with lines* called **isobars** (eye-suh-barz). He also marks the *boundaries, or* **fronts,** *between different air masses* and shades locations where rain or snow is falling. This gives a more graphic picture of the total weather conditions which exist throughout the country.

★ **13. Weather observers measure atmospheric pressure in millibars.** Physicists usually measure atmospheric pressure in centimeters, millimeters, or inches of mercury. But meteorologists throughout the world use another unit of pressure called a *millibar.* A pressure of 1000 millibars equals 29.53 inches of mercury. The table at the bottom of the page shows the relation between barometric pressure in inches and millibars.

The isobars on a weather map are drawn at 3 millibar intervals. For example, an isobar is drawn through all points reporting a barometric pressure of 1020 millibars. Other isobars are drawn through those points reporting

pressures of 1023, 1026, 1029 millibars, and so on. The centers of these higher pressure regions are marked "High." Other isobars are drawn through points reporting lower pressures, 1017, 1014, 1011 millibars, and so on. The center of low pressure areas is marked "Low."

★ **14. Studying a weather map.** Fig. 4-20 shows a somewhat simplified weather map of the type prepared by the Weather Bureau. At each of the locations from which data are recorded, we see the station model with its symbols. These symbols indicate the weather conditions at this particular point at the time of observation. Even though the names of the cities do not appear on this map, you probably can locate the station model for New York City. It is also shown in Fig. 4-21. Examine this station model to see whether you can interpret it. The circle is one-quarter darkened, which means that the sky is $\frac{2}{10}$ to $\frac{3}{10}$ covered with clouds. The arrow representing wind direction is from the northwest. The tail of the arrow tells you that the wind velocity is between 19 and 24 miles per hour. The present temperature is 44° F. The atmospheric pressure is indicated by the number 146. This means that the pressure, corrected to sea level, is 1014.6 millibars. The symbol +8 means that the barometer has risen 0.8

Inches	Millibars	Inches	Millibars
27.0	914	29.5	999
27.5	931	30.0	1016
28.0	948	30.5	1033
28.5	965	31.0	1050
29.0	982	31.5	1067

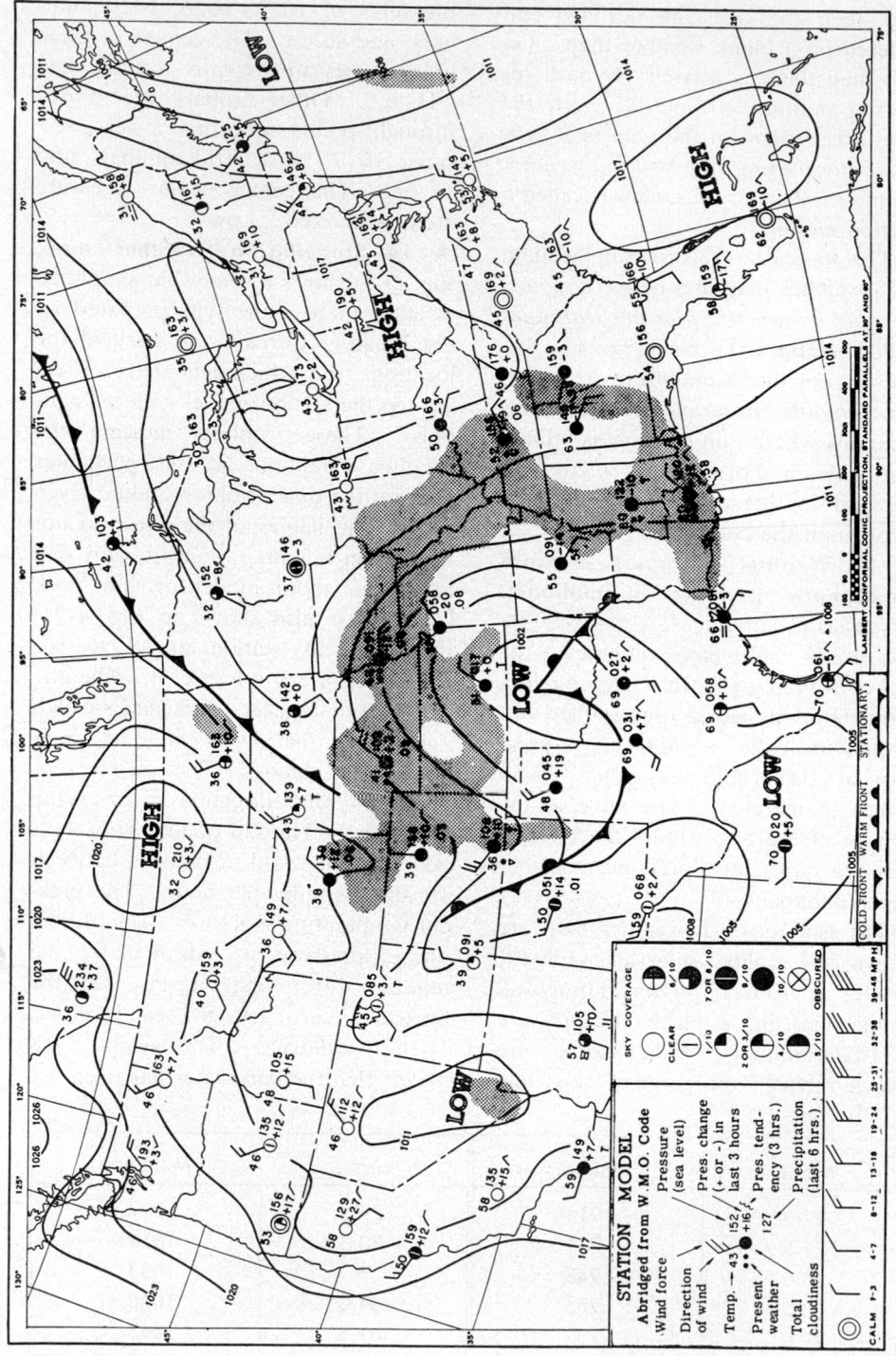

Fig. 4-20.   The Daily Weather Map shows at a glance the weather for the whole country.

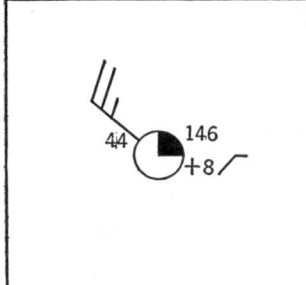

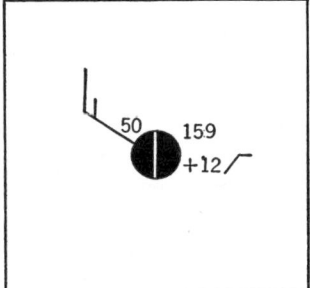

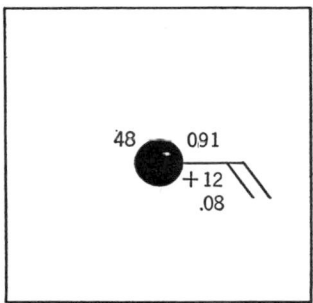

Fig. 4-21. Station model, New York City.

Fig. 4-22. Station model, San Francisco.

Fig. 4-23. Station model, Omaha, Nebraska.

millibars in the three hours prior to the observation.

The solid lines on the map are the isobars. They show the weather forecaster the position of the important atmospheric disturbances and locate their centers. The broad lines which have triangles or half circles on them are the fronts. It is along these lines that that greatest changes in weather conditions are taking place.

Now examine the direction of the winds about the very prominent low pressure area centered in Oklahoma. Notice that the winds circle such a low pressure area in a counter-clockwise direction. As a result, when a " Low " is approaching a particular locality, it appears to be coming from almost the opposite direction.

Around the high pressure areas, like that centered over West Virginia, we find the winds blowing in a clockwise direction. The general circulation of the air on the earth's surface is from areas of high pressure to those of low pressure. At the high pressure areas, air is descending from the upper levels of the atmosphere. In a low pressure area, the air is rising because it is being pushed upward by the air flowing into this area along the surface of the

ground. The air entering a high pressure area from the upper levels of the atmosphere is warmed because its pressure is being increased. As a result, we find clear skies in these locations. In low pressure areas, the rising air is cooled by expansion. This produces cloudiness and precipitation.

★ **15. What are warm fronts and cold fronts?** A " Low " such as that centered over Oklahoma in the weather map, Fig. 4-20, is formed from two great currents of air. One of these currents is warm air; the other one is cold air. The fronts develop at the boundaries between these air masses.

At the **warm front,** to the east, *the warm air flows against and over the cold current of air.* As a result this warm air is cooled by expansion. Since it originally came from the Gulf of Mexico, it contains considerable water vapor. The cooling of this moist air produces the precipitation that has fallen to the east and northeast of the surface location of the warm front.

To the south and west of the " Low," we find a **cold front.** *Along this front, the colder air* from the northwest *is sweeping under the warm air, and forcing it to rise.* The precipitation northwest of the " Low " is produced by this

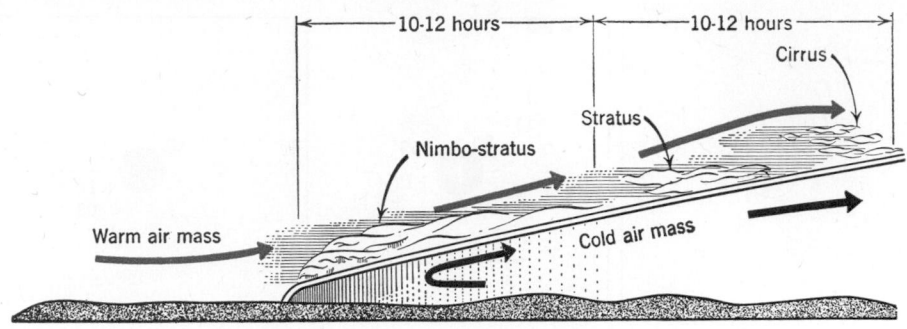

Fig. 4-24. A warm front tends to ride up over a mass of cold air. As it does this, the air is cooled by expansion and the water vapor it contains is condensed and produces precipitation.

condition. Notice the difference in the surface temperatures on either side of these two fronts. Notice, too, that between the fronts we have a region which, while cloudy, is warm and without precipitation.

★ **16. The movement of weather conditions across the United States.** During the long period in which the Weather Bureau has taken observations, meteorologists have learned numerous facts about the movement of weather disturbances. They have found that " High " and " Low " pressure areas generally travel in an easterly direction across the United States in more or less well-defined paths. By studying the movement of air masses and the locations of the " fronts," skilled observers can be remarkably accurate in their predictions. It has also been found that the velocity of " Highs " and " Lows " usually varies from 400 to 700 miles per day. However, storms may suddenly slow down, speed up, or remain stationary for several hours. As warm and cold fronts pass successively over one place after another, they bring with them their own characteristic weather conditions. " Highs " and " Lows " generally succeed each other in a given location at two- to three-day intervals. These " High " and " Low " pressure areas are generally from 500 to 1500 miles in diameter.

Usually weather predictions are made 24 hours in advance, with new predictions made approximately every six hours.

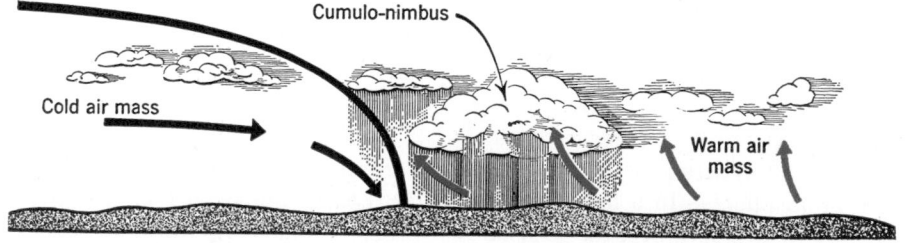

Fig. 4-25. A cold front sweeps under masses of warm air, causing them to rise. The cooling of the warm air by expansion often causes precipitation.

Summary

Man slowly is reaching out toward the edge of the atmosphere. Already he has conquered the highest mountain on earth, has flown an airplane to an altitude of about 20 miles, and has fired rockets to a height of about 250 miles.

The layers of the atmosphere are the troposphere in which we live; the stratosphere, a region of almost uniform temperature; the chemosphere, where ultraviolet rays are absorbed; the ionosphere, from which radio waves are reflected; and the exosphere, which stretches to the outer edge of the atmosphere.

Air has weight. One liter of dry air at a temperature of 0° C and a pressure of 760 mm of mercury weighs 1.293 g. Air also exerts pressure. At sea level the pressure is 14.7 lb/in². The rise of liquids in exhausted tubes is caused by air pressure. Torricelli showed that air pressure supports a column of mercury 76 centimeters high. Pascal showed that air pressure decreases with increasing elevation. Von Guericke invented the first vacuum pump.

A barometer is an instrument used to measure atmospheric pressure. There are several types of barometers: the mercurial barometer, the aneroid barometer, and the altimeter.

Weather maps are based upon weather observations made four times daily at about 750 weather offices in the North American area. Weather maps show "High" and "Low" pressure areas, as well as the regions in which weather disturbances are taking place. Meteorologists measure atmospheric pressure in millibars. The principal types of weather disturbance are warm fronts, in which warm air flows against and up over a cold current of air, and cold fronts, in which cold air sweeps under a blanket of warm air. Weather disturbances usually move across the United States from west to east.

Terms to Define . . .

Altimeter	"High"	Stratosphere
Aneriod barometer	Ionosphere	Torricellian apparatus
Atmosphere	Isobar	Tropopause
Atmospheric pressure	"Low"	Troposphere
Aurora	Magdeburg hemispheres	Variation of barometer reading at different altitudes
Barograph	Mercurial barometer	
Chemosphere	Millibar	Warm front
Cold front	Pressure of air	Weather map
Exosphere	Specific gravity of gases	Weather observations
Four atmospheres pressure	Station model	Weight of air

Questions

at Omaha, Nebraska, as shown in the station model, Fig. 4-23 on page 77.

★ **14.** What prediction would you make for the weather during the next 24 hours at Chicago, as indicated by the weather map?

GROUP A

★ **1.** From what sources is the information obtained that is used in making a weather map?

★ **2.** How frequently are weather maps compiled by the United States Weather Bureau?

★ **3.** What specific kinds of information are used in making a weather map?

★ **4.** What is meant by "station model"?

★ **5.** How is an isobar drawn on a weather map? What is the pressure interval between isobars on a weather map?

★ **6.** What is a "High"? What is a "Low"?

★ **7.** What are the two types of fronts? How are they indicated on a weather map?

★ **8.** In which direction do winds circle a low pressure area? In which direction do they circle a high pressure area?

GROUP B

★ **9.** Why do winds circle a low pressure area in the direction they do? Why do winds circle a high pressure area in the direction they do?

★ **10.** Describe the movement of the air masses and the type of weather conditions to be expected as a cold front passes.

★ **11.** Describe the movement of the air masses and the type of weather conditions to be expected as a warm front passes.

★ **12.** Interpret the present weather conditions at San Francisco, as shown in the station model, Fig. 4-22 on page 77.

★ **13.** Interpret the present weather conditions

Problems

In the Mathematics Refresher, refer to Sections 8 and 16.)

GROUP A

★ **1.** The barometer reading at Minneapolis-St. Paul, as shown on the weather map, is 1015.2 millibars. What will be the barometer reading in inches of mercury?

★ **2.** The barometer reading at San Antonio, Texas, is 1005.8 millibars. What is this reading in inches of mercury?

★ **3.** Convert a barometer reading of 29.2 inches of mercury to the corresponding reading in millibars.

★ **4.** Convert a barometer reading of 30.65 inches of mercury to the corresponding reading in millibars.

GROUP B

★ **5.** The barometric pressure in Boston, as on the weather map, is 1012.5 millibars. What is the pressure in millimeters of mercury?

★ **6.** The station model near Yellowstone Park shows a barometer reading of 1014.9 millibars. What is this pressure in millimeters of mercury?

Things to Do

1. Look up the current altitude records for balloon ascents, for rocket airplane flights, and for rockets.

2. Maintain a record of weather observations made twice daily for a period of two weeks. During each observation determine the temperature, barometric pressure, sky condition, wind direction, and amount of precipitation.

3. Many newspapers print some form of daily weather map. Collect these maps for two weeks. Write a report which gives your opinion concerning the way in which the weather travels across the United States.

4. Take an aneroid barometer into a valley and to the top of a hill and note the variation in its reading with changes of altitude.

Chapter 5

Mechanics of Gases

---

1. COMPRESSION AND EXPANSION OF GASES

1. The volume of a gas depends on the pressure. If we put a pint of milk into a quart bottle, the milk will not expand to fill the entire bottle. But if we let the air out of an inflated inner tube, the air expands and occupies more space than it did in the inner tube. Since liquids have a definite volume, we can easily measure quarts of milk or liters of water. Gases, however, expand and completely fill their containers.

The volume occupied by a particular weight of gas depends on the pressure exerted on it. Suppose we blow up a rubber balloon until it is about half inflated. Next let us put it under a bell jar, as shown in Fig. 5-1, and gradually exhaust the air that surrounds the balloon. As we remove air from the jar, we reduce the pressure on the outside of the balloon. The air inside the balloon expands and increases the volume of the balloon. If we let air flow into

the bell jar until the pressure is the same as before, the balloon shrinks to its original size. This experiment shows that the volume occupied by a gas depends on the pressure. It also shows that gases are perfectly elastic.

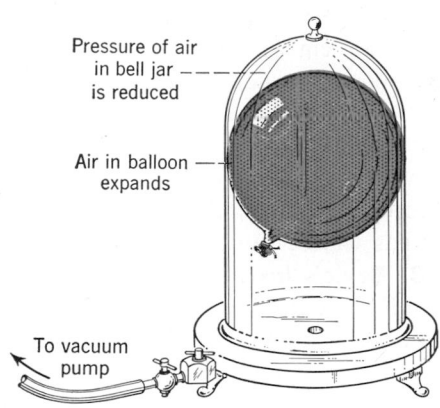

Fig. 5-1. The gas inside the balloon expands when the pressure on the outside of the balloon is decreased.

Vocabulary

BOYLE'S LAW. The volume of a dry gas varies inversely with the pressure exerted on it, provided the temperature remains constant.

STANDARD PRESSURE. The pressure of a column of mercury 760 mm high.

STANDARD TEMPERATURE. The temperature of melting ice, 0° C.

2. What are standard temperature and pressure?   The dimensions of both solids and liquids change slightly with changes in temperature and pressure.   But the variation is so small that it is usually neglected.   If a carpenter wishes to cut a board 12 feet long he does not bother to read the thermometer or the barometer.

On the other hand, gas volumes vary so much that it is always necessary to consider both the temperature and the pressure when we measure them. Physicists use *the temperature of melting ice,* which is 0° C (32° F) as the **standard temperature** for measuring gas volumes.

The pressure of a column of mercury 760 mm high, or 76 cm high, is used as the **standard pressure.**   The abbreviation *S. T. P.* is used to indicate *standard temperature and pressure.* For example, a gas may have a volume of 1000 cm³ at S. T. P.   This means that 1000 cm³ is the volume which the gas occupies when its temperature is 0° C, and the pressure applied to it is one atmosphere, or 760 mm of mercury.   At a different temperature and pressure, the volume of that particular gas will be quite different.

3. Boyle's law.   An English scientist, Robert Boyle (1627–1691), was the first person to perform experiments on what he called the " springiness of the air."   No doubt other scientists living at that time knew about compressed air.   But none of them had performed experiments to learn how the volume of a gas is affected by the pressure exerted on it.

In his experiments, Boyle used a J-shaped tube similar to that shown in Fig. 5-2.   He poured just enough mercury into the tube to fill the bent por-

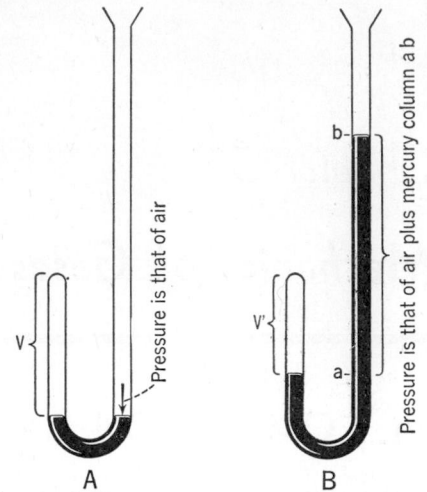

Fig. 5-2.   J-tube apparatus used to demonstrate Boyle's law.

tion.   He then adjusted the mercury levels so that they would be at the same height in both arms of the tube.   In this way, Boyle trapped a volume of air, *V,* in the short arm of the tube. Next he measured the length of the tube so that he could determine the volume of the confined gas.   He knew that this gas must be under atmospheric pressure, because the mercury levels were the same.   See Fig. 5-2*A.* By reading the barometer, Boyle found the exact pressure exerted on the volume of gas, *V.*   Let us call that pressure *p.*

Next he added more mercury to the long arm of the tube, as shown in Fig. 5-2*B.*   By measuring the length of the column of air in the short arm he could determine its new volume, *V'.*   He could find the new pressure, *p',* on this volume of gas by measuring the length of the mercury column *ab,* and adding that length to the barometer reading.

As a result of several trials with this type of apparatus, Boyle found that increasing the pressure upon a volume of confined gas reduced its volume correspondingly. Doubling the pressure reduced the volume to one-half. Tripling the pressure reduced the volume to one-third.

BOYLE'S LAW may be stated as follows: *The volume of a dry gas varies inversely with the pressure exerted upon it, provided the temperature remains constant.*

★ **4. A graph of Boyle's law.** Suppose we take 2000 cm³ of a gas measured at a pressure of 200 mm of mercury. Let us subject it to each of the pressures indicated at the left in the following table. By experiment, we then find the volume occupied by this gas at each pressure.

Pressure	Volume
200 mm	2000 cm³
250	1600
333	1200
400	1000
500	800
800	500
1000	400
1200	333
1600	250
2000	200

We have plotted this data in Fig. 5-3, using the pressures as abscissas, and the volumes as ordinates. This is a graph of Boyle's law. A graph of this shape represents an *inverse proportion.*

Since one factor increases as the other decreases, *the product of a pressure and its corresponding volume is always a constant quantity.* In equation form,

$$pV = \text{a constant.}$$

In all cases, except under very high pressures,

$$pV = p'V'.$$

p is the original pressure, V is the original volume. p' represents the new pressure, and V' the new volume. See Sample Problem at the bottom of page 84.

5. How does a change in pressure affect the density of a gas? There is no change in the weight of a gas when its volume is changed by a difference in the pressure exerted upon it. When the volume of a certain weight of gas is decreased, its density is increased. Since an increase in pressure produces a decrease in the volume of a gas, it must also increase the density of the gas. See Fig. 5-4. *The density of a gas varies directly with the pressure exerted on the gas.* A liter of air weighs 1.29 g at a pressure of one atmos-

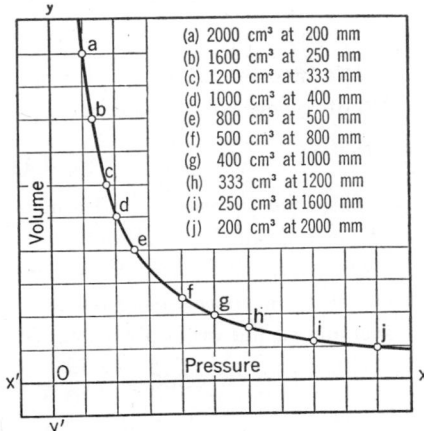

(a) 2000 cm³ at 200 mm
(b) 1600 cm³ at 250 mm
(c) 1200 cm³ at 333 mm
(d) 1000 cm³ at 400 mm
(e) 800 cm³ at 500 mm
(f) 500 cm³ at 800 mm
(g) 400 cm³ at 1000 mm
(h) 333 cm³ at 1200 mm
(i) 250 cm³ at 1600 mm
(j) 200 cm³ at 2000 mm

Fig. 5-3. The graph shows the relationship between the pressure on a gas and its volume. This is the graph of two quantities which are inversely proportional.

phere. A liter container can hold four times 1.29 g, or 5.16 g, of air under a pressure of four atmospheres. In this case the air is four times as dense. See Sample Problem at top of page 85.

6. The vacuum and compression pump. A simple type of air pump is shown in Fig. 5-5. It consists of a piston, which can move up-and-down within a cylinder, and a pair of valves, which control the direction in which the air flows. In the cylinder the piston fits so tightly that air can not pass around it. However, air may enter the

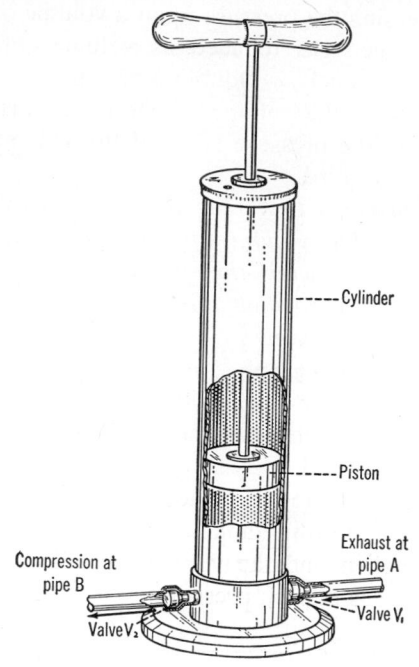

Fig. 5-5. This simple pump may be used either as a vacuum pump or as a compression pump.

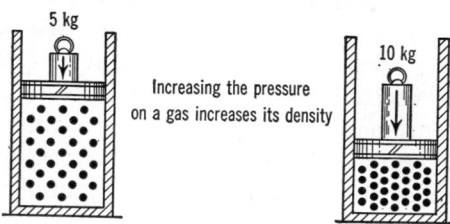

Fig. 5-4. When we increase the pressure on a gas, we also increase its density.

SAMPLE PROBLEM

We measure 500 cm³ of a gas under a pressure of 750 mm of mercury. What volume will this gas occupy if the pressure is increased to 800 mm?

SOLUTION No. 1

Since the pressure is to be increased from 750 mm to 800 mm, the volume of the gas will be decreased. It will be decreased by the ratio of the pressures, $\frac{750}{800}$. (Because the volume is *decreased*, the *smaller* pressure is the numerator in the pressure ratio.)

Multiplying the original volume, 500 cm³, by the pressure ratio, $\frac{750}{800}$,

$$500 \times \frac{750}{800} = 468.8 \text{ cm}^3, \text{ the new volume.}$$

★ SOLUTION No. 2

We may also use the formula $pV = p'V'$ to solve this problem.
Substituting, $750 \times 500 = 800 \times V'$.
Solving, $V' = 468.8$ cm³, the new volume.

SAMPLE PROBLEM

A certain gas has a density of 1.5 g/l at a pressure of 760 mm. What will be its density if the pressure is decreased to 730 mm?

SOLUTION

Since the density varies directly with the pressure, a decrease in pressure will produce a decrease in density.

We multiply the original density, 1.5 g/l, by the ratio of the pressures, $\frac{730}{760}$. (Since the density is to be *decreased*, the *smaller* pressure is the numerator of the pressure ratio.)

$1.5 \times \frac{730}{760} = 1.44$ g/l, the new density.

cylinder through valve V_1 and is expelled from the cylinder through valve V_2. In operation, on the upstroke of the piston, the air above it is pushed out of the cylinder. Valve V_2 is closed. Valve V_1 opens to let air enter through A. Air enters the cylinder because the pressure at A is greater than the pressure in the cylinder. On the downstroke, valve V_1 closes and V_2 opens as the piston pushes the air out of the lower part of the cylinder.

This type of pump may be used either as a vacuum pump or as a compression pump. If a container is attached at A, the contents will be evacuated as the pump operates. Air may be compressed in a container attached at B.

★ **7. The rotary vacuum pump.** The rotary vacuum pump, Fig. 5-6, will produce a high vacuum quickly. Fig. 5-7 shows how the pump operates. Cylinder C rotates inside a case about an off-center axis. Vane V pushes down on the cylinder and divides the air space inside the case. As the cylinder turns, the space connected to the intake increases. Air flows into this

space. The rotating cylinder then closes the intake and pushes the air around to the outlet. With each revolution of the cylinder more air enters through the intake, becomes trapped, and is pushed around to the outlet. A container attached to the intake side of this pump is quickly evacuated. The moving parts of the pump are made to fit precisely. They rotate in a bath of special oil which coats them and prevents leakage of air between them. With such pumps it is possible to reduce the pressure in an airtight container to 0.025 mm of mercury.

★ **8. What is an aspirator?** An instrument called an *aspirator* (*ass*-per-ayt-er) is often used in the laboratory to produce a partial vacuum or to provide gentle suction. It is screwed to a water faucet, and the container to be evacuated is attached to the tube on its side. A diagram of an aspirator is shown in Fig. 5-8. As a stream of water flows rapidly through the inner tube, it drags along with it air molecules from the container which is being evacuated. The air in the container expands and more molecules are

Fig. 5-6. A rotary vacuum pump.

carried away by the running water. A fairly low pressure, about 40 mm of mercury, can be obtained by this par-

ticular method of using an aspirator.

The same principle is applied in the mercury diffusion pump, Fig. 5-9. In

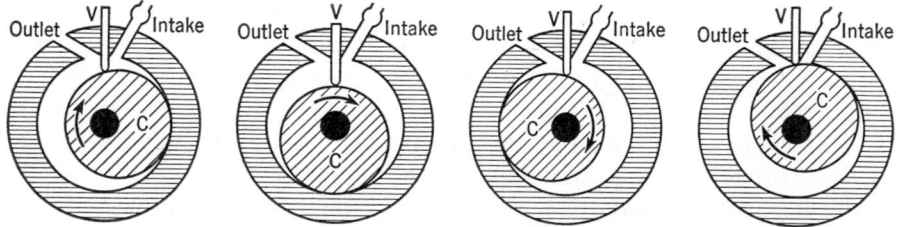

Fig. 5-7. As the cylinder C of this vacuum pump rotates, air enters through the intake. This air is then caught between the cylinder and the case, and finally expelled through the outlet. As the cylinder continues to turn, more air is removed from the intake side to increase the vacuum.

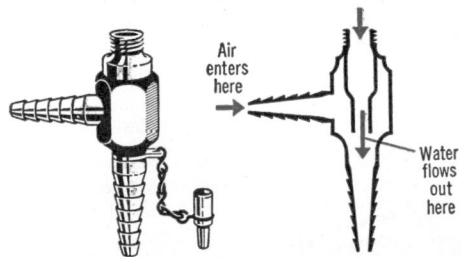

Fig. 5-8. As a stream of water flows through the inner tube of the aspirator, it drags along gas molecules from the container attached to the side arm.

ken into a fine spray by the blast of air from the cylinder.

★ When wind blows across the top of a chimney, it carries away some of the gas molecules within the chimney. The gases within the chimney expand. This decreases their density. Consequently, a chimney draws much better on a windy day. See Fig. 5-11.

10. Applications of the vacuum pump. A vacuum pump is used to remove part or all of the air from a con-

place of a moving stream of water, this pump uses moving mercury vapor. The vapor traps the molecules of air and carries them away. At the outlet of the pump the mercury vapor is cooled until it condenses to a liquid. The air molecules which it carried along are removed by a rotary vacuum pump. A mercury diffusion pump in combination with a rotary vacuum pump can produce a pressure lower than 0.000001 mm of mercury.

9. How does a garden sprayer work? A hand-type garden sprayer used for dispersing small quantities of insecticides is shown in Fig. 5-10. A small tube extends into the tank of the sprayer. Fastened to the tank is a cylinder fitted with a piston. At the end of the cylinder, a second small tube is set at right angles to and just on a level with the tube from the tank. When the piston is pushed forward in the cylinder, a stream of air blows across the top of the vertical tube. This reduces the pressure inside the vertical tube because some of the molecules of gas inside it are carried away by the stream of air blowing across the top. The air inside the tank expands and pushes the liquid insecticide up the vertical tube. The liquid then is bro-

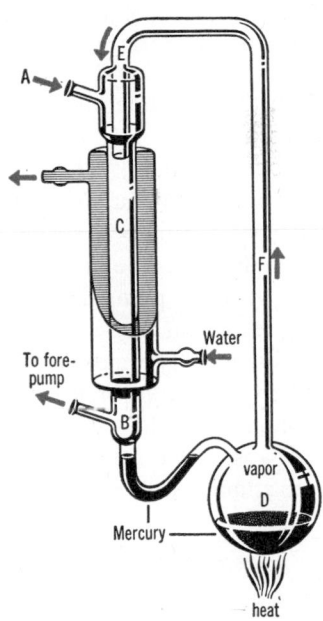

Fig. 5-9. Mercury is evaporated from the reservoir D, and its vapor passes upward through F and into E. It is condensed to a liquid in the condenser C, collects in the trap below, and returns to D. The movement of the mercury vapor through C pushes molecules of gas downward to B where they are drawn off by a rotary pump used as a forepump. More gas then flows into the condenser from A until the vessel connected with A is almost perfectly exhausted.

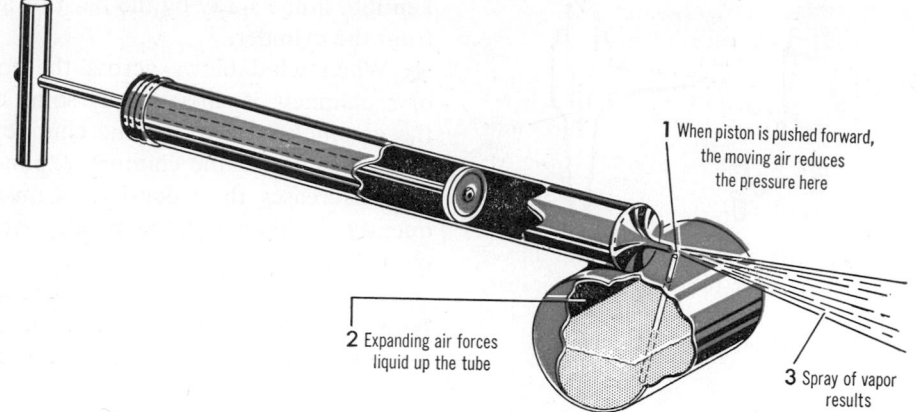

1 When piston is pushed forward, the moving air reduces the pressure here

2 Expanding air forces liquid up the tube

3 Spray of vapor results

Fig. 5-10. The insecticide which rises through the tube is broken up into a fine spray by the blast of air produced by the moving piston.

tainer. In the manufacture of electric light bulbs all of the air must be removed from the bulb, otherwise the filament would burn out immediately. In some types the bulb is refilled with a gas which increases the life of the filament. A vacuum pump is used also in making television tubes, radio tubes, X-ray tubes, and Thermos bottles.

Liquids boil at a lower temperature in a vacuum than they do at atmospheric pressure. Even if they are not heated to their boiling temperature,

they evaporate much more rapidly in a vacuum. The principle of vacuum drying is used when dyestuffs, chemical crystals, and certain drugs are dried in *vacuum pans*. Some dried or dehydrated foods have had much of the

Fig. 5-12. Vacuum pumps are used to remove the air from television picture tubes during the final stage of their manufacture.

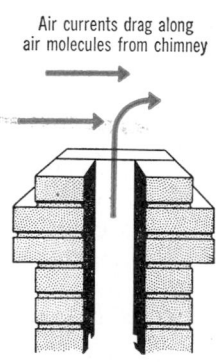

Air currents drag along air molecules from chimney

Fig. 5-11. The movement of air across the top of a chimney causes movement of air up the chimney. As a result, a chimney draws better on a windy day.

Fig. 5-13. Vacuum pans used for low temperature evaporation of water during the preparation of frozen, concentrated orange juice.

water they contained removed in a vacuum pan. Concentrated fruit juices for canning or freezing are prepared by evaporating, at low pressure, some of the water they contain. In sugar refineries vacuum pans are used for evaporating the sugar solution. Even though a low temperature is used to prevent the sugar crystals from scorching, evaporation takes place rapidly.

11. Fans are used to move gases. While fans do not produce very low pressures, they are used effectively for moving gases from one location to another. Exhaust fans are used to remove cooking odors from a kitchen and poisonous gases from a laboratory or a shop. A vacuum cleaner contains an exhaust fan. The fan pushes the air away in front of the blades and reduces the pressure on the other side of the fan. As the air rushes in through the nozzle or tube leading to the fan chamber, it carries with it the dust particles from the article that is being cleaned. A revolving brush is sometimes used to sweep the rug at the same time in order to loosen the dirt. The fan behind the radiator in an automobile is used to draw air through the radiator. This cools the water heated by the engine as the water passes through the radiator. A fan is often used with a hot-air heating system to force the heated air through ducts to all parts of the house.

Fig. 5-14. The fan mounted in the attic helps cool this house by drawing heated air from the rooms and forcing it out the attic louvres. Cool air then enters the rooms from outside to replace the heated air removed by the fan.

12. There are several types of compression pumps. One of the simplest compression pumps is a bicycle or automobile tire pump. This pump is used to push more air into a container. In a simple type, shown in Fig. 5-15, a leather disc attached to the piston permits air to flow past it on the upstroke but it fits the cylinder walls tightly on the downstroke. The leather disc takes the place of one of the valves in the vacuum-compression pump we studied in Section 6. The other valve may be placed in the outlet tube. With tire pumps, however, the valve in the valve stem of the tire may serve as the outlet valve.

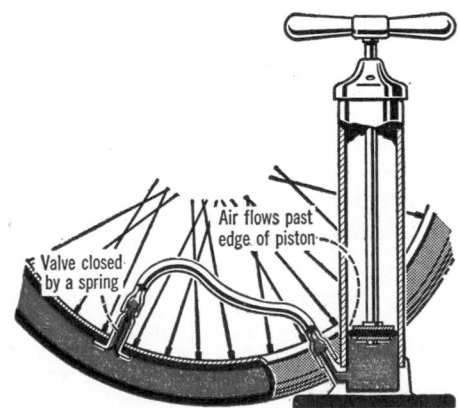

Fig. 5-15. A simple compression pump used to inflate a bicycle or automobile tire. The air flows from the pump through the valve and so into the tire.

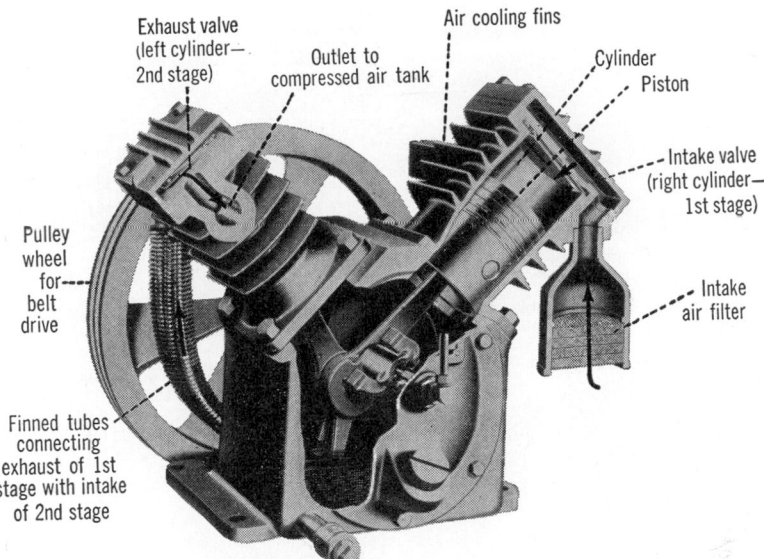

Exhaust valve (left cylinder— 2nd stage)

Outlet to compressed air tank

Air cooling fins

Cylinder

Piston

Intake valve (right cylinder— 1st stage)

Intake air filter

Pulley wheel for belt drive

Finned tubes connecting exhaust of 1st stage with intake of 2nd stage

Fig. 5-16. A two-stage reciprocating air compressor. Air enters the right cylinder where it is partially compressed. It then passes through finned pipes to the left cylinder where it is further compressed before being delivered to the compressed air storage tank.

★ The *reciprocating air compressor* is a modification of the vacuum-compression pump. Air flows into a cylinder through an open valve during the intake stroke. The valve then closes. As the piston moves toward the end of the cylinder during the compression stroke, a second valve opens. The piston forces the air through this second valve into a tank. The action of the piston maintains air in the tank at a higher pressure. This is called a reciprocating compressor because of the back-and-forth movement of the piston in the cylinder. The compressed air in the tank may be used to operate various pneumatic appliances. During the compression stroke, an automobile engine acts as a compressor. See Section 10, Chapter 16.

★ A *rotary-type compressor* is shown in Fig. 5-17. As the toothed wheels turn, they trap successive, small quantities of gas between the teeth and the outside casing. Since the teeth mesh closely at the center of the pump, air can not return to the intake side. Consequently, an increased air pressure is built up on the outlet side. Such pumps may be used to move a large volume of gas quickly at moderate pressures. They are used to furnish fresh air to the cylinders of a Diesel engine. See Section 14, Chapter 16.

★ *Turbo-compressors* are used in jet engines and gas turbines. They consist of several rows of small windmill-like blades mounted on a common shaft. Between each row of rotating blades is a series of fixed blades. These fixed blades alter the direction of the air coming off each set of movable blades so that the air may be picked up

Fig. 5-17. A rotary-type air compressor is attached to the side of this Diesel engine. The two rotating three-toothed wheels trap air between them and compress it. This compressed air is delivered to the engine cylinders at the end of each power stroke.

and further compressed by the next set of movable blades. The length of both the fixed and movable blades decreases toward the high pressure end of the compressor. Fig. 5-18 is a cut-away illustration of one type of jet engine. The compressor is shown at the left.

13. Uses of compressed air. Compressed air is useful because of two properties: (1) when air is under a pressure of several atmospheres, it can exert a great expansive force; (2) this force can be transmitted for a great distance through strong-walled tubes.

The following five examples show uses to which compressed air is put.

(1) *Tires and air-cushion springs.* Compressed air in automobile, truck,

and airplane tires acts as an elastic cushion to help absorb the shocks produced by rough pavements. When we inflate an automobile tire, we are applying Pascal's principle to gases. The pressure applied at the valve stem is transmitted undiminished to every unit area inside the tire.

Eight flexible rubber-and-nylon air cushions containing compressed air are used in place of metal springs on some new buses. These doughnut-shaped cushions are mounted between the axles of the bus and the body. The pressure in each cushion is regulated automatically to insure a smooth, comfortable ride.

(2) *Westinghouse air brakes.* This

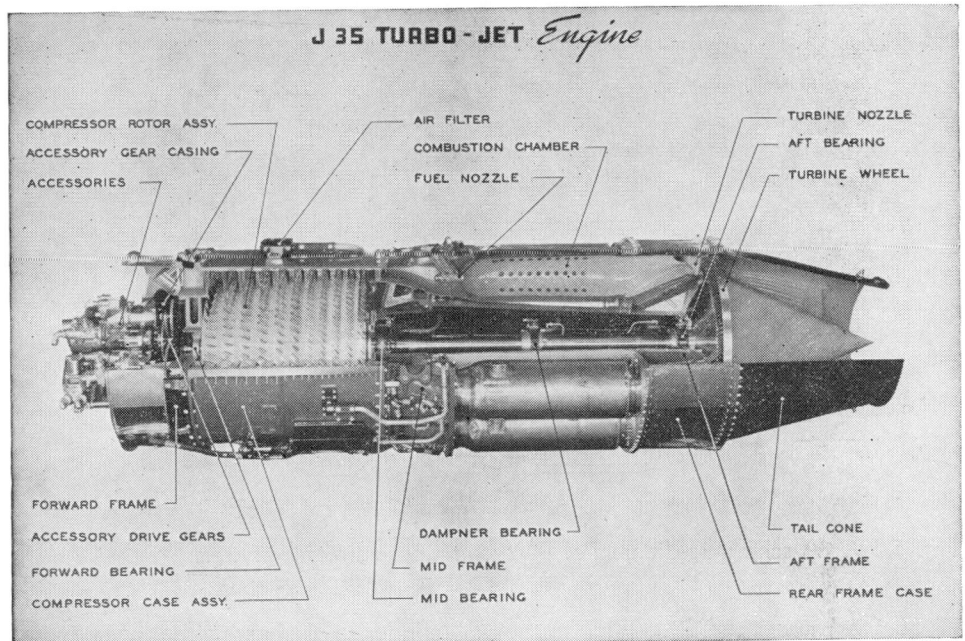

Fig. 5-18. A cutaway model of a turbo-jet engine, showing the turbo-compressor at the left.

air brake, invented by George Westinghouse (1846–1914), contributes greatly to the safety of railroad transportation. The brake may be operated directly from the locomotive or automatically by a reservoir of compressed air located under each car. As shown in Fig. 5-20, compressed air from the locomotive is transmitted to each car through a brake pipe. This brake pipe under each car is connected by the hose and coupling at either end of the car to the brake pipe of the cars ahead and behind when the train is made up. A pressure of about five atmospheres is maintained in these pipes throughout the entire length of the train. The brake pipe is connected through the valve with the auxiliary reservoir, the emergency reservoir, the brake cylinder, and the pressure retaining valve. Both the auxiliary reservoir and emergency reservoir are charged from the compressed air in the brake pipe.

When the pressure in the brake pipe is reduced by the engineer, the valve

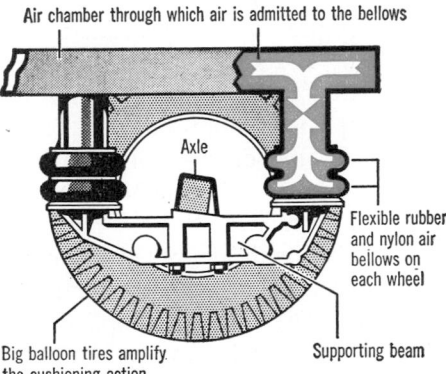

Air chamber through which air is admitted to the bellows

Axle

Flexible rubber and nylon air bellows on each wheel

Big balloon tires amplify the cushioning action

Supporting beam

Fig. 5-19. Compressed air takes the place of metal springs on some new busses.

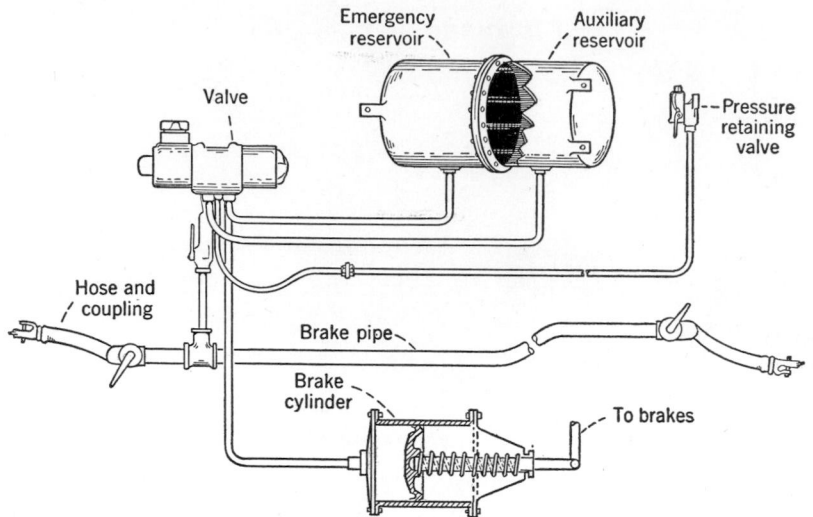

Fig. 5-20. A schematic diagram of a Westinghouse air-brake system.

on each car opens the brake pipe to the atmosphere. In this way the pressure in the brake pipe system is very quickly lowered throughout the entire length of the train. The valve simultaneously connects the auxiliary reservoir with the brake cylinder in order to set the brakes.

When pressure is restored in the brake pipe, the valve releases air from the brake cylinder. A strong spring moves the piston back to its original position. The auxiliary reservoir is then recharged. The emergency reservoir provides additional pressure to operate the brake cylinder if it is necessary to stop the train before the auxiliary reservoir is fully charged. It also is used if it is necessary to stop the train very quickly in an emergency. Since a reduction of pressure in the brake pipe sets the brakes, a car which becomes uncoupled by accident will be stopped automatically.

The pressure retaining valve is adjusted by hand to permit the brake cylinder to discharge either directly into the atmosphere or to retain some air when the brakes are released. It is desirable to retain some air in the brake cylinder when the train crew wish to keep the brakes partially applied while recharging the system, or when the train is descending a long, steep grade.

(3) *Diving bells and diving suits.* If we push a glass tumbler under water mouth downward, the pressure of the water compresses the air retained in the tumbler. The amount of compression depends upon the depth. The air in a diving bell is compressed in a similar method as the diving bell is lowered into the water. This is shown in Fig. 5-21. In a modern bell the men in it are supplied with air forced through a tube connected to a compressor at the surface. The air is supplied fast enough to force all the water out of the bell and to keep a stream of bubbles flowing out from under the lower edges. See Fig. 5-22.

A diving suit usually is supplied with

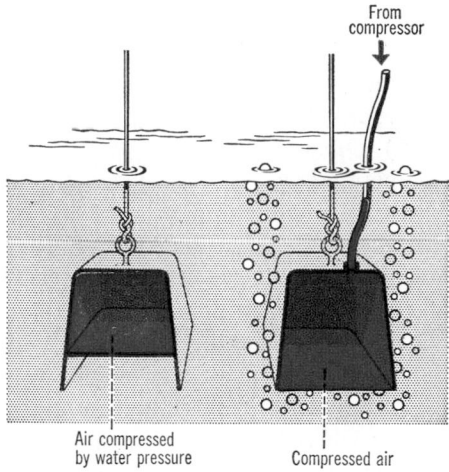

From compressor

Air compressed by water pressure

Compressed air

Fig. 5-21. Left. When a diving bell is lowered into the water, the water pressure compresses the air in the bell.

Fig. 5-22. Right. When compressed air from the surface is supplied to a diving bell, it forces the water from the bell.

compressed air in the same manner as a diving bell. In other cases the diver carries a tank of compressed air and can move about without fear of cutting his air line on some sharp object. By opening a valve he permits air to escape just fast enough to keep his suit, or perhaps just a helmet or facepiece, filled with air.

(4) *Caissons.* These devices are used when constructing bridge piers or foundations under water. The *pneumatic caisson* (*kay*-sun) is open at the lower end. It is weighted so that it will sink not only through the water, but also into the mud at the bottom, as shown in Fig. 5-24. Compressed air keeps the water out of the caisson. The workmen enter through air locks, or airtight doors, and material is passed down to them this same way. The

Fig. 5-23. An experienced diver who carries a supply of air in a tank strapped to his back can move around under water with great freedom of movement. Here a diver so equipped is riding a vehicle that pushes him rapidly forward when he operates foot pedals. The pedals turn the propeller on the shaft behind him, giving him speed.

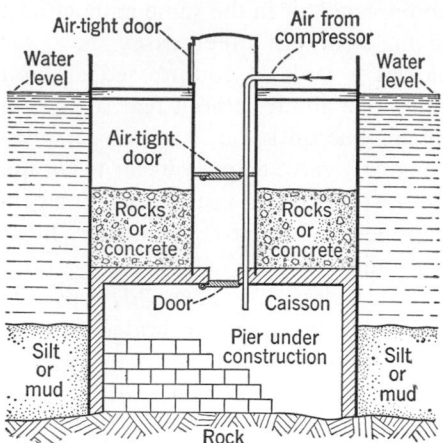

Fig. 5-24. The higher air pressure inside a pneumatic caisson prevents the water from entering.

foundation being constructed is built inside the caisson. In tunnel construction under a river, jacks are used to push forward a cylindrical shield as the river bottom material is removed by workmen. The tunnel lining is then constructed inside the shield.

(5) *Operation of tools.* Many tools are operated by compressed air. These include riveting hammers, rock-drills, pneumatic drills for breaking up concrete or asphalt pavement, sand blasting equipment, and paint sprayers.

14. Compressed air ventilates long tunnels. The longest automobile tunnel in the United States, the Brooklyn-Battery Tunnel, was opened in 1950. This tunnel is actually two parallel tunnels placed 15 feet apart. Each tube is 31 feet in diameter, and is 9117 feet (or almost two miles) long.

The ventilation of tunnels like this one is an engineering problem. Every car or truck passing through gives off

Fig. 5-25. Interior of the Brooklyn-Battery Tunnel. Notice the fresh air inlets along both sides of the roadway, and the exhaust ports in the ceiling of the tunnel.

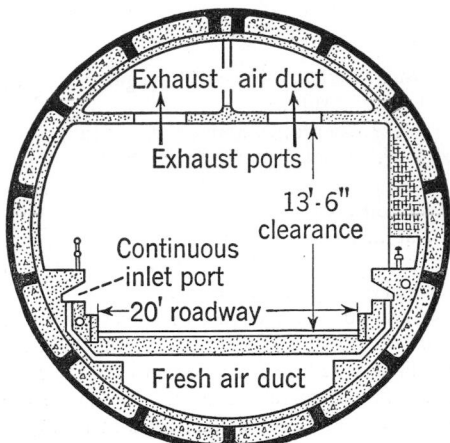

Exhaust air duct

Exhaust ports

13'-6"
clearance

Continuous
inlet port

20' roadway

Fresh air duct

Fig. 5-26. Cross-section of one of the tunnels under the Hudson River. Notice how the ventilating air is circulated upward through the tunnel.

in its exhaust some deadly carbon monoxide gas. Unless this gas is removed by proper ventilation the tunnels would soon become unusable. Three ventilation buildings were built for the Brooklyn-Battery Tunnel. One is located at each end while the third is about half way, where the tunnel passes the tip of Governor's Island. Fresh air is forced from each ventilation building through ducts beneath the roadway. The air is started into the tunnel at 60 miles per hour by 27 fans, some as large as 8 feet in diameter. The circulation in the tunnel itself is vertically upward from the roadway. At the top of the tunnel the exhaust air is then sucked back toward the ventilation buildings. It has been estimated that each car or truck gets 4 tons of fresh air during the $3\frac{1}{2}$ minute passage through the tunnel. Automatic analyzers keep a continuous record of the percentage of carbon monoxide in each section of the tunnel.

QUESTIONS

GROUP A

1. What two conditions must be specified when measuring the volume of a gas?
2. What is standard temperature? What is standard pressure? What does S. T. P. mean?
3. How many cubic centimeters are there in a liter? How many millimeters are there in a centimeter? In a meter?
4. Give the statement of Boyle's law. Explain the term "inversely."
5. How is the density of a gas affected by the pressure on it?
6. Using Fig. 5-5 to help you, explain how a simple vacuum and compression pump works.
7. What are the main uses for vacuum pumps? For vacuum pans?
8. Give five examples of the use of fans for moving air.
9. What takes the place of the intake and outlet valves in a simple tire pump?
10. Why is compressed air useful for transmitting force?
11. How are large tunnels successfully ventilated?

★ **12.** What is the formula which expresses Boyle's law?

GROUP B

13. What are some other applications of the sprayer principle put to use in the hand garden sprayer?
14. By referring to Fig. 5-20, explain what happens when a railroad car accidentally breaks loose from the rest of the train.
15. Why is the density of a gas affected by the pressure on it?
★ **16.** How is the air removed from a vessel by an aspirator?
★ **17.** What are the differences between reciprocating, rotary, and turbo-type compressors?
★ **18.** What is the shape of the graph relating two quantities which are directly proportional? Inversely proportional?
★ **19.** What features in the construction of a rotary vacuum pump enable it to produce pressures as low as 0.025 mm of mercury?
★ **20.** Using Fig. 5-9, explain the operation of the mercury diffusion pump.

PROBLEMS

(In the Mathematics Refresher, refer to Sections 8, 10, 12, and 16.)

GROUP A

1. A steel tank whose volume is 10 ft³ contains air under a pressure of 60 lb/in². What volume will this gas occupy if released at 15 lb/in²?

2. How many pounds of air were in the tank of Problem 1?

3. The volume of an inflated automobile tire is 10 liters. If the tire is to be inflated to a pressure of 2.5 atmospheres, what volume of air at one atmosphere will be required?

4. What weight of air in grams is required to inflate the tire of Problem 3?

5. What will be the weight of 100 ft³ of compressed air at a pressure of 5 atmospheres?

6. A tank contains 65 liters of air at a pressure of 5700 mm of mercury. How much does this air weigh?

7. What pressure must be exerted on 1200 cm³ of oxygen at one atmosphere pressure to reduce its volume to 600 cm³? To 400 cm³? To 300 cm³? To 200 cm³? To 100 cm³?

8. What pressure must be exerted on 25 ft³ of hydrogen gas at 5 atmospheres pressure in order to make its volume 125 ft³? 62.5³ ft? 12.5 ft³? 10 ft³? 5 ft³?

9. Two liters of nitrogen are measured at 735 mm pressure. What volume will this gas occupy at standard pressure?

10. Thirty cubic feet of air are measured at 22.5 lb/in² pressure. What volume will this gas occupy at 15 lb/in² pressure?

GROUP B

11. A certain gas occupies 500 ml at 750 mm pressure. What volume will the gas occupy at 800 mm pressure?

12. A cylinder for compressed gas has a volume of 2 ft³. What volume of oxygen at 15 lb/in² can be put in the cylinder under a pressure of 100 lb/in²?

13. John measures 15 ft³ of natural gas when the pressure is 14.5 lb/in². What volume does the gas occupy at 14.7 lb/in²?

14. The volume occupied by some oxygen at 740 mm pressure is 1500 ml. What pressure is required to reduce this volume to 1000 ml?

15. What pressure is required to change the volume of 75 ft³ of methane gas at 20 lb/in² pressure, to 100 ft³?

16. On a certain day, when the barometer reads 720 mm of mercury, Charles finds the volume of some hydrogen to be 650 ml. On the following day, the barometer has risen to 730 mm. What volume will the hydrogen now occupy? What volume will the hydrogen occupy at standard pressure?

● **17.** What will be the weight of 500 ml of chlorine at 0° C and 770 mm pressure? (See Appendix B, Table 5, for the specific gravity of chlorine.)

● **18.** What volume will 5 g of carbon dioxide occupy at 0° C and 725 mm pressure?

● **19.** The piston of an air brake is under an effective pressure of 4 atmospheres. If the diameter of the piston is 5 inches, what is the total force available to set the brakes?

● **20.** The diameter of the piston of an automobile tire pump is 1 inch. If the tire is partially inflated to an effective pressure of 20 lb/in², what force must be overcome on the downstroke of the pump in order to further inflate the tire?

2. OTHER PROPERTIES OF GASES

15. What is a lift pump? A lift pump is used to raise water from cisterns or from shallow wells. It consists of a cylinder, a piston, and two valves. The cylinder usually rests on a platform near the surface of the ground. From the lower end of the cylinder a pipe extends down into the well and

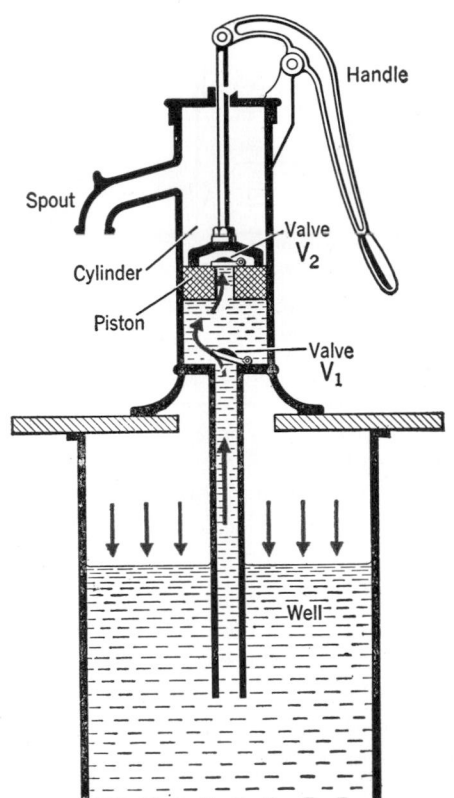

Fig. 5-27. This is a sectional view of the common lift pump used to raise water from a well.

dips beneath the surface of the water. Fig. 5-27 is a diagram of a typical lift pump.

When the end of the pump handle is pushed down, the piston is raised. The valve V_2 in the piston is closed and the air above the piston is pushed out of the top of the cylinder. Raising the piston lowers the pressure beneath it. The downward pressure of the air upon the surface of the water in the well now pushes some water up through the pipe into the cylinder. The valve V_1 opens to permit this water to pass through. On the next downstroke of the piston, valve V_1 closes so that the water can

not flow back into the well. The only place it can go is up through valve V_2 to occupy part of the space above the piston. The next upstroke of the piston *lifts* this water so that it flows out of the spout. At the same time more water is being pushed up into the lower end of the cylinder by the air pressure on the water surface.

Air pressure can raise water to a height of about 34 feet. Consequently, a lift pump can not be used if the cylinder of the pump is more than 34 feet above the level of the water in the well. In actual practice, a lift pump is not used if the height to which the water is to be raised is more than about 28 feet. Leakage around the piston and through the valves makes it impossible to secure a perfect vacuum.

16. The centrifugal pump. *Centrifugal* (sen-*trif*-yuh-gul) *pumps* are used for most commercial pumping op-

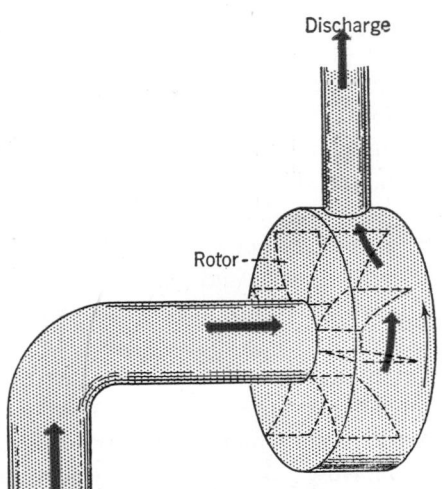

Fig. 5-28. As the rotor of this centrifugal pump is turned, it moves the water through the pump in the direction indicated by the colored arrows.

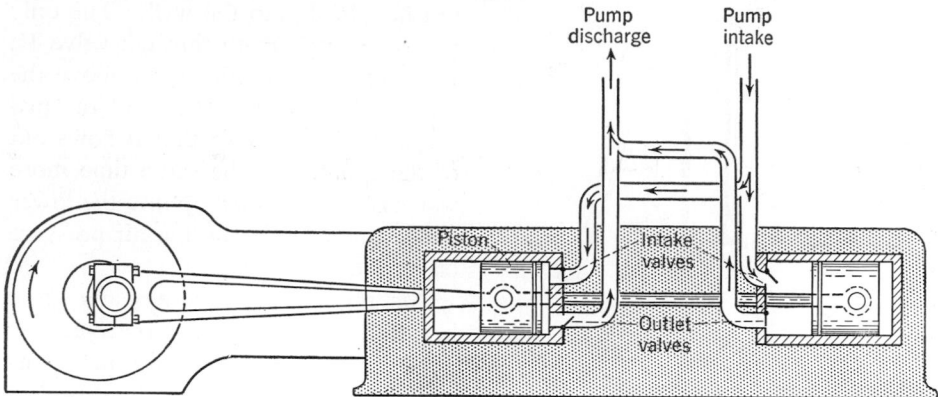

Fig. 5-29. This cross-section of a two-cylinder reciprocating pump shows that, as one cylinder is filled with liquid, the other cylinder is discharged. Such a two-cylinder pump moves a larger volume of liquid at a more uniform rate than a single-cylinder pump.

erations. Such a pump consists of a rotor which revolves within a casing, as shown in Fig. 5-28. The intake is at the center of the rotor. As the rotor turns, its blades throw the liquid against the casing and force it out through the discharge. The air pressure on the surface of the liquid below the pump then forces more liquid up the intake pipe into the pump.

Centrifugal pumps can raise water only about 15 to 20 feet. However, they do move large volumes of liquid with a smooth, continuous flow. Also, they are compact and require no valves or packing. Consequently they can be used for pumping liquids which contain solid materials. The rotor is usually connected directly to the shaft of the electric motor which turns it.

★ **17. How does a reciprocating pump operate?** A *reciprocating* (reh-*sip*-ruh-kay-ting) *pump* consists of a piston which moves back and forth within a cylinder. The cylinder is equipped with intake, or suction, valves and discharge, or outlet, valves. Water

or other liquid is drawn in through the suction valves on the intake stroke. At the end of the intake stroke the suction valves close and the outlet valves open. On the discharge stroke the water is forced out of the cylinder through the outlet valves. Since liquid leaves the cylinder only on the discharge stroke, the flow of liquid is not uniform. Some pumps of this type have two pistons. As one cylinder is being filled, the other is being discharged. This tends to make the flow of liquid continuous. The amount of liquid moved depends on the speed at which the pump is operated. A reciprocating pump may raise water as high as 25 feet.

★ **18. The rotary pump.** The *rotary pump* for liquids operates on the same principle as the rotary pump for gases. Small quantities of liquid are trapped by the toothed wheels and forced from one side of the pump to the other. The flow from such a pump is continuous. Rotary pumps are of simple construction and have a large capacity in comparison with their size.

They are used for pumping oil, grease, soap, and other liquids that are thick and which normally flow slowly.

19. How does a siphon work? It often is necessary to transfer a liquid from a large drum or other heavy container. Such a drum is usually too heavy to lift. Also, we would find it difficult to pour the liquid without spilling some. A bent tube, with arms of unequal lengths, may be used to transfer liquids over an elevation from one container to another at a lower level. A tube used for this purpose is called a *siphon* (sy-fun). It generally is made of rubber, glass, or plastic.

Suppose we fill the siphon tube *ABCD*, Fig. 5-30, with water and close the ends with our fingers. Next we invert the siphon into containers of water. The water flows from the container at *A* through the siphon and into the lower container at *D*. We can explain why this happens by calculating the effective pressures at *A* and *D*. The air pressure upon each liquid surface is approximately 14.7 lb/in². Suppose the short arm of the siphon, *AB*, is one foot long. Then the water pressure from such a column of water is 0.43 lb/in². The effective air pressure at *A* then becomes only 14.7 − 0.43, or only 14.27 lb/in². Suppose the long arm of the siphon, *CD*, is 3 feet long. Then the air pressure at *D* is supporting a column of water 3 feet high. The effective pressure here is 14.7 − 3(0.43) or 13.41 lb/in². Because there is less pressure at *D* than at *A*, the water will flow from *A* to *D*.

It is really the difference between the water pressures in the two arms of the siphon that makes the effective air pressures unequal. Consequently, the rate of flow of a siphon will increase if

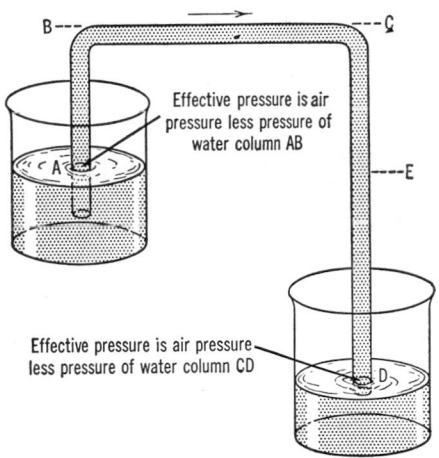

Fig. 5-30. Water flows through this siphon from *A* to *D* because of the difference in the effective air pressure at the two points.

Effective pressure is air pressure less pressure of water column AB

Effective pressure is air pressure less pressure of water column CD

we increase the difference in the lengths of the two arms. For every foot we increase the arm length, *DE*, the pressure causing the siphon to flow increases 0.43 lb/in². If we reduce the length *DE* to zero, the siphon will stop flowing.

★ **20. What is the Cartesian diver?** The bottle imp, or *Cartesian* (kahr-*tee*-zhun) *diver*, illustrates several laws and principles of physics. It gives us an opportunity to review many of the important ideas we have already studied in physics.

By careful adjustment, it is possible to put into a small vial or test tube just enough water so that the specific gravity of the combination of vial and water is very slightly less than that of water. Any pressure applied to the vial as it floats mouth downward in a container of water, or any increase in its specific gravity, will cause it to sink. Let us stretch a rubber membrane over the top of the container, as shown in Fig. 5-31. When we apply pressure to

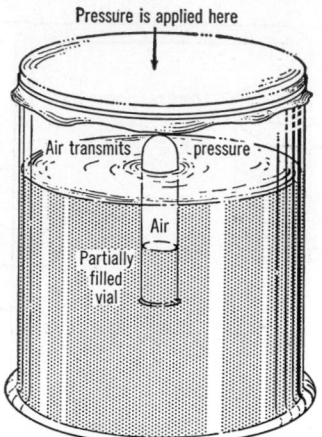

Fig. 5-31. The Cartesian diver demonstrates many laws and principles of the mechanics of both liquids and gases.

the membrane, the vial slowly sinks. It rises again as we remove the pressure. Why does this happen? Let us study it.

(1) The air beneath the membrane is compressed. (Boyle's law)

(2) The increased air pressure is applied to the surface of the water. It is transmitted by the water equally and undiminished in all directions. (Pascal's principle)

(3) The gas in the upper part of the vial is compressed. More water flows into the vial. This increases the specific gravity of the vial and its contents. (Specific gravity and density)

(4) The weight of the water displaced by the vial is now less than the weight of the vial, and the vial sinks. (Archimedes' principle)

(5) As we remove the pressure, the air in the vial expands (Boyle's law) and pushes some water out of the vial. Its specific gravity again becomes slightly less than that of water, and it rises to the surface. (Archimedes' principle) .

It is possible to use just enough pressure to keep the vial stationary at any position beneath the surface of the water.

21. Gases exert a buoyant force. Archimedes' principle applies to all fluids, gases as well as liquids. Just as water exerts a buoyant force on submerged objects, air exerts a buoyant force on objects submerged in it. An object which displaces exactly one liter of air will weigh 1.293 g more in a vacuum than it does in air at S. T. P. This shows that the buoyant force of air is 1.293 g/*l*. An object will rise in air if the buoyant force which the air exerts on it is greater than the object's own weight.

22. The buoyant force of the air causes balloons and airships to rise. A balloon is essentially a strong, airtight bag filled with a gas less dense than air. The balloon will rise if its weight plus the weight of the gas it contains is less than the weight of the air it displaces. If the balloon is filled with hydrogen (a gas which weighs only 0.09 g/*l*), then every liter of air the balloon displaces exerts a lifting force equal to the difference between the weight of one liter of air and one liter of hydrogen; that is, 1.29 g − 0.09 g = 1.20 g. While it is the buoyant

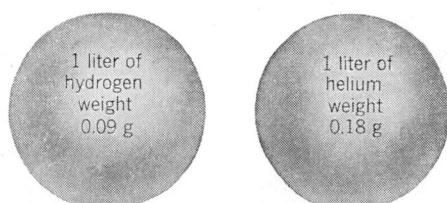

1 liter of air pushes upward with a force of 1.29 g

Fig. 5-32. The upward push of the air is the same in both cases, but the helium weighs more than the hydrogen.

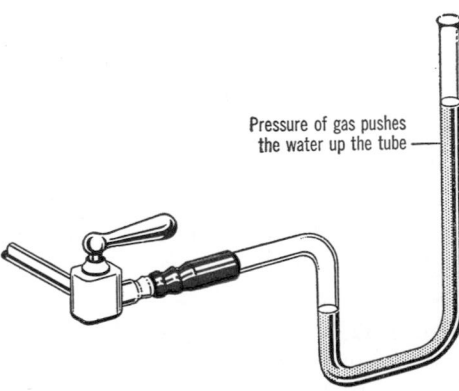

Fig. 5-33. The flight of an airship is an application of Archimedes' principle. The airship displaces a weight of air slightly greater than its own weight. The buoyant force of the air causes the airship to rise.

force of the air displaced that actually causes a balloon to rise, we commonly speak of it as the *lifting force* of hydrogen. This lifting force of hydrogen is 1.20 g/l. Since there are 1000 liters in a cubic meter, the lifting force of hydrogen is equal to 1200 g/m³ or approximately 1.2 oz/ft³. See Fig. 5-32.

Hydrogen is the gas of lowest density, but it burns. Consequently, it is dangerous to use for filling balloons. Helium is a gas which is twice as dense

Pressure of gas pushes the water up the tube

Compressed air

B

A

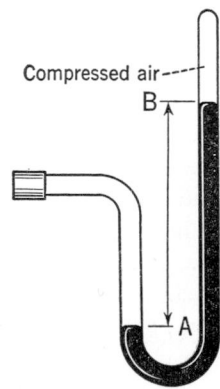

Fig. 5-34. An open manometer may be used to measure gas pressure.

Fig. 5-35. A closed manometer is used to measure high pressure.

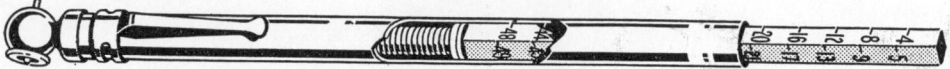

Fig. 5-36. A pencil-type gauge is used for measuring the air pressure in automobile tires.

as hydrogen, but it does not burn. It is the gas used for filling balloons and airships in the United States. The lifting power of helium is 1.29 g − 0.18 g = 1.11 g/l, 93% that of hydrogen. Fig. 5-33 shows a type of airship used for observation purposes.

23. How high does a balloon rise? Since air is very compressible, the layers near the surface of the earth are compressed by the weight of the layers above. Consequently, air has its greatest density at sea level. As a balloon rises, the density of the surrounding air gets less and less. The buoyant force of the air decreases accordingly. A balloon will continue to rise until the weight of the balloon and its contents exactly equals the weight of the air displaced.

24. How can we measure the pressure of a gas? We buy gas for cooking and heating purposes at a certain price per 1000 ft³. The density of a gas varies with the pressure exerted upon it. Consequently it makes considerable difference whether the gas is measured at a low pressure or at a high pressure.

Suppose we put enough water into a bent tube, like that shown in Fig. 5-34, so that it stands about 4 inches high in each arm. When we attach the tube to a gas valve, we find that the water will rise a few inches higher in the open arm when the gas valve is opened. The difference in height enables us to measure the amount by which the gas pressure exceeds the atmospheric pressure. Mercury may also be used in this type of manometer. For high pressures, a closed manometer like that shown in Fig. 5-35 may be used.

A spring gauge, similar to the one shown in Fig. 5-36, is used to check the pressure of air in automobile tires. Most gauges show a reading of zero at normal atmospheric pressure. The actual pressure, or the *absolute pressure,* equals the *gauge pressure* plus 14.7 lb/in². Manometers and gauges may also be used to measure reduced pressures. Engineers speak of a " 27 inch

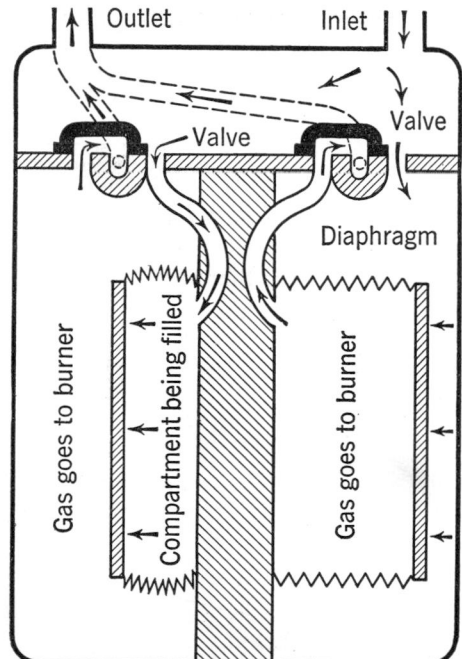

Fig. 5-37. The movement of the diaphragms inside a gas meter turns the dials which indicate the amount of gas consumed.

vacuum " or a " 28 inch vacuum " in referring to reduced pressures. A " 28 inch vacuum " means that the pressure is 28 inches less than one atmosphere, which is 30 inches. The gas in a " 28 inch vacuum " exerts a pressure of just 2 inches of mercury.

25. How does the gas meter work? A gas meter is a metal box divided by flexible diaphragms into four compartments. A slide valve connects these compartments alternately with the gas supply and with the gas-consuming appliances in the home, workshop, or school. While the gas in two of the compartments is being used, the other two gas compartments are being filled. This is shown in Fig. 5-37. The movement of the diaphragms operates the slide valve. This movement also controls the dials which indicate the number of cubic feet of gas that passes

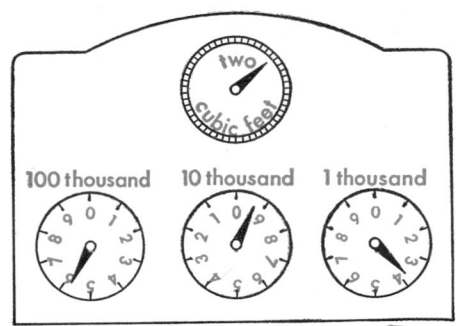

Fig. 5-38. Dials of a gas meter.

through the meter. Fig. 5-38 shows the dials of a gas meter. The meter is read at regular intervals. The amount of gas used between readings is found by subtracting the previous reading from the present one. The dials in Fig. 5-38 indicate 59,300 ft³. When the hand stands between two numbers, the lower number is then taken as the reading.

Summary

If a gas is placed in a container, it expands and fills the container. A gas may be easily compressed. Standard temperature for measuring gas volumes is 0° C. Standard pressure is 760 mm of mercury. S. T. P. is the abbreviation for standard temperature and pressure.

Robert Boyle found that at constant temperature the volume of a dry gas varies inversely with the pressure exerted upon it. The density of a gas varies directly with the pressure exerted upon it.

Gases may be removed from vessels with an aspirator, a vacuum pump, or a mercury diffusion pump. Vacuum pumps are used for exhausting Thermos bottles, electric light bulbs, and radio and television tubes. Solutions may be concentrated at low temperature in vacuum pans.

There are several types of compression pumps. These include the tire pump, the reciprocating air compressor, the rotary-type compressor, and the turbo-compressor. Compressed air is used in automobile tires, air brakes, diving bells and suits, caissons, and in various pneumatic tools.

The lift pump, the centrifugal pump, the reciprocating pump, the rotary pump, and the siphon depend upon the pressure of the air for their operation.

Archimedes' principle applies to gases. The buoyant force a gas exerts is equal to the weight of the gas displaced.

Terms to Define...

Absolute pressure	Garden sprayer	Rotary pump
Air brake	Gas meter	Siphon
Air-cushion spring	Gauge pressure	Standard pressure
Aspirator	Inverse proportion	Standard temperature
Boyle's law	J-tube apparatus	S. T. P.
Buoyant force of gases	Lifting force	Tire pump
Caisson	Lift pump	Tunnel ventilation
Cartesian diver	Manometer	Turbo-compressor
Centrifugal pump	Pressure ratio	25-in vacuum
Compression pump	Reciprocating air	Vacuum pan
Diffusion pump	compressor	Vacuum pump
Diving bell	Reciprocating pump	Variation of gas density
Fans used to move air	Rotary compressor	with pressure.

Questions

GROUP A

1. How do the valves of a lift pump work, simultaneously or alternately? Why must they work in such a fashion?

2. As the piston of a lift pump is raised, water flows into the cylinder beneath the piston. What causes it to do this?

3. What type of pump is used for most commercial pumping operations? Why do you believe that this type of pump has become most popular?

★ **4.** What are the principal uses for rotary pumps for liquids?

5. What causes a siphon to flow? Will it flow in a vacuum?

6. Why does a balloon filled with hydrogen or helium rise through the air?

7. What will determine the height to which a balloon rises?

8. What devices are used for measuring the pressure of gases?

9. What is the difference between absolute pressure and gauge pressure?

10. What is a "28 inch vacuum"?

GROUP B

11. Draw a diagram of a lift pump. Using your diagram, explain how the pump operates.

12. Does the barometric pressure have any effect on the height over which a liquid may be siphoned?

13. What do we mean by the "lifting force" of hydrogen?

14. To what height must the container shown in Fig. 5-39 be filled before liquid will flow out the pipe at the bottom? How long will the liquid continue to flow out of this pipe? To what height must the liquid rise before it flows out a second time?

15. Refer to Fig. 5-37. With the help of this diagram, explain the operation of a gas meter.

16. Does the specific gravity of a liquid have any effect on the height over which it may be siphoned?

★ **17.** Compare a reciprocating pump for liquids to a reciprocating pump for gases.

★ **18.** How does the Cartesian diver illustrate Boyle's law? The properties of floating and sinking objects? Archimedes' principle?

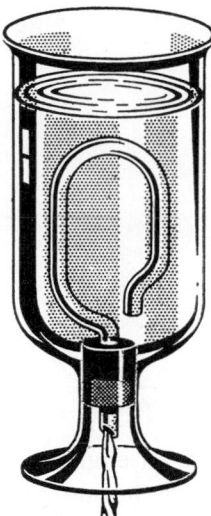

Fig. 5-39. The intermittent siphon.

(In the Mathematics Refresher, refer to Sections 8, 10, and 16.)

GROUP A

1. Water can be raised by a certain lift pump to a height of 26 ft. To what height can this same pump raise gasoline? The specific gravity of gasoline is 0.7.

2. What is the lifting force of 15 liters of helium?

3. What is the maximum height in meters over which alcohol may be siphoned if the barometric pressure is 735 mm of mercury? Specific gravity of alcohol is 0.8.

4. Some larger, low pressure automobile tires are designed to be inflated to 25 lb gauge pressure. What is the absolute pressure of the air in the tire? Remember that tire gauges read zero when the atmospheric pressure is 15 lb/in^2.

5. If a barometer reads 24 inches of mercury at Denver, what is the greatest elevation over which water could be siphoned in that city? In how deep a well could a lift pump be used?

6. A centrifugal pump can raise water to a height of 17 ft. To what height could this pump raise oil which has a density of 50 lb/ft^3?

7. What will be the weight of the air in a tire whose capacity is 800 in^3 if the tire is inflated to 23 lb gauge pressure?

8. Theoretically, to what height in feet could a lift pump raise salt water, specific gravity 1.15, when the barometric pressure is 28.3 inches of mercury?

GROUP B

9. If the total weight of a balloon is 2500 lb, what volume of helium in cubic feet will be required to lift it?

10. How much greater is the lifting force of 1000 ft^3 of hydrogen than that of the same volume of helium?

● **11.** What will be the volume in cubic meters of a balloon filled with helium which carries a gross load of 4000 kg?

● **12.** What total force must be exerted by the piston of a reciprocating pump which raises water to a height of 1500 ft if the area of the piston is 30 in^2?

● **13.** What total force must be exerted by the piston of a reciprocating pump to raise water to a height of 50 meters? The area of the piston is 25 cm^2.

Things to Do

1. Read an account of the discovery of Boyle's law. Find out how large a J-tube apparatus Boyle used.

2. Make a report to the class on the exploits of the U.S. Navy "frogmen" during World War II.

3. If you live in or near a city in which there is an artificially ventilated automobile tunnel, visit the ventilating plant to learn how the ventilating system operates.

4. Assemble the Cartesian diver apparatus. Show it and explain its operation in class.

Unit 3

Molecular Physics

Have you ever stopped to wonder how an engineer can design and then supervise the construction of a great bridge like the one shown? Each piece of steel girder, each length of wire cable, each part of the roadway surface must all fit together precisely as the bridge is being built. The finished bridge must support its own weight and the weight of the vehicles which move over it.

In this unit we are going to study some of the properties of molecules — those small particles of which all matter is composed. We shall find that in the solid steel of a bridge, in the water that flows beneath the bridge, and in the air surrounding the bridge there are molecules. These molecules are constantly in motion. Physicists and engineers know a great deal about the behavior of molecules. Thus, they can design the various parts of a bridge so that the parts will fit together and be strong enough to support the load of traffic crossing over.

Chapter 6

The Behavior of Molecules

1. THE KINETIC THEORY

1. The kinetic theory of gases. Scientists continually are trying to find explanations for the changes they observe. *An explanation which can be tested by observations and experiments is called a* **theory.** In this section we shall study a theory which helps us to understand the behavior of molecules. It is called the *kinetic* (kih-*net*-ik) *theory.*

In our study of Boyle's law, we found that the volume occupied by a gas varies inversely with the pressure exerted on it. This is a very simple

Vocabulary

ADHESION. The force of attraction between different kinds of molecules.

ADSORPTION. Condensation of a gas on the surface of a solid.

BRITTLE. Easily broken.

CAPILLARITY (kap-ul-*air*-ih-tee). The elevation or depression of liquids in small-diameter tubes.

COHESION. The force of attraction between the same kind of molecules.

DIFFUSION. Mixing of molecules of gases, liquids, or solids without regard to weight.

DUCTILE (*duk*-tul). Capable of being drawn into wire.

ELASTICITY. The ability of a solid to resume its original shape after being distorted.

EVAPORATION. Changing from a solid or liquid into a gas.

HARD. Not easily scratched or worn away.

KINETIC (kih-*net*-ik) **THEORY.** A theory of matter which assumes that the molecules of matter are in constant motion.

MALLEABLE (*mal*-ee-uh-bul). Capable of being hammered out or rolled.

MENISCUS (meh-*niss*-kus). The crescent-shaped surface of a liquid column.

OSMOSIS (oz-*moh*-sis). The diffusion of a liquid through a membrane.

SOLUTE. The substance which is dissolved.

SOLUTION. The mixture of a solvent and a solute.

SOLVENT. The substance in which the solute is dissolved.

STRAIN. The distortion produced by a stress.

STRESS. The force which tends to distort an object.

SURFACE TENSION. The tendency of a liquid surface to contract.

TENSILE STRENGTH. The force required to break a wire or rod of unit cross-sectional area.

THEORY. A scientific explanation which can be tested but not definitely proved by observations and experiments.

109

way for a gas to behave. If we *double* the pressure on a gas, its volume becomes *one-half* as great. If the pressure is reduced to *one-third* of the original value, the volume is *tripled*. Apparently a gas is not a very complicated state of matter, otherwise gases would not behave in such an easily predictable fashion.

We know that it is possible to compress a large volume of gas into a much smaller container. This makes us believe that gases are mostly empty space. But, because it has weight, a gas must contain matter in some form. Most gases consist of widely-scattered molecules. These molecules must be in very rapid motion because they exert a pressure against the walls of a container as they bump into it. Also, because gas molecules do not ultimately settle to the bottom of their container, they must be in continuous motion. This is the description of a gas proposed by the **kinetic theory,** *which states that the molecules of matter are in constant motion.*

The diameter of a molecule is about 0.00000001 cm. This is more conveniently written 10^{-8} cm. (See Section 15 in the Mathematic Refresher for an explanation of this method of writing very small numbers.) For an idea of how very small this is, refer to Section 5, Chapter 1.

Let us suppose that the molecules of a gas are magnified until they are like perfectly elastic rubber balls having a diameter of $2\frac{1}{4}$ inches. The container for this gas is a cubical box, 500 feet on a side. Because this imaginary gas is at standard temperature and pressure, there will be about 100,000 molecules in the container. On an average, these molecules should be approximately 6 feet apart. They move in a most haphazard way at a speed of about one million miles per second. They collide with one another about every 200 feet that they move. If these gas molecules are reduced to their actual size, and the container is reduced correspondingly, the length of one side of the container would be only fifteen-millionths of a centimeter. This is too small an object to be seen except as a tiny speck under the best high-powered microscope!

2. The kinetic theory of liquids and solids. We have found from our study of the properties of liquids that the molecules in liquids must be much closer than in gases. We can compress gases easily, but liquids are almost in-

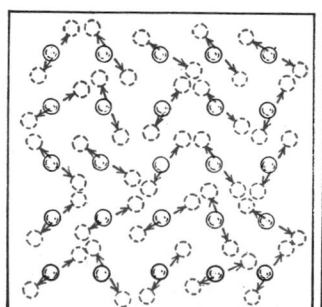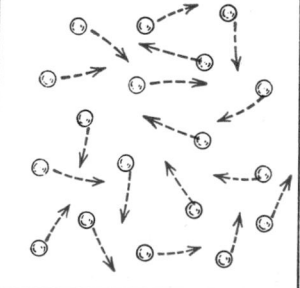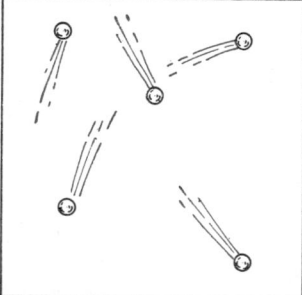

| Molecules of a solid vibrate about fixed positions | Molecules of a liquid slide over one another freely | Molecules of a gas are widely separated and move rapidly |

Fig. 6-1. Molecular motion in solids, liquids, and gases.

Fig. 6-2. The haphazard movement of the large particle is caused by its collisions with the molecules of liquid in which it is suspended.

compressible. Nevertheless the molecules forming a liquid are in motion. They also slide over one another easily as the liquid is stirred or poured.

Molecules are a little closer together in most solids than they are in liquids. They can no longer move freely over one another. Their motion is generally restricted to vibrating back and forth about a fixed position.

3. What is Brownian movement? In 1827 an English botanist, Robert Brown (1773–1858), made an important discovery. He placed some pollen grains in water and dropped a bit of this suspension on a small, glass slide. When he looked at the material under a microscope, he found that the pollen grains were in constant motion. They vibrated in a very haphazard way. The path of one particle would be like that shown in Fig. 6-2. Today we know that **Brownian movement,** as it is called, *is caused by the ceaseless bombardment of particles by the molecules of the liquid in which they are suspended.* Can you imagine the irregular path traced by a person helplessly caught in an uncontrolled, moving mob? He is pushed first one way by the crowd, then another, forward and backward, from side to side. It is in this way that the molecules of a liquid push suspended particles around. Tiny oil drops suspended in air undergo the same zigzag motion as they are driven about by rapidly moving air molecules. In this way molecules show us that they are in constant motion. Brownian movement gives us one of the necessary proofs to indicate the correctness of the kinetic theory.

2. MOLECULAR MOTIONS IN GASES

4. Gases expand. When someone accidently leaves a gas valve open in the laboratory, you can soon smell the gas, no matter where you are in the room. Suppose we unstopper a small bottle of bromine vapor and invert a large beaker over it. Soon the reddish-brown gas may be seen expanding and mixing with the air in the beaker. These gas molecules move in all directions until they become thoroughly mixed with the molecules of the air. The expansion of gases is one proof that gas molecules move.

5. Gases exert pressure. Automobile tires may burst from the pressure which the air inside them exerts on the tire walls. This pressure is caused by the constant bombardment of the tire wall by billions of moving molecules of air. Suppose we pump an additional two cubic feet of air into

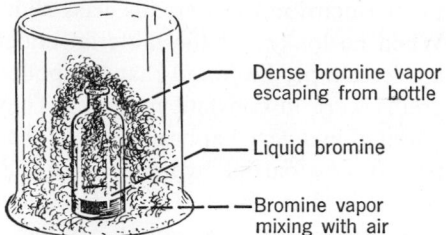

— Dense bromine vapor escaping from bottle

— Liquid bromine

— Bromine vapor mixing with air

Fig. 6-3. The escape of the bromine vapor from the bottle and its subsequent mixing with the air in the beaker show that the molecules of gaseous bromine expand because they are in motion.

a space already occupied by one cubic foot. We now have three times as many molecules bombarding the walls of the container, and the pressure is three times as great. From Fig. 6-4 we see that tripling the number of molecules in a given space triples the pressure. There are three times as many impacts against the walls as before.

A boiler may produce steam at a pressure of 200 pounds per square inch. Molecules of steam must be widely separated from one another in comparison with the diameter of the mole-

cules themselves. This is proved by the fact that when steam condenses into water the water occupies only about $\frac{1}{1700}$ of the volume of the original steam. The high temperature increases the velocity of the steam molecules. These rapidly moving molecules can exert great pressure.

6. Diffusion of gases. Hydrochloric acid is a water solution of a dense gas called hydrogen chloride. Household ammonia, or aqua ammonia, is a water solution of a low density gas, ammonia. When these gases combine they form a cloud of fine, white particles.

Suppose we put a few drops of hydrochloric acid in a warm bottle, and an equal amount of aqua ammonia in a second warm bottle. Then we cover the mouth of each bottle with a glass plate, and invert the bottle containing ammonia over the one containing hydrogen chloride, as shown in Fig. 6-5. We let the bottles stand for a minute or two. Then we slide out the glass plates, leaving the bottles mouth-to-mouth. We can tell from the white

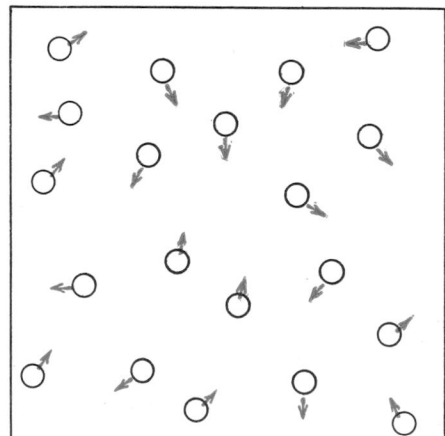
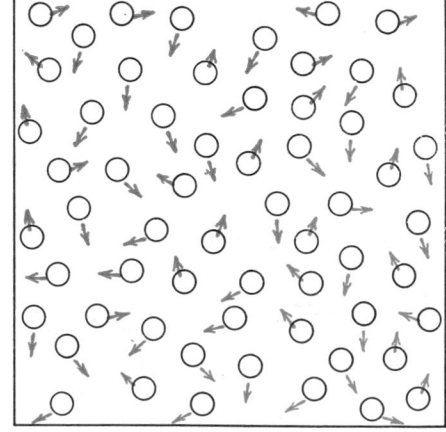

Fig. 6-4. Increasing the number of gas molecules in a container increases the pressure exerted by the gas against the walls of the container.

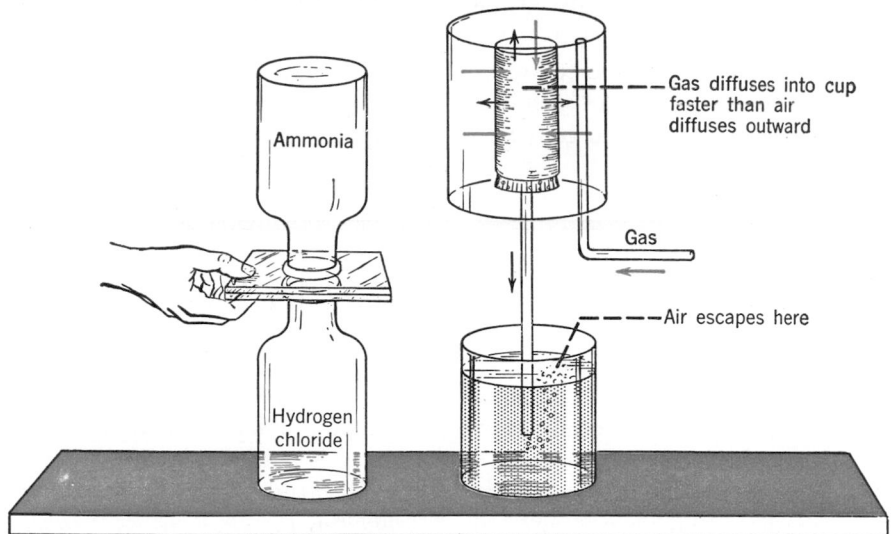

Fig. 6-5. When the glass plates are removed, the gases mix by diffusion. The dense hydrogen chloride molecules move upward and the less dense ammonia molecules move downward.

Fig. 6-6. The more rapid diffusion of gas into the cup increases the pressure within the cup. As a result, some of the air is forced down the tube and bubbles through the liquid.

smoke produced that the less dense ammonia gas *descends* and mixes with the more dense hydrogen chloride. The hydrogen chloride also *rises* and mixes with some of the ammonia remaining in the upper bottle. The movement of these two gases apparently contradicts gravity.

If the denser gas had been placed at the top, we could explain this phenomenon by the action of gravity. But since the gases move in apparent violation of gravity, the molecules of gases must be in motion. *Mixing of gases without regard to weight is called* **diffusion.**

7. Gases diffuse through porous solids. In the apparatus shown in Fig. 6-6, an unglazed earthenware cup is closed with a rubber stopper. A glass tube which dips into a colored liquid fits into a hole in the stopper.

A large beaker is placed over the cup, and gas from the gas valve is led into the beaker. Air begins to bubble through the colored liquid immediately. This experiment shows that gases diffuse through a porous solid. It also shows that the lighter molecules of gas move faster than the heavier molecules in the air. If a dense gas like carbon dioxide is led into the beaker, molecules from the air flow out through the porous cup faster than the carbon dioxide molecules enter. This reduces the pressure inside the cup and the colored liquid rises in the tube. Diffusion through a porous solid always takes place more rapidly from a less dense to a more dense medium.

Diffusion of gases through the membranes of plants, animals, and man is a very important process. In a person's ordinary breathing, the oxygen of the air passes through the walls of the capillaries in the lungs and enters the blood. It passes through the cell walls in the same manner. Similarly, carbon dioxide is liberated from the cells into the blood, and from the blood into the lungs, from which it is exhaled. Diffusion of this same sort occurs in plant tissues. Without diffusion of gases, living things could not exist.

3. MOLECULAR MOTION IN LIQUIDS

8. Why do liquids evaporate? Water that is put in an open container soon disappears by evaporation. How can we explain this disappearance of a liquid unless we assume that the molecules of the liquid are in motion? In Fig. 6-7, we show what we believe happens constantly in a liquid exposed to the air. The molecules of the liquid move in all directions. Those moving upward with sufficient speed can break through the surface of the liquid and escape into the air. Some of those just getting into the air may collide with gas molecules already there and be bounced back into the liquid. If we remove some of the air above the liquid,

the liquid molecules find it easier to escape. And they are not bumped back into the liquid as readily. Consequently, liquids evaporate more rapidly in a vacuum. *Evaporation may be defined as the changing of a substance from a solid or liquid into a gas.*

9. Diffusion of liquids is slower than that of gases. Let us pour enough concentrated copper sulfate solution into a tall cylinder to form a layer of blue liquid two or three inches deep. Next we float a flat cork on the

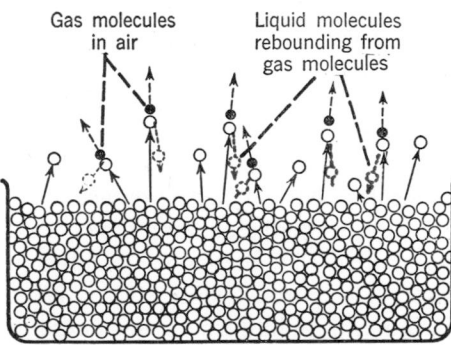

Gas molecules in air   Liquid molecules rebounding from gas molecules

Fig. 6-7. Molecules at the surface of a liquid which are moving with sufficient speed escape into the air. Some are bounced back into the liquid again by collisions with molecules in the air.

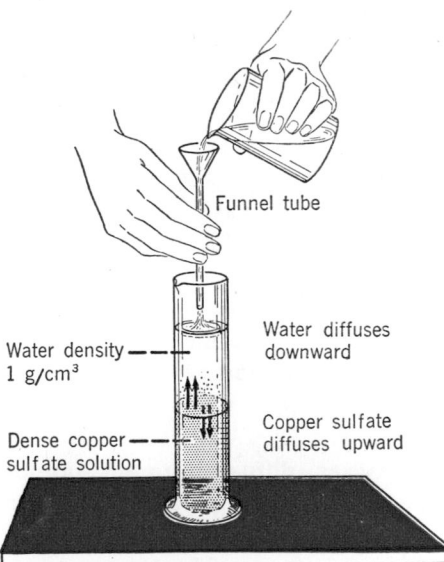

Funnel tube

Water density —— 1 g/cm³

Dense copper —— sulfate solution

Water diffuses downward

Copper sulfate diffuses upward

Fig. 6-8. Liquids diffuse more slowly than gases.

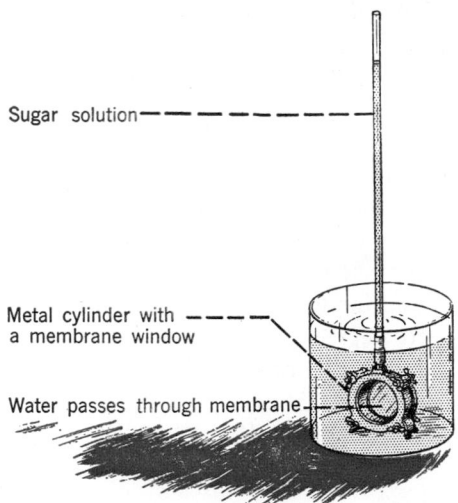

Sugar solution

Metal cylinder with
a membrane window

Water passes through membrane

Fig. 6-9. The diffusion of a liquid through a membrane is called osmosis.

surface of the solution. We now pour water carefully through a funnel tube onto the top of the cork, as shown in Fig. 6-8. The water will spread out over the surface of the blue liquid, forming two distinct layers. The liquids separate into layers because the water is of much lower density than the copper sulfate solution.

After this cylinder stands for a few days the boundary between the layers becomes less distinct. Some of the blue solution has moved upward and mixed with the water above. Some of the water molecules have moved down-

ward into the copper sulfate solution. This experiment shows that diffusion also occurs in liquids. However, it may require weeks or months before the diffusion is complete. This is much slower than the diffusion of gases.

10. Diffusion of liquids is called osmosis. By using the apparatus shown in Fig. 6-9, we can demonstrate the diffusion of liquids through membranes. The metal box with membrane " windows " is filled with a 2% sugar solution to which a few drops of food coloring have been added. The box then is immersed in water. Within a short time the liquid begins to rise in the tube. In 24 hours it will probably reach a height of several feet. The lightweight water molecules move much more rapidly than the heavy sugar molecules. Consequently they pass through the membrane into the box more rapidly than sugar molecules move through the membrane out of the box. The result is an accumulation of molecules in the box, which increases the volume of the liquid. *Diffusion of liquids takes place more rapidly from the less dense to the more dense liquid.* The diffusion of a liquid, which is generally water, is called **osmosis** (oz-*moh*-sis). The pressure due to the osmosis of liquids may equal several atmospheres.

4. MOLECULAR MOTION IN SOLIDS

11. Evaporation of solids. It is not too well known that solids evaporate. However, several illustrations will convince us that solids do evaporate, even though in most cases the process takes

place very slowly. Most of us are familiar with the odor of moth crystals. We know that these crystals will disappear in a short time if exposed to the air. The odor of the crystals and their disappearance prove that they evaporate. A lump of camphor or a crystal of iodine will evaporate in a day or two. Snow and ice evaporate readily. This is what causes them to disappear on days when it is too cold for them to melt. It is probable that many solids evaporate. But the evaporation takes place so slowly that in most cases we do not notice it. The evaporation of solids furnishes evidence that their molecules are in motion. If a solid has an odor, the odor can be detected only when some of the evaporated molecules reach the nose. At that point, the sense organs detect the odor.

12. Solids diffuse very slowly. If a lead plate and a gold plate are placed in close contact and left in this condition for several months, particles of gold may be detected in the lead. This shows that solids diffuse. Other solids show a similar effect if we increase the temperature by several hundred degrees. From the evaporation and diffusion of solids it is evident that molecular motion exists, even in compact, dense, solids.

QUESTIONS

GROUP A

1. What is a scientific theory?

2. How is the gaseous phase of matter described in terms of the kinetic theory?

3. Describe the motion of the molecules of a liquid as proposed by the kinetic theory.

4. What molecular motion is believed to occur in solids?

5. Describe the behavior of particles which show Brownian movement.

6. What do we believe causes the pressure exerted by a confined gas?

7. What do we mean by the term *diffusion?* Give examples of the diffusion of gases, liquids, and solids.

8. Describe what we believe happens to the molecules of a liquid as the liquid evaporates.

9. Why will a liquid evaporate much more rapidly in a vacuum than when its surface is exposed to the air?

10. Compare the rates of diffusion of solids, liquids, and gases.

11. What does the term *osmosis* mean?

12. What observations prove that solids evaporate?

GROUP B

13. In what way does Brownian movement offer proof of the correctness of the kinetic theory?

14. Describe two experiments which prove that gases expand.

15. Why can we put as much as 100 ft³ of a gas at one atmosphere pressure into a strong-walled tank whose volume is only 1 ft³?

16. What determines the rate of diffusion of a gas?

17. Where does gaseous diffusion occur in our bodies?

18. Where does osmosis occur in our bodies?

5. FORCES BETWEEN MOLECULES

13. Molecular forces in solids. The movement of molecules in a solid tends to make them escape from the solid. But there are also forces between molecules in a solid which counteract this tendency to escape. We know that enormous strength is required to pull many solids apart. Thus, in spite of molecular motion, there are strong forces which bind together the mole-

Fig. 6-10. The Golden Gate Bridge, San Francisco, California. The girders and cables of such a bridge must have high tensile strength in order to support both the weight of the bridge and the traffic passing over it.

cules of such solids. *This very strong force of attraction between the same kind of molecules is known as* **cohesion.**

Molecules of different kinds sometimes attract each other strongly. Chewing gum sticks to the leather of our shoes. Glue sticks to wood. When we write on the blackboard, some of the chalk particles adhere to the slate. It would be impossible for you to write with your pencil upon paper if the molecules of graphite in the lead did not stick to the paper more strongly than they stick to each other. *The force of attraction between differ-* *ent kinds of molecules is called* **adhesion.**

14. What is tensile strength? Several properties of solids depend on the cohesive forces between molecules. One of these properties is called *tensile strength.* Suppose we take two threads of the same diameter, one cotton and one silk. We use a special machine which pulls upon these threads until they break. Testing them in this manner, we find that the silk thread withstands more pull than does the cotton thread. Thus we find that silk thread is stronger than cotton thread of the same diameter. If we test two wires of the same diameter, one copper and the other steel, we find that the copper is more easily broken than the steel. Therefore we say that steel has a higher *tensile strength* than copper. *The* **tensile strength** *of a material is the force required to break a rod or wire of that material having a unit cross-sectional area.* This area may be 1 in² or 1 cm². (See Table 6, Appendix B.)

15. What is ductility? The ductility of a metal is determined by the force of cohesion between its molecules. Let us make a point on one end of a copper rod so that the rod will pass through a tapering hole in a tungsten carbide die. The pointed end, after being pushed through the die, is fastened to a wheel. As the wheel turns it pulls, or draws, the rod through the opening. See Fig. 6-11. As the rod is pulled through, its diameter is decreased but the length is increased, and the rod becomes a wire. *A metal that can be drawn into a wire is said to be* **ductile**

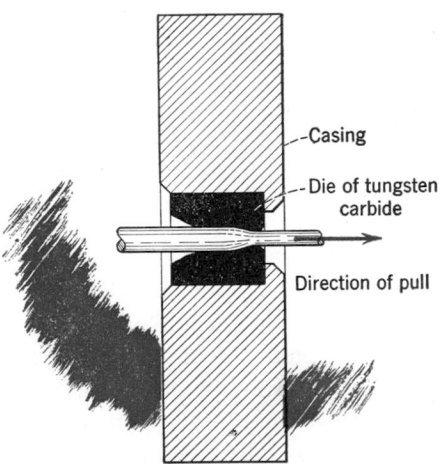

Casing

Die of tungsten carbide

Direction of pull

Fig. 6-11. Because of the cohesive force between the molecules of this metal, it can be drawn through a die and formed into a wire of smaller diameter. Such metals are said to be ductile.

(*duk*-tul). Gold, silver, and iron are examples of other ductile metals.

16. What is malleability? Iron, copper, lead, aluminum, platinum, and gold may be hammered or rolled into sheets. These metals are *malleable* (*mal*-ee-uh-bul). *That property of metals which gives them the ability to be hammered or rolled into sheets is called* **malleability**. There are strong cohesive forces in malleable metals.

17. What is hardness? A diamond will cut or scratch glass. Steel will cut tin or copper. *A substance is* **hard** *if it can not be easily scratched or worn away.* Hardness is a comparative property. For example, glass is harder than wood, but, as was just mentioned, glass is easily scratched by a diamond. Soapstone is soft enough to be scratched with your thumbnail. When two substances of unequal hardness are rubbed together, the harder one always wears away the softer one more rapidly unless the soft substance is driven at a high speed. Hard substances like sand, emery, silicon carbide, and diamonds are used extensively for cutting, grinding and polishing. The hardness of these substances is due to the cohesion of their molecules.

Fig. 6-12. Wire, which has been formed by being pulled through the die at the left, is wound on a large drum.

Fig. 6-13. Because steel is a malleable metal, the spinning rolls in these finishing stands can change a red-hot billet of steel into a quarter-mile-long sheet in just a few seconds.

18. What is brittleness? Glass and porcelain break easily when they are struck sharply. *A substance that is easily broken is said to be* **brittle**. Hardness and brittleness are often confused. Glass is hard and brittle, whereas steel is hard and tough. Steel is tempered to give it the proper degree of hardness. Glassware can be annealed to make it less brittle.

19. What is elasticity? *A solid,* such as a rubber band, *which requires a certain amount of force to stretch it and then tends to resume its original shape when the distorting force is removed has the property of* **elasticity.** The elasticity of solids depends on cohesion. *The force which acts on a body and tends to distort it is called a* **stress.** *The change, or distortion, which is produced is called the* **strain.** If we squeeze a tennis ball, it becomes distorted. However, it tends to recover its original shape and size when the stress is removed. This is an example of *elasticity of compression.*

The type of elasticity illustrated by the stretching of a rubber band is called *elasticity of extension.* The twisting of a coiled spring is an example of *elasticity of torsion.* An illustration of the *elasticity of flexion* is the bending of a strip of steel. In all these cases the material tends to resume its original form when the stress is removed.

20. Hooke's law and the elastic modulus. The beams and girders used in buildings and bridges are continually acted on by varying forces or stresses. It is important for the engineers to know what distortion or strain these forces will produce. In order to do this, they must have some way to measure the elasticity of materials.

If we stretch a coiled spring, as shown in Fig. 6-15, it probably will return to its exact original form after the removal of the stress. If it does, it is said to be *perfectly elastic.* If the spring is stretched too far, so that it remains permanently distorted, it has exceeded its *elastic limit.* Every mate-

K I N D S   O F   E L A S T I C I T Y

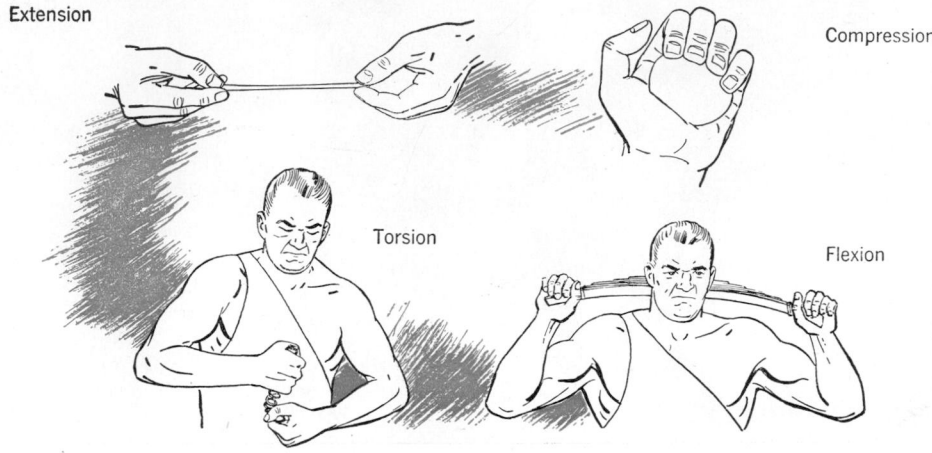

Fig. 6-14. Examples of each of the four kinds of elasticity.

rial has a certain range of perfect elasticity through which it may be distorted before its elastic limit is reached.

Suppose we fasten one end of a steel wire to a beam, as in Fig. 6-16. Now let us add weights to the hanger attached to the lower end. The wire will be stretched gradually as weights are added one by one. We find that a weight of 100 g stretches the wire 1 mm. When the weight is removed, the wire returns to its original length. Making the weight 200 g stretches the wire 2 mm. Again the wire returns to its original length when the weight is removed. The wire is stretched 3 mm by a weight of 300 g. It returns to its original length when we take this weight off. Eventually a point is reached where the wire readily stretches a short distance with only a slight addition to the weight. This is the elastic limit. If we remove the weights, the wire remains distorted. It does not return to its original length.

By such a method Robert Hooke (1635–1703) found that the amount of distortion in elastic materials is directly proportional to the distorting force, provided the elastic limit is not exceeded. HOOKE'S LAW states that *within the limits of perfect elasticity, strain is directly proportional to stress.*

The value of the ratio, $\frac{\text{stress}}{\text{strain}}$, is different for different materials. It is, however, reasonably the same for the same material, even though the material may be fashioned in different shapes and sizes. This ratio, $\frac{\text{stress}}{\text{strain}}$, gives us a means of comparing the elasticity of various materials; it is called the *elastic modulus.*

Suppose we have two wires of different material but of the same cross-sectional area. By experiment we may find that twice as much stress is required to stretch the first wire a certain distance as is required to stretch the second the same amount. Consequently, the first wire has an elastic modulus twice as high as the second. Steel has a high elastic modulus be-

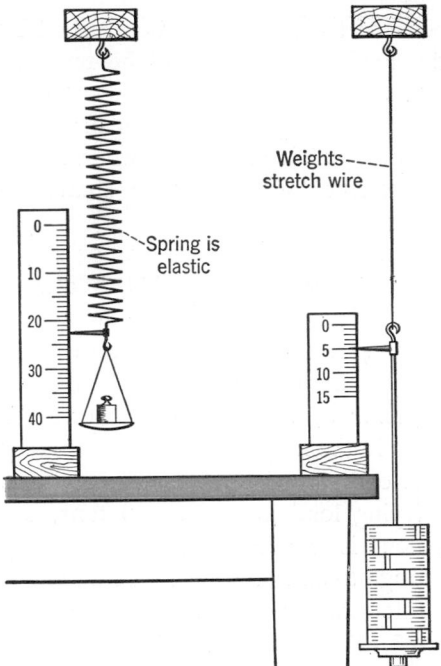

Fig. 6-15. Left. If the pointer attached to this spring returns to the zero mark after the weight is removed, this spring is perfectly elastic.

Fig. 6-16. Right. If the weights stretch the wire to its elastic limit, the pointer will not return to zero when the weights are removed.

cause a large stress produces only a small strain. Lead, on the other hand, has a small elastic modulus.

While we think of rubber as an elastic material, its elasticity is of a different nature from that found in metals, wood, glass, and other common structural materials. In rubber, small stresses produce extremely large strains, but the elasticity of rubber does not follow Hooke's law.

Liquids are perfectly elastic; they have high elasticity. Gases have low elasticity, since very little force is needed to compress them. They are, however, perfectly elastic. Only the elasticity of compression of liquids and gases is important.

⭐ **21. How does an elastic object rebound?** If we throw an elastic object against a hard surface, the object rebounds. When a batted ball comes toward him, the shortstop on a baseball team must be able to judge the angle which the ball will make with the earth. He must also spot the point at which it will strike the ground and estimate the angle at which it will rebound. If he has done all this accurately, he can place his glove in position to catch the ball as it rebounds.

In tennis, basketball, billiards, and other games, the player constantly makes use of the rebound of elastic objects. In Fig. 6-18, let the horizontal line *MN* represent the ground and *O* the point at which the ball hits the ground. We erect *CO* perpendicular to *MN* at *O*. The line *AO* shows the path of the ball toward the ground and *OB* shows the line along which it rebounds. If the ball is perfectly elastic and the surface is hard, the ball will rebound so that angle *BOC* equals angle *AOC*. The angle of rebound, *BOC,* is equal to the angle of incidence, *AOC.* Note that the angles of incidence and rebound are measured *from the perpendicular,* and not from the ground.

When a ball that is not perfectly elastic, for example, a dead tennis ball, is driven against a hard surface, the angle of rebound, *ROC,* is greater than the angle of incidence.

Thus far we have not considered the effect of rotation on the rebound of an elastic body. A ball spinning on its axis as it moves will not rebound as shown in Fig. 6-18. The path it takes after striking the hard surface depends

Fig. 6-17. In order to be a successful shortstop like Mickey Mantle, a baseball player must be able to judge the rebound of a ball in order to catch it easily and accurately.

on the angle of incidence and the direction and rate of its spin. A tennis ball that is " cut " to make it rotate is harder to handle, since the player who receives it can not judge just how it will rebound. Furthermore, a ball that is spinning travels in a slightly curved path, and not in a straight line.

★ **22. How can we find the strength of materials?** It is very important for builders to know the elastic modulus of structural materials. It is just as essential for engineers to know the breaking strength of the materials which they use. In physical testing laboratories, strong machines are used to measure the strength of materials. Such machines test the tensile strength of cables, ropes, wires, belts, and similar items. Tests are made of the compression strength of materials used for piers, pillars, posts, and foundations,

because these must not be crushed by the load which they will be required to sustain. The propeller shaft of a steamship and the crankshaft of an automobile must transmit power without permanent twisting of the shafts involved.

When designing machines or structures of any kind, engineers always plan to use materials heavy enough to carry several times the load that is likely to be put upon them. This gives a *factor of safety,* which allows for flaws in the material and for temporary overloading. A bridge which has its carrying load limited to 10 tons, but which is made of material heavy enough to carry 50 tons, is said to have a safety factor of five.

23. Molecular forces in liquids. If you stick your finger into thick molasses and then try to pull it out, you discover that a certain amount of force is needed to pull apart the molecules of the molasses. We can use the following experiment to show that some force is necessary to overcome the cohesion of water molecules. We attach a clean glass plate to one pan of a balance and place enough weights on the other pan to counterbalance the plate. Next, we place a jar of water under

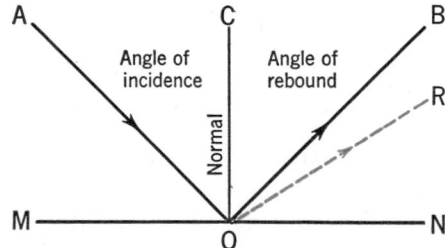

Fig. 6-18. When a perfectly elastic, non-spinning ball strikes a hard surface, the angle of rebound equals the angle of incidence.

Fig. 6-19. A machine which tests the strength of metal rods. The metal rod in the photograph has been pulled with such force that it is about to break. Notice the decrease in diameter at the point where the break will occur.

the plate so that the plate's lower surface just touches the surface of the water. Several small weights must now be added to the right-hand balance pan in order to lift the plate. See Fig. 6-20. Since the plate is wet when it is pulled away, the additional weights must have been used to overcome the force between the water molecules. The adhesion of water molecules to glass is greater than their cohesive force. Consequently, water wets glass.

If we use mercury, the glass will not be wet by the mercury. The cohesion of mercury molecules is greater than their adhesion to glass. For this reason, a finger dipped into mercury does not get wet. Cohesive forces vary in different liquids. They are smaller in liquids than in solids.

24. What is surface tension? Have you ever floated a sewing needle or a safety-razor blade on the surface of a glass of water? If you place them carefully on the surface they will float, even though their density is about seven times that of the water. If you look closely at the water surface, you will notice that the needle or razor blade floats in a hollow in the water surface. *The water acts as though a thin elastic film had been stretched over its surface.* This property of liquids is due to *surface tension.* The weight of the needle or razor blade is not great enough to break the film.

All liquids show surface tension. Mercury has a very high surface tension. However, in many liquids the surface film is not as strong as that of water or mercury. The cleaning action of some detergents is better because they lower the surface tension of water. This makes it possible for the water and detergent to penetrate more readily between the fibers or into the pores of the substance being cleaned.

By studying Fig. 6-21, we can understand why a liquid has surface tension. A molecule at *A* is attracted equally in all directions by the cohesion of the surrounding molecules. A molecule at *B* is attracted sideward and downward, but not as strongly in an upward direction. The molecule at *C* is not attracted in an upward direction

Weight needed to tear apart water molecules

Fig. 6-20. A method of measuring the cohesion of water molecules.

at all. We see that there is an unbalanced force tending to pull such molecules toward the interior of the liquid. This unbalanced contracting force causes the surface to act like an elastic film. *The tendency of a liquid surface to contract is called* **surface tension.**

⭐ **25. Liquid films are elastic.** If you blow a soap bubble and then remove the pipe from your mouth, the bubble slowly contracts, forcing the air out of the pipestem. See Fig. 6-22. If we dip a wire ring containing a loop of thread, Fig. 6-23A, into a dish of strong soapsuds, a film is formed across the ring. If we break the film inside the loop with a hot wire, the unbroken

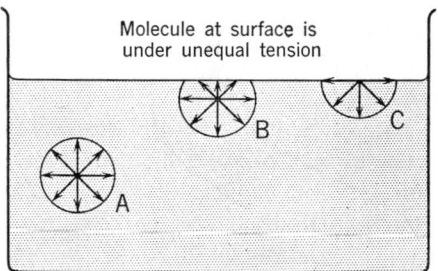

Fig. 6-21. The unbalanced downward force on molecules near the surface of a liquid causes surface tension.

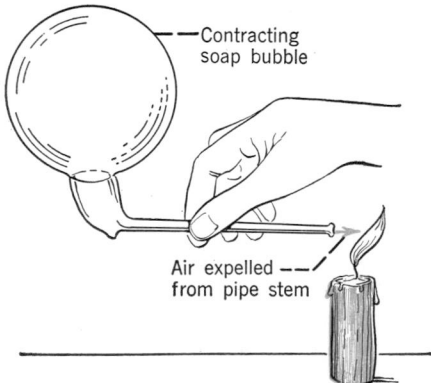

Fig. 6-22. The elasticity of the liquid film forces air out of the pipestem.

film outside the loop contracts and pulls the thread into the form of a circle, as shown in Fig. 6-23B. These experiments show that *surface films of liquids are elastic.*

26. What is the shape of liquid surfaces? If we examine the surface of water in a glass container, we find that it is not exactly level. It is actually very slightly curved, and from above the curvature is concave. The edge of the surface where it comes in contact with the glass is lifted a little above the general level. This is shown in Fig. 6-24A. *The crescent-shaped surface of a liquid column is called the* **meniscus** (meh-*niss*-kus). In reading the height of the water surface in a graduated cylinder or a burette, read the *lower part* of the meniscus. The actual volume of liquid lifted above this level is small. The water at the edge is lifted above the normal level because

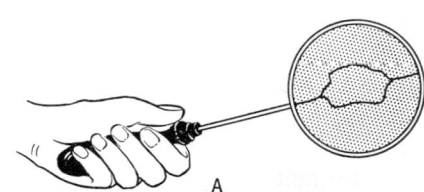

A

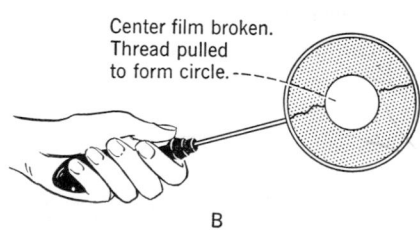

Center film broken.
Thread pulled
to form circle. - - - -

B

Fig. 6-23. A. The soap film is formed across the ring. B. When the center of the film is broken, the outer portion of the film contracts and pulls the loop of thread into a circle.

the adhesion of water for the glass is greater than the cohesion between water molecules.

When mercury is used instead of water, the edges of the liquid are depressed and the surface is *slightly convex*. See Fig. 6-24B. In this case the cohesion between mercury molecules is greater than their adhesion to glass. When finding the height of a mercury column, read the graduation at the *top* of the meniscus.

★ **27. The shape of free liquids.** A free liquid is one which is not acted upon by any force or pressure. Water poured on the floor is not a free liquid. The action of gravity spreads the water out in all directions, since water molecules slide over one another readily. Rain drops, however, are common examples of free liquids. They are nearly spherical in shape. Suppose we fill a glass cylinder half full of water and then float a layer of alcohol on the surface of the water. Now, if we lower a drop of oil carefully into the liquid, the forces of the alcohol and water on the oil drop will practically nullify the force of gravity. The oil is denser than the alcohol, but not as dense as the water. The drop of oil floats at the interface, as in Fig. 6-25. *Its shape is spherical.*

From geometry we learned that a sphere has a smaller surface area for a given volume than any other solid. As the internal forces act on the surface molecules, they tend to reduce the surface area. This pulls the liquid into the shape of a sphere. When mercury is spilled on a table, it breaks up into small drops. These drops are spherical since the effect of gravity is small compared to the cohesive forces of the molecules of mercury. Larger glob-

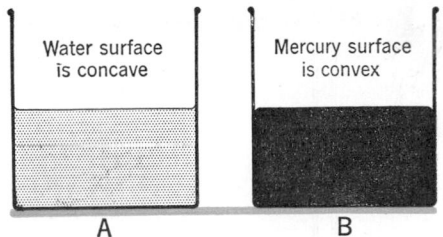

Fig. 6-24. A. Liquids which wet the surface of their containers have concave surfaces. B. Liquids which do not wet vessels have convex surfaces.

ules are distinctly flattened.

28. What is capillarity? In Section 6, Chapter 3, we learned that liquids stand at the same level in connecting tubes. This statement is true if the tubes have a large enough diameter so that the center of the liquid surface is flattened. For smaller tubes, a correction must be made. Experiments show that *water does not stand at the same level in connecting tubes of varying small diameters*. The height to which it rises increases as the diameter of the tube decreases. See Fig. 6-26A.

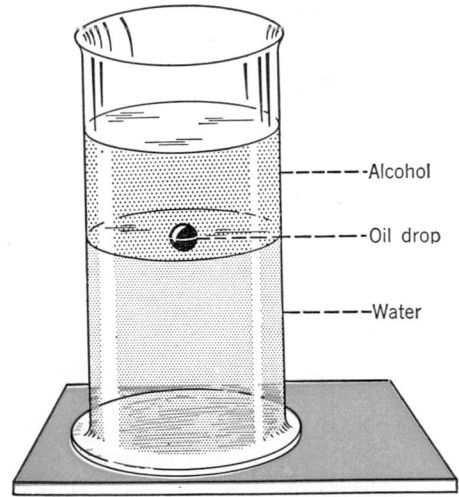

Fig. 6-25. A drop of liquid which is free from the distorting force of gravity takes a spherical shape.

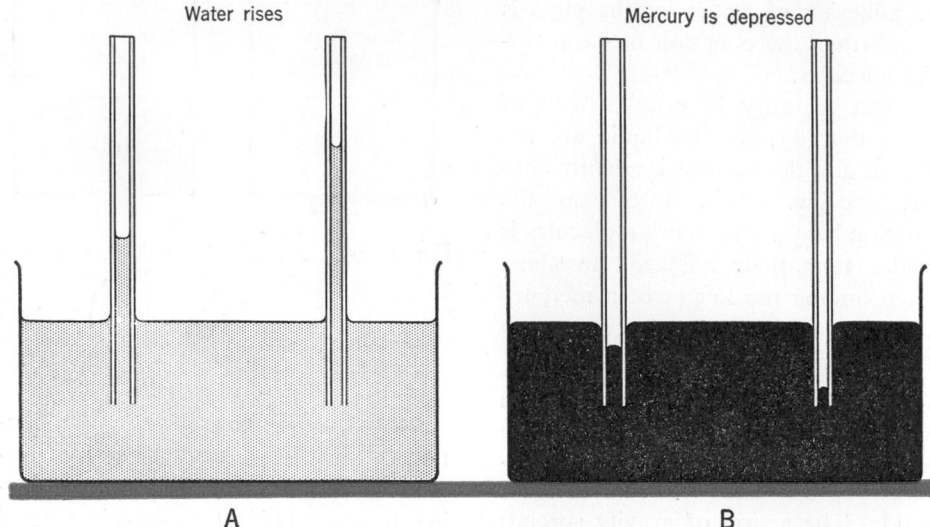

Water rises

Mercury is depressed

A   B

Fig. 6-26. A. Capillary action of water. B. Capillary action of mercury.

When mercury is used, the depression of the surface is greater as the diameter of the tube is reduced. See Fig. 6-26B. *This elevation, or depression, of liquids in small diameter or capillary (hair-like) tubes is called* **capillarity** (kap-ul-*air*-ih-tee).

Capillarity depends on both adhesion and surface tension. The adhesion of water to glass causes the surface of the water to become concave. Surface tension tends to flatten this surface by contraction. The combined action of these two forces acts to raise the water above its surrounding level. The water level will rise until the forces are counterbalanced by the weight of the elevated liquid. Why is a liquid like mercury depressed in capillary tubes?

Several conclusions about capillarity have been verified by experiment: (1) *Liquids rise in capillary tubes if they wet the tubes; liquids that do not wet them are depressed.* (2) *The elevation, or depression, is inversely proportional to the diameter of the tube.* (3) *The amount of elevation or depression decreases as the temperature increases.*

★ **29. Capillarity in everyday life.** When we hold one corner of a towel in water, water quickly soaks into the towel. The spaces between the fibers act as capillaries in which the liquid rises. Drying our hands on a towel is an application of capillarity. The absorption of ink by blotting paper, and the rise of lighter fluid in the wick of a cigarette lighter are other examples.

Capillarity plays an important part in the conservation of moisture in the soil. Rain water disappears in several ways: (1) part of it runs off directly, (2) part evaporates, (3) some trickles through the soil and enters the subterranean drainage system, (4) some of it is absorbed and held by the soil where it can be used by the plant roots. The amount retained in this way depends upon the kind of soil and upon its porosity. In very fine, compact soil, the pores are small. Capillary action in such a soil brings the water to the surface, where it is lost by evaporation. Soil conditioners coagulate the fine particles of such soils and increase their porosity. The soil may then hold more moisture. Also, stirring the surface soil breaks up its capillary contact with the soil beneath. This retains soil moisture by reducing evaporation.

30. Solubility and solutions. When a lump of sugar or a piece of salt is put into a glass of water, *the salt or sugar dissolves, that is, it goes into* **solution.** Water is called the **solvent,** *or the substance in which the solute is dissolved,* while the salt or sugar is the **solute,** *or substance which is dissolved.* We believe a substance dissolves because the force of adhesion between its molecules and those of the solvent is greater than the cohesive force binding its molecules together. The molecules of the solute occupy spaces between the molecules of solvent. It is probable that molecular motion plays an important part in the movement of solute molecules through the solvent.

The following lists several important properties of solutions:

(1) A solution is the same throughout. Each unit volume of solvent contains the same amount of solute. A teaspoonful of sweetened coffee is just as sweet when taken from one part of the cup as from another.

(2) The solute does not separate from the solvent upon standing unless the temperature changes or some of the solvent is lost by evaporation.

(3) Only a definite amount of solute can be dissolved at a certain temperature. If the solvent holds all the solute it can at that temperature, it is said to be *saturated.*

(4) The solubility of a solid generally increases with a rise of temperature. Boiling water dissolves salt or sugar more quickly than cold water does. Therefore, more solute is needed to saturate boiling water.

(5) Dissolving certain substances in water will change the temperature of the solvent. Dissolving salt in water lowers the temperature. A greater lowering of temperature occurs when ammonium chloride, potassium iodide, or ammonium thiocyanate is dissolved. On the other hand, when sulfuric acid is dissolved in water, the temperature of the water is raised considerably.

(6) The solubility of a solid varies with the nature of the solid and with the solvent used. For example, salt dissolves readily in water, but glass is only very slightly soluble. Rosin and shellac are almost insoluble in water, but they dissolve readily in alcohol. Grease is insoluble in water, but it quickly dissolves in gasoline. Many substances that are insoluble in alcohol or gasoline dissolve easily in water. Water is one of the best solvents known.

(7) The freezing point of a solution is lower than the freezing point of the pure solvent. During cold weather, alcohol or ethylene glycol (Prestone) is added to the water in an automobile radiator. The addition of these solutes lowers the freezing point of water. In this way, the engine and radiator are protected from the damage which might be caused by expansion when the water changes into ice.

(8) The boiling point of a solution may be higher than the boiling point of the pure solvent. The syrup which is heated to make fudge or rock candy

Fig. 6-27. Large crystals of ethylene diamine tartrate are being "grown" here in solution. Notice their geometrical shape, which is caused by the regular fashion in which the molecules in solution deposit themselves on the outer surface of the "growing" crystal.

boils at a higher temperature than pure water.

31. The formation of crystals. When a saturated solution of a solid is cooled or evaporated, some of the solid separates from the solvent in the form of crystals. Crystallization may also take place when a substance changes from a liquid to a solid. During crystallization the molecules and atoms of a solid arrange themselves in regular geometric patterns. The arrangement of the atoms and molecules determines the angles between the faces of a crystal. The shape of a crystal thus depends upon its composition and the conditions under which crystallization takes place. Granulated sugar, rock candy, and snowflakes are familiar examples of this phenomenon.

★ **32. What is an emulsion?** We know from using antifreeze in an automobile radiator that it is possible to make a solution of one liquid in another. In such cases, either liquid may be considered the solvent. When two liquids are mutually soluble, they are said to be *miscible*. For example, water and alcohol will mix in all proportions. But oil and water are immiscible; that is, they do not mix. When an oily liquid is vigorously shaken with water, finely divided particles of the oil remain *temporarily* suspended in the water, forming an *emulsion*. Milk is a good example of an emulsion. When milk is homogenized, the fat globules are broken up so finely that they remain suspended in the milk almost indefinitely.

33. How are gases adsorbed by solids? Some porous solids, like charcoal, meerschaum, and silica gel have a great capacity for *adsorbing* gases. Freshly heated charcoal adsorbs 90 times its own volume of ammonia gas. It will adsorb 35 times its volume of carbon dioxide. *The **adsorption** of gases by solids appears to be due to a condensation of the gas upon the surface of the solid.* Consequently, porous solids, having large surface areas, have a great capacity for adsorption. Tailors put fuller's earth on a grease spot and then add a solvent. The grease is dissolved by the solvent, and the liquid is adsorbed by the fuller's earth.

Charcoal is a good deodorizing agent, since it readily adsorbs the gases that produce bad odors. Sometimes

drinking water is filtered through a layer of charcoal to improve the taste.

Activated carbon is much more efficient as an adsorbing agent than ordinary charcoal. Carbon may be activated by heating it under pressure with steam, and then suddenly releasing the pressure. Samples of activated carbon have been made which are capable of adsorbing 900 times their own volume of gas. Gas mask canisters for industrial and military use contain activated carbon. The carbon is impregnated with various chemicals to make it more effective.

34. Gases may be dissolved in liquids. If we heat a test tube that is half full of water, bubbles of gas soon begin to rise through the water. This

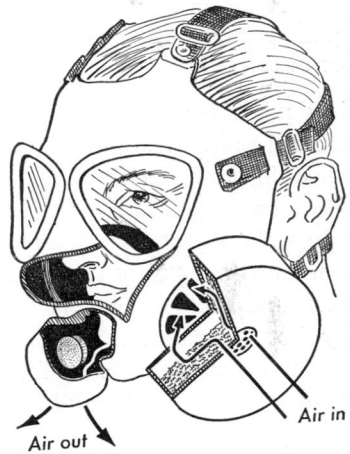

Air out

Air in

Fig. 6-28. This Army gas mask shows the passage of inspired and expired air. The canister, which is mounted on the left cheek so that it will not interfere with the soldier aiming his rifle, contains two different materials in separate layers. The first is a special kind of cellulose to remove finely divided solid particles from the inspired air. The second layer is activated carbon which adsorbs poison gases in the air breathed by the soldier.

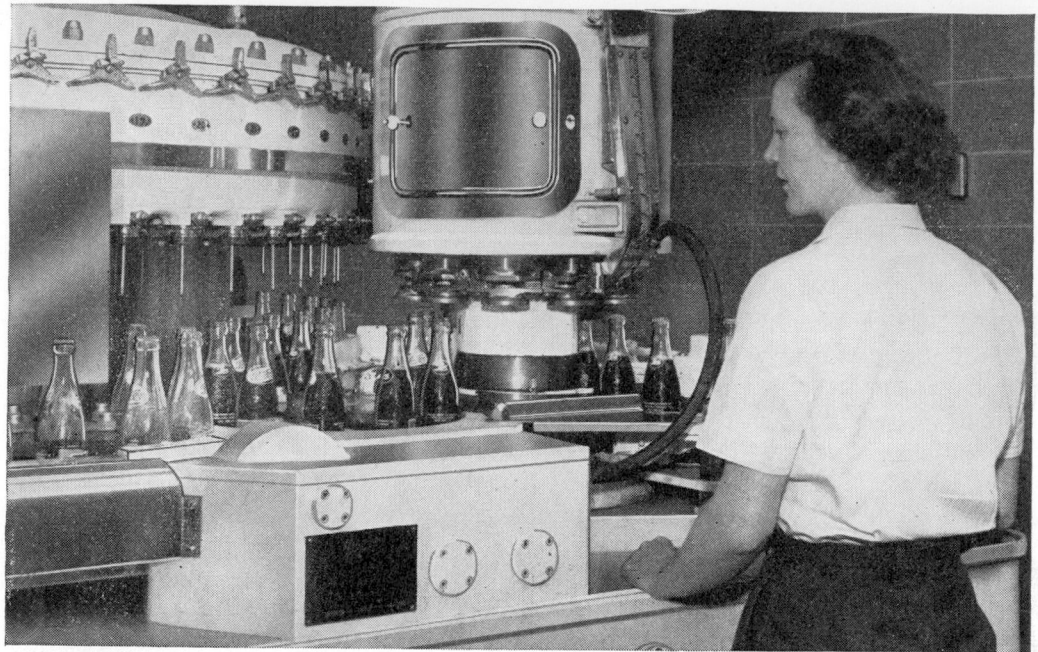

Fig. 6-29. Beverage manufacturers use the principle of increased solubility of gases in liquids under pressure. Here a machine adds carbon dioxide under pressure to bottles of soft drinks and then caps them to prevent escape of the gas.

gas is a mixture of oxygen and nitrogen from the air. Water dissolves carbon dioxide more readily than it does air. Ammonia gas is so soluble that it is possible to dissolve nearly 1300 liters of ammonia gas, at standard temperature and pressure, in one liter of water whose temperature is 0° C.

Heating a liquid decreases the solubility of the gases dissolved in it. Gases are less soluble in hot water than they are in cold water. Consequently air bubbles are formed when we heat water in a test tube.

Gases may be divided roughly into two classes based on their solubility in water. Some gases are very slightly soluble. Oxygen, hydrogen, and nitrogen are examples. These gases are probably held in solution physically. Others, like carbon dioxide, ammonia, and hydrogen chloride are very soluble in water. These gases actually react with water, so that the solution of these gases in water has different properties from pure water.

An increase of pressure increases the solubility of gases in liquids. In making soda water or in bottling carbonated beverages, carbon dioxide gas is forced into the liquid under a pressure of several atmospheres. When the pressure is released, part of the dissolved gas bubbles off and escapes at the surface of the liquid. The effect of pressure upon the solubility of a gas was studied by William Henry (1774–1836). He found that for slightly soluble gases, *the amount of gas that can be dissolved in a liquid is directly proportional to the pressure.* This statement is known as HENRY'S LAW. At a pressure of two atmospheres, we can dissolve twice the amount of gas in water that we can dissolve when the pressure is only one atmosphere.

Summary

Scientists believe that matter is made up of exceedingly small particles called molecules, and that these molecules are always in motion. This description of matter is called the kinetic theory. There are several observations which lead us to believe that the kinetic theory is correct: gases expand indefinitely; the movement of fine particles in suspension can be detected with a very high-powered microscope; gases exert pressure on the walls of their containers; gases diffuse rapidly through one another; gases also diffuse through membranes. The diffusion, evaporation, and osmosis of liquids are all evidence that their molecules are in motion. The diffusion and evaporation of solids show us that their molecules move, too.

Cohesion is the force of attraction between the same kind of molecules. Adhesion is the force of attraction between different kinds of molecules. Several properties of matter, such as tensile strength, ductility, malleability, hardness, brittleness, and elasticity, depend on cohesive forces between molecules. Hooke found that the amount of distortion in elastic materials is directly proportional to the distorting force, provided the elastic limit is not exceeded. In other words, strain is directly proportional to stress. When an object rebounds, the angle of rebound is equal to the angle of incidence, provided the object is perfectly elastic.

Liquids behave as though a thin elastic film were stretched over their surfaces. Liquid surfaces have a tendency to contract, which is called surface tension. Surface tension pulls free liquids into a spherical shape. The elevation or depression of liquids in tubes of small diameter is called capillarity. Liquids that wet the tubes are elevated by capillarity; those that do not wet the tubes are depressed. The amount of elevation or depression is inversely proportional to the diameter of the tube. The amount of elevation or depression decreases as the temperature increases.

The solubility of a solid usually increases as the temperature is increased. Cooling a saturated solution, or evaporating some of the solvent, causes some of the solute to separate as crystals.

Certain porous solids have the ability to adsorb large volumes of gases. Gases may be dissolved in liquids, but the solubility of a gas decreases with an increase in temperature. The amount of a slightly soluble gas that can be dissolved in a liquid is directly proportional to the pressure. This is known as Henry's law.

Terms to Define...

Adhesion	Elasticity of extension	Malleable
Adsorption of gases	Elasticity of flexion	Meniscus
Brittle	Elasticity of liquid films	Miscible
Brownian movement	Elasticity of torsion	Osmosis
Capillarity	Elastic limit	Perfect elasticity
Cohesion	Elastic modulus	Pressure exerted by gases
Comparison of molecular	Evaporation of liquids	Properties of solutions
motion in solids, liquids,	Evaporation of solids	Rebound of an elastic object
and gases	Expansion of gases	Shape of a free liquid
Crystallization	Factor of safety	Solubility of gases in liquids
Diffusion of gases	Hard	Solute
Diffusion of liquids	Henry's law	Solvent
Diffusion of solids	Hooke's law	Strength of materials
Ductile	Immiscible	Surface tension
Elasticity of compression	Kinetic theory	Tensile strength

Questions

GROUP A

1. What name is given to the force of attraction between molecules of the same kind?

2. What name is given to the force of attraction between different kinds of molecules?

3. What property must elevator cables possess to a great degree?

4. How is a metal drawn into the form of wire? What property is possessed by those metals which can be drawn into wire?

5. What property does gold have which enables us to make it into gold leaf?

6. What property do we desire in materials which are used as grinding wheels?

7. What do we mean by the term *brittle?*

8. Name the four types of elasticity. Give an example of each type.

9. State Hooke's law. Define the terms used.

10. Why does water wet glass? Why does mercury not wet glass?

11. What behavior does surface tension impart to a liquid surface?

12. List and explain five important properties of solutions.

13. What is adsorption? How is the phenomena of adsorption used in a practical way in (1) water purification? (2) removing grease spots from clothing? (3) gas masks?

14. If a bottle of a carbonated beverage is chilled before removing the cap, the carbonation does not escape as rapidly as if the bottle were at room temperature when opened. Explain why this is so.

GROUP B

15. What do we mean when we speak of "the elastic modulus of steel"?

16. Why is it possible to float a greased needle or razor blade on water, even though the density of both the needle and the razor blade is greater than that of water?

17. A column of water in a glass tube has a concave meniscus. Why? What is the shape of the meniscus of a column of mercury? Why?

18. From what source do fish obtain the oxygen required for their respiration?

★ **19.** Why is it important for a billiard player to be familiar with the way in which objects rebound? Why would he be particularly interested in the effect which the spin of a ball on its axis has on its direction of rebound?

★ **20.** Bridge builders generally allow a safety factor of five. What does this mean?

★ **21.** Why does a drop of a free liquid assume a spherical shape?

22. What is capillarity? Upon what properties of a liquid does it depend? Why does it vary with temperature?

23. Why does the cultivation of the top layer of the soil help to prevent loss of moisture from the lower layers of the soil?

24. Explain the difference between a solution and an emulsion.

Problems

(In the Mathematics Refresher, refer to Sections 8, 12, and 16.)

GROUP A

1. A coiled spring is stretched 5 cm when a 50-g weight is hung from one end. How far will the spring be stretched by a 100-g weight? What weight will stretch the spring 3 cm?

2. The hook of a spring balance is pulled down 2 inches by a 10-lb weight. If a weight of 25 lb is now substituted for the 10-lb weight, how far will the hook be pulled down? How far apart will the 1-lb graduations be?

3. A wire with a cross-sectional area of 5 mm² is stretched 0.1 mm by a certain weight. How far will a wire of the same material and the same length, but with a cross-sectional area of 10 mm², be stretched by this same weight? (The strength of a wire varies directly with its cross-sectional area.)

4. One liter of water at 0° C absorbs 1.71 liters of carbon dioxide under a pressure of one atmosphere. How many liters of carbon dioxide will be absorbed if the pressure is four atmospheres?

5. If 31.0 cm³ of oxygen will dissolve in a liter of water at 20° C under a pressure of one atmosphere, what volume of oxygen will be dissolved under a pressure of 8 atmospheres? If the density of oxygen is 1.429 grams per liter, what weight of oxygen is this?

6. The cross-sectional area of a wire is 0.0005 in². If a force of 50 lb is required to break this wire, what is its tensile strength?

7. What force will be needed to break a piano wire, 0.0007 in² in cross-sectional area, if its tensile strength is 375,000 lb/in²?

8. An elevator is rated to carry 3000 lb. If a safety factor of 5 has been provided, what maximum load can the elevator cables actually lift?

9. A bridge is so designed that it will actually support a load of 80 tons. If a safety factor of 10 has been provided, what should its rated capacity be?

GROUP B

10. The tensile strength of copper wire is 65,000 lb/in². What force will be required to break a piece of No. 18 wire, which has a diameter of 0.040 inch?

11. A piece of tungsten wire 0.01 inch in diameter is broken by a force of 46 lb. What is the tensile strength of tungsten wire in pounds per square inch?

12. Two wires are identical except that one is 100 cm long and the other is 200 cm long. The first wire is broken by a force of 50 kg-wt. What force is needed to break the second wire?

13. Aluminum wire has a tensile strength of 40,000 lb/in². What force will be required to break a piece of aluminum wire 0.065 inch in diameter?

14. How much force would be required to pull apart one of the cables of the George Washington Bridge, which spans the Hudson River at New York City? The cables are 36 inches in diameter. Assume that the steel has a tensile strength of 150,000 lb/in².

Things to Do

1. Set up an osmosis apparatus according to the directions given in the text. Use it as a demonstration for the class. To what height does the liquid rise in the tube because of osmotic pressure?

2. Demonstrate the diffusion of liquids. Use saturated cupric sulfate solution and water as described in the text. How long does it take before diffusion of the sulfate solution and the water is complete?

Unit 4 — Force and Motion

Outer space has aroused man's adventuresome spirit for many years. We find this interest expressed in imaginative stories of trips by rocket ship to the moon, and to the other planets in our solar system.

During the last fifteen years American scientists have made great advances toward building rockets which can rise into outer space. The photograph shows the Viking No. 11 rocket leaving its launching platform at White Sands Proving Grounds, New Mexico. This rocket ascended to an altitude of 158 miles, the greatest height achieved by any American-built single-stage rocket.

In this unit on Force and Motion we shall study some of the important physical principles which govern the flight of rockets and projectiles. Today we are using these ideas of forces, as well as the effects they have on the motion of bodies, in attempts to probe the vastness of outer space. Yet they were originally proposed almost three hundred years ago by one of the most important early physicists, Sir Isaac Newton.

Chapter 7

Force

1. FORCE IS A VECTOR QUANTITY

1. What is force? We already have seen how forces act in a variety of situations. A liquid exerts a force against the bottom and sides of its container. It exerts an upward, buoyant force on objects placed in it. The force of compressed air may be used to stop a train or to drive a riveting hammer. Forces may act to produce distortions in matter. There are forces between the molecules of which matter is composed. We originally defined force as a push or a pull because that definition was sufficient for certain applications.

Now we begin a more detailed study of force. We shall find that some combinations of forces just balance each other, and the object on which they act remains stationary. In other cases, balanced forces may keep an object moving at a constant speed. A force acting on an object may also increase or decrease its rate of speed.

We exert a force if we push against

Vocabulary

CENTER OF GRAVITY. That point at which all the weight of an object appears to be concentrated.

COEFFICIENT OF FRICTION. The ratio of the force of friction to the normal force pressing the surfaces together.

EQUILIBRANT FORCE. The force which produces equilibrium.

EQUILIBRIUM. The condition of a body when no unbalanced forces act upon it.

FORCE. That which produces or prevents motion, or has a tendency to do so.

FRICTION. The force which opposes motion.

PARALLEL FORCES. Forces acting in the same or opposite directions.

POUND. The English system unit of force. It equals the weight of the standard pound at sea level and 45° latitude.

RESOLUTION OF FORCES. Separation of a single force into two forces acting in definite directions upon the same point.

RESULTANT FORCE. The single force which has the same effect as two or more forces acting together.

ROTARY MOTION. Motion about a point which acts as a pivot.

SCALAR (*skay*-ler) **QUANTITY.** A quantity which has only magnitude.

TORQUE (*tork*). The product of a force times the length of the arm on which it acts.

TRANSLATORY (*trans*-luh-tor-ee) **MO-TION.** Motion along a line.

VECTOR. An arrow used to represent a vector quantity.

VECTOR QUANTITY. A quantity which has magnitude and direction.

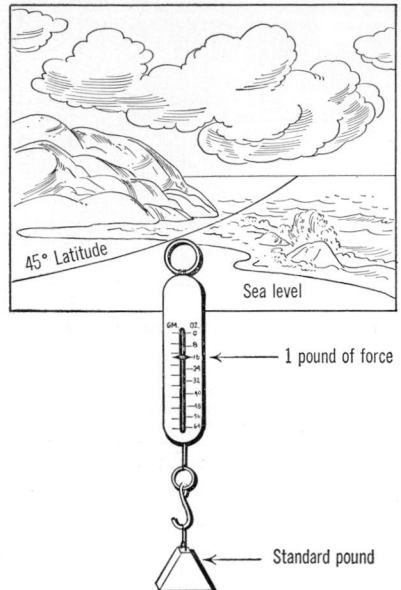

Fig. 7-1. At 45° latitude and at sea level, one pound of force is needed to overcome the earth's attraction for the standard pound.

a truck. We may move the truck, or only tend to move it. We exert a force if we pull on a heavy piano. We may move the piano, or we only tend to move it. **Forces** *produce or prevent motion, or they have a tendency to do so.*

2. Forces acting on a body. Most of the forces which act on an object are caused by other objects in contact with it. When we exert a force to close a door, our hand is in contact with the door. The liquid which exerts a force against the container is in contact with the container. Other forces may act on a body without being in actual physical contact with it. Some of these forces are magnetic or electrical. For the present, however, we shall be concerned only with one force of this type: the force of gravitation

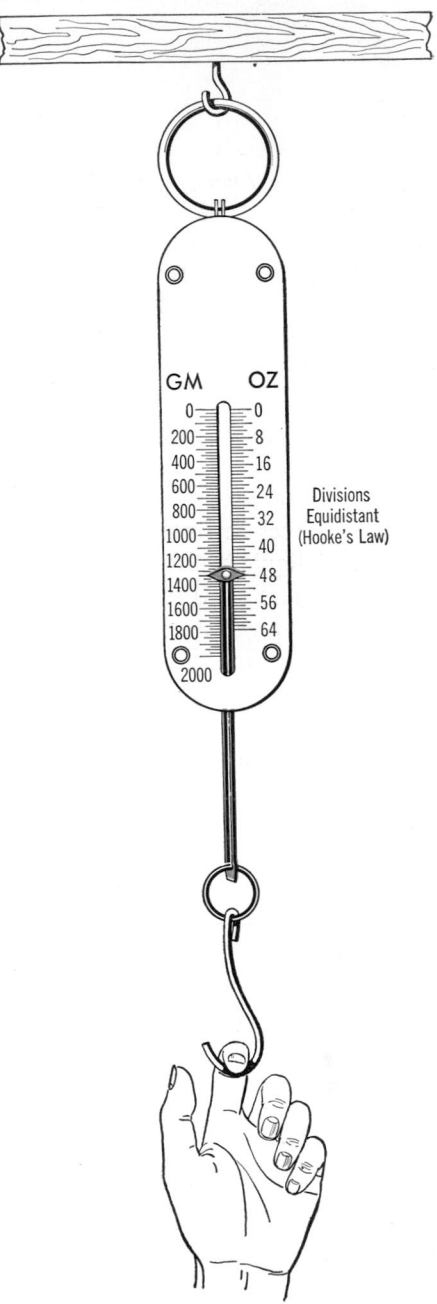

Fig. 7-2. A spring balance is used to measure force. Here it measures the downward force exerted by the hand pulling on the hook of the balance.

exerted by the earth. This is the force which causes bodies to fall toward the earth. This is the force we measure when we find the *weight* of an object.

3. The pound is a unit of force. In Chapter 2 we learned about certain standards of measurement in both the metric and English systems. The standard mass in the metric system is the platinum-iridium cylinder called the *standard kilogram*. By official action of the Congress of the United States a similar cylinder, having only 0.4535924277 the mass, is called the *standard pound*. The pound, the English system *unit of force,* is defined as the weight of the standard pound. The pound of force equals the force of attraction of the earth for the standard pound. We shall learn later that the gravitational attraction of the earth for a certain object is different at various locations on the earth's surface. Therefore, a further condition to *the definition of the* **pound** *of force is that it equals the weight of the standard pound at sea level and 45° latitude.* There also are units of force in the metric system in addition to the gram-weight and kilogram-weight we have used so far. We shall study them later.

4. How is force measured? A spring balance is commonly used to measure force. This device is an application of Hooke's law. The pull of the earth upon a standard pound suspended from the hook of the balance will stretch the spring a certain distance. Any other object which stretches the spring this same distance will also weigh a pound. Two such objects will stretch the spring twice as far. Three of them will stretch the spring three times as far, and so on. Graduations corresponding to these distances are marked on the face of the balance. A pointer attached to the spring indicates the reading. A typical spring balance appears in Fig. 7-2.

5. Scalar and vector quantities. There are some quantities in physics which require both a magnitude, or size, and a direction in order to express them completely. Force is one of these quantities. When a force is exerted, we are not only interested in the size of the force, but also in the direction the force acts. Force is therefore said to be a **vector quantity,** *or a quantity which has magnitude and direction. Vector quantities may be represented by an arrow. The arrow is called a* **vector.**

Quantities like volume or density are not connected with any particular direction. *They are completely expressed when we give just their magnitude. These are called* **scalar** (*skayler*) **quantities.**

2. COMPOSITION OF FORCES

6. Force vectors. The arrow, or vector, used to represent a force is called a *force vector*. Suppose we draw a vector to represent a force of 10 pounds acting eastward upon point *P*. We use a straight line ten units long, drawn eastward from point *P,* as shown in Fig. 7-3. A force vector is always represented as a *pull* upon the point where the force acts. The arrowhead at the end of the line indicates the direction in which the force acts. Any convenient unit may be selected to represent one pound of force. But it is necessary to use the same unit in each case when several forces are represented in the diagram. We may let ¼ inch represent 1 pound, or we may use some other convenient scale. The choice of the unit will depend upon the amount of space available for the diagram.

In Fig. 7-4 we have two forces represented. One force of 15 pounds acts westward upon point *P*. The other force, 20 pounds, acts southward upon the same point.

7. What is a resultant force? Usually, two or more forces act simultaneously upon the same object. We may wish to find the magnitude and direction of a single force which could produce the same effect as all the forces acting together. *The resultant of two or more forces applied at a point is that single force applied at the same point which could produce the same effect as the two or more forces acting together. This is the* **resultant force.**

The resultant of two or more forces is really a substitute for those forces. If we use the resultant we assume that it takes the place of two or more forces. After we have found their resultant, the separate forces may be ignored. Unlike the football substitute, who does not always produce the same effect as the man he replaces, *the resultant force*

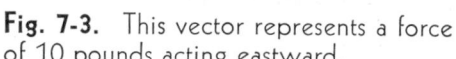

Fig. 7-3. This vector represents a force of 10 pounds acting eastward.

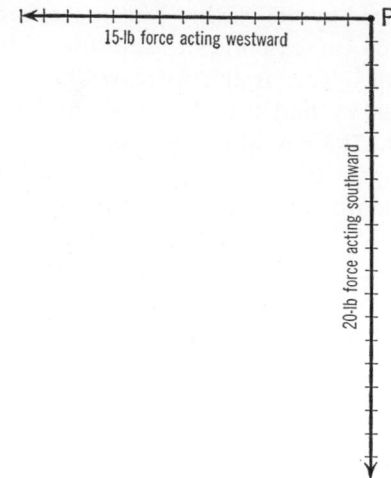

15-lb force acting westward

20-lb force acting southward

Fig. 7-4. These vectors represent two forces acting in different directions upon the same point.

must produce exactly the same effect as all the forces for which it is substituted.

8. The resultant of forces acting in a straight line. If one boy pulls on a rope with a force of 40 pounds, and another boy joins him and pulls on the rope in the same direction with a force of 60 pounds, the resultant force equals the *sum of the two separate forces.* If the boys stopped pulling, one man taking their place could produce the same effect by pulling on the rope in the same direction with a force of 100 pounds.

If one boy pulls in one direction with a force of 40 pounds and another boy pulls on the same point in the opposite direction with a force of 60 pounds, the resultant force will be *the difference between the two separate forces.* In this case, a force of 20 pounds pulling on the point in the direction of the *greater* force would produce the same effect as that produced by the two boys.

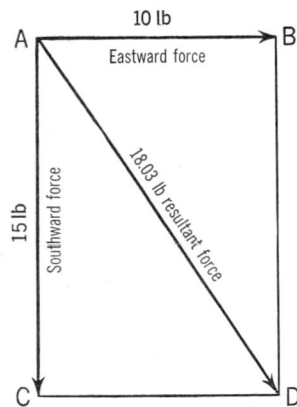

Fig. 7-5. A method of graphically finding the resultant of two forces acting at right angles.

9. The resultant of forces acting at right angles. Suppose one force of 10 pounds acts eastward upon an object at point A. Another force of 15 pounds acts southward upon the same point. Let us first draw vectors to represent these two forces, as shown in Fig. 7-5. From our drawing, we see that the first force tends to move the object along AB to B. The second force tends to move the object along AC to C. If the forces act *simultaneously,* the object moves along the diagonal of the parallelogram of which the two forces are sides, or

along AD to D. *The resultant of two forces acting at an angle upon a given point is equal to the diagonal of a parallelogram of which the two force vectors are sides.* In this case the parallelogram of forces is a rectangle, and we can easily calculate the value of the resultant. The diagonal divides the rectangle into two right triangles. The square of the hypotenuse of a right triangle equals the sum of the squares of the two sides, $c^2 = a^2 + b^2$. Here c represents the hypotenuse length, a and b the lengths of the two sides. See Sample Problem below.

10. Finding the resultant of forces acting at any angle. The angle between two forces acting on the same point is generally not a right angle. In Fig. 7-6 we have represented the vec-

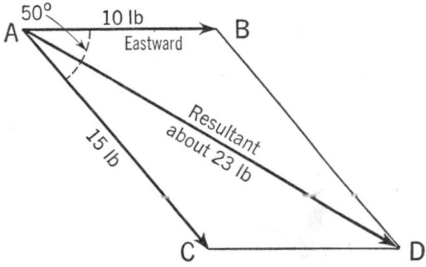

Fig. 7-6. A method of graphically finding the resultant of two forces acting at an acute angle.

SAMPLE PROBLEM

Find the resultant of the two forces acting on point A as shown in Fig. 7-5.

SOLUTION

Since the parallelogram of forces is a rectangle, we may use the formula, $c^2 = a^2 + b^2$.

Substituting, c^2 (the resultant squared) $= (10)^2 + (15)^2$.

Solving, $c^2 = 100 + 225 = 325$. Extracting the square root of 325, $c = 18.03$ lb, the resultant force. (See Section 2 in the Mathematics Refresher for the method of extracting square root.)

tors for two forces, 10 pounds and 15 pounds, which act on point *A*. The angle between the two forces is 50°. Unless you have already studied trigonometry, you can not *calculate* the resultant of these two forces acting at this angle. We can, however, find an approximate value of the resultant graphically. First, we draw the parallelogram to scale, using the two force vectors *AB* and *AC* as sides. We must use a protractor to make the angle between them 50°. From point *A* we draw a diagonal and measure it carefully. Since we know the scale we are using, we can find the magnitude of the resultant force in pounds from the length of the diagonal. Observe that the diagonal vector representing the resultant is drawn from the point on which the two original forces are acting. The other diagonal of the parallelogram, *BC,* is not the resultant of the two forces.

The resultant is decidedly different if we use the same two forces but make the angle between them 140°. The parallelogram is constructed to scale in the same manner, using the force vectors as sides, and making the angle between them 140°. This parallelogram is shown in Fig. 7-7. The diagonal must be drawn from *A,* the point on which the two forces are acting. The length of the diagonal *AD*

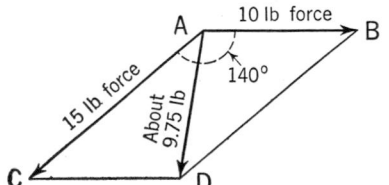

Fig. 7-7. A method of graphically finding the resultant of two forces acting at an obtuse angle.

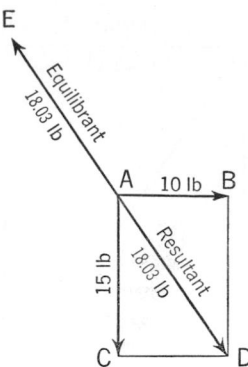

Fig. 7-8. The equilibrant of two forces acting at a point is applied at the same point. It equals the magnitude of their resultant, but acts in the opposite direction.

is measured, and its value is determined from the scale used in making the diagram.

★ Sometimes three or more forces act at different angles upon the same point. We may find their resultant by first finding the resultant of two of them. We use the vectors of these first two forces as sides of a parallelogram, and find the diagonal. Then we construct a second parallelogram using this diagonal and the third force vector as sides. The diagonal of the second parallelogram is the resultant of the three concurrent forces.

11. What is an equilibrant force? In working with forces, it is also desirable to find the point of application, the magnitude, and the direction of a force which could be applied to produce *equilibrium,* or to *prevent motion.* One boy pulls on a wagon with a force of 40 pounds. Another boy pulls on the wagon with a force of 40 pounds in exactly the opposite direction. The second boy prevents motion; he produces equilibrium. The force he uses is called the *equilibrant.*

It is easy to find the equilibrant of two or more forces acting upon the same point. First we find their resultant. The equilibrant force then acts in the opposite direction. In Fig. 7-5, we found that a single force, *AD,* can be substituted for the two forces *AB* and *AC.* In order to counteract the resultant force *AD,* an equilibrant force *AE,* Fig. 7-8, must be applied at the same point *A.* Its direction must be exactly opposite to that of the resultant, and its magnitude must be equal to that of the resultant. *The equilibrant of two or more forces acting at a point is applied at the same point. It always equals the magnitude of their resultant but acts in the opposite direction. We call this the* **equilibrant force.**

QUESTIONS

GROUP A

1. What new definition of force have we learned in this chapter?

2. Exactly what do we measure when we weigh an object?

3. What is the basic unit of force in the English system of measurement? Define this unit. What units of force in the metric system have we been using?

4. What instrument do we normally use for measuring forces? Of what law of physics is it an application?

5. What is a scalar quantity? What is a vector quantity? How may we represent vector quantities graphically?

6. What three facts about a force are represented by a force vector?

7. What is a resultant force?

8. How do we calculate the value of the resultant of two forces which are acting in the same direction as well as in the same straight line?

9. How do we calculate the value of the resultant of two forces which act on the same point, but in exactly opposite directions?

10. How may we calculate the magnitude of the resultant of two forces which act at right angles to each other upon the same point?

11. How may we determine the magnitude of the resultant of two forces which act at any angle to each other upon the same point?

12. What is an equilibrant force? At what point must it be applied? How does it compare with a resultant force?

GROUP B

13. Give some examples of forces which act on an object because other objects are in contact with it. Give some examples of forces which act on an object without being in actual physical contact with it. What is the most common force of this type?

☆ **14.** What method must be followed when we wish to find the magnitude of the resultant of three or more forces which act simultaneously upon the same point?

PROBLEMS

(In the Mathematics Refresher, refer to Sections 2, 10, 11, and 16. You will need a ruler and protractor for solving these problems. Use a scale of 1 inch = 10 lb for the drawing for each problem.)

GROUP A

1. Draw a force vector which represents a force of 25 lb acting westward upon point *A.*

2. Using a protractor, draw the vector which represents a force of 35 lb acting in a direction 15° south of east on point *B.*

3. Two forces are acting simultaneously upon point *C.* One is a force of 5 lb acting northward. The other is a force of 15 lb which also acts northward. Represent these forces graphically, and find the resultant force.

4. There are three forces acting simultaneously upon point *D.* One acts eastward with a force of 10 lb; the second acts westward with a force of 20 lb; the third acts eastward with a force of 5 lb. Represent these three forces graphically, and find the resultant.

5. A force of 15 lb acts southward from point *E*. A force of 20 lb acts westward from point *E*. Represent these forces graphically, and *graphically* find the resultant. In which direction does the resultant force you obtained by this method act?

6. A force of 5 lb acts westward from point *F*. A force of 30 lb acts northward from point *F*. Draw the vectors which represent these forces. *Graphically* find the resultant. In which direction does the resultant force you obtained by this method act?

7. Two forces act upon point *G*. One force of 20 lb acts northward. The second force of 20 lb acts in a direction 45° south of east. Draw the vectors which represent these forces. Graphically find the resultant force. In which direction does this resultant force act? Draw the vector which represents the equilibrant force. What are the magnitude and direction of the equilibrant force?

8. A force of 25 lb acts southward upon point *H*. A force of 20 lb acts in a direction 20° east of north upon point *H*. Represent these forces graphically. Draw the resultant force vector and graphically find its magnitude. Draw the vector which represents the equilibrant force. In what direction do you find that it acts?

GROUP B

9. *Calculate* the value of the resultant force acting upon point *E* in Problem 5.

10. *Calculate* the value of the resultant force acting upon point *F* in Problem 6.

11. A force of 10 lb acts eastward upon point *J*. A second force of 30 lb acts in a direction 30° south of west upon point *J*. Find the magnitude and direction of the resultant force by the graphical method. What is the magnitude and direction of the equilibrant force?

12. One force acts 25° west of north upon point *K*. A second force acts 35° east of north upon point *K*. Find the direction and magnitude of the equilibrant force by the graphical method.

● **13.** Three forces act simultaneously upon point *L*. One force of 10 lb acts northward. The second force of 15 lb acts westward. The third force, also 15 lb, acts in a direction 30° east of north. Graphically find the magnitude of the resultant force and its direction.

● **14.** A force of 25 lb acts in a direction 30° south of east upon point *M*. A second force of 15 lb acts in a direction 15° west of north upon point *M*. A third force of 30 lb acts upon this same point in a direction 20° south of west. Graphically find the magnitude and direction of the equilibrant force.

---

3. RESOLUTION OF FORCES

12. How is a force resolved into two components? We have just learned how to find the single force which can produce the same effect as two *component* forces acting upon the same point. We next must learn how to find the value of the components if we are given the magnitude and direction of a single force and the directions in which its components act.

This problem in *resolution of forces* is the converse of a problem in *composition of forces*. We are given the diagonal of a parallelogram, and the angle between the diagonal and each side. We must construct the parallelogram and find the length of the sides. *Resolution of forces is the separation of a single force into two forces acting in definite directions upon the same point. Usually, the two components into which a single force is to be resolved act at right angles to each other.*

13. Applications of the resolution of forces. When we roll a lawn, as shown in Fig. 7-10, we push the roller

SAMPLE PROBLEM

A force of 10 lb acts on point A in a direction 37° east of south. Find the eastward and southward components of this force.

SOLUTION

Draw a vector representing a 10-lb force acting in a direction 37° east of south, as shown in Fig. 7-9. From point A draw lines southward and eastward, because these are the directions of the two components. Then from point C, the opposite end of the vector, drop perpendiculars to these southward and eastward lines. These perpendiculars intersect the southward line from A at B, and the eastward line from A at D. Placing arrowheads at B and D completes the two vectors, AB and AD. These are the southward and eastward components, respectively, of the force AC. By measuring AB and AD, we find that they represent forces of 8 lb and 6 lb respectively. (Note: This method of constructing the force parallelogram applies only when the components of the given force act at right angles to each other. The force parallelogram in such cases is always a rectangle.)

at an angle to the ground. This is the convenient way to push, even though we wish the roller to move horizontally over the lawn. The force we apply is resolved into two components. One component pushes the roller forward. The other acts perpendicularly to it and tends to push the roller into the ground. Suppose we push with a force of 80 pounds at the angle shown in the figure. By constructing a parallelogram to scale, we find that the horizontal component is about 74 pounds. The vertical component, which tends to push the roller into the ground, is approximately 31 pounds.

When a boy pulls a loaded wagon, the force which he exerts is resolved into two components. The horizontal component draws the wagon forward. The vertical component tends to lift the wagon.

When a sailboat is moving with the wind, the full force of the wind drives the boat forward. When the boat is moving at an angle with the direction of the wind, part of the force of the wind drives the boat forward while the other component tips the boat sideways. See the diagram, Fig. 7-11.

The boom of a power shovel must resist with a thrust force the combined effect of the weight on the cable and the tie force. If the thrust force

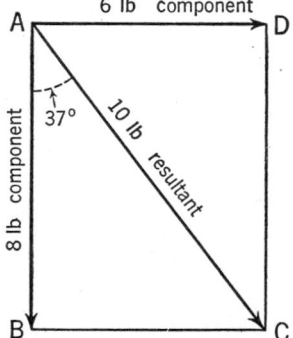

Fig. 7-9. A method of graphically finding the southward and eastward components of a single force acting 37° east of south.

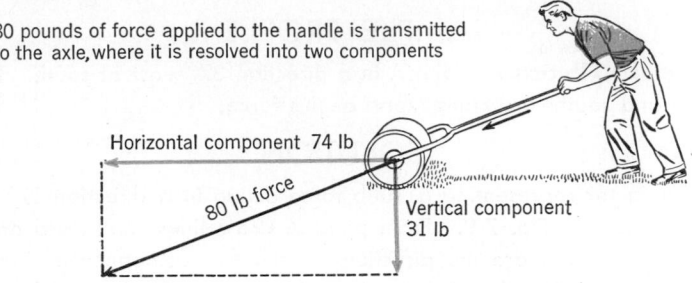

80 pounds of force applied to the handle is transmitted to the axle, where it is resolved into two components

Horizontal component 74 lb

80 lb force

Vertical component 31 lb

Fig. 7-10. The force applied to the handle of the lawn roller is resolved into a horizontal and a vertical component.

is known, together with the angles at which the other forces act, the value of the tie force and the weight may be calculated. In this example the two component forces *do not act at right angles to each other.* See Fig. 7-12. The weight of the roof of a house acts downward and outward upon the walls. From Fig. 7-13 we see how the weight of the roof is resolved into these two components. The weight of the roof *OW* is resolved into the two components *OX* and *OY,* which act in the directions of the supporting rafters. The rafters transmit these forces to their point of contact with the walls. The force *OX* which was applied to *O* is the same as force *AD* applied at *A*. *AB* is the component of *AD* tending to spread the walls. *AC* is the component which acts downward.

★ **14. Resolving the force of gravity.** A force may act on an object in a direction in which the object can not move. However, it may be possible to resolve this force into two components. The object may then move in the direction of one of the components, just as though that were the only force acting upon the object.

An object placed on an inclined plane is attracted by the earth. The force of attraction is the weight of the object. See Fig. 7-14. The plane prevents the motion of the object along *OE,* the direction in which the earth's attraction acts. The force of attraction may, however, be resolved into two components. One component, *OD,* acts perpendicular to the surface of the plane and tends to break the plane. The other force, *OF,* acts parallel to the plane and tends to pull the object down the plane.

Using *OE* as the diagonal, we can construct the parallelogram *ODEF* and find the relative values of the sides

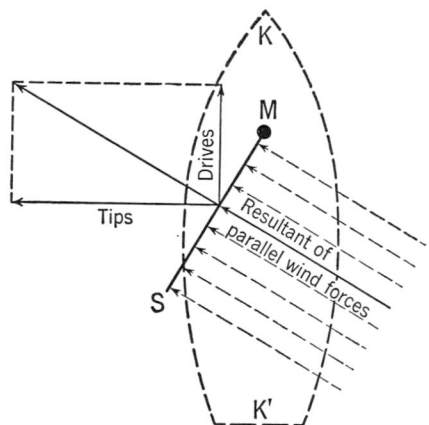

Fig. 7-11. The sail resolves the force of the wind into two components. One component drives the boat forward; the other tends to tip it over.

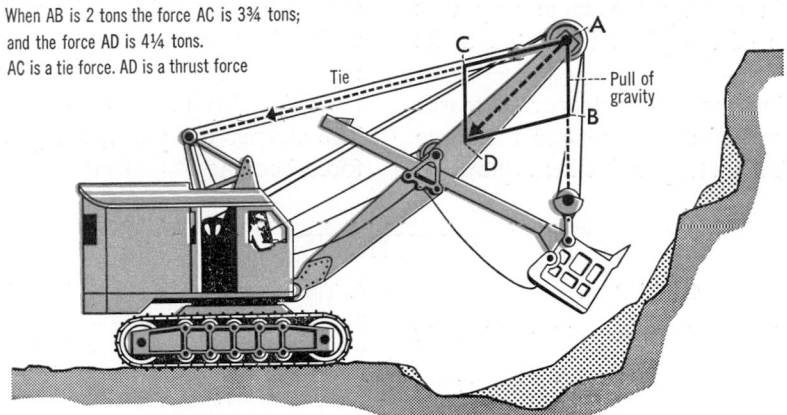

When AB is 2 tons the force AC is 3¾ tons; and the force AD is 4¼ tons. AC is a tie force. AD is a thrust force

Tie

Pull of gravity

Fig. 7-12. The thrust force exerted by the boom of a power shovel must counteract the resultant of the tie force and the weight of the load.

OF and OD by plotting to scale. In this special case, we also can calculate these values if the height and length of the inclined plane are known. The triangles ABC and OEF are similar. (The sides are mutually parallel or perpendicular.) Therefore, $OE : OF = AB : BC$. But OE represents the weight of the object, $W;$ $OF,$ the force W_p tending to pull the object down the plane; $AB,$ the length of the plane, $l;$ $BC,$ the height of the plane, $h.$ The weight of the object is related to the force tending to pull it down the plane

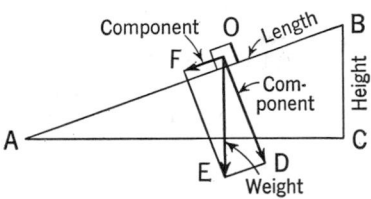

Fig. 7-14. Resolving the force of gravity into two component forces. One component acts down the plane; the other acts against the plane.

in the same way that the length of the plane is related to its height, or,

$$W : W_p = l : h.$$

In a similar fashion it may be shown that the force tending to break the plane is related to the weight of the

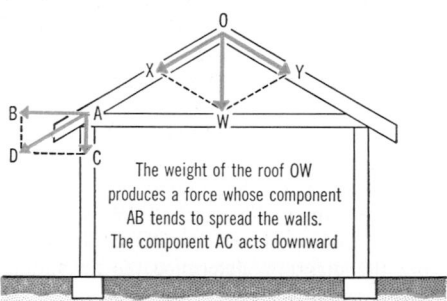

The weight of the roof OW produces a force whose component AB tends to spread the walls. The component AC acts downward

Fig. 7-13. The weight of the roof may be resolved into a force acting downward and a force acting to spread the walls.

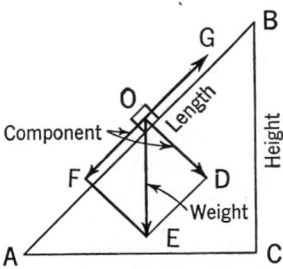

Fig. 7-15. When the inclined plane is made steeper, the component acting down the plane is increased.

object in exactly the same way that the base of the plane is related to its length.

Making the plane steeper increases the force *OF* and decreases the force *OD*. This steeper inclined plane is shown in Fig. 7-15. The vector *OG*, which is equal and opposite to *OF*, represents the force needed to keep the object from sliding down the plane. The steeper the plane, the greater this force becomes.

QUESTIONS

GROUP A

1. What is meant by "composition of forces"? By "resolution of forces"?

2. What is a "component force"? What is the usual angle between component forces?

3. How does a problem in the resolution of forces differ from a problem in the composition of forces?

4. When we push on the handle of a lawnmower, into what two components may the force we exert be resolved?

5. A boy pulls a sled along a level, snowy road by means of a rope which extends at a 30° angle from the front of the sled to his hand. Into what two components may the force he exerts upon the rope be resolved?

6. The antenna tower of a radio station is supported by guy wires which extend from the top of the tower to the ground. The wires make a 60° angle with the tower. Into what two components is the force which the tower exerts on each guy wire resolved?

GROUP B

★**7.** A large crate rests on an inclined plane. Into what two forces may the weight of the crate be resolved? Which force may cause the crate to move?

★**8.** John parks his automobile on a hill. Into what two components may the weight of the automobile be resolved? Which force is counteracted by the brakes of the automobile?

PROBLEMS

(In the Mathematics Refresher, refer to Sections 2, 8, 10, 11, and 16. You will need a ruler and protractor for solving these problems. Use a scale of 1 inch = 10 lb for the drawings in Problems 1 through 6.)

GROUP A

1. A force of 20 lb acts northeast upon point *A*. Resolve this force graphically into the northward and eastward components. From your diagram, find the value of each of these components.

2. A force of 15 lb acts in a direction 30° west of south upon point *B*. Resolve this force graphically into its westward and southward components. From your diagram, find the magnitude of each component.

3. A force of 25 lb is exerted in a direction 35° north of west upon point *C*. Graphically resolve this force into its northward and westward components. From the diagram find the magnitude of these two component forces.

4. A force of 35 lb acts in a direction 10° north of east upon point *D*. By using the graphical method, resolve this force into its northward and eastward components. From your diagram, read the magnitude of each of the component forces.

5. Frank pushes with 30 lb of force upon the handle of a lawn roller. The angle between the handle and the ground is 45°. By the graphical method, resolve this force into its horizontal and vertical components. From the diagram, read the value of each component force.

6. Ralph pulls a loaded wagon with a force of 25 lb. The handle of the wagon makes an angle of 30° with the ground. Graphically resolve the force with which Ralph pulls into both its horizontal and vertical components. From the diagram, determine the magnitude of each component force.

GROUP B

7. *Calculate* the magnitude of each component force in Problem 5.

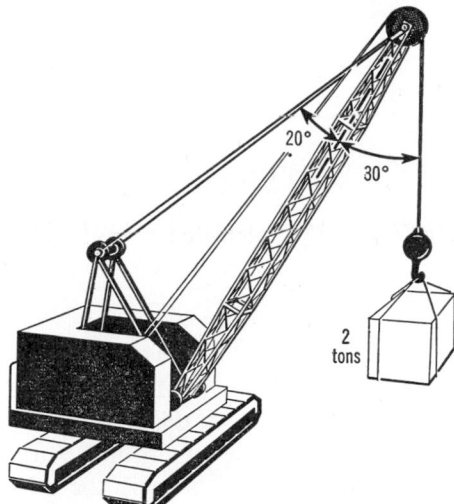

Fig. 7-16. Forces acting about the boom of a crane.

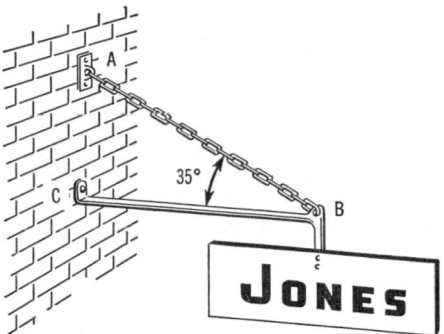

Fig. 7-17. The forces which support an overhanging sign.

8. *Calculate* the magnitude of each component force in Problem 6. (Remember that in a 30°–60°–90° right triangle, the hypotenuse is twice as long as the shorter side of the triangle.)

9. A block of stone weighing 2 tons is to be raised by a crane. The angle between the load cable and the crane boom is 30°. The boom is held in place by a tie cable which forms an angle of 20° with the boom. See Fig. 7-16.

Graphically find the thrust force of the boom and the force on the tie cable.

10. A sign weighing 100 lb is supported as shown in Fig. 7-17. Calculate the forces exerted by *AB* and *CB*. In which direction do these forces act?

★ **11.** A truck weighing 10 tons is parked on a hill which rises 3 ft in each 100 ft of road. What force tends to make the truck roll down the hill?

★ **12.** A safe which weighs 500 lb is being rolled up an inclined plane. The plane is 10 ft long, with the upper end 4 ft above the lower end. What force tends to make the safe roll back down the plane? What is the force that the safe is exerting perpendicular to the inclined plane?

4. PARALLEL FORCES

15. What are parallel forces? Suppose two boys carry a heavy load on a stick between them. The boys push up on each end of the stick. The load itself acts as a force in a downward direction. These obviously are two parallel forces. **Parallel forces** *act in the same or opposite directions. The resultant of two parallel forces in the same direction equals the sum of the forces.*

16. The moment of a force — torque. Before we can understand how a load is distributed between two parallel forces, we must learn about the moment of a force, or the *torque* (*tork*) produced by a force. Suppose we have a rigid bar, *AB,* such as shown in Fig. 7-18. At end *A,* force *F′,* 40 pounds, acts downward. At end *B,* force *F,* 20 pounds, acts downward. The bar can pivot about the fixed point

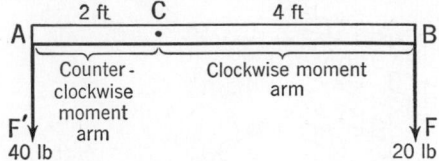

Fig. 7-18. The torque produced by a force equals the product of the force times the length of the arm on which it acts.

C. The force *F* is attempting to turn the bar *AB* about *C* in a clockwise direction. The force *F'* tends to turn the bar in a counterclockwise direction. How effective is each force in producing rotation? Experiments show that the effectiveness of any force in producing rotation depends on the magnitude of the force and the length of the arm on which it acts. The effectiveness of a force in producing rotation is called *the moment of a force, or the torque produced by the force. The moment of a force, or its **torque**, equals the product of the force times the length of the arm on which it acts.* For example, the force *F,* 20 pounds, acting upon the lever *BC,* 4 feet long, has a clockwise torque of 80 pound-feet. The force *F',* 40 pounds, acting upon the arm *AC,* 2 feet long, has a counterclockwise torque of 80 pound-feet also.

★ If the force *F* is not applied per-

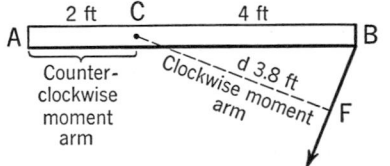

Fig. 7-19. If the force does not act at right angles to the bar, the length of the arm upon which the force acts is the perpendicular distance from the line of direction of the force to the pivot point.

pendicularly to the bar *AB* but is applied as shown in Fig. 7-19, the length of the arm upon which this force acts is no longer *BC*. The length of the arm upon which force *F* acts is the perpendicular distance *d* from the line of the direction of the force to the pivot point. The torque in this case equals the product of the force *F* times the distance *d*.

17. How do we use torques? Again two boys carry a load on a stick between them. The force diagram is shown in Fig. 7-20. The stick is 8 feet long. The load, which weighs 160 pounds, is placed 3 feet from the boy at *A,* and 5 feet from the boy at *B.* What part of the load does each boy carry? To find the upward force exerted by the boy at *A,* we shall consider that the hand of the boy at *B* acts as a pivot. The boy at *A* is pulling upward, or clockwise, upon an arm 8 feet long. Suppose we let *x* equal the force he exerts. Then the clockwise torque is 8 *x*. The load *W* is pulling downward, or counterclockwise, with a force of 160 pounds upon an arm 5 feet long. Its torque is $5 \times 160 = 800$ pound-feet. If the bar is in equilibrium, the two torques must be equal. Thus, 8 *x* = 800. Solving, *x* = 100 pounds, the force exerted by the boy at *A.* To find the force exerted by the

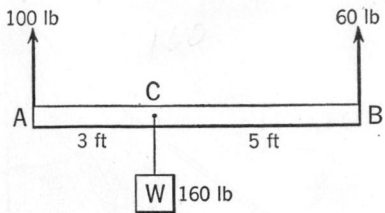

Fig. 7-20. We calculate the load which each boy carries by using the principles of torques.

SAMPLE PROBLEM

The bridge shown in Fig. 7-21 is 100 ft long.   A weight of 10,000 lb rests on the bridge 30 ft from one end.   Find the upward force which must be exerted by each pier to support this weight.   Neglect the weight of the bridge.

SOLUTION

We first letter the bridge AB.

Let x equal the upward force exerted by pier A.   Using B as a pivot, the clockwise torque of the upward force at A is 100 x.   The counterclockwise torque of the weight on the bridge is 70 × 10,000, or 700,000 lb-ft.   But these torques are equal.   100 x = 700,000.

Solving, x = 7000 lb, the upward force exerted by pier A.

Let y equal the upward force exerted by pier B.   Using A as the pivot, the counterclockwise torque is 100 y.   The clockwise torque of the weight on the bridge is 30 × 10,000 or 300,000 lb-ft.   100 y = 300,000.

Solving, y = 3000 lb, the upward force exerted by pier B.

boy at *B,* we use *A* as a pivot.   The upward force at *B,* which we shall represent by *y,* acts counterclockwise upon an arm 8 feet long.   This counterclockwise torque is 8 *y.*   The load, 160 pounds, acts clockwise upon a 3-foot arm.   The clockwise torque is 480 pound-feet.   Since 8 *y* = 480, *y* = 60 pounds, the force exerted upward by the boy at *B.*   In this problem the stick's weight is neglected.

Refer to the Sample Problem which is shown above.

When you solve problems in which parallel forces are exerted on a pivoted beam or pole, use the pivot point as the point about which to calculate the torques.   If the beam or pole is not pivoted, any point may be used as the point about which to calculate the torques.   It usually is easier to select one end as an imaginary pivot point.

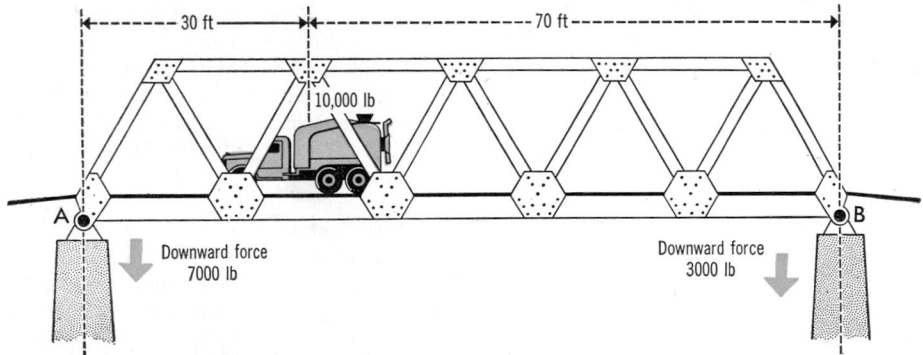

Fig. 7-21.   Parallel forces are exerted by the truck and by the piers supporting the bridge.

QUESTIONS

GROUP A

1. What are parallel forces? How can we calculate the resultant of two parallel forces which act in the same direction? How can we calculate the resultant of two parallel forces which act in opposite directions?

2. How do we calculate the torque produced by a force which acts at right angles to a pivoted bar? In what unit is torque measured in the English system?

3. If a pivoted bar on which parallel forces act is to be in equilibrium, what must be true of the clockwise and counterclockwise torques?

4. What is the most convenient point about which to calculate the torques in a parallel force problem?

GROUP B

5. Two boys are carrying a load suspended from a stick between them. How may the position of the load be adjusted so that the stronger boy carries his proper share of this particular load?

★ **6.** How do we calculate the torque produced by a force which does not act at right angles to a pivoted bar?

PROBLEMS

(In the Mathematics Refresher, refer to Section 16.)

GROUP A

1. Paul and Henry are carrying a sack weighing 120 lb on a pole between them. If the pole is 6 ft long, and the load is 2 ft from Paul, how much does each boy carry? Neglect the weight of the pole.

2. A bridge is 40 ft long. What force must the pier at each end of the bridge exert to support an automobile weighing 2 tons which is parked 15 ft from one end of the bridge? Neglect the weight of the bridge.

3. A painter stands on a plank 8 ft long which is supported at each end by a stepladder. The painter weighs 160 pounds. If he stands 3 ft from one end of the plank, what force is exerted by each stepladder? Neglect the weight of the plank.

4. Two boys weigh 100 pounds and 125 pounds respectively. They wish to balance on a see-saw. If the 100-pound boy sits 5 ft from the center, how far from the center must the 125-pound boy sit? Neglect the weight of the see-saw.

GROUP B

5. George is chinning himself on a bar 4 ft long. His left hand is placed 1 ft from the left end of the bar. His right hand is 2 ft from the right end of the bar. George weighs 150 pounds and his weight is supported equally by his hands. What force must be exerted by the poles which support the ends of the chinning bar? Neglect the weight of the bar.

6. A bricklayer weighing 175 pounds stands 2 ft from one end of a scaffold 6 ft long. Two feet from the other end of the scaffold is a pile of bricks weighing 64 lb. What force must be exerted on each end of the scaffold in order to support it? Neglect the weight of the scaffold.

7. A wooden bar 10 ft long is pivoted 3 ft from end A. A weight of 250 lb is attached at end A. At the other end of the bar a weight of 75 lb is attached. Where must a weight of 100 lb be attached to the bar in order to make the clockwise and counterclockwise torques equal? Neglect the weight of the bar.

8. A steel beam 12 ft long is pivoted in the center. At end A of the beam a 200-lb weight is attached. Two feet in from A a weight of 50 lb is attached. At end B a 400-lb weight is attached. Three feet in from B a weight of 200 lb is attached. Where on the beam must a weight of 400 lb be attached in order to make the clockwise and counterclockwise torques equal? In this problem neglect the weight of the beam.

5. CENTER OF GRAVITY AND EQUILIBRIUM

18. The center of gravity. Fig. 7-22 represents a stone lying on the ground. Since we know every part of the stone has weight, every part of the stone must be attracted by the earth. All of the downward forces exerted by the stone because of its weight are parallel. The actual weight of the stone is the resultant of all these separate parallel forces, and the point of application of this resultant force is called the *center of gravity*. The **center of gravity** *of any object is that point at which all its weight appears to be concentrated.*

If we attach a string to this stone at a point directly above the center of gravity and pull upward, the stone may be lifted without any rotation. An object may be balanced on the point of a knife placed directly beneath its center of gravity. Suppose we try to overturn the stone shown in Fig. 7-22. If we exert our lifting force at *A, B* becomes the pivot point. Force *A* acts clockwise upon the lever arm *AB*. The weight of the stone, concentrated

at *C,* is a counterclockwise force. The length of its lever arm is *CB*. Since the force at *A* is applied on a longer lever arm than is the weight of the stone, the force needed to overturn the stone will be less than that required to lift it completely off the ground.

★ **19. Finding the center of gravity experimentally.** Suppose we tie a weight at one end of a piece of twine. Then we hold the twine by the other end so that the weight is free to swing. The weight finally comes to rest in such a position that if the line of the cord is extended downward, it will pass through the center of gravity of the earth. This weight and cord form a *plumb (plum) line*. We may use it to find experimentally the center of gravity of an irregular object such as that shown in Fig. 7-23. First we suspend the object from one point, such as

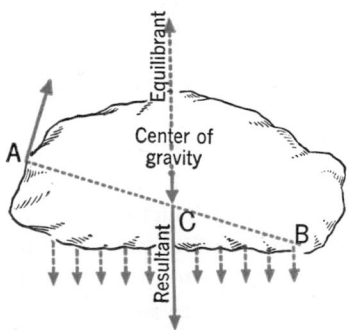

Fig. 7-22. All the weight of the stone appears to be concentrated at its center of gravity.

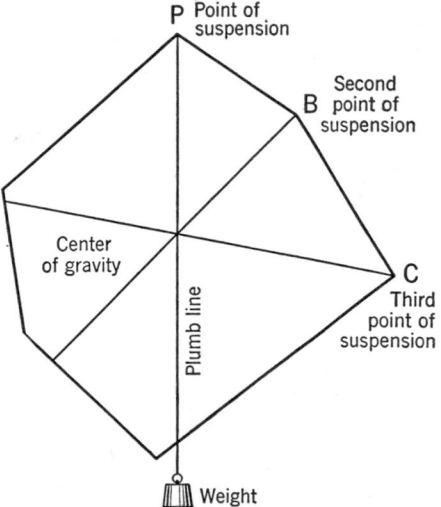

Fig. 7-23. An experimental method for finding the center of gravity.

P in the diagram, so that it is free to turn about the point of suspension. The object may swing about this point, but it finally comes to rest with its center of gravity directly below the point of suspension. If we drop the plumb line from point *P,* the center of gravity of the object will lie somewhere on this line. A line drawn on the object along the plumb line must pass through the center of gravity. Let us next suspend the object from point *B* and again draw a line along the plumb line. In order to check our results, we may suspend the object from a third point, *C*. Again we draw a line along the plumb line. Each of these lines passes through the center of gravity. Therefore, the center of gravity must lie at the point where these lines intersect.

20. When are parallel forces in equilibrium? When this book rests on your desk, it pushes down upon the desk with a force equal to its weight. If the book is to be in equilibrium, your desk must push upward against the book with an equal force. In order to keep the book, or any other object, in equilibrium, there must be no *unbalanced* force acting upon it. A push from one side must be balanced by an

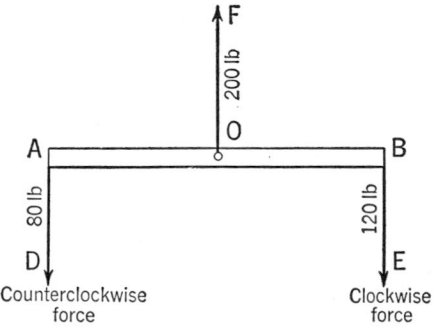

Fig. 7-24. Placing a 200-lb force at any point, O, prevents translatory motion.

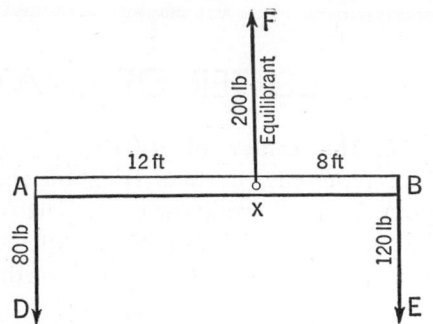

Fig. 7-25. Placing the 200-lb force at X prevents both translatory and rotary motion, and produces equilibrium.

equal push from the opposite side. *An object is said to be in* **equilibrium** *when no unbalanced force acts upon it.* In other words, *the resultant of all the forces acting upon the object is zero.*

To secure equilibrium, there are two kinds of motion which must be prevented. These are **translatory** (trans-luh-tor-ee) **motion,** or *motion along a line,* and **rotary motion,** or *motion about a point acting as a pivot.* Suppose we have two parallel forces, *D* and *E,* of 80 pounds and 120 pounds respectively. These two forces act upon a bar at points *A* and *B,* Fig. 7-24. A force of 200 pounds applied in the opposite direction at any point, *O,* will prevent translatory motion since this force equals the sum of the two forces, 80 lb + 120 lb. In order to prevent rotary motion, this 200-pound force must be located at such a point on the bar that the clockwise and counterclockwise torques are equal. In order to calculate this position, let us use *B* as a pivot point. The counterclockwise torque will be that of the 80-pound force acting on the 20-foot lever arm, or 1600 lb-ft. The clockwise torque will be that of the 200-pound force acting on a lever arm of unknown length from point B. Let us call this unknown length x. The clockwise torque will be 200 x. For equilibrium, the two torques must be equal.   Therefore 200 x = 1600. Solving, x = 8 ft, the distance from B at which the 200-pound force must be applied to prevent rotary motion. See Fig. 7-25.

Any number of parallel forces are in *equilibrium if the sums of the opposite forces are equal, and the sums of all the clockwise torques are equal to the sums of all the counterclockwise torques.*

★ **21. When is an object in stable equilibrium?** If the position of an object in stable equilibrium is slightly altered, the object will tend to return to its original position. An object in

---

SAMPLE PROBLEM

A bar, *AB*, 30 ft long is shown in Fig. 7-26. The bar weighs 100 lb, and its center of gravity, *C*, is 10 ft from *A*. At *A* a force of 200 lb acts downward. At *B* a force of 250 lb acts downward. At *D*, 4 ft from *B*, a force of 80 lb acts upward. At *E*, 2 ft from *A*, a force of 250 lb acts upward. What force must be used to produce equilibrium? In which direction must it act? Where must it be placed?

SOLUTION

The weight of the bar, 100 lb, acts like a 100-lb force pulling downward at the center of gravity, *C*. In order to prevent translatory motion, the sum of the forces acting upward must equal the sum of the forces acting downward.

250 + 80 = 330 lb, total upward force.

200 + 100 + 250 = 550 lb, total downward force.

550 − 330 = 220 lb, additional upward force needed to prevent translatory motion.

We next must find where this 220-lb force must be applied to prevent rotary motion. Let us use *A* as the imaginary pivot point. Let x be the distance from *A* to the point where the 220-lb force must be applied. In order to prevent rotary motion, the total clockwise torque must equal the total counterclockwise torque.

Clockwise torque: 100 × 10 = 1000
                   250 × 30 = 7500
Total clockwise torque   8500 lb-ft

Counterclockwise torque: 250 × 2 =   500
                          80 × 26 = 2080
                          220 × x =   220 x
Total counterclockwise torque (2580 + 220 x) lb-ft

For rotary equilibrium these torques are equal:
8500 lb-ft = (2580 + 220 x) lb-ft.
Solving, 220 x = 5920, x = 26.9 ft, the distance from *A* to the point where the 220-lb force must be applied.

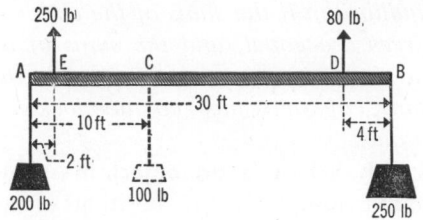

Fig. 7-26. In order to produce equilibrium, we must apply a force which prevents both translational and rotary motion.

stable equilibrium can not be overturned without first raising its center of gravity. Both bricks shown in Fig. 7-27 are in stable equilibrium, but their degree of stability differs. To turn brick (*A*) on its edge, *P,* the center of gravity, *C,* must be raised to the point *E.* When the center of gravity passes beyond the vertical line *EA,* it is no longer over the area *originally* included within the base. The brick now falls into the position shown by the dotted lines. In falling, its center of gravity is lowered from *E* to *B.* The brick is once again in a state of stable equilibrium. Let us now look at brick (*B*). This represents the same brick, but its original position this time is standing on end. In order to overturn this brick, we must raise its center of gravity from *C'* to *E.* Now the center of gravity is no longer over the area of the original base (the end of the brick). The brick falls to the position shown by the dotted lines. It falls because this lowers its center of gravity.

With the brick originally on its side, the center of gravity must be raised the distance from *A* to *E,* Fig. 7-27(*A*), before the brick may be turned on end. When the brick is originally on end, the center of gravity must be raised the distance from *D* to *E,* Fig. 7-27(*B*), before the brick falls on its side. *EA* is much greater than *ED.* Consequently the brick has much greater stability when it is on its side. *The stability of an object may be increased by enlarging the base, and by having the center of gravity as low as possible.*

A truck loaded with steel sheets is less likely to upset than a truck loaded with barrels made from this same weight of steel. The center of gravity of the load of steel sheets is much lower. In Fig. 7-28, the loaded truck on the sloping road will upset if the load is high enough to raise the center of gravity to *C'.* A plumb line dropped from *C'* falls outside the

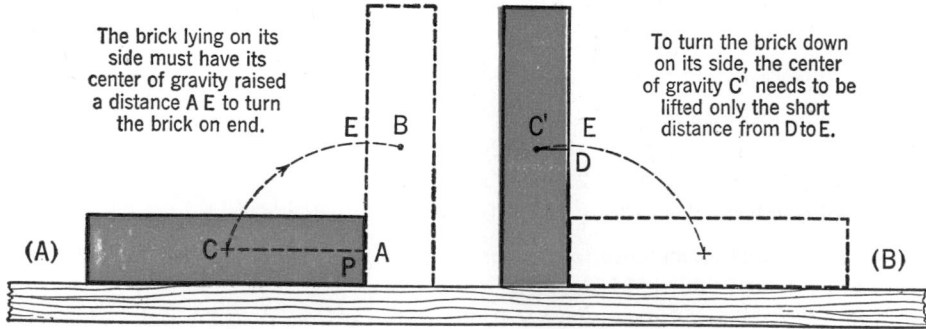

Fig. 7-27. To make an object more stable, we may broaden its base or lower its center of gravity.

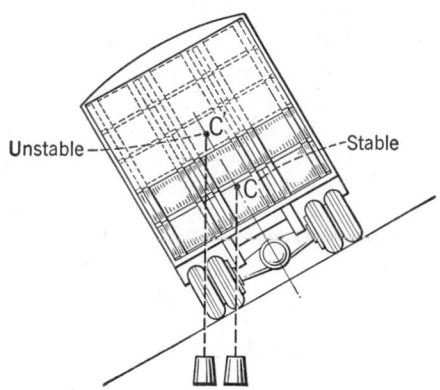

Fig. 7-28. The truck is stable when a plumb line dropped from the center of gravity falls within the area described by the wheel base.

wheel base. If the top of the load is removed, the center of gravity will be lowered, perhaps to *C*. A plumb line dropped from *C* falls within the area described by the wheel base, showing that the load is stable.

★ **22. When is an object in unstable equilibrium?** An egg standing on its end is in unstable equilibrium. A person walking a tightrope is another example of unstable equilibrium. In either case, as soon as the slightest movement occurs the center of gravity falls outside a plumb line dropped to the point of support. The center of gravity begins to be lowered at once and the object falls. In unstable equilibrium, the center of gravity is above the point of support.

★ **23. When is an object in neutral equilibrium?** A ball lying on a table is in neutral equilibrium. A cylinder or a cone lying on its side, and a wheel free to turn on its axle are other examples of neutral equilibrium. These objects come to rest in any position since the center of gravity is neither raised nor lowered when the object is overturned. Fig. 7-29 illustrates the differences between stable, unstable, and neutral equilibrium.

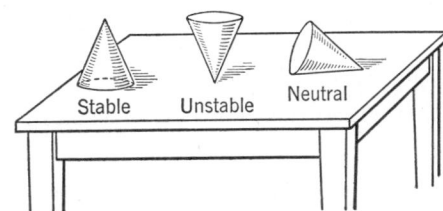

Fig. 7-29. Types of equilibrium.

QUESTIONS

GROUP A

1. What is the center of gravity of an object?
2. What conditions must be met in order for an object to be in equilibrium? What two kinds of motion must be prevented in order to secure equilibrium?
3. What conditions must be met before any number of parallel forces are in equilibrium?
4. What is meant by stable equilibrium? How may we increase the stability of an object?
5. When is an object in unstable equilibrium? In neutral equilibrium?
6. Explain two possible adjustments that can be made so two young boys of unequal weight may balance on a see-saw.

7. In building railroad passenger cars, as much of the heavy mechanical equipment as possible is hung below the floor level. Will this increase the stability of the car? Why?
8. Ocean freighters add ballast if carrying a light cargo. What is its purpose and where would it be placed?

GROUP B

7. Why does all the weight of an object appear to be concentrated at its center of gravity?
★ 8. Describe how you could find experimentally the center of gravity of an irregularly shaped object.

PROBLEMS

(In the Mathematics Refresher, refer to Sections 2, 11, and 16.)

GROUP A

1. A steel beam of uniform cross section weighs 500 lb. If it is 10 ft long, what force is needed to lift one end of it?

2. A wooden telegraph pole 15 ft long is tapered so that the center of gravity is 6 ft from one end. It weighs 400 lb. What force is required to lift the heavy end? The light end?

3. A bar 12 ft long weighs 75 lb. Its center of gravity is 4 ft from one end. If a weight of 50 lb is attached to one end and a weight of 80 lb is attached at the other end, what is the value of the equilibrant? In which direction must it act? Where must it be located?

4. A bridge 60 ft long is supported by a pier at each end. The bridge weighs 50 tons. If a load of 7.5 tons is located 15 ft from one end, what load does each pier support?

GROUP B

5. A bar 15 ft long has its center of gravity 5 ft from the heavy end. If it is placed on the edge of a block 5 ft from the light end and a weight of 150 lb is added to the light end, it will be balanced. What is the weight of the bar?

6. A painter's scaffold 10 ft long is supported by ropes attached at each end. If the scaffold weighs 100 lb, what is the tension on each rope? If a painter weighing 150 lb stands on the scaffold 4 ft from one end, find the tension on the ropes. Suppose a second painter, whose weight is 175 lb, steps on the scaffold 2 ft from the other end. What is the tension on each rope now?

7. A uniform pole 25 ft long weighs 750 lb. From end *A* a weight of 500 lb is hung. At *B*, the other end of the pole, there is a weight of 700 lb. Two feet from *B*, there is an upward force of 600 lb. Four feet from *A*, there is an upward force of 800 lb. What is the value of the equilibrant? In which direction must it act? Where must it be applied?

8. A paperhanger weighing 150 lb stands in the center of a plank 8 ft long. The plank weighs 50 lb. It is supported at each end by stepladders which have an angle of 60° between each pair of legs. Calculate the force exerted by each of the four legs of each stepladder in supporting the plank and paperhanger.

---

6. FRICTION

24. What is friction? When we attempt to roll or slide one object over another we find that *there is a force which opposes the motion. This force is called* **friction.** Several ideas have been presented to explain friction. Some physicists believe that friction is caused by irregularities in the surfaces of the objects being rubbed together. The uneven surfaces tend to interlock and offer resistance to motion. If surfaces are polished, we should expect friction between them to be lessened. Experiments have shown, however, that there is a limit to the amount by which friction may be reduced by polishing the surfaces. If the surfaces are made too smooth, the friction between them actually increases. Friction in the bearings and cylinders of automobiles is reduced by making one of the sliding surfaces rougher than the other.

Still other physicists believe that electrical forces similar to those which hold atoms and molecules together are partly the cause of friction.

Friction may also be caused by the adhesion of molecules of one surface to those of the other surface. By using radioactive materials, scientists

Fig. 7-30. The treads on this tractor enable it to pull heavy loads over rough terrain. They increase the friction between the tractor and the earth.

have learned that in sliding over one another, minute quantities of one surface are rubbed off on the other surface.

25. How does friction help us? Have you ever seen a driver trying to start up his automobile on an icy pavement? The rear wheels spin but the car does not go forward. We need friction between the tires and the pavement before the automobile can move. We would be unable to walk if there were no friction between the soles of our shoes and the sidewalk.

Whenever you apply the brakes on an automobile, the friction of the brake lining on the brake drum slows down the wheels. The friction between the tires and the roadway enables you to bring the car to a stop.

Friction helps us in less obvious ways. Friction holds a screw in wood. It also enables us to use nails to fasten boards together. If friction were eliminated, dishes would slide off the table unless the table were perfectly level.

26. Friction may be a hindrance, too. When we wish to move an object, friction is a disadvantage. We mount heavy pieces of furniture on wheels. We polish and lubricate bearings to reduce friction. The proper maintenance of automobiles, bicycles, motors, and other machines depends upon regular lubrication.

27. What do we know about sliding friction? Friction experiments are very difficult to perform, and the results are not always easy to express in a simple fashion. The following statements about sliding friction hold true in many cases. There are, however, outstanding exceptions to them.

(1) *Friction depends upon the materials and their surfaces.* Friction is not only different between different

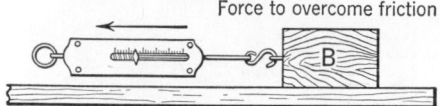

Force to overcome friction

Fig. 7-31. Measuring the force needed to overcome sliding friction.

materials, but it is different between the same material if the surfaces are different.

(2) Suppose we hook a spring balance to an object and pull horizontally. We find that it takes more force to start the object sliding than it does to keep it sliding. *Sliding friction is less than starting friction.*

(3) We do not find much difference in the friction of sled runners on snow when we change the speed at which we pull a sled. But if a person attempts to stop his automobile with a steady pressure on the brake pedal, the car comes to a jolting halt. In this case, friction

apparently increases with a decrease in speed. With objects moving at high velocities, a bullet moving through a gun barrel for example, friction decreases with an increase in velocity. Ultimately, a speed is reached beyond which there is little decrease in friction. At this speed the friction between the surfaces of the bullet and the gun barrel produces enough heat to melt them. Then, the moving bullet is surrounded by a thin film of molten metal. Within the range of medium speeds, *sliding friction is nearly independent of velocity.*

(4) The force needed to slide a brick along a table is almost the same whether the brick lies on a side, on edge, or on end. *Friction is practically independent of the area of contact between the surfaces.*

(5) It does not require as much force to slide an empty chair across the floor

Fig. 7-32. Sand is being placed on the rail just in front of one of the driving wheels of a locomotive. This increases the friction between the wheel and the steel rail so that the wheel will not slip when the locomotive is started.

SAMPLE PROBLEM

A block weighs 100 lb. A force of 30 lb is required to keep it in uniform motion on a horizontal surface. What is the coefficient of friction?

SOLUTION

Since the block is moving on a horizontal surface, its weight is the normal force pressing the surfaces together. We may substitute directly in the formula, $\mu = \dfrac{f}{N}$.

This gives us $\mu = \dfrac{30 \text{ lb}}{100 \text{ lb}}$.

Solving, $\mu = 0.3$, the coefficient of friction.

(Note: If the block is not moving on a horizontal surface, the weight of the block must first be resolved into the components tending to move the block along the surface and pushing the block against the surface. The component of the weight tending to move the block along the surface will either aid or hinder the force overcoming friction. The force pushing the block against the surface is the normal force needed in the formula.)

as it does to slide the same chair when a 200-pound man is sitting on it. *Friction is directly proportional to the force pressing the two surfaces together.*

Some very special experiments have shown, however, that the force of friction is directly proportional to the area of contact and is independent of the force holding the surfaces together. But in practical cases, the force holding the surfaces together deforms the surfaces and determines the actual area in contact. Consequently the statements given in (4) and (5) on the preceding page concerning friction hold true.

28. The coefficient of friction. From what we have learned about the force of friction in Section 27, we see that, for practical purposes, it depends only upon the surfaces and upon the force pressing them together. We may compare the friction between different surfaces by using the coefficient of fric-

tion. *The **coefficient of friction** is the ratio of the force of friction to the normal force pressing the surfaces together.* The coefficient of friction may be represented by the Greek letter μ (mu).

Fig. 7-33. Roller bearings are used to reduce friction on modern railroad cars. They are tapered to resist sidewise movement of the axle.

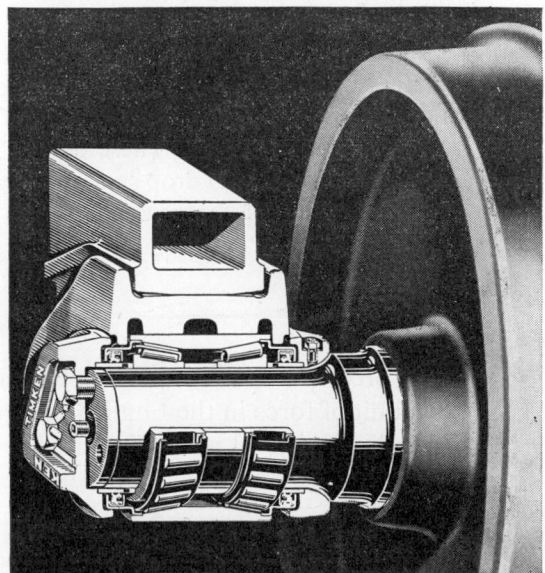

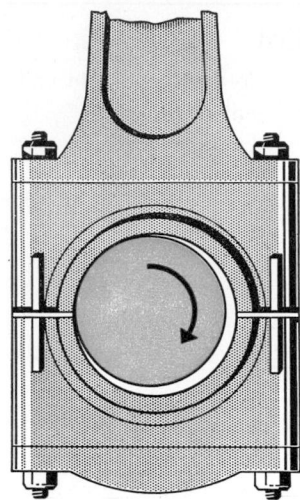

Fig. 7-34. The lubricant flows in the space between the shaft and the bearing, and substitutes fluid friction for sliding friction. The clearance between the shaft and the bearing is exaggerated in this drawing for emphasis.

If the force of friction is represented by f and the normal force by N, then,

$$\mu = \frac{f}{N}.$$

The coefficient of friction varies with the nature of the material and the degree of polish of the surface. See Sample Problem on page 159.

29. How can we increase friction? A train engineer sands the rails so that the drive wheels of the locomotive will not slip. Some buses and trucks are equipped with sanders. These devices enable their drivers to drop sand or fine gravel in front of the rear wheels so that they will not spin on icy pavements. We use chains or snow tires on the rear wheels of automobiles when roads are covered with snow and ice. We throw cinders on slippery hills and curves during the winter to increase friction.

30. How can we reduce friction? We use several methods to reduce friction. Machines which must operate with very little friction may be designed with one or more of the following:

(1) *Polished bearings.* If a wheel is to turn easily on an axle, both of the contact surfaces must be polished. The material must be hard so that it will not wear away rapidly or easily become grooved.

(2) *Anti-friction metals.* When steel slides over an alloy of lead and antimony, the coefficient of friction is less than when steel slides on steel. Bearings are sometimes packed with such an alloy to reduce friction.

(3) *Ball bearings or roller bearings.* The coefficient of friction of steel balls rolling on steel may be as low as 0.002. This is only about $\frac{1}{100}$ as much as that of steel sliding on steel. Roller bearings are made in various designs to reduce friction in different kinds of machines.

(4) *Lubricants.* If oil is used as a lubricant, an oil film flows between the bearing surfaces. This separates them so that fluid friction is substituted for solid friction. Fluid friction is generally much less than the solid friction.

Summary

Forces produce or prevent motion, or they have a tendency to do so. The unit of force in the English system is the *pound*, the weight of the standard pound at sea level and 45° latitude. Spring balances are commonly used to measure forces.   Force is a vector quantity because it has both magnitude and direction.   Forces may be represented graphically by arrows which are called vectors.

The resultant of two or more forces applied at a point is that single force, applied at the same point, which could produce the same effect as the two or more forces acting together.   The resultant of forces acting in the same direction is their sum.   The resultant of forces acting in opposite directions is their difference.   The resultant of two forces acting at an angle upon a given point is equal to the diagonal of a parallelogram of which the two force vectors are sides.   The equilibrant of two or more forces acting at a point is applied at the same point.   It always equals the magnitude of their resultant but acts in the opposite direction.

A single force may be resolved into two or more components.   In such a case, the single force is represented by the diagonal of a parallelogram of which the two components are sides.

The torque produced by a force equals the product of the force times the length of the arm on which it acts.

The center of gravity of a body is that point at which all its weight appears to be concentrated.   An object is said to be in equilibrium when no unbalanced force acts upon it.   Both translatory and rotary motion must be prevented in order to produce equilibrium with parallel forces.   The stability of an object is increased in two ways: (1) by broadening its base and (2) by lowering its center of gravity.

Friction is the force which opposes motion.   The coefficient of friction is the ratio of the force of friction to the normal force pressing the surfaces together. Friction is sometimes a desirable force.   At other times, when undesirable, it is reduced by using special bearings and lubricants.

Terms to Define . . .

Center of gravity	Neutral equilibrium	Sliding friction
Coefficient of friction	Parallel forces	Spring balance
Definition of the pound as a unit of force	Parallelogram of forces	Stable equilibrium
	Pivot point	Standard kilogram
Equilibrant force	Plumb line	Standard pound
Equilibrium	Reducing friction	Starting friction
Force	Resolution of forces	Torque
Force vector	Resolution of the force of gravity	Translatory
Friction		Unstable equilibrium
Increasing friction	Resultant force	Vector
Lubricant	Rotary	Vector quantity
Moment of a force	Scalar quantity	Weight

GROUP A

1. What is friction?   What do physicists believe may be the cause of friction?

2. Give several examples of the way in which friction may be helpful.

3. What methods do we use to reduce friction?

4. Why is it possible for bulldozers to clear land rapidly in almost any sort of terrain?

5. If there were no friction, would it be possible to tie a knot in a piece of string?   Would it be possible to make the string itself?

6. How does sliding friction compare with starting friction?

7. In most cases, what does the amount of sliding friction depend upon?   Of what is it independent?

8. What is the *coefficient of friction?*

GROUP B

9. Suppose that you are driving an automobile down a long hill.   The hill is not steep enough to require shifting into a lower gear, but the car will go too fast if the brakes are not applied.   How should the brakes be applied — with a light but constant pressure, or more heavily and intermittently?

10. In what ways do we increase the friction between the soles of our shoes and the surface with which they come in contact?

11. Name as many devices as you can which are used to increase the friction between the tires of an automobile and the pavement over which it is moving.

12. What advantages would roller bearings have over conventional bearings in the trucks of railroad freight cars?   What disadvantages?

13. Why does the use of a lubricant reduce the friction in a bearing?

(In the Mathematics Refresher, refer to Sections 8, 10, and 16.)

GROUP A

1. A wooden block weighs 0.5 lb.   A force of 0.15 lb is required to keep it in motion on a horizontal surface.   What is the coefficient of sliding friction?

2. The coefficient of sliding friction between two metal surfaces is 0.15.   What force will be required to slide a block of metal weighing 4 lb over the metal top of a table?

3. In a coefficient of friction experiment, a force of 45 lb was needed to slide an object weighing 125 lb over a horizontal surface. Calculate the coefficient of friction.

4. A force of 10 lb is required to move a loaded sled weighing 60 lb over the snow on a level road.   What is the coefficient of friction?

GROUP B

● **5.** A crate weighing 250 lb slides down an inclined plane at uniform speed.   The plane is 10 ft long.   The height of the plane is 5 ft. What is the coefficient of friction of the crate against the inclined plane?

● **6.** A block of wood just slides down a 3-ft-long inclined plane when one end of the plane is raised 1 ft.   The block of wood weighs 0.2 lb. Calculate the coefficient of friction.

Things to Do

1. Look around school for applications of composition of forces, resolution of forces, and parallel forces.   Examine such things as gymnasium equipment and fire escapes.

2. If your instructor has the double cone and inclined plane apparatus and the "Tower of Pisa" apparatus, use them to demonstrate the principles of center of gravity and stability.

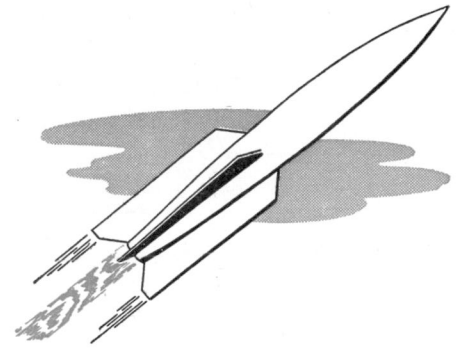

Chapter 8

Motion

1. VELOCITY

1. What is motion? If you drive across Texas from Dallas to El Paso, you have moved from one location to another. You may fly from Cheyenne, Wyoming, to Seattle, Washington. Again you have changed your place as shown on a map of the United States. Finally, you may go from physics class in one room to English class in another room. During the time you were making all of these changes, your body was in motion. **Motion** *may be defined as a continuous change of place or position.*

In our study of forces we found that there were two kinds of motion which must be prevented in order to produce equilibrium. These were translatory motion and rotary motion. *Translatory motion is motion in a straight line.* It is also called **rectilinear** (rek-tin-*lin*-ee-er) *motion. Rotary motion is motion in a curved path.* This is sometimes also called *circular motion.*

2. What is speed? Every automobile has a device called a speedometer. This instrument tells you your **speed,** or *rate of motion,* at each particular instant as you drive along. When you

---
Vocabulary

ACCELERATION (ak-sel-uh-*ray*-shun). Rate of change in velocity.

CENTRIFUGAL (sen-*trif*-yuh-gul). Acting away from a center.

CENTRIPETAL (sen-*trip*-uh-tul). Acting toward a center.

GRAVITATION. The mutual force of attraction between bodies.

IMPULSE. The product of a force times the length of time it acts.

INERTIA (in-*er*-shuh). The property of matter which makes it necessary for a force to be exerted on the matter in order to accelerate it.

MASS. A measure of the inertia of a body.

MOMENTUM. The product of the mass of an object times its velocity.

MOTION. A continuous change of place or position.

PENDULUM. A body suspended in such a manner that it can swing to-and-fro about a horizontal axis.

RECTILINEAR (rek-tih-*lin*-ee-er). In a straight line.

SPEED. Rate of motion.

VELOCITY (vuh-*loss*-ih-tee). Rate of motion in a particular direction.

163

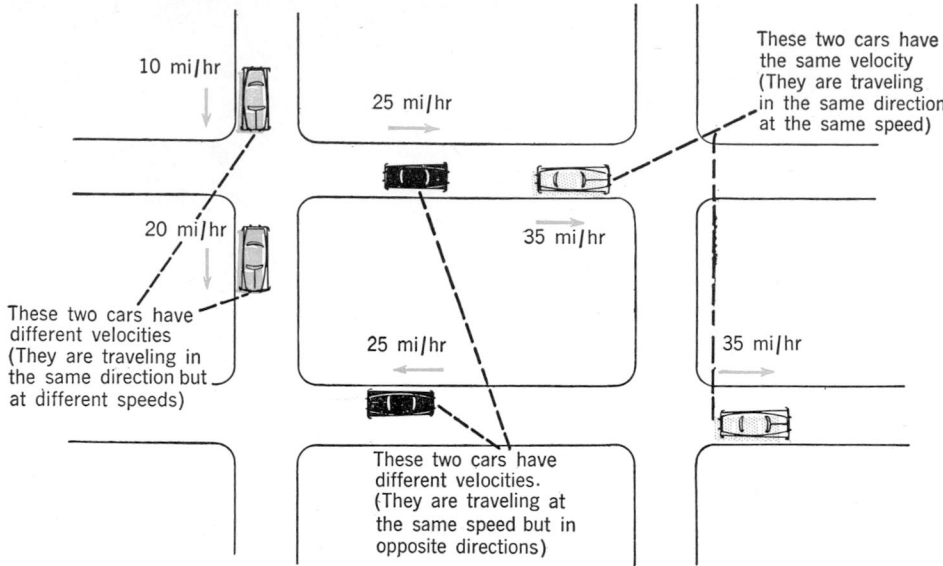

10 mi/hr

25 mi/hr

These two cars have
the same velocity
(They are traveling
in the same direction
at the same speed)

20 mi/hr

35 mi/hr

These two cars have
different velocities
(They are traveling in
the same direction but
at different speeds)

25 mi/hr

35 mi/hr

These two cars have
different velocities.
(They are traveling at
the same speed but in
opposite directions)

Fig. 8-1. Speed is rate of motion, but velocity is rate of motion in a particular direction.

go on a long automobile trip, you are interested in the *average speed* you have maintained during each day. Suppose you traveled from Dallas to El Paso, a distance of 637 miles, in $13\frac{1}{2}$ hours. Your average speed would be 637 mi ÷ $13\frac{1}{2}$ hr = 47.2 mi/hr.

$$\text{Average speed} = \frac{\text{distance traveled}}{\text{elapsed time}}.$$

We may measure speed in several types of units. Speed generally is measured in mi/hr. However, we may also use ft/sec, cm/sec, and m/sec.

3. What is velocity? *Speed* and *velocity* (vuh-*loss*-ih-tee) are commonly given the same meaning. In physics, speed and velocity have definite, separate meanings. The speed of an object indicates how fast it is going. It tells us the distance the object will travel in a given time. But it tells us nothing about the direction in which the object is moving. Suppose you start from Chicago and travel for 10

hours at an average *speed* of about *45 miles per hour*. At the end of this time, you may be in Minneapolis, Nashville, or Pittsburgh. If you drive in a circular path, you may even be back in Chicago.

The quantity in physics which combines the speed of an object with the direction in which it moves is called velocity. **Velocity** *may be defined as the rate of motion in a particular direction.* In the example given above, if you travel from Chicago for 10 hours with a velocity of about *45 miles per hour northwestward,* you arrive in Minneapolis. If your velocity is 45 miles per hour *southward,* you reach Nashville. If your velocity is 45 miles per hour *southeastward,* you reach Pittsburgh.

Motion is said to be *uniform* when the velocity is constant; that is, when the object moves the same distance in the same direction in each succeeding unit of time. An automobile that main-

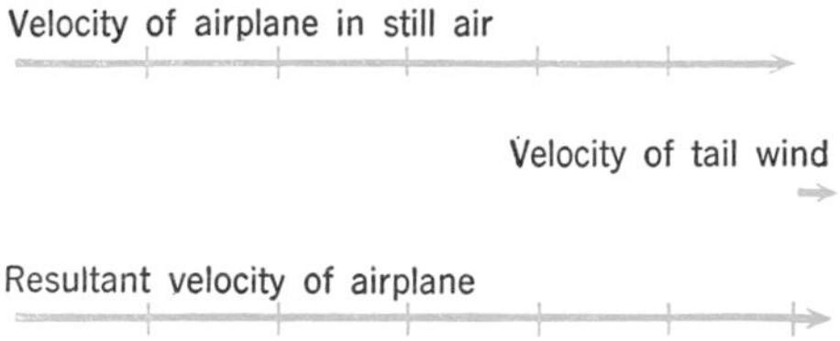

Velocity of airplane in still air

Velocity of tail wind

Resultant velocity of airplane

Fig. 8-2. The resultant of two velocities in the same direction is the sum of the two velocities. It has the same direction as the component velocities.

Velocity of airplane in still air

Velocity of head wind

Resultant velocity of airplane

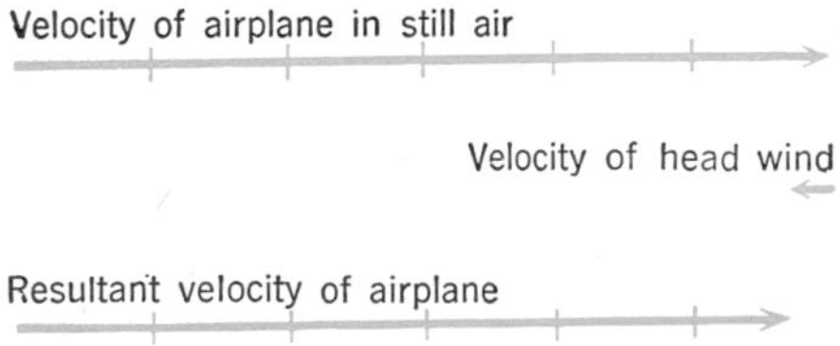

Fig. 8-3. The resultant of two velocities in opposite directions is the difference between the two velocities. It has the same direction as the greater velocity.

tains a velocity of 50 mi/hr along a perfectly straight, level road is an example of uniform motion. If either the speed of the car or the direction in which it is going is changed, its motion is *variable*. When the motion is variable, the distances a car travels in a particular direction in equal periods of time are unequal.

4. Velocity is a vector quantity. Since velocity has both magnitude and direction, *velocity is a vector quantity.* We may apply the same principles of vectors, which we learned about in Chapter 7, to the solution of problems involving velocities.

Suppose an airplane flies eastward through still air with a velocity of 300 mi/hr. Suddenly a tail wind with a velocity of 15 mi/hr eastward springs up. What is the resultant velocity of the airplane? Since these two velocities have the same direction, the resultant velocity is the sum of the separate velocities. Therefore, 300 mi/hr east-

ward + 15 mi/hr eastward = 315 mi/hr eastward, the resultant velocity of the airplane. This is shown graphically in Fig. 8-2.

Now let us take the opposite case. The airplane flies eastward, but the wind is a head wind. Its velocity is 15 mi/hr westward. What is the resultant velocity of the airplane? Since these velocities have opposite directions, the resultant will be the difference between them. It will have the direction of the greater velocity. Therefore, 300 mi/hr eastward − 15 mi/hr westward = 285 mi/hr eastward. The vectors for this problem are shown in Fig. 8-3.

We have still a third case to consider. The airplane still flies eastward with a velocity of 300 mi/hr. But now the wind has a velocity of 25 mi/hr southward. What is the resultant velocity of the airplane? We may solve this problem graphically. See Fig. 8-4. First let us draw the vector *AB* to rep-

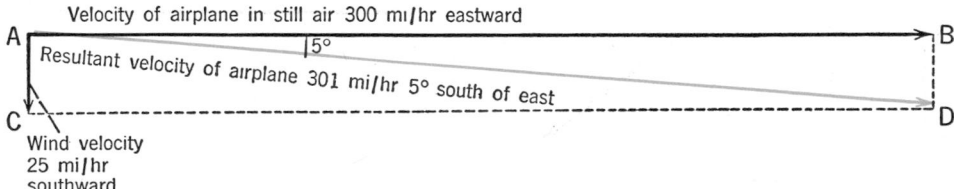

Velocity of airplane in still air 300 mi/hr eastward

Resultant velocity of airplane 301 mi/hr 5° south of east

Wind velocity
25 mi/hr
southward

Fig. 8-4. The resultant of two velocities acting at right angles to each other is the diagonal of the rectangle constructed by using the component velocity vectors as sides.

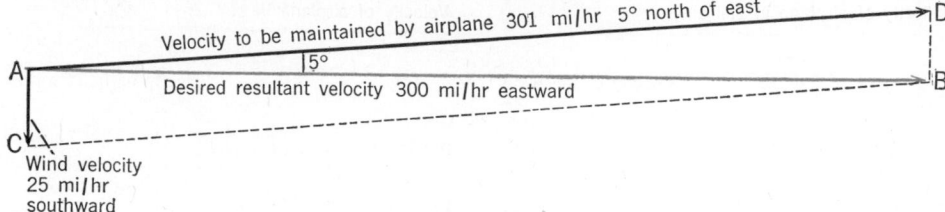

Fig. 8-5. Finding a second component velocity when one component velocity and the resultant velocity are known.

resent the velocity of the airplane, 300 mi/hr eastward. The vector representing the velocity of the wind, 25 mi/hr southward, is *AC*. To find the resultant velocity, we construct the parallelogram of velocities, *ABDC*. The diagonal of this parallelogram *AD* is the resultant velocity. From the scale of our diagram, we find that its magnitude is approximately 301 mi/hr. Its direction is nearly 5° south of east.

However, the pilot of this airplane does not want to get 25 miles south of his course for each hour of flight. What change must he make in the velocity of his airplane so that he stays on course despite the wind blowing from the north? Our problem is now one in the resolution of velocities. The

resultant velocity we wish to obtain is 300 mi/hr eastward. This is represented by the vector *AB* in Fig. 8-5. It will be the diagonal of our velocity parallelogram. We know one component of this velocity, that of the wind, 25 mi/hr southward. This is represented by the vector *AC*. To complete our parallelogram, we first draw *CB*. Then from *A,* we draw *AD* parallel and equal to *CB*. Connecting *D* with *B* completes the parallelogram. The side *AD* represents the velocity the airplane must maintain. From our diagram we find that this velocity is approximately 301 mi/hr in a direction 5° north of east. By pointing his airplane 5° north of east, and increasing his speed to 301 mi/hr, the pilot will actually travel along an eastward path with a speed of 300 mi/hr. See Sample Problems on page 167.

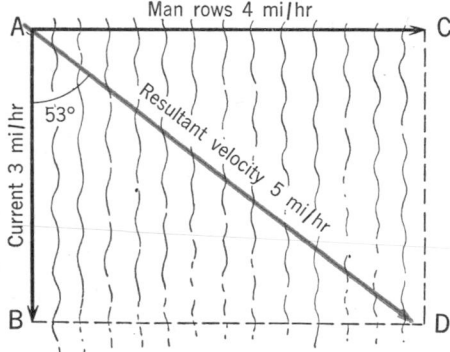

Fig. 8-6. Finding the resultant of two velocities acting at right angles to each other.

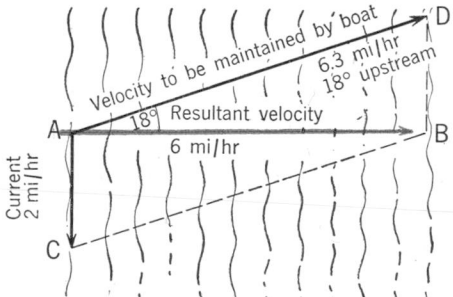

Fig. 8-7. Finding a second component velocity when the resultant velocity and one component are known.

SAMPLE PROBLEM

A man rows a boat at the rate of 4 mi/hr in still water. He heads the boat directly across a stream which flows at the rate of 3 mi/hr. What is his resultant velocity?

SOLUTION

In Fig. 8-6, we have drawn the vector AC to represent the velocity at which the man rows the boat. The vector AB is the velocity of the current of the stream.

Constructing the parallelogram of velocities, ACDB, we find the resultant velocity AD. Its magnitude may be found graphically.

Or we may find it by using the equation, $c^2 = a^2 + b^2$. $c^2 = (4)^2 + (3)^2$. Solving, $c^2 = 25$. $c = 5$ mi/hr. This velocity vector of 5 mi/hr forms an angle of approximately 53° with the stream current vector.

SAMPLE PROBLEM

What must be the velocity of a boat in order for it to cross a river $1\frac{1}{2}$ miles wide in 15 min? The river flows at the rate of 2 mi/hr.

SOLUTION

The resultant velocity of the boat must be $1\frac{1}{2}$ miles directly across the river in 15 min. This is a speed of 6 mi/hr at an angle of 90° with the current of the river. In Fig. 8-7, the vector AB represents the resultant velocity, 6 mi/hr. The vector AC represents the velocity of the river, 2 mi/hr.

We construct the velocity parallelogram, ACBD. Then the side of the parallelogram AD represents the velocity which the boat must maintain in order to follow a path directly across the river.

From the diagram we find this velocity is 6.3 mi/hr in a direction approximately 18° upstream.

QUESTIONS

GROUP A

1. What is motion? What is rectilinear motion? What is circular motion?

2. What is speed? In what units is it commonly measured?

3. What is velocity? How does it differ from speed?

4. If a body is to move with uniform motion, what must be true of its velocity?

5. What changes in velocity may occur to cause the motion of a particular body to be variable?

6. Why is velocity a quantity which may be represented by a vector?

GROUP B

7. What is measured by a speedometer? If you have a compass mounted on the instrument panel of your automobile, can you tell your velocity?

8. How do we calculate the resultant of two velocities which are at right angels to each other?

9. How may we graphically find the resultant of two velocities which act at any angle to each other?

10. Describe how to resolve graphically a single velocity into two velocities which act in fixed directions.

PROBLEMS

(In the Mathematics Refresher, refer to Sections 2, 10, 11, and 16.)

GROUP A

1. A motor boat travels 10 mi/hr in still water. What will be the resultant velocity if this boat is directed upstream on a river which is flowing at the rate of 2 mi/hr?

2. An airplane flying toward Chicago has a velocity with respect to the ground of 275 mi/hr northward. However, there is a wind blowing southward with a velocity of 15 mi/hr. What is the velocity of the airplane with respect to the air?

3. It takes 4 hours and 35 minutes to drive from Cleveland to Detroit, a distance of 167 miles. What is the average speed for this trip?

4. In driving from Cincinnati to St. Louis, Walter covered the distance of 341 miles in 8 hours and 20 minutes. What was his average speed?

5. Arthur can row a boat at the rate of 3 mi/hr in still water. He heads directly across a river which flows at the rate of 1 mi/hr. What is his resultant velocity? Solve the problem graphically.

6. An airplane flies westward at a velocity of 220 mi/hr. If the wind is blowing southward with a velocity of 20 mi/hr, what is the resultant velocity of the airplane? Solve the problem graphically.

7. The velocity of an airplane is 325 mi/hr northward. If there is a wind blowing at 25 mi/hr from the southwest, what will be the resultant velocity of the airplane? Solve the problem graphically.

8. A speed boat travels at 30 mi/hr in still water. What will be its resultant velocity if it heads directly across a river which is flowing at a speed of 5 mi/hr? Solve the problem graphically.

GROUP B

9. Calculate the value of the resultant velocity in Problem 5.

10. Calculate the value of the resultant velocity in Problem 6.

11. In order to maintain a velocity of 325 mi/hr northward, what should be the speed and direction of the airplane of Problem 7 to counteract the effect of the southwest wind of 25 mi/hr?

12. If a boat is to go straight across a river with a resultant velocity of 15 mi/hr, what should be its speed and direction to counteract the current of the river which flows at 3 mi/hr?

---

2. UNIFORMLY ACCELERATED MOTION

5. What is acceleration? Only under very special circumstances do we ever drive an automobile at constant velocity. When we drive through a large city we must continually stop for red traffic lights. When they change to green we start on our way again. In addition to stopping and starting, we may drive at various speeds because different parts of the city have different speed limits.

When we change the velocity of our automobile, we accelerate it. If the velocity goes from 25 mi/hr to 35 mi/hr, we have changed our velocity 10 mi/hr. If this change in velocity takes place in 5 seconds, the rate of change of velocity is 10 mi/hr in 5 sec, or 2 mi/hr/sec. In physics, *the rate of change of velocity is called* **acceleration** (ak-sel-uh-*ray*-shun).

An object that moves 1 foot the first second, 3 feet the next second, 5 feet the third second, and so on, is an example of accelerated motion. In each second the velocity has increased 2 ft/sec. The acceleration is 2 ft/sec/ sec. If an automobile moves 1 mi/hr

Fig. 8-8. Galileo Galilei (1564–1642), a great Italian scientist. He formulated the laws of accelerated motion and falling bodies. We will learn later about his discoveries of the important facts about the motion of a pendulum and his invention of the air thermometer.

the first second, 3 mi/hr the next second, and 5 mi/hr the third second, the increase in velocity during each second is 2 mi/hr. The acceleration is 2 mi/hr/sec. In both of these examples the acceleration is constant. Such motion is *uniformly accelerated motion*. An object that moves 2 feet the first second, 5 feet the next second, and 10 feet the third second is also an example of accelerated motion. In this case, however, the acceleration is not uniform, it is *variable*.

Since acceleration is the rate of change of a rate of motion, time enters into the unit twice. Examples of this are mi/hr/sec, or ft/sec/sec. Where the two units of time are the same as in ft/sec/sec, these may be represented

as ft/sec². Ft/sec/sec actually means ft/sec × 1/sec. In other words, the acceleration or rate of change of velocity is so many ft/sec. Since this much acceleration takes place each second, we simply express it as so many ft/sec/sec, or ft/sec².

In bringing a vehicle to a stop, it may move 7 feet, 5 feet, 3 feet, and 1 foot in each of four successive seconds. This is an example of negatively accelerated motion. It is also called retarded or *decelerated* (dee-*sel*-er-ay-ted) *motion*. In each second 2 ft/sec are subtracted from the velocity. The vehicle's motion is uniformly retarded.

We may also have variably retarded motion. In stopping an automobile we first exert a gentle brake pressure. Then we push harder on the brake pedal until the car slows down. Finally we ease up on the brake pedal until the car comes to a smooth stop.

6. Equations for uniformly accelerated motion. Acceleration and its effect on the motion of objects was first clearly explained by Galileo Galilei (1564–1642). He performed many experiments to determine the rate at which objects fall and the rate at which balls roll down an inclined plane.

Suppose we repeat one of Galileo's experiments. We raise one end of a

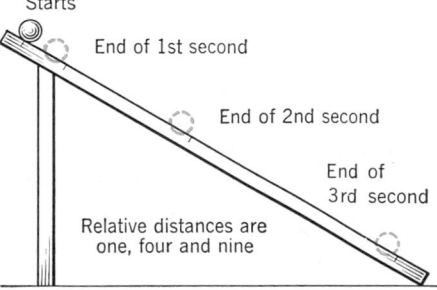

Fig. 8-9. The ball rolls down the plane with uniformly accelerated motion.

board so that it is just steep enough to cause a ball to roll down it at the rate of 1 foot in the first second. Our apparatus is shown in Fig. 8-9. As the ball rolls down the board, we determine its position at one-second intervals. The data we obtain is shown in the following table:

Elapsed Time	Total Distance	Distance Each Successive Second
1 sec	1 ft	1 ft
2 sec	4 ft	3 ft
3 sec	9 ft	5 ft
4 sec	16 ft	7 ft
5 sec	25 ft	9 ft

The motion of a ball rolling down an inclined plane is uniformly accelerated motion. The distance rolled each second is 2 feet greater than that rolled the second before. Thus the acceleration is 2 ft/sec/sec, or 2 ft/sec². When an object starts from rest and travels with uniformly accelerated motion, the acceleration equals twice the distance the object travels during the first second.

The initial velocity of the ball is zero. Its acceleration, or gain in velocity, is 2 ft/sec². Therefore, its velocity at the end of *the first second* is 2 ft/sec. If at that instant the ball ceased to be accelerated, it would continue to move with a constant velocity of 2 ft/sec. At the end of the next second, its velocity is 4 ft/sec. In five seconds, 5×2 ft/sec, or 10 ft/sec is added to its original velocity. Its velocity at the end of the fifth second is 10 ft/sec. Thus we find that the final velocity equals the product of the acceleration by the time.

(1) *If the acceleration of an object is uniform, its velocity at the end of any second is directly proportional to the time.*

Using v to represent final velocity, a to represent acceleration, and t to represent time, we show this statement by the following equation:

$$v = at. \qquad \text{(Equation 1)}$$

★ In Section 3 we learned that the total distance traversed, s, equals the average velocity, $\bar{v}$, times the number of seconds, t. Thus,

$$s = \bar{v}t. \qquad \text{(Equation 2)}$$

★ The average velocity for any given number of seconds equals one-half the sum of the initial velocity, v_i, and final velocity, v_f,

$$\bar{v} = \frac{v_i + v_f}{2}. \qquad \text{(Equation 3)}$$

★ For an object starting from rest, the initial velocity is zero; the final velocity equals at. Therefore,

$$\bar{v} = \frac{0 + at}{2}. \qquad \text{(Equation 4)}$$

We now substitute Equation 4 in Equation 2. This gives us,

$$s = \tfrac{1}{2}at^2. \qquad \text{(Equation 5)}$$

The meaning of this equation is as follows:

(2) *If the acceleration of an object is uniform the distance it travels in any given number of seconds equals one-half the acceleration times the square of the number of seconds.*

We see from the data table on the experiments with the rolling ball that the total distance is proportional to the square of the number of seconds. In this particular case, the acceleration was 2 ft/sec². One-half of this acceleration equals 1 ft/sec². Consequently, the total distance was numerically equal to the square of the number of seconds. ★ Now let us solve Equation 5 for t, and substitute this value of t in Equation 1. From Equation 5,

$$t = \sqrt{\frac{2s}{a}}.$$

★ Substituting in Equation 1,

$$v = a\sqrt{\frac{2s}{a}}.$$

Squaring a, including it under the radical, and then simplifying, we obtain,

$$v = \sqrt{2as.} \qquad \text{(Equation 6)}$$

The equation, $\boxed{s = \tfrac{1}{2}a(2t - 1)}$,

may be used to find the distance traveled by an object in any given second. If we wish to find the distance traveled in the eighth second, we let $t = 8$.

We may use Equation 1 to find v, a, or t, if two of these quantities are known. If any two of the following, a, t, and s, are known, the third may be found by using Equation 5. If we are given any two of the quantities a, v, and s, we may use Equation 6 to find the third. See Sample Problem below.

7. Equations for uniformly retarded motion. The equations given in Section 6 also apply to uniformly retarded motion. We use them when we wish to know how far an automobile will travel after the brakes are applied before it can be stopped. We may also wish to find the length of time required to stop the car. See the Sample Problem on page 172.

8. Equations for freely falling bodies. In the experiments with a ball rolling down an inclined plane, the acceleration was produced by a com-

SAMPLE PROBLEM

A ball starting from rest rolls down an inclined plane with uniformly accelerated motion. If its acceleration is 20 ft/sec², find: (1) its velocity at the end of the tenth second; (2) the distance it travels in 10 seconds; and (3) the distance it rolls in the eighth second.

SOLUTION

(1) To find the final velocity, we use the formula, $v = at$.
Substituting, $v = 20 \times 10$.
Solving, $v = 200$ ft/sec, the velocity at the end of the tenth second.

(2) To find the total distance traveled, we must use the formula $s = \tfrac{1}{2}at^2$.
Substituting, $s = \tfrac{1}{2} \times 20 \times (10)^2$.
Solving, $s = 1000$ ft, the distance traveled in 10 seconds.

(3) To find the distance rolled in the eighth second, we use the formula $s = \tfrac{1}{2}a(2t - 1)$.
Substituting, $s = \tfrac{1}{2} \times 20[(2 \times 8) - 1]$.
Solving, $s = 150$ ft, the distance traveled in the eighth second.

ponent of the force of gravitation. If we make the plane steeper, we increase this component. When the plane is vertical, the acceleration is the result of the action of the entire force of gravitation. The ball becomes a freely falling body.

If one gram of mass is allowed to fall freely at the latitude of New York, the force of gravitation gives it a velocity of 9.8 meters per second in one second of time. Since $v = at$, the acceleration of gravity equals 9.8 m/sec² at this latitude. We must give a particular location for this value of the acceleration of gravity, since it differs for different locations on the earth's surface. Corresponding values for the acceleration of gravity are 980 cm/sec² and 32.16 ft/sec².

The equations for accelerated motion apply to freely falling bodies also. Since the acceleration caused by the force of gravity is the same for all objects at a given location, we may substitute the letter g for a in the equations. These now become,

$$v = gt$$
$$s = \tfrac{1}{2}gt^2$$
$$v = \sqrt{2gs}$$
$$s = \tfrac{1}{2}g(2t - 1)$$

9. Objects fall at the same rate in a vacuum. When Galileo performed his experiments with falling bodies, he discovered that dense objects fell slightly faster than those of lower density. There was so little difference that he concluded that the unequal rate must be caused by the resistance of the air. He believed that all objects would fall at the same rate in a vacuum.

With the invention of the vacuum pump, it became possible to test Galileo's idea. A long glass tube filled with air and which contains a feather and a coin is inverted. The feather

SAMPLE PROBLEM

An automobile is traveling 30 mi/hr. Its brakes are capable of retarding it at the rate of 20 ft/sec². How long will it take to stop the car? What distance will the car travel after the brakes are applied?

SOLUTION

Since we know velocity and acceleration, the time may be found by using the equation $v = at$. First, however, we must convert 30 mi/hr to the corresponding velocity in ft/sec.

$$30 \text{ mi/hr} \times \frac{88 \text{ ft/sec}}{60 \text{ mi/hr}} = 44 \text{ ft/sec.}$$

Substituting in the equation, 44 ft/sec = 20 ft/sec² × t.
Solving, $t = 2.2$ sec.

In order to find the distance the automobile travels after the brakes are applied, we use the equation $v = \sqrt{2as}$.
Substituting, 44 ft/sec = $\sqrt{2 \times 20 \text{ ft/sec}^2 \times s}$. Squaring both sides of the equation, 1936 ft²/sec² = 40 ft/sec² × s.
Solving, $s = 48.4$ ft, the distance the automobile travels after the brakes are applied.

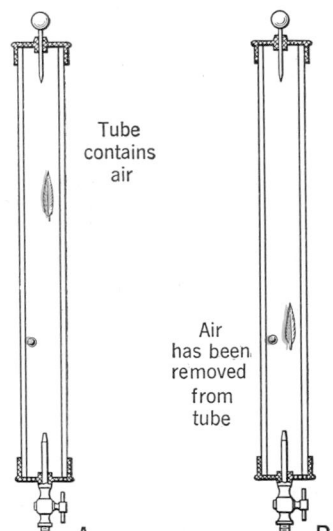

Tube
contains
air

Air
has been
removed
from
tube

A   B

Fig. 8-10. Objects fall at the same rate in a vacuum.

apply with exactness only to objects falling freely in a vacuum. They apply with reasonable correctness to dense and compact objects, such as baseballs or lead shot, falling through the air. Of course, they will not apply to leaves or feathers dropping through the air. Neither will they apply to a descending parachutist.

10. What altitude will be reached by an object projected upward? An object thrown upward is uniformly retarded by the force of gravitation until it finally stops rising. Then, as it falls, it is uniformly accelerated by the force of gravitation. If we know the initial velocity with which it is projected upward, we may apply the equations in Section 8 to find how high it will rise and how long it will take for the ascent. See the Sample Problem below.

★ **11. The path of a projectile.** The path of a projectile is determined principally by two types of motion. The projectile maintains a constant velocity in the direction it is fired. It is also acted on by the force of gravitational

flutters down slowly, striking the bottom long after the coin, as shown in Fig. 8-10*A*. If we pump the air from the tube, and again invert it, both the coin and the feather fall at the same rate. This is shown in Fig. 8-10*B*.

The equations given in Section 8

SAMPLE PROBLEM

An object is projected upward with a velocity of 100 mi/sec. To what height will it rise? How long will be needed for the ascent? What will be the total time elapsed before it strikes the earth?

SOLUTION

In order to find the height to which the object will rise, we use the equation $v = \sqrt{2gs}$.

Substituting, $100 = \sqrt{2 \times 9.8 \times s}$.

Solving, $s = 510.2$ m.

From the formula $v = gt$, we find the time for the ascent.

Substituting, $100 = 9.8t$.

Solving, $t = 10.2$ sec.

Because it takes this same amount of time for the object to fall, the total time elapsed will be 2×10.2 sec $= 20.4$ sec.

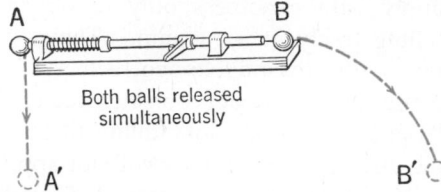

Fig. 8-11. Even though ball *B* has a horizontal velocity, the force of gravitational attraction acts in the same way on both balls *A* and *B*, causing them to strike the floor at the same time, as shown by balls *A'* and *B'*.

attraction, which pulls it toward the earth. These act independently on the moving body. This may be demonstrated by means of the apparatus shown in Fig. 8-11. If balls are placed at *A* and *B* and the trigger released, ball *A* merely drops to the floor. Ball *B* is given a horizontal velocity, but it is also acted on by gravity. Since both balls strike the floor at the same time, this shows that the action of gravity is independent of the horizontal velocity of ball *B*.

Suppose a bullet is fired horizontally from a rifle with a velocity of 3000 ft/sec. If we neglect the air resistance, the bullet will have traveled 3000

feet by the end of the first second. But gravity begins acting on the bullet immediately after it leaves the muzzle of the gun. During the first second, a freely falling body drops 16.08 feet. Consequently this bullet will strike 16.08 feet below the bull's-eye of a target 3000 feet away. In 2 seconds the bullet will travel 6000 feet, but it also drops 64.32 feet. The greater the velocity of the projectile, the more nearly a straight line its path will be. The path of a slow-moving projectile is quite noticeably curved. Fig. 8-12 compares the paths of high and low velocity projectiles.

In order to counteract the effect of gravity on a bullet and thus increase its range, a rifle generally is fired at a small upward angle. This angle is determined by raising the rear sight to the proper range marking. Then, when the rifle is aimed, its muzzle is directed upward at the correct angle. This gives a slight upward component to the velocity of the bullet. The component is enough to overcome the force of gravitation until the bullet has time to reach its distant target.

The muzzle of a field gun is always

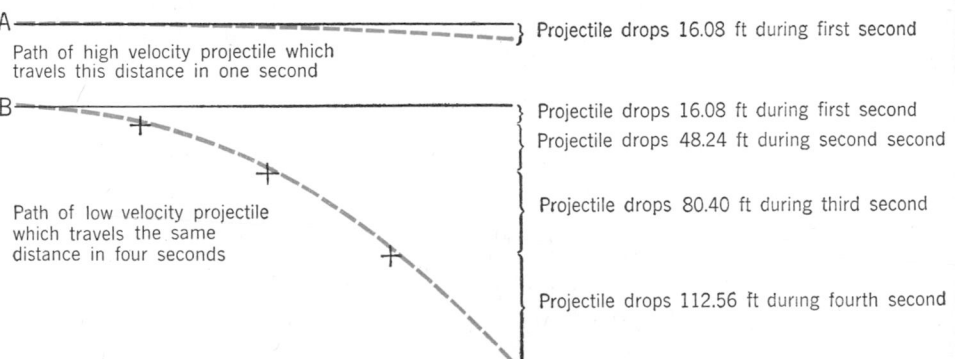

Fig. 8-12. The effect of the force of gravitational attraction on high velocity and low velocity projectiles.

Path of bullet

Line of sight

Fig. 8-13. In order to counteract the action of the force of gravity on the bullet, a rifle is aimed the necessary distance above the target by raising the rear sight.

elevated so that the projectile is fired at an angle. Fig. 8-14 shows the path such a projectile may take. The angle *BAC* is the angle of elevation. *AC* and *AD* are the horizontal and vertical components of the velocity. *AR* is the range. The path *ABR* is called the *trajectory* (trah-*jek*-tor-ee).

QUESTIONS

GROUP A

1. What is the definition of acceleration? Why do the units in which we measure acceleration have a unit of time in them twice?

2. How does an object move in successive units of time when it is uniformly accelerated? How does an object move in successive units of time if it is variably accelerated?

3. An automobile travels 22 ft, 18 ft, 14 ft,

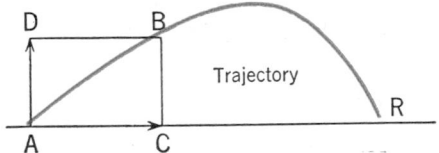

Fig. 8-14. The path of a projectile that is fired at an angle.

10 ft, and 6 ft in each of five successive seconds. What kind of motion is this?

4. Why does the velocity of a falling body increase?

5. Why would a bomb dropped from an airplane flying at an altitude of 25,000 ft take longer to reach the earth than is calculated from the formula, $s = \frac{1}{2}gt^2$?

6. How does the force of gravitation act on a baseball thrown directly upward?

GROUP B

★ **7.** What forces govern the path of a projectile? What effect does each have on its path?

★ **8.** What adjustment is made on the rear sight of a rifle when the distance to the target is increased? How would the use of a higher velocity bullet affect the adjustment?

PROBLEMS

(In the Mathematics Refresher, refer to Sections 2, 10, 11, and 16.)

GROUP A

1. An automobile is accelerated at the rate of 4 ft/sec². How many seconds will be required for this car to attain a velocity of 50 ft/sec?

2. A ball rolling down an inclined plane is accelerated at the rate of 5 cm/sec². What velocity will it attain after 4 seconds?

3. What velocity, in ft/sec, will a freely falling stone attain after it has dropped for 7 seconds? Acceleration of gravity is 32 ft/sec².

4. A large rock is dropped from a bridge into the river below. If the time required for it to drop is 1.5 seconds, with what velocity, in m/sec, does it hit the water? Acceleration of gravity is 9.8 m/sec².

5. How many seconds does it take for a metal ball to drop 400 ft?

6. An object is accelerated at the rate of 8 cm/sec². How far will the object have moved in 5 seconds? What distance will it move in the fifth second?

7. What velocity is attained by an object which is accelerated at the rate of 0.25 m/sec², when it has covered a distance of 50 meters?

8. How many feet will a bomb which is dropped from an airplane fall in the tenth second after it is released?

9. If the brakes of an automobile can decelerate it at the rate of 10 ft/sec², how long will it take to stop a car traveling at a velocity of 30 mi/hr? (30 mi/hr equals 44 ft/sec.) How far will the car travel before it is stopped?

10. How far must a brass weight fall before it attains a velocity of 100 m/sec?

GROUP B

11. A bomb is dropped from an airplane flying at an altitude of 25,600 ft. How long will it take for this bomb to reach the earth?

12. The Eiffel Tower in Paris is about 300 m high. A golf ball is dropped from the top of the tower. With what velocity will it strike the earth?

13. A baseball player sends a fly ball to a height of 144 ft. After the bat strikes the ball how much time will there be for a fielder to get into position to make the catch?

14. With what velocity must a bullet be fired upward in order to reach an altitude of 500 meters?

15. How long will it take for the bullet in Problem 14 to return to the earth?

16. The opening near the top of the Washington Monument is 504 ft above the ground. With what velocity will a baseball tossed out of this opening strike the ground?

● **17.** The barrel of a field gun is elevated at an angle of 45°. The velocity of a projectile leaving the muzzle of the gun is 1000 ft/sec. Calculate (1) the vertical and horizontal components of the muzzle velocity; (2) the height of the trajectory; (3) the time which elapses before the projectile returns to the earth; (4) the range of the gun.

● **18.** A shell is fired from a gun whose barrel is elevated 30° above the horizontal. The muzzle velocity is 250 m/sec. Calculate height of the trajectory and the range of the gun.

● **19.** If a train travels the distance between consecutive mile posts in 50 seconds, what is the velocity of the train in mi/hr? In ft/sec?

---

3. NEWTON'S LAWS OF MOTION

12. The three laws of motion. Sir Isaac Newton (1642–1727) formulated three laws of motion that help explain some very important principles of physics. While they are, in some cases, idealistic and can not be proved, actual observations and experiments make us sure that they are true. These laws may be applied to objects on the earth. Also, they may be applied to the earth

Fig. 8-15. Sir Isaac Newton (1642–1727) formulated three important laws of motion which explain how forces act on matter. He also is famous for his statement of the law of gravitational attraction and for his discovery that sunlight is composed of seven spectral colors.

itself, and to the sun, moon, and the stars. We have been explaining some simple ways in which objects move. Newton's laws explain why these objects move. The laws tell us the relationship existing between force and motion.

13. Newton's first law of motion. Suppose you bring your car to a stop on a perfectly level street and you forget to pull up the hand brake. What will happen to your car? As long as it is not touched, it will not move. But suppose someone pulls into the parking space behind and carelessly bumps your car. What happens? Your car starts to move, but will gradually come to a stop. Why? The bump against your car is a force acting upon it. It

moves your car; that is, it increases its velocity from zero to perhaps one mile per hour. A change in velocity is acceleration. Therefore an unbalanced force produces acceleration. But the car eventually stops. What force produces the deceleration? Probably the most important force is friction. The friction in the wheel bearings and the friction of the tires on the street bring the car to rest. Suppose there is no friction. Then it is logical to assume that the car will continue to roll at constant speed.

We may state NEWTON'S FIRST LAW OF MOTION: *A body continues in its state of rest or uniform motion in a straight line unless an unbalanced force acts on it.*

14. Inertia. When a body is in a state of rest, or when it is moving at a constant speed in a straight line, its velocity is constant. The velocity of a body does not change unless an unbalanced force acts upon it. We change the velocity of an object when we speed it up, slow it down, or change the direction in which it moves. When we change the velocity of an object, we accelerate it. Consequently, *an unbalanced force accelerates an object.*

What property does an object have which makes it necessary for us to exert a force in order to accelerate it? This property is called the **inertia** (in-er-shuh) of the body. If the body is stationary, we say its inertia tends to keep it stationary. We have to overcome the inertia in order to move the body. The inertia of a coin placed on a card over the mouth of a tumbler enables us to flick away the card so that the coin then drops into the tumbler. If a body is in motion, its inertia tends to keep it in motion. If you are stand-

Fig. 8-16. The inertia of the coin enables us to flick the card from beneath it.   The coin then drops directly into the glass.

ing on a crowded bus and the driver makes a sudden stop, your body continues to move forward because of its inertia.   In order to swing a stone attached to a cord in a circular path, you must exert a continual force on the cord.   The inertia of the stone resists the continual change of direction as the stone is swung around.   *The amount of inertia possessed by a body is called the* **mass** *of the body.*

15. Newton's second law of motion.   In our discussion of inertia, we mentioned three quantities which are apparently related to one another. These are force, acceleration, and mass. In order to find out how they are related, we shall perform two imaginary experiments.   For these we need a spring balance, some weights, and a smooth surface on which the weights can move without friction.   These experiments are imaginary in the sense that they can not be performed in exactly the way we shall describe.   Real experiments show that if we could perform these imaginery experiments, we should obtain the results we shall describe.

(1) We exert successive forces of 1 pound, 2 pounds, 3 pounds, and so on, on a 1-kg weight, and measure the acceleration produced.   The forces are measured by the spring balance.   A stop watch and meter stick are used to measure the accelerations.   See Fig. 8-17.   We find that, for the *constant mass* of the one kilogram, *the acceleration is directly proportional to the force applied.*   The acceleration is in the same direction as the applied force.

$$a \propto F \qquad (m \text{ is constant})$$

The symbol $\propto$ is read "varies as." This is another way of saying that a is directly proportional to F.   As F increases, a increases in a corresponding fashion.

(2) Next we take a second kilogram weight and verify that its mass is the same as that of the first.   We do this by observing whether equal forces produce equal accelerations on both weights. Now we determine the acceleration produced by a certain force acting on one kilogram.   Then, using the two kilograms together, we determine the acceleration produced by this same force.   We may take three kilograms and repeat the experiment.   When we do, we find that the acceleration produced by the same force each time is inversely proportional to the mass being accelerated.

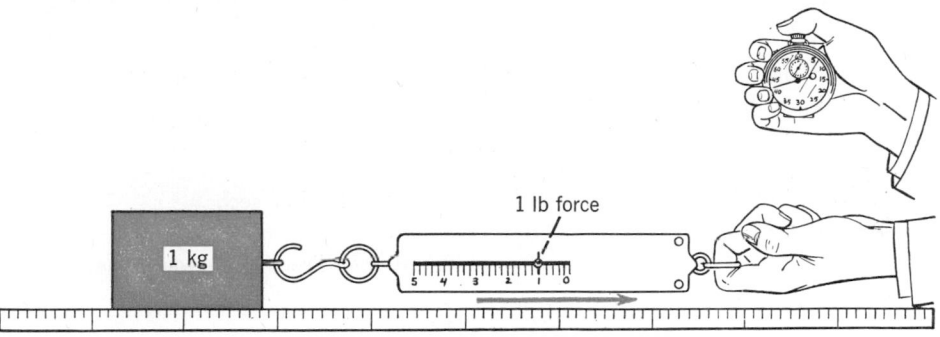

Fig. 8-17. An imaginary experiment for the derivation of Newton's second law of motion — measuring the acceleration of a mass of one kilogram when acted on by a force of one pound.

$$a \propto \frac{1}{m} \qquad (F \text{ is constant})$$

Since we have found that the acceleration varies directly with the force and inversely with the mass, we may combine the two equations and obtain

$$a \propto \frac{F}{m}.$$

The acceleration of a body is directly proportional to the force exerted on the body, is inversely proportional to the mass of the body, and is in the same direction as the force. This is a statement of NEWTON'S SECOND LAW OF MOTION.

16. Units of force and mass. We may convert the proportion type expression for Newton's second law into an equation by inserting the constant *k,* and transposing,

$$F = kma.$$

It would be more convenient to let $k = 1$, for then F would equal *ma*. We may do this only if we are willing to define one of the quantities in the equation in terms of the other two. This is what physicists have done.

Consequently, in terms of the units we are about to define,

$$\boxed{F = ma.}$$

In the MKS system, the unit of mass is the kilogram, and the unit in which acceleration is expressed is meter per second per second. The force required to accelerate 1 kilogram of mass at the rate of 1 meter per second per second is *1 kg-m/sec²*. This force is called *1 newton.* Newton is abbreviated: *nt.*

★ In the CGS system, the unit of mass is the gram, and the unit in which acceleration is expressed is centimeter per second per second. The force required to accelerate 1 gram of mass at the rate of 1 centimeter per second per second is *1 g-cm/sec²*. This force is called *1 dyne.* One newton equals 10^5 dynes.

In the English system, the unit of force is the pound, and the unit in which acceleration is expressed is feet per second per second. The *mass* of a body which will be accelerated at the rate of 1 foot per second per second when 1 pound of force acts upon it is *1 slug.*

SAMPLE PROBLEM

What force, in newtons, is required to accelerate a small cart with a mass of 10 kg at the rate of 5 m/sec² in an eastward direction?

SOLUTION

Substituting in the formula $F = ma$, $F = 10$ kg $\times$ 5 m/sec².
Solving, $F = 50$ newtons, the force required.
This force must act eastward because this is the direction in which the cart is accelerated.

SAMPLE PROBLEM

The acceleration of gravity is 9.8 m/sec². What force, in newtons, is needed to lift a mass of 25 kg?

SOLUTION

Using $F = ma$, $F = 25$ kg $\times$ 9.8 m/sec².
Solving, $F = 245$ newtons, the necessary force.

SAMPLE PROBLEM

What is the mass, in slugs, of a 10-lb bag of sugar?

SOLUTION

The acceleration of gravity is 32 ft/sec². Substituting in $F = ma$,
10 lb $= m \times$ 32 ft/sec².
Solving, $m = 0.31$ slug, the mass.

★ **17. Forces on bodies of known weights.** In the experiments we used to derive the equation, $F = ma$, we learned that the acceleration acquired by a particular object was directly proportional to the amount of force applied. We may express this as the proportion,

$$F : F' = a : a'.$$

In the case of a freely falling body, one of the forces is known because it equals the weight, w, of the body. The acceleration, g, is also known. It is the acceleration due to gravitational attraction, 32 ft/sec². Making these substitutions, the proportion becomes,

$$F : w = a : g.$$

By using this formula, we can calculate the force needed to impart to a body of known weight any desired acceleration. See Sample Problem on page 182.

★ **18. What are impulse and momentum?** We already have learned that acceleration is the rate of change of velocity. This may be expressed as:

$$a = \frac{v}{t}.$$

If we substitute this expression for a in the equation $F = ma$, we get,

$$F = \frac{mv}{t}.$$

By transposing,

$$Ft = mv.$$

This equation defines and gives the relationship between two important quantities, *impulse* and *momentum*. The product of a force times the length of time it acts is called **impulse**. The product of the mass of an object times its velocity is called **momentum**. We see that impulse and momentum are equal. A force, *F*, acting on an object for time, *t*, will change its momentum by an amount, *mv*.

Suppose you place your hand flat on the table, palm upward. If a 1-pound weight is lowered gradually on your hand, the impact is bearable. Since the 1-pound weight is gently lowered onto your hand, only a small force acts on the weight to move it in the direction of your palm. The time during which this force acts is also small. These combine to give a small impulse. Consequently, the weight lowered onto

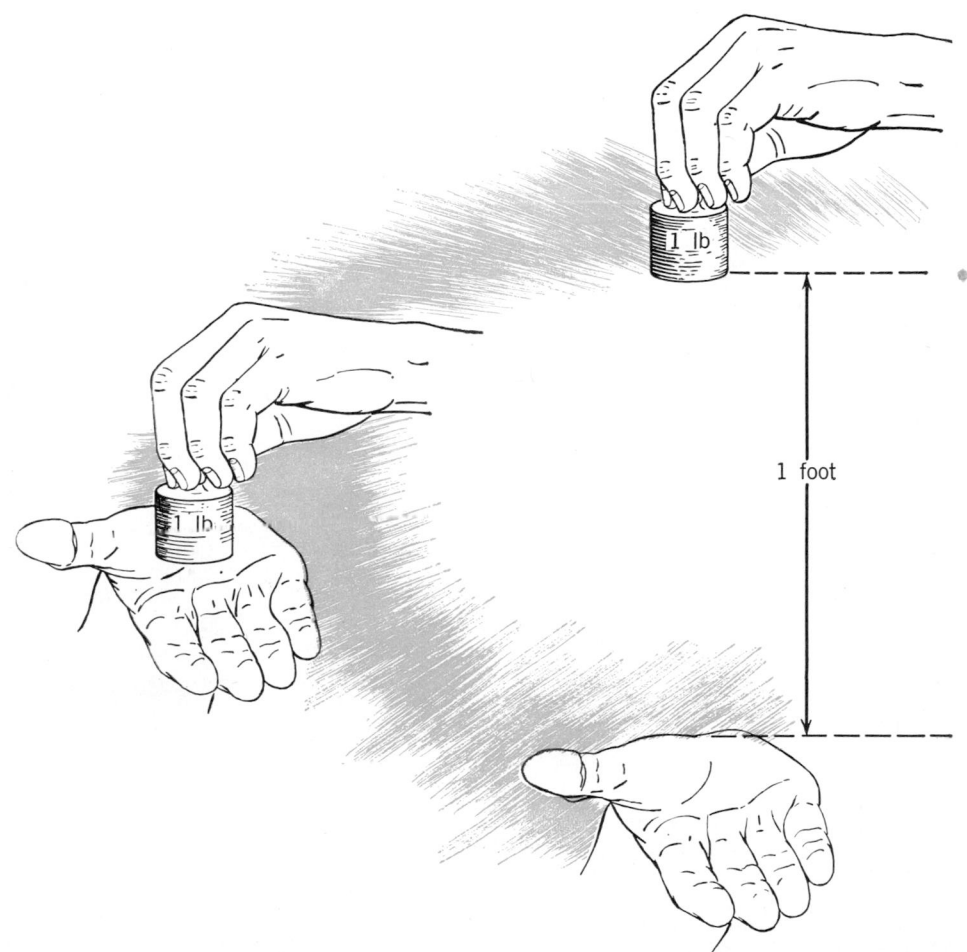

Fig. 8-18. When the weight is lowered onto your hand, as at the left, the impulse and momentum are small, and the impact is bearable. If the weight is dropped onto your hand from a height of one foot, as at the right, the impulse and momentum are much larger, and the impact may injure your hand.

SAMPLE PROBLEM

A car weighs 4000 lb. What force is needed to give it an acceleration of 10 ft/sec²?

SOLUTION

By substitution in the formula $F : w = a : g$, we obtain

$F : 4000$ lb $= 10$ ft/sec² $: 32$ ft/sec². Cross multiplying, $32F = 40,000$ lb.

Dividing, $F = 1250$ lb, the force required to produce the acceleration of 10 ft/sec².

your hand acquires only a small amount of momentum, and you find the impact bearable.

Now, however, suppose the 1-pound weight is dropped from a height of 1 foot onto your hand. You can im-agine that the effect would be unpleasant, and it might injure your hand. In this case the full force of gravity acts on the mass of the 1-pound weight. If we assume that the time during which this force acts is the same as in the first

Fig. 8-19. Even though this ferry boat moves slowly when docking, its great mass gives it high momentum.

SAMPLE PROBLEM

The mass of an automobile is 1800 kg. If its velocity is 15 m/sec northward, what is its momentum? How long must a force of 1350 nt act on the automobile to give it this momentum?

SOLUTION

Momentum equals the product mv.

1800 kg $\times$ 15 m/sec = 27,000 kg-m/sec northward.

This momentum also equals the product Ft.

27,000 kg-m/sec = 1350 nt $\times$ t.

Solving, t = 20 sec, the time required.

case, you can easily see that the falling weight has many times the momentum of the gently lowered weight. The impact of the falling weight is greater because of its greater momentum.

The mass of a body is a scalar quantity. But its velocity is a vector quantity. Consequently the product, momentum, is also a vector quantity. The direction of momentum of an object is the same as the direction of the velocity of the object.

A ferryboat moves very slowly in docking, but if you catch your foot between the slowly moving boat and the dock, it will surely be crushed by the momentum of the boat. A rifle bullet has a terrific impact against the object it strikes. Its velocity may be from 1500 to 3000 ft/sec. Its small mass of only a fraction of a slug multiplied by such a large velocity gives it the large momentum. See the Sample Problem above.

19. Newton's third law of motion. Let us describe some of the forces which are exerted when you place this book on the top of a level table. The weight of the book is a force which acts downward. Because the book does not move, there can be no unbalanced

forces acting upon it. The table top, therefore, must exert an upward force on the book equal to the downward force the book exerts upon the table top. In order to walk forward, you exert a force against the floor with your feet. The floor pushes against your feet with an equal force.

In each example there are two objects involved. In the first example, the objects are the book and the table top. In the second, they are the foot and the floor. There are also two forces involved in each example. In the first one they are the force of the book against the table and the force

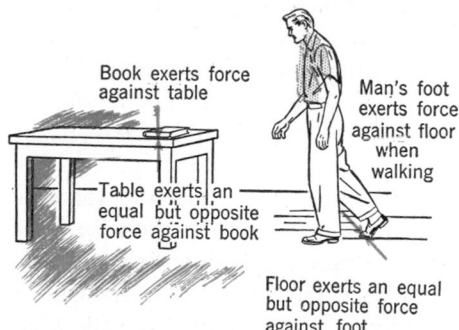

Book exerts force against table

Man's foot exerts force against floor when walking

Table exerts an equal but opposite force against book

Floor exerts an equal but opposite force against foot

Fig. 8-20. Whenever one body exerts a force upon a second body, the second body exerts an equal and opposite force upon the first.

Fig. 8-21. The balances both show the same reading because the action force equals the reaction force.

of the table against the book. In the second, they are the force of the foot against the floor and the force of the floor against the foot. In cases such as these, one force may be called the *action,* while the second force may be called the *reaction.* NEWTON'S THIRD LAW OF MOTION states: *Whenever one body exerts a force upon a second body, the second exerts an equal and opposite force upon the first.* In other words, *action is equal and opposite to reaction.*

★ We have been considering action and reaction in fixed bodies. The same law holds true if the bodies are free to move. A boy rows a boat toward the shore of a lake. When he is three or four feet from shore, he steps on the bow and attempts to leap ashore. He exerts a force against the boat. The boat exerts an equal but opposite force against the boy. However, since both objects are now free to move, the force the boy exerts against the boat accelerates it. The force the boat exerts against the boy will accelerate him in the opposite direction. The amount of acceleration of each object will be inversely proportional to its mass. The boy will probably judge the force he must exert to reach shore on the basis of his experience in jumping the same distance from a fixed object. Consequently, when he jumps from the boat, he probably will not reach shore but instead will fall into the water.

Suppose we fasten one spring balance to a table leg and hook another

spring balance to it, as shown in Fig. 8-21. Now, if we pull steadily, we find that both balance readings are the same. The pull of the first balance on the second equals the pull of the second on the first. The action is equal but opposite to the reaction.

You may try to argue that motion can not occur if action and reaction are equal. If two boys pull with equal force but in opposite directions upon a lightweight wagon, the wagon will not move. But this is not an example of action and reaction. There are two forces, it is true, *but they are both exerted on the same object.* Action and reaction are shown in the force which each boy's feet exert against the ground and the equal but opposite force the ground exerts against the feet.

20. Applications of Newton's third law of motion. There are many every-

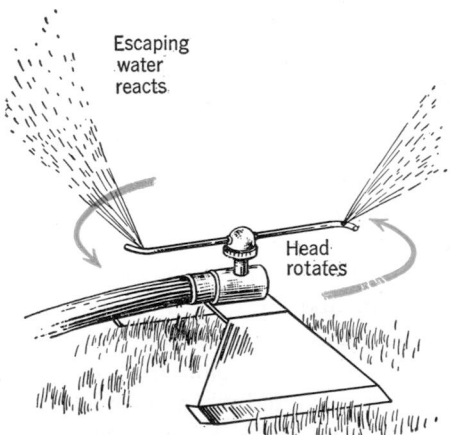

Fig. 8-22. The reaction force of the water against the nozzles causes the sprinkler to rotate.

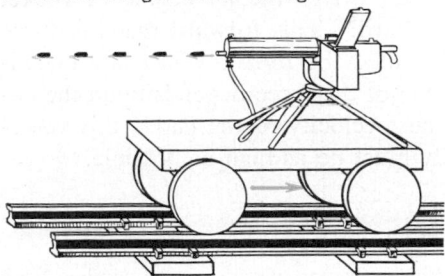

Reaction force of bullets on gun accelerates the gun toward the right

Fig. 8-23. The unbalanced force of the bullets on the gun accelerates the gun toward the right.

day happenings in which Newton's third law of motion plays an important part. When we row a boat, the oars exert a force against the water and the water exerts an opposite force against the oars. Air reacts against the propellers of an airplane, so that the propellers pull the airplane through the air.

Water reacts against the nozzle of a garden hose. If the hose is not held in place, it will be driven backward by this force. This same force is used to drive a rotary lawn sprinkler.

★ **21. How do jets and rockets exert a force?** Suppose we have a machine gun mounted on wheels so that it may move along a track, as shown in Fig. 8-23. Bullets fired from the gun leave the barrel with a certain muzzle velocity, which we shall call v. Since the bullets have a total mass, m, the combined momentum of these bullets will be mv. But, from Section 18, we know this momentum equals the impulse of the gun, Ft. The force exerted by the gun will equal the combined momentum of the bullets divided by the time required to fire them, $F = mv/t$. According to Newton's third law of motion, this force equals the reaction force of the bullets on the gun. This reaction force acts in the opposite direction. It accelerates the machine gun, which then moves toward the right with increasing velocity.

Jet engines and rockets exert a force in a similar manner. Instead of the

Fig. 8-24. The mass of hot gases roaring at high velocity from the exhaust of these jet fighters produces the thrust which speeds them through the air.

mass of bullets leaving the muzzle of the gun in a certain time, we have a mass of hot gases issuing from the exhaust in a given time. In place of the muzzle velocity of the bullets, we have the jet velocity of the gases relative to the engine. The product of these two quantities gives the reaction force which drives the jet engine or rocket forward. This forward reaction force is called the *thrust*. Since the magnitude of the force depends upon the exhaust velocity of the gases, this velocity must be as high as possible.

QUESTIONS

GROUP A

1. If you place a steel ball in the center of the top of a level table, the ball will remain there. What forces are acting in this situation? Are there any unbalanced forces acting on the ball? Why does it remain at rest?

2. If you give the steel ball in Question 1 a slight push, what happens to the ball? What forces are acting in this situation? Are there any unbalanced forces acting on the ball? If so, what are they? How do they affect the motion of the ball?

3. Suppose you tie an 18-inch length of strong cord to the ball and fasten the end of the cord to a nail driven into the table top. Now, when you push the ball, what path does it follow? What forces act in this situation? How do they affect the motion of the ball?

4. What is Newton's First Law of Motion?

5. What name do we give to the property of matter which makes it necessary for us to exert a force on a body in order to accelerate it?

6. What property of an object do we measure when we measure its mass?

7. How does the acceleration of a body vary with the amount of force applied? How do the direction of the acceleration and the direction of the applied force compare?

8. How does the acceleration which is produced on different bodies by identical forces vary with the mass of the body?

9. State Newton's Second Law of Motion. What is the equation which expresses the relationship of force to mass and acceleration?

10. Why is it necessary, in the MKS and CGS systems of units, to define the units of force in terms of the units for mass and acceleration? What are the units of force in these systems? To what are they equal? How are they related?

11. Why is it necessary, in the English system of measurement, to define the unit of mass in terms of the units for force and acceleration? What is the unit of mass in the English system? How is it defined?

12. Suppose you suspend a weight from a rigid support by means of a 1-ft length of string. What downward force acts on the weight? If this force is the action force, what force is the reaction force?

13. What upward force acts on the suspended weight of Question 12? If this force is the action force, what force is the corresponding reaction force?

14. What force acts on the rigid support from which the weight of Question 12 is suspended? What is the corresponding reaction force?

15. State Newton's Third Law of Motion. How many forces are involved? How many objects are involved?

GROUP B

16. Why does a falling object undergo acceleration at a constant rate?

17. In Fig. 8-25, the segment of string supporting the ball is cut from the same piece as the segment attached below the ball. If you pull with a quick jerk at *A*, the string will break below the weight. If you pull steadily at *A*, the string will break above the weight. Why?

18. Explain how a rotary lawn sprinkler works. What are the two objects involved? What are the two forces? Which force produces the rotation? Why?

★ **19.** How can we calculate the amount of force which is needed to impart a certain acceleration to an object of known weight?

★ **20.** How is impulse defined? What do we mean by momentum? How are they related?

★ **21.** Why will a slowly docking ferryboat and a speeding rifle bullet both have a large amount of momentum?

★ **22.** Identify each of the following as a scalar or as a vector quantity. (1) Mass; (2) Force; (3) Acceleration; (4) Velocity; (5) Time;

(6) Impulse;   (7) Momentum;   (8) Speed; (9) Weight; (10) Acceleration of gravity.

⭐ **23.** What name is given to the force which drives a jet or rocket forward? What is the origin of this force? What conditions determine its magnitude?

PROBLEMS

(In the Mathematics Refresher, refer to Sections 8, 10, and 16.)

GROUP A

1. An object which has a mass of 3 kg is accelerated upward at the rate of 5 m/sec². What force acted on the object to produce this? In what direction did the force act?

This heavy ball has a great deal of inertia

A

Fig. 8-25. The inertia of the heavy ball enables you to break the string at A with a quick jerk.

⭐ **2.** What force, in dynes, will be required in order to lift a 5-g weight? Acceleration of gravity is 980 cm/sec².

3. What is the mass, in slugs, of an object which can be accelerated at the rate of 10 ft/sec² by a force of 25 lb?

4. A body with a mass of 20 kg is accelerated eastward at the rate of 50 cm/sec². What force, in newtons, produced this acceleration? ⭐ What was the force in dynes?

5. What is the mass, in slugs, of a 94-lb bag of cement? Acceleration of gravity is 32 ft/sec².

6. What acceleration is experienced by an object whose mass is 0.5 kg when acted upon by a southward force of 10 nt?

7. What gravitational force, in newtons, acts on a body whose mass is 750 g? Acceleration of gravity is 9.8 m/sec².

8. What acceleration is experienced by an object whose mass is 10 slugs when a force of 50 lb acts northward on it?

GROUP B

⭐ **9.** A truck weighs 10 tons. What force will give it an acceleration of 5 ft/sec²?

⭐ **10.** If a force of 2 nt acts on a body for 5 sec, what momentum is imparted to the body? If the mass of the body is 1 kg, what velocity does it acquire?

⭐ **11.** How long must a force of 5 nt act on a body whose mass is 4 kg to impart to it a velocity of 20 cm/sec?

● **12.** What is the weight of an automobile which can be accelerated at the rate of 10 ft/sec² by a force of 1000 lb?

● **13.** The jet velocity of a rocket is 6000 ft/sec. If 1300 lb of gas issue from the exhaust per second, what is the thrust of the rocket?

4. UNIVERSAL GRAVITATION

22. The force of gravitational attraction. Even before you began to walk you learned about the force of gravitation. You learned that objects, including yourself, fall toward the earth. We say that bodies fall toward the earth because they are attracted by gravity. They are acted on by the force of **gravitation,** *which is the mutual force of attraction between bodies.*

The force of gravitation is a property *of all bodies.* But the effects of gravitation which we readily observe are those caused by large bodies like the earth, the moon, and the sun. Nevertheless, gravitational forces are mutually interacting forces. A falling apple is attracted to the earth, but the apple attracts the earth as well. The earth attracts the moon, and the moon attracts the earth.

The magnitude of the force of gravitational attraction depends upon two things: (1) the masses of the bodies; (2) the square of the distance between their centers. It takes twice the force to lift two bricks that it does to lift one brick. This is because we must now overcome the attraction of the earth for twice as much mass. The force of attraction decreases rapidly as the distance between the two bodies increases. The force of attraction varies inversely as the square of the distance between their centers. Newton formulated the following LAW OF UNIVERSAL GRAVITATION: *Every body in the universe attracts every other body with a force that is directly proportional to the product of their masses and inversely proportional to the square of the distance between their centers.*

An object on the surface of the earth is about 4000 miles from its center. If it were taken up to a height of 4000 miles, it would be 8000 miles from the earth's center. The earth's attraction for it would then be only $(4000)^2 \div (8000)^2$, or $\frac{1}{4}$ as much as before. A person who weighs 144 pounds on the earth's surface would weigh only 36

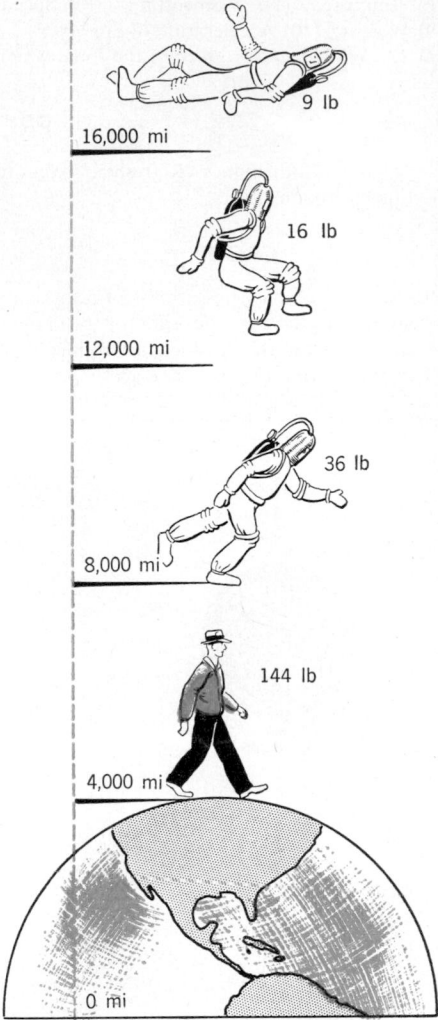

Fig. 8-26. The weight of a man decreases as his distance from the center of the earth increases.

pounds at a height of 4000 miles above the surface of the earth. At a height of 8000 miles, 12000 miles from the earth's center, he would weigh only 16 pounds. See Fig. 8-26.

23. The weight of an object depends upon its location. We have already defined the weight of a body as the measure of the earth's attraction for

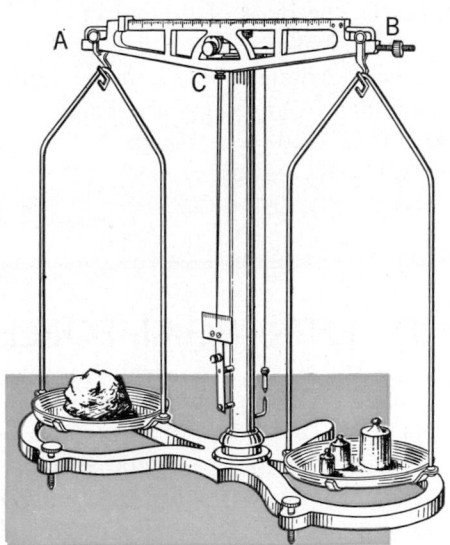

Fig. 8-27. The equal-arm beam balance is used for comparing masses. The mass of the stone on the left-hand balance pan equals the combined masses of the weights on the right-hand balance pan.

that body. When we say that a man weighs 200 pounds, we mean that the earth attracts him with a force of 200 pounds. He also attracts the earth with a force of 200 pounds. Since all parts of the earth's surface are not the same distance from its center, the weight of an object varies in different localities. A body weighs a little less on top of a mountain than it does in a valley. Since the earth is slightly flattened at the poles, a man will weigh a little more at the North Pole than he does at the Equator. A man who weighs 189 pounds at the Equator will weigh about 190 pounds at either pole.

If we bore a hole down into the earth and are lowered into it, our weight does not keep increasing as we are lowered beneath the surface. It is true that we would be getting nearer the earth's center, but the gravitational attraction of the material above us causes us to weigh *less* when we are beneath the surface. A body will have its greatest weight *on that part of the surface of the earth which is nearest the earth's center.* It loses weight if carried above the surface or lowered beneath it.

24. An equal-arm balance is used to compare masses. In Fig. 8-27, *AB* represents the beam of an equal-arm balance. This beam is carefully constructed so that it is light in weight yet rigid enough so that it will not bend when a load is applied at its ends. It rests on a knife-edged agate bearing located exactly at the mid-point of the beam, *C.* When balance pans of equal weight are attached at each end, the center of gravity of the beam lies directly below this point of suspension.

Now let us put an object of unknown *mass* on the left-hand balance pan. The earth attracts this object with a force equal to its *weight*. This force, acting on the arm of the balance *AC,* creates a counterclockwise torque. If we place known masses from a set of weights on the right-hand balance pan, we can bring the beam of the balance into equilibrium. The attraction of the earth for these known masses is a force which acts on the right-hand portion of the beam of the balance to produce a clockwise torque. When equilibrium is attained, the clockwise torque equals the counterclockwise torque.

In constructing the balance, the balance arms were made of equal length. This means that when the balance is in equilibrium, *the forces on the ends of the beam are equal.* Furthermore, *the acceleration due to gravity is the same on the objects placed on the balance pans.* (For practical purposes they are at the same spot on the surface of the earth.) Since the forces are equal, and the acceleration of gravity is equal, *the masses must be equal.* We know the masses of the individual weights. The weights were made in comparison with the standard kilogram. Conse-

quently, the mass of the object on the left-hand balance pan equals the sum of the individual masses on the right-hand pan. An equal-arm balance is therefore used as a means by which to compare masses.

★ 5. CIRCULAR MOTION AND CENTRIFUGAL FORCE

★ 25. How is circular motion produced? From Newton's first law we learned that a body which has acquired velocity continues to move in a straight line. If a second force acts upon the moving body at right angles to its path, the body will be deflected from its straight line. Its motion will become circular. Suppose we tie one end of a string to a ball. If we hold the other end of the string firmly, we may swing the ball in a circle with our hand as a center. The pull of the hand upon the cord deflects the ball from its rectilinear path and in toward the center, as shown in Fig. 8-28. As the ball moves along the circumference from *B* to *A,* the pull toward the center has deflected it a distance equal to *AO.* The constant pull that deflects a body from its rectilinear path and compels it to move along a curve, is called *centripetal* (sen-*trip*-uh-tul) force. **Centripetal** *means acting toward a center.*

★ 26. What is centrifugal force? According to Newton's third law of motion, to every action there is an equal and opposite reaction. We have seen that the string exerts a centripetal force on the ball, causing it to move in a curved path. But the ball exerts an equal and opposite force on the string, tending to break the string. This force

is called the **centrifugal** (sen-*trif*-yuh-gul) *force, and acts away from a center.* These forces, centripetal and centrifugal, are equal in magnitude but act in opposite directions. Centripetal force is the force exerted by the string on the ball. Centrifugal force is the force exerted by the ball on the string. If the string breaks, the ball will continue to move in a straight line tangent to the curved path. This agrees with Newton's first law, because, when once the string is broken, no forces act on the ball.

★ 27. Calculating centrifugal force. Suppose we use a device which measures the pull which the ball of Fig. 8-28 exerts on the string. Then, if we use a

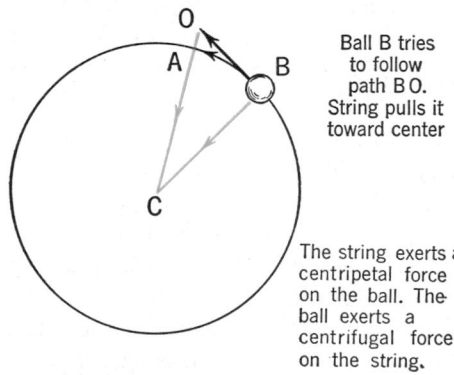

Ball B tries to follow path B O. String pulls it toward center

The string exerts a centripetal force on the ball. The ball exerts a centrifugal force on the string.

Fig. 8-28. The ball tends to break the string and follow path *BO.*

SAMPLE PROBLEM

A ball having a mass of 0.05 kg is attached to the end of a cord 1.5 m long. The ball is swung in a circular path at the end of the cord with a velocity of 8 m/sec. What is the force in newtons which tends to break the string?

SOLUTION

Substituting the quantities given in the problem in the equation, C.F. $= \dfrac{mv^2}{r}$,

$$\text{C.F.} = \frac{0.05 \text{ kg} \times (8 \text{ m/sec})^2}{1.5 \text{ m}}.$$

Solving, C.F. $= 2.13$ kg-m/sec$^2 = 2.13$ nt, the force tending to break the string.

ball which has double the mass, we find that the pull on the string is twice as great. We conclude that the centrifugal force is directly proportional to the mass. If we shorten the string, the ball is pulled from its path faster and it reacts with greater force to break the string. Careful measurements show that centrifugal force is inversely proportional to the radius of curvature. As we swing the ball faster, its velocity along the curve increases, and the ball pulls more strongly on the cord. Accurate measurements show that the centrifugal force is directly proportional to the square of the velocity. If m is the mass of the body, v is its velocity, and r is the radius of its path,

$$\text{centrifugal force} = \frac{mv^2}{r}.$$

See the Sample Problem which is at the top of this page.

Fig. 8-29. The curves on this modern superhighway are banked to counteract the effect of centrifugal force on automobiles as they take the curves at high speed.

★ **28. How can we counteract the effects of centrifugal force?** We are all too familiar with the damage caused by the uncontrolled centrifugal force which sends an automobile spinning off the road if the driver attempts to round a sharp curve too fast. Modern highways are banked at the curves to help counteract the effect of centrifugal force. " Banking a curve " means to make the outside edge of the curve higher than the inside edge. When we ride a bicycle, or a motorcycle, or when we skate, we tend to lean toward the center when we are rounding a curve.

★ **29. Applications of centrifugal force.** Centrifugal separators are used to separate cream from milk. Milk enters the top of the separator and is thrown against the surfaces of several funnel-shaped discs, or blades, that rotate at a high speed. The cream, being less dense than milk, rises to the top surface of the blades. It issues from

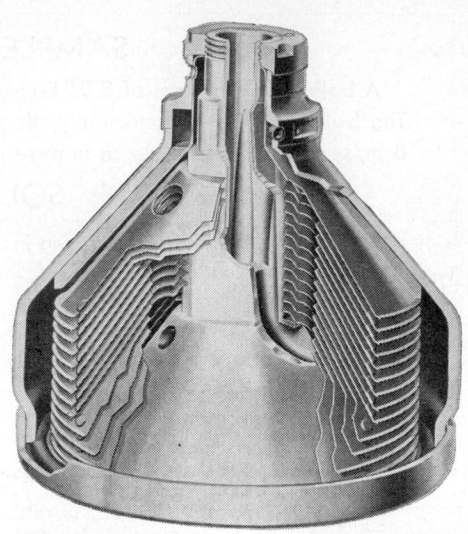

Fig. 8-31. The whole milk enters at the top and is separated by centrifugal force. The blades, or discs, rotate at a speed of from 6000 to 8000 revolutions per minute. The skim milk, which is denser, is thrown against the lower surfaces of the discs and passes down to the outer edge of the bowl. The cream, which is less dense than the milk, passes upward and inward toward the center.

an opening near the center. See Figs. 8-30 and 8-31. The skim milk passes to the outside of the rotating blades, where it is drawn off through a separate outlet.

Wet solids may be partially dried by putting them in a perforated cylinder, which is then rapidly rotated. The water is thrown out through the openings. Crystals are dried in this manner. Many washing machines use centrifugal force for drying clothes. Fig. 8-32 shows the spinner of one type of washing machine.

Liquids that contain sediment are often *centrifuged* (*sen*-trih-fyoojd) instead of being filtered. A small laboratory centrifuge is shown in Fig. 8-33.

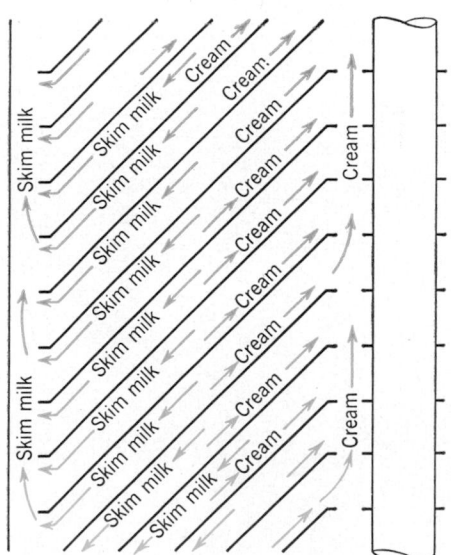

Fig. 8-30. The blades of a cream separator.

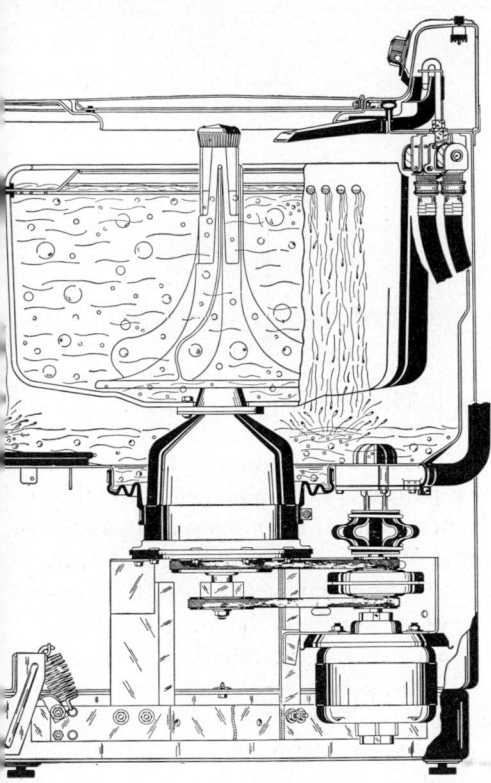

Fig. 8-32. The spinning wash basket exerts centrifugal force on the wash water, which is thrown up and out through the holes near the top of the wash basket.

The sediment from varnish is removed by using large industrial centrifuges.

★ **30. What is a gyroscope?** Fig. 8-34 shows a *gyroscope* (jy-roh-skohp), which consists of a heavy wheel mounted so that it is free to rotate on its axis within a lightweight frame. When you spin the wheel, the frame will stay in a position that might ordinarily be one of unstable equilibrium. Considerable force must be used to change the plane of rotation of the wheel.

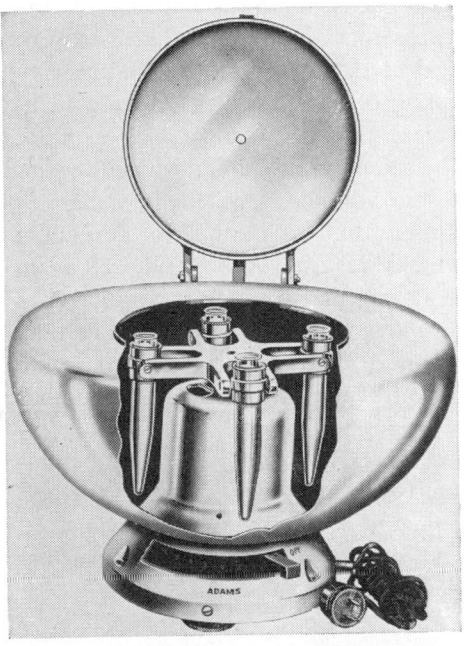

Fig. 8-33. A laboratory centrifuge for separating suspended matter from small quantities of solution.

★ 6. PERIODIC MOTION — THE PENDULUM

★ **31. What is periodic motion?** Automobiles racing around a circular track at constant speed are examples of periodic motion. They move along the same path at the same rate of speed. The same amount of time is required for each lap they go. If we suspend a weight at the end of a spring and then cause it to vibrate up and down, its motion is periodic. The vibrating weight travels up and down along the same path. While its velocity is not constant, the time for each vibration is the same. Later we shall study other examples of periodic motion. These include the vibration of strings and air columns in musical instruments. Periodic motion is also important in the study of light and electricity.

★ **32. What is a pendulum?** *A body suspended so that it can swing to-and-fro about a horizontal axis is called a* **pendulum.** The simple pendulum is a small, dense mass suspended by a cord whose mass is so small that it may be neglected. A simple pendulum consisting of a ball suspended by a light-weight thread is shown in Fig. 8-35. The point, or axis, about which the pendulum vibrates is called the *center of suspension.* As the ball, or pendulum bob, moves from *A* to *B* and back again to its starting position *A,* it makes a *complete vibration,* or *cycle.* The time required for the cycle is known as the *period* of the pendulum. The number of cycles per second is called the *frequency.* The *displacement* of a pendulum is the changing distance of the bob from the center point of its swing, *C.* The *amplitude* is the maximum displacement.

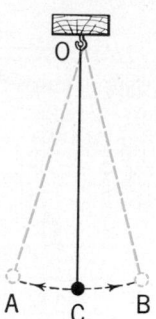

Fig. 8-35. The simple pendulum.

★ **33. What determines the period of a pendulum?** Galileo was probably the first to study the motion of a pendulum. While sitting in the cathedral at Pisa, Galileo watched the gentle swaying of a sanctuary lamp. Using his pulse as a timer, he found that successive vibrations were made in equal lengths of time.

The facts about the period of a pendulum are summarized below:

(1) *The period of a pendulum is independent of the mass or material of the pendulum.* This is strictly true only if the pendulum vibrates in a vacuum. Air resistance has more effect on a ball of cotton used as a pendulum bob than it does on a ball of lead.

(2) *The period of a pendulum is independent of the amplitude if the arc is small.* A pendulum usually swings through an arc of 10° or less.

(3) *The period of a pendulum is directly proportional to the square root of its length.* We may express this algebraically as follows:

$$t : t' = \sqrt{l} : \sqrt{l'}.$$

If we have two pendulums, one 25 cm long and the other 100 cm long, the period of the longer one will be twice that of the shorter one. The square roots of 25 and 100 are 5 and

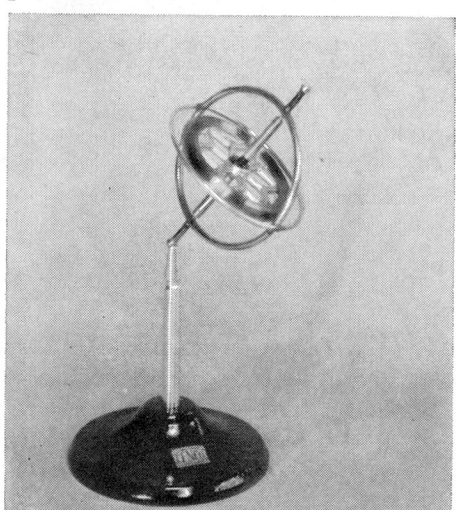

Fig. 8-34. A simple gyroscope.

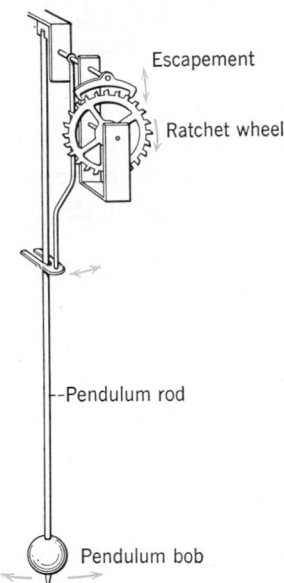

Fig. 8-36. The swinging of the pendulum bob operates the escapement, which in turn controls the rate at which the ratchet wheel turns.

10 respectively. Thus the periods are in the ratio of 5 to 10, or 1 to 2.

(4) *The period of a pendulum is inversely proportional to the square root of the acceleration due to gravity.* A pendulum vibrates slightly faster at the North Pole than at the Equator. If we use the letter *l* to denote the length of a pendulum, and *g* to denote the acceleration due to gravity, the period *t* is:

$$t = 2\pi\sqrt{\frac{l}{g}}.$$

See the Sample Problem below.

★ **34. Uses of the pendulum.** The chief use of a pendulum is in keeping time. The movement of the hands of a clock may be controlled by the swinging of a pendulum. In Fig. 8-36 the escapement wheel is one of a train of gear wheels that move the hands. Although these wheels are driven by a weight or spring, the escapement wheel is released one cog at a time by the vibrating pendulum. This controls the rate at which the hands move. The slight push from each cog as it escapes keeps the pendulum vibrating.

Jean Bernard Leon Foucault (1819–1868) used a heavy pendulum bob suspended by a long wire to prove that the earth rotates on its axis. A stylus attached to the bob traced its paths across a sanded curved floor. Foucault's pendulum continually vibrated in the same plane. Its tracings moved about the floor because the earth rotates. A pendulum may also be used to measure the acceleration of gravity.

SAMPLE PROBLEM

Find the length of a pendulum which has a period of 1 sec for a complete vibration at a location where $g = 9.8$ m/sec^2.

SOLUTION

Substitute the values in the formula $t = 2\pi\sqrt{l/g}$, or $t^2 = \dfrac{4\pi^2 l}{g}$.

This gives $1 = \dfrac{4 \times 9.870 \times l}{9.8}$.

Solving, $39.48l = 9.8$ m, and $l = 0.248$ m, the length of the pendulum.

(Note: The Standard Seconds Pendulum has a period of one second for a single vibration.)

Summary

Motion is a continuous change of place or position. Motion may be rectilinear or circular, uniform or variable. Speed is the rate of motion. Velocity is the rate of motion in a particular direction. Since velocity is a vector quantity, the resultant of two velocities may be found by the parallelogram method.

Acceleration is the rate of change of velocity. If acceleration is uniform, the final velocity equals the product of the acceleration times the elapsed time; the distance an object travels equals one-half the acceleration times the square of the elapsed time. The equations for accelerated motion apply to uniformly retarded motion. Since freely falling bodies are uniformly accelerated, these equations also apply to objects acted on by the force of gravitational attraction. The acceleration of gravity is 9.8 m/sec^2 or 32.16 ft/sec^2.

Newton formulated three laws of motion: (1) A body continues in its state of rest or uniform motion in a straight line unless an unbalanced force acts on it. (2) The acceleration of a body is directly proportional to the force exerted on the body, is inversely proportional to the mass of the body, and is in the same direction as the force. (3) Whenever one body exerts a force upon a second body, the second body exerts an equal and opposite force upon the first body.

The units of force in the metric system, the newton and the dyne, are defined by Newton's second law of motion. The unit of mass in the English system, the slug, is also defined by this law.

The product of a force times the length of time it acts is called impulse. The product of the mass of an object times its velocity is called momentum. Impulse and momentum are equal. Newton also formulated the law of universal gravitation: Every body in the universe attracts every other body with a force that is directly proportional to the product of their masses and inversely proportional to the square of the distance between their centers. While the mass of an object does not change, its weight is greatest on that part of the surface of the earth which is nearest the earth's center. An equal-arm balance is used to compare masses.

Centrifugal force increases with the mass; it is directly proportional to the square of the velocity; also it is inversely proportional to the radius of curvature.

The period of vibration of a pendulum is independent of the mass, material, or amplitude; it is directly proportional to the square root of the length; and it also is inversely proportional to the square root of the acceleration due to gravity.

Terms to Define...

Acceleration	Final velocity	Retarded motion
Acceleration of gravity	First law of motion	Rotary
Action and reaction	Gyroscope	Scalar quantity
Amplitude	Impulse	Second law of motion
Average velocity	Inertia	Slug
"Banking a curve"	Initial velocity	Speed
Center of suspension	Law of universal gravitation	Third law of motion
Centrifugal force	Mass	Thrust
Centrifuge	Meaning of $\propto$	Trajectory
Centripetal force	Momentum	Translatory
Circular	Motion	Uniformly accelerated motion
Cycle	Newton (unit)	Uniform motion
Decelerated motion	Pendulum	Variable motion
Displacement	Period	Variably accelerated motion
Dyne	Rectilinear	Vector quantity
Equal-arm balance	Resultant velocity	Velocity

Questions

GROUP A

1. What force acts on a baseball which is falling toward the earth? What force is acting on the earth?

2. Upon what two factors does the magnitude of the force of gravitational attraction depend?

3. Why must we exert five times as much force to lift a 5-kg weight as we must to lift a 1-kg weight?

4. Assuming his mass remains constant, how will a man's weight vary as he climbs from Crawford Notch, New Hampshire, elevation 1900 ft, to the top of Mount Washington, elevation 6288 ft?

5. Even though your mass remains constant, what happens to your weight as you drive from the entrance to Death Valley National Monument, elevation 5250 ft, down to the lowest spot in Death Valley, 280 ft below sea level?

6. When we "weigh" some particular object on an equal-arm balance, what are we actually doing?

GROUP B

★ 7. Explain why centrifugal and centripetal forces are examples of Newton's third law of motion.

★ 8. Why is a body which moves at constant speed in a circular path being accelerated? What is the force that is producing this acceleration?

★ 9. What conditions determine the magnitude of the centrifugal force which a rotating object exerts?

★ 10. How is the track of a roller coaster laid in order to counteract the centrifugal force of the cars as they round a sharp curve?

★ 11. Give several examples of how we use centrifugal force to our advantage.

★ 12. How do bicycles and motorcycles illustrate the principle of the gyroscope?

★ 13. What is a complete vibration, or cycle, of a pendulum? What is its amplitude? Its frequency? Its period?

★ 14. What factors determine the period of vibration of a pendulum?

★ 15. How could a pendulum be used to measure the value of g, the acceleration of gravity? Since the value of g varies from place to place, it should be determined for each physics laboratory where advanced experiments are conducted.

Problems

(In the Mathematics Refresher, refer to Sections 2, 10, and 16.)

GROUP A

1. The force of gravity on the moon is about one-sixth that on the earth. If a man weighs 160 lb on the earth, what will be his weight on the moon?

2. If a rocket ship weighing 50 tons on the earth reached an altitude of 4,000 miles above the earth, what would be its weight at that altitude?

3. What will be the weight, in newtons, of an object whose mass is 5 kg at a spot where the acceleration of gravity is only 9.78 m/sec²?

4. The acceleration of gravity at Cincinnati, Ohio, is 980.004 cm/sec². At Colorado Springs, Colorado, it is 979.490 cm/sec². What will be the force of gravitational attrac-

tion, in newtons, on a mass of 250 g at each of these locations?

GROUP B

★ **5.** A ball, whose mass is 25 g, is swung at a velocity of 5 m/sec at the end of a string 1 m long. What is the centrifugal force, in newtons, exerted by this ball?

★ **6.** An automobile weighs 3000 lb. Calculate its mass at a location where the acceleration of gravity is 32 ft/sec². If this car is driven around a curve which has a radius of 500 ft at the rate of 45 mi/hr, what is the centrifugal force, in pounds, exerted by the car? (45 mi/hr = 66 ft/sec.)

★ **7.** A pendulum 25 cm long vibrates once in one second. What is the period of vibration of a pendulum 100 cm long?

★ **8.** What is the period of a pendulum 2 m long? Use $g = 9.8$ m/sec².

● **9.** What is the length, in feet, of a pendulum which has a time of vibration of 5 sec? Acceleration of gravity is 32 ft/sec².

● **10.** If at Denver, Colorado, a pendulum 1 m long vibrates with a period of 2.0065 sec, what is the value of the acceleration of gravity?

Things to Do

1. Look up the account of Galileo's life in an encyclopedia. Report to the class upon his scientific accomplishments.

2. Have the driver education instructor or a representative of the local automobile club visit the class and explain the importance of proper methods of accelerating and decelerating an automobile.

3. Make a report to the class on rocket research. Learn what you can about the altitudes

reached, fuels used, and materials of which the rockets are built.

4. Demonstrate to the class the proper method of making a weighing on a sensitive equal-arm balance.

5. Get a small gyroscope. Observe its extreme stability while it is rotating.

6. Examine a pendulum clock to learn how the pendulum controls the rate of the clock. How is the period of the pendulum varied?

Chapter 9

Fluids in Motion

1. BERNOULLI'S PRINCIPLE

★ **1. What is streamline flow?** The motion of fluids is very complex. If we watch the waves along the shore of an ocean or a large lake, we soon realize how complicated is their movement. The unpredictable nature of tornadoes shows that the movement of gases is complex, too. Consequently we shall limit our study of the motion of fluids to a few examples which we can explain in simplified terms.

Suppose we have a tube whose diameter varies like that shown in Fig. 9-2. If water is flowing through the tube, we find that it flows smoothly. Water molecules entering the tube at *A, B,* or *C* follow the paths shown by the dotted lines. Since the volume of water passing any cross-sectional area of the tube will be the same in any given length of time, the water must flow more rapidly through the narrow portion of the tube than it does through the wide portion. *This smooth flow*

of a fluid through a tube is called **streamline flow.** If the velocity of the fluid becomes too great, or if there are too abrupt changes in the diameter or direction of the tube, the fluid will not flow smoothly. The flow then is said to be *turbulent.*

★ **2. The Venturi meter.** Water is moving with streamline flow through the tube shown in Fig. 9-3. Because the diameter of the center portion is less than that at either end, the water flows faster through the narrow part of the tube. Suppose we use vertical tubes as pressure gauges. They fill with liquid until the pressure due to the weight of the liquid in the tube equals that of the moving liquid. These gauges show that the pressure is higher where the velocity of the fluid is lower. Where the velocity of the fluid is higher, the pressure it exerts is lower. This is the principle of the *Venturi* (ven-*too*-ree) *meter.* This device enables

Vocabulary

BERNOULLI'S (ber-*noo*-lees) **PRINCIPLE.** For the horizontal flow of a fluid through a tube, the sum of the pressure and the kinetic energy per unit volume of the fluid is a constant.

CAMBER. The curvature of the surface of an airplane wing.

DRAG. The force which tends to retard the movement of an airplane through the air.

LIFT. The component of the forces on the upper and lower surfaces of an airplane wing which acts in an upward direction.

STREAMLINE FLOW. The smooth flow of a fluid.

Fig. 9-1. The irregularity of the shape of these waves rolling onto the shore shows us how complicated the motion of a liquid can be.

us to calculate the velocity of water in the horizontal tube from the difference in pressure in the vertical tubes.

A Venturi meter also can be used to measure the velocity of gases.

⭐ **3. What is Bernoulli's principle?** The explanation for the variation in pressure exerted by a moving fluid when its velocity is changed was given by Daniel Bernoulli (Ber-*noo*-lee) (1700–1782). He found that, *for the horizontal flow of a fluid through a tube, the sum of the pressure and the kinetic energy per unit volume of the fluid is a constant.* This statement usually is called BERNOULLI'S PRINCIPLE.

The kinetic energy of a moving fluid is directly proportional to the square of its velocity. But Bernoulli's principle states that the sum of the pressure and the kinetic energy per unit volume is a constant. As the velocity of a moving fluid increases, its kinetic energy increases. Consequently, the pressure it exerts must correspondingly decrease. This explains the results we observed in the Venturi meter.

⭐ **4. How does a carburetor work?** An application of Bernoulli's principle

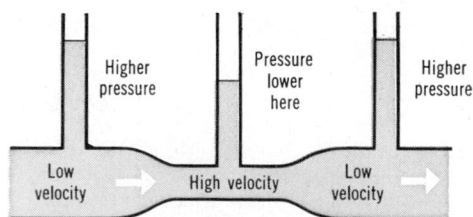

Fig. 9-3. As the water flows more rapidly through the narrow portion of the tube, the pressure is lowered.

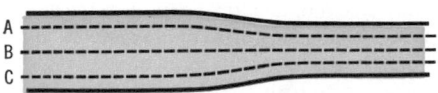

Fig. 9-2. Streamline flow of water through a tube.

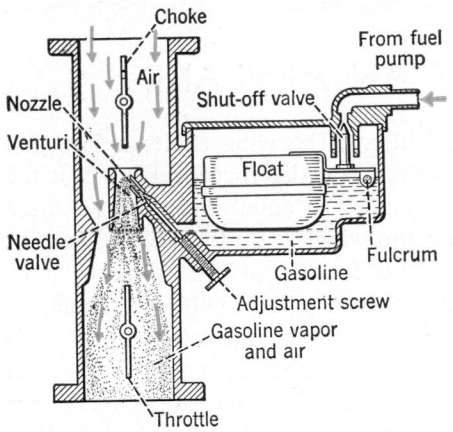

Fig. 9-4. The carburetor vaporizes gasoline and mixes it with air to form an explosive mixture.

is the automobile carburetor, shown in Fig. 9-4. The purpose of a carburetor is to mix gasoline vapor and air in the correct proportions so that they form an explosive mixture. Gasoline is fed from a tank to the carburetor by means of a fuel pump. The liquid level in the gasoline well is controlled by a small float with a needle valve attached. When the engine is running, a partial vacuum is produced in the chamber by the action of the pistons. The throttle is opened. Air entering in the direction shown by the arrows sweeps past the end of the nozzle and mixes with the gasoline which is escaping. The space around the nozzle is narrowed to give the air a greater velocity. This reduces the pressure that the air exerts. The gasoline escapes from the nozzle and vaporizes more readily in this low pressure area. The throttle controls the amount of air-and-gasoline vapor mixture which is admitted to the cylinders. In this way it controls the speed of the engine. At the air intake, the choke valve controls the proportion of air and gasoline vapor in

the mixture that is fed to the cylinders. When the choke is open, as shown in Fig. 9-4, the mixture has a large proportion of air compared to the amount of gasoline vapor present. This is called a lean mixture. When the choke is closed, as in starting or when warming up a cold engine, the proportion of air decreases. This makes for a rich mixture. As soon as the engine is warmed up, the choke is opened to permit more economical operation. Many automobiles have an automatic choke which is opened when the engine reaches the proper operating temperature.

★ **5. A spinning baseball moves in a curved path.** A baseball which is not spinning may travel in a straight line. However, a spinning ball will move along a curved path. Look at Fig. 9-5. The ball, spinning in a counterclockwise direction, drags the adjacent air around with it, as represented by the dashed circles. At the top of the ball, this air current is moving with the air current set up by the forward motion of the ball. At the bottom, it is moving against this current. The air at the top moves faster, and the pressure there is reduced. Thus, the ball will move along the path shown by the dashed curve.

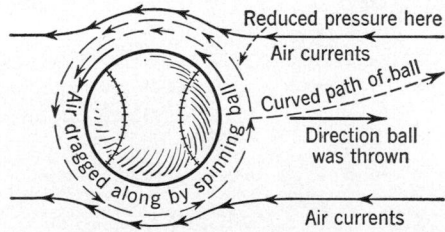

Fig. 9-5. A spinning baseball follows a curved path because its motion makes the air pressure less on one side than on the other.

★ 2. THE FLIGHT OF AN AIRPLANE

★ **6. The forces that lift an airplane.**
A balloon rises because it is buoyed up by the air it displaces. The weight of this displaced air is greater than the weight of the balloon. An airplane, however, weighs more than the air it displaces. It can not rise unless it is acted on by forces which are produced by its own movement through the air. An airplane moves through the air because of the action of its conventional engines and propellers, its jet engines, or its rocket engines.

Fig. 9-7 shows a cross-section of an airplane wing with air flowing past it from left to right. The lower surface of the wing is at a slight angle to the direction of moving air. This air flowing past the lower surface is deflected slightly. The wing exerts a force on the air in order to deflect it. But the air exerts an equal and opposite force on the wing. The upward component of this force provides about 15% of the force required to lift an airplane.

The remaining part of the force needed to lift the airplane is produced by the movement of the air across the upper surface of the wings. An airplane wing is so shaped that air moving across the upper surface must travel a greater distance to get from the leading edge to the trailing edge. Yet the air above the wing travels this distance in the same time as the air moving beneath. Consequently, the air moving over the top surface of the wing exerts less pressure than that moving beneath

Fig. 9-6. The Douglas DC-7, a modern, high-speed passenger airplane.

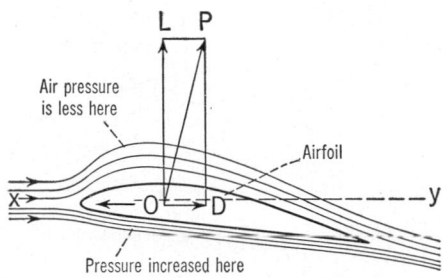

Air pressure is less here

Airfoil

Pressure increased here

Fig. 9-7. The movement of air over the wing produces a difference in pressure between the upper and lower surfaces. The force produced in this manner may be resolved into an upward lift force and a horizontal drag force.

it. This is in accordance with Bernoulli's principle. The difference in pressure between the top of the wing and the bottom of the wing provides most of the lifting force which enables an airplane to rise into the air. A difference in air pressure of only 2.5 oz/in² will produce a lifting force of more than 20 pounds on each square foot of wing surface. *The combined upward-acting effect of the forces on the upper and lower surfaces of an airplane wing is called* **lift**.

⭐ **7. The forces that retard the motion of an airplane.** We have seen that there are two forces which act to lift an airplane. But neither of these forces acts in a vertical direction. They both act at an angle on the wings. Only the vertical component of these forces acts to lift the airplane. *The horizontal component of these forces will tend to retard the movement of the airplane through the air.* Such a horizontal component is called **drag**. Work must be done by the engine of the airplane to overcome this retarding force.

In Fig. 9-7, the resultant lifting force on the airplane wing is represented by the vector *OP*. The vertical component (lift) is then *OL,* while the horizontal component (drag) is *OD.*

⭐ **8. The shape of an airplane wing.** Engineers have experimented with planes and wings in wind tunnels to determine how the shape of an airplane wing affects the lifting force. Many different shapes have been tried, varying from the flat wing to the curved wing. Experiments show that for most purposes a curved wing is better. *The amount of the curve of the surface of a wing is called its* **camber.**

⭐ **9. The angle of incidence.** A straight line from the leading edge of an airplane wing to the trailing edge is called the *chord.* The wings are attached to the body, or *fuselage (fyoozul-ij)*, in such a way that they make a slight angle with the longitudinal axis of the airplane. This angle is called the *angle of incidence.*

⭐ **10. The angle of attack.** In all kinds of flight the direction of the relative wind is opposite to the movement of the airplane. The wind is horizontal in ordinary level flight. But when the nose is tilted downward, the relative wind seems to come from above. In taking off, when the nose of the plane points upward, the relative wind appears to come from below. The angle between the chord of an airplane wing and the direction of the relative wind is called the *angle of attack.* The angle of incidence for any given airplane is fixed, since the wings are rigidly attached and their angle with the longitudinal axis does not vary. The angle of attack, however, changes as the airplane ascends or descends. As the airplane rises, the angle of attack is considered positive.

Different angles of attack are shown

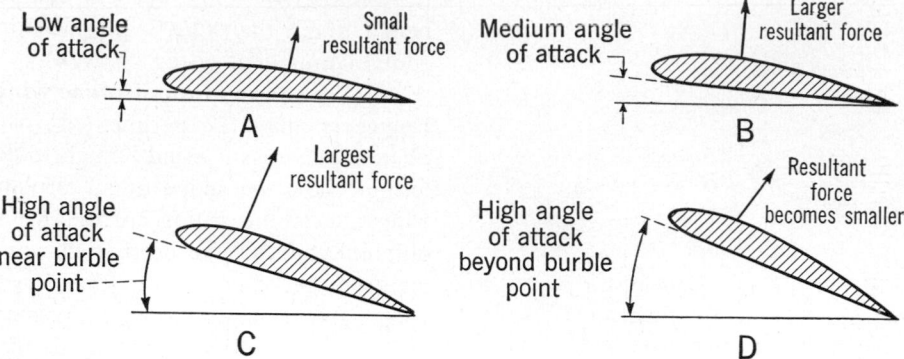

Fig. 9-8. Variation of the resultant force on a wing with increasing angle of attack.

in Fig. 9-8. The lifting force on an airplane wing varies with the angle of attack. Generally, the lifting force increases as the angle of attack increases. However, if the angle of attack becomes too great, the air no longer flows smoothly over the cambered surfaces, but begins to burble, as shown in Fig. 9-9. Bernoulli's principle no longer applies, and the lifting force decreases rapidly, as shown in Fig. 9-9. The angle just below that at which burbling begins to reduce the lifting force is called the *stalling angle*.

★**11. How can we control the direction of flight of an airplane?** Before a plane can rise, it must taxi along the ground. In this way it gains enough velocity so that the lifting force at a small angle of attack is slightly higher than the weight of the plane with its load.

Fig. 9-10 shows the various parts of an airplane. The center of gravity lies within the fuselage of the plane at the point where the wings are attached. Forces acting on the tail tilt the nose of the plane upward or downward, and to the left or to the right. The horizontal tail plane, or *stabilizer*, helps keep the airplane on an even keel when flying. The *elevators*, which are hinged to the rear edge of the stabilizer, are tilted up and down when the pilot pulls the control stick backward or forward. As the plane taxies along the ground, the elevators are turned slightly downward to keep the nose of the plane toward the ground until proper flying speed is attained.

When the plane gains enough speed to rise, the pilot pulls the control stick backward. This tilts the elevators upward. The increased force of the air against the upper surfaces of the elevators pushes the tail of the plane down and the nose up. The lift force increases with the increased angle of attack, and the airplane takes off. When the pilot shoves the stick forward, the elevators swing down. The air pres-

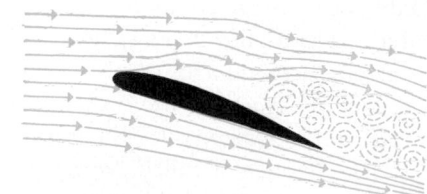

Fig. 9-9. When the angle of attack is too great, air no longer flows smoothly over the upper surface of the wing. This burbling decreases the lifting force.

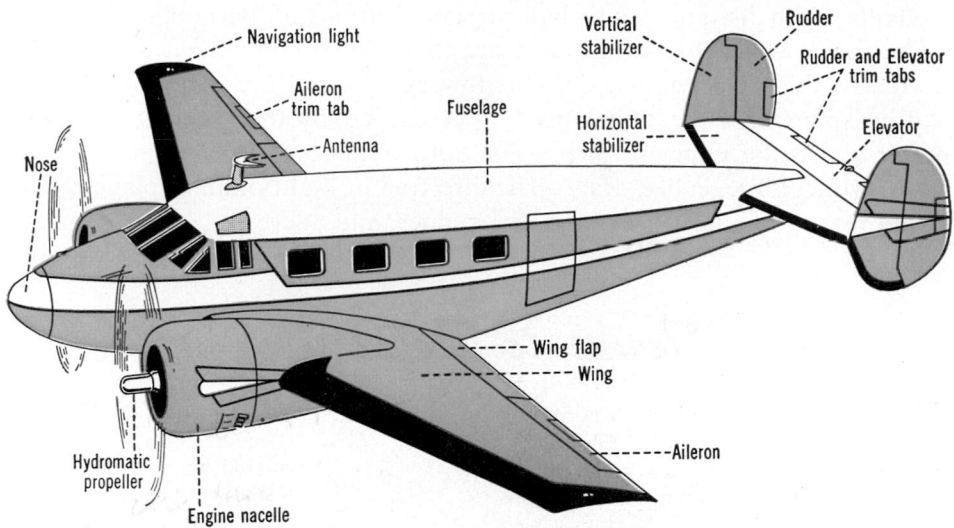

Fig. 9-10. The parts of a small, twin-engine transport airplane.

sure on their lower surfaces pushes the tail up and causes the plane to nose downward. Thus, by means of the elevators, upward or downward direction of the plane is controlled.

An airplane may be rotated about its vertical axis. Mounted on the tail at right angles to the stabilizer is a vertical plane called the *fin*. The fin increases the sidewise stability of the airplane. Hinged to the rear edge of the fin is the *rudder*. When the pilot moves the rudder to the right, the airplane swings toward the right. When he moves the rudder to the left, the plane swings to the left. This action is like that of a boat rudder which swings the stern from side to side and controls the direction of the boat.

We know that an automobile rounding a curve at high speed may skid outward because of centrifugal force. An airplane turning may also skid outward. To prevent an airplane from skidding when turning, *ailerons* (*ayler-onz*) are used. One aileron is hinged to the rear edge of each wing. When the pilot pushes the control stick to the right in making a turn, the right aileron is pushed up and the left aileron is pulled down. The increased force of the air above the right wing pushes that wing down, while at the same time the left wing is pushed up.

Summary

The smooth flow of a fluid through a tube is called streamline flow. When a fluid does not flow smoothly, its flow is said to be turbulent. A Venturi meter may be used to measure the rate of flow of a fluid through a tube.

Bernoulli's principle states that for the horizontal flow of a fluid through a tube the sum of the pressure and the kinetic energy per unit volume of the fluid is a constant. The automobile carburetor and the curved flight of spinning baseballs, softballs, and tennis balls are applications of Bernoulli's principle.

The forces which lift an airplane are the vertical component of the force exerted by the air moving against the lower surface of the wing, and the vertical component of the unbalanced force caused by the greater velocity of the air across the upper surface. The horizontal component of these forces is a retarding force, called drag. The direction of flight of an airplane is controlled by the stabilizer, elevators, fin, rudder, and ailerons.

Terms to Define...

Aileron	Chord	Rich mixture
Angle of attack	Drag	Rudder
Angle of incidence	Elevator	Stabilizer
Bernoulli's principle	Fin	Stalling angle
Camber	Fuselage	Streamline flow
Carburetor	Lean mixture	Turbulent flow
Choke	Lifting force	Venturi meter

Questions

GROUP A

★ **1.** What is smooth flow of fluids called?

★ **2.** What causes turbulent flow in a fluid?

★ **3.** How does the pressure exerted by a smoothly moving fluid vary with its rate of flow? What is a practical application?

★ **4.** What is the purpose of the narrow air passage near the nozzle of a carburetor?

★ **5.** What is the function of the throttle? Of the choke?

★ **6.** What is meant by a "rich mixture"? A "lean mixture"?

★ **7.** How is a balloon supported in the air? How is an airplane supported in the air?

★ **8.** How does the shape of an airplane wing affect the amount of lifting force?

★ **9.** What is the angle of incidence? The angle of attack?

★ **10.** How does lifting force on an airplane wing change as angle of attack increases?

GROUP B

★ **11.** What is Bernoulli's principle?

★ **12.** Explain why a spinning baseball travels in a slightly curved path.

★ **13.** Into what two components may the resultant force of the air moving over an airplane wing be resolved? Which component is useful? Which component acts as a retarding force?

★ **14.** How are the ailerons and rudder of an airplane changed when turning to the right?

★ **15.** How do airplanes change altitude?

Things to Do

1. Get a copy of *Life* magazine for July 27, 1953. Report to the class on the article on page 104 on the curve of a spinning baseball.

2. Visit your community airport. Examine the different types of airplanes which you find there. Identify the parts studied in this Chapter.

Unit 5 Work, Power, and Energy

The pile driver shown in the photograph illustrates the physical concepts of work, power, and energy. In order to raise the hammer of the pile driver, a certain force must be exerted over a given distance. When this happens, physicists say that work has been done on the hammer. Because this work raises the hammer, the energy of position, or the potential energy of the hammer, is increased. When the hammer is released, its potential energy is transformed into energy of motion, or kinetic energy. The kinetic energy of the hammer enables it to do work in driving a wood or metal pile into the ground. The rate at which the pile driver works is called its power. The more powerful this machine is, the more rapidly it can do its work of driving piles.

Chapter 10

Work — Power — Energy

1. WORK

1. The scientific meaning of work. In everyday language we use the word *work* to describe any form of activity in which we exert muscular or mental effort. In physics, the word *work* has a very special meaning. No matter how long you hold a 50-lb bag of plant food on your shoulder, you are not doing any work in a scientific sense. You are merely exerting an upward force which counteracts the downward force due to the weight of the plant food. You do work in a scientific sense when you raise the bag to your shoulder, or when you carry it up a flight of stairs. In these cases, you exerted a force, and *the force moved the object.* But you do not do any work when you carry the bag of plant food with a constant velocity along a horizontal walk. It is true that the bag is in motion, but the *upward force* you exert on it does not produce its *horizontal motion. If a force acts upon a body and moves it, the force has done work upon the body.*

2. How is work measured? Two factors must be considered in measuring work: the force applied, and the distance through which the force acts.

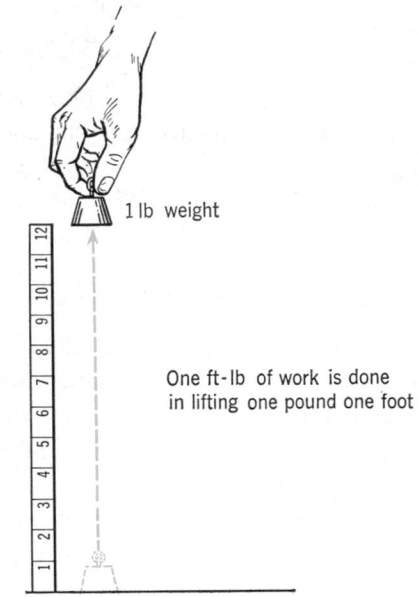

1 lb weight

One ft-lb of work is done in lifting one pound one foot

Fig. 10-1. Definition of the *foot-pound* as a unit of work.

Vocabulary

KINETIC ENERGY. Energy of motion.

POTENTIAL ENERGY. Energy of position, or stored energy.

POWER. The rate of doing work.

WORK. The product of a force times the distance through which the force acts.

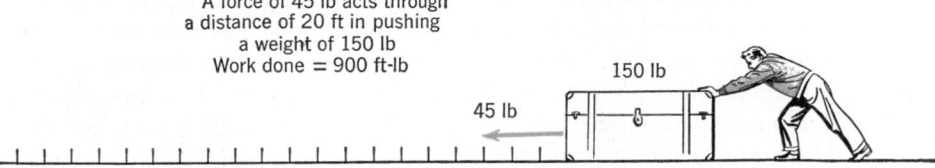

A force of 45 lb acts through
a distance of 20 ft in pushing
a weight of 150 lb
Work done = 900 ft-lb

150 lb

45 lb

20 19 18 17 16 15 14 13 12 11 10 9 8 7 6 5 4 3 2 1

Fig. 10-2. The work done in pushing an object equals the force needed to overcome friction multiplied by the distance.

*The amount of **work** done is equal to the product of force times distance,*

$$W = Fs.$$

If either the force or the distance is zero, no work is done.

(1) English system. *If one pound of force acts through a distance of one foot, it does one foot-pound of work.* This unit of work almost defines itself. See Fig. 10-1. The "foot-pound" is used to distinguish this unit of work from the unit of torque, the pound-foot.

A man who weighs 150 lb does 1500 ft-lb of work in climbing a flight of stairs 10 ft high. He lifts his own weight 10 ft against the force of gravitational attraction. When an object is lifted vertically, the amount of work done always equals the *weight of the object* times the *vertical height* through which it is lifted. In such cases, the force which must be applied is that which overcomes the weight of the object. We must use a force of 100 lb to lift a weight of 100 lb.

Suppose that we push a large trunk weighing 150 lb across a platform 20 ft long, as shown in Fig. 10-2. What work is done? In order to push the trunk, the only force needed is that required to overcome friction. Suppose the coefficient of friction is 0.3. Then the force needed to keep the trunk moving is $0.3 \times 150 = 45$ lb. The amount of work done equals the force applied, 45 lb, times the distance, 20 ft. This product is 900 ft-lb. In order to carry the same trunk up a flight of stairs 20 ft high, we must do 20 ft $\times$ 150 lb = 3000 ft-lb of work.

(2) Metric system — MKS units. If the force is measured in newtons and the distance is measured in meters, the product which represents the work will be given in *joules (jowls)*. *A force of one newton, acting through a distance of one meter, does one joule of work.* This unit of work was named for the English physicist, James Prescott Joule (1818–1889).

★ (3) Metric system — CGS units.

SAMPLE PROBLEM

How much work is done in raising a mass of 5 kg to a height of 10 m?

SOLUTION

The force required to lift a mass of 5 kg is 5 kg $\times$ 9.8 m/sec^2 = 49 nt. The work done will be 49 nt $\times$ 10 m = 490 joules.

If the force is measured in dynes, and the distance is measured in centimeters, the work will be in ergs. *A force of one dyne, acting through a distance of one centimeter, does one erg of* *work.* One joule equals 10^7 ergs. See the Sample Problem on page 109. See Section 15, Mathematics Refresher, for an explanation of this exponential method of writing large numbers.

PROBLEMS

(In the Mathematics Refresher, refer to Sections 10 and 16.)

GROUP A

1. A man weighing 200 lb climbs a flight of stairs 15 ft high. What work did he do?

2. In order to lift a 1-kg weight, we must exert a force of 9.8 nt. How much work do we do when we lift the weight a height of 5 m?

3. A force of 50 lb is needed in order to push a loaded wheelbarrow. If the wheelbarrow is pushed 100 ft, how much work is expended?

4. A large box, having a mass of 50 kg, is to be lifted to a platform 1.5 m high. What work must be done in lifting this box? Acceleration due to gravity is 9.8 m/sec².

5. What work is done when John lifts a 2.5-kg package from the floor and places it on a shelf 2 m high?

6. Paul has a can of paint weighing 4 kg. If he lifts it 0.75 m, how much work must he do?

7. The coefficient of friction between a large packing case and the floor is 0.25. If the case weighs 250 lb, what force is required to move it across the level floor? If the packing case is to be moved 20 ft, what work must be done?

8. If the coefficient of friction between a metal safe and the floor is 0.15, what force, in newtons, is required to roll this 25-kg safe across the floor? How much work is done if the safe is rolled a distance of 15 m?

GROUP B

9. A loaded trunk has a mass of 35 kg. The coefficient of friction between the trunk and the floor is 0.2. How much work will be done in moving the trunk 12 m across a level floor and then lifting it into the back of a truck 0.5 m above the floor?

● **10.** A certain pump has a capacity of 5 ft³/min. How much work is done by this pump in one hour if it raises water from a well 20 ft deep?

★ **11.** What work, in ergs, is done when a 50-g weight is raised a distance of 30 cm?

★ **12.** The coefficient of friction between a small box and a table top is 0.40. If the box has a mass of 125 g, what work, in ergs, is done when the box is moved 75 cm?

2. POWER

3. What is power? Just as there are different everyday and scientific meanings for the word *work,* there are different everyday and scientific meanings for the word *power.* When we say a person has great power, we usually mean he has great strength, or he wields great authority. In physics, the term **power** means *the rate of doing work.*

A man does the same amount of work when he climbs a flight of stairs in one minute that he does if he climbs the same flight of stairs in one hour. But he does not use the same amount of power. Power depends upon three factors: the force exerted, the distance the force moves, and the time required.

4. How is power measured? (1) English system. *If one foot-pound of work is done in one second of time, the power is one foot-pound per sec-*

ond. However, this unit is too small to be used conveniently. The common unit of power in the English system is the *horsepower* (hp); it equals 550 ft-lb/sec or 33,000 ft-lb/min.

$$hp = \frac{\text{total work in ft-lb}}{550 \times \text{time in sec}},$$

or, $hp = \dfrac{Fs}{550t}$.

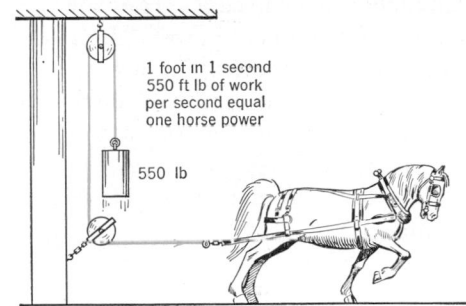

1 foot in 1 second
550 ft lb of work
per second equal
one horse power

550 lb

Fig. 10-3. Definition of the *horsepower* as a unit of power.

This unit was originated by James Watt (1736–1819), the inventor of the steam engine. He found by a series of experiments that a horse pulling a heavy wagon could continue, for a reasonable length of time, to work at the rate of 550 ft-lb/sec.

(2) Metric system — MKS units. Work is measured in joules in the MKS system. Time is measured in seconds. *The unit of power is one joule per second.* One joule per second is called *one watt*. This unit is named in honor of James Watt. But it, too, is an inconveniently small unit. Power is more commonly measured in units of 1000 watts, called *kilowatts* (kw).

Because you have heard the terms watt and kilowatt used frequently in connection with electricity, you may think that these terms are used only when discussing electrical power. This

SAMPLE PROBLEM

What horsepower engine is required to hoist 100 tons of coal per hour from a mine 200 feet deep?

SOLUTION

A ton equals 2000 lb. Substituting in the formula,

$hp = \dfrac{Fs}{550t}$, we obtain, $hp = \dfrac{100 \text{ tn} \times 2000 \text{ lb/tn} \times 200 \text{ ft}}{550 \text{ ft-lb/sec} \times 60 \text{ sec/min} \times 60 \text{ min/hr}}$.

Solving, hp = 20.2, the horsepower engine required.

SAMPLE PROBLEM

Paul's mass is 75 kg. If he walks up a flight of stairs 12 m high in 30 sec, what power has he used?

SOLUTION

The force Paul must use to raise a mass of 75 kg is 75 kg × 9.8 m/sec = 735 nt. The work done will be 735 nt × 12 m = 8820 joules. The power used will be 8820 joules ÷ 30 sec = 294 watts.

definitely is not the case. They are the MKS system units of power. It makes no difference whether the power is mechanical or electrical. We could measure the power consumption of an electric lamp in horsepower. Again we could rate an automobile engine in kilowatts.

★ (3) Metric system — CGS units. The power unit in this system is *one erg per second*. It has no special name.

One horsepower equals 746 watts, or 0.746 kilowatt. It is useful to remember that 1 hp = about ¾ kw. See the Sample Problems, page 211.

PROBLEMS

(In the Mathematics Refresher, refer to Sections 10 and 16.)

GROUP A

1. A power shovel raised 500 lb of earth to a height of 10 ft in 5 sec. What was the horsepower used?

2. What horsepower is required for an ore bucket to raise 10 tons of ore to a height of 50 ft in 20 sec?

3. How many kilowatts of power are required to raise a mass of 50 kg to a height of 10 m in 15 sec? Acceleration due to gravity is 9.8m/sec².

4. The loaded cage of an elevator has a mass of 3000 kg. If it is raised in 10 sec to the top story of a building, a height of 50 m, how many kilowatts of power were used?

5. The elevator in the Empire State Building in New York City makes the ascent to the 80th floor in 50 sec. If the height is 989 ft, what horsepower is used to lift a man weighing 160 lb to this floor?

6. How many kilowatts of power are required for hoisting 100,000 kg of coal per hour from a mine which is 300 m deep?

7. The mass of a large steel ball is 1500 kg. What power is used in raising this steel ball to a height of 15 m if the work is done in 5 sec?

8. An elevator in a garage can raise an automobile weighing 2 tons to a height of 30 ft in 2 minutes. What horsepower is required?

GROUP B

9. An automobile engine is rated to give 235 hp. What is this power in kilowatts?

● **10.** A pump can deliver 10 liters of gasoline per minute. What power, in kilowatts, is expended by the pump in raising gasoline a distance of 5 m? Specific gravity of gasoline, 0.70.

● **11.** If the effective coefficient of friction is 0.02, what horsepower will be required to move a railroad car which weighs 50 tons at the rate of 60 mi/hr? (60 mi/hr = 88 ft/sec.)

● **12.** How many gallons of water will be pumped from a well 20 ft deep by a ½-hp motor in 1 minute? One gallon of water weighs 8 lb.

3. ENERGY

5. What is energy? In Chapter 1 we defined *energy as the capacity or ability for doing work.* An object acquires energy when work is done in raising it to an elevated position. It also acquires energy when it is set in motion. The water in a swiftly flowing river has energy. Winds possess energy too. Destruction caused by waves shows they have energy.

6. Kinetic and potential energy. In mechanics there are two kinds of energy, *kinetic energy* and *potential energy.* **Kinetic energy** *is the energy of motion.* A body has kinetic energy because of its velocity. A moving automobile, a bullet leaving the muzzle of a gun, strong winds, and falling or running water all possess kinetic energy.

Potential energy *is stored energy, or energy of position.* A rock resting on the edge of a cliff has potential energy. This energy becomes kinetic if the rock falls over the edge. The coiled mainspring of a watch has potential energy. Work was done in winding the spring. As the spring unwinds, its potential energy becomes kinetic. If we pull a heavy pendulum bob to one side, we are storing up energy by raising the bob against the force of gravity. As the bob swings downward and forward, the potential energy becomes kinetic. This kinetic energy is sufficient to carry the bob upward again on the opposite side. Here kinetic energy is changed back into potential energy. We see from this example that it is possible to change potential energy into kinetic energy, and that it is also possible to change kinetic energy into potential energy.

7. How is potential energy measured? Since energy is the capacity for doing work, *we may use work units for measuring both potential and kinetic energy.* If we lift a 40-lb block from the floor to a table 3 ft high, we have done 120 ft-lb of work. In being raised 3 ft above the floor, the block acquired 120 ft-lb of potential energy. If the block falls to the floor, it can do 120 ft-lb of work. See Fig. 10-4.

Potential energy may be calculated by means of the following formula:

$$\text{P.E.} = mgh.$$

In this formula m represents the mass of an object, g the acceleration due to gravity, and h the vertical distance

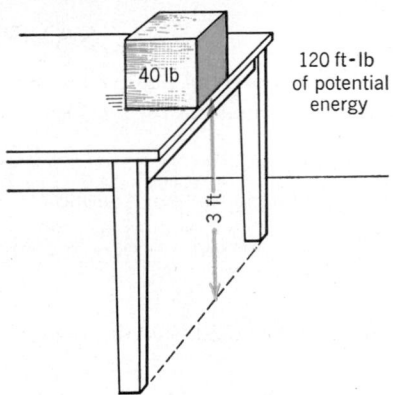

Fig. 10-4. When the 40-pound block is raised 3 feet above the floor, it acquires 120 foot-pounds of potential energy.

through which it is raised. See Sample Problem at the top of page 214.

(1) English system. When using this formula with English system units, we must remember that the product mg equals the force required to lift the object. That is, mg equals the weight of the object. If this weight is expressed in pounds and the distance in feet, the potential energy will be given in foot-pounds.

(2) Metric system — MKS units. If the mass of the object is given in kilograms, the acceleration of gravity is 9.8 meters per second per second, and the height or distance is given in meters, then the potential energy will be expressed in joules.

★ (3) Metric system — CGS units. Here the mass of the object will be expressed in grams. The acceleration of gravity is 9.8 cm/sec². The height or distance will be measured in centimeters. The calculated energy will be given in ergs.

8. How is kinetic energy measured? The velocity of a freely-falling body in terms of the acceleration of gravity and

SAMPLE PROBLEM

What potential energy has been acquired by a block of steel, whose mass is 50 kg, when it is raised 5 m?

SOLUTION

Substituting in the equation P.E. = mgh, we obtain P.E. = 50 kg × 9.8 m/sec² × 5 m. Multiplying, P.E. = 2450 joules.

the distance traveled is given by the formula

$$v = \sqrt{2gs}.$$

Solving for s, we obtain

$$s = \frac{v^2}{2g}.$$

But s in this equation means the same quantity as h in P.E. = mgh. So let us substitute for h the expression we have just derived for s. Since this object is moving with velocity v, it possesses kinetic energy. We then obtain,

$$\text{K.E.} = mg \times \frac{v^2}{2g}, \text{ or,}$$

$$\text{K.E.} = \tfrac{1}{2} mv^2.$$

(1) English system. In using this equation with English units, m must be given in slugs, and v in ft/sec. Remember that under the conditions of standard gravity, 32 pounds of force are required to lift a mass of one slug. Kinetic energy is given in foot-pounds. See the Sample Problem below.

(2) Metric system — MKS units. The mass m must be given in kilograms, and v in m/sec. Then K.E. will be measured in joules.

★ (3) Metric system — CGS units. The mass m must be given in grams and v in cm/sec. Then K.E. will be calculated in ergs.

See the Sample Problem on page 215. Also see the table, Fig. 10-5 for a list of the units in mechanics.

9. Mass and energy. In Chapter 1 we learned that matter and energy were interchangeable. The Einstein equation for the relation between matter and energy is $E = mc^2$, where E is the energy in joules, if m is the mass in kilograms, and c is the velocity of light,

SAMPLE PROBLEM

Find the kinetic energy of a bullet weighing 0.10 lb if its velocity is 2000 ft/sec.

SOLUTION

If the weight of the bullet is 0.10 lb, its mass is 0.10 lb ÷ 32 ft/sec² = 0.00313 slug.

Substituting in the formula K.E. = $\tfrac{1}{2} mv^2$, we have K.E. = $\tfrac{1}{2}$ × 0.00313 × (2000 ft/sec)².

Solving, K.E. = 6260 ft-lb.

SAMPLE PROBLEM

A baseball has a mass of 0.14 kg. If it is thrown with a velocity of 7.5 m/sec, what is its kinetic energy?

SOLUTION

Substituting in the formula K.E. $= \frac{1}{2} mv^2$, we obtain K.E. $= \frac{1}{2} \times 0.14$ kg $\times (7.5$ m/sec$)^2$.

Solving, K.E. $= 39.4$ joules.

3×10^8 m/sec. Since c^2 equals 9×10^{16} m²/sec², we can readily understand that a tremendous amount of energy may be produced from a very small quantity of matter. In a powerful atomic explosion, 1 g of matter may be transformed into energy. How much energy will be produced from this gram? Converting the mass to kilograms, 1 g $= 10^{-3}$ kg. Substituting in $E = mc^2$, $E = 10^{-3}$ kg $\times 9 \times 10^{16}$ m²/sec². Solving, $E = 9 \times 10^{13}$ joules. In order to produce this same amount of energy, it would be necessary to burn over 3000 tons of coal. (In the Mathematics Refresher, refer to Section 15 for the method of writing very small numbers using negative exponents.)

★ One of the basic steps in the reasoning which produced this equation is the idea that the mass of an object varies with its velocity. Up to this point we have assumed that the mass of an object does not vary with its location or condition. For the velocities attained by usual quantities of matter the variation of mass is so slight we

---

Length	Mass	Time	Velocity	Acceleration	Force	Work	Power
s	m	t	$v = s/t$	$a = v/t$	$F = ma$	$W = Fs$	$P = W/t$
MKS system —							
meter (m)	kilogram (kg)	second (sec)	m/sec	m/sec²	$\frac{\text{kg-m}}{\text{sec}^2}$ newton (nt)	nt-m joule	joule/sec watt
CGS system —							
centimeter (cm)	gram (g)	second (sec)	cm/sec	cm/sec²	$\frac{\text{g-cm}}{\text{sec}^2}$ dyne	dyne-cm erg	erg/sec 10^{-7} watt
English system —							
foot (ft)	slug	second (sec)	ft/sec	ft/sec²	pound (lb)	ft-lb	$\frac{\text{ft-lb}}{\text{sec}}$ $550 \frac{\text{ft-lb}}{\text{sec}} = 1$ hp

UNITS IN MECHANICS*

* The basic units in each system are shown in italics.

Fig. 10-5. A table listing the units in mechanics.

Fig. 10-6. The transformation of a small amount of matter into a tremendous amount of energy produced the destruction caused by this atomic bomb explosion.

can not detect it. But for velocities near that of light, the increase in mass is appreciable. Experiments on rapidly moving electrons confirm this.

★ The mass of a body increases as its velocity increases according to:

$$m = \frac{m_0}{\sqrt{1 - (v^2/c^2)}}.$$

In this formula, m is the mass of the object at velocity v; m_0 is the mass of the object when its velocity is zero; and c is the velocity of light, 3×10^8 m/sec.

★ The following table shows how the mass of a 1-g body varies with velocity. The velocity is expressed as a percentage of the velocity of light. That is, a

velocity of 50% is half the velocity of light. See how rapidly mass increases above 90% of the velocity of light.

Velocity of Object (Per cent of velocity of light)	Mass
0%	1.00g
25%	1.03g
50%	1.15g
75%	1.51g
80%	1.67g
85%	1.88g
90%	2.30g
95%	3.16g
99%	7.07g
99.9%	22.4 g

Summary

If a force acts upon a body and moves it, the force has done work upon the body.   The amount of work done is equal to the product of force times distance.   Units of work are the foot-pound, the joule, and the erg.

Power is the rate of doing work.   The horsepower, the watt, and the erg-sec are the units of power.   One horsepower equals 550 foot-pounds per second. One watt is one joule per second.

Energy is the capacity or ability for doing work.   Kinetic energy is the energy of motion, while potential energy is stored energy, or energy of position. Units of work are used for measuring both potential and kinetic energy.

Matter and energy are interchangeable.   A very small amount of matter will produce a tremendous amount of energy.   The mass of an object varies with its velocity.   However, the variation is not very pronounced until the object reaches a velocity which is about 75% of the speed of light.

Terms to Define...

$E = mc^2$	Horsepower	Power
Energy	Joule	Variation of mass with
Erg	Kilowatt	velocity
Erg/sec	Kinetic energy	Watt
Foot-pound	Potential energy	Work

Questions

8. How are horsepower and kilowatts related?
9. What is energy? What are the two important kinds of energy? How do they differ?
10. In what units do we measure energy? How do we calculate potential energy? How do we calculate kinetic energy?

GROUP A

1. What conditions must be met before work, as we use the term in physics, has been done?
2. How do we calculate the amount of work?
3. In what unit is work generally measured in the English system?
4. What is the unit of work in the MKS system of measurement? ★ In the CGS system?
5. How is the term "power" used in physics?
6. What is the common unit for measuring power in the English system?
7. What is the common unit for measuring power in the MKS system of measurement?

GROUP B

11. If there were no friction, would it require work to keep an automobile moving in a straight path on a perfectly level road at constant speed?
12. With what power can an average person work continuously?
13. What is Einstein's equation relating mass and energy? Identify each of the terms used in this equation, and mention the units in which they usually are measured.
★ 14. How does the velocity of a body affect its mass?

Problems

(In the Mathematics Refresher, refer to Sections 2, 7, 10, 15, and 16.)

GROUP A

1. By virtue of its position, what potential energy is possessed by 500 lb of water at the top of Niagara Falls? The falls are 167 ft high.

2. John places a 1-kg weight on a table 0.80 m high. What potential energy, in joules, is now possessed by this weight?

3. A large rock has a mass of 10 slugs. If it rests at the top of a steep cliff 100 ft high, what potential energy does it have?

4. The mass of a large block of steel is 5000 kg. If this block of steel is lifted to a height of 7.5 m, what potential energy has it acquired? How does this compare with the amount of work done in lifting the block?

5. How much kinetic energy is possessed by an automobile weighing 2500 lb when it is traveling at the rate of 44 ft/sec?

6. The mass of a bomb is 250 kg. If it strikes the earth with a velocity of 50 m/sec, what is its kinetic energy?

7. A baseball has a mass of 0.14 kg. If it is thrown with a velocity of 20 m/sec, what is its kinetic energy?

8. What kinetic energy does a 20-ton truck have if it moves at a velocity of 65 ft/sec?

GROUP B

9. How much matter must be transformed into energy in order to provide 1,000,000 joules of energy?

● **10.** Calculate the mass that a 1-g weight would have traveling at 99.99% of the velocity of light.

Things to Do

1. If you have the opportunity, observe a pile driver in operation. Note how the potential energy of the lifted weight is transformed into the kinetic energy which drives the piles into the ground.

2. Make a pictorial chart showing the approximate ranges of horsepower for an average man; a small gasoline engine such as would be used on a power mower or motor bike; automobile engines; Diesel locomotives; airplane engines of conventional type; jet engines; and so forth.

Unit 6 · Machines

This power shovel is a complicated-looking piece of heavy-duty earth-moving equipment, isn't it? It is used to scoop out large bucketfuls of earth and load them into waiting trucks.

While the entire power shovel is complicated, its various parts may be analyzed and separated into just a few simple machines. The six simple machines are the lever, the pulley, the wheel and axle, the inclined plane, the screw, and the wedge. We shall study them in this unit.

After you have learned about the simple machines, you will find it easy, with the help of the Trans-Vision insert which follows page 248, to analyze this complicated power shovel and to pick out the simple machines of which it is composed.

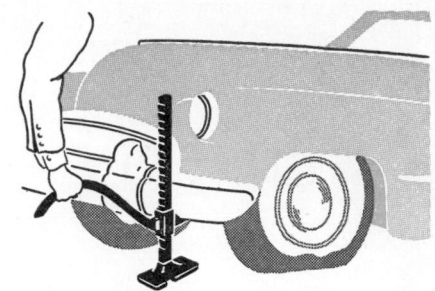

Chapter 11

Machines

1. GENERAL PRINCIPLES OF MACHINES

1. Man uses machines for many purposes. From the very earliest times man has used machines to help him in his work. Now we have become dependent on machines for almost every task we perform.

Some machines are used to *transform energy*. A generator transforms mechanical energy into electrical energy. A steam turbine or gas turbine transforms heat energy into mechanical energy. The chemical energy stored in gasoline is transformed into mechanical energy in the engine of our automobile. And electrical energy is transformed into sound energy by the loudspeakers of our radios and TV's.

We use machines to *transfer energy* from one place to another, too. The connecting rods, crankshaft, drive shaft, and rear axle transfer energy from the explosions in the cylinders of an automobile to the tires on the rear wheels. A system of gear wheels transfers the energy of a small electric motor to the hands of a clock. The belts on washing machines, power mowers, and many home workshop outfits transfer energy from an electric or gasoline motor to the working parts of such apparatus.

You do not ordinarily attempt to pull out nails with your fingers. You use a claw hammer as a lever. In or-

Vocabulary

EFFICIENCY. The ratio of useful work to total work.

INCLINED PLANE. A slanted surface.

INPUT. The product of the acting force by the distance it moves.

LEVER (*lev*-er). A rigid bar which is free to turn about a fixed point.

MECHANICAL ADVANTAGE. The ratio of the resisting weight to the acting force; or, the ratio of the distance through which the force is exerted divided by the distance the weight is raised.

OUTPUT. The product of the resisting weight by the distance it moves.

PULLEY. A wheel which turns readily on an axle mounted in a frame.

SCREW. An inclined plane wound on a cylinder.

WATER TURBINE. A device for changing the potential energy of water into the kinetic energy of a rotating shaft.

WEDGE. A double inclined plane.

WHEEL AND AXLE. A wheel or crank rigidly attached to an axle.

der to raise the frame of an automobile to change a wheel and tire, you use a jack. If a garage mechanic wishes to lift the motor out of an automobile, he can use a system of pulleys to make the job easier. In all these cases, a machine multiplies the force we exert. *An important use of machines is to multiply force.* But when we multiply force, we increase the time required to do the job. *We gain force at the sacrifice of time or speed.*

A bicycle is a machine which is used to gain speed. We gain speed by exerting additional force. When we try to ride a bicycle up a steep hill, we soon realize that we gain speed at the expense of force. It is impossible to gain both force and speed at the same time. *Machines may be used to multiply speed.*

Machines have still another use. We usually raise a flag on a pole by means of a rope threaded through a pulley at the top of the pole. We attach the flag to hooks on the rope near the ground. Then by pulling on the rope, we raise the flag. The single pulley at the top of the pole does not multiply force. It does not multiply speed, either. Its purpose is to change the direction of the downward force which we exert into an upward force which raises the flag. *A machine can be used to change the direction of a force.*

2. There are six simple machines. These are the *lever,* the *pulley,* the *wheel and axle,* the *inclined plane,* the *screw,* and the *wedge.* Other machines are either modifications of one of these simple machines or combinations of two or more of them. It is quite easy to show that the pulley and the wheel and axle are really levers.

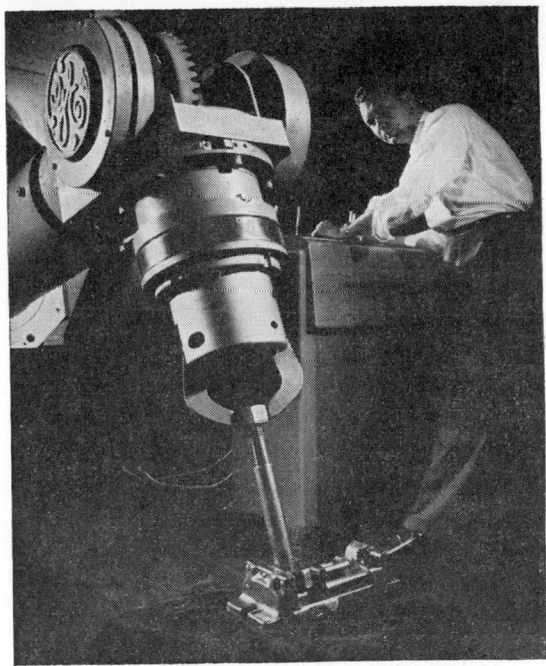

Fig. 11-1. Engineers have invented this machine to work in radioactive areas where human hands can not work without harm. While designed to perform heavy tasks, this overhead manipulator can also do a delicate job of tightening a nut on a bolt, as shown in the photograph.

The wedge and screw are inclined planes.

3. What is mechanical advantage? In Section 17, Chapter 3, we learned that a machine has a mechanical advantage of 5 if by its use, a force of 1 pound can counterbalance a weight of 5 pounds. There are two ways to find the mechanical advantage of a simple machine. (1) By using a spring balance, the acting force, F, can be measured. The weight being raised, w, can be measured in the same manner. Then the mechanical advantage equals w/F, provided friction is neglected. (2) With a meter stick or similar measuring instrument we may measure the distance the acting force moves, s_F. We may also measure the distance the resisting weight is raised, s_w. Then the mechanical advantage equals s_F/s_w. Thus it is seen that **mechanical advantage** *is the ratio of the resisting weight to the acting force; or, the ratio of the distance through which the force is exerted divided by the distance the weight is raised.*

4. The input and output of a machine. In Section 3 we derived two statements for the mechanical advantage of a machine. These two statements are equal. Consequently,

$$\frac{w}{F} = \frac{s_F}{s_w},$$

and, by transposing terms,

$$F \times s_F = w \times s_w.$$

In all frictionless machines, the acting force multiplied by the distance through which this force moves equals the resisting weight multiplied by the distance through which this weight moves.

The acting force times the distance it moves equals the work put into the machine. This work is called the **input.** *The resisting weight times the distance it moves equals the work accomplished by the machine. This work is called the* **output.**

5. What is efficiency? If you move a load of sand from one place to another with a wheelbarrow, you not only have to exert enough force to move the sand, but you have to exert enough force to move the wheelbarrow as well.

SAMPLE PROBLEM

A force of 40 lb moves through a distance of 20 ft in lifting a weight of 180 lb to a height of 4 ft. What is the efficiency?

SOLUTION

The useful work of lifting the 180-lb weight to a height of 4 ft is 180 lb × 4 ft = 720 ft-lb.

The total work performed by the force of 40 lb moving a distance of 20 ft is 40 lb × 20 ft = 800 ft-lb.

The efficiency is therefore $720/800 = 0.90$. Expressed in percentage, $0.90 = 90\%$.

SAMPLE PROBLEM

A machine has a mechanical advantage of 5. But a force of 25 lb is actually required to support a weight of 100 lb. What is the efficiency of this machine?

SOLUTION

Theoretically, a force of 100 lb ÷ 5, or 20 lb should be needed to support this weight. The efficiency of the machine is thus 20 ÷ 25 or 80%.

Moving the wheelbarrow from one place to another is *extra, wasted* work. No machine ever runs without some friction. Overcoming this friction wastes work, too. Consequently, the work we put into a machine is always greater than the work performed by the machine. We are usually more interested in what a machine actually does than in what it should do theoretically. We are concerned with the useful work that is accomplished. *The* **efficiency** *of a machine is the ratio of* *the useful work accomplished to the* *total work expended.* Or,

$$\text{efficiency} = \frac{\text{useful work}}{\text{total work}}.$$

Efficiency may also be defined as:

efficiency =

$$\frac{\text{actual mechanical advantage}}{\text{theoretical mechanical advantage}}.$$

If a machine has an input of 1000 ft-lb and its useful output is 800 ft-lb, the machine's efficiency is 80%. See Sample Problems on page 222.

---

2. THE LEVER

6. What is a lever? When we pry the lid off a can of paint with a screwdriver, we are using the screwdriver as a lever. The oars of a boat are levers we use to move it through the water. A shovel and a wheelbarrow are other common levers. A **lever** (*lev*-er) consists of a rigid bar which is free to turn about a fixed point called the *fulcrum* (*ful*-krum). The fulcrum is the pivot point. The effort force is exerted upon one lever arm and tends to rotate the lever in one direction. The resisting weight is exerted upon the other lever arm, and tends to rotate the lever in the opposite direction. In studying the lever, we apply the principles learned in Chapter 7 for producing equilibrium.

7. The mechanical advantage of the lever. In Fig. 11-2 the letter F represents the fulcrum of the lever ER. At E the effort force is exerted upon the arm EF and tends to produce *counterclockwise* rotation. The resisting weight, or resistance, acts at R upon the arm RF and tends to produce *clockwise* rotation. If the effort force moves from E to E′ the resistance will move from R to R′. But,

$$\frac{EE'}{RR'} = \frac{EF}{RF}.$$

(Arcs of circles subtended by equal central angles are directly proportional to the radii of the circles.) Consequently, the distance moved by the effort and the distance moved by the resistance are proportional to the

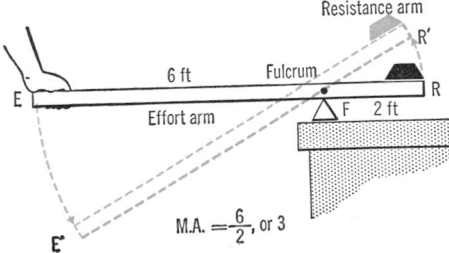

Fig. 11-2. The mechanical advantage of a lever is the length of the effort arm divided by the length of the resistance arm.

First-class levers

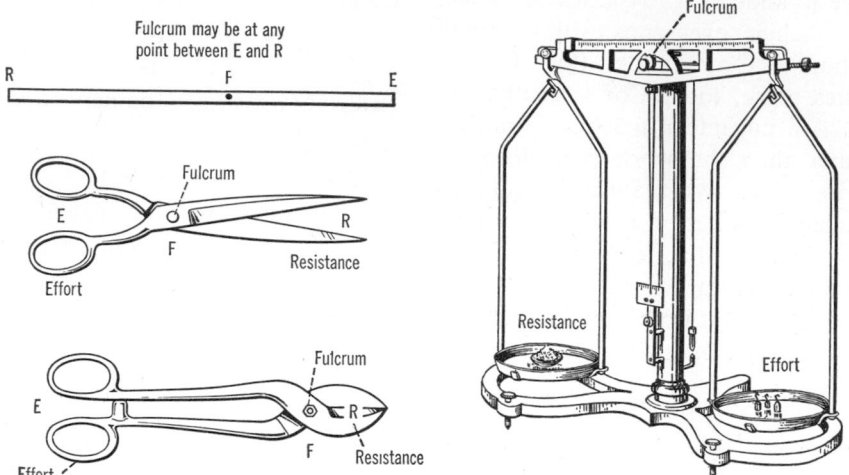

Fig. 11-3. In all first-class levers the fulcrum is located between the effort force and the resisting weight.

Fig. 11-4. In all second-class levers the resisting weight is located between the effort force and the fulcrum.

Second-class levers

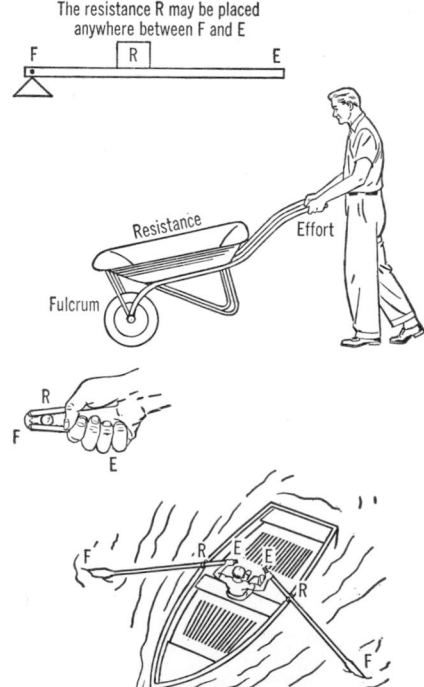

lengths of the lever arms upon which they act or,

$$\frac{s_F}{s_w} = \frac{\text{EF}}{\text{RF}}.$$

But for any frictionless machine,

$$\text{mechanical advantage} = \frac{s_F}{s_w}.$$

Therefore, for all kinds of levers,

$$\text{mechanical advantage} = \frac{\text{EF}}{\text{RF}}.$$

The mechanical advantage of any lever equals the length of the effort arm divided by the length of the resistance arm. If EF is 6 ft long, and RF is only 2 ft long, the mechanical advantage is $6 \div 2 = 3$.

8. The three classes of levers. (1) *First-class lever.* If the effort force acts at one end of a lever, the resisting weight acts at the other end, and the fulcrum is between them, the lever is called a *first-class lever.* See Fig. 11-3. This lever may be used to gain speed, to gain force, or to change direction.

Third-class levers

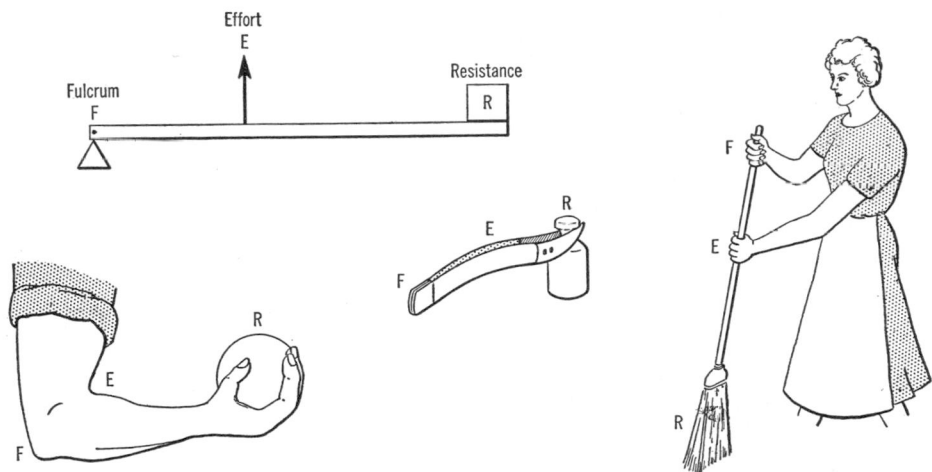

Fig. 11-5. In all third-class levers the effort force is located between the resisting weight and the fulcrum.

If EF is longer than RF, the lever has a mechanical advantage of force. The pump handle shown in Fig. 5-27 is an example of such a lever. Tinner's shears are another example. In these levers, the mechanical advantage is *more than one* because the effort arm is longer than the resistance arm.

Sometimes a first-class lever is used to gain speed. In such levers, the effort arm is shorter than the resistance arm. The mechanical advantage of force for such a lever is a *fraction between zero and one*. Ordinary scissors or tailer's shears are examples of first-class levers used to gain speed.

(2) *Second-class lever.* Sometimes the effort force is applied at one end of a lever and the fulcrum is at the other end. The resisting weight is placed between the effort and the fulcrum. This is a *second-class lever.* See Fig. 11-4. In a wheelbarrow, the axle of the wheel is the fulcrum. The effort force is applied at the ends of the handles. The load or resisting weight is placed between the fulcrum and the effort. Since the effort arm of a second-class lever is the *entire* lever, and the resistance arm is only a *part* of the lever, EF is always greater than RF. The mechanical advantage of a second-class lever is always *more than one*.

(3) *Third-class lever.* If the resisting weight is applied at one end of a lever, the fulcrum is located at the other end, and the effort force is applied between the two, then the lever is of the *third class.* See Fig. 11-5. Our forearm is a third-class lever. The resisting weight will be in our hand. Our elbow acts as the fulcrum. The tendons attached to the bones of the forearm just below the elbow exert the effort force. In third-class levers, the resistance arm is longer than the effort arm. Consequently, such a lever may be used to gain speed. The mechanical advantage of force of a third-

class lever is always a fraction between zero and one. The force we exert will be greater than the resistance we move. A broom, a shovel, or a garden fork with which we turn over the soil may be used as third-class levers. However, sometimes we use these particular im-plements so that they are first-class levers.

9. How is a lever affected by its own weight? So far, we have not considered the weight of the levers we have been using. But in any practical situation, we must take the weight of

---

SAMPLE PROBLEM

In Fig. 11-6 the uniform bar, ER, is 12 ft long. It weighs 60 lb. At R, 2 ft from the fulcrum, there is a resisting weight, w, of 500 lb. What effort force, F, must be applied at E to produce equilibrium?

SOLUTION

For equilibrium, the clockwise torque must equal the sum of the counter-clockwise torques.

The clockwise resistance torque is 300 lb × 2 ft = 600 lb-ft. The effort torque acts counterclockwise. It will be x lb × 10 ft = 10x lb-ft. The weight of the lever, acting at the center of gravity of the lever, 4 ft from the fulcrum, also produces a counterclockwise torque. This torque is 60 lb × 4 ft = 240 lb-ft. Setting the clockwise torque equal to the sum of the counterclockwise torques, we have, 600 lb-ft = 10x lb-ft + 240 lb-ft.

Solving, x = 36 lb, the effort force needed.

SAMPLE PROBLEM

Fig. 11-7 represents a second-class lever 12 ft long. The lever is uniform, and weighs 60 lb. What effort must be applied at the end of the lever to balance a weight of 300 lb placed 2 ft from the fulcrum?

SOLUTION

In order to secure equilibrium, the clockwise torque must equal the sum of the counterclockwise torques.

The clockwise torque will be produced by the effort acting at the end of the lever. It will be x lb × 12 ft = 12x lb-ft. The counterclockwise torque pro-duced by the 300-lb weight is 300 lb × 2 ft = 600 lb-ft. The weight of the lever acting at the center of gravity also produces a counterclockwise torque, 60 lb × 6 ft = 360 lb-ft. Next we set the clockwise torque equal to the sum of the counterclockwise torques, 12x lb-ft = 600 lb-ft + 360 lb-ft.

Solving, x = 80 lb, the effort force needed to produce equilibrium.

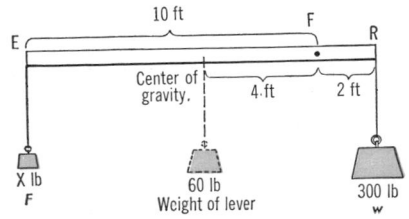

Fig. 11-6. The weight of this lever acts as a counterclockwise force and aids the effort force. See the Sample Problem at the top of page 226.

the lever into account. *The weight of a lever acts as if it, the weight, were all concentrated at the center of gravity of the lever.*

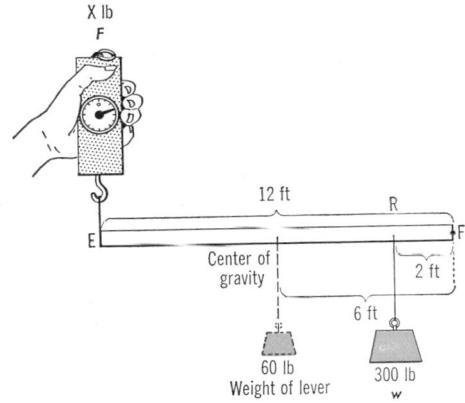

Fig. 11-7. The weight of this lever acts as a counterclockwise force and hinders the effort force.

QUESTIONS

GROUP A

1. Which of the following machines transform energy from one form to another, and which merely transfer energy from one spot to another: (1) electric motor; (2) gear wheels in a watch; (3) fan belt and pulleys in an automobile engine; (4) gasoline engine on a lawn mower; (5) the drive shaft, differential gears, and rear axle of an automobile?

2. What changes in the magnitude or direction of a force can be produced by machines? Give an example of a machine which produces each type of change.

3. If a machine is used to gain speed, what is necessarily lost?

4. What are the six simple machines? Into what two general classes may they be grouped?

5. What is "useful work"? What is "total work"? How do we determine the efficiency of a machine?

6. What is the position of the effort force, the fulcrum, and the resisting weight in each of the following: (1) a claw hammer used for pulling nails, Fig. 11-8; (2) the oar of a rowboat; (3) forceps used for handling small weights; (4) your lower jaw; (5) a see-saw?

7. In what two ways may we calculate the mechanical advantage of a lever?

8. Why is it impossible to gain speed by using a second-class lever?

9. How is a first-class lever used to gain a mechanical advantage of force? How is it used to gain a mechanical advantage of speed?

10. How is a mechanical advantage of speed obtained with a third-class lever?

GROUP B

11. What are the two general ways of determining the mechanical advantage of a machine? Which is the more accurate method for determining the theoretical mechanical advantage?

12. Can a machine have an efficiency greater than 100%? Explain.

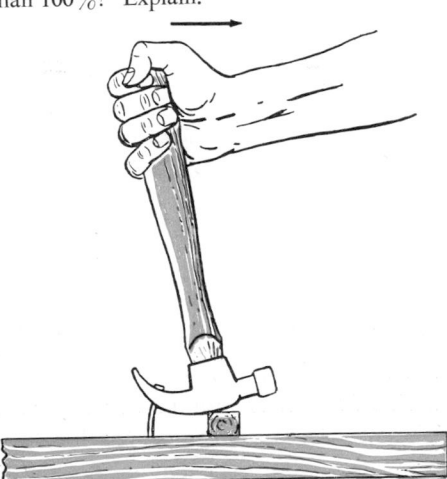

Fig. 11-8. Where are the effort, resistance, and fulcrum located in this lever?

PROBLEMS

(In the Mathematics Refresher, refer to Sections 6, 10, and 16.)

GROUP A

1. What is the mechanical advantage of a machine in which an acting force of 50 lb counterbalances a resisting weight of 250 lb?

2. In a certain machine the acting force moves 25 cm in order to move a resisting weight 7.5 cm. What is the mechanical advantage?

3. What is the efficiency of a machine which has an input of 400 ft-lb, and an output of 300 ft-lb?

4. The mechanical advantage of a certain machine is 6. However, a force of 25 lb is required in order to raise a weight of 100 lb. What is the efficiency of the machine?

5. A screwdriver is used as a first-class lever to pry the lid off a can of paint. The distance from the edge of the blade to the pivot point against the rim of the can is $\frac{1}{4}$ in, while an effort of 3 lb is exerted 8 in from this pivot point. What force is prying the lid from the can?

6. John must use a force of 50 lb in order to lift the handles of a loaded wheelbarrow. The handles are 4 ft long. If the loaded wheelbarrow weighs 150 lb, how far is its center of gravity from the wheel? What is the mechanical advantage of this wheelbarrow?

7. Paul's forearm is 14 in long. If the muscle is attached 2 in below the elbow, what force must he exert to lift a baseball which weighs 5 oz? What is the mechanical advantage of speed of this forearm?

8. An oar is 12 ft long, with the oarlock 2 ft from the handle. What is the mechanical advantage? If a force of 20 lb is used on each of a pair of such oars, what force will move the boat through the water?

GROUP B

9. A force of 15 nt moves through a distance of 2 m while raising a mass of 5 kg to a height of 0.25 m. What is the efficiency?

10. A plank 5 m long is used as a first-class lever. The fulcrum is 2 m from the resistance. What is the mechanical advantage of this lever? What force, in newtons, is needed to counterbalance a mass of 10 kg which is used as the resistance?

11. A fishing rod is 12 ft long. It weighs 5 lb, and its center of gravity is 2 ft from the handle. If you place one hand at the end of the rod to act as a fulcrum, and place the other hand 1 ft away to act as the effort force, what force is required to pull a 10-lb fish out of the water?

12. A gangplank is 25 ft long and weighs 200 lb. It is resting on the end of a pier with 5 ft of its length extending out over the water. A man who weighs 175 lb walks out on the gangplank, and stands at the far end. Now suppose another man, weighing 175 lb, walks out on the plank to join the first man. How far out from the pier can he walk before the gangplank starts to tip over?

---

3. THE PULLEY

10. What is a pulley? The simple machine called the **pulley** *consists of a wheel which turns readily on an axle, which in turn is mounted in a frame.* The wheel is usually grooved for rope or wire cable. The frame, or block, may be metal or wood. Also, two or more wheels may be mounted in the same frame. They also may be mounted on the same axle, as in Fig. 11-9, or on different axles, as in Fig. 11-10. When two or more wheels are mounted in the same block, the pulley is said to have two or more *sheaves*. For the sake of clearness, pulleys of the type shown in Fig. 11-10 will be

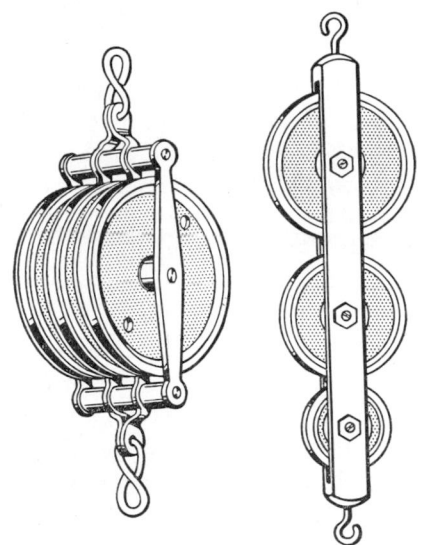

Fig. 11-9. Left. A usual type of pulley with three sheaves all on the same axle.
Fig. 11-10. Right. A pulley with three sheaves, each on a different axle.

used in diagrams, although those of the type shown in Fig. 11-9 are more often used in actual practice.

11. Uses of pulleys. The cords that support a window sash pass over fixed pulleys in the window frame. Pulleys are used with ropes for raising flags, awnings, and Venetian blinds. Painters use pulleys to raise or lower scaffolding needed when working on buildings. An elevator cable passes over a pulley to a drum upon which the cable is wound as the elevator is lifted.

12. A single fixed pulley is a first-class lever. Fig. 11-11 shows a single fixed pulley. This pulley acts like a first-class lever, EFR. But EF equals RF, so its mechanical advantage is one. When an effort force of 1 lb, F, pulls downward through a distance of 1 ft, a resisting weight of 1 lb, w, is raised 1 ft. A single fixed pulley gains neither force nor speed. Such a pulley

only changes the direction in which a force is applied.

13. A single movable pulley is a second-class lever. A single movable pulley is shown in Fig. 11-12. The effort force, F, acts upon the arm EF, which is the *diameter* of the pulley. The resisting weight, w, acts upon the arm RF, which is the radius of the pulley. Since the diameter is twice the radius, the mechanical advantage of a single movable pulley is two. When the effort, F, moves 2 ft, the resistance, w, is lifted 1 ft. If we fasten both ends of the cord, it is obvious that each cord must support one-half the weight.

14. Pulley combinations. Many different combinations of fixed and movable pulleys are possible. We shall consider two cases. In both of these the cord or rope is continuous. The effort force is applied to one end of the cord. The other end of the cord may be attached either to the movable block or to the fixed block.

(1) *To the movable block.* Such an arrangement of pulleys is shown in Fig. 11-13. One end of the cord is

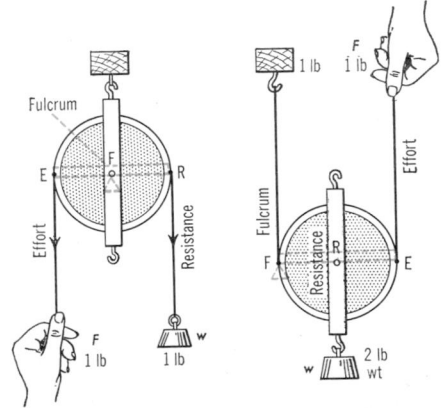

Fig. 11-11. Left. The mechanical advantage of a single fixed pulley is one.
Fig. 11-12. Right. The mechanical advantage of a single movable pulley is two.

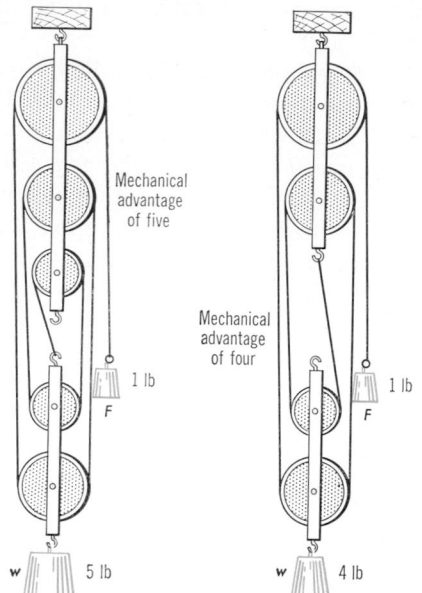

Fig. 11-13. Left. Five strands support the movable block.

Fig. 11-14. Right. Four strands support the movable block.

attached to the movable block, then passes over a fixed pulley, and so on.

The effort force F must pull downward a distance of 5 ft to lift the resisting weight w a height of 1 ft. Therefore the mechanical advantage is 5, which is exactly *equal to the number of strands supporting the movable block.* The strand of cord on which the effort force acts *does not support* the movable block. It does not increase the mechanical advantage, but is used to change the direction of the effort force.

(2) *To the fixed block.* In Fig. 11-14, one end of the cord is attached to the fixed block. The number of strands now supporting the movable block is four. The last strand, on which the effort force acts, does not support the movable block. It is used to change the direction of the effort force.

If we let the letter n represent the number of strands which support the movable block in a pulley system, the pulley formula becomes

$$nF = w.$$

4. THE WHEEL AND AXLE

15. What is a wheel and axle? The simple machine called the **wheel and axle** *consists of a wheel or crank which is rigidly attached to an axle.* They make the same number of revolutions per second.

In Fig. 11-15 we have two wheels of unequal diameter which are fastened so they turn together around the axis, F. In one revolution, the acting force, F, moves a distance equal to the circumference, C, of the wheel. During this time, the resistance, w, will travel a distance equal to the circumference, c, of the axle. Since $s_F = C$, and $s_w = c$,

$$\text{mechanical advantage} = \frac{C}{c}.$$

We may also use the following expressions for the mechanical advantage of the wheel and axle:

$$\text{mechanical advantage} = \frac{D}{d}, \text{ or}$$

$$\text{mechanical advantage} = \frac{R}{r}.$$

In these expressions, D is the diameter of the wheel, d is the diameter of the axle, R is the radius of the wheel, and r is the radius of the axle. We may use these expressions because the diameter or radius of a wheel is directly proportional to its circumference.

See the Sample Problem below.

16. Applications of the wheel and axle. The steering wheel and the rear driving wheels of an automobile are applications of the wheel and axle. Doorknobs, faucet handles, and gas valves are further examples of the wheel and axle. In the kitchen we find the wheel and axle applied to such a device as the egg beater.

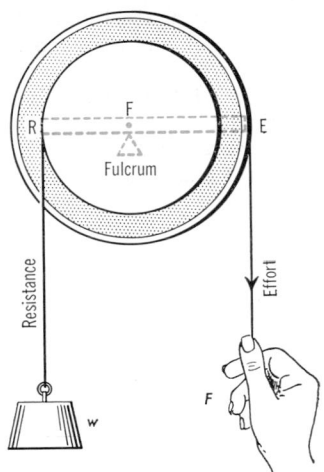

Fig. 11-15. The wheel and axle is similar to a lever with unequal arms.

SAMPLE PROBLEM

A wheel having a diameter of 2 ft is attached to an axle which has a diameter of 4 in. If a weight of 600 lb is attached to the axle, what force must be applied to the rim of the wheel to produce equilibrium?

SOLUTION

The mechanical advantage of this wheel and axle equals D/d.

In order to have both diameters measured in the same units, we change the diameter of the wheel, 2 feet, to inches. 2 ft $\times$ 12 in/ft = 24 in.

The mechanical advantage will be 24 in $\div$ 4 in = 6. With a mechanical advantage of 6, a force of 600 lb $\div$ 6 = 100 lb must be applied to the rim of the wheel.

PROBLEMS

(In the Mathematics Refresher, refer to Sections 6, 10, 12, and 16.)

GROUP A

1. Make a diagram showing how a system of fixed and movable pulleys may be used to raise a weight of 10 lb by exerting a force of 2 lb.

2. Show by a diagram how you would connect a single-sheave and a double-sheave pulley to obtain the highest possible mechanical advantage.

3. A block and tackle is to be used to raise a load weighing 400 lb. If the maximum force which can be exerted is 125 lb, at least how many strands of rope must support the movable block?

4. Robert and Paul are using a windlass to raise a weight of 1500 lb. The radius of the wheel is 1 ft and the radius of the axle is 1.5 in. What is the mechanical advantage? If each boy exerts an equal force, how much force must each apply?

5. What is the mechanical advantage of a

screwdriver, used as a wheel and axle, if its blade is 0.35 in wide and the handle is 1.40 inches in diameter?

6. A crank handle is 8 in long. It is attached to a shaft which has a radius of 0.5 in. What is the mechanical advantage? If a force of 40 lb is exerted on the crank handle, what weight may be raised?

7. A block and tackle is arranged so that 6 strands support the movable block. How much force must be exerted in order to raise a load weighing 540 lb?

8. A wrench is being used to tighten a bolt. The head of the bolt is square, and is 0.5 inch on a side. The handle of the wrench is 10 in long. If a force of 25 lb is exerted at the end of the wrench handle, what force is being used to tighten the bolt?

GROUP B

9. Three strands are used to support the movable block in a block-and-tackle system. If 60 lb of force are needed to lift a weight of 150 lb, what is the efficiency of this system?

10. A force of 100 lb is exerted on the rope of a block and tackle, and the rope is pulled in 30 ft. This work causes a weight of 500 lb to be raised 5 ft. What work was put into this machine? What was the output? What was the

theoretical mechanical advantage? The actual mechanical advantage? The efficiency?

● **11.** The theoretical mechanical advantage of a system of pulleys is 4. George raises a weight of 200 lb by pulling 100 ft of rope through his hands with a force of 55 lb in 5.5 sec. What was the horsepower input? The horsepower output? The efficiency?

● **12.** A force of 100 lb is exerted by each of two men in turning a wheel 20 inches in diameter. The force is exerted on the circumference of the wheel. If the radius of the axle is 2 in, what load can they raise? If they each work at the rate of 0.10 hp, how long will it take to raise this load 50 ft?

● **13.** The length of the crank handle on a windlass is 10 in. The diameter of the axle is 1 in. What is the mechanical advantage? If a force of 50 lb on the crank handle can raise a load of 600 lb, what is the efficiency of this windlass?

● **14.** The handle of a crank can opener is 4 inches long. Attached to the same axle as this crank is a toothed wheel which presses against the rim of the can and causes the can to turn while being opened. The diameter of the toothed wheel is 0.5 inch in diameter. If a force of 5 lb is applied to the crank, how much work must be done in opening a can which has a top 3 inches in diameter? If done in 5 sec, what horsepower was expended?

---

5. THE INCLINED PLANE

17. The inclined plane. When we wish to increase the height or elevation of an object without exerting the force to lift it vertically, we use an **inclined plane;** *that is, a slanted surface.* Barrels may be rolled up an inclined plank in order to load them onto a truck. When a power shovel is to be transported by trailer to a new construction job, an inclined plane of heavy timbers is built at the rear of the trailer. The shovel can then run onto the trailer under its own power. We build inclined ramps instead of

stairs in stadiums and large auditoriums. They are safer, and people can move along them more rapidly. In parking garages, an attendant drives

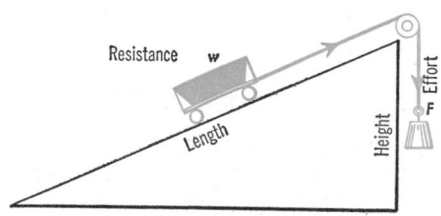

Fig. 11-16. The mechanical advantage of this inclined plane is the length of the plane divided by its height.

SAMPLE PROBLEM

An inclined plane is 18 ft long and 2 ft high. Neglecting friction, what force will be required to slide a weight of 2000 lb up the plane?

SOLUTION NO. 1

We may use the equation $\dfrac{w}{F} = \dfrac{l}{h}$.

By substitution, 2000 lb/F = 18 ft/2 ft.

Solving, F = 222.2 lb, the force required.

SOLUTION NO. 2

The mechanical advantage of this inclined plane is $\dfrac{l}{h}$.

18 ft ÷ 2 ft = 9, the mechanical advantage.

With a mechanical advantage of 9, the force required to move a resistance of 2000 lb will be 2000 lb ÷ 9. This equals 222.2 lb, the force required.

---

your car up an inclined plane to the upper storage floors.

When an inclined plane is used, less force is required to move the resisting weight up the slanted surface than to lift it vertically. However, the force must be applied over the entire length of the plane in order to raise the load the height of the plane, *if the force is applied parallel to the plane.* See Fig. 11-16. Since s_F is the length, l, of the plane, and s_w is the height, h,

$$\text{mechanical advantage} = \frac{l}{h}.$$

Theoretically, 1 lb of force will push a weight of 5 lb up an inclined plane 20 ft long and 4 ft high.

$$\frac{w}{F} = \frac{l}{h}.$$

See Sample Problem above.

Fig. 11-17. In order to conquer the grade encountered in constructing a railroad across the Allegheny Mountains this long, inclined Horseshoe Curve was built.

In certain cases, the force may be applied *parallel to the base of the plane.* If *b* represents the base of the plane, then,

$$\text{mechanical advantage} = \frac{b}{h}.$$

★ **18. What is meant by " grade "?** The advantage of an inclined plane becomes greater as the slope is made more gradual. Engineers use the term " grade " to express the ratio of the height of an incline to its length. A road which rises 5 ft in 100 ft of its length has a grade of 5%. If it rises 3 ft in 100 ft of its length, its grade is 3%. A grade of 3% is about the maximum for a good road.

6. THE WEDGE

19. What is a wedge? *The wedge is really a double inclined plane.* See Fig. 11-18. There is so much friction in using a wedge that a theoretical mechanical advantage is of no significance. A wedge which is long in proportion to its thickness is easier to drive. Consequently, we may say that its mechanical advantage depends upon the ratio of its length to its thickness.

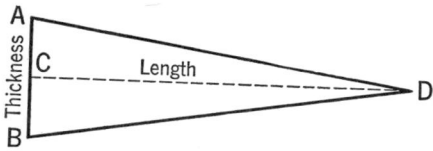

Fig. 11-18. The wedge is a double inclined plane.

A wedge is used for various purposes. An ax or hatchet may be used for chopping or splitting wood. Nails, pins, and needles act as wedges when they are pushed or driven through some resisting objects.

7. THE SCREW

20. What type of machine is a screw? Let us cut a sheet of paper in the shape of a right triangle and wind it on a pencil, as shown in Fig. 11-19. This reveals that *a* **screw** *is really an inclined plane wound upon a cylinder.* The distance between the threads is called the *pitch* of the screw. The effort force is often applied at one end of a lever which is set in the head of the screw. It may also be applied to a screwdriver set in a groove in the head of the screw. Or it may be applied to a wrench which is attached to the head of the screw. While the effort force describes a complete circle, the head and axis of the screw make one complete turn, and the resistance moves a distance equal to the pitch of the screw. If *r* is the length of the lever arm upon which the force *F* acts, then, for one revolution, s_F equals $2\pi r$. As *F* moves this distance, the resisting weight *w* moves the distance

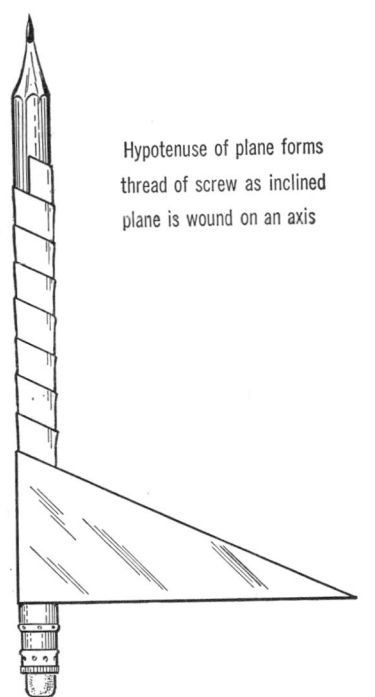

Fig. 11-19. The screw is an inclined plane wound on an axis.

Hypotenuse of plane forms thread of screw as inclined plane is wound on an axis

21. The uses of the screw. Bolts, nuts, and screws of all kinds are examples of this simple machine. When the threads on a bolt are cut so that the nut must be turned in a clockwise direction as it is tightened, the screw is said to be a right-handed one. When the nut must be turned in a counterclockwise direction to tighten it, the screw or thread is said to be left-handed. Examples of right and left-handed threads are shown in Fig. 11-21. A carpenter's or machinist's vise is an example of a screw. The jackscrew, which is used for lifting buildings and other heavy objects, is a screw having a very high mechanical advantage.

For measuring the thickness of paper and foil, or for finding the diameter of a wire, or for measuring precisely machined parts, a fine-threaded screw is used. Such a screw is contained in a *micrometer* (my-*krom*-uh-ter) *caliper*. The handle of the caliper, which is actually the head of the screw, may be divided into 25 parts, as shown in Fig. 11-22. The threads of the screw of this micrometer are 0.025 in apart. Consequently, when the head is turned

d, which is the pitch of the screw. But d is s_w. Consequently,

$$\text{mechanical advantage} = \frac{s_F}{s_w} = \frac{2\pi r}{d}.$$

SAMPLE PROBLEM

The lever of a screw is 21 in long. If the screw has 4 threads to the inch, find the mechanical advantage of this machine. Neglecting friction, what force is needed to lift 40,000 lb?

SOLUTION

Since there are 4 threads to the inch, the pitch of the screw is $\frac{1}{4}$ in, or 0.25 in.

Substituting in the formula, mechanical advantage $= \dfrac{2\pi r}{d}$, we obtain

$$\frac{2 \times 3.14 \times 21 \text{ in}}{0.25 \text{ in}} = 527.5, \text{ the mechanical advantage of this screw.}$$

To lift 40,000 lb, a force of 40,000 lb ÷ 527.5 = 75.65 lb is needed.

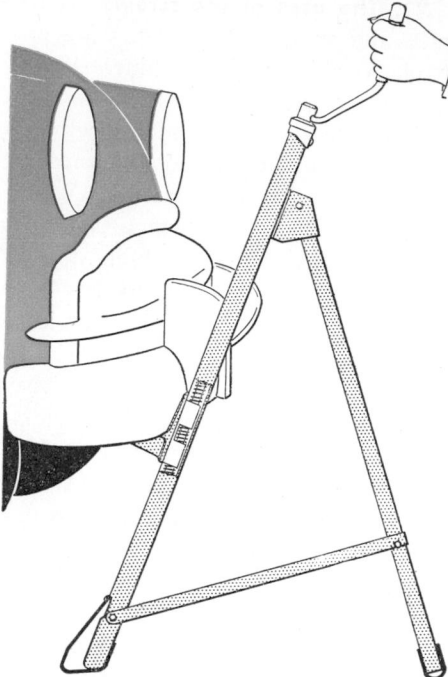

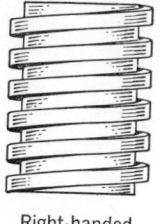
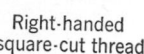

Right-handed
square-cut thread

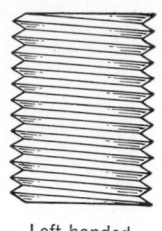

Left-handed
V-cut thread

Fig. 11-20. This automobile bumper jack is an application of the screw. As the crank is turned in a clockwise direction, the automobile is raised. When the crank is turned counterclockwise, the automobile is lowered.

Fig. 11-21. Examples of right- and left-handed screws. Square-cut and V-cut threads.

from one division to the next, the caliper is opened or closed by 0.001 in.

22. How efficient are the simple machines? It is impossible to make any machine 100% efficient because we can not totally eliminate either the friction or the weight of the parts of the machine. In the various types of levers the efficiency may be nearly 100%. Friction is small, but the weight of the lever may lower the efficiency. The efficiency of the block and tackle is usually not more than 60%. The rigidity of the ropes, the friction of the sheaves, and the weight of the movable block are all factors which tend to reduce the efficiency of this simple machine. If the surface of an inclined plane is very smooth and hard, the efficiency of the plane may be as high as 80%. Friction plays such an important part in the use of the wedge that it is almost impossible to estimate its efficiency. While the jackscrew has a high mechanical advantage, friction, however, is so great that the efficiency may be no more than 25%.

QUESTIONS

GROUP A

1. Explain why a single fixed pulley acts as a first-class lever.

2. Use a diagram to show how a single movable pulley is similar to a second-class lever.

3. How is the theoretical mechanical advantage of a pulley system determined?

4. Which of the wheels of a bicycle is an application of the wheel and axle? Why?

5. Why are sloping ramps easier to climb than a flight of stairs?

6. Why is it impractical to calculate a theoretical mechanical advantage for a wedge?

7. What is meant by the expression "pitch of a screw"?

8. Show how the wedge and the screw are actually applications of the inclined plane.

9. Why is the efficiency of the automobile bumper jack, shown in Fig. 11-20, rather low?

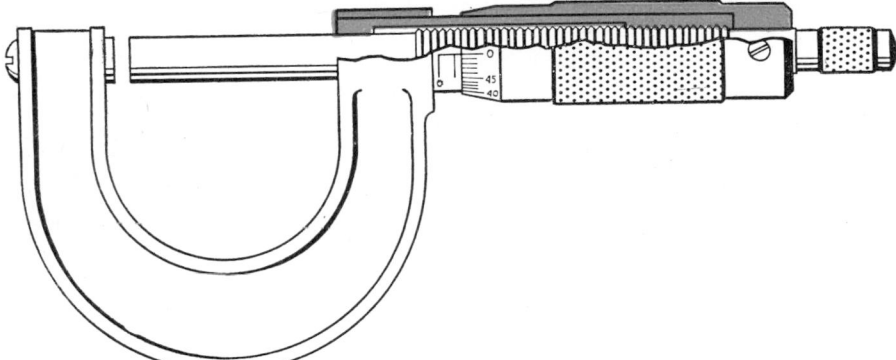

Fig. 11-22. The accuracy of a micrometer depends on a precisely threaded screw.

10. What factors lower the efficiency of a block and tackle?

GROUP B

11. The mechanical advantage of a wheel and axle is the ratio of the circumference of the wheel to the circumference of the axle. Prove that the mechanical advantage is also the ratio of the diameter of the wheel to the diameter of the axle. Prove that the mechanical advantage is also the ratio of the radius of the wheel to the radius of the axle.

★ **12.** The maximum grade on a highway is 1.8%. What does this mean?

PROBLEMS

(In the Mathematics Refresher, refer to Sections 6, 7, 8, 10, 11, and 16.)

GROUP A

1. The raised end of an inclined plane 12 ft long is 3 ft high. What is the mechanical advantage of this inclined plane? What force, if we should neglect friction, is required to roll a steel drum weighing 150 lb up this inclined plane?

2. An inclined plane 20 ft long has one end 5 ft higher than the other. What is the theoretical mechanical advantage? If 60 lb of force must be exerted to pull a loaded wagon up the plane, what is the combined weight of the wagon and its load?

3. What mechanical advantage is obtained by using a wrench with a 6-in handle to tighten bolts having 16 threads to the inch?

4. What is the mechanical advantage of a small jackscrew which has 10 threads to the inch if the lever arm is 5 in long? What weight may be raised if a force of 25 lb is exerted at the end of the lever arm?

GROUP B

5. A plank 13 ft long is used as an inclined plane to a platform 5 ft high. What force, neglecting friction, must be used to keep a block of ice weighing 195 lb from sliding down the plank? If the coefficient of friction is 0.1, what force then must be used to keep the block from sliding down? What force must be used to push the block up the plank?

6. A ramp 100 ft long connects two floors in a parking garage. If 300 lb of force are required to push an automobile weighing 1.5 tons up the ramp, what is the vertical distance between the floors?

● **7.** A jackscrew has a lever arm 2 ft long. The screw has 3.5 threads to the inch. If 50 lb of force must be exerted in order to raise a load of 6 tons, calculate the efficiency.

● **8.** A housemover's jackscrew, exerting a force of 11 tons on a house, can raise one corner 6 inches in 10 minutes. If the efficiency of this jackscrew is 30%, what is the work output? The work input? The horsepower output? The horsepower input?

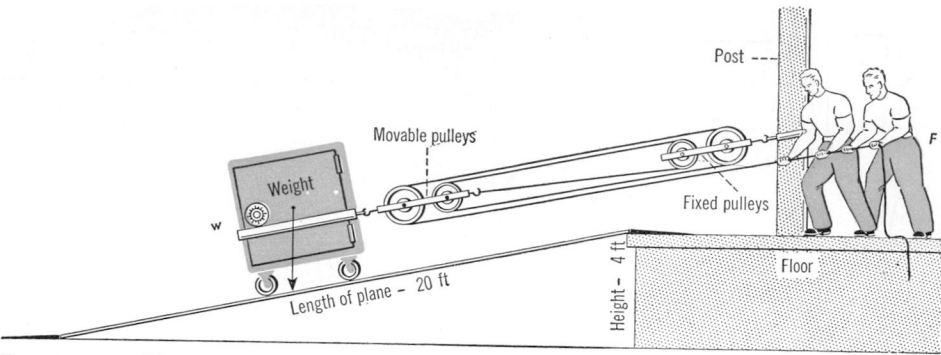

Fig. 11-23. The mechanical advantage of a compound machine is usually the product of the mechanical advantages of the simple machines of which it is composed. What is the mechanical advantage of this compound machine?

8. COMPOUND MACHINES

⭐ **23. What is a compound machine?** Many complicated-looking machines are just combinations of two or more simple machines. A food chopper has a crank which works on the principle of the wheel and axle. The crank turns a screw which forces the food through small holes, where it is chopped off by the wedge action of a cutting disc. *Such a combination of two or more simple machines is called a compound machine.*

Fig. 11-23 shows a safe which weighs 4000 lb. We wish to move it onto a raised floor 4 ft above the lower level. An inclined walk 20 ft long leads onto the raised floor. The mechanical advantage of the inclined plane is 20 ft ÷ 4 ft = 5. But this means that we still have to exert a force of 400 lb ÷ 5 = 80 lb to pull the safe up the walk. If we attach the movable block of a block and tackle to the safe, and the fixed block to the post, we have a pulley system which

has a mechanical advantage of 5. (Five strands support the movable block.) Now a force of 800 lb ÷ 5 = 160 lb must be applied to the rope to pull the safe up the incline. The combined mechanical advantage of the two machines is 5 × 5, or 25. *In nearly all cases of compound machines, the total mechanical advantage is the product of the separate mechanical advantages.* If one machine

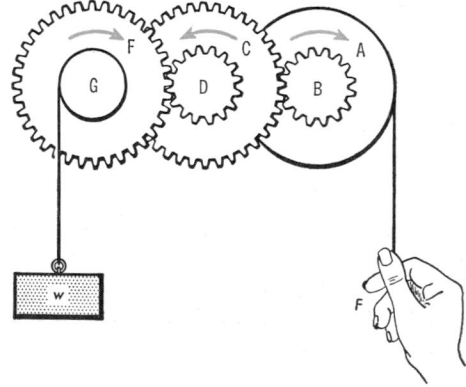

Fig. 11-24. A train of gear wheels.

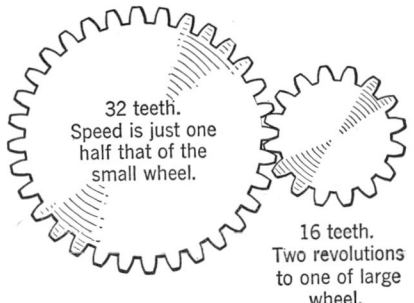

32 teeth.
Speed is just one half that of the small wheel.

16 teeth.
Two revolutions to one of large wheel.

Fig. 11-25. Gear wheels of different diameters are used to vary speed.

multiplies the effort force by 5 and a second machine multiplies it again by 5, then both acting together will multiply it by 25.

★ **24. Combinations of gear wheels.** Fig. 11-24 shows several gear wheels in combination. This device is usually called a train of gear wheels. It has a high mechanical advantage. The effort force is applied at A, which makes one revolution in the same time as its axle B. But wheel C makes only that fraction of a revolution which is equal to

$$\frac{\text{number of cogs in } B}{\text{number of cogs in } C}.$$

The wheel G, too, will revolve only a fraction as rapidly as D. The wheels

A and H are essentially a wheel and axle. Therefore, the total mechanical advantage equals

$$\frac{\text{radius of } A}{\text{radius of } H} \times \frac{\text{no. of cogs in } C}{\text{no. of cogs in } B}$$
$$\times \frac{\text{no. of cogs in } G}{\text{no. of cogs in } D}.$$

Gear wheels are used to vary the speed or direction of a twisting force. Suppose a wheel that has 32 gear teeth is meshed with a wheel that has only 16 teeth, as shown in Fig. 11-25. If we apply the effort force to the first one we gain speed, since the second wheel will make two revolutions while the first is making one. If we apply the effort force to the second wheel we gain force, and have a mechanical advantage of 2.

In a bicycle, the sprocket wheels on separate shafts are connected by a chain. In Fig. 11-26 the front sprocket wheel has 28 teeth and the rear one only 7. During one complete revolution of the pedals, the rear wheel of the bicycle will make four complete revolutions.

★ **25. The worm wheel.** A worm wheel is shown in Fig. 11-27. It con-

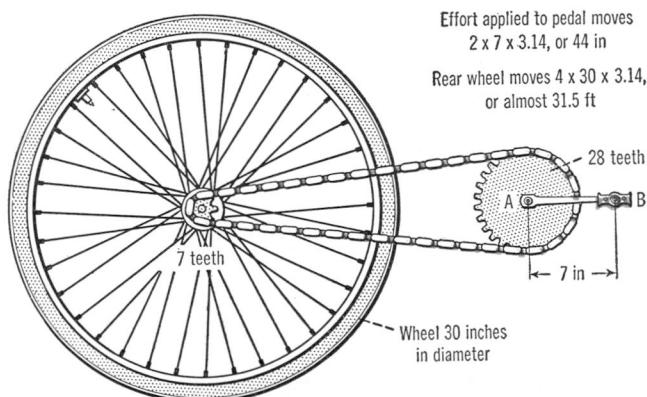

Effort applied to pedal moves
2 x 7 x 3.14, or 44 in

Rear wheel moves 4 x 30 x 3.14, or almost 31.5 ft

28 teeth

A   B

7 in

7 teeth

Wheel 30 inches in diameter

Fig. 11-26. The bicycle has a mechanical advantage of speed.

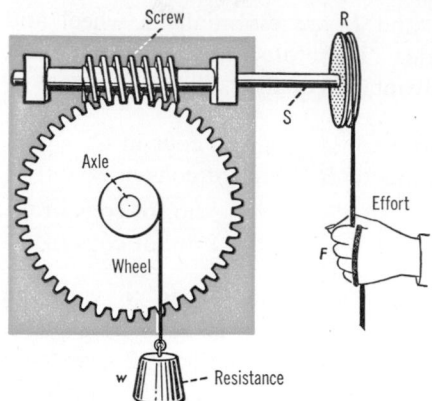

Fig. 11-27. The worm gear has a high mechanical advantage, but friction may lower its efficiency.

sists of an endless screw which is meshed with a gear wheel. The effort force is used to turn the worm wheel. If there are 50 teeth in the gear wheel, one complete turn of the worm will turn the gear through $\frac{1}{50}$ of a revolu-

tion. The resisting weight acts on the axle of the gear wheel. If we let *l* represent the length of the crank lever upon which the effort force acts, and *n* the number of teeth in the gear wheel, with *r* the radius of the axle, the mechanical advantage of the worm wheel equals nl/r.

★ **26. The differential pulley.** This compound machine consists of two wheels of unequal diameter. They are fastened together and turn on the same axle. An endless chain connects the two wheels with a movable pulley. A diagram of a differential pulley is shown in Fig. 11-28. The endless chain is made of links which fit into notches in the rims of the pulley wheels so that the chain will not slip on the wheels.

Suppose the effort force *F* shortens the chain by winding on the wheel *A* a length of chain equal to its circum-

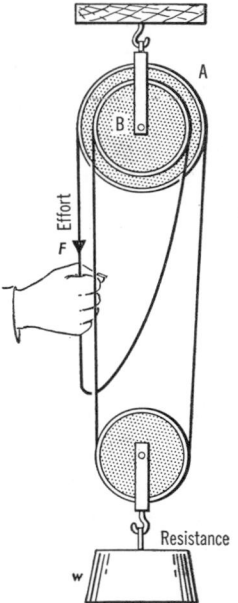

Fig. 11-28. A diagram of a differential pulley.

Fig. 11-29. A commercial differential pulley.

ference C. While this is being done, a length of chain equal to the circumference c of the wheel B will be unwound. The chain is thus shortened a distance equal to $C - c$. The resisting weight, which is attached to the movable pulley, will be lifted a distance equal to $\frac{1}{2}(C - c)$. Therefore s_F equals C, and s_w equals $\frac{1}{2}(C - c)$. The equation will thus become as is shown in the following,

$$\text{mechanical advantage} = \frac{2C}{C - c}.$$

A commercial type of differential pulley is shown is Fig. 11-29. The differential pulley is used in garages, boathouses, and in machine shops for raising heavy objects.

9. THE WATER TURBINE

★ **27. How does a water turbine work?** *The water turbine is a device for transforming the potential energy of a water reservoir into the kinetic energy of a rotating shaft.* The energy of the rotating shaft may be used to turn an electric generator.

A diagram of a water turbine installation is shown in Fig. 11-30. The water is stored in a reservoir above the turbine. It is delivered to the turbine through a large pipe called a *penstock*. From the penstock, the water flows into the turbine casing. Within the casing are large, fixed blades which give the flowing water a spiral motion. Between these fixed blades and the turbine are large gates to control the flow of water to the turbine. The " waterwheel " part of the turbine, called the *runner,* consists of a series of blades

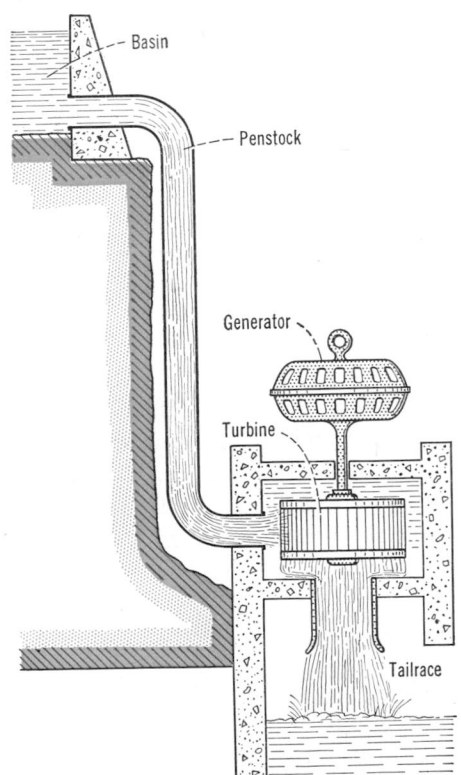

Fig. 11-30. A cross-section of a waterwheel generator installation.

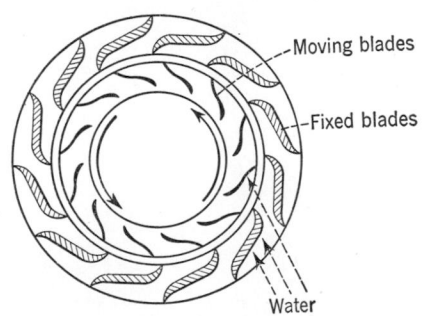

Fig. 11-31. Fixed blades direct the water against the movable blades of the water turbine.

mounted on a vertical shaft. These blades are mounted in a slightly inclined position so that the full force of the spiral movement of the water will act upon them and cause the turbine to turn. See Fig. 11-31. The water from the turbine is discharged downward through the center of the runner. This method of discharge transfers more energy from the water to the turbine. In operation, the entire turbine is immersed in water. A water turbine of the standard type may have an efficiency of about 90%.

10. POWER TRANSMISSION

★ **28. How may mechanical power be transmitted?** If you have a home workshop, you possibly have several machines which are driven by the same electric motor. In larger machine shops, each individual machine may be driven by its own electric motor. How is the power of the rotating shaft

Fig. 11-32. The interior of one of the two powerhouses at Grand Coulee Dam. There are nine 125,000-kilowatt water-wheel generators in this generator room. The tremendous size of these generators can be judged by comparison with the men standing in the foreground.

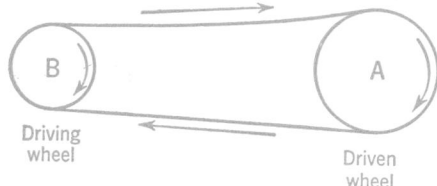

Fig. 11-33. Both wheels A and B turn in the same direction.

of an electric motor transmitted to the lathe, the planer, the grinder and polisher, or to a circular saw?

In some machines power is transmitted by means of a belt and pulleys. Usually, the belt is connected as shown in Fig. 11-33. Then the driven wheel will rotate in the same direction as the drive wheel mounted on the shaft of the motor. If the belt is twisted, then the wheels will turn in opposite directions. See Fig. 11-34. The ratio of the speeds at which the wheels turn is inversely proportional to the circum-

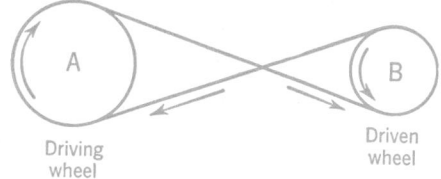

Fig. 11-34. The driving wheel A and the driven wheel B turn in opposite directions with such a belt transmission.

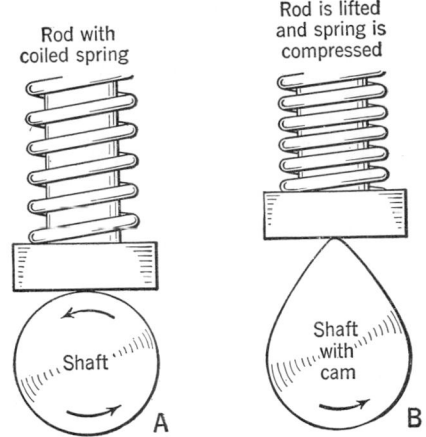

Fig. 11-35. By means of a cam, rotary motion is changed to an up-and-down motion, or a back-and-forth motion. This is called reciprocating motion.

ferences, or diameters, of the wheels. For example, if wheel *A* has a diameter of 10 in and wheel *B* has a diameter of 5 in, then *B* will make *two* revolutions while *A* is making *one*.

In some machines, like grinders and polishers, the shaft of the motor may be connected to the rotating shaft of the machine by means of a train of gear wheels.

★ **29. How is rotary motion transformed into reciprocating motion?** In transmitting mechanical power, it is often desirable to change rotary motion into reciprocating motion. We can do this by the method shown in Fig. 11-35. If the circular shaft shown at *A* rotates, it slides around under the vertical rod, but does not move the rod

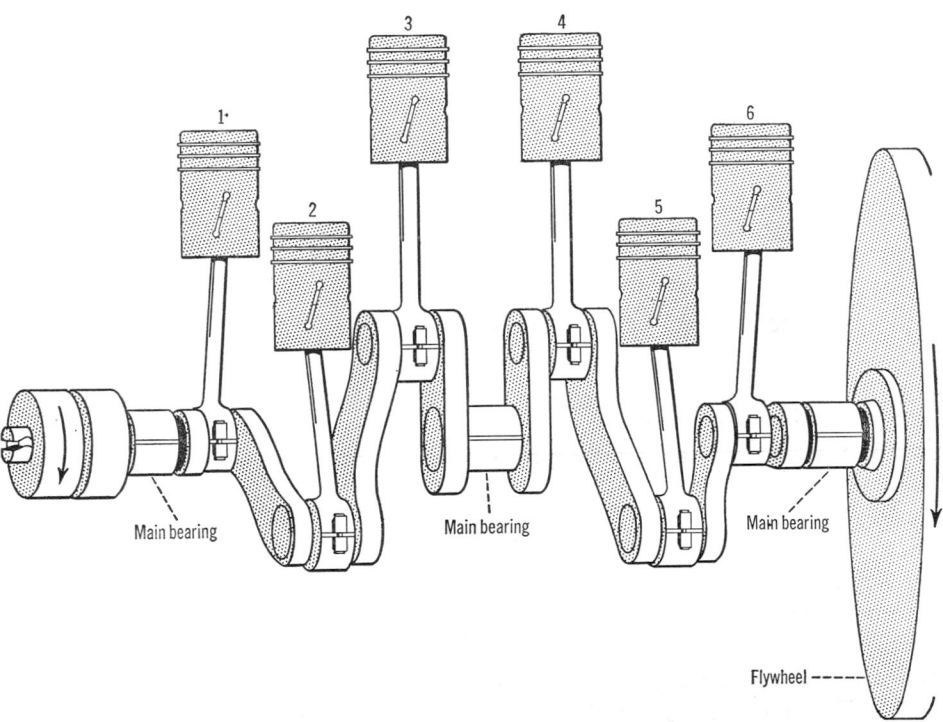

Fig. 11-36. The pistons, connecting rods, and crankshaft of a six-cylinder engine. The reciprocating motion of the pistons is transformed into the rotary motion of the crankshaft.

Fig. 11-37. The chassis of a modern automobile. Locate the position of the flywheel, clutch, transmission, drive shaft, universal joints, differential gears, and rear axle.

up and down. The shaft at *B* has a projection on one side. As the projection slides under the rod, the rod is lifted. A spring keeps the rod pressed against the shaft. Consequently, the rod will move down again after the projection has passed. This projection is called a *cam*. The shaft on which the cam is mounted is called a *camshaft*. The intake and exhaust valves of automobile engines are controlled by cams and camshafts.

★ **30. How may reciprocating motion be transformed into rotary motion?** The pistons of an automobile engine move up and down within the cylinders. This reciprocating motion is transformed into rotary motion by means of the connecting rods and the " off-center " bearings of the crankshaft. These off-center bearings are sometimes called *eccentrics* (ek-*sen*-triks). See Fig. 11-36.

Suppose the explosion of the mixed gasoline vapor and air in cylinder 3 is forcing the piston down. This force is transmitted by the connecting rod to the eccentric on the crankshaft. The eccentric is moved downward, but this downward motion is transformed by the eccentric into rotary motion of the crankshaft. The crankshaft turns in a clockwise direction when viewed from the front of the engine. Near the end of the power stroke in cylinder 3, the piston in cylinder 1 reaches the top of its compression stroke. The mixture of gases in the cylinder explodes, and piston 1 transmits power to the crankshaft. The downward force against the piston in cylinder 1 is transformed as before into rotary motion of the crankshaft by an eccentric. The inertia of the flywheel keeps the crankshaft turning between successive power strokes. With the 6-cylinder engine, Fig. 11-36, there is a power stroke for each 120° the crankshaft turns.

★ **31. The drive mechanism of an automobile.** We know how the downward power strokes in the automobile engine are transformed into the rotary motion of the crankshaft. Now we are ready to learn how the motion of the crankshaft is varied in speed and direction and transmitted to the rear wheels so as to move the automobile. The crankshaft rotates in bearings at the lower part of the engine. A flywheel is mounted on the crankshaft toward the rear of the engine. Behind the flywheel is the transmission, which may be either manual or automatic. The friction or fluid clutch mechanism is part of the transmission. The transmission connects the crankshaft to the drive shaft. There are two universal joints in the drive shaft which permit it to bend up and down, or from side to side. The drive shaft is connected through the differential gears to the rear axle.

★ **32. How does the clutch work?** A gasoline engine can not be started well under a load. Consequently, the automobile engine must be disconnected from the rest of the driving mechanism while it is being started, and until it comes up to proper operating speed. After the engine has reached this speed, it must be connected smoothly to the transmission and drive shaft. The device which performs these various functions is called the *clutch*. There are two general types of clutches used on automobiles today: the friction clutch and the fluid clutch.

(1) *The friction clutch.* A plate, or a series of plates covered with " friction " material is attached to the shaft leading into the transmission. This ring of friction material can be pressed against the face of the flywheel by means of strong springs. A pedal, which is actually a lever operated by the left foot of the driver, is used to engage or disengage the clutch. When the clutch pedal is pushed in, the clutch is disengaged and the clutch plate is pushed backward. This disconnects the crankshaft from the drive shaft. Then the engine " idles," or runs without moving the car. When the clutch pedal is released, the springs push the clutch plate forward. It slips a little as it is engaged gently, and then holds firmly. See Fig. 11-38.

(2) *The fluid clutch.* This clutch is an important part of an automatic drive mechanism. At the end of the crankshaft there is a set of blades similar to those of a water wheel. Facing this wheel is a second set of blades mounted on the end of the transmission shaft. Both sets of blades are enclosed in a sealed housing filled with oil. As the engine picks up speed, the blades attached to the crankshaft through the flywheel set the oil in motion, and the moving oil, as it acts upon them, turns the blades attached to the transmission shaft. Thus the power is transmitted from the crankshaft to the transmission. A modification of the fluid clutch, called a *torque converter,* is an important part of some types of automatic transmissions.

★ **33. What is the transmission?** A transmission is a device which connects the clutch and the drive shaft. It is used to change the drive shaft speed

Fig. 11-38. The parts of a friction clutch.

Fig. 11-39. A disassembled fluid clutch showing the interior blades.

without greatly varying the engine speed. Manually operated transmissions have the conventional gearbox shown in Fig. 11-40. This gearbox has three shafts: the *pinion* (*pin*-yun) *shaft* and the *drive shaft* are both in the same straight line; the *countershaft* is always connected at one end to the pinion shaft. The countershaft may be connected by sliding gears to the main drive shaft. The pinion shaft is connected to the engine through the clutch. When the clutch is engaged, the pinion shaft turns at the same rate as the crankshaft. The gear wheels *E* and *F* can be moved forward or backward along the drive shaft, which is square or grooved. When these particular gear wheels turn, the drive shaft also turns.

The diagrams used to explain the operation of the transmission have been simplified. Actually, a transmission consists of beveled gears, cone gears, and gears with teeth cut in them at an angle in order to make them easier to mesh and to provide quiet operation. Fig. 11-41 shows a cutaway view of an automobile transmission.

The following is an explanation of

how gears are shifted and what happens each time.

Neutral. In starting the engine, the gearshift lever is at the position *N* of Fig. 11-42. The gears are then in the position shown in Fig. 11-40. The pinion gear and the countershaft both turn. The drive shaft and the rear wheels do not turn because the gears are not meshed with those of the countershaft.

Low gear. When the driver disengages the clutch and pulls the gearshift lever back to position 1 of Fig. 11-42, he slides the gear *E* forward until it meshes with the small gear *G* on the countershaft. See Fig. 11-43. We have two gear reductions, *AB* and *GE*, and the car is now in *low gear*. The

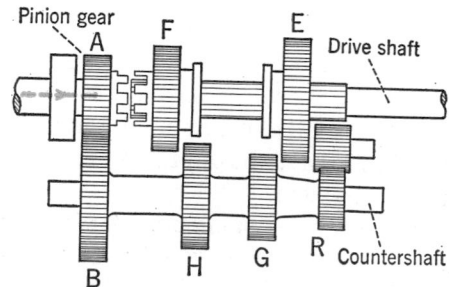

Fig. 11-40. Transmission gears in neutral.

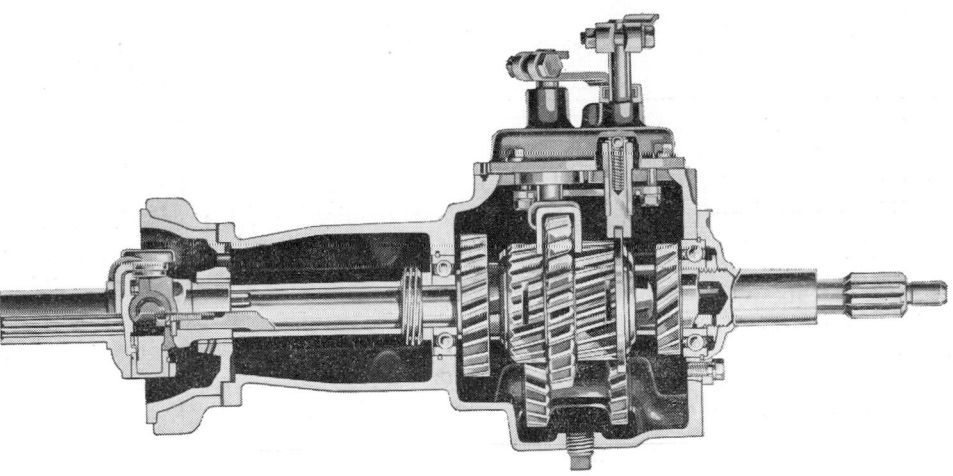

Fig. 11-41. A cutaway view of an automobile transmission.

power in this case is transmitted through *A*, *B*, *G*, and *E* to the drive shaft, as shown by the dotted lines.

Second gear. As the gearshift lever is shoved into position 2, Fig. 11-42, it moves the gear wheel *E* backward, and at the same time moves *F* back until it meshes with the gear wheel *H*. See Fig. 11-44. The dotted lines show the power transmission through *A*, *B*, *H*, and *F* to the drive shaft.

High gear. When the gearshift is pulled back to position 3 of Fig. 11-42, the gear wheel *F* is pushed forward until it is locked to the pinion gear by

means of teeth on the sides of the two gear wheels. See Fig. 11-45. The power now is transmitted directly from the crankshaft to the drive shaft and the rear wheels.

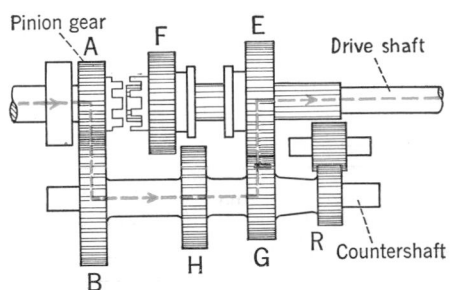

Fig. 11-43. The transmission in low gear.

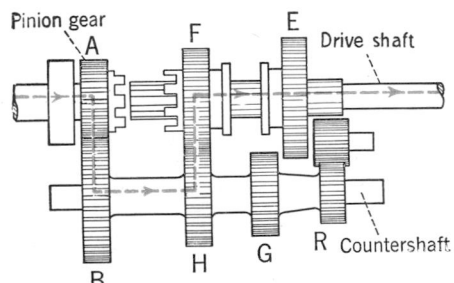

Fig. 11-44. The transmission in second gear.

Fig. 11-42. A diagram to show gear-shift positions.

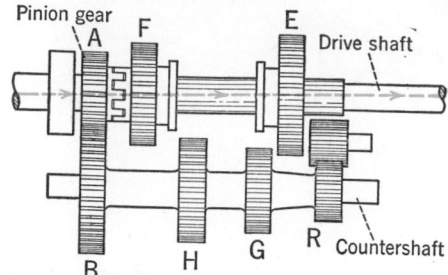

Fig. 11-45. The transmission in high gear.

Reverse gear. When the driver pushes the gearshift lever to the position *R,* Fig. 11-42, the sliding gear wheel *E* meshes with a small idler gear and the gear *R.* See Fig. 11-46. The three gears are now meshed as shown in Fig. 11-47. Observe that the crankshaft turns in the same direction as before, but that the drive shaft turns in the opposite direction. The crankshaft itself is never reversed.

⭐ **34. Automatic drives make car operation easier.** There are now several types of automatic drive mechanisms used in automobiles. They range from a fluid clutch and hydraulically-operated gearbox to combinations of torque converters and special planetary gears. They are extremely complicated devices. With most types of

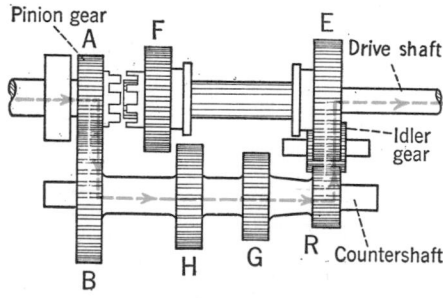

Fig. 11-46. The transmission in reverse gear.

automatic devices, we just set the selector lever for " forward drive," step on the accelerator pedal, and drive away. The automatic drive changes the ratio between the speed of the crankshaft and the drive shaft to suit the required driving speed. Special adjustments usually must be made for locking the drive shaft when parking and for reverse. Some makes of automobiles have a fourth forward speed called an " overdrive." The overdrive mechanism automatically cuts in at a predetermined forward speed to give more economical engine operation. In overdrive, the crankshaft turns more slowly than the drive shaft.

⭐ **35. What is the differential?** The transmission system is connected with the *differential gears* on the rear axle by means of two universal joints and the drive shaft. In going around a curve, the outer wheel of an automobile must turn faster than the inside

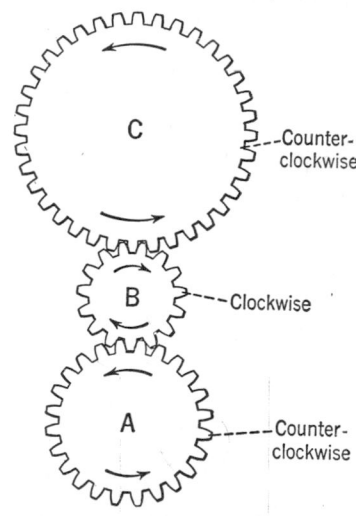

Fig. 11-47. The countershaft and the crankshaft turn in the same direction as in the forward speeds, but *B,* the idler gear, reverses the direction of the drive shaft.

THE POWER SHOVEL

as seen by the "Trans-Vision" process

THE POWER SHOVEL is an application of many different simple and compound machines. Consequently it provides an excellent opportunity for you to review the principles you have learned in this unit on Machines.

By turning the pages of this "Trans-Vision" insert, you can see the complete exterior of the power shovel, as well as the inner mechanism, in a way not possible even by watching a real power shovel in operation. The labeling which has been superimposed on the drawings will help you to identify easily the simple machines which make up this complex piece of earth-moving equipment.

You will find the six types of simple machines illustrated here. These include the three classes of levers, fixed and movable pulleys, the wheel and axle, the wedge, the screw, and the inclined plane. In addition, you will find various types of belt, chain, and gear drives.

The right-hand pages show the front view of the power shovel. The left-hand pages show the power shovel as viewed from the rear. In this way, you can see from opposite pages just how the various parts are located with respect to each other, and how they fit and operate together.

The drawings are the work of Mr. F. R. Gruger, Jr. They are greatly simplified from photographs and drawings which were generously supplied by the Marion Power Shovel Company, Marion, Ohio.

On the last page of this "Trans-Vision" insert, you will find a key to the machines shown and the page on which each occurs.

SIMPLE MACHINES :

LEVERS : 1ˢᵀ CL   2ᴺᴰ CL   3ᴿᴰ CL

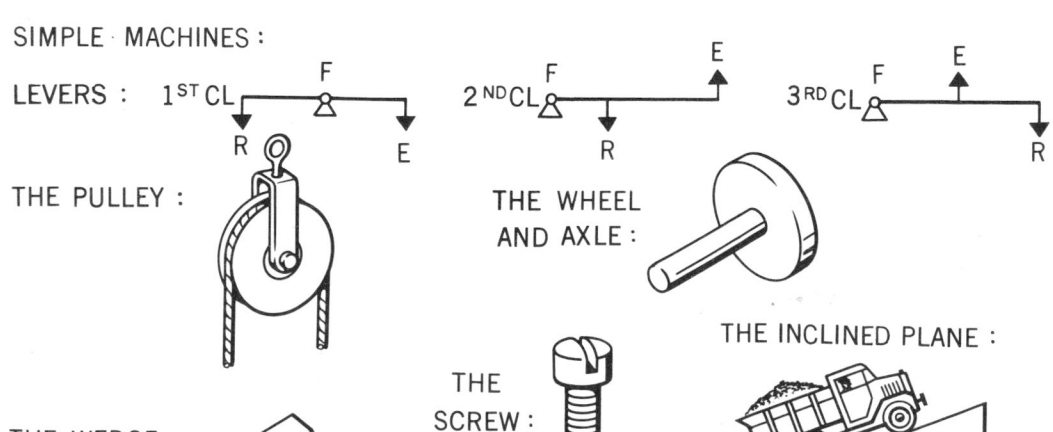

THE PULLEY :

THE WHEEL AND AXLE :

THE INCLINED PLANE :

THE SCREW :

THE WEDGE :

I   **FRONT VIEW OF POWER SHOVEL.** The power shovel itself is an example of
a bent first-class lever. The center of gravity of the cab is the point at which
the effort force is applied. The resisting weight is applied at the bucket. The fulcrum of this first-class lever is located at the near edge of the flexible tread. The
effort distance, s_F, and the resistance distance, s_W, are shown above.

In this view of the power shovel we also have examples of fixed and movable
pulleys. The fixed pulley is identified by the number **(1).** What is its function
during the operation of the power shovel? The movable pulley is number **(2).**
What is its mechanical advantage?

The application of the wedge as a simple machine is found in the teeth **(3)**
attached to the bucket of the power shovel.

II   REAR VIEW OF BOOM AND BUCKET OF POWER SHOVEL. This view shows the second- and third-class levers in the power shovel. The boom is a second-class lever. The fulcrum is at the bottom of the boom at the point where the boom is pivoted to the turntable. The effort is applied at the top of the boom. The resistance acts at a point between the effort and fulcrum. Why must s_F of this lever be measured in the manner indicated? Explain why the bucket and the beams which connect it to the boom constitute a third-class lever.

V BACKGROUND. The sixth simple machine, the inclined plane, is shown in this background view. We see a loaded truck being driven up the inclined plane (**20**) in order to get it up out of the excavated area. How is the mechanical advantage of this inclined plane calculated? Another example of the wheel and axle as a machine is the rear axle and wheel of the truck (**21**).

KEY TO MACHINES

wheel. Since the driving power of the engine is transmitted to the rear axle, a device must be used so that the two rear wheels will drive together. It must also permit one wheel to travel faster than the other on curves. The differential, which is placed between the two parts of the divided rear axle, accomplishes both of these purposes. See Fig. 11-48. The driving pinion *A,* which is attached to the drive shaft, rotates the bevel gear, *B.* This gear is attached to the frame, *F,* in which the gears *C* and *E* are mounted. These parts all rotate as a unit within the housing of the differential. The left and right axles are free to rotate

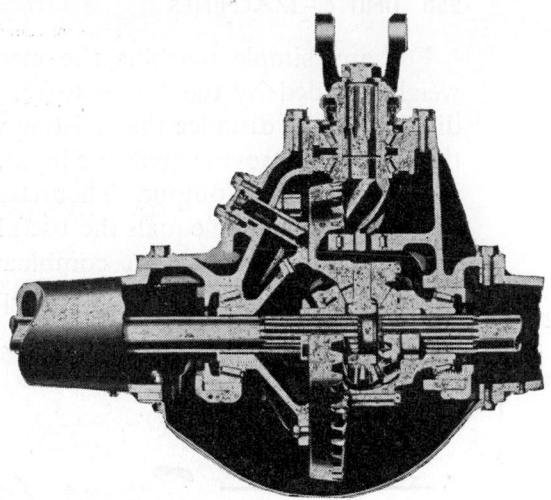

Fig. 11-49. A cutaway view of the differential.

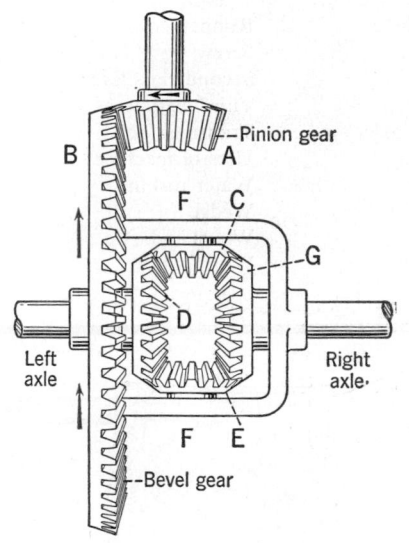

Fig. 11-48. Differential gears.

in bearings within the frame. On a straight road, the gears *C* and *E* do not rotate on their axes, but they are carried around with the frame, *F.* As they revolve with the frame, they turn the gears *D* and *G* at the same speed. These gears are attached to the inner ends of the divided rear axle. As they turn the axles, the rear wheels, which are rigidly attached to the other ends of these axles, move the car. When the right axle turns faster than the left on a curve, the gears *C* and *E* turn on their axes in opposite directions to compensate for the difference in speed of the two rear wheels. Fig. 11-49 shows a sectional view of a rear axle with the housing cut away to show the differential.

Summary

Machines are used to transform energy, transfer energy, multiply force, multiply speed, or to change the direction of a force. There are six simple machines, the lever, the pulley, the wheel and axle, the inclined plane, the screw, and the wedge.

For any simple machine the mechanical advantage equals the resisting weight divided by the acting force, or the distance the acting force moves divided by the distance the resisting weight is raised. The acting force times the distance it moves equals the input. The resisting weight times the distance it moves equals the output. Theoretically, input equals output. The efficiency of a simple machine equals the useful work divided by the total work.

Compound machines are combinations of two or more simple machines. The mechanical advantage of a compound machine in nearly all cases is the product of the separate mechanical advantages of the simple machines of which it is composed.

Terms to Define...

Belt drive	Inclined plane	Pitch
Cam	Input	Pulley
Compound machine	Lever	Pulley as 1st or 2nd class
Differential	M.A. of compound machine	lever
Differential pulley	M.A. of inclined plane	Runner
Eccentric	M.A. of lever	Screw
Efficiency of machines	M.A. of pulleys	Second class lever
First class lever	M.A. of screw	Third class lever
Fixed block	M.A. of wheel and axle	Transmission
Fluid clutch	Mechanical advantage	Uses of machines
Friction clutch	Micrometer caliper	Water turbine
Fulcrum	Movable block	Wedge
Gear wheel combinations	Output	Wheel and axle
Grade	Penstock	Worm wheel

GROUP A

★ **1.** How may the mechanical advantage of a compound machine be calculated?

★ **2.** What will be the ratio between the number of teeth in the gear wheel attached to the second hand of a watch and the number of teeth in the gear wheel attached to the minute hand?

★ **3.** Explain how the counter shown in Fig. 11-50 can be used to determine the number of revolutions per minute.

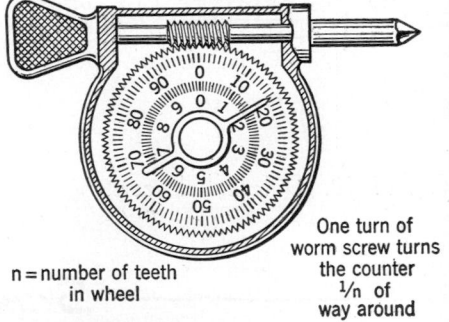

n = number of teeth in wheel

One turn of worm screw turns the counter $1/n$ of way around

Fig. 11-50. The worm gear can be used as a speed counter. How many teeth are there in the wheel?

★ **4.** What well-known method is used for transforming rotary motion into reciprocating motion? For transforming reciprocating motion into rotary motion?

★ **5.** Why should a flywheel be rather heavy yet easy to rotate?

★ **6.** What are the main parts of the drive mechanism of an automobile?

★ **7.** Which type of clutch mechanism is found on your family's automobile? Explain how it operates.

★ **8.** What is the function of the transmission of an automobile?

★ **9.** Why are differential gears needed for connection between the drive shaft and the rear axles of an automobile?

★ **10.** Why is one tire chain of no value in driving on icy pavements?

GROUP B

★ **11.** The turnbuckle shown in Fig. 11-51 acts upon one rod which has a right-hand thread; it also acts upon another rod which has a left-hand thread. If each rod has 10 threads to the inch, how much is the space between the ends increased or decreased by one complete revolution of the turnbuckle?

★ **12.** Why would a differential pulley be useful in a garage which services trucks and buses?

★ **13.** What factors in the design of a water turbine increase the efficiency with which it converts the potential energy of elevated water into the kinetic energy of the rotating turbine shaft?

★ **14.** What devices do you have in and around your home which include either belt or chain drive power transmission?

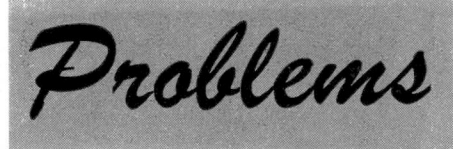

(In the Mathematics Refresher, refer to Sections 6, 7, 10, and 16.)

GROUP A

★ **1.** A block and tackle is used to pull a large block of granite up an inclined plane. If the

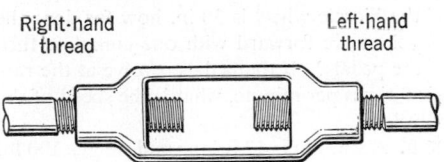

Right-hand thread	Left-hand thread

Fig. 11-51. A turnbuckle.

mechanical advantage of the plane is 10 and the mechanical advantage of the block and tackle is 4, what is the mechanical advantage of the combination?

★ **2.** The pulley wheel on the shaft of an electric motor has a diameter of 2 in. The drive wheel of the fan run by the motor has a diameter of 4 in. What is the mechanical advantage of this belt drive? How does the number of revolutions per minute of the motor compare with the number of revolutions per minute of the fan?

★ **3.** The large wheel of a differential pulley has a circumference of 30 in. The small wheel has a circumference of 27 in. What is the theoretical mechanical advantage of this differential pulley? If a force of 75 lb is required in order to raise a motor block weighing 1000 lb, what is the actual mechanical advantage? What is the efficiency?

★ **4.** What is the mechanical advantage of the train of gear wheels shown in Fig. 11-24? The radius of *A* is twice that of *G*. *B* and *D* each have 16 teeth, while *C* and *F* each have 36 teeth.

★ **5.** A worm drive, like that shown in Fig. 11-27, has 90 teeth in the gear wheel. If the radius of the drive wheel is 2 ft, and the radius of the axle is 2 in, what load can be lifted by a force of 10 lb?

GROUP B

★ **6.** A safe weighing 4000 lb is to be pulled up an inclined plane 20 ft long onto a platform 4 ft high. A block and tackle having a mechanical advantage of 5 is attached to the safe. If it requires two men, each pulling with a force of 125 lb, to move the safe, what is the efficiency?

★ **7.** The diameters of the wheels of a differential pulley are 15 in and 12 in respectively. What is the mechanical advantage? If a force of 50 lb is required in order to raise a block weighing 300 lb, what is the efficiency of this pulley system?

★ **8.** The front sprocket wheel of a bicycle has 28 teeth; the rear wheel has 7. If the diameter of the bicycle wheel is 30 in, how far does the bicycle move forward with one complete turn of the pedals? If the pedals revolve at the rate of 60 times per minute, what is the speed of the bicycle?

★ **9.** A scaffold is 12 ft long and weighs 100 lb. Each end is supported by a block and tackle in which 4 strands support the movable block. If a painter, who weighs 150 lb, stands 1 ft from one block, with what force must he pull to raise the end of the scaffold?

● **10.** The crank handle of the hoist on a wrecking truck is 18 in long. On the same shaft there is a gear wheel which has 25 teeth. This gear wheel meshes with another one having 100 teeth, which is fastened to the axle shaft. This axle, on which the chain is wound, is 2 inches in diameter. The chain passes over a single fixed pulley at the end of the boom, through a single movable pulley to which the hoisting block is attached, and is fastened to the top of the boom. This hoist operates at 60% efficiency. What effort applied to the crank handle is required to raise the front of an automobile 16 ft long and weighing 4000 lb? The center of gravity of the car is 6 ft from the front.

Things to Do

1. Examine one room in your home, the kitchen for example, and identify all the devices which are applications of one or more of the machines studied in this chapter. Make a list of these devices.

2. Make a list of the devices visible on an automobile, without lifting the hood, which are applications of one or more simple machines.

3. Make a report to the class on types of automatic transmissions. Explain their similarities of operation and their differences.

4. Visit a large garage or machine shop and examine the various devices used for exerting large forces with little expenditure of effort.

Unit 7 Heat

Heat is the second of the major divisions of physics which we are going to study. We shall learn that heat is a form of energy. A problem that has confronted physicists and engineers for many years is finding the most efficient method of converting the heat energy from burning fuels into mechanical energy.

A device which offers great promise as a more efficient method of converting heat energy into mechanical energy is the gas turbine. The sleek, streamlined automobile shown in the photograph is powered by a gas turbine which generates 370 horsepower. This experimental model is about 19 feet long, 6.5 feet wide, and less than 3.5 feet high at the plastic dome of the cockpit.

Along with the gas turbine, we shall study in this unit such other devices for converting heat into work as the steam turbine, the gasoline engine, and the Diesel engine.

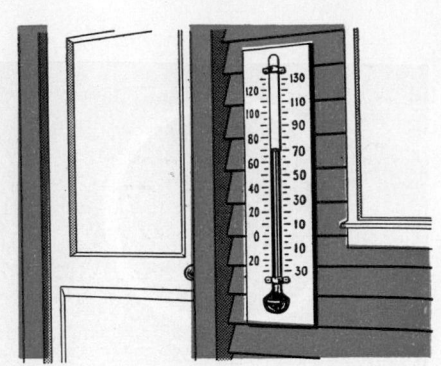

Chapter 12

Heat and Thermometry

1. What is the nature of heat? Until about the middle of the nineteenth century heat was thought to be an invisible, weightless fluid called *caloric*. When a substance like wood or coal was burned, large quantities of caloric were produced. This caloric could be transferred to other materials, and as a result they were warmed. When a hot substance cooled off, it was said to have lost caloric.

About 1800, Count Rumford (1753–1814), a military expert as well as scientist, was watching a cannon being bored for the Bavarian government. In order to keep the boring tools cool, the barrel of the cannon was kept filled with water. This water boiled away as the boring tools cut into the metal. But it also boiled away even when the tools became so blunt that they were no longer cutting. Rumford concluded that the heat which could be obtained in this way

from friction alone was apparently limitless. This meant that heat could not be some kind of a substance. It must be related to the motion of the tool in the bore of the cannon. About 40 years later, James Prescott Joule, after many careful experiments, showed that a definite amount of mechanical energy could always be transformed into the same amount of heat. Consequently, heat must be another form of energy.

2. What are the sources of heat energy? The most important of these sources are as follows.
(1) *The sun.* Directly or indirectly, nearly all our heat may be traced to the sun. Heat from the sun makes it possible for plants to grow. Animals require these same plants for food. On a hot, sultry summer day it seems that we must be getting a large portion of the sun's heat. It has been estimated, however, that the earth as a whole

----

Vocabulary

HEAT. Thermal energy which is being transferred from one body to another.

TEMPERATURE. The "hotness" or "coldness" of a body as determined by the thermal energy it possesses.

THERMAL ENERGY. The combined potential energy and kinetic energy of the atoms of a body.

THERMOMETER. A device for measuring temperature.

receives only one two-billionth of all the heat which the sun gives off.

(2) *The earth's interior.* The molten lava from volcanoes and the boiling water which spurts from geysers are both evidence that the interior of the earth is much hotter than is its surface.

(3) *Chemical action.* We use fuels such as coal, oil, gas, and wood as our main sources of artificial heat. In our bodies the oxygen we breathe unites with the food we eat. This supplies our bodies with enough heat to maintain a body temperature of about 98.6° F.

(4) *Mechanical energy.* We have already seen from the experiments of Rumford and Joule that mechanical energy can be changed into heat. Work that is used to overcome friction appears as heat energy. The force of impact of a lead bullet against a steel plate may be transformed into sufficient heat to melt the bullet. When we compress gases into a smaller volume, the cylinder of our pump or mechanical compressor becomes hot. Most of this heat comes from the gas while it is being compressed.

(5) *Electrical energy.* Heat is produced from electricity by the resistance of coils of certain kinds of wire to the passage of the electric current. An electric iron and a toaster are heated this way.

(6) *Nuclear energy.* This promises to be an important future source of large amounts of energy. The heat from nuclear reactors is used to change water into steam. Then the steam may turn a turbine connected to an electric generator.

3. What are some of the things that heat can do? The effects that heat produces are both interesting and of practical importance.

(1) As heat is absorbed by a substance, the temperature of the substance generally rises. Water in a pan over a gas flame rises in temperature as it absorbs heat.

(2) The heat absorbed by a solid may

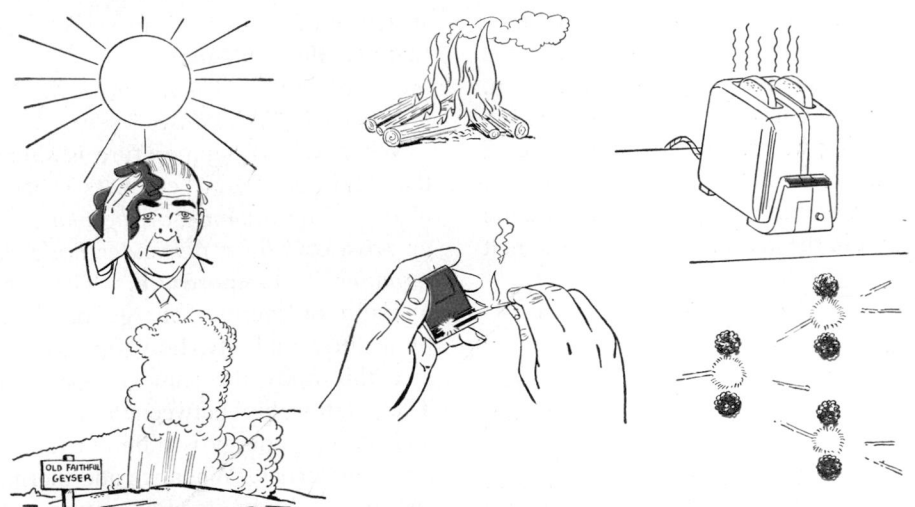

Fig. 12-1. The six most important sources of heat energy. Can you identify each source of energy?

cause the solid to melt, or to change from the solid to the liquid phase. Ice melts and forms water when it is heated.

(3) A liquid may absorb sufficient heat to cause it to evaporate, or to change from the liquid phase into a vapor. When water is sufficiently heated, it changes into steam.

(4) The volume of almost any object increases when it is heated. The mercury in a thermometer expands as the temperature rises.

(5) Heat causes many chemical changes to occur. During the cooking of foods we apply heat to produce chemical reactions.

(6) Heat produces many physiological effects in both plant and animal life.

(7) We shall discover that heat can produce an electric current when two different metals are in contact.

4. The difference between heat and temperature. We know from experience that heat and temperature are related. However, a difference exists between them. A burning match has a much higher temperature than a steam radiator, but the heat from the match is not enough to warm a room. Suppose we have a teakettle that is full of boiling water. If we pour some of the water into a cup, the temperature of the water in the cup will be the same as that in the kettle. But we could melt

Fig. 12-2. The pail of water and the tub of water at the left have the same temperature but different quantities of heat. The pail of water and the tub of water at the right have different temperatures and different quantities of heat.

more ice with the water in the kettle than we could with the water in the cup because the water in the kettle can give up more heat. Ten pounds of water at 80° F will melt more ice than one pound of water at 100° F. The ten pounds of water can evolve more heat, but the one pound of water is at a higher temperature. From these observations we learn that it is possible for a body to have a high temperature and give out little heat; it may have a high temperature and give out a great amount of heat; it may have a low temperature and give out little heat; or it may have a low temperature and give out a large quantity of heat.

You may have heard someone say that an electric iron has more heat when it is hot than when it is cold. This is a popular mode of expression, but it is not accurate in a strict scientific sense. The correct statement is that such an iron has more *thermal energy* when it is hot than when it is cold. We do not know the exact relationship between thermal energy and the atomic structure of matter. But we do know that *the* **thermal energy** *of a body is the total potential and kinetic energy possessed by its atoms.*

What we call temperature is simply the " hotness " or " coldness " of an object. *The quantity of thermal energy possessed by a particular body determines its* **temperature.** The same quantity of thermal energy possessed by a different body, however, will not give this body the same temperature. The relationship between temperature and thermal energy is different for different materials. When we add thermal energy to a body, its temperature ordinarily rises. If the body gives up thermal energy, its temperature ordinarily

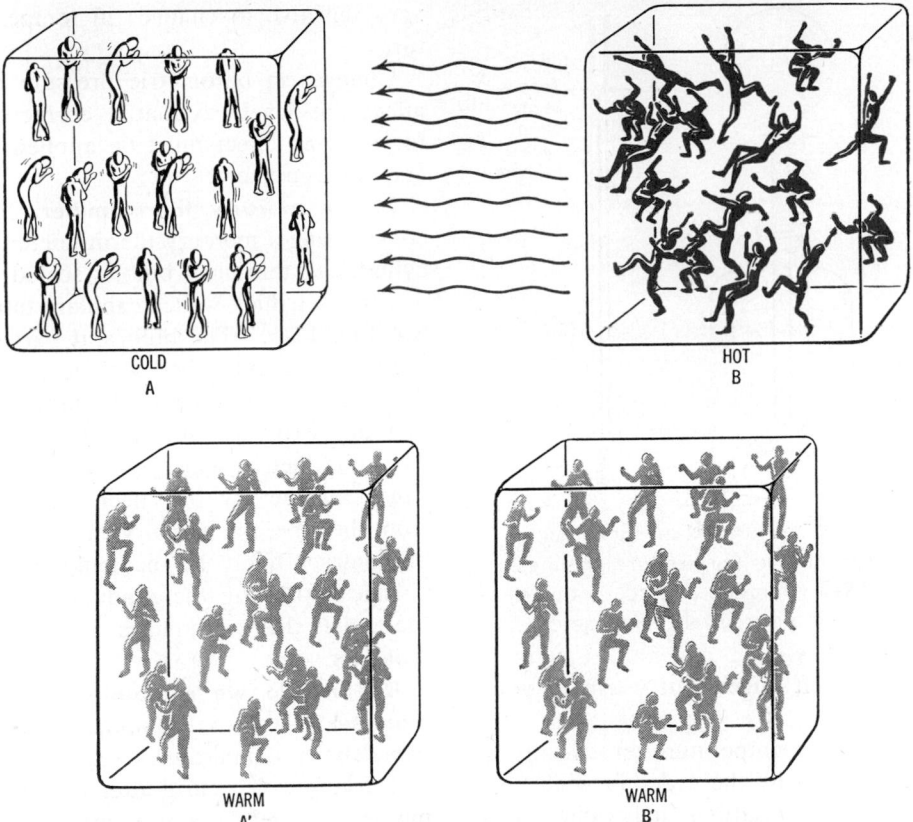

Fig. 12-3. The molecules of block *A*, represented by the shivering figures, possess little thermal energy.   Block *A* therefore has a low temperature — it is cold.   The molecules of block *B*, represented by the jumping figures, possess a great amount of thermal energy.   Block *B* therefore has a high temperature — it is hot.   Since block *B* is at the higher temperature, it can transfer some of its thermal energy in the form of heat to block *A* until the molecules of both blocks have an equal amount of thermal energy — their temperatures are the same.   See blocks *A'* and *B'*.

goes down.   *Thermal energy which is being added to a body, or being given up by a body is called* **heat.**   The temperature of a body determines its ability to give up heat to other bodies.

5. What do we mean by " hot " and " cold "?   We use such terms as " hot," " cold," " warm," and " cool " to indicate temperature.   It is easy to show that these terms are only relative, and mean very little scientifically.

The following experiment proves our point.   Take three drinking glasses and fill the one at your left with *hot* water, the middle one with *warm* water, and the one at your right with *ice* water.   For a few moments hold the index finger of your left hand in the hot water and the index finger of your right hand in the ice water.   Then dip both fingers into the glass of warm water.   You will have the sensation of feeling that the warm water is both warm and cold at the same time.   It will feel cold

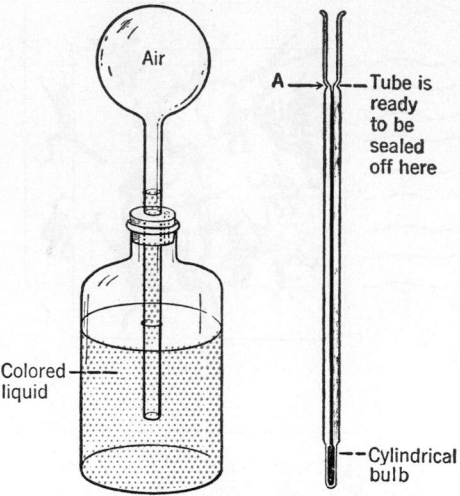

Fig. 12-4. Left. The air thermometer is very sensitive to temperature changes.
Fig. 12-5. Right. A step in the manufacture of a mercurial thermometer.

to your left finger, but warm to your right.

Since our temperature sense is affected so much by the order in which we experience sensations, it is quite unreliable for precise determinations. Several types of **thermometers** *have been developed for measuring temperatures.*

6. The air thermometer. The air thermometer is one of Galileo's inventions. It consists of a long tube with a thin-walled glass bulb on one end. The open end of the tube dips into some colored liquid, as shown in Fig. 12-4. To use the thermometer, some air must be expelled from the bulb and tube. This is done by warming the air in the bulb so that it expands and the desired quantity escapes by bubbling from the end of the tube up through the liquid. As the air in the bulb cools, the atmospheric pressure causes some of the liquid to rise in the tube. The level of the liquid in the tube is

very sensitive to changes in temperature.

Changes in barometric pressure do affect this level, so that a correction for such an effect must be applied to each measurement.

7. The mercury thermometer. In constructing a mercury thermometer, a cylindrical, thin-glass bulb is sealed to one end of a thick-walled capillary tube. See Fig. 12-5. The bulb and part of the stem are then filled with mercury. The bulb next is heated until the mercury expands and fills the tube. The tube then is sealed off at *A*. Because all the air has been expelled from the tube, the mercury can expand or contract freely as the temperature changes. Placing the graduations on the tube then completes the thermometer.

8. How do we graduate a thermometer? Two *fixed points,* that is, two definite temperatures must be selected before we can graduate a thermometer. The freezing point and the boiling point of water are two definite temperatures which can be reached easily and precisely. These are called, respectively, the *ice-point* and the *steam-point.*

The bulb and lower portion of the stem of a thermometer, as constructed by the method described in Section 7, are packed in a funnel containing melting ice. See Fig. 12-6. Melting ice produces the same temperature as freezing water, and is much more convenient to use. The lowest point to which the mercury falls is marked as the ice-point.

Next, in order to determine the steam-point, the thermometer is suspended in steam from boiling water. See Fig. 12-7. Since the boiling point of water varies with the atmospheric pressure, we must adjust our apparatus so that the water is boiling under a pressure of exactly 760 mm of mercury. The highest point to which the mercury rises is marked as the steam-point.

9. How are the degrees marked on a thermometer? The two fixed points we have marked on our thermometer now enable us to set up a thermometer scale. While several types of scales with degrees of different size have been devised, we shall study only two, the

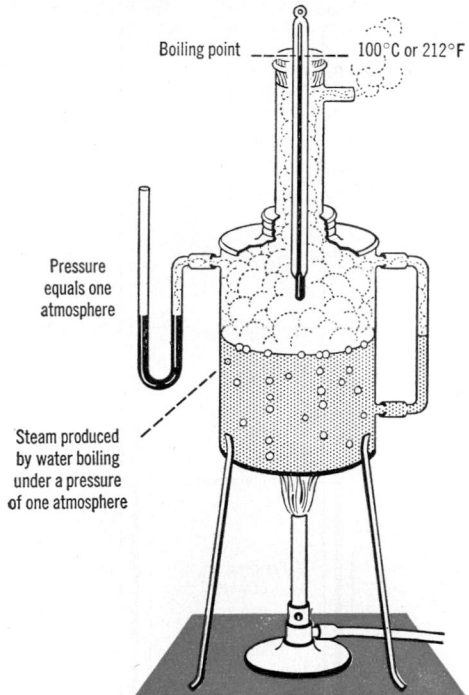

Fig. 12-7. Checking the steam-point, 100° C, on a thermometer.

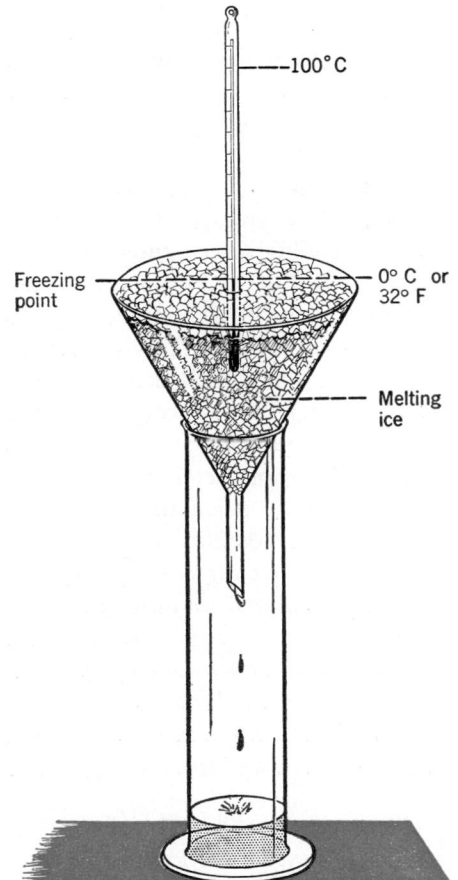

Fig. 12-6. Checking the ice-point, 0° C, on a thermometer.

Centigrade (*Sent*-ih-grayd) and the *Fahrenheit* (*Far*-un-hyte) *scales*.

(1) *Centigrade scale*. This scale, which was devised by a Swedish astronomer, Anders Celsius (*Sel*-see-us) (1701–1744), is the one commonly used in many foreign countries. It officially is called the Celsius scale, but this name has not been generally accepted in the United States. The Centigrade scale is used for scientific work in the United States. On a Centigrade thermometer, the ice-point is marked *0*, and the steam-point is marked *100*. The space between the fixed points is divided into one hundred equal parts, called *degrees*. The divisions between the parts are thus numbered from 0° to 100°. From one marked division to the next is a *temperature interval of*

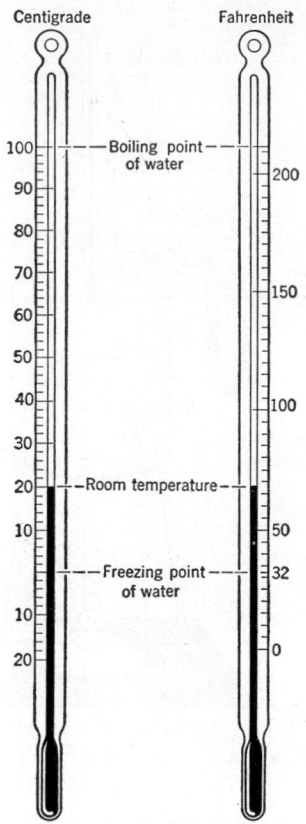

Centigrade   Fahrenheit

100 — Boiling point — —
     of water
90   200
80
70   150
60
50
40   100
30
20 — Room temperature — —
10   50
     — Freezing point — — 32
     of water
10
20   0

Fig. 12-8. Comparison of Centigrade and Fahrenheit thermometers.

one Centigrade degree, or 1 C°. The graduations are continued both below 0° and above 100° by marking off scale divisions of similar size.

(2) *Fahrenheit scale.* This scale, devised in 1714 by Gabriel Daniel Fahrenheit (1686–1736), is used in the United States for weather observations and for most general purposes. On a Fahrenheit thermometer the ice-point is marked 32, and the steam-point is marked 212. The space between these two fixed points on a Fahrenheit thermometer is divided into 180 degrees. Graduations are extended above and below these fixed points in

the same manner as for a Centigrade thermometer.

10. How do we convert a temperature reading on one scale to the equivalent temperature on the other scale? Just as we found it necessary to change meters into yards, and inches into centimeters, we may have the problem of changing a Fahrenheit temperature reading to the corresponding Centigrade reading, or vice versa. In order to do this, we must first recognize that 0° C and 32° F are the same temperature. 100° C and 212° F are also the same temperature. Between the ice-point and the steam-point on a Centigrade thermometer, there are 100 degrees. Between the same points on a Fahrenheit thermometer, there are 180 degrees. Consequently 100 Centigrade degrees equal 180 Fahrenheit degrees. Or 1 Centigrade degree (1 C°) equals $\frac{9}{5}$ Fahrenheit degrees ($\frac{9}{5}$ F°).

If the reading on a Centigrade thermometer is 20°, it means that the temperature is 20 Centigrade degrees above the ice-point. This equals 20 × $\frac{9}{5}$, or 36 Fahrenheit degrees above the ice-point. But the ice-point on the Fahrenheit scale is 32°. Therefore the Fahrenheit thermometer will read 32° + 36°, or 68°, when the Centigrade thermometer reads 20°.

To change Centigrade readings to Fahrenheit readings, multiply the Centigrade readings by $\frac{9}{5}$, and add 32. To change Fahrenheit readings to Centigrade readings, subtract 32 from the Fahrenheit readings and multiply by $\frac{5}{9}$. ★ These two procedures are expressed:

$$t_F = \tfrac{9}{5} t_C + 32, \text{ and } t_C = \tfrac{5}{9}(t_F - 32),$$

Here t_F represents the Fahrenheit temperature; t_C, the Centigrade temperature.

SAMPLE PROBLEM

Change 10° C to the equivalent Fahrenheit reading.

SOLUTION

First, multiply $10 \times \frac{9}{5} = 18$. Then add 32. $18 + 32 = 50$. Thus $10° C = 50° F$.

SAMPLE PROBLEM

Convert $-58°$ F to the corresponding Centigrade temperature.

SOLUTION

We *subtract* 32 from -58. $-58 - 32 = -90$. Then multiply by $\frac{5}{9}$. $\frac{5}{9} \times -90 = -50$. Therefore, $-58° F = -50° C$.

11. There are other types of thermometers. The useful temperature range of mercury as a thermometer liquid is generally limited by its freezing point, $-39°$ C, and its boiling point, 357° C. For measuring temperatures outside this range, other types of thermometers have been devised.

The other familiar liquid-in-glass thermometer is the *alcohol thermometer*. It is useful for making some measurements below the range of the mercury thermometer, since alcohol does not freeze until the temperature reaches approximately $-115°$ C. A red or blue dye normally is added to the alcohol so that it can be seen readily.

★ The *constant-volume gas thermometer* is useful over a wide range of tem-

Fig. 12-10. An optical pyrometer is used to check the temperature of molten steel as it pours from a ladle into the ingot molds.

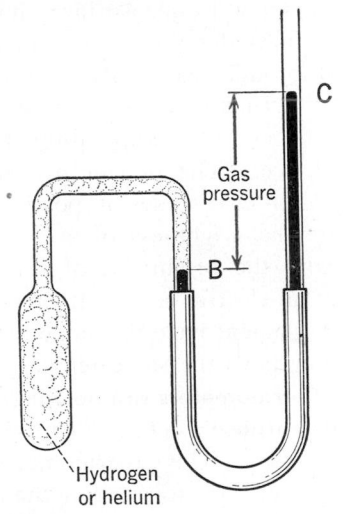

Fig. 12-9. The constant-volume gas thermometer.

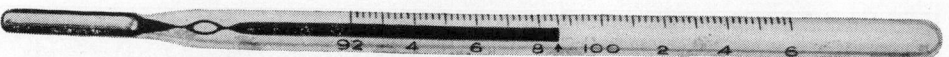

Fig. 12-11. A clinical thermometer. Notice the constrictions in the bore which prevent the mercury from returning to the bulb until shaken down.

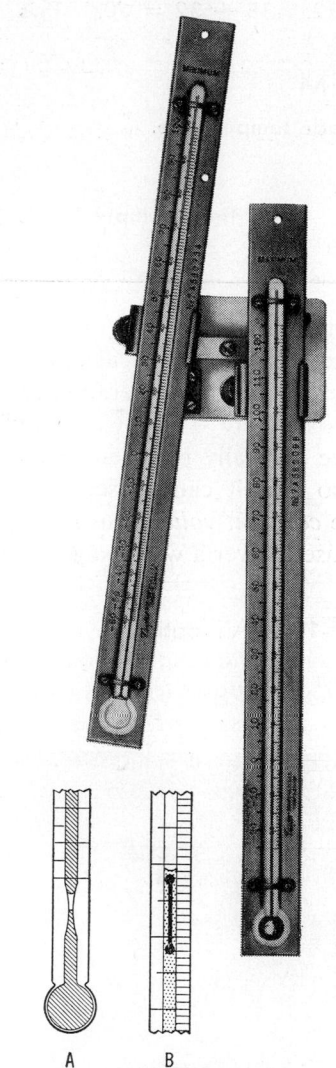

A   B

Fig. 12-12. The official United States Weather Bureau maximum and minimum thermometers. Insert *A* shows the constriction above the bulb of the maximum thermometer, while insert *B* shows the glass index in the bore of the minimum thermometer.

peratures. See Fig. 12-9. The bulb of this thermometer usually contains hydrogen or helium. If the temperature of the gas is lowered the gas contracts, and mercury in the manometer will rise at *B* and drop at *C*. Since *B* and *C* are connected by flexible tubing, *C* can be lowered until the mercury level in *B* is restored to its original reading. By thus changing the pressure we can keep the gas at constant volume. By measuring the change in pressure which is required to maintain the gas at constant volume, the temperature of the gas may be calculated. ★ The electrical resistance of metals increases when their temperature is increased. The *platinum resistance thermometer* indicates temperature by the amount of its resistance to an electric current. This is one of the most precise temperature-measuring instruments. Two different metals in contact will produce electricity when heated. This principle is used in the *thermocouple,* another temperature measuring device. The *optical pyrometer* (py-*rom*-eh-ter) makes it possible to compare the brightness of a very hot body with the brightness of the filament of an electric lamp. If this body and the filament have the same brightness, they have the same temperature.

12. Thermometers are designed for special purposes. (1) *The clinical thermometer.* This thermometer is used by physicians for reading the temperature of the human body. It usually is graduated from 92° F to 110° F. This small range is adequate because normal body temperature is 98.6° F, and the variation is only a few degrees in either direction.

In order that the mercury reading will remain at its highest value, the tube is constricted to reduce the size of the bore just above the cylindrical bulb. The mercury can force its way past this constriction as it expands. But the cohesion of the mercury molecules is not great enough to pull the mercury column back past the constriction. The mercury continues to indicate the highest reading until it is shaken back.

(2) *Maximum thermometer.* This type of thermometer may be used to show the highest temperature during a given period of time. One type of maximum thermometer is constructed like the clinical thermometer. It may be set at a certain hour each day by shaking the mercury down into the bulb. Then as the temperature goes up, the mercury rises in the tube and stands at the highest temperature reached during the day.

(3) *Minimum thermometer.* In one type of minimum thermometer the bulb is filled with alcohol. The surface tension of the alcohol drags a small glass index along the tube as the alcohol contracts. This index is left at the lowest temperature reading for the time interval, since the alcohol flows

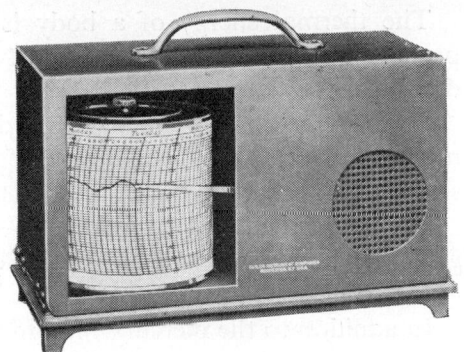

Fig. 12-13. The thermograph.

past it when expanding again. This thermometer is reset by inverting it until the glass index drops to the surface of the alcohol.

(4) *The thermograph.* A thermograph is a self-recording thermometer. It contains a special metal strip which is sensitive to temperature changes. A long pointer is attached to this strip. As this strip moves with changes in temperature, it swings the long pointer up and down. An ink pen mounted at the end of this arm records these movements as temperature changes. The recordings are made on a sheet of graph paper wound on a cylinder. A clock mechanism turns the cylinder through one complete rotation per week. The pointer traces a continuous line which shows the temperature at any day and hour of the week.

Summary

Heat is a form of energy. The sun, the earth's interior, chemical action, mechanical, electrical, and nuclear energy are the chief sources of heat.

When heat is absorbed by a body, its temperature generally rises. The absorption of heat may cause a solid to melt or a liquid to boil. The volume of an object nearly always increases when it is heated.

Thermal energy which is being added to a body or being given up by a body is called heat.

The thermal energy of a body is the total potential and kinetic energy possessed by its atoms. The quantity of thermal energy possessed by a body determines its temperature.

Sensation is an unreliable method of determining temperature. A thermometer is an instrument devised for that purpose. The two temperature scales used in the United States are the Centigrade scale and the Fahrenheit.

To change Centigrade readings to Fahrenheit readings, multiply the Centigrade readings by $\frac{9}{5}$ and add 32. To change Fahrenheit readings to Centigrade readings, subtract 32 from the Fahrenheit readings and multiply by $\frac{5}{9}$.

In addition to the mercury thermometer, scientists have devised the alcohol thermometer, the constant-volume gas thermometer, the platinum resistance thermometer, the thermocouple, and the optical pyrometer.

——— *Terms to Define...* ———

Air thermometer	Fahrenheit scale	Pyrometer
Alcohol thermometer	Heat	Sources of heat energy
Caloric	Ice point	Steam point
Centigrade scale	Maximum thermometer	Temperature
Clinical thermometer	Mercury thermometer	Thermal energy
Constant-volume gas thermometer	Minimum thermometer	Thermocouple
Effects of heat	Platinum resistance thermometer	Thermograph
		Thermometer

GROUP A

1. What are the usual sources from which we obtain heat? Give a specific example to illustrate each source you name.

2. Compare the amount of thermal energy possessed by each of the following: (1) a soldering iron and a needle at 300° F; (2) a four-section radiator and a 10-section radiator, both at 220° F; (3) a teakettle of boiling water and a cup of boiling water; (4) fifty pounds of ice at −10° C and 25 lb of ice at −10° C; (5) a quart of liquid air and a gallon of liquid air, both at −189° C.

3. How does the thermal energy a body possesses determine its temperature?

4. How do heat and temperature differ?

5. Why are our senses not especially reliable for measuring differences in temperature?

6. Why do atmospheric pressure changes, as well as temperature changes, affect the reading of an air thermometer?

7. Why is mercury used in thermometers?

8. For what purposes is the Centigrade scale used in the United States? For what purposes is the Fahrenheit scale used?

9. Why does the reading of a clinical thermometer remain at its highest value even after the thermometer is removed from the mouth?

GROUP B

10. What reasoning led Rumford to believe that heat could be produced from mechanical energy?

11. The temperature of the melting point of ice and the temperature of the boiling point of water are called "fixed points" in calibrating a thermometer. Why?

12. If you examine several similar laboratory thermometers, you may find that the distance between 0° C and 100° C is not exactly the same on all of them. Why is there such a difference when they are all the same make and model?

★ 13. Why is a constant-volume gas thermometer useful even though making a reading with this thermometer is much more difficult than reading a mercury thermometer?

★ 14. What device would you use to measure the temperature of a furnace containing melted iron?

★ 15. Why are maximum and minimum thermometers useful to weather observers?

(The odd-numbered problems are temperature conversions from Fahrenheit to Centigrade. The even-numbered problems are temperature conversions from Centigrade to Fahrenheit. In the Mathematics Refresher, refer to Section 10.)

GROUP A

1. The temperature in a classroom is 72° F. What is the Centigrade reading?

2. Acetone, a colorless liquid used as a solvent, boils at 56.5° C. What is this temperature on the Fahrenheit scale?

3. During an illness, John's temperature rose to 102° F. Convert this reading to the corresponding Centigrade reading.

4. Carbon tetrachloride, which is sometimes used as a dry-cleaning fluid, boils at 76° C. Calculate its boiling point, Fahrenheit scale.

5. On a hot summer day, William read the Fahrenheit thermometer and saw that it was 90°. What was the Centigrade temperature?

6. Lead melts at 327.4° C. What Fahrenheit temperature is this?

7. The temperature in the stratosphere is about −80° F. Convert this to the corresponding temperature on the Centigrade scale.

8. The lowest temperature theoretically attainable is −273.16° C. Find the corresponding Fahrenheit temperature.

9. Copper, which is used for electric wiring, melts at 1980° F. What is the Centigrade temperature?

10. Liquid nitrogen boils at −196° C. What is the reading on the Fahrenheit scale?

11. In a limestone mine in Pennsylvania, the temperature remains constant at 53° F throughout the entire year. What is this temperature in degrees Centigrade?

12. If water is cooled from 50° C to 10° C, what is the temperature change in Fahrenheit degrees?

13. During a summer thunderstorm the temperature dropped 15 Fahrenheit degrees. What was the drop in Centigrade degrees?

14. Ether, used as an anesthetic, is a colorless liquid which freezes at −116.3° C. Calculate its freezing point on the Fahrenheit scale.

15. On a day in January the temperature was 10° F. What is the Centigrade temperature which corresponds to this?

16. Alcohol freezes at about −115° C. What is it on the Fahrenheit scale?

17. The lowest temperature ever recorded in the United States was −70° F at Rogers Pass, Montana, on January 20, 1954. What is this temperature on the Centigrade scale?

18. Tungsten, the metal used in the filaments of electric light bulbs, melts at 3370° C. On the Fahrenheit scale, what is this temperature?

19. Mercury freezes at −38.0° F. Convert to the equivalent Centigrade reading.

20. The melting point of helium under a pressure of 26 atmospheres is −272.2° C. What is this temperature Fahrenheit?

21. At what temperature is the reading the same on Centigrade and Fahrenheit scales?

Things to Do

1. Look up the account of the life of Count Rumford and make a report to the class.

2. Examine as many different types of temperature measuring devices as are available. These should include mercury- and alcohol-filled Centigrade and Fahrenheit thermometers in various ranges, a clinical thermometer, thermocouple, metallic thermometer, maximum and minimum thermometer, air thermometer, and, possibly, a thermograph. Discover how each one operates in registering temperature. What is the useful range of each instrument?

Chapter 13

Thermal Expansion

1. Solids become larger when heated. Sometimes when drinking glasses are stacked one inside another in the cupboard, two of them become stuck together. If we try to pull them apart, we may break one or both of them. Here is a safe way to separate these glasses: Put very cold water into the upper glass and immerse the outside of the lower glass in hot water. Usually, after a minute or two, the glasses should loosen. Why does this procedure work? When we put cold water into the upper glass, we lower the temperature of the glass and make it get very slightly smaller. Immersing the lower glass in hot water increases its temperature, so that it expands slightly. These small changes in the sizes of the glasses loosen them from each other. This simple experiment illustrates the fact that with few exceptions, *solids expand when they are heated and contract when they are cooled.* They not only increase in length, but they also increase in width and thickness.

When both the iron ring and the ball shown in Fig. 13-1 are at room temperature, the ball will pass through the ring. Now let us heat the ball in the flame of a burner. When we try to pass the ball through the ring, we find that the ball has expanded. It will no longer go through the ring. If we heat the ring, however, we find that the heated ball will pass through the heated ring. Note that when the ring expanded, it expanded in all dimensions — including the size of the hole!

2. How much do solids expand? Suppose we have an apparatus into which we can put a rod of aluminum one foot long. By applying heat to our

---

Vocabulary

ABSOLUTE ZERO. That temperature attained by matter when it has given up all the thermal energy it can; $-273.16°$ C or $-459.69°$ F.

BIMETALLIC STRIP. Two strips of different metals which have been riveted or welded together.

COEFFICIENT OF LINEAR EXPANSION. The increase in a unit length of a solid when its temperature is increased one degree.

COEFFICIENT OF VOLUME EXPANSION. The increase in a unit volume of a solid or a liquid when its temperature is increased one degree.

apparatus, we raise the temperature of the aluminum rod one Centigrade degree. By using the precise measuring instrument on our apparatus, we measure the increase in the length of our rod when it is heated. We find that when an aluminum rod one foot long is heated one Centigrade degree, its increase in length is 0.000023 foot. Let us substitute an iron rod of the same length for the aluminum rod, and repeat the experiment. We find that the iron rod expands only 0.000011 foot when its temperature is raised one Centigrade degree. Different materials of the same length expand different amounts for the same change in temperature. *The increase in unit length of a solid when its temperature is increased one degree is called its* **coefficient of linear expansion.**

In this experiment, we found that 1 ft of aluminum expands 0.000023 ft when its temperature is raised 1 C°. The coefficient of linear expansion of aluminum is therefore 0.000023/C°. Likewise the coefficient of linear expansion of iron is 0.000011/C°. Since the coefficient of linear expansion is defined as *the increase in unit length,* its value does not depend upon any particular length unit. Its value, however, does depend upon the size of the degree used to measure the temperature change. Table 7, Appendix B shows the coefficient of linear expansion for several solids. This table gives the coefficient of linear expansion for *Centigrade degrees.* The coefficient of expansion for *Fahrenheit degrees* will be just $\frac{5}{9}$ as much.

So far, we have been working with one-foot lengths of aluminum and iron, and have raised the temperature only one Centigrade degree. If we raise the

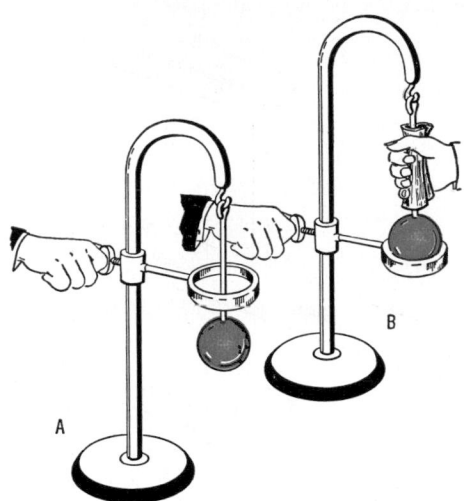

Fig. 13-1. *A. When the metal ball is at room temperature, it can pass easily through the ring. B. When the metal ball has been heated, it expands and cannot pass through the ring.*

temperature of 10 ft of aluminum rod 1 C°, the expansion is 10 times as much as the expansion of the 1-ft length. $10 \times 0.000023 = 0.00023$ ft. If the temperature of this 10 ft of aluminum is raised 10 C°, the increase is 10 times as great as for 1 C°. 10×0.00023 ft = 0.0023 ft. We conclude from these observations that *the total increase in the length of a solid when it is heated equals its length times its change in temperature times its coefficient of linear expansion.*

★ This may be expressed by the formula,

$$\Delta l = \alpha l\ (t - t_o),$$

where Δl is the increase in length, α is the coefficient of linear expansion, l is the original length, t is the final temperature, and t_o is the original temperature. See Sample Problem, page 268.

3. Solids expand in all directions when heated. We must remember

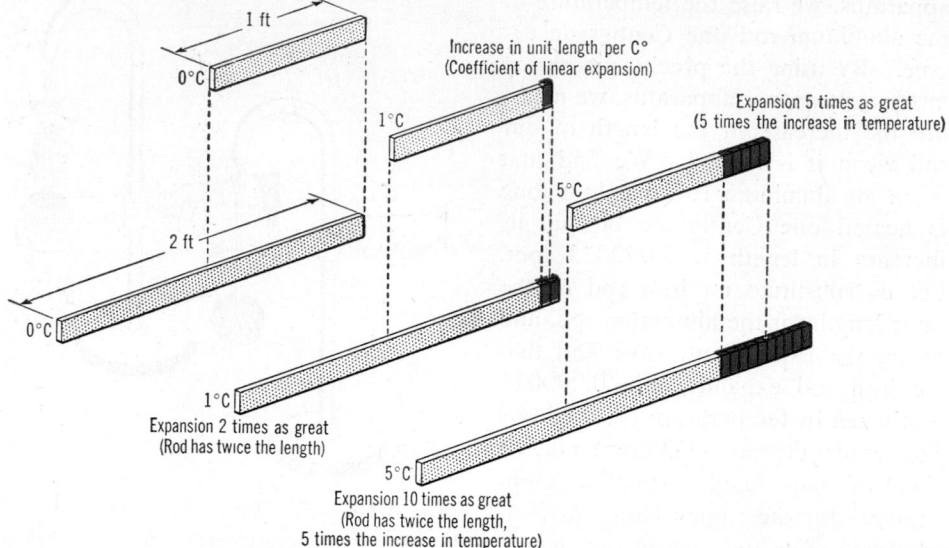

Fig. 13-2. The increase in unit length of a solid when it is heated one degree is the coefficient of linear expansion. The total increase in the length of a solid when it is heated equals its length times its change in temperature times its coefficient of linear expansion.

that when solids are heated, they do not just increase in length — they increase in all dimensions. The *coefficient of area expansion,* or the increase in unit area per degree, is approximately *twice* the coefficient of linear expansion. The **coefficient of volume expansion,** or *the increase in unit volume*

SAMPLE PROBLEM

An iron rod is 60 cm long at 0° C. How much will it expand when heated to 80° C? What will be its length at 80° C?

SOLUTION NO. 1

From Table 7, Appendix B, we find that 1 cm of iron expands 0.000011 cm when heated 1° C. 60 cm of iron will then expand $60 \times 0.000011 = 0.00066$ cm when heated 1° C. The change in temperature is 80° C, so the actual increase is $80 \times 0.00066 = 0.0528$ cm.

The length of the rod at 80° C will be 60.0528 cm, the original length plus the expansion.

★ SOLUTION NO. 2

Substituting the appropriate data in the formula, $\Delta l = \alpha l(t - t_o)$, $\Delta l = 0.000011 \times 60(80 - 0)$.

Solving, $\Delta l = 0.0528$ cm, the increase in length. The new length at 80° C is $60 + 0.0528 = 60.0528$ cm.

Fig. 13-3. In these pipes, which are used for carrying superheated water to a sulfur well, the loops permit expansion without any danger of the pipes breaking.

Fig. 13-4. When the hot rivet cools, it will contract and make a very tight joint.

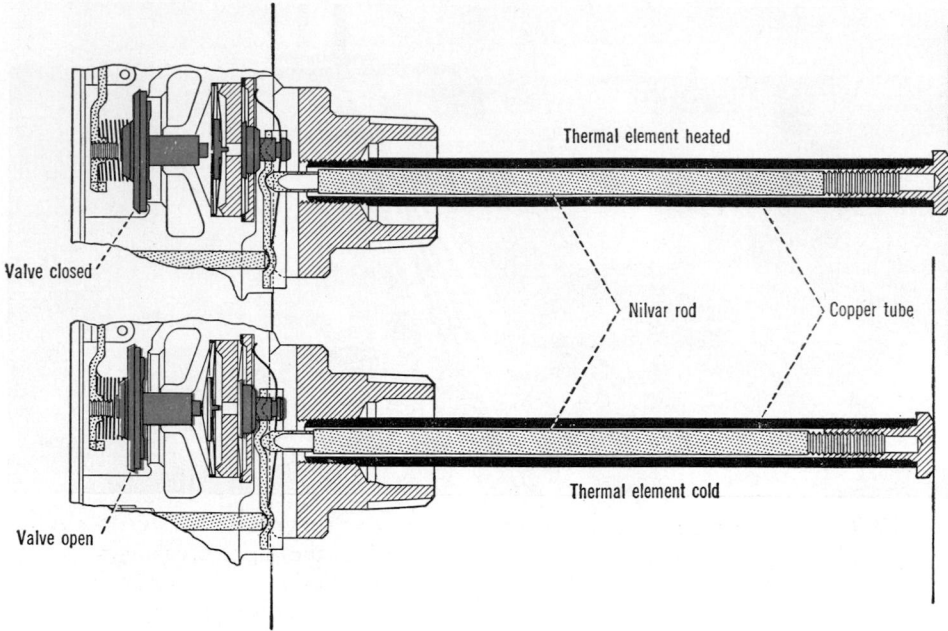

Thermal element heated

Valve closed

Nilvar rod

Copper tube

Valve open

Thermal element cold

Fig. 13-5. The valve of one type of hot-water heater is controlled by the expansion of a copper tube. The movement of this tube is conducted to the valve by a Nilvar rod which has negligible expansion.

when a solid is heated one degree, is approximately *three times* the coefficient of linear expansion.

4. The expansion of solids may be useful. In constructing tall buildings and bridges, the steel girders and beams are partially assembled before being shipped to the building site. This assembly usually consists of riveting several pieces of steel together to form the girder. Often the angle brackets used in fastening it to other girders are riveted in place, too. The metal rivets are heated red hot before they are put through the holes in the pieces to be joined. A powerful hammer spreads the hot metal end of each rivet. As the rivets cool, they contract and make a very tight joint.

In one type of automatic water heater, a rod of " Nilvar," an alloy of very low coefficient of linear expansion, is used. It is attached to a copper tube and regulates the amount of gas needed to keep the water in the hot-water tank at a desired temperature. As the copper tube expands, the " Nilvar " rod closes the valve regulating the flow of gas. As the copper tube cools and contracts, the " Nilvar " rod opens the gas valve.

5. How engineers solve the problems of expansion. The next time you cross a long highway bridge, see whether you can find where the engineer who designed the bridge provided for its expansion. Usually you will find on the roadway plates with interlocking metal fingers, like those shown in Fig. 13-6. As the bridge expands in hot weather, these fingers move closer together. In the winter, when it

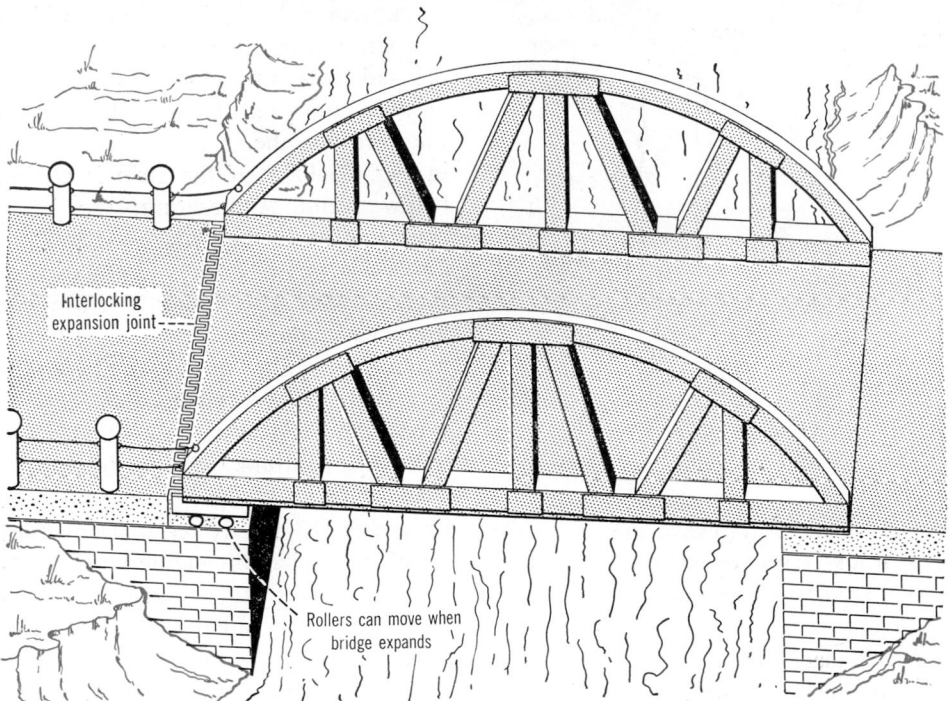

Interlocking
expansion joint

Rollers can move when
bridge expands

Fig. 13-6. Engineers provide for the expansion of bridges by rollers and interlocking expansion joints.

is cold, the fingers are farther apart. But this is just one way to allow for expansion. If you look beneath the roadway at the steel construction, you will find that the bridge is divided into sections. Each section is connected rigidly to a pier at one end. The other end of each section is mounted on rollers, or constructed in some other way so that it can move slightly on its supporting pier. In this way, when the bridge expands, the free ends of each section roll toward the next section. Enough space is provided between sections so that they will never fit tightly against each other.

When a contractor lays a concrete road, he provides space between each section for expansion. This space is usually filled with a semi-plastic bi-

tuminous material. Steel rails usually are laid with space for expansion be-

Fig. 13-7. The laying of continuous steel rail. The elasticity of this steel rail is great enough to overcome the stress caused by expansion when the temperature rises.

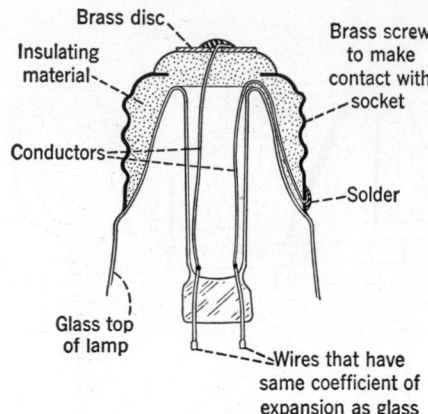

Fig. 13-8. The "lead-in" wires have the same coefficient of expansion as glass.

tween the ends. However, in some recent track-laying operations, the rails are welded together into one continuous piece.

Pyrex glass has a coefficient of expansion about one-third that of ordinary glass. Consequently, dishes and other types of glassware made of Pyrex are not as likely to break when their temperature is suddenly changed.

The two wires that lead into the filament of the ordinary household electric lamp must be sealed in the glass so perfectly that no gases can get into the lamp or escape from it. The wires must have the same coefficient of expansion as glass. Otherwise, unequal expansion and contraction would break the seal. Engineers use wires of nickel-iron alloy which have been coated with a film of a chemical adherent and sheathed with copper. See Fig. 13-8.

6. What is a bimetallic strip? Let us *take two flat strips of different metals,* such as brass and iron, *and rivet or weld them together,* as shown in Fig. 13-9*A.* This is called a **bimetallic strip.** If the strip is straight at

room temperature, it will curve if its temperature is either increased or decreased. If the temperature is increased, the brass expands more than the iron, and the strip curves as shown in Fig. 13-9*B.* If the strip is cooled below room temperature, the brass contracts more than the iron, and the curvature of the strip is that shown in Fig. 13-9*C.* Brass and iron are not the only metals from which we may make a bimetallic strip. Any two metals which have different coefficients of expansion may be used.

7. Applications of the bimetallic strip. (1) *Metallic thermometers.* From Fig. 13-10, we see that one end, *A,* of a circular bimetallic strip is attached firmly to the base of the thermometer. The end *B* is connected by a chain to the rotating shaft *C* on which a pointer is attached. The chain *BC* is kept under tension by a spring on shaft *C* which can rotate the shaft and pointer in a clockwise direction. The metal on the outside of the bimetallic strip has the greater coefficient of expansion. When the strip is

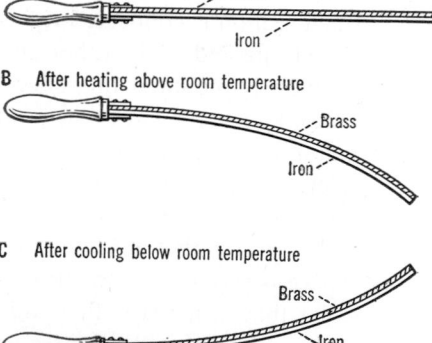

Fig. 13-9. The different rates of expansion of the two metals in a bimetallic strip cause the strip to bend when exposed to changes in temperature.

heated, it bends inward. The tension on the chain is reduced and the spring turns the shaft and pointer in a clockwise direction along the scale. Many oven thermometers and some industrial thermometers are of this type.

(2) *The thermostat.* A thermostat is a device containing a bimetallic strip which is used for regulating temperatures. We find thermostats used to control the burning of fuel in a furnace, so that our homes may be maintained at a healthful and comfortable temperature during changing cold weather. A thermostat can control the temperature in a refrigerator, the temperature of an electric iron, or the temperature of the air circulated by a room air conditioner.

A thermostat for controlling the operation of a gas or oil furnace is shown in Fig. 13-11. The bimetallic strip in this thermostat has been coiled. The expansion and contraction of the bimetallic strip operates a mercury switch.

As the temperature in the room falls, the bimetallic strip becomes more tightly coiled. At the desired mini-

Fig. 13-11. A circular thermostat in which the bimetallic strip operates a mercury switch.

mum temperature, the tension in the coil is sufficient to tilt the right end of the mercury switch down and complete the circuit. This turns on the furnace. As the temperature rises, the bimetallic strip expands. Finally, at the desired maximum temperature, the tension in the coiled strip becomes sufficient to tilt the right end of the mercury switch upward and break the circuit, thus shutting off the furnace.

(3) *The balance wheel.* An increase in temperature causes an ordinary balance wheel in a watch to expand. This makes the watch run too slowly. In order to correct this defect, more expensive watches have compensated balance wheels. Such a wheel is shown in Fig. 13-12. As the radius of this wheel expands and tends to slow up the movement, the bimetallic strips bend the ends W and W' inward enough to keep the period of vibration almost constant.

8. The expansion of liquids. Suppose you fill the gasoline tank of your automobile on a cool morning and then

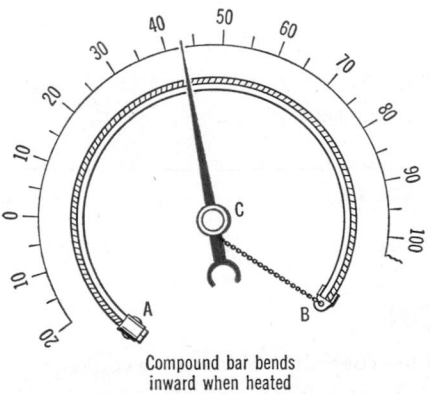

Compound bar bends
inward when heated

Fig. 13-10. A bimetallic strip controls the movement of the pointer in this metallic thermometer.

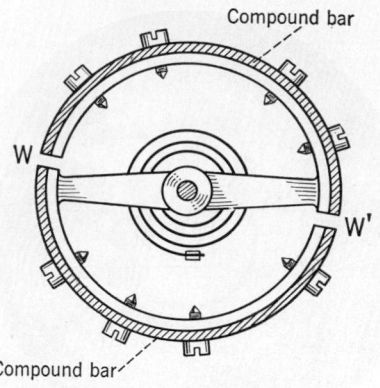

Fig. 13-12. A compensated balance wheel.

park your car in the sun. You may discover, when you return, that some of the gasoline has overflowed from the tank. Heat caused the gasoline to expand. Thermometers contain either mercury or alcohol because these liquids expand as the temperature rises.

Since liquids do not have a definite shape but take the shape of their container, we are concerned only with their expansion in volume. An apparatus like that shown in Fig. 13-13 may be used to measure the volume expansion of a liquid.

We find that liquids expand more than solids do. Consequently they have higher coefficients of volume expansion. The coefficients of volume expansion for several liquids are given

in Table 8, Appendix B. See the Sample Problem below.

9. The peculiar expansion of water. Suppose we fill an expansion bulb, like that shown in Fig. 13-13, with water at room temperature. As we cool the bulb and water, the water gradually *contracts* until a temperature of 4° C is reached. As we lower the temperature of the water below 4° C, the water *expands* until its freezing point, 0° C, is reached. Because the volume of water decreases as the temperature is lowered to 4° C, the density of the water increases. (The mass of the wa-

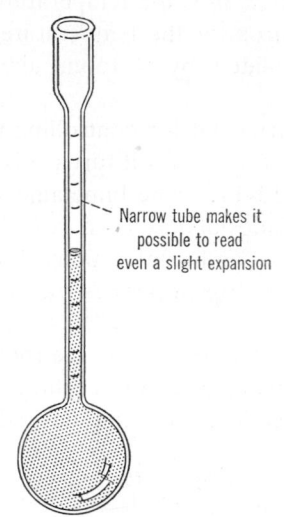

Narrow tube makes it possible to read even a slight expansion

Fig. 13-13. A tube used for measuring the volume expansion of liquids.

SAMPLE PROBLEM

One hundred gallons of petroleum are measured at 0° C. What will be the volume of the petroleum at 30° C?

SOLUTION

From Table 8, Appendix B, we learn that the coefficient of volume expansion for petroleum is 0.00096/C°. 0.00096 × 30 = 0.0288 gal, the expansion of 1 gal when heated 30 C°. 0.0288 × 100 = 2.88 gal, total expansion. 100 + 2.88 = 102.88 gal, the new volume.

ter is constant.) Therefore, water has its maximum density, 1.0000 g/cm³, at 4° C. The density of water at various temperatures is given in Table 9, Appendix B. The unusual way in which the density of water varies with the temperature is shown in the graph, Fig. 13-14.

10. Gases expand when heated, too. When your mother bakes a cake, the gas produced by the baking powder expands when the batter is heated. This makes the cake "rise." By experiment we can show that all gases expand when they are heated. Solids and liquids have coefficients of expansion which vary for different materials. But *gases have approximately the same coefficient of expansion.* Also, *the coefficient of expansion is nearly uniform at all temperatures,* except for those near the liquefying temperature of the gas. The coefficient of volume expansion for gases is $\frac{1}{273}$ of the volume at 0° C, or 0.003660/C°. This is about 20 times the expansion of mercury, and almost 60 times the volume expansion of aluminum.

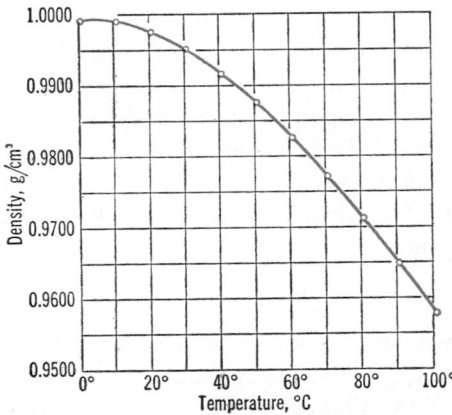

Fig. 13-14. The variation of the density of water with temperature. The density of water is greatest at 4° C.

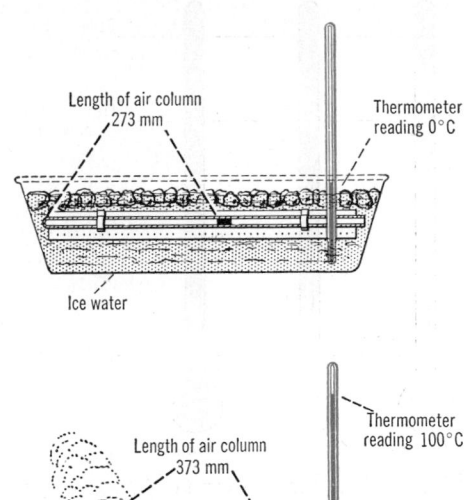

Fig. 13-15. For each degree rise in temperature a gas expands $\frac{1}{273}$ of its volume at 0° C.

If a gas is confined so that it can not expand when it is heated, it will exert a greater pressure. Suppose the tires on your automobile are inflated to 25 lb gauge pressure when the temperature is 32° F. If the temperature rises to 68° F, the pressure in the tires will probably increase to 28 lb. When the thermal energy of a gas is increased, the velocity of the molecules becomes greater. They bombard the inner walls of the tire more vigorously. This increases the pressure exerted by the gas.

11. How can we measure the coefficient of expansion of a gas? In 1787, Jacques Charles (1746–1823), a Frenchman, performed some important experiments with gases. These

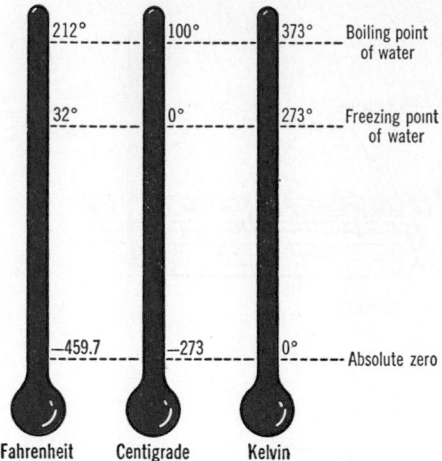

Fig. 13-16. Comparison of temperatures on Fahrenheit, Centigrade, and Kelvin thermometers.

experiments proved that all gases expand the same amount when heated one degree if the pressure is kept constant.

In order to determine the rate at which gases expand, we shall need a capillary tube sealed at one end, as shown in Fig. 13-15. A certain mass of air is trapped in this capillary tube by a globule of mercury, M. First, we measure the length of the air column when the tube is immersed in a mixture of ice and water. Next, we measure the length of the air column when the tube is surrounded by steam. Comparing these two readings, we find that the air column increased by $\frac{100}{273}$ of its original length when heated from 0° C to 100° C. For each degree of temperature change, the expansion was $\frac{1}{273}$ of the volume at 0° C. When gases other than air are used, similar results are obtained.

12. What is the lowest possible temperature? We know that materials possess thermal energy. When the amount of thermal energy is increased by the addition of heat, the temperature of the material rises. When the amount of thermal energy is decreased because heat is transferred from the material, its temperature drops. *When a material gives up all the thermal energy it can,* its temperature can go no lower. The material is as cold as it can get. *It is at the* **absolute zero of temperature.** On the ordinary temperature scales, *absolute zero is* $-273.16°$ *C or* $-459.69°$ *F.* Scientists have been able to reach temperatures within a few thousandths of a degree of absolute zero.

13. What is the Kelvin scale? This temperature scale was devised by Lord Kelvin (Sir William Thomson, 1824–1907). The zero point on this temperature scale is absolute zero. The degrees, however, are the same size as Centigrade degrees. For comparison, here are a few temperatures on both the Centigrade and Kelvin scales:

$$-273° \text{ C} = 0° \text{ K}$$
$$0° \text{ C} = 273° \text{ K}$$
$$100° \text{ C} = 373° \text{ K}$$

From this table we see that a Kelvin temperature is 273 degrees higher than the corresponding Centigrade temperature. *To change from Centigrade scale to Kelvin scale, add 273 degrees to the Centigrade reading.* In equation form,

$$T = t_C + 273,$$

where T is Kelvin temperature and t_C is Centigrade temperature.

14. Charles' law. The following table gives the volume occupied by a certain mass of gas at various Centigrade and Kelvin temperatures.

Volume	Centigrade	Kelvin
373 cm³	100°	373°
323 cm³	50°	323°
273 cm³	0°	273°
223 cm³	— 50°	223°
173 cm³	—100°	173°

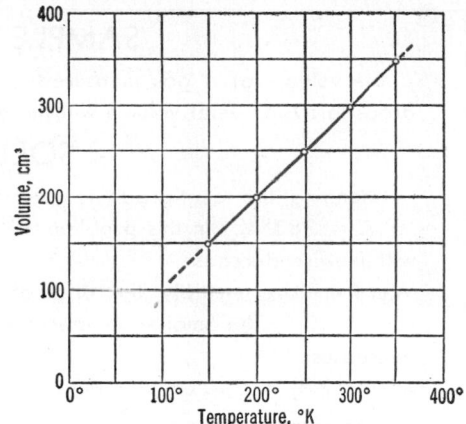

Fig. 13-17. The volume of a gas varies directly with the Kelvin temperature.

From this table, we see that the volume of a gas varies directly with the Kelvin temperature. CHARLES' LAW is: *If the pressure is constant, the volume of a dry gas is directly proportional to the Kelvin temperature.*

We may plot the Kelvin temperatures and gas volumes given in the table above to show Charles' law graphically. The resulting curve is shown in Fig. 13-17. This straight line relationship between Kelvin temperatures and volumes is proof they are directly proportional. See the Sample Problem below and at the top of page 278.

It is suggested that this method of solving Charles' law problems as shown in the unstarred samples is more desirable. For those who wish to use the formula method see the starred Sample Problem, bottom of page 278.

15. Combining Charles' and Boyle's laws. When working with gases, it frequently happens that temperature and pressure conditions both change. In order to find the new volume that a gas will occupy in such a case, we combine the effects of Boyle's law and Charles' law. This may be done in separate steps by first correct-

---

SAMPLE PROBLEM

At − 23° C, the volume of a gas is 1000 cm³. What will be the volume of this gas at 27° C?

SOLUTION

Since Charles' law states that the volume is proportional to the Kelvin temperature, we must first change the two Centigrade temperatures to Kelvin scale. −23° C + 273 = 250° K. 27° C + 273 = 300° K. Since the temperature is raised, the volume of the gas will increase.

To find the new volume we multiply the original volume by a ratio of the two Kelvin temperatures; $\frac{300}{250}$. The larger of the two temperatures is placed in the numerator of this fraction, because we know that the volume will increase. 1000 × $\frac{300}{250}$ = 1200 cm³, the new volume.

SAMPLE PROBLEM

The volume of a gas measured at 60° C is 400 cm³. If the temperature drops to 10° C, what volume will the gas occupy?

SOLUTION

Changing the Centigrade temperatures to Kelvin scale, 60° C = 333° K; 10° C = 283° K. In this problem the temperature is decreased, so the volume will likewise decrease.

We therefore multiply the original volume, 400 cm³, by the temperature ratio, $\frac{282}{333}$. The smaller temperature is the numerator, because the volume decreases.

$400 \times \frac{283}{333} = 340$ cm³, the new volume.

★ SAMPLE PROBLEM

At 20° C, a gas occupies 500 cm³. What will be the volume of this gas at 70° C?

SOLUTION

Since Charles' law states that the volume of a gas is directly proportional to the Kelvin temperature, we may use the formula, $\frac{V}{V'} = \frac{T}{T'}$. V is the original volume; V', the new volume; T, the original Kelvin temperature; and T', the final Kelvin temperature. 20° C = 293° K; 70° C = 343° K. By substitution in the formula, $\frac{500}{V'} = \frac{293}{343}$. Transposing to isolate V',

$$V' = \frac{500 \times 343}{293}.$$

Solving, $V' = 585.3$ cm³, the new volume.

ing the original volume to the new pressure conditions. Then this volume is corrected for the temperature change. Usually, however, these two steps are combined. The first solution to this problem, page 279, illustrates the reasoning method. The second one shows the solution by formula.

16. How great is the force of expansion? The force of expansion or contraction is enormous. Broken wires in winter and the bursting of tires when highly heated all testify to the great force exerted by a change in temperature. Concrete walks buckle under the force of expansion. The magnitude of this force seems to be limited only by the breaking strength of the material at a certain specified temperature.

SAMPLE PROBLEM

We have 500 cm³ of gas at 20° C and 750 mm pressure. What volume will the gas occupy at 30° C and 760 mm pressure?

SOLUTION NO. 1

First, let us derive an expression which, if solved, would give us the new volume corrected for the change in pressure alone. This will be the original volume, 500 cm³, multiplied by the pressure fraction, $\frac{750}{760}$. In the pressure fraction, the smaller pressure goes in the numerator because the pressure is being increased and the resulting volume must be smaller. The new volume, corrected for pressure alone, equals $500 \times \frac{750}{760}$. We don't need to find the actual value. We can apply the temperature correction directly to this expression.

Converting to the Kelvin temperatures, 20° C = 293° K; 30° C = 303° K. Since the temperature rises, the volume change, produced by the temperature change alone, is an increase. The temperature fraction must therefore have the larger number in the numerator, $\frac{303}{293}$. Multiplying the expression for the pressure correction by this temperature correction, we obtain,

$500 \times \frac{750}{760} \times \frac{303}{293} = 510.2$ cm³, corrected volume.

★ SOLUTION NO. 2

The formula for finding the corrected volume of a gas when temperature and pressure both change is $\dfrac{pV}{T} = \dfrac{p'V'}{T'}$.

Here, p, V, and T represent the original pressure, volume, and Kelvin temperature respectively; p', V', and T' represent the new pressure, volume, and Kelvin temperature. Substituting the appropriate values in this formula,

$$\frac{750 \times 500}{293} = \frac{760 \times V'}{303}.$$

Transposing so that V' is the only term on the left side of the equation,

$$V' = \frac{750 \times 500 \times 303}{293 \times 760}.$$

Solving, V' = 510.2 cm³, the corrected volume.

Summary

In general, solids expand when heated and contract when cooled. The increase per unit length per unit degree is called the coefficient of linear expansion. The increase in area, or the coefficient of area expansion, is approximately twice the coefficient of linear expansion. The increase in volume, or the coefficient of volume expansion, is three times the coefficient of linear expansion.

Liquids have a much higher coefficient of expansion than solids. Water has its maximum density at 4° C. If heated above or cooled below this temperature, water expands.

The coefficient of expansion of all gases is nearly the same, 0.003660 per Centigrade degree.

The lowest possible temperature is absolute zero, −273.16° C or −459.69° F. The Kelvin temperature scale was devised with its zero point at absolute zero. The degrees on the Kelvin scale are the same size as Centigrade degrees. To convert Centigrade readings to Kelvin scale, add 273 degrees.

Charles' law states that if the pressure is constant, the volume of a dry gas is directly proportional to the Kelvin temperature. Charles' law and Boyle's law may be combined in the formula, $\dfrac{pV}{T} = \dfrac{p'V'}{T'}$.

—————— *Terms to Define...* ——————

Absolute zero	Coefficient of volume expan-	Kelvin scale
Bimetallic strip	sion	Metallic thermometer
Coefficient of area expan-	Compensated balance wheel	Pyrex glass
sion	Expansion of bridges	Thermostat
Coefficient of linear expan-	Expansion of gases	Riveting
sion	Expansion of water	Volume expansion of liquids

Questions

GROUP A

1. How does running hot water over the cap of a jar of pickles help loosen the cap?

2. What is coefficient of linear expansion?

3. What provision is made to allow for expansion of (1) concrete highways? (2) railroad tracks? (3) piston rings?

4. How does the coefficient of volume expansion for mercury compare with the coefficient of volume expansion for glass?

5. What season is the best time to string a wire fence in order that it remain tight?

6. What is the temperature of a body when it has given up all the thermal energy it can?

7. With what two properties of a gas is Charles' law concerned?

8. A hole, 0.25 inch in diameter, is drilled through a piece of steel at 20° C. What happens to the diameter of the hole as the steel is heated to 100° C?

9. How does the Centigrade scale compare with the Kelvin scale?

10. What happens to the length of the heating wires in your electric toaster as they get warm?

GROUP B

11. Does the coefficient of linear expansion depend on the unit of length used?

12. Explain how the coefficient of linear expansion per Centigrade degree compares with the coefficient of linear expansion per Fahrenheit degree.

13. Why are brass and iron used for making bimetallic strips?

14. Do you get more gasoline for your money in the winter or in the summer, providing it sells for the same price per gallon during both seasons?

15. Explain how a dial-type oven thermometer operates.

16. Why are the coefficients of volume expansion for various gases very nearly the same?

17. A platinum wire may be easily sealed into a glass tube. However, a copper wire does not form a tight seal with glass. Explain.

If Richard now measures the volume, what will he find it to be?

8. What is the increase in volume of a gallon of turpentine when it is warmed from $10°$ C to $55°$ C?

9. Five liters of oxygen are measured when the temperature is $27°$ C. What volume will the gas occupy at $77°$ C?

10. What will be the decrease in volume of 50 ft³ of natural gas, measured at $17°$ C, when the temperature is lowered to $-23°$ C?

11. A certain gas occupies a volume of 250 ml at $37°$ C. What is its volume at $67°$ C?

12. To what temperature must 1000 ml of gas at $0°$ C be heated to increase the volume to 1500 ml?

(In the Mathematics Refresher, refer to Sections 8, 10, and 16.)

GROUP A

1. A piece of copper pipe is 15 ft long at $20°$ C. If it is heated to $70°$ C, what will be the increase in its length?

2. A rod of silver is 100 cm long at $0°$ C When heated to $100°$ C, its length becomes 100.19 cm. What is its coefficient of linear expansion?

3. The steel cables on a bridge are 5000 ft long on a day when the temperature is $30°$ C. What will be their length when the temperature drops to $10°$ C?

4. The boiling point of liquid oxygen is $-183.0°$ C. What is this temperature in degrees Kelvin?

5. What will be the boiling point of helium in the Centigrade scale if its boiling point on the Kelvin scale is $4.1°$?

6. Ten gallons of ethyl alcohol are placed in a tank when the temperature is $15°$ C. What will be the volume of this alcohol when the temperature rises to $25°$ C?

7. Richard pours 500 ml of carbon tetrachloride, temperature $20°$ C, into a flask. He then heats the carbon tetrachloride to $45°$ C.

GROUP B

13. The diameter of a hole drilled through a piece of brass is 0.500 cm when the temperature is $20°$ C. What will be the diameter of the hole if the brass is heated to $150°$ C?

14. An aluminum rod 60.0 cm long is heated from $20.0°$ C to $100.0°$ C. The screw micrometer which measures the change in length has an original reading of 2.1735 cm and a final reading of 2.0631 cm. What is the coefficient of linear expansion per Centigrade degree?

15. One cubic centimeter of mercury at $20°$ C has a mass of 13.546 g. What will be the mass of 1 cm³ of mercury at $100°$ C?

16. Find the volume at S. T. P. of 350 ml of hydrogen measured at $27°$ C and 740 mm pressure.

● **17.** What volume of air at a pressure of 15 lb/in² and $17°$ C can be pumped into an "empty" 25 ft³ tank to raise the gauge pressure to 75 lb/in² if the temperature is raised to $47°$ C?

● **18.** The spaces between 40 ft steel rails are 0.20 in at a temperature of $0°$ F. If the rails close up at $90°$ F, what is the coefficient of linear expansion per Fahrenheit degree? Per Centigrade degree?

● **19.** A new refrigerator is being installed in a room which contains dry air at a temperature of $98.6°$ F and a barometric pressure of 760 mm of mercury. During installation the door of the refrigerator stood open. When the refrigerating mechanism is turned on, the door is immediately closed. What is the difference in the pressures inside and outside the refrigerator when the temperature inside the refrigerator drops to $42.8°$ F?

Chapter 14

Change of Phase

1. HEAT UNITS—SPECIFIC HEAT

1. The measurement of heat. We already have learned about the construction of several types of thermometers. We found that each type has a useful temperature range, and that by using the proper thermometer, we may measure almost any temperature. The measurement of heat is not so simple. We don't have any instrument which will tell us directly the amount of thermal energy a body can give out or absorb. Therefore, *we measure quantities of heat by the effects which they produce.* For example, the amount of heat given out when a fuel burns may be measured by the temperature change it produces in a known quantity of water. If one sample of coal heats 1000 g of water 1 C°, and another sample heats 1000 g of water 2 C°, then twice as much heat was given out by the second sample.

Vocabulary

BRITISH THERMAL UNIT. The quantity of heat which raises the temperature of one pound of water one Fahrenheit degree.

CALORIE. The quantity of heat which raises the temperature of one gram of water one Centigrade degree.

DEW POINT. The temperature at which the moisture in the air begins to condense.

FUSION. The change of phase from a solid to a liquid.

HEAT CAPACITY. The quantity of heat needed to raise the temperature of a body one Centigrade degree.

HEAT OF FUSION. The number of calories needed to melt one gram of a substance without increasing its temperature; or the number of British thermal units needed to melt one pound of a substance without increasing its temperature.

HEAT OF VAPORIZATION. The number of calories needed to vaporize one gram of a liquid without increasing its temperature; or the number of British thermal units needed to vaporize one pound of a liquid without increasing its temperature.

HUMIDITY. Amount of water vapor in air.

KILOCALORIE. 1000 calories.

SPECIFIC HEAT. The number of calories needed to raise the temperature of one gram of a substance one Centigrade degree; or the number of British thermal units needed to raise the temperature of one pound of a substance one Fahrenheit degree.

SUBLIMATION. The evaporation of a solid to a gas directly without passing through a liquid phase.

VAPORIZATION. The change of phase from a liquid to a vapor.

2. What are the units of heat? In defining the three common units for measuring thermal energy, we find that water again serves as a standard.

(1) *The calorie. The quantity of heat needed to raise the temperature of one gram of water one Centigrade degree is called the* **calorie,** abbreviated cal. When the temperature of one gram of water drops one Centigrade degree, it gives out one calorie of heat. Warming one gram of water ten Centigrade degrees requires ten calories. Ten calories could also warm ten grams of water one Centigrade degree.

(2) *The kilocalorie.* As you probably gathered from its name, the **kilocalorie** *is 1000 calories.* The *kilocalorie,* abbreviated kcal, *is the quantity of heat needed to raise the temperature of one kilogram of water one Centigrade degree.* This unit is the " calorie " which the biologist and dietician use in measuring the fuel value of foods.

(3) *The British thermal unit.* This is the heat unit used in the English system. *The* **British thermal unit,** abbreviated Btu, *is the quantity of heat needed to raise the temperature of one pound of water one Fahrenheit degree.*

Since these units are energy units, they may be related to each other as well as to the energy units which we studied in Mechanics. *One Btu equals 252 calories.* The relation between calories and joules, and between British thermal units and foot-pounds will be given in Chapter 16.

3. Substances have different heat capacities. Fig. 14-1 shows blocks of five different metals, aluminum, iron, copper, zinc, and lead. They all have a mass of 100 g and have the same cross-sectional area. Because these metals have different densities, the pieces have different heights. We first place all of them in a pan of boiling water to heat them to the same temperature. Then we transfer them to a block of ice. The diagram shows us the relative depths to which they melt the ice. We see that the aluminum block melts the most ice. Iron follows as a poor second, while copper and zinc are tied for third. The lead melts ice the least. This experiment shows us that different materials absorb or give out different amounts of heat, even though the materials have the same mass and undergo the same temperature change. We say that such substances differ in *heat capacity.* Those with a high heat capacity warm up more slowly because they must ab-

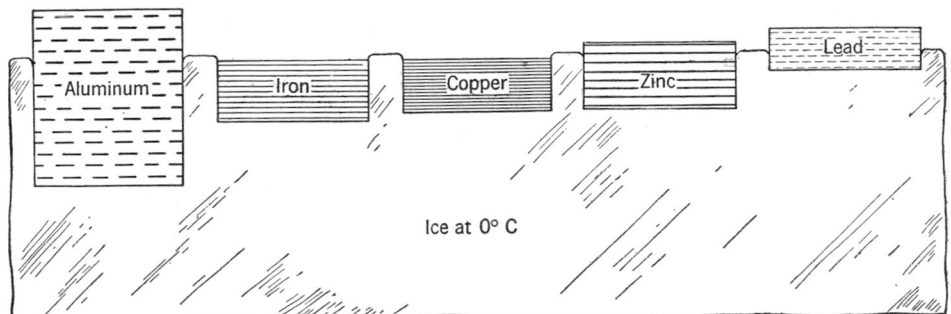

Fig. 14-1. Because metals have different heat capacities, these blocks, all of equal mass and heated to the same temperature, melt to different depths in the ice.

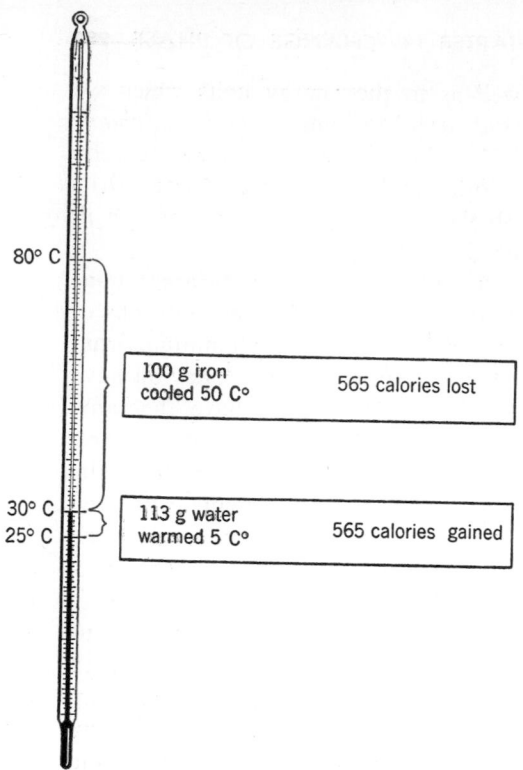

Fig. 14-2. When 100 g of iron at 80° C are added to 113 g of water at 25° C, the final temperature of the mixture is 30° C. The number of calories lost by the iron equals the number of calories gained by the water.

sorb a greater number of calories. They cool down more slowly, too, because they must give out more heat. *The **heat capacity** of a body may be defined as the quantity of heat needed to raise its temperature 1 C°.*

4. What is specific heat? The heat capacity of a body does not tell us very much about the thermal properties of the material of which the body is made. For example, the heat capacity of 100 g of copper is different from the heat capacity of 100 g of aluminum. But the heat capacity of 100 g of aluminum is also different from that of 200 g of aluminum. In order to obtain a figure which is characteristic of copper or aluminum, we must compare the heat capacities of equal masses. Here again we use water as our standard. The specific heat capacity of water is the heat capacity of a unit mass of water. Let us use 1 g as our unit mass. Then, since 1 calorie is needed to raise the temperature of 1 g of water 1 C°, the specific heat capacity of water is 1 cal/g C°. The phrase "specific heat capacity" is usually spoken of simply as *specific heat*. Using 1 lb as the unit mass in the English system, the specific heat of water becomes 1 Btu/lb F°. Because of the way in which the calorie and the Btu are defined, the specific heat of water is *numerically* 1.00 in both the metric and the English system. The specific heats of other substances are likewise *numerically* equal in the two systems of measurement.

*The **specific heat** of a substance equals the number of calories needed to raise the temperature of 1 g of the substance 1 C°. The specific heat of a substance also equals the number of Btu needed to raise the temperature of 1 lb of the substance 1 F°.*

By experiment, we find that a given mass of iron can be heated from room temperature to 100° C in about $\frac{1}{9}$ the time it takes to heat an equal mass of water through the same temperature change. Apparently the specific heat of iron is about $\frac{1}{9}$ that of water. The average of a large number of experiments shows that it requires only 0.107 calorie to warm one gram of iron one Centigrade degree. The specific heat of iron is therefore 0.107 cal/g C°. It is also 0.107 Btu/lb F°. From Table 10, Appendix B, we learn that the specific heat of most substances is rather small when compared with water.

5. The amount of heat needed to raise the temperature of materials. We know that one calorie warms one gram of water one Centigrade degree. Then 100 cal will warm 100 g of water 1 C°. Or 100 cal can also warm 1 g of water 100 C°. To find the amount of heat needed to produce a certain temperature change in a specific material, multiply *mass (g) × change in temperature (C°) × specific heat = heat required (cal)*; or *mass (lb) × change in temperature (F°) × specific heat = heat required (Btu)*.

★ The general formula is

$$Q = mc\Delta t,$$

where Q is the amount of heat required to produce a change in temperature, Δt, in a mass, m, of a substance having a specific heat, c. If m is given in g, and Δt in C°, Q will be in cal; when m is in lb, and Δt in F°, Q will be in Btu; c is numerically the same whether metric or English units are used.

6. The method of mixtures. If a cup of coffee is too hot to drink, we may cool it quickly by adding some cold water. The temperature of the coffee is lowered, but the temperature of the water we add is raised. The final temperature of the mixture lies between the original temperatures of the coffee and the cold water. Each time we bring into contact or mix two substances of *unequal* temperature, we find that *the warmer one loses heat and the cooler one gains heat until they both finally reach the same temperature.* Heat is a form of energy. No heat energy is lost when substances of unequal temperatures are mixed. *The heat given off by hot objects equals the heat received by cold objects.* The total number of heat units given off by warmer substances equals the total number of heat units received by cooler substances. *Calories lost = calories gained; or Btu's lost = Btu's gained.*

In a laboratory experiment, 100 g

SAMPLE PROBLEM

How many calories are needed to raise the temperature of 300 g of aluminum 50 C°?

SOLUTION

From Table 10, Appendix B, we find the specific heat of aluminum is 0.214. To calculate the heat needed, we multiply the mass of aluminum, 300 g, by the temperature change, 50° C, and by the specific heat, 0.214.
300 × 50 × 0.214 = 3210 cal.

★ SAMPLE PROBLEM

How many calories of heat will be given out when 200 g of water cool from 80° C to 20° C?

SOLUTION

The specific heat of water is 1.00. The temperature change, Δt, is 60 C°. Substituting in the formula, $Q = mc\Delta t$, we have $Q = 200 \times 1.00 \times 60$. Solving, $Q = 12,000$ cal.

of iron at 80° C were added to 107 g of water at 25° C. The final temperature of the mixture was 30° C. Refer to Fig. 14-2. The iron cooled 50 C°, from 80° C to 30° C. How many calories did it give off? We multiply the mass of the iron, 100 g, by the change in temperature, 50 C°, and then by the specific heat of iron, 0.107. 100 × 50 × 0.107 = 535 calories given off by the iron. The water was warmed from 25° C to 30° C, a temperature change of 5 C°. How many calories did it receive? Multiplying the mass of the water, 107 g, by the temperature change, 5 C°, and then by the specific heat of water, 1.00, we obtain 107 × 5 × 1.00 = 535 calories received by the water. This equals the number of calories given off by the iron.

7. Measuring specific heat. If we have a lump of brass, how can we find its specific heat? We do this by using the method of mixtures. The procedure includes the following steps:

(1) Find the mass of a metal cup, or *calorimeter* (kal-er-*im*-eh-ter), whose specific heat is known.

(2) Pour some cold water into the calorimeter. Then find the combined mass of calorimeter and water. By subtraction, calculate the mass of the water.

(3) Find the mass of the lump of brass. Then heat the brass by suspending it in steam over boiling water. It must be heated long enough to acquire the temperature of the steam, which is taken with a thermometer.

(4) The temperature of the water in the calorimeter is also taken. The lump of brass then is quickly transferred to the water in the calorimeter.

(5) The water in the calorimeter is stirred. We watch the rise in temperature of the water as shown by a ther-

Boiling water

Hot brass cylinder

Thermometer

Cold water

Fig. 14-3. Finding the specific heat of brass by the method of mixtures.

mometer. When the mercury in the thermometer stops rising we know that the brass, the water, and the calorimeter have reached the same temperature. This is the final temperature of the mixture. The brass lost heat; the calorimeter and the water gained heat.

In order to illustrate the calculations of this method, let us use the following data:

Mass of calorimeter	110 g
Specific heat of calorimeter	0.09 cal/g C°
Mass of water	405 g
Mass of brass	201.9 g
Initial temperature of the water	20° C
Initial temperature of brass	100° C
Final temperature of water, calorimeter and brass	23.5° C

The heat lost by the brass is:

Mass (g) × change of temperature (C°) × specific heat = heat lost (cal). By substituting from our data, 201.9 × (100 − 23.5) × specific heat = heat lost.

The heat gained by the calorimeter and the water is:

110 × (23.5 − 20) × 0.09 = 34.7 cal, gained by the calorimeter.
405 × (23.5 − 20) × 1.00 = 1417.5 cal, gained by the water.
Total heat gained = 1452.2 cal.

Since the heat lost by the brass equals the heat gained by the calorimeter and water,

201.9 × 76.5 × specific heat = 1452.2
Solving, specific heat = 0.094 cal/g C°. This is the specific heat of the brass.

This method is a general one. In all problems involving heat exchange and specific heat, you must identify the substances which lose heat and those which gain heat. Also, you must remember that the heat lost by the warmer bodies equals the heat gained by the cooler ones. Finally, mass (g) × change in temperature (C°) × specific heat = amount of heat transferred (cal).

★ **8. Effects of the high specific heat of water.** Sometimes in early June in the northern states the weather becomes quite balmy. We become anxious to go out for the first swim of the season. What a shock it is to find that though the air and ground are warm, the water in the lake or ocean is still too cold for comfort! In the spring, water increases in temperature more slowly than does the land. In late September and early October the reverse is true. We may enjoy a late summer swim, but when we come out the air feels quite chilly. Water warms slowly and cools slowly.

Cities which are located on large bodies of water do not experience the extremes of temperature often found in inland cities. San Francisco and St. Louis are at about the same latitude. However, San Francisco, with its weather tempered by the Pacific Ocean, has a more even climate than St. Louis. While New York City is on the ocean, its climate is subject to greater variations than that of San Francisco because it is affected by the prevailing westerly winds which blow across North America.

QUESTIONS

GROUP A

1. What is a calorie? A kilocalorie? A British thermal unit? How many calories equal 1 Btu?

2. Two cylinders having the same mass and the same cross-sectional area, but composed of different metals, are heated to the same temperature. They are then placed on a one-half inch thick piece of paraffin. If one cylinder takes twice as long to melt through the paraffin, how do they compare in heat capacity?

3. What is the specific heat of a substance?

4. How do the specific heats of most common substances compare with the specific heat of water?

5. How do we calculate the amount of heat required to produce a given temperature change in a substance?

6. What happens when a hot object is brought into contact with a cold object? Compare the amount of heat lost by the hot object with the amount of heat gained by the cold object.

GROUP B

7. Since we have no instrument which measures heat directly, how do we measure quantities of heat?

8. Why are specific heats numerically equal in the English system and the metric system of measurement?

★ **9.** Why is it not comfortable to swim in Lake Erie until July?

★ **10.** In what way would you expect the Pacific Ocean to affect the climate of a city like Portland, Oregon?

PROBLEMS

(In the Mathematics Refresher, refer to Sections 10 and 16.)

GROUP A

1. How many calories will be needed to change the temperature of 500 g of water from 20° C to 100° C?

2. A cube of iron weighs 5 lb. How many Btu will be needed to raise its temperature from 70° F to 300° F?

3. How much heat is given out when 75 g of lead cool from 200° C to 0° C?

4. An aluminum cylinder is heated to 500° F. If the cylinder weighs 3 lb, how many Btu are given out as the cylinder cools to 50° F?

5. Paul mixes 10 g of water at 0° C with 20 g of water at 30° C. What will be the final temperature of the mixture?

6. A piece of tin having a mass of 250 g and a temperature of 100° C is dropped into 100 g of water at a temperature of 10° C. If the final temperature of the mixture is 20° C, what is the specific heat of tin?

7. An aluminum calorimeter has a mass of 60 g. Its temperature is 25° C. What will be the final temperature attained when 60 g of water at 100° C is poured into it?

GROUP B

8. The mass of a certain block of metal is 1000 g. It is heated to a temperature of 300° C and then placed in 100 g of water at 0° C in a calorimeter. The mass of the calorimeter is 100 g; its specific heat is 0.1. If the final temperature is 70° C, find the specific heat of the metal.

9. A block of brass, having a mass of 500 g and a temperature of 100° C, is placed in 300 g of water, temperature 20° C, in an aluminum calorimeter which has a mass of 75 g. The final temperature is 30° C. What is the specific heat of the brass? (Use 0.2 as the specific heat of aluminum.)

10. A copper ball has a mass of 95 g and a specific heat of 0.092. It is heated to 90° C and then placed in 75 g of turpentine, temperature 20° C. The temperature of the mixture, after stirring, is 35° C. What is the specific heat of turpentine?

● **11.** A 450-g metal cylinder at 100° C is dropped into a 150-g iron calorimeter which contains 300 g of water at 21° C. The specific heat of the calorimeter is 0.1. If the resulting temperature is 30° C, calculate the specific heat of the cylinder.

2. FUSION

9. What is fusion? As a solid absorbs heat, its temperature rises. Upon reaching a certain temperature, the solid melts and becomes a liquid. *This change of phase, or change of state, from a solid to a liquid is called* **fusion.**

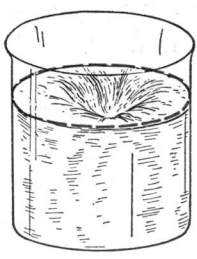
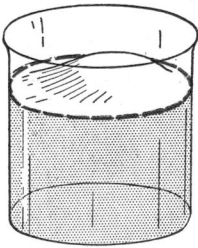

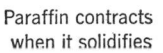

Paraffin contracts
when it solidifies

Water expands
when it freezes

Fig. 14-4. Most substances are like paraffin and contract when they solidify. Water is one of a few substances which expand when they solidify.

Fusion is the scientific term for what we commonly call melting, or liquefaction. The temperature at which this change occurs is called the *melting point*. Pure substances generally have a definite melting point, and different solids have different melting points.

When a substance changes from a liquid to a solid, it is said that it freezes. The physicist calls this change of phase *solidification*. The temperature at which solidification occurs is known as the *freezing point*. For crystalline substances, melting point and freezing point are the same temperature.

Non-crystalline substances like glass and paraffin have no definite melting point. When they are heated, they soften gradually. Such substances may be heated until they soften, and then be bent, molded, or welded.

10. Volume changes during solidification. If we pour melted paraffin into a glass jar and let it harden, the center will become indented, or depressed, as shown in Fig. 14-4. This happens because paraffin contracts when it solidifies. All but a very few substances behave thus when they change from the liquid to the solid phase.

Water is the most important exception to the rule that a substance contracts when it changes from a liquid to a solid. The level of the water in the sections of an ice cube tray is uniform when the tray is placed in the freezing compartment. But when the ice cubes are formed, each one will have a slightly raised spot in the center. The volume occupied by ice is about 1.1 times that occupied by the water from which it was formed. The force of expansion when water freezes is enormous.

Bismuth and antimony are two metals which expand when they solidify. Antimony is a constituent of type metal. Because it expands when the molten metal is poured into a mold, the type is sharp and clear-cut.

Fig. 14-5. Showing expansion as water becomes ice. These tubes of Alathon 10 polyethylene were filled with water and sealed. The tube on the left was then frozen. Expansion amounted to .136 inch. (Normally, freezing of plastic tubing is not recommended.)

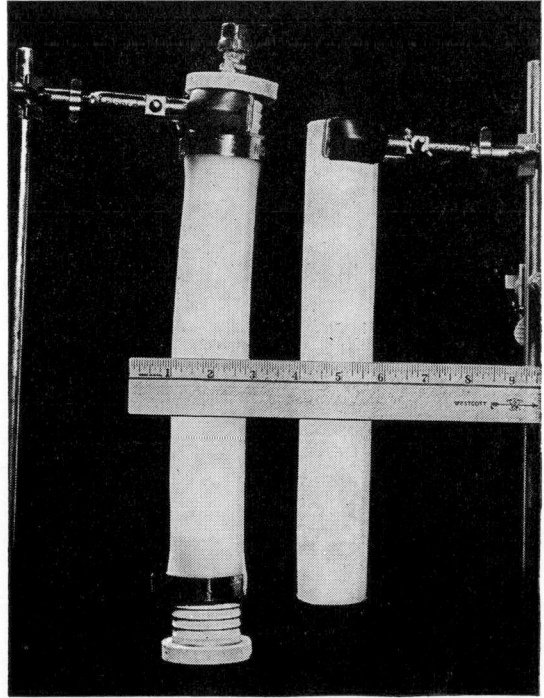

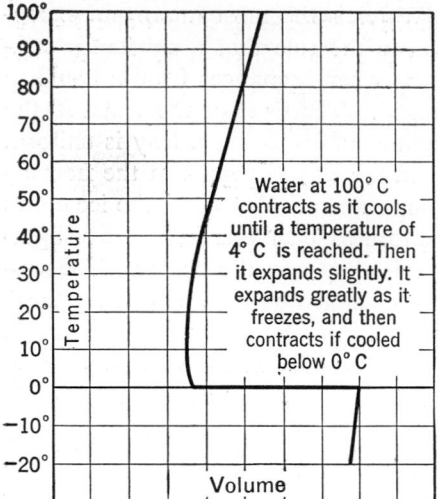

Fig. 14-6. A curve showing the variation in the volume of a given mass of water as it is cooled, changed into ice, and further cooled.

11. The expansion of water upon freezing. Water contracts as it cools until a temperature of 4° C is reached. Then the water expands slightly as it cools to its freezing point, 0° C. If water did not expand slightly below 4° C and expand much more as it freezes, the ice which forms on the surface of a pond or stream would immediately sink to the bottom. During the cold winter months, ice would continue to form until the pond or stream was frozen solid. In the summer months only a few feet of ice at the top of the lake would melt. However, no ice can form at the surface until all the water in the pond is cooled to 4° C. Then as the surface is cooled further, and freezes at 0° C, the ice remains on the surface.

Fig. 14-6 is a graph which shows the contraction of a given mass of water as it is cooled to 4° C, the expansion from 4° C to 0° C, the sharp expan-

sion on freezing, and the slight contraction as ice is cooled below 0° C.

★ 12. How does pressure affect the melting point? When most substances freeze, they contract, like the paraffin in Fig. 14-4. The molecules of the solid are closer together than the molecules of the liquid. By exerting additional pressure on it, can we cause such a liquid to solidify at a higher temperature than its normal melting point under atmospheric pressure? Experiments show that we can. An increase in pressure will raise the freezing temperature of most substances. Some of the rocks in the interior of the earth are probably hot enough to melt at normal pressure. But they remain solid because of the tremendous pressure. If pressure is released, as when a volcano erupts, the rocks melt, forming lava.

What effect does an increase in pressure have on the freezing point of a substance like water, which expands as it freezes? In such a substance we may assume that the molecules are farther apart in the solid than they are in the

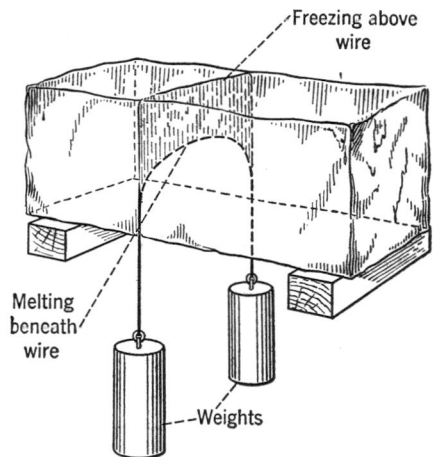

Fig. 14-7. The melting under pressure and freezing again after the pressure is released is called regelation.

Fig. 14-8. The movement of this glacier down into the valley is made possible by the melting of the ice under pressure and its refreezing again after the pressure is released. This phenomena is an example of regelation.

liquid. Then, an increase in pressure makes it more difficult for the solid phase to form. This means that the freezing point will be lowered if the pressure is raised.

We may illustrate this by the following experiment. Let us suspend two brass weights by means of a strong wire over the surface of a large cake of ice. This is shown in Fig. 14-7. The pressure of the wire on the ice lowers the melting point of the ice immediately below the wire. This part of the ice melts, and the molecules of water are forced upward around the wire. When they reach a spot above the wire, the pressure returns to normal, and the water molecules freeze again. In this way, the wire may cut its way through the cake of ice, and yet leave the ice completely solid. This melting under pressure and freezing again after the pressure is released is called *regelation* (reh-jel-*ay*-shun).

An increase in pressure produces only a slight effect on the melting point of ice. At two atmospheres pressure, the melting point of ice is lowered only to $-0.0075°$ C. The property of snow to pack into snowballs results from the change in melting point with pressure. When we make a snowball, we squeeze the snow together, causing some crystals to melt. When the pressure is released and the water freezes again, the snowball stays together. However, on very cold days we find that snow does not pack, because we can not exert sufficient pressure with our hands to cause it to melt.

13. How much heat do we need to melt one gram of ice? Suppose we take a tray of ice cubes, crush them, and place them in a pan. Now let us heat the pan of crushed ice over a gas-burner or electric hot-plate. If we stir the ice and water mixture that is being formed, we find that the temperature is 0° C when we start. The temperature does not rise above 0° C until all the ice is melted. We are continuously adding heat to the mixture, but since the temperature does not rise, this heat must be used to change the solid ice into liquid water.

We know that the atoms and molecules of a solid vibrate about definite fixed positions. The atoms and molecules in a liquid, while not much farther apart than in a solid, have enough energy to slip around each other. Evidently the heat which we apply to ice at 0° C to change it into water at 0° C increases the energy of the atoms and molecules. Since the heat that is added to produce such a change does not produce an increase in temperature, it is sometimes called *latent* (hidden) *heat*.

The number of calories needed to melt one gram of a substance without increasing its temperature is called its **heat of fusion.** The heat of fusion of ice is approximately 80 cal/g. This means that 80 cal must be added to 1 g of ice at 0° C to convert it into water at 0° C. Ice melts because it absorbs heat from its surroundings. Thus it lowers the temperature of substances placed near it. It acts as a refrigerating agent. *The heat of fusion in the English system is the number of*

SAMPLE PROBLEM

A calorimeter has a mass of 100 g. Its specific heat is 0.09. It contains 400 g of water at 40° C. When 91 g of ice are added and completely melted, the temperature of the water is 18.2° C. What is the heat of fusion of ice?

SOLUTION

The method of mixtures is based on the equation, *calories lost by hot objects = calories gained by cold objects.* First we must calculate the amount of heat lost by the hot objects, the calorimeter, and the water.

Heat lost by calorimeter:

$100 \times (40 - 18.2) \times 0.09 = 196.2$ cal

Heat lost by water:

$400 \times (40 - 18.2) \times 1.00 = 8720$ cal

Total heat lost:

$196.2 + 8720 = 8916.2$ cal

These 8916.2 cal did two things; first, they melted 91 g of ice; second, they warmed the 91 g of water thus formed from 0° C to 18.2° C.

Heat gained by the water:

$91 \times (18.2 - 0) \times 1.00 = 1656.2$ cal

By subtraction:

$8916.2 - 1656.2 = 7260$ cal, heat used to melt the ice.

$7260 \div 91 = 79.8$ cal/g, heat of fusion of ice.

In such a problem it is important to remember that every gram of ice that melts produces one gram of water. Part of the heat that is lost by the hot water is gained by this cooler water as it warms to the final temperature.

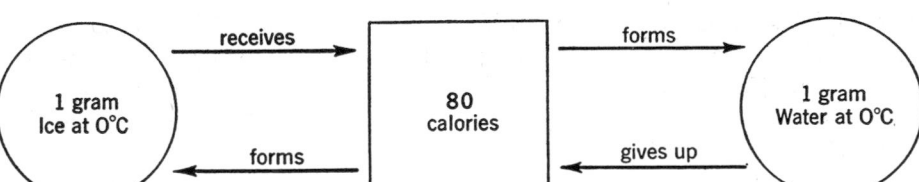

Fig. 14-9. The reversible energy change between one gram of ice and one gram of water at zero degree Centigrade.

British thermal units needed to melt one pound of a substance without increasing its temperature. In the English system the heat of fusion of ice is 144 Btu/lb at 32° F. The heat of fusion of some other substances is given in Table 10, Appendix B.

14. Measuring the heat of fusion. We use the method of mixtures to determine the heat of fusion of a solid. Suppose we wish to find the heat of fusion of ice. Since hot water melts ice, we must find out how many grams of ice can be melted by a known mass of water at a known temperature. We shall need the following data: mass of calorimeter; specific heat of calorimeter; mass of water; initial temperature of water; mass of ice; and the final temperature when all the ice is melted. See the Sample Problem, page 292.

15. Water gives up heat when it freezes. The heat added to ice to make it melt increases the thermal energy of its atoms and molecules and changes it into water. Is this same energy given out when water freezes? Yes, this is a reversible energy change. Each gram of water at 0° C that forms ice at 0° C gives off 80 cal. When the atoms and molecules of water return to their fixed positions in ice, they give up the energy, which enabled them to slide over one another, in the form of heat. Fig. 14-9 shows the reversible energy change between 1 g of ice and

1 g of water at 0° C. To change the ice to water, 80 cal must be added. To change the water to ice, 80 cal must be taken away.

★ If pure water is very carefully cooled without being disturbed, temperatures as low as −40° C may be reached without the water becoming frozen. Water that is cooled below the normal freezing point is said to be *supercooled.* If a piece of ice is added to such water, freezing takes place rapidly and the temperature will rise to 0° C, the normal freezing point. The formation of ice takes place readily at 0° C if there is some dust or other foreign matter on which the first crystals of ice can condense. Supercooling results when these are not present because of the difficulty in forming the first small ice crystal.

★ **16. Producing low temperatures in the laboratory.** In order to demonstrate the expansion of water on freezing, or the solidification of mercury, we must be able to produce low temperatures conveniently. A salt-ice mixture may be used to freeze water. When salt is put on ice, it dissolves in the surface moisture. This absorbs heat. Moreover, a solution of salt in water has a lower freezing point than pure water. A saturated salt solution freezes at −21° C. Since the salt solution has a lower melting point than water, salt added to ice makes the ice melt rapidly. Both the more rapid melting of the ice and the dissolving of the salt absorb heat.

Temperatures down to $-78.5°$ C may be obtained from a mixture of solid carbon dioxide, "Dry-Ice," and a liquid such as acetone or ether. This mixture may be made in an unstoppered vacuum bottle so that it does not absorb heat too rapidly from its surroundings.

★ **17. Industry uses low temperatures.** Many new low temperature processes are being developed by various industries. We are all familiar with the freezing of foods to preserve them. The frozen food industry provides us with a wide variety of meats, fish, poultry, fruits, and vegetables all year round. Blood plasma is prepared for storage by freezing it, too. Temperatures between $32°$ F and $-40°$ F are used in these freezing processes.

The use of solid carbon dioxide for storing ice cream has become quite popular. Soft manufactured parts, such as those made of rubber, may be smoothed by hardening them at $-100°$ F and then tumbling them in revolving containers. Liquid carbon

Fig. 14-10. The photograph at the left shows a scientist holding a coil of wire through which electricity is flowing to the electric lamp. Notice how dimly the lamp glows. The photograph at the right shows the scientist immersing the coil of wire in liquid air. At this low temperature, the wire becomes a better conductor, because now the lamp glows much more brightly.

dioxide is used as a cooling agent in certain grinding operations.

In order to produce special hard steels, the metal is chilled by liquid air at $-300°$ F and then rolled at below zero temperatures. These low temperatures are also used for shrink-fitting parts into each other. The inner part is chilled in liquid air or liquid nitrogen and then placed in position with the other part. As it warms up,

it expands and fits tightly inside the other part.

Temperatures near that of liquid helium, $-454°$ F, offer interesting industrial possibilities. Matter sometimes behaves in unexpected fashion at this very low temperature. For instance, materials that are poor electrical conductors at room temperature become super conductors when cooled in liquid helium.

QUESTIONS

GROUP A

1. What is meant by the expression "change of phase"? By the term "fusion"?

2. What change in volume takes place when most substances solidify? What important substance does not behave in this fashion? How does it behave?

3. The air above the ice of a pond is $-10°$ C. What probably will be the temperature of the upper surface of the ice? The lower surface? The water just beneath the surface? The water at the bottom of the pond?

4. Why do we call the heat necessary to melt ice "hidden heat"?

5. Why does it often happen that the temperature of the air slowly rises during a prolonged snowfall?

GROUP B

★ **6.** What effect does an increase in pressure have on the freezing point of a substance which contracts as it freezes? What effect does an increase in pressure have on the freezing point of a substance which expands as it freezes?

★ **7.** What effect will a drop in temperature from 25° F to 0° F probably have on the coefficient of sliding friction between the runners of a sled and the snow?

★ **8.** How is water supercooled?

★ **9.** Describe two convenient methods for producing low temperatures in a high school physics laboratory.

★ **10.** Why can typical molded rubber parts be easily smoothed if they are first cooled to $-100°$ F?

PROBLEMS

(In the Mathematics Refresher, refer to Sections 10 and 16.)

GROUP A

1. How many calories will be absorbed by 75 g of ice at 0° C as it melts?

2. A 50-lb block of ice melts completely into water at 32° F. How many Btu were required to produce this change of phase?

3. Robert heats a 500-g aluminum block to 250° C. How many grams of ice at 0° C will the aluminum be able to melt on cooling?

4. To what temperature must a 5-lb iron ball be heated in order that it may completely melt 2 lb of ice at 32° F?

5. An aluminum tumbler has a mass of 50 g. It contains 100 g of water at 20° C. How many grams of ice at 0° C must be added to reduce the temperature of the mixture to 5° C?

6. To what temperature must a 500-g brass weight be heated in order to convert 60 g of ice at $-20°$ C into water at 20° C?

GROUP B

7. What will be the final temperature reached by a mixture of 50 g of ice at 0° C and 50 g of water at 80° C?

8. What is the final temperature attained when 300 g of ice at 0° C, 500 g of ice water at 0° C, and 1200 g of water at 100° C are mixed?

● **9.** A calorimeter, specific heat 0.1, has a mass of 200 g. It contains 300 g of water at 40° C. If 50 g of ice at 0° C are dropped into the water and stirred, the final temperature of the mixture when all the ice has melted, is 23.8° C. From this particular experiment calculate the heat of fusion of ice.

● **10.** A block of silver, mass 500 g, temperature 100° C, is placed in a calorimeter with 300 g of water, temperature 30° C. The mass of the calorimeter is 50 g and its specific heat is 0.1. A block of ice, mass 50 g, temperature −10° C, is also placed in the calorimeter. What is the final temperature?

---

3. VAPORIZATION AND CONDENSATION

18. What is vaporization? If we place some alcohol or ether in a shallow dish, we notice in a short time that the quantity of liquid is getting smaller. Water acts the same way, though not so rapidly. What happened to these liquids? Some of their molecules absorbed enough energy from the surroundings to overcome the forces holding them to the body of the liquid. They escaped from the surface of the liquid and became molecules of vapor. *The process of converting a liquid into a vapor is called* **vaporization.** When this process occurs slowly without visibly disturbing the liquid, it is called *evaporation.* However, if we heat a pan of water, bubbles of vapor will form on the bottom and sides of the container. When these bubbles rise into the cooler layers of liquid above them, they collapse. But when the entire quantity of water is heated enough, these bubbles reach the surface freely. Vaporization takes place so rapidly that the liquid becomes agitated. Rapid vaporization in which the liquid is disturbed is called *boiling.*

19. The rate of vaporization. We can see from the examples just given that the rate of evaporation varies with the temperature. Furthermore, it is different for different liquids. The process of vaporization consists of transferring energy to the molecules of a liquid so that they may escape from the surface of the liquid. Any method which speeds up this process will increase the rate of vaporization.

(1) *Effect of temperature.* Hot water evaporates faster than cold water. We expect this because the higher thermal energy of hot water means that its molecules move more rapidly. We conclude, therefore, that *the rate of vaporization increases with an increase in temperature.*

(2) *Effect of area.* Suppose we have one quart of water in a milk bottle and another quart of water in a broad, shallow pan. From which one will the water evaporate more rapidly? From the shallow pan. Therefore, we say that *the rate of vaporization increases as the surface area of the liquid increases.*

(3) *Nature of the liquid.* Alcohol evaporates much more rapidly than water. Ether evaporates faster than alcohol. There are some liquids, like glycerin and olive oil, that do not seem to evaporate at all. *The rate of vaporization varies with the nature of the liquid itself.*

(4) *Effect of the air pressure above the liquid.* Water molecules escaping

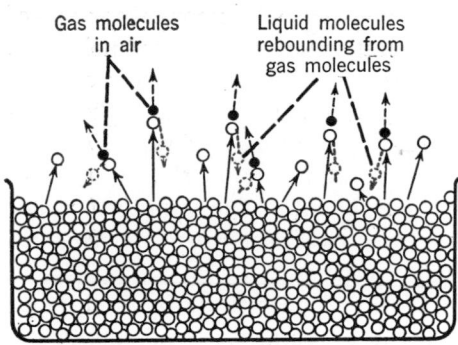

Fig. 14-11. The gas molecules in the air retard evaporation.

from the surface of a liquid meet a barrage of nitrogen and oxygen molecules from the air. Some of the molecules trying to escape collide with molecules in the air and rebound into the water again, as shown in Fig. 14-11. If we take some of the molecules above the surface away, these collisions will be less frequent. The vaporization will then be faster. It becomes extremely rapid in a vacuum. We conclude that *the rate of vaporization is increased when the atmospheric pressure is reduced.*

(5) *Effect of water vapor in the air.* When water molecules escape from the surface of the liquid, they occupy a part of the space between the gas molecules of the air. This makes a more crowded barrier for other water molecules which are trying to escape. Now, in addition to collisions with oxygen and nitrogen molecules, they may collide with other water molecules. This action is represented in Fig. 14-12. As the air becomes saturated with water vapor, evaporation takes place very slowly. When the number of water molecules returning to the water surface exactly equals the number of water molecules escaping per second, the

air is *saturated with water vapor. The rate of vaporization of water is decreased when the amount of water vapor in the air is increased.*

(6) *Effect of air movement above the liquid.* Wet clothes dry quickly when they are blown by the wind. In this case, the air which becomes saturated with water vapor is moved away. It is replaced by fresh, unsaturated air. *The rate of vaporization increases with the rate of change of the air in contact with the liquid surface.*

★ **20. The vaporization of solids.** Occasionally, in the winter you will notice that ice disappears from sidewalks and steps on days when the temperature does not get above freezing. This ice does not melt. It disappears without forming any water. Evidently the ice has been transformed directly into water vapor. At temperatures below 0° C, molecules of ice which acquire enough thermal energy can become molecules of water vapor directly. *They do not have to pass through the liquid phase. Such evaporation of solids directly into the gaseous state is called* **sublimation.** Some solids will

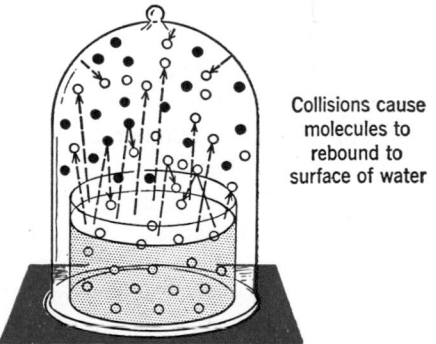

Collisions cause molecules to rebound to surface of water

Fig. 14-12. The additional pressure exerted by the water vapor molecules against the walls of the bell jar is called the saturated vapor pressure.

sublime at ordinary room temperatures. Camphor, iodine, and naphthalene ("moth balls") are well-known examples.

21. The vapor pressure of water. We have seen that both water and ice evaporate slowly at a temperature below 100° C under normal atmospheric pressure. When water is heated to 100° C, however, evaporation suddenly becomes so very rapid that the entire liquid is agitated. Why is there this distinct difference depending on the temperature? Let us look again at Fig. 14-12. When we place the bell jar over the container of water, there are as many molecules of the gases of the air trapped beneath the bell jar as we would find in an equal volume of air outside the bell jar. The pressure exerted by the oxygen and nitrogen molecules on the inside walls of the bell jar is the same as the pressure such molecules are exerting on the outside walls. The pressure of the gas in the bell jar is at one atmosphere. However, as the water evaporates, water molecules become mixed with the gas molecules. This increases the number of molecules striking the inside walls of the bell jar. The pressure against these inside walls thus becomes higher. Eventually, the number of water molecules returning to the surface of the liquid will equal the number escaping from the liquid. Then the number of water vapor molecules in the gas in the bell jar becomes constant. The molecules exert a pressure against the walls of the bell jar. This pressure is in addition to that exerted by the molecules of the gases of the air alone. Such added pressure of the water vapor molecules is called the *saturated vapor pressure*. Since the saturated vapor pressure depends upon the rate of evaporation of the water molecules, and since we know that the molecules evaporate more rapidly at higher temperatures, the *saturated vapor pressure must depend only on the temperature of the liquid. The saturated vapor pressure increases when the temperature increases.*

Now we understand why a substance like ice evaporates. Solid substances, like liquids, exert a vapor pressure. The saturated vapor pressure of ice at 0° C is equal to about 4.5 mm of mercury. With solids, however, the vapor pressure is much less than with liquids, and they evaporate more slowly. Since they do exert a vapor pressure, there is a slight tendency for the molecules of a solid to escape and to be transformed into molecules of vapor.

If we reduce the pressure on the surface of a solid or a liquid, we should make it easier for the molecules to escape. Evaporation should take place more rapidly. When the pressure of the atmosphere is reduced to the value of the saturated vapor pressure of a liquid, the liquid evaporates so very rapidly that we say it boils.

22. How does pressure affect the boiling temperature of water? Table 11, Appendix B gives the saturated vapor pressure of water at various temperatures. We show the graph of these data in Fig. 14-13, where the pressures are used as ordinates and the temperatures as abscissas. This is the vapor pressure curve of water. It also is used to determine the boiling temperature of water at varying pressures.

Since the vapor pressure of water at 100° C is 760 mm of mercury, or one atmosphere pressure, this is the normal boiling point of water. Suppose we

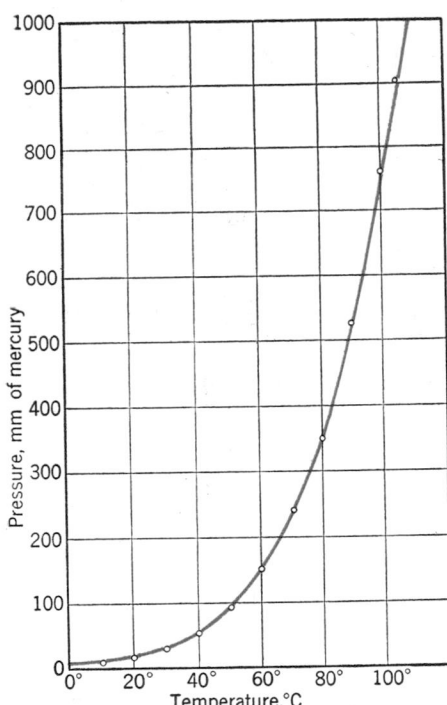

Fig. 14-13. The vapor pressure of water increases rapidly as the temperature is raised.

should reduce the air pressure to 525.8 mm of mercury. Water now boils at 90° C, since at this temperature the vapor pressure of water is 525.8 mm of mercury. In order to make water boil at 50° C, the pressure must be reduced to 92.5 mm. If we increase the pressure above one atmosphere to 787.5 mm of mercury, water will not boil until its temperature reaches 101° C. *The boiling temperature of water increases as the air pressure upon its surface increases.*

★ **23. Why do we use pressure cookers?** If you live in Denver, Colorado, or in Salt Lake City, Utah, you find the air pressure so very low that water boils at temperatures between 90° and 95° C. For approximately each 900 ft

of elevation above sea level, the boiling temperature of water drops 1 C° below the normal boiling point. This drop of 5 to 10 C° in the boiling temperature of water at Denver and Salt Lake City makes it difficult to cook foods in boiling water.

This difficulty may be overcome by using a pressure cooker. This is a strong-walled vessel in which a pressure higher than the outside atmospheric pressure can be maintained. One type of pressure cooker is shown in Fig. 14-14. The food is put into the cooker, together with a little water; then the lid is fastened firmly into place. When the water inside the cooker boils, the pressure of its vapor adds to the pressure of the air inside the cooker. As the pressure rises, the boiling temperature of the water rises too. The pressure maintained in such cookers is indicated by either a pressure gauge or a weight which permits steam to escape if the pressure gets above a certain value. The amount of heat supplied is adjusted so that the desired pressure is maintained in the cooker. If the pressure in the cooker is 15 lb/in² higher than the outside pressure, the boiling temperature of water may be increased to 110°–

Fig. 14-14. A pressure cooker enables us to cook foods more rapidly because of the higher boiling temperature of the water inside.

120° C. At such temperatures food cooks in one-half to one-third the time needed at 100° C.

★ **24. How are vacuum pans used?** Let us take a round-bottomed flask, pour a little water in it, and heat the water to boiling. Then we remove the flask from the flame and stopper the flask tightly. Now let us turn the flask upside down and clamp it in the position shown in Fig. 14-15. The flask contains only water and steam. If we dip a cellulose sponge in cold water and let the water from the sponge flow over the flask, some of the steam inside will condense. This reduces the pressure on the surface of the liquid, and the water will start to boil vigorously. When the boiling stops, the pressure may again be reduced by pouring more cold water over the outside of the flask.

The principle of boiling at reduced pressure, and consequently at a reduced temperature, is used in *vacuum pans*. Sugar crystals can be obtained from sugar syrup by boiling the syrup in a vacuum pan. The liquid evaporates quickly, and at the low temperature used there is no danger of scorching the sugar. Concentrated fruit juices, evaporated milk, certain drugs, and dyestuffs are prepared in a similar manner.

25. Summary of conditions affecting boiling. The experiments and practical applications given in the last few paragraphs illustrate several conditions which affect the boiling point of a liquid.

(1) The temperature at which the saturated vapor pressure of a liquid equals the pressure on its surface is the boiling point of the liquid. When the pressure on the surface of the liquid

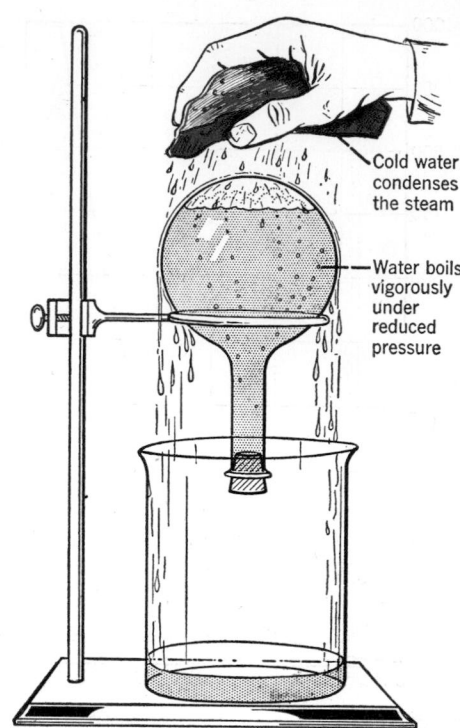

Cold water condenses the steam

Water boils vigorously under reduced pressure

Fig. 14-15. Water boils at a lower temperature when the pressure is reduced.

equals 760 mm of mercury, the temperature at which this liquid boils is called the *normal boiling point*.

(2) The boiling point of a liquid is a characteristic of that liquid. Consequently, this property may be used to identify a liquid, or to measure its purity.

(3) While water or any other liquid is boiling, it does not get hotter. Water boiling rapidly has the same temperature as water which is simmering. We find that while a liquid is boiling away, the boiling point does not change. It remains constant until all the liquid has vaporized.

(4) From our study of pressure cookers and vacuum pans, we know that the

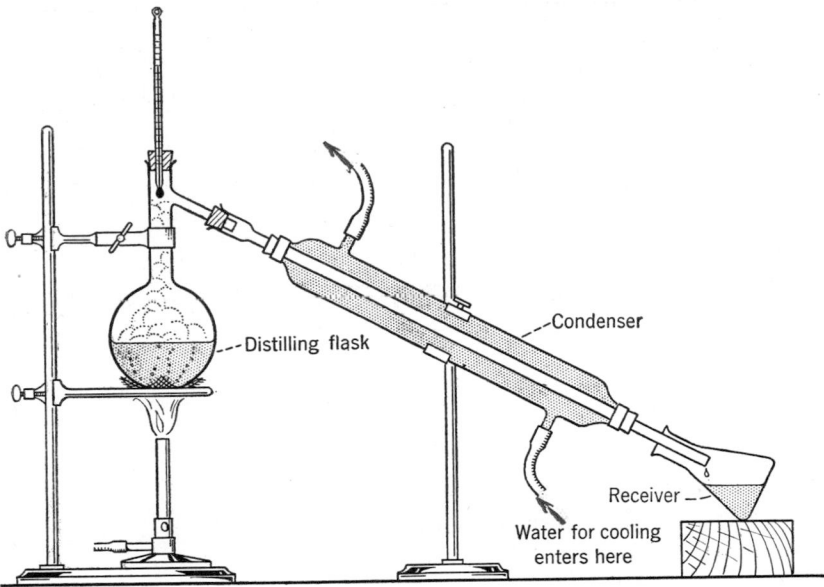

Fig. 14-16. Distillation is the process of converting a liquid to a vapor and then condensing it to a liquid again.

boiling point of a liquid rises as the pressure on its surface is increased. The boiling point falls as the pressure is decreased.

(5) When solids or gases are dissolved in a liquid, they change the boiling point of the liquid. Salt water boils at a higher temperature than pure water. In general, solids dissolved in liquids raise the boiling point. Gases dissolved in liquids usually lower the boiling point.

(6) If we mix ethyl alcohol with water and boil the mixture, we find that the boiling point is not the same as the boiling point of either alcohol or water. Alcohol boils at 78° C and water boils at 100° C. The boiling point of this mixture will be between 78° C and 100° C, depending on the proportions of alcohol and water that were mixed. When two or more liquids having different boiling points are mixed, the mixture has a different boiling point.

26. What is distillation? We need water which is free from dissolved mineral matter for the storage batteries of our automobiles, for making up certain solutions in a chemical laboratory, and for preparing drugs for injection. Insoluble impurities can be removed by filtration. We remove dissolved impurities by vaporizing the water. The impurities remain behind. The pure water vapor then is condensed into liquid again. This process is called *distillation*. We do it in the laboratory with the apparatus shown in Fig. 14-16. The distilling flask contains the impure water. As the water boils, the vapor passes through the inner tube of the condenser. Since the condenser is cooled by water running through the jacket surrounding it, the water vapor is condensed into liquid.

Fig. 14-17. One of the steps in the manufacture of petroleum products at a refinery such as this is the fractional distillation of petroleum to separate it into gasoline, kerosene, oils, and other products.

Many liquids, in addition to water, are purified by the process of distillation.

★ **27. Fractional distillation.** If you use an alcohol-type antifreeze in your automobile radiator, you must check its effectiveness periodically. Why? The boiling point of ethyl alcohol is about 78° C. The boiling point of the water with which it is mixed is 100° C. During a long, hard drive, or during unseasonably warm weather in the winter, the alcohol will be changed into vapor faster than the water will. In other words, one part or fraction of the liquid mixture evaporates or distills off more rapidly than the other fraction. It is possible to separate two or more liquids which have different boiling points. We distill the mixture and separate it into several fractions depending upon the boiling temperature. These are then redistilled one at a time, and a new set of fractions obtained. By repeating the process three or four times, a rather complete separation may be made.

★ **28. How do radiator air vents work?** Each radiator of a single pipe steam heating system must be provided with a vent which permits air to escape. But this must not permit either steam or water to escape. One type of radiator vent is shown in Fig. 14-18. It contains a float with a flexible metal

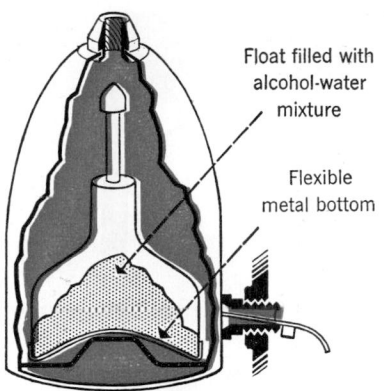

Float filled with alcohol-water mixture

Flexible metal bottom

Fig. 14-18. A radiator vent permits air to escape, but closes when either steam or water enters it.

bottom. The float contains a mixture of alcohol and water under reduced pressure. Attached to the float is a pointed rod which can close the opening at the top of the vent. As steam enters the radiator, it pushes out the air. The air escapes through the vent. When steam reaches the vent, its higher temperature causes the alcohol-water mixture within the float to vaporize. The pressure exerted by this vapor bulges out the flexible metal bottom of the float. This bulge, pressing against the bottom of the valve, pushes the pointed rod against the opening at the top of the vent. This closes the vent while steam is present, and prevents the steam from escaping. When the temperature in the radiator drops because steam is no longer present, the vapor in the float condenses. The flexible metal bottom returns to its original shape. The vent opens, air re-enters.

If water enters the vent instead of steam, the float is pushed up by the water. The pointed rod closes the vent, and water can not escape. When the water drains from the vent, the float drops to permit the passage of air.

29. How much heat do we need to vaporize one gram of water? Suppose we put a quart of water having a temperature of 0° C in a pan and heat it on the stove. Let us check the time when we start to heat the water, the time when it starts to boil, and the time when all the water has boiled away. During the time the water is heating from 0° C to 100° C, each gram of water absorbs 100 cal. If we continue to supply heat to the water at the same rate, we find that it takes more than five times as long to boil the water away as it did to heat the water from 0° C to 100° C. Apparently, each gram of water absorbs more than 500 calories when it changes into steam. Since the temperature of the boiling water does not change, and the steam has the same temperature as the boiling water, this is another example of latent (hidden) heat. *The heat required to vaporize one gram of liquid without changing its temperature is called its* **heat of vaporization.**

The heat of vaporization of water is about 539 cal/g. For solving problems, however, we shall use the number 540, since it will simplify our calculations. *In order to convert 1 g of boiling water at 100° C into steam at the same temperature, 540 cal of heat must be added. In English system units, 970 Btu are required to change 1 lb of water at 212° F into steam at the same temperature.*

30. Measuring heat of vaporization. We use the method of mixtures to determine the heat of vaporization of water. As shown in Fig. 14-19, steam is passed into cold water, and we find the increase in temperature. We make sure that only steam enters the water in the calorimeter by using a

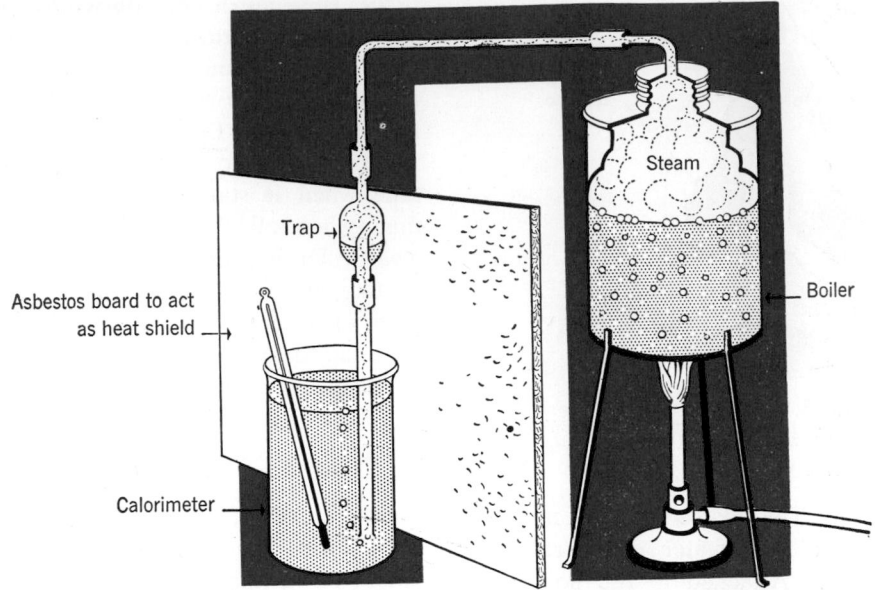

Fig. 14-19. Finding the heat of vaporization of water by the method of mixtures.

trap which will catch any condensed water from the steam generator. In order to make our measurement, we must find the mass of the calorimeter and its specific heat. We also need to know the mass of the water and the steam. Then, we must get the original temperatures of the steam, the cold water, and the calorimeter, and final temperature of the mixture. Thus:

Mass of calorimeter	120 g
Specific heat of calorimeter	0.1 cal /g C°
Mass of water	402 g
Mass of steam	23.5 g
Initial temperature of cold water	6° C
Temperature of steam	100° C
Final temperature of water	40° C

Heat absorbed by calorimeter:
$120 \times (40 - 6) \times 0.1 = 408$ cal

Heat absorbed by water:
$402 \times (40 - 6) \times 1.0 = 13,668$ cal

Total heat absorbed:
$408 + 13,668 = 14,076$ cal

When 23.5 g of steam condense, 23.5 g of water at 100° C are formed. This water loses heat to the calorimeter and the cold water. Heat lost by hot water: $23.5 \times (100 - 40) \times 1.0 = 1410$ cal

Heat lost by steam in condensing:
$14,076 - 1410 = 12,666$ cal

This is the heat lost by 23.5 g of steam in condensing. $12,666 \div 23.5 = 539.0$ cal /g, heat of vaporization of water.

31. Steam gives out heat as it condenses. Heat is absorbed during vaporization. This increase in thermal energy of the atoms and molecules of a liquid enables them to break away from the body of the liquid and become molecules of vapor. When the vapor condenses into a liquid, this thermal energy is lost. Heat is given out by a vapor when it condenses into the liquid phase. Fig. 14-20 shows this reversible thermal energy change in graphic form. We use this reversible heat effect in a steam heating system. The heat of vaporization is added to the water in the

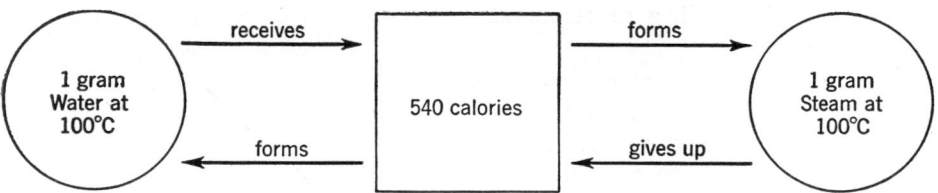

Fig. 14-20. It takes 540 calories to change water at 100° C into steam.   Steam at 100° C sets free this much heat in changing to water.

boiler and changes the water into steam. This steam expands into the radiators, where it gives up its heat of vaporization and condenses to a liquid.

Even though steam and boiling water are at the same temperature, steam can produce a more severe burn. We readily see why this happens when we remember that steam has absorbed 540 more calories per gram than has hot water. When steam condenses, 540 cal/g are given out. Then the water which is formed starts to give out the same amount of heat that boiling water does as it cools.

32. A summary of the effect of heat on water. We have learned about several effects which the addition or subtraction of heat produces in water. We can summarize all of these changes in a graph. Fig. 14-21 shows what happens from the time heat is added to

ice at −10° C until it becomes steam at 120° C. Heat units (calories) are plotted as abscissas, and temperatures (°C) are plotted as ordinates. Since the specific heat of ice is 0.5, 1 g of ice absorbs 5 cal in being warmed to 0° C. When this ice melts, 80 cal of heat are absorbed. There is *no temperature change* while this heat is being absorbed. As we continue to add heat, the temperature of the water rises. The addition of 100 cal increases the temperature to 100° C. The water begins to boil. We need 540 cal of heat to convert 1 g of water at 100° C into steam at 100° C. During this change of phase, there is *no temperature change*. If the steam is maintained under one atmosphere pressure, its specific heat is about 0.5. To heat the steam to 120° C, 10 cal will be needed. It requires 720 cal to change 1 g

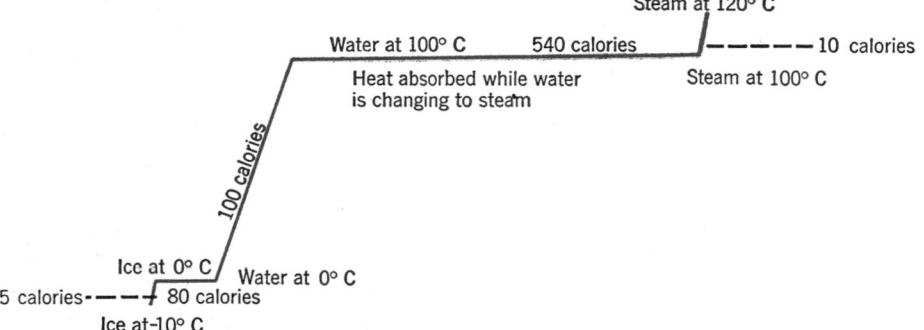

Fig. 14-21. Graph showing the heat absorbed as one gram of ice at −10° C is converted into steam at 120° C.

of ice at 0° C into 1 g of steam at 100° C.

33. The liquefaction of gases. So far we have been studying the vaporization and condensation of water. There are other substances whose evaporation and liquefaction we should study also. Some of these substances are liquids, but many of them are gases at ordinary temperatures. Michael Faraday (1791–1867) conducted an important series of experiments on liquefying gases. He used a thick-walled tube of the type shown in Fig. 14-22. In one experiment he filled the tube with chlorine gas. One end of the tube was packed in a freezing mixture of salt and ice. Faraday heated the other end of the tube. The gas in the heated end expanded and increased the pressure exerted on the gas in the cold end. By the combined effect of increasing the pressure and cooling the gas, Faraday condensed chlorine to a liquid. Using this same method, he succeeded in liquefying such gases as ammonia and carbon dioxide. But he could not liquefy oxygen, hydrogen, and nitrogen in this manner.

We now know that Faraday's freezing mixture was not cold enough to liquefy these gases no matter what pressure is exerted upon them. Oxygen must be cooled to −119° C, nitrogen to −147° C, and hydrogen to −240° C before they will liquefy at any pressure. The temperature to which any gas must be cooled before it can be liquefied by pressure is called its *critical temperature*. The pressure needed to liquefy a gas at its critical temperature is called its *critical pressure*. All known gases have now been liquefied by greatly compressing them, cooling them, and allowing them to ex-

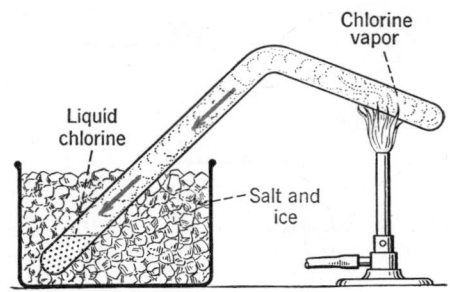

Fig. 14-22. The type of apparatus used by Faraday in his experiments on liquefying gases.

pand, which process cools them further. Successive compressions and coolings are needed to condense gases with very low boiling points.

★**34. How is liquid air made?** In the type of apparatus illustrated in Fig. 14-23, the air is first compressed. The hot, compressed air is then cooled as it goes through the coils of the condenser. It passes to the liquefier. As the compressed air escapes through the needle valve, it expands rapidly. This expansion lowers its temperature. The expanded air now returns to the compressor through the outer concentric coil. On its way it cools the air in the inner coil. By continually compressing the air, absorbing the heat of compression, and then letting the air expand, we make the air become colder and colder. Finally, some of the air reaches its critical temperature and changes into a liquid.

Liquid air under atmospheric pressure boils at temperatures from −183° C to −196° C, depending upon the amount of nitrogen present. Liquid hydrogen boils at −253° C, while liquid helium boils at −269° C. We transport liquid air in large double-walled insulated bottles, similar in construction to a Thermos bottle.

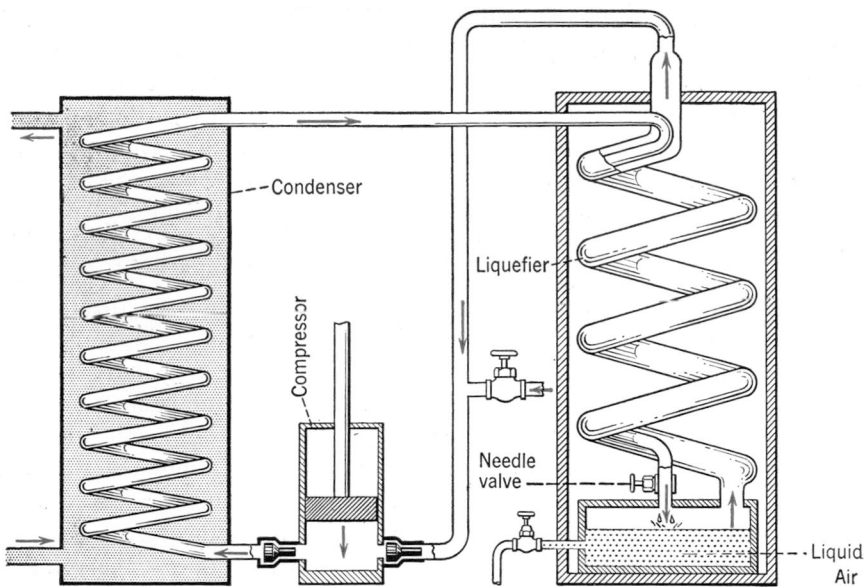

Fig. 14-23. One type of apparatus that is used for making liquid air.

★ **35. How are gases sold?** Gases usually are sold to laboratories, hospitals, and industrial users in strong steel tanks or cylinders. The gas is forced into these tanks under high pressure. Oxygen and hydrogen can not be liquefied at ordinary temperatures by pressure alone. But gases like ammonia, sulfur dioxide, and carbon dioxide condense to liquids at the high pressure in the tanks. Carbon dioxide is also sold in the solid phase as " Dry Ice." Solid carbon dioxide sublimes at ordinary temperatures and pressures. Because of its extreme cold, about −80° C, and the fact that it does not get wet, solid carbon dioxide is a very useful refrigerant.

36. Evaporation produces a cooling effect. When you climb onto the dock after a swim on a windy summer day, the wind on your wet body seems much colder than it did before you went into the lake. The wind helps to evaporate the water from your body. But in order for water to evaporate, each gram must gain 540 calories of heat. The water takes this heat from your skin. Losing heat from the skin produces a cooling effect. As soon as your body dries, the wind does not seem as cold.

Our body uses this same system to control its temperature. When we become too warm, we give off noticeable amounts of water through the skin. This water evaporates. Since the heat of vaporization comes from the skin, we are cooled. If we sit in a breeze where perspiration may evaporate more rapidly, we cool off faster. When it is hot and humid, we have difficulty keeping cool. Perspiration does not evaporate as readily on such days.

37. All liquids absorb heat when they evaporate. You are probably familiar with the cooling effect of an alcohol rub. If you pour ether over your hand, your hand feels cold. In both cases, the liquid evaporates very rapidly. Since the heat of vaporization comes from your body, the liquid feels cold on your skin.

Liquefied gases behave in a similar fashion. Certain gases which may be liquefied easily by pressure alone at room temperature are important refrigerants. These gases are compressed and then cooled to room temperature. In this process they give off heat and condense to liquids. Then they are allowed to expand and evaporate. For this process they must gain heat from their surroundings. By recycling the gas through this process, the gas can be made to transport heat from one location to another. In practice, the heat required for evaporation and expansion is absorbed from the freezing compartment. This heat is given up to the air of the room when it cools the gas in the condenser coils.

★ **38. How is ice made commercially?** The commercial method of making ice depends on the cooling effect of an evaporating liquid. In this process the evaporating liquid is ammonia, which boils at −34° C under atmospheric pressure. If we compress ammonia gas and then cool it to 20° C, it will liquefy. When liquid ammonia evaporates at this temperature, one gram absorbs about 284 calories of heat from its surroundings. At lower temperatures the heat of vaporization is somewhat higher.

Fig. 14-24 shows a diagram of an ice-making plant. Ammonia gas is compressed in the cylinder by the piston. The heat of compression is absorbed by the cold water which flows down over the cooling coils. The ammonia then liquefies. As the liquid ammonia flows through the expansion valve into the coils in the brine tank, it evaporates and expands. Both of these changes absorb heat. The heat comes from the surrounding brine, which is cooled to −10° C, or lower. Cans of fresh water immersed in the brine are frozen into cakes of solid ice in 24 to 48 hours.

Circulation of low-temperature brine may also be used in frozen-food locker

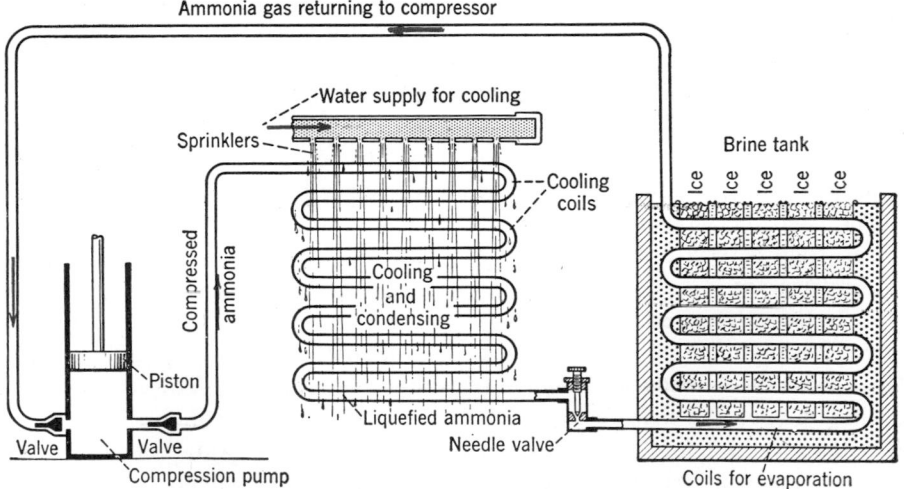

Fig. 14-24. A diagram of a plant for making ice.

plants to keep the stored food at a temperature of about −20° C. The brine circulates through small pipes attached to the metal shelves on which the food is placed.

39. How does the electric refrigerator work? The refrigerant in most modern refrigerators is a substance with the chemical name of *di-chloro-difluoro methane*. Its commercial name is Freon. Freon boils at about −30° C when the pressure is one atmosphere. At this temperature its heat of vaporization is approximately 40 cal/g.

Liquid Freon circulates through coils surrounding the freezing compartment of the refrigerator. Since the pressure in these coils is low, the Freon expands and evaporates. It takes its heat of vaporization from the inside of the refrigerator. This action cools the foods stored there and converts trays of water into ice cubes. The evaporated Freon then passes through tubing to the compressor. The compressor is driven by a small electric motor of about one-sixth horsepower. The compressor forces the Freon at high pressure into the condenser. In the condenser coils, the Freon is cooled by the air of the room. The combination of high pressure and room temperature is sufficient to liquefy the Freon. The liquid Freon then is forced back through an expansion valve into the low pressure coils of the freezing compartment. Here it vaporizes again, absorbing more heat from the inside of the refrigerator. This process goes on as long as the compressor motor is operating. Proper temperatures are maintained in the food and freezing compartments by a thermostat which automatically starts and stops the motor.

Fig. 14-25. The storage room in a frozen food locker plant. The coils through which the cold circulating brine passes are shown at the top of the picture.

Home freezers are very similar to the freezing compartment of a refrigerator. The difference is in their size and in the amount of insulation. Home freezers are large boxes or cabinets surrounded by the evaporating pipes through which the refrigerant circulates. This makes all the walls of the freezer effective freezing surfaces, and maintains a temperature of −20° C.

40. The gas-type refrigerator. This refrigerator also operates on the cooling effect produced when a liquid evaporates. A simplified diagram of this refrigerator is shown in Fig. 14-27. Water, ammonia gas, and hydrogen are placed in the pipes, and the system is sealed. When the water solution of

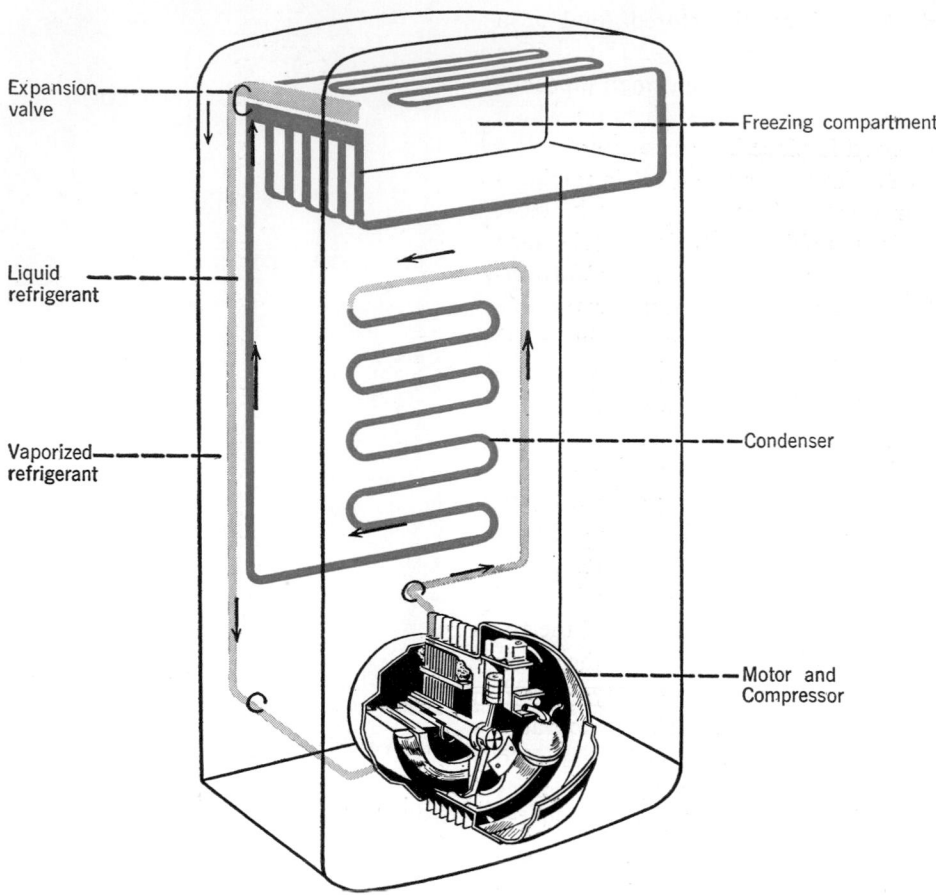

Expansion valve

Liquid refrigerant

Vaporized refrigerant

Freezing compartment

Condenser

Motor and Compressor

Fig. 14-26. The essential parts of an electric refrigerator.

ammonia is heated in the generator, the ammonia is driven out of the water. The water and ammonia are separated by the vapor and liquid separator. The rapid expulsion of the ammonia gas from the water compresses it. As the ammonia gives off its heat in the condenser, it is converted into a liquid. The liquid ammonia then passes to the freezing compartment, where it evaporates in the presence of hydrogen gas. The heat of vaporization is absorbed from the freezing compartment. Now the ammonia gas, mixed with hydrogen, passes to the absorber where the am-

monia is once again dissolved in water. Hydrogen, being insoluble, returns to the evaporator. The purpose of the hydrogen is to equalize the pressure in the evaporator and absorber. It enables the liquid ammonia to evaporate more rapidly in the freezing coils, and aids the flow of ammonia gas back to the absorber. This process is repeated continually. A thermostat inside the refrigerator controls the flow of gas to the burner, thus regulating the temperature. The gas refrigerator is silent in its operation because it has no moving parts.

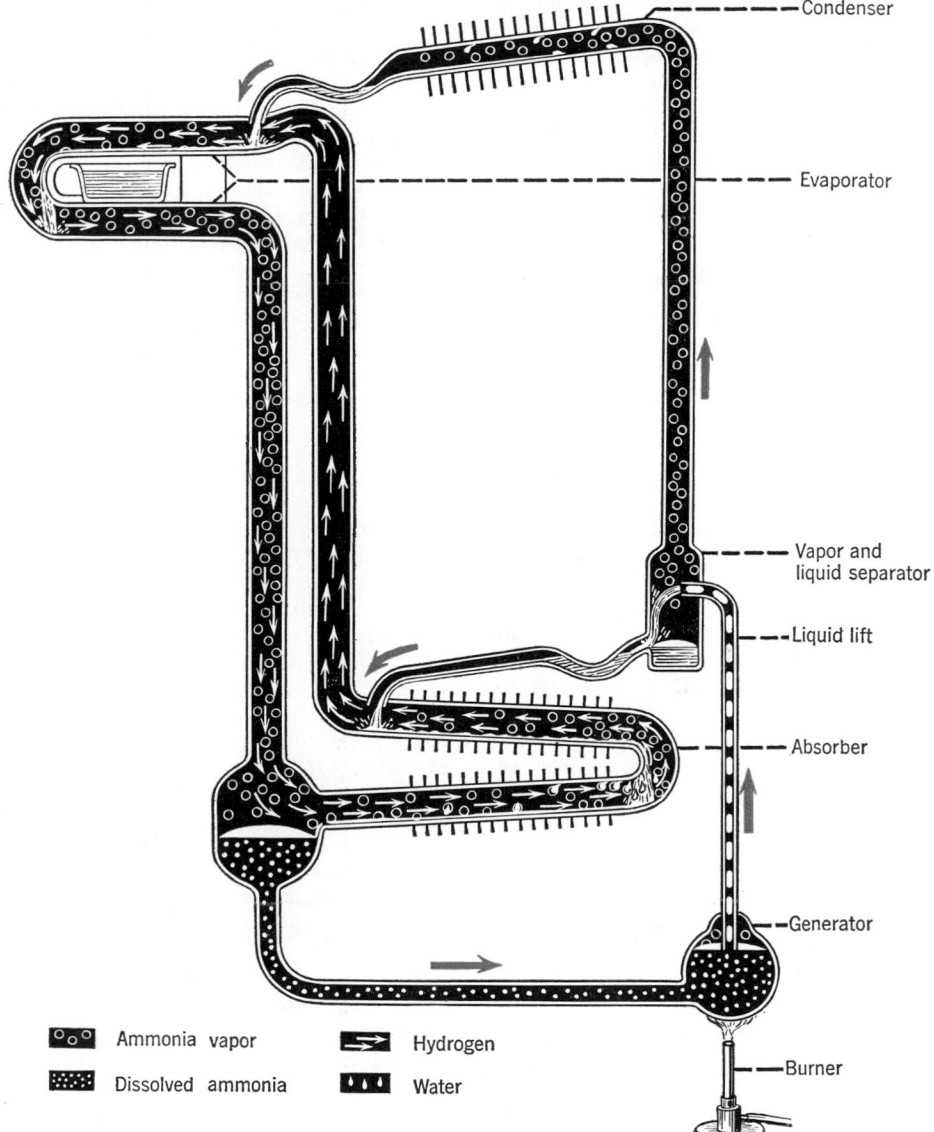

Fig. 14-27. The principle of operation of the gas-type refrigerator.

Condenser

Evaporator

Vapor and
liquid separator

Liquid lift

Absorber

Generator

Burner

Ammonia vapor	Hydrogen
Dissolved ammonia	Water

QUESTIONS

GROUP A

1. Explain the difference between vaporization, boiling, and evaporation.

2. What is the value of the heat of vaporization of water in the metric system? In the English system?

3. Why do you receive a more severe burn from steam at 212° F than from water at 212° F?

4. Why do liquids exert a vapor pressure?

5. How is fractional distillation used in separating the different materials found in crude oil?

6. Why is it possible to liquefy chlorine but not oxygen by compressing the gas and cooling it with a freezing mixture of ice and salt?

7. Why does an easily vaporized liquid such as ether or acetone feel cool if it is accidentally spilled on the skin?

8. What is the function of the heater in a gas-type refrigerator?

GROUP B

9. If an electric refrigerator is operated in a closed room into which no heat may enter and from which no heat may escape, what will happen to the temperature of the room?

10. In terms of the kinetic theory, explain why

(1) liquids evaporate more rapidly at higher temperatures; (2) the rate of evaporation increases as the surface area of the liquid increases; (3) evaporation is more rapid when the pressure is reduced; (4) water evaporates more slowly when the humidity is high; (5) ether evaporates more readily than water.

★**11.** What advantages do pressure cookers offer in the preparation of food?

★**12.** If water is to be removed from sugar syrup or milk, this removal must be done at a fairly low temperature. Why? How is this accomplished?

★**13.** Using Fig. 14-23, explain how liquid air is produced.

★**14.** Why is solid carbon dioxide a convenient refrigerant to use to keep ice cream frozen?

PROBLEMS

(In the Mathematics Refresher, refer to Sections 10 and 16.)

GROUP A

1. How many calories of heat are needed to vaporize 50 g of water at 100° C?

2. Sufficient steam at 212° F condenses to produce one cubic foot of water at the same temperature. How much heat was liberated?

3. How many grams of mercury may be vaporized at its boiling point, 356.58° C, by the addition of 1000 cal of heat?

4. Calculate the number of Btu given off when 10 lb of steam at 212° F are condensed, cooled, and changed into ice at 32° F.

5. A calorimeter contains 400 g of water at 20° C. How many grams of steam at 100° C will be needed to raise the temperature of the water and calorimeter to 90° C? The calorimeter has a mass of 100 g; its specific heat is 0.1.

GROUP B

6. In an experiment to determine the heat of vaporization of water, 15 g of steam at 100° C

were added to 150 g of water at 20° C in a calorimeter. The mass of the calorimeter is 75 g; its specific heat is 0.1. The equilibrium temperature of the mixture was 73.9° C. What is the heat of vaporization of water?

7. The mass of a mixture of ice and water is 200 g. This mixture is in a 100-g calorimeter, specific heat, 0.2. When 40 g of steam are added to the mixture, the temperature is raised to 60° C. How many grams of ice were originally in the calorimeter?

8. A block of frozen mercury at −50° C has a mass of 100 g. How many calories will change it into liquid mercury at 20° C?

● **9.** An aluminum cylinder, mass 50 g, is placed in a 100-g brass calorimeter with 250 g of water at 20° C. What equilibrium temperature will be reached after the addition of 25 g of steam at 120° C?

●**10.** A copper ball weighing 10 lb is removed from a furnace and dropped into 3 lb of water, temperature 72° F. After the water stops boiling, the combined weight of the ball and water is 12 lb. What was the furnace temperature?

4. HUMIDITY

41. What is humidity? We learned in Sections 19 and 20 that water and ice continually evaporate. This means

that there is always some water vapor in the air. However, the amount of water vapor may differ from place to place. It will vary in a given location depending on the temperature, wind, rainfall, and other weather factors. The term *humidity* (hyoo-*mid*-eh-tee) *is used to describe the amount of water vapor in the air.*

42. What is the capacity of the air? The amount of moisture which the air can hold when it is saturated is called its *capacity*. Capacity usually is measured in grains per cubic foot, abbreviated gr/ft³. Table 12, Appendix B, shows how many grains of moisture one cubic foot of air can hold at various temperatures. The capacity increases with an increase in temperature.

43. What is absolute humidity? Suppose we have a bottle that just holds one quart. Then one quart is its capacity; that is the most it can hold. If we pour one pint of milk into the bottle, then the amount of liquid which the bottle holds is one pint. Just as a quart bottle may not always hold one quart of liquid, the air may not always be filled to capacity with water vapor. The amount of water vapor in one cubic foot of air at any given time is its *absolute humidity*.

44. What is relative humidity? When a quart bottle contains one pint of liquid, it is 50% full. If a cubic foot of air that could hold 4 grains of water vapor holds only 2 grains, it is 50% full, or half saturated. Such air has a relative humidity of 50%. The *relative humidity* of the air may be defined as the ratio of the amount of moisture which the air actually contains to what it could contain. We can find the relative humidity by dividing the absolute humidity by the capacity. This quotient is usually expressed in per cent.

45. Relative humidity varies with the temperature. A cold room in a house usually feels damp. But if the same room is heated, the dampness seems to disappear and the room becomes dry. The amount of moisture in the room has not been reduced by heating the room. However, the capacity of the air in the room for moisture increased when its temperature was raised. An example will illustrate this. Suppose the air in a room at 32° F contains 2 grains of water vapor per cubic foot. From Table 12, Appendix B, we see that the capacity of air at 32° F is 2.118 gr/ft³. The relative humidity will be 2 ÷ 2.118, or 94%. This air will feel damp. When the temperature is raised to 68° F, the amount of moisture in the air remains the same. But the capacity of the air has been increased to 7.56 gr/ft³. The relative humidity is now 2 ÷ 7.56, or 26%. This air will feel dry. We see that increasing the temperature decreases the relative humidity. On the other hand, if the temperature is lowered, the relative humidity will be increased.

46. We may measure relative humidity with a wet-and-dry-bulb thermometer. One of the easiest ways to measure the relative humidity is by using two thermometers, one having a dry bulb and the other a wet bulb. The dry-bulb thermometer indicates the actual temperature of the air. A wet-bulb thermometer has a cloth wick surrounding its bulb. This wick is moistened with water. When the air is dry, the rapid evaporation of the water from the wick cools it. This lowered temperature is indicated by the reading of the wet-bulb thermometer. The lower the relative humidity, the more

Fig. 14-28. A dial-type humidity indicator.

rapidly the water evaporates and the greater will be the difference between the wet and dry-bulb readings. Tables have been prepared which enable us to read the relative humidity directly when we know the two thermometer readings. See Table 13, Appendix B.

The dial-type humidity indicator, shown in Fig. 14-28, contains a human hair, or sometimes a special synthetic fiber. The length of the strand of hair or fiber increases in proportion to the relative humidity. As the relative humidity goes up, the hair or fiber gets longer. Then the tension spring mounted on the pointer pulls the pointer to the right over the numbered dial. When the relative humidity decreases, the hair or fiber gets shorter, and it will pull the pointer back to the left.

47. The dew point and precipitation. Cooling the air increases its relative humidity. What will happen if we cool the air until its relative humidity reaches 100%? At such humidity, we find that water vapor from the air begins to condense. Depending on the temperature and other atmospheric conditions, this condensed water vapor will form fog, rain, snow, frost, dew, sleet, or hail. *The temperature at which the moisture in the air begins to condense is called the* **dew point.** Before precipitation can occur, the temperature of the air must be reduced to the dew point.

For example, suppose we have air containing 8 gr/ft³ of water vapor at 84° F. From Table 12, Appendix B, we see that this air will become saturated with water vapor when it is cooled to about 70° F. Below this temperature it will begin to lose moisture by condensation, since the relative humidity can never exceed 100%. If the air cools to 60° F, each cubic foot of air loses 2.2 grains of moisture.

Several remarkable effects have been produced by the discharge of dry ice pellets and silver iodide smoke in the air. It is possible to cause the formation of ice crystal clouds by " seeding " with dry ice the areas of the atmosphere which contain supercooled droplets of water. The dry ice provides the nuclei on which ice crystals may form. Dry ice pellets dropped into stratus clouds produce snow.

Summary

Quantities of heat are measured by the effects which they produce. The calorie is the quantity of heat needed to raise the temperature of one gram of water one Centigrade degree. The British thermal unit is the quantity of heat

Fig. 14-29. The storm system shown in the photograph is believed to have been produced by the dispersion of silver iodide particles from a ground generator. The radar equipment in the truck detected precipitation falling from the distant clouds.

needed to raise the temperature of one pound of water one Fahrenheit degree.

Fusion is the change of phase from a solid to a liquid. The temperature at which fusion occurs is called the melting point. An increase in pressure raises the melting point of substances that contract when solidifying, and lowers the melting point of substances that expand when solidifying.

To change one gram of ice at $0°$ C to water at the same temperature requires 80 calories. To change one pound of ice at $32°$ F to water at the same temperature requires 144 British thermal units. These quantities of heat are called heats of fusion. This heat is liberated when these quantities of water freeze. Vaporization is the change of phase from a liquid to a vapor. The temperature at which vaporization occurs is called the boiling point. At this temperature the vapor pressure of the liquid equals the atmospheric pressure.

To change one gram of water at $100°$ C into steam at the same temperature requires 540 calories. To change one pound of water at $212°$ F into steam at the same temperature requires 970 British thermal units.

The amount of moisture which the air can hold when it is saturated is called its capacity. The amount of water vapor the air does hold is its absolute humidity.

Terms to Define...

Absolute humidity	Freezing point	Method of mixtures
Boiling	Fusion	Pressure cooker
Boiling point	Gas-type refrigerator	Regelation
British thermal unit	Heat capacity	Relative humidity
Calorie	Heat of fusion	Solidification
Calorimeter	Heat of vaporization	Specific heat
Capacity	High specific heat of water	Sublimation
Cooling effect of evaporation	Humidity	Supercooled
Critical pressure	Kilocalorie	Vacuum pans
Critical temperature	Latent heat	Vaporization
Dew point	Liquefaction of gases	Vapor pressure
Distillation	Liquid air	Wet-and-dry bulb thermometer
Electric refrigerator	Melting point	

Questions

GROUP A

1. What is meant by "capacity" of the air? By "absolute humidity"? By "relative humidity"?

2. What is the highest value the relative humidity may have? What are the probable weather conditions when this value is attained?

3. A cold room feels damper than a warm one, even though the amount of moisture in the air in each room is the same. Explain.

4. Why do we feel very uncomfortable on a hot summer day if the relative humidity is 90%?

5. Explain why a wet-bulb thermometer ordinarily shows a lower reading than a dry-bulb thermometer.

6. What is the "dew point"?

7. What belief do scientists hold concerning the way in which dry ice will act on clouds to produce snow?

Problems

(In the Mathematics Refresher, refer to Sections 4, 6, 7, 10, and 16.)

GROUP A

1. What is the relative humidity of air which contains 2.9 gr/ft³ of water vapor at 60° F?

2. If the relative humidity is 35%, how much water vapor does 1 ft³ of air contain at 80° F?

3. The dry-bulb thermometer reads 72° F, while the wet-bulb thermometer stands at only 62° F. What is the relative humidity?

4. What is the difference between the readings of wet- and dry-bulb thermometers at 84° F, if the relative humdity is 50%?

5. On a certain day the temperature is 66° F and the relative humidity is 40%. What is the temperature of the dew point?

6. If the temperature is 90° F and the dew point is 45° F, what is the relative humidity?

Things to Do

1. Devise an experiment which proves that solids evaporate. Use it as a class demonstration.

2. Investigate the method of producing frozen fruit juices. How many of the principles studied in this chapter are used in this process?

3. Make a record of the temperature and humidity three times daily for a period of a week. What are the maximum and minimum temperatures you observe? What are the maximum and minimum values of the relative humidity?

Chapter 15

Transfer of Heat

1. How is heat transferred? Heat energy may be transferred from one body to another. Heat from the sun warms the earth. A hot plate heats water to its boiling point. Heat is absorbed by the melting ice in a glass of lemonade. A refrigerator transports heat from one location to another. Now we shall study the methods by which heat is transferred. We also shall study how we apply these methods in order to make our homes comfortable throughout the year. We add heat to substances whose temperature we wish to raise. We take heat away from materials we wish to cool. In both cases we use insulation to help prevent undesirable transfer of heat.

1. CONDUCTION

2. What is conduction? If you happen to leave your spoon in some hot soup, you discover very shortly that the handle becomes hot to the touch. You use a pot holder to remove a hot sauce pan from the stove. Otherwise your fingers might be burned by the hot metal. These examples show us that thermal energy can be *conducted* from one part of an object to another. We know that the thermal energy of a body is associated with the motion of its atoms and molecules. Molecules which are near the source of heat vibrate rapidly as their energy is increased. By collisions with adjacent molecules, some of the energy is passed on. In this way the thermal energy is

Vocabulary

CONDITIONED AIR. Filtered and gently circulating air with a temperature of 68°–78° F, and a relative humidity of 40–60%.

CONDUCTION. The transmission of thermal energy from molecule to molecule.

CONVECTION (kun-*vek*-shun). The transmission of thermal energy by moving currents of molecules.

RADIATION. The transmission of thermal energy by electromagnetic waves.

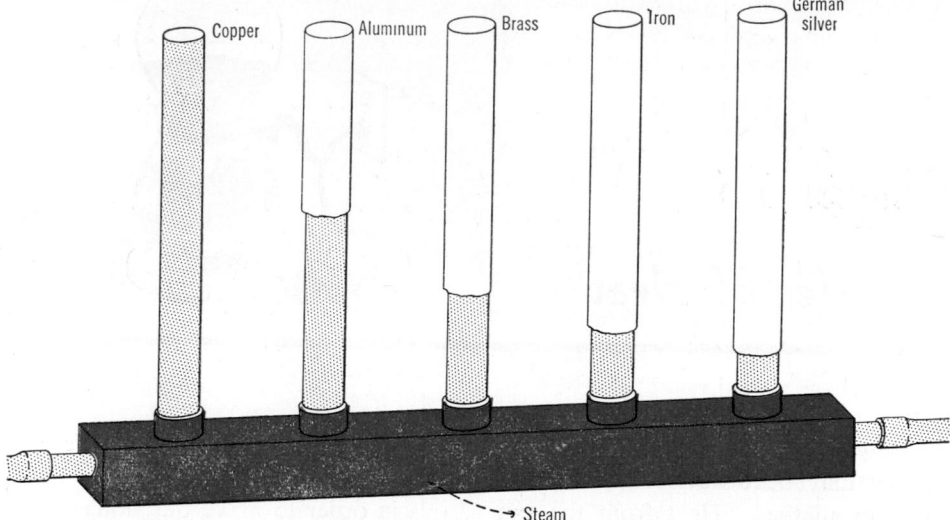

Fig. 15-1. The heights to which the paraffin has melted show that metals conduct heat at different rates.

increased molecule by molecule until the entire object becomes hot. *The transmission of thermal energy from molecule to molecule is called* **conduction.** Conduction of heat in a body will take place only when one part of the body has a higher temperature than another. The heat will be transferred from the part at higher temperature to the part at lower temperature.

3. Heat conduction in solids. We know from experience that some solids, particularly metals, are good conductors of heat. We can show the relative rates of conduction of heat for some metals by the following experiment. We use a *conductometer* (kon-duk-*tom*-eh-ter) illustrated in Fig. 15-1. The metal rods are coated with paraffin or with a paint which changes color as the temperature rises. Steam is passed through the base of the apparatus. We follow the rate of heat conduction by observing the melting paraffin or the color of the paint.

Of all the materials we know, silver is the best conductor of heat. Copper and aluminum are much better conductors than other common metals. German silver, which is an alloy of copper, zinc, and nickel, is a poor conducting metal. The order of conductivity of the five metals shown is copper, aluminum, brass, iron, and German silver. Metals are generally much better conductors of heat than wood or stone. The relative conductivity of various common substances is given in Table 14, Appendix B.

4. Heat conduction in liquids. Let us put a piece of ice in the bottom of a test tube. Now weight the ice down and fill the tube two-thirds full of water. See Fig. 15-2. By heating the upper part of the test tube, we may boil the water for several minutes before enough heat is conducted down through the water to melt the ice. We see that water does conduct heat, but that it is a poor conductor.

We may carry on a more sensitive test of heat conduction by water with the apparatus shown in Fig. 15-3. Here we have the bulb of an air thermometer immersed in water in a large funnel. The stem of the thermometer contains some colored liquid. We pour some ether on the surface of the water, and ignite it. Although the air thermometer is very sensitive, we find that the liquid column is lowered only slightly. This experiment shows again that water is a poor conductor of heat. Other liquids, likewise, are poor conductors.

5. Heat conduction in gases. Experiments show that gases are even poorer conductors than liquids. We expect this, because the molecules of gases are farther apart. It is much more difficult for a gas molecule to pass on its additional kinetic energy through collision. Silver conducts heat about 700 times as fast as water, and about 17,500 times as fast as air. The air spaces in porous solids are largely responsible for their poor conductivity. A vacuum does not conduct heat, although we shall learn later that heat

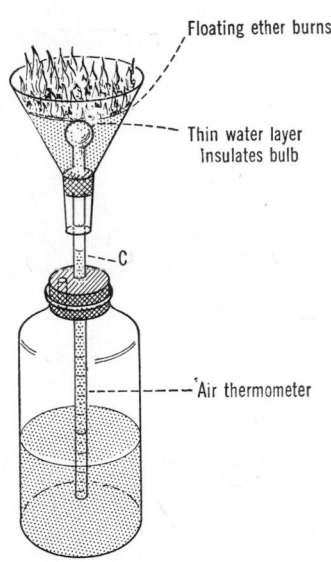

Fig. 15-3. Very little heat from the burning ether reaches the bulb of the air thermometer because of the poor conduction of the thin water layer between them.

may be transferred through a vacuum by another method.

6. Conductivity affects our sense of temperature. We learned in an earlier section that our sense of temperature is not overly accurate, and that it is greatly affected by environment. The following is another example. If you walk into the bathroom on a cold morning, you find that the tile floor feels much colder than the rug which covers part of the floor. Yet a thermometer will show that both have the same temperature. The tile feels colder because it conducts heat away from your feet more rapidly than does the rug.

7. How is conduction useful? When we start a campfire, we heat part of the sticks of wood to their kindling temperature with burning paper. As the sticks start to burn, heat is con-

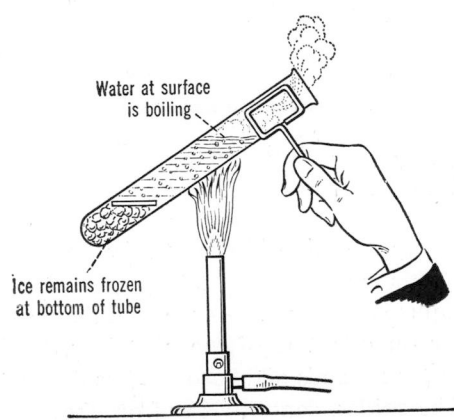

Fig. 15-2. Water is a poor conductor of heat.

Fig. 15-4. The outer surface of the cylinders of most airplane engines consists of many thin metal fins. They conduct heat away from the cylinder and make possible the air cooling of the engine.

ducted slowly along them until their entire length is ablaze. Without conduction, fire would not spread through a fuel so rapidly. We use aluminum or iron cooking utensils. The heat from a gas flame or electric coil is conducted through the utensils to the food we are cooking. The conductivity of the metal makes all parts of the utensil hot, even though heat is supplied to only one area of the particular pot or pan we are using.

2. CONVECTION

8. How is heat transferred by convection? Suppose we fill a large Pyrex glass container almost full of water. Let us support this container so that one side of it may be heated with a burner, as shown in Fig. 15-5. Next we drop several small crystals of potassium permanganate into the water. These crystals will drop to the bottom of the container and dissolve, forming a purple solution. As we heat the water on one side of the container, the water expands and becomes less dense. The colder, denser, water from the opposite side of the container flows across and pushes up this less dense water.

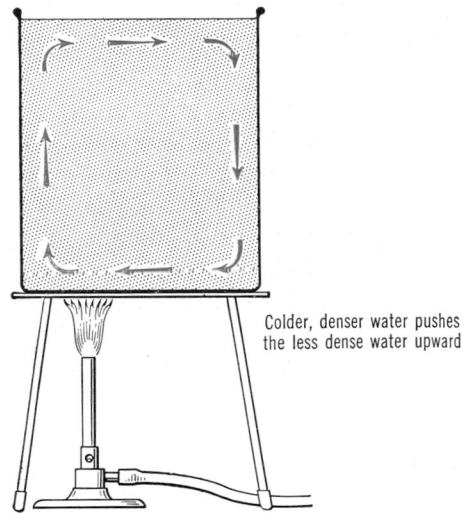

Colder, denser water pushes the less dense water upward

Fig. 15-5. Unequal heating of the water in the container sets up convection currents which travel around inside the container.

Convection (kun-*vek*-shun) *currents* are thus set up in the water as shown by the arrows in the diagram. The circulatory motion of the water will be clearly indicated by the path of the colored streams from the potassium permanganate.

If we build a fire in a space heater in the center of a large room, the air over the heater will expand. This less dense air is pushed upward by the colder, more dense air flowing in along the floor to the center of the room. As the warm air reaches the ceiling, it spreads out toward the walls, and, as it cools, sinks to the floor. **Convection currents** *may be set up in either liquids or gases by unequal heating. Heat is transmitted by the molecules in these moving currents.*

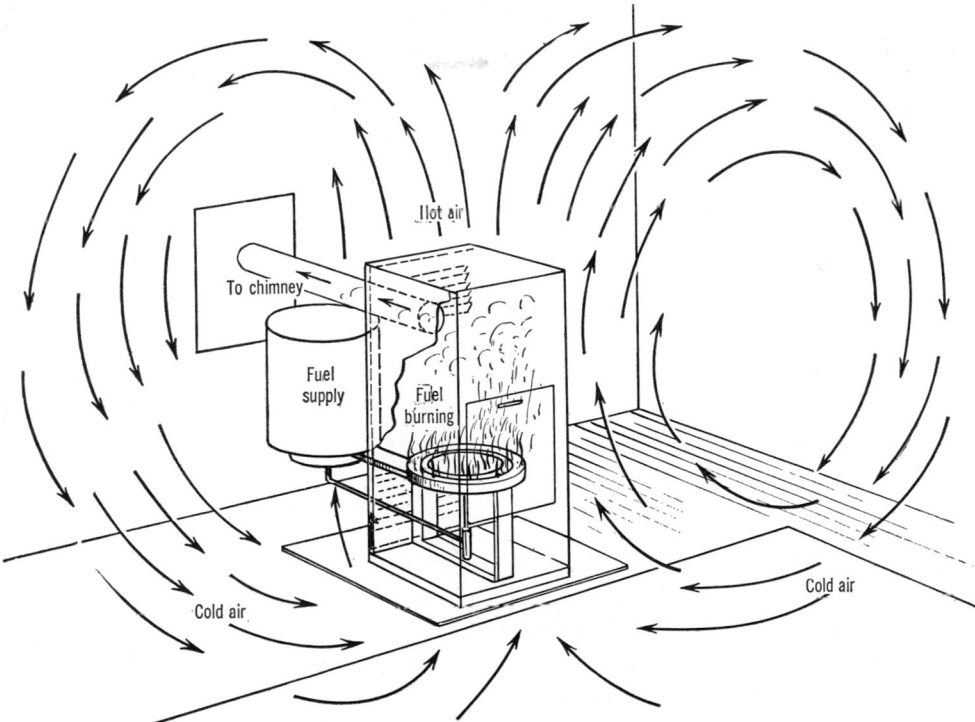

To chimney

Hot air

Fuel supply

Fuel burning

Cold air

Cold air

Fig. 15-6. A space heater heats a room by means of convection currents.

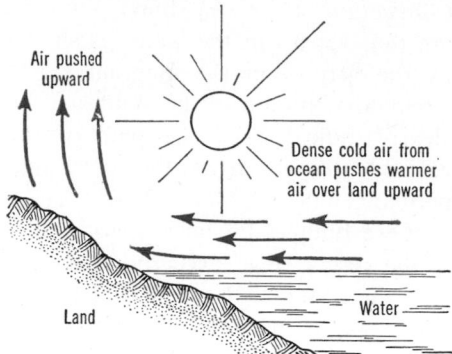

Fig. 15-7. Sea breezes blow toward the land during the day.

9. What causes winds? Unequal heating of the air at different places on the earth's surface causes huge convection currents in the atmosphere. These convection currents are *winds*. (1) *Land and sea breezes.* The water of the ocean heats more slowly than land along the shore. Consequently, by mid-morning on a sunny day the land and the air above it will be more highly heated. Then the colder, denser air from the ocean can blow in and force the less dense air upward. This causes a *sea breeze*. It blows from mid-morning until late evening.

At night, the land cools more quickly than the water. Consequently, the air over the ocean remains warmer than that over the land. Now a convection current of air may flow from the land. This is a *land breeze*. It usually begins to blow just before midnight.

(2) *Trade winds.* The direct rays of the sun strike the equator in March and September. At these times this area is heated so strongly that upward air currents are produced. At places where the air rises, there is not much wind on the surface of the earth, and the *equa-*

torial calm belt is formed. Colder, denser air blows toward the equator from both the north and the south. These convection currents are the *trade winds.* They blow continually throughout the year. We would expect the trade wind south of the equator to blow due north, and the one north of the equator to blow due south. However, the rotation of the earth on its axis deflects them. In the southern hemisphere we have the *southeast trades,* and in the northern hemisphere, the *northeast trades.* Where the air which rose at the equator descends, we find high pressure areas. In March and September, these are over the Tropic of Capricorn and the Tropic of Cancer. These descending air currents produce the *Calms of Cancer and Capricorn.* Fig. 15-9 shows the general atmospheric circulation in the spring and fall. During summer in the northern hemisphere, the calm belts and the trade winds shift northward. During winter, they shift southward.

(3) *The jet stream.* At altitudes between 10,000 and 40,000 feet above the earth's surface there are narrow streams of air which move at speeds of 200 to 300 miles per hour. These *jet streams* move in a general westerly

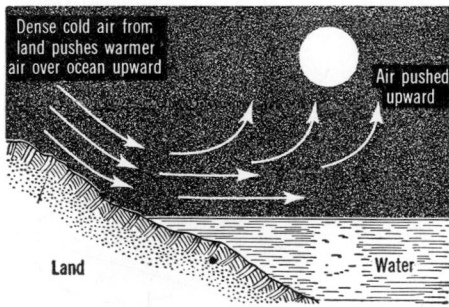

Fig. 15-8. Land breezes blow toward the ocean at night.

direction, and may be thousands of miles long. It is believed that these strange winds connect with each other forming a mass of rushing air which circles the northern hemisphere. The path of this air lies between the Arctic Circle and the Tropic of Cancer. Preliminary investigations indicate the possibility of a similar jet stream above the southern hemisphere.

★ **10. Newton's Law of Cooling.** The transfer of heat by convection is too complicated a process to be reduced to a simple formula. Newton, however, discovered a relationship between the rate of cooling and the difference in temperature of two bodies. This holds true experimentally for small differences in temperature when most of the heat loss is by convection.

Suppose we put two cups of warm water in a refrigerator to cool. The air in the refrigerator has a temperature of 40° F; one cup of water is 45° F, and the temperature of the

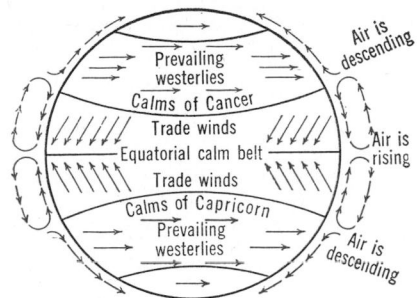

Fig. 15-9. The circulation of the atmosphere when the direct rays of the sun shine on the equator.

other is 50° F. By using a thermometer, we discover that the cup of water at 50° F cools twice as fast as the one at 45° F. The 50° F water is 10° warmer than the air in the refrigerator. The 45° F water is only 5° warmer. NEWTON'S LAW OF COOLING states that *the rate of cooling or warming of a body is proportional to the difference between the temperature of the body and the temperature of the surrounding medium.*

---

3. RADIATION

11. How is heat transferred by radiation? Have you ever used a heat lamp to relieve aching joints or muscles? If so, you know that the heat does not travel from the lamp to your body by either conduction or convection. The air between the lamp and your body is a poor conductor. Probably the lamp was directed downward, which is certainly not the position to make air transfer heat by convection. Yet heat traveled from the lamp to you without appreciably warming the air in between. This heat was transferred

Fig. 15-10. Heat is transmitted from the heat lamp to the man's shoulder by radiation.

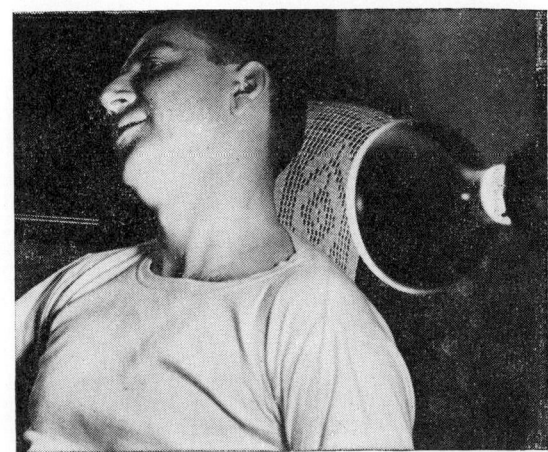

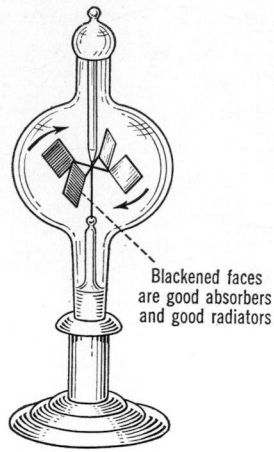

Blackened faces
are good absorbers
and good radiators

Fig. 15-11. A Crookes' radiometer.

by **radiation,** *which is the transmission of thermal energy by electromagnetic waves.* We get heat from the sun by radiation. Radiant heat energy probably is produced by the internal vibration of atoms and molecules of a heat-producing body, and appears to travel through space as a wave. Radiant energy is just one type of electromagnetic wave. Other types are light waves, X rays, and radio waves. These waves are all alike in that they travel through a vacuum at a speed of 186,000 miles per second. They differ in wave length and frequency of vibration. *Radiant energy is not heat itself. The absorption of radiant energy increases the thermal energy of the absorbing substance. Materials which are easily penetrated by heat waves are warmed very little by their passage.*

12. Radiant energy may be reflected, absorbed, or transmitted. When heat waves strike a body, part of them may be reflected, part may be absorbed and warm the body, and part may be transmitted through the body. Polished metals are excellent heat reflectors. Consequently they make poor

heat absorbers. And poor heat absorbers are poor radiators. A roughened teakettle absorbs heat more readily than a highly polished one. Also, it loses heat faster by radiation.

The color of a substance affects its absorbing power. Black surfaces absorb heat faster than white ones. As a result, we find a light-colored linen suit is more comfortable in the summer than a dark-colored one.

A *Crookes' radiometer,* shown in Fig. 15-11, demonstrates these facts nicely. This interesting device consists of a partially exhausted glass bulb. A rotating wire shaft with four aluminum vanes is mounted vertically inside. Each vane is polished on one surface, and blackened on the other. When exposed to a source of radiant energy — sunlight, for example — the vanes turn very rapidly. The black

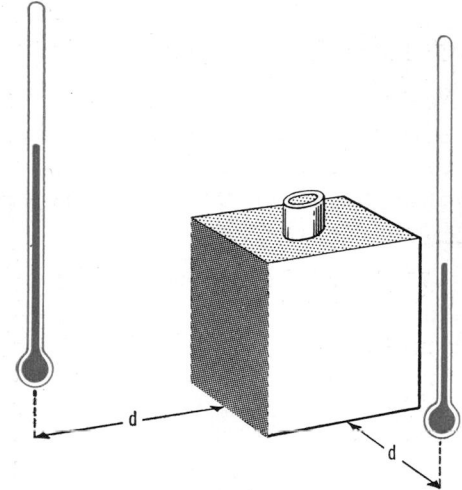

Fig. 15-12. Even though the sides of the cube are at the same temperature and the thermometers are the same distance away, the thermometer near the blackened side has a higher reading. The blackened side is therefore the better radiator.

surfaces absorb more radiant energy than the polished surfaces, and heat the adjacent air more highly. This air moves away from the black surfaces rapidly, and exerts a greater pressure on them. This causes the wire shaft to rotate in the direction shown in Fig. 15-11.

By the following experiment we can show that a good absorber is a good radiator, and that a poor absorber is a poor radiator. We have a cubical metal box, like the one shown in Fig. 15-12. One side of this box is polished metal, another side is painted dull black. We fill the box with very hot water and place thermometers at equal distances from these two different sides. Since the thermometer near the blackened side shows the higher reading, this side must give off more radiant energy.

★ **13. What is Stefan's Law?** We have just seen that good absorbers are good radiators. If we wish to make the best possible radiator, it should also be the best possible absorber. Paints or surface coatings are not especially effective. The best known device for absorbing radiation is a hollow carbon box with a small hole in one side. Radiation entering through the hole will be reflected from surface to surface inside the box until it is absorbed. Very little radiation will be reflected out through the hole. If this box is heated to a high temperature, the radiation coming from the hole will be of greater intensity than the radiation from the same area of any other kind of surface at the same temperature. This device is called an *ideal radiator*.

Josef Stefan (1835–1893) discov-

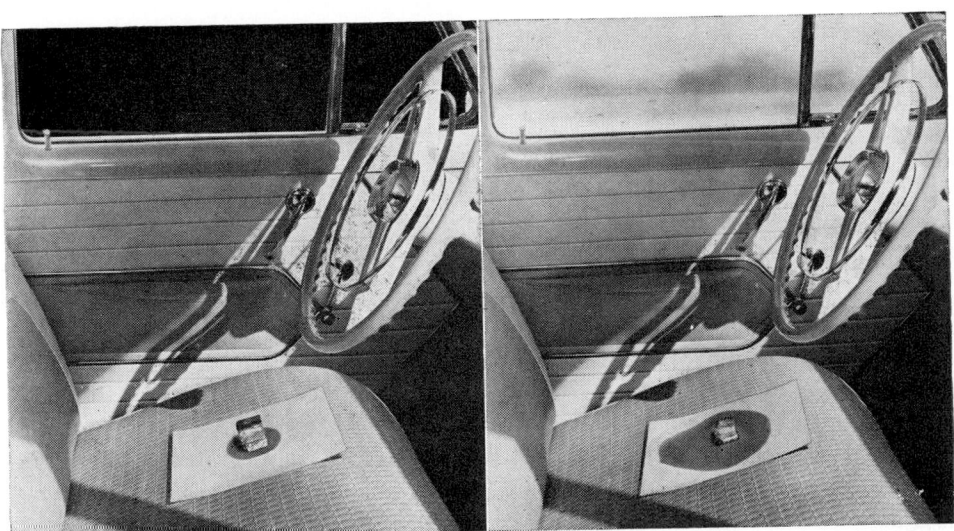

Fig. 15-13. The tinted glass used in some automobiles does not transmit radiant heat waves. As a result, the interior of the automobile is cooler. This is shown by the smaller amount of water formed by the ice cube melting on the seat of the car equipped with tinted glass windows in the photograph on the left. The photograph on the right shows the amount of water formed by an ice cube melting under similar conditions on the seat of a car equipped with ordinary glass windows.

ered that *the amount of energy emitted by an ideal radiator is directly proportional to the fourth power of its Kelvin temperature.* This is STEFAN'S LAW.

If the radiation from a heated body is not focused in a particular direction, but spreads out from the source in all directions, *the intensity of the radiation received is inversely proportional to the square of the distance from the source.* We know that a person sitting near a campfire receives more heat than one who is farther away.

★ **14. Heat transparency.** A substance like dry air which is not warmed very much by the passage of radiant energy is said to be *transparent* to heat. Clouds and moist air are more *opaque* to heat. Consequently, clouds absorb some of the sun's heat. They also prevent the loss by radiation of some of the earth's heat. Certain substances — alum, for example — are transparent to light, but are opaque to heat. On the other hand, iodine solution is opaque to light, but transparent to heat.

Heat from the sun readily enters through the glass windows of a building. Heat from a room, however, does not so readily escape by radiation through glass. The wave length of the radiation makes the difference. The waves from the sun are short and extremely penetrating. Those given off by objects in a room are long and much less penetrating. Glass is used for covering greenhouses and cold frames.

★ 4. HEAT TRANSFER WITHIN OUR HOMES

★ **15. Maintaining proper temperatures.** There are important examples of heat transfer occurring in our homes all the time. These range from the breeze blowing through a window to the operation of an all-year air conditioning system. Heating water, cooking foods, and drying clothes in an automatic dryer involve the transfer of heat.

16. Natural ventilation. Ordinary ventilation depends entirely on convection. Warmer air in a room, being less dense, rises to the ceiling. Cooler air is found near the floor. By opening windows from the top and bottom, natural convection currents change the air in the room. Open windows in rooms on opposite sides of the house permit outside winds to move air through these rooms. Exhaust fans are sometimes used to remove cooking odors from the kitchen so that they do not spread to other parts of the house. A large exhaust fan will increase the rate of air movement and provide better ventilation for hot, summer evenings.

★ **17. What is conditioned air?** Four things should be done to condition the air of our homes. Properly **conditioned air** enables us to enjoy maximum health and comfort, and to work more efficiently. (1) Air must be warmed in winter and cooled in summer. We can adapt ourselves to extremes of temperature. But we feel most comfortable when *the temperature range is from 68° F to 78° F.* (2) *The relative humidity should be* between 40% and 60%. (3) *Air should be filtered* to remove particles of dust and bacteria present in the air. (4) *The air should be kept in constant, gentle motion.*

While a great many homes are not equipped with complete air conditioning systems, we usually have devices which perform two or three of these functions. Heating units are found practically everywhere. Air conditioning systems are familiar in theaters, stores, office buildings, and trains. Room air conditioners are becoming more popular for bedrooms and living rooms. Each year more new homes are built with all-year air conditioning.

★ **18. The heating of air.** There are three well-known types of fuels used to supply energy for heating air. These are coal in its various forms, natural or manufactured gas, and fuel oil. Most heating systems can be adapted to the combustion of any one of these fuels.

(1) *Space heaters.* These are stoves which are used for heating a single

Fig. 15-14. An exhaust fan is used to ventilate a kitchen by removing the warm, odor-filled air to the outside, leaving the interior fresher.

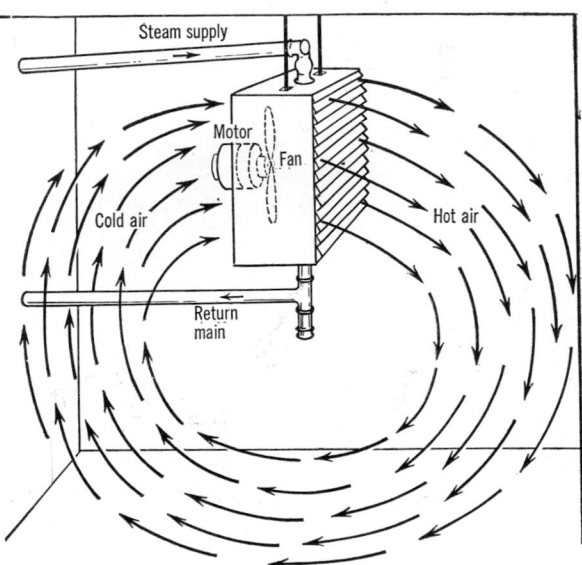

Fig. 15-15. A unit heater.

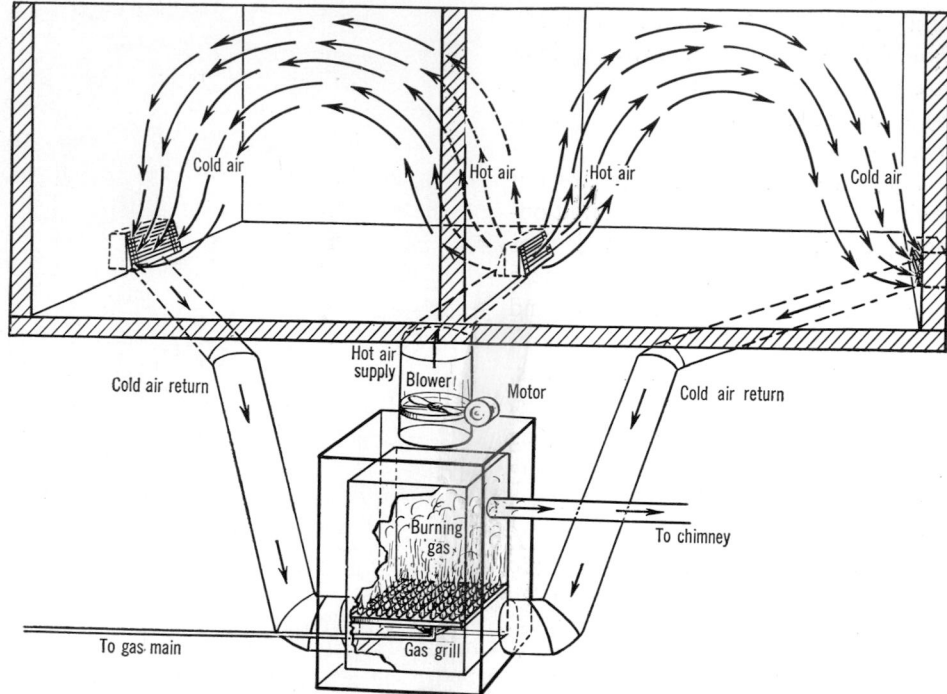

Fig. 15-16. A gas-fired forced hot air heating system.

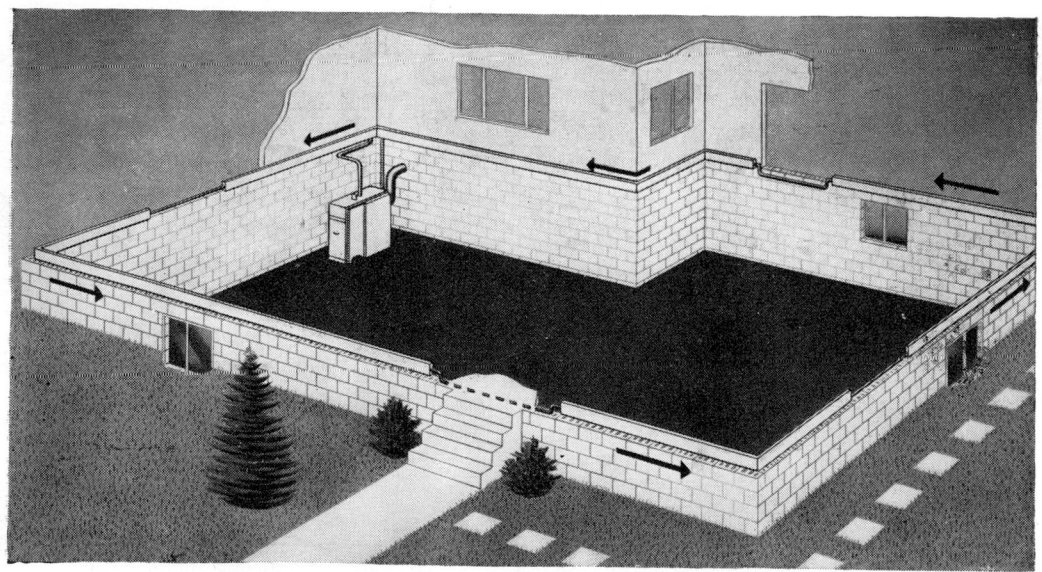

Fig. 15-17. An installation of an oil-fired boiler hot water heating system. A pump circulates the hot water through the baseboard radiators in the direction shown by the arrows.

large room. Cool air enters the heater at the bottom. It is warmed by passing around the hot firebox, and circulates throughout the room by convection currents. Sometimes a blower is used to increase the circulation of the air. A water pan may be used for increasing the humidity. See Fig. 15-6.

(2) *Unit heaters.* Stores, factories, and garages are often equipped with unit heaters. In this heater, a fan forces the cool air over steam or gas-heated metal coils. These heaters are useful for warming large areas. The heat from them may be directed toward the particular spot where it is most needed.

(3) *Forced hot-air heating system.* Air from outside, or, more frequently, that returned from the rooms, is circulated around the hot firebox. This warmed air is then distributed through ducts to the rooms by the action of a circulating fan. A separate set of ducts returns the cooled air to the furnace. Since the air is forced to circulate, it may be filtered and also humidified by appropriate apparatus near the furnace.

In older homes, the circulation of hot air may be by convection alone. In such cases larger ducts must be used, and filtration of the air is not possible.

(4) *Circulating hot water heating system.* Heat is carried to the rooms by water which has been warmed in coils surrounding the firebox of the furnace. A pump forces the hot water through the system from the furnace to some form of room radiator and back again to the furnace. This system is most popular when panel heating or baseboard heating is desired. A panel heating system has coils of pipe imbedded in the floors, walls, or ceilings of the rooms. The heat of the water circulated through these pipes warms the room by radiation. Baseboard radiators or standard type radiators warm a room mostly by convection. In spite of their name, they give off very little heat by radiation.

Two pipes are used in the hot-water system. One is for the hot water which goes to the radiators, the other acts as the return pipe. Since water expands when heated, an expansion tank containing some air is inserted in the system. The air in the tank is compressed by the expanding water. A valve releases water from the system to the outside if the pressure gets too high.

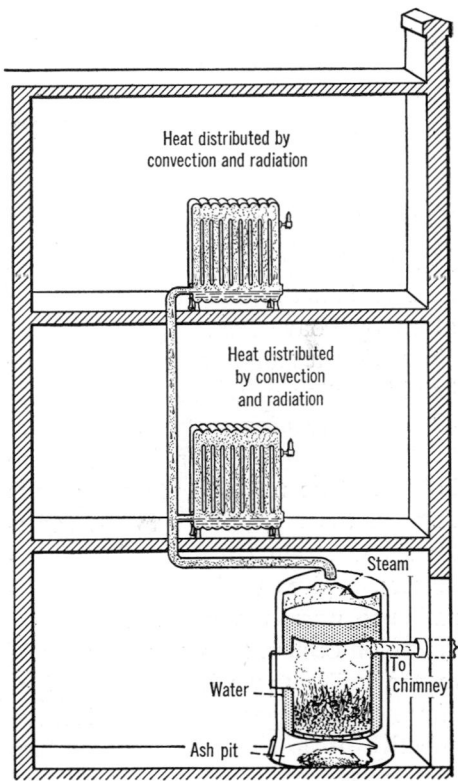

Fig. 15-18. A coal-fired single-pipe steam heating system.

Fig. 15-19. This workman is plastering over the electric cable which will provide radiant heat to this room from the ceiling.

When larger pipes are used, the water circulation in this system may take place by convection. However such circulation responds very slowly to the heating action of the furnace.

(5) *Steam heating systems.* In steam heating systems, water is heated to boiling. The resulting steam expands through the pipes and into the radiators. As steam condenses in the radiators, it gives up its heat of vaporization to warm the room. After condensation occurs, the water may return to the boiler through the same pipe. However, in larger buildings, it is more effective if a separate water return pipe is used. Since the temperature of steam is higher than that of hot water, smaller radiators may be used for steam heating. Rooms are warmed principally by convection from these radiators.

The vapor system of steam heating operates in a manner similar to a regular steam heating system, except that the system is kept at a lower operating pressure by means of a vacuum pump. With lowered pressure, the water does not need to be heated to so high a temperature to be converted into steam. Two pipes are used in this system. Special care must be taken to make sure that the entire system is free from leaks which might raise the pressure.

(6) *Electric heating.* We are familiar with the small, portable electric heater used to heat a room. Now it is possible to heat an entire home by elec-

tricity. Low temperature electric heating cables are mounted on the ceilings when the house is built. They are then covered with plaster. Consequently, no heating apparatus is visible. In operation, the cables heat the ceiling so that it becomes a low temperature, radiant heating surface.

(7) *The heat pump.* A heat pump operates like a refrigerator in transporting heat from one location to another. For winter heating operation, heat is absorbed from the earth by the evaporation of a refrigerant in a long coil laid in the ground below the frost line. The refrigerant is then drawn into the house by a compression pump. As the pump compresses the refrigerant, it gives out heat. The condensation of the refrigerant gives out still more heat. The heat given out on compression and condensation warms the air being circulated through the house. The condensed refrigerant then circulates back into the underground coils to evaporate and repeat the process.

This heat pump can be used for summer cooling merely by reversing the process. The refrigerant now evaporates in coils over which the air in the house is circulating. This absorbs heat from the air in the house and cools it. The refrigerant is then compressed, and sent through the ground coils where it gives up its heat, and condenses.

★ **19. Comparison of the common heating systems.** (1) The mechanical warm-air system provides the cheapest satisfactory installation. It is easily controlled in mild weather when little heat is needed. The duct openings are inconspicuous compared with radiators. This system has the distinct advantage of being the easiest to convert to all-year air conditioning. Filtering and humidifying the air are easily included. Replacement of the filters at intervals is necessary. The noise of the circulating fan may be annoying to some persons. (2) Circulating hot water systems provide uniform heating. They are proving to be the most

Fig. 15-20. The heat pump can be used to cool a home in summer and to heat it in winter. During summer operation the refrigerant evaporates in the piping, absorbing heat from the air circulating inside the home. During winter operation the refrigerant cools after being compressed, giving out heat to the air circulating inside the home.

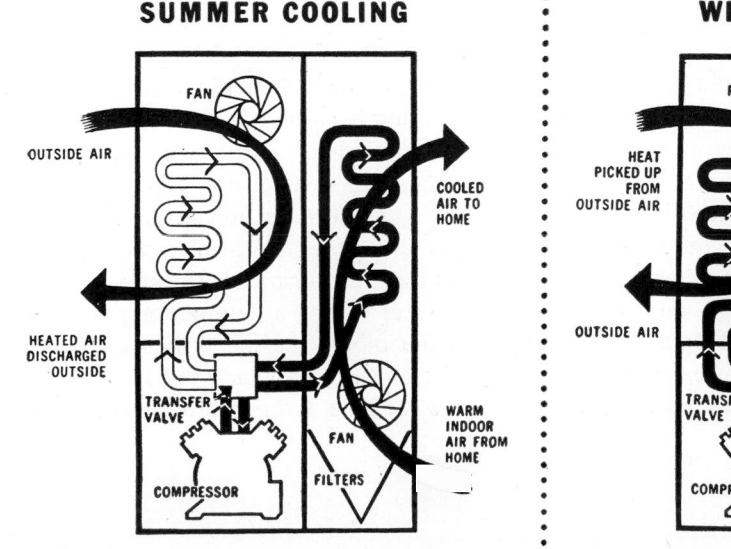
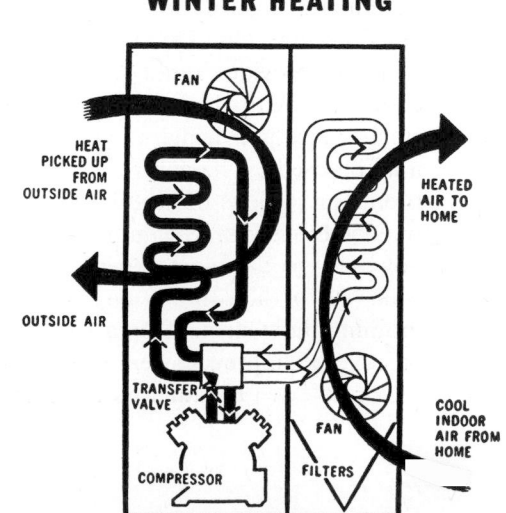

Fig. 15-21. A cutaway diagram of a room air conditioner. Warm air from the room is drawn by an enclosed fan through the filter and cooling coils at the left and discharged to the room through the directional grille at the top. In the outdoor portion of the unit, at the right, are the compressor, the condenser coils, and the condenser fan.

popular choice when panel or baseboard heating is desired. It is possible to use this system with a window unit which brings heated, outside air into the room. If cold water is circulated through the pipes in the summer, this window unit will also provide cooling. Hot-water systems require a lot of piping. Provision for complete drainage of the system is necessary. Corrosion or mineral deposits in the piping will cut down the circulation. (3) Steam systems provide rapid heating and cooling. With higher temperatures, smaller size unit heaters and radiators may be used. The control of separate rooms or sections of a building is easily done by valves. Steam heating may, however, be the most expensive to install. Provision must be made for draining the system. Steam pipes must be covered to prevent heat loss, as well as for safety. If radiators are located

beneath the level of the boiler, a pump must be provided to return the condensed water.

★ **20. The cooling of air.** Unless large quantities of cold water are available, air is cooled by refrigeration. Either the mechanical refrigerator or the gas-type refrigerator may be adapted to this purpose. Air is circulated over the coils in which the refrigerant is evaporating. This absorbs heat from the air, and cools it. Heat from the compression and condensation of the refrigerant is discharged to the outside atmosphere. Such refrigerating mechanisms may be easily installed in the basement beside the forced warm-air furnace. In this way, warm or cool air is circulated through the home to maintain a temperature at a comfortable level.

Room air conditioners operate on the same principle. Outside air or recirculated inside air is drawn over cooling coils by the action of a fan. The air is filtered and humidity reduced by the condensation of moisture on the cooling coils. The heat of compression and condensation of the refrigerant, as well as the moisture from the cooling coils, are discharged to the outside air by the action of a second fan.

★ **21. Regulation of humidity.** We have just described the way in which humidity is partially controlled in room air conditioners. In a home heating or cooling system the humidity may be regulated more precisely. Humidifiers are generally of two types. In one type, the air passes through a spray of water having a definite temperature. In the other, the air passes over wet coils or surfaces which are maintained at a definite temperature. The temperature of the water spray or of the wet coils determines the humidity of the air. The higher these temperatures are, the higher the relative humidity will be.

★ **22. Filtration of air.** A filter is placed in a circulating air system so that all the air must pass through it. The job of the filter is to remove dust, dirt, lint, bacteria, and any other fine particles which are being carried by the air. Filters may consist of a mat of glass fibers or of coated, fine metal screening. Electronic filters have been devised, also. (See Section 22, Chapter 24.) All of these must be cleaned or replaced periodically as they become clogged. In some installations, ultraviolet light is used to kill air-borne bacteria.

★ **23. Circulation of air.** Either a blade-type or centrifugal-type fan is used to keep the air in circulation. These fans are usually mounted on rubber so that the noise of their operation is reduced. They also are controlled by thermostats in the furnace or air-cooling unit so that they do not operate unless the air to be circulated is within the proper temperature range.

★ **24. How does a chimney work?** We know from Bernoulli's principle that air moves upward in a chimney when wind blows across the top. But even on a calm day there is an upward draft in a chimney. Before a fire is started in a furnace, or fireplace, the air inside the chimney has the same density as the air outside. But when the fire is started, it heats the air in the chimney and causes the air to expand. This action decreases its density. Colder, denser air from the outside then pushes the warm air up the chimney. At the same time the hot waste

products of combustion are carried away.

A tall chimney draws better than a short one. There is a greater difference in weight between the hot gases inside the chimney and an equal volume of cooler air outside.

★ **25. The hot water heater.** Hot water heaters are of two types: the tank type, and the instantaneous type. (1) *Tank type.* This consists of a large insulated metal tank in which a

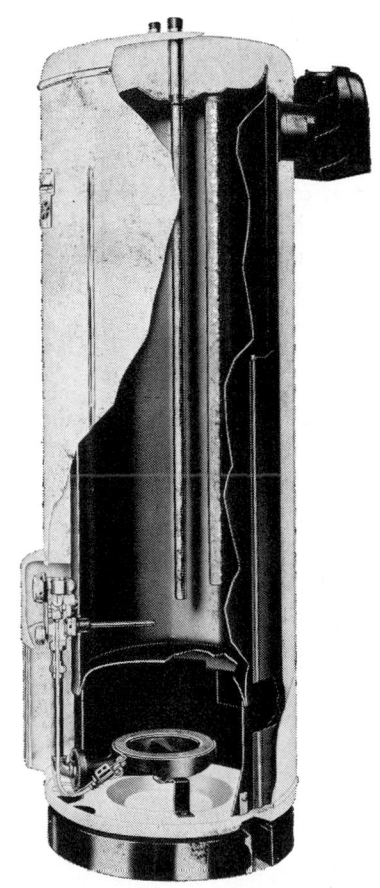

Fig. 15-22. A cutaway view of a gas-fired tank-type hot water heater. Notice the inlet and outlet pipes, the thermostat, and the insulation between the walls of the tank.

quantity of water is maintained at the desired temperature. The water in the tank is heated by convection currents set up in the water itself. See Fig. 15-22. The source of heat may be a side-arm coil which passes into the steam or hot-water boiler of the house heating system. It may also be a separate gas burner which heats the water in a side-arm coil. Still another type has the gas burner mounted at the bottom of the tank. Electric water heaters are considered to be tank type heaters.

(2) *Instantaneous type.* In this type, large gas burners heat water flowing through coiled copper tubing. Cold water is raised to the desired temperature as it flows through the heater on its way to the hot water faucet. The gas burns only when hot water is needed.

★ 5. PREVENTING THE TRANSFER OF HEAT

★ 26. Heat transfer through the walls of our homes. Since we wish to keep our homes warmer in winter and cooler in summer than the outside temperature, we must keep the transfer of heat through the walls as low as possible. Various materials and techniques are used to do this. By studying Fig. 15-23, we see that the walls of many houses consist of alternate layers of material separated by air spaces. From the outside, going in, we find a single course of brick, an air space, the sheathing, the studding with air spaces between, and finally the plasterboard and plaster. Air spaces make good insulators, because air is a poor conductor of heat. It is important that the materials making up the wall be poor conductors of heat, too.

★ 27. What materials are used for sheathing? A variety of substances is pressed or formed into large sheets for sheathing. Among these materials are corkboard, wood fiberboard, asbestos millboard, and sugarcane fiberboard. Usually these are impregnated with asphalt or some other moisture-proof coating.

★ 28. Other insulating materials used in home construction. The air spaces between the studs and the ceiling above the upper floor may also be insulated. For this purpose, rock wool, mineral wool, or glass fibers in various forms may be used. These come in blankets to be tacked to the studding, or as pellets or granules to be poured between the rafters above the upper ceiling. These materials reduce the transfer of heat because they are poor conductors. Aluminum foil blankets combine the property of poor conduction through internal air spaces

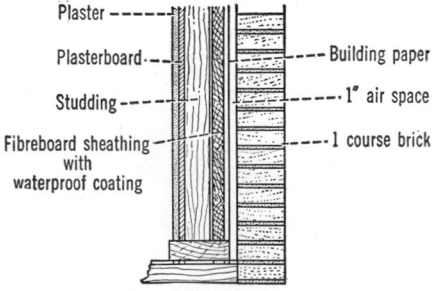

Fig. 15-23. A cross section of the brick-veneer walls of a house.

Plaster

Plasterboard

Studding

Fibreboard sheathing with waterproof coating

Building paper

1″ air space

1 course brick

Fig. 15-24. Insulation stapled between the studs of the walls of a house helps prevent the transfer of heat through the walls.

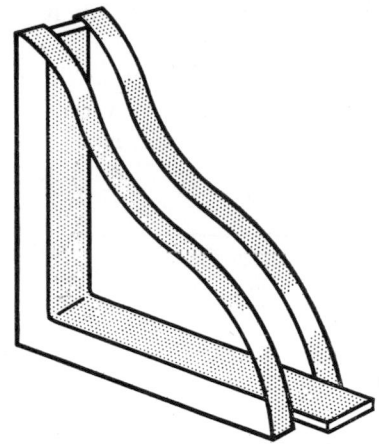

Fig. 15-25. The dead air space between the two panes of glass acts as an insulator.

with excellent reflection of heat radiation at the polished metal surfaces. In order to prevent heat transfer through our glass windows, we sometimes install storm windows. The air trapped between the two panes of glass acts as an insulator. Window units consisting of two sheets of glass separated by an air space are available also.

★ **29. Insulating home appliances.** The hot water tank is probably insulated with mineral wool or glass fibers to keep the heated water hot. A refrigerator may be insulated with corkboard or glass fibers to prevent heat of the room from passing through its walls, while the door is fitted with a rubber gasket to prevent heat from entering there. The oven in a stove has walls insulated with mineral wool or asbestos material.

★ **30. How is heat transfer prevented in a vacuum bottle?** Hot liquids poured into a vacuum bottle stay hot a long time, and cold liquids stay cold. The vacuum bottle is constructed to prevent heat transfer by conduction,

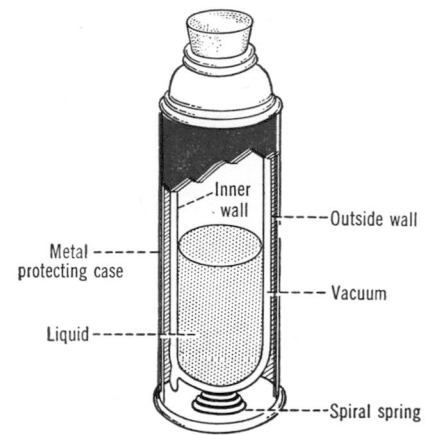

Metal protecting case

Inner wall

Outside wall

Vacuum

Liquid

Spiral spring

Fig. 15-26. The vacuum bottle is constructed to prevent heat transfer by conduction, convection, and radiation.

convection and radiation. It is really a two-walled bottle, as shown in Fig. 15-26. The space between the walls is highly evacuated. A vacuum is a non-conductor of heat. Heat can not be lost through such a double wall by convection, either, since there is no fluid present. Also, the walls of a vacuum bottle are silvered to prevent the transmission of radiant energy.

Summary

Heat may be transferred by conduction, convection, and radiation. Conduction is the transmission of thermal energy from molecule to molecule. Solids conduct heat better than liquids or gases.

Convection currents are set up in fluids because of the difference in density of unequally heated regions. Heat is transmitted by the molecules in such convection currents. Atmospheric circulation depends on convection currents.

Radiation is a method of transferring heat by electromagnetic waves. Radiant energy is not heat itself, but the absorption of radiant energy increases the thermal energy of the absorbing substance. Good absorbers of heat are good radiators. Good reflectors are poor absorbers and poor radiators.

Ordinary ventilation depends upon convection. In order to be properly conditioned, air must be warmed in winter and cooled in summer; the relative humidity must be maintained between 40% and 60%; the air should be filtered; and the air should be kept in constant, gentle motion. There are many methods of heating. These include space heaters, unit heaters, steam heating, forced hot-air heating, circulating hot-water heating, electric heating, and the heat pump. Air is cooled by refrigeration. The humidity of the air may be controlled by passing air over wet coils or through a spray of water.

Heat transfer is prevented by poorly conducting materials used as insulators.

Terms to Define...

Circulating hot-water
  heating system
Circulation of
  air
Conditioned air
Conduction
Conductometer
Convection
Cooling of air
Electric heating
Filtration of
  air

Forced hot-air heating
  system
Heat conduction through
  gases
Heat conduction through
  liquids
Heat conduction through
  solids
Heat pump
Hot-water heater
Insulating materials in home
  construction

Jet stream
Land breeze
Newton's Law of Cooling
Radiation
Regulation of humidity
Sea breeze
Space heater
Steam heating system
Stefan's law
Trade Winds
Unit heater
Vacuum bottle

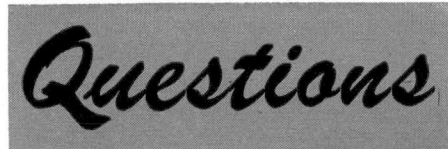

GROUP A

1. Explain how the end of the handle of a spoon left in a cup of coffee becomes hot.

2. In what direction does heat transfer occur spontaneously? How can we cause the transfer of heat to take place in the opposite direction?

3. Arrange the following metals in order of their conductivity of heat: aluminum, brass, copper, gold, iron, mercury, platinum, silver, steel, zinc.

4. Arrange the following insulating materials in order of their conductivity of heat: air, asbestos, brick, concrete, cork, magnesia, paper, sawdust.

5. What is the chief method of heat transfer in liquids?

6. On the way to school one morning, you find a steel penny and a copper penny side by side on the pavement. Which penny is colder? Which feels colder when you pick the pennies up?

7. How are air-cooled engines designed so that the rate of heat loss to the air is as great as possible?

8. A living room is heated by hot water passing through the tubes of a baseboard radiator. What method of heat transfer warms the air in all parts of the room?

9. Why does unequal heating of fluids set up convection currents in the fluids?

10. Explain why winds usually blow from large bodies of water onto the land during the day and from the land onto the water at night.

11. How does the jet stream in the Northern Hemisphere affect weather conditions?

12. What causes the Calms of Cancer and Capricorn?

13. Name some types of electromagnetic radiation. What property do all these types have in common?

14. What effect does the passage of radiant heat waves have on the temperature of a substance which transmits them readily?

15. What color should a radiator be painted in order that it radiate heat most efficiently?

GROUP B

★ **16.** One cup of water at 55° F and another cup of water at 50° F are placed in a refrigerator which has a temperature of 45° F. How do cooling rates of the two cups of water compare?

★ **17.** Describe an ideal radiator. Upon what does its rate of energy emission depend?

★ **18.** Why will radiant heat waves from the sun pass through glass windows into our houses easily, yet little heat from the room is lost through the windows by radiation?

★ **19.** What should be the relationship between the inside and outside temperatures if a large exhaust fan is to be effective in cooling a house? Would such a fan have a beneficial effect at any other time? Explain.

★ **20.** What are the four characteristics of properly conditioned air?

★ **21.** What are the advantages of unit heaters? For what heating requirements are they particularly useful?

★ **22.** Which type of heating system is most adaptable to the addition of a refrigeration unit to provide air cooling?

★ **23.** In homes where forced air is used for both heating and cooling, the ducts through which air enters the room open into the room about halfway up the wall. Why are they placed in this position, rather than at the top or bottom of the wall?

★ **24.** Why does a forced hot-water system provide more even heat for rooms than a gravity-flow hot-water system?

★ **25.** In what type of climate would a home steam heating system be most effective?

Things to Do

1. Prepare a diagram of the heating system in your home. Include the furnace, together with all the pipes or ducts. Show how the system is controlled.

2. Examine a house which is in process of construction. How are the walls made? What insulating materials are used, and where are they put?

Chapter 16

Heat and Work

1. How are heat and work related?
When we first began to study heat, we learned about Count Rumford and his discovery that friction produced heat. The friction resulted from work which was wasted in the boring of a cannon. Then Joule found that a definite amount of mechanical energy could always be transformed into the same amount of heat. These discoveries showed that heat was another form of energy, and could therefore be related to work.

Joule used an interesting method to find the relation between heat and work. A simplified form of his apparatus is shown in Fig. 16-1. The weights are permitted to fall a certain distance. As they fall, the cord to which they are attached turns the shaft and paddles. The constant paddling of the water warms it by friction. All the work put into this machine is transformed into heat.

By multiplying the amount of weight used by the distance it falls, we calculate the number of foot-pounds of work wasted during the experiment. By multiplying the mass of water by the number of Fahrenheit degrees its temperature was raised during the experiment, we compute the number of British thermal units of heat produced by the wasted work. Joule found that 772 ft-lb of work produced one Btu of heat. The average of a large number of more recent experiments shows that *778 ft-lb of work are equivalent to one Btu of heat.* In the metric system, work is measured in either joules or ergs. *One calorie equals 4.19 joules, or 4.19 × 10⁷ (41,900,000) ergs.*

2. How is heat converted into work? We have just seen how work may be completely converted into heat. This conversion is reversible. That is, we also can change heat into work. Experiments have shown that *one British thermal unit of heat can do*

Vocabulary

EXTERNAL COMBUSTION ENGINE. An engine in which the heat of the burning fuel is used to vaporize a liquid under pressure. The vaporized liquid is then permitted to expand in the cylinder or turbine chamber of the engine.

INTERNAL COMBUSTION ENGINE. An engine in which the fuel is burned directly in the cylinders or turbine chamber.

MECHANICAL EQUIVALENT OF HEAT. The conversion factor which relates heat units to work units.

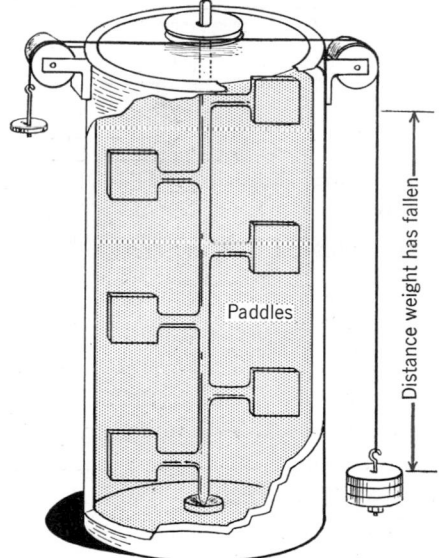

Fig. 16-1. A simplified form of the apparatus Joule used to determine the mechanical equivalent of heat.

*778 ft-lb of work. One calorie can do 4.19 joules or 4.19 × 10⁷ ergs of work. These numbers give the **mechanical equivalents of heat.***

We have several methods by which we convert heat into useful work.

(1) *In our own bodies.* You may have learned in biology that a thick slice of bread furnishes 100 kilocalories, or 100,000 calories of heat. This value is the amount of heat which can be given out by the bread when it is completely oxidized. This would provide enough energy to perform 419,000 joules of work. At an efficiency of 100%, that heat energy would enable a 125-lb boy to climb a mountain almost 2500 ft high. Experiments have shown however that only about 25% of the heat energy in our food is converted into muscular energy.

(2) *By the use of steam.* We generate steam by adding enough heat to

water to make it boil. This heat may come from burning wood, coal, or oil. When water is converted into steam under normal atmospheric pressure it expands about 1700 times. In a boiler, however, the steam is confined and exerts a considerable pressure in all directions. The pressure of this steam may be used to do work in one of two ways. It may exert its force against the piston of a steam engine, or its force may turn the blades of a steam turbine. In either case, the heat of the burning fuel is transformed into work through the use of steam.

(3) *By the use of burning gases.* When we use steam to produce work, we must first generate the steam by *burning a fuel outside the engine which converts into vapor a liquid under pressure.* Such engines are called **external combustion engines.** If we convert heat into work by using burning gases, we have eliminated the need for a boiler. We may use the pressure of burning gases to convert heat into work in the same two ways that steam

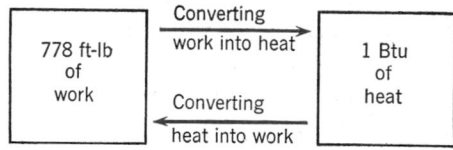

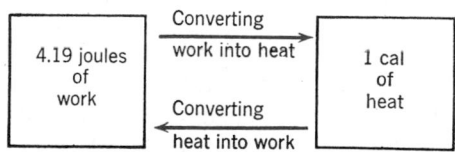

Fig. 16-2. The mechanical equivalents of heat.

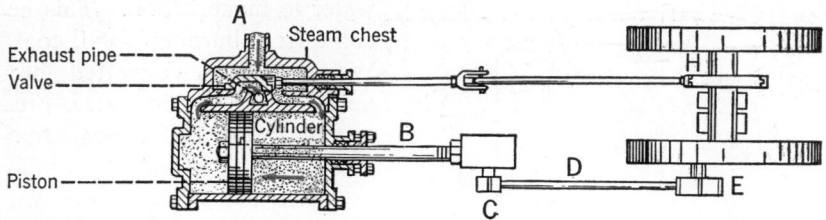

Fig. 16-3. The essential parts of a steam engine as viewed from above.

is used. Burning gases may exert their force to move a piston, or their force may turn the blades of a turbine. Since *the burning of the fuel occurs within the cylinder or turbine chambers, such engines are called* **internal combustion engines.**

3. The steam engine. In Fig. 16-3 we see the principal parts of a steam engine. The steam is led from the boiler through pipe *A* into the steam chest. When the slide valve is in the position shown in the figure, the steam goes from the steam chest into the right end of the cylinder. Here it expands and pushes the piston with great force toward the left end of the cylinder. The steam that was used in the previous stroke is pushed out the left end of the cylinder and through the exhaust pipe. The path of the expanding steam is shown by arrows.

When the piston has nearly reached the end of its stroke to the left, the valve slides to the right. Now the left end of the cylinder is connected with the steam chest, and the right end of the cylinder is connected to the exhaust. The steam enters the left end of the cylinder and pushes the piston to the right. As the valve moves back and forth, steam is admitted alternately to the ends of the cylinder. This causes the piston to be pushed back and forth. This kind of motion, as

mentioned before, is called reciprocating motion. When one end of the cylinder is connected to the steam supply, the slide valve automatically connects the other end of the cylinder with the exhaust.

4. How does the moving piston rod turn a wheel? The to-and-fro motion of the piston rod is not a very useful type of motion. The turning of a wheel, or *rotary motion,* is more desirable. How can we convert reciprocating motion into rotary motion? In Figs. 16-3 and 16-4 we see that the piston rod *B* is pivoted at *C* to a connecting rod *D*. This rod, in turn, is attached to an eccentric *E* on the flywheel shaft. As the piston moves the length of the cylinder to the left, *C* moves this same distance. In doing so, it causes the end of the eccentric to describe a circular path up and around from *G* to *F*. The diameter of the circle *FG* must be the same as the length of travel of the piston in the cyl-

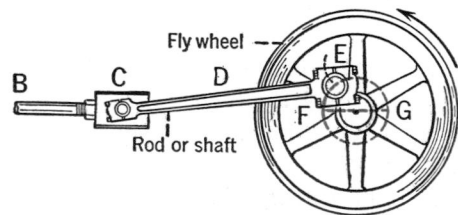

Fig 16-4. The eccentric attached to the flywheel converts reciprocating motion into rotary motion.

Fig. 16-5. This streamlined passenger locomotive is one of the few modern steam locomotives used on American railroads today. It operates at a steam pressure of 300 lb/in²; its cylinders are 27 inches in diameter and have a 32-inch stroke. The tender holds 35 tons of coal and 20,000 gallons of water.

inder. During the return stroke of the piston, *C* moves to the right and pushes the eccentric down around the other half-circle from *F* to *G*. The inertia of the heavy flywheel carries the piston past the two points where there is no steam pressure. These two points are known as " dead centers."

5. How is the sliding valve controlled? From Fig. 16-3 we see that the motion of the sliding valve is controlled by a second eccentric *H* mounted on the flywheel shaft. By means of a slide valve rod, the rotary motion of the flywheel shaft is converted back into the reciprocating motion needed to control the slide valve. As the eccentric *H* moves counterclockwise, the valve is pulled to the right. This shuts off the steam entering the right side of the cylinder, and permits steam to enter the left side of the cylinder for the back stroke of the piston.

6. The two types of steam engines. (1) *Non-condensing engines.* In a non-condensing engine, the spent steam is discharged directly into the atmosphere. Suppose the steam entering the cylinder is at a pressure of 85 lb/in². The spent steam, which is discharged into the air, meets a backward pressure of one atmosphere, nearly 15 lb/in². As a consequence, the net pressure exerted on the piston by the expanding steam is only 70 lb/in². If

we require an effective steam pressure of 85 lb/in² for the operation of our engine, we must boost the pressure in the steam chest to 100 lb/in². The best examples of non-condensing steam engines are steam locomotives.

(2) *Condensing engines.* Stationary steam engines are equipped ordinarily with a condenser. In the condenser the spent steam is changed into liquid by cooling, usually with water. The condensation of the spent steam reduces the pressure behind the piston, perhaps to only 1 lb/in². In this case a pressure of 86 lb/in² in the steam chest is approximately as effective as a pressure of 100 lb/in² in a non-condensing engine.

7. How is the steam produced? Boilers for generating steam are designed so that the heat from the burning fuel is transferred as completely as possible to the water and steam. (1) *Water-tube type.* This type of boiler is shown with an automatic stoker in Fig. 16-6. It is used with stationary engines and with steam turbines. The flames and hot exhaust gases travel a circuitous path over and around the pipes filled with water. They also strike the bottom of the boiler itself. In this way heat is more effectively transferred to the water. The automatic stoker feeds fuel to the fire at the proper rate. Additional hot

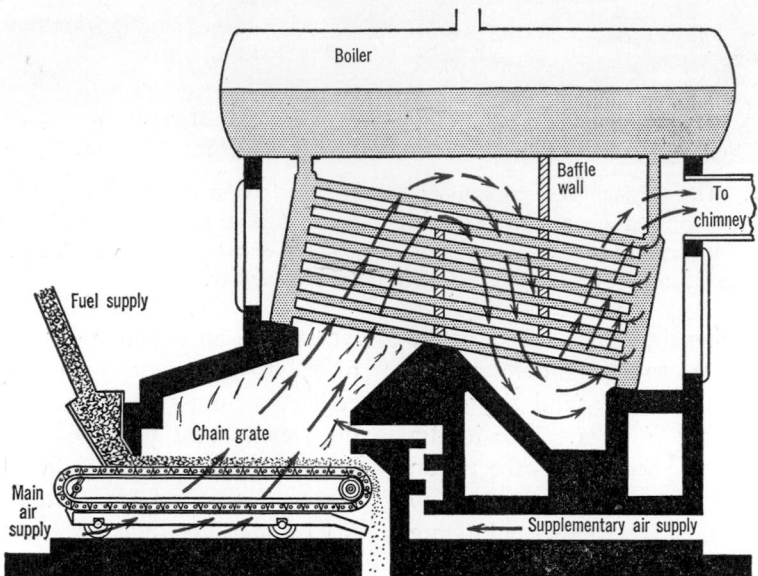

Fig. 16-6. A water-tube boiler fired by an automatic coal stoker.

air is fed into the flames to make combustion more complete.

(2) *Fire-tube type.* This type of boiler is used on steam locomotives. From the firebox, the flames are drawn through long horizontal tubes which are surrounded with water. The exhaust steam is given off through the smokestack and produces the draft.

8. The steam turbine. We already have learned how moving water, striking the blades of a water turbine, causes the turbine to rotate. Steam under high pressure can do the same thing. We see the principle of the steam turbine illustrated in Fig. 16-7. The steam is directed through nozzles against a set of movable, cupped buckets.

A large steam turbine consists of two main parts, (1) a rotor, and (2) a stator. The rotor consists of a long shaft on which are mounted wheels containing a large number of

buckets. These are set much like the blades of a windmill. See Fig. 16-8. The stator, in which the rotor is mounted, contains a large number of fixed nozzles. The steam enters near one end of the turbine and strikes the first set of movable buckets. After passing through this set the steam is redirected by a set of fixed nozzles.

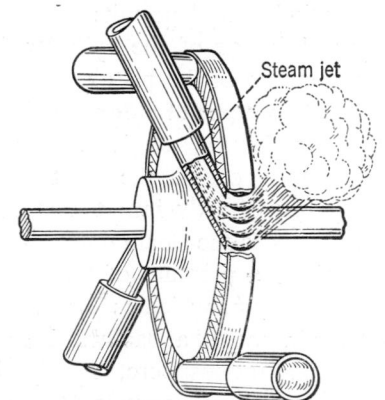

Fig. 16-7. The force of the steam against the cupped buckets causes them to move.

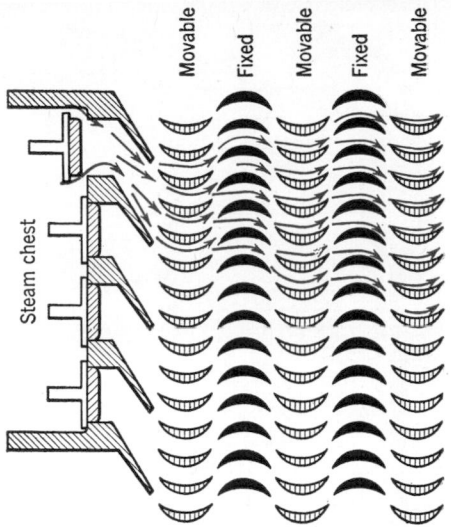

Movable · Fixed · Movable · Fixed · Movable

Steam chest

Fig. 16-8. Path of steam through a turbine.

The steam then strikes a second set of movable buckets and gives up more of its force. Again its direction is restored by fixed nozzles. The force of the steam against the movable buckets makes them turn. This causes the shaft on which they are mounted to rotate. The diameters of both the rotor and the stator are made larger near the outlet end. The pitch of the buckets changes, too. In this way the expansive force of the steam is most completely used.

In a modern turbine, steam may enter at 1200–2000 lb/in². On its way through the turbine — a distance of 15 or 20 feet — the steam passes through about 20 bucket wheels and the same number of nozzles. It pushes against 5000 or more buckets. Its temperature drops from 900° to 70° F. All this happens in one-thirtieth of a second. A condenser for the spent steam converts it into water so rapidly that

Fig. 16-9. The rotor of a 100,000 kilowatt steam-turbine generator set being lowered into position.

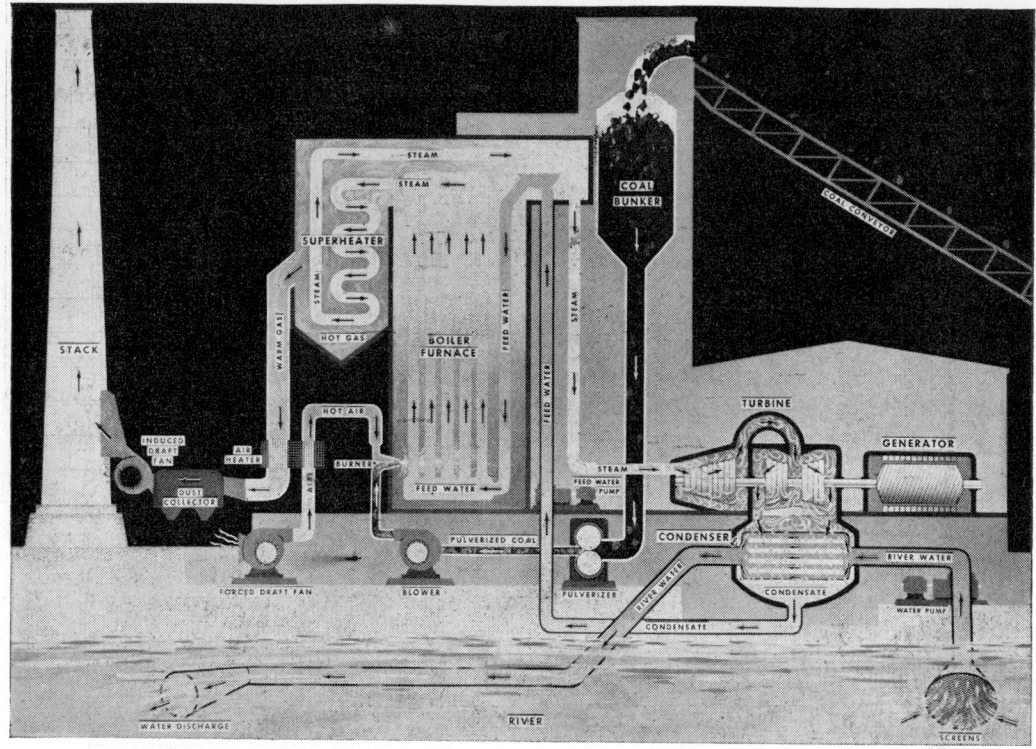

Fig. 16-10. Schematic diagram showing the cross-section of a steam turbine generating station. Trace the flow of water or steam through the boiler, superheater, turbine, and condenser.

the pressure in the cool end of a turbine is less than that of the atmosphere.

9. Comparing the steam turbine and the steam engine. The steam turbine is the device most frequently used today for changing the heat of steam into useful work. However, some steam engines still remain in older installations and as steam locomotives.

For a given horsepower, the steam turbine occupies less space and has less weight than a reciprocating engine. The rotary motion of a turbine causes much less vibration than the to-and-fro motion of a reciprocating engine. Steam turbines are high speed machines. The steam enters at 1200 miles per hour. The wheels turn at

600 mi/hr. The shaft of a turbine may be directly connected to the electric generator which it drives.

A steam turbine is not as efficient at low speed as the reciprocating engine. Steam must travel through a turbine at high speed, otherwise much of its expansive force is lost. A reciprocating engine is easily reversed. The turbine can not be reversed.

10. The gasoline engine. The gasoline engine is our most familiar internal combustion engine. The fuel to be burned in the cylinders of this engine is a mixture of gasoline vapor and air which is prepared in the carburetor. (Refer to Section 4, Chapter 9.) This mixture is ignited in the cylinder by an electric spark. The energy from

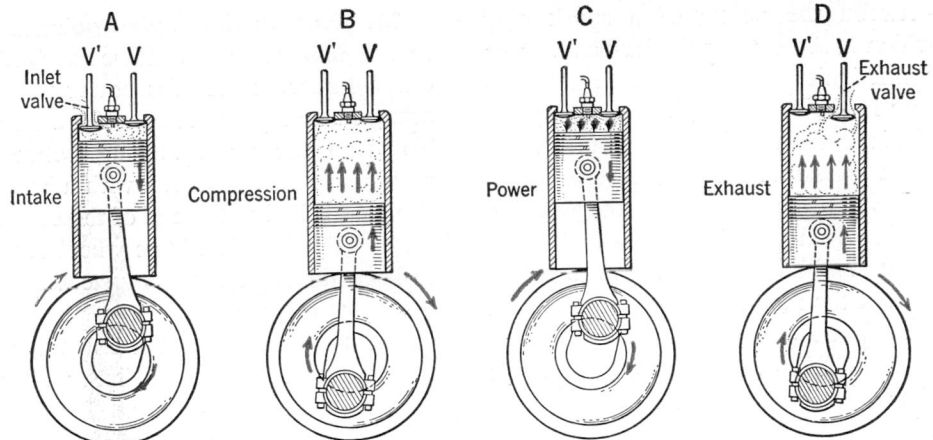

Fig. 16-11. The four strokes of a gasoline engine.   A. Intake.   B. Compression.
C. Power. D. Exhaust.

the explosion pushes the piston down. This force is transmitted by the connecting rod to the crankshaft. (See Section 30, Chapter 11.) The cylinder has thick walls. The piston fits the cylinder so tightly that gases can not pass it. The cylinder has one valve to let in the fuel mixture and another valve to let the burned gas escape.

Let us see what happens in a single-cylinder, four-stroke engine:

STROKE 1. To start the engine, we pull the piston down from a position near the top of the cylinder. In an automobile engine this is done by an electric motor which we call the " starter." As the piston moves down, the intake valve opens, and fuel is drawn from the carburetor into the cylinder. During this stroke the exhaust valve is closed. This stroke is called the *intake stroke*. It fills the cylinder with an explosive mixture of gases.

STROKE 2. As the starter continues to crank the engine, the intake valve closes, and the piston moves upward. During this stroke the explosive

gases are compressed to one-seventh or one-eighth of their original volume. This is the *compression stroke*. Both valves must be tightly closed during this time, otherwise the gas would not be compressed.

STROKE 3. Just before the piston reaches the top of the compression stroke, an electric spark is produced

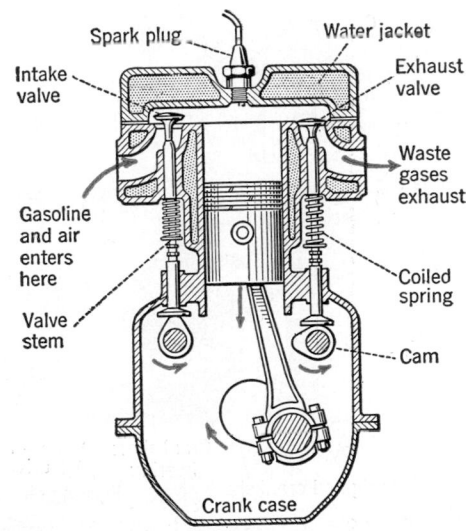

Fig. 16-12. A sectional view of a gasoline engine.

between the points of a spark plug which is set in the cylinder head. The spark ignites the compressed gas mixture in the cylinder. The resulting explosion produces hot gases which exert great pressure. The pressure forces the piston down. This is the working stroke of a piston, and is called the *power stroke*. Both valves are closed so that the motor gets full benefit from the expansion of the burning gases.

STROKE 4. The cylinder now is filled with burned gases. On the next upstroke of the piston, these gases are pushed out of the cylinder through the exhaust valve. This *exhaust stroke* completes the operation. Then the whole process starts over again.

11. Keeping the engine going between power strokes. If we have only one cylinder, it provides power to the crankshaft only one-fourth of the time. To keep the parts moving between power strokes, a flywheel with a heavy rim is attached to the end of the crankshaft. The inertia of this wheel tends to keep the engine running steadily.

Automobiles are usually powered with six- or eight-cylinder engines, although there are four-cylinder Jeeps and 16-cylinder Cadillacs. By using more cylinders, the power strokes on the crankshaft occur more often. When we have only one cylinder, there is one power stroke for two complete turns of the crankshaft. Six cylinders

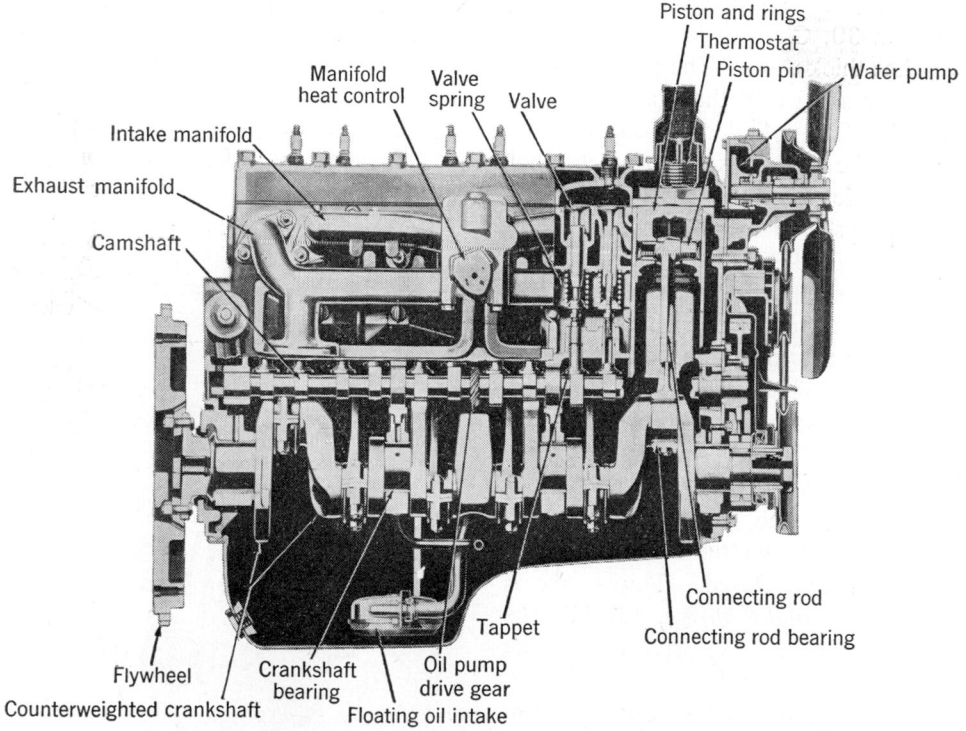

Fig. 16-13. A cross-sectional view of a gasoline engine. Notice the crankshaft, camshaft, and flywheel. Also, at the top and to the right, notice the thermostat which controls the amount of water being used to cool the engine.

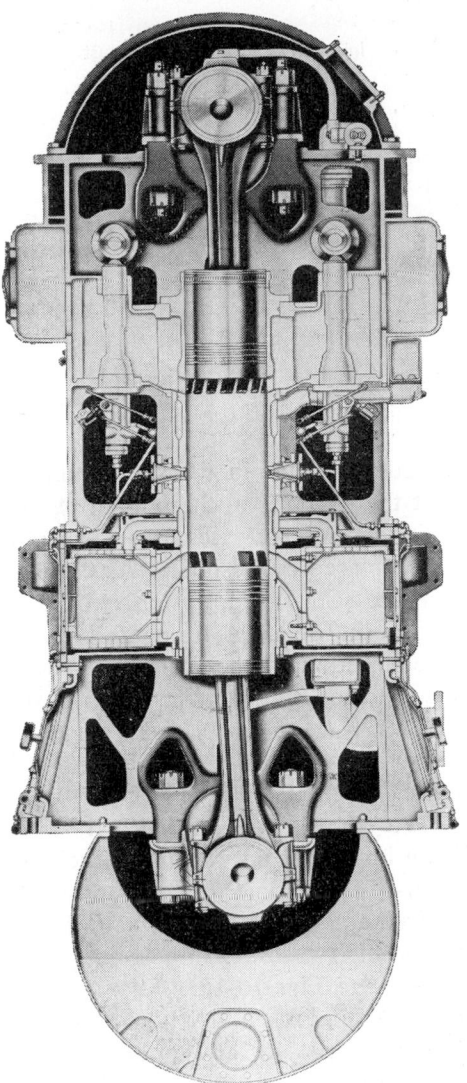

Fig. 16-14. A cross-section of a large Diesel opposed-piston engine.

provide a power stroke for each one-third turn of the crankshaft. Eight cylinders provide a power stroke each one-quarter turn. Since these engines provide more frequent power strokes, the operation is smoother.

12. How are the valves controlled? It is important that the valves open and close at exactly the right time if we are to get maximum power from the engine. The valves are controlled by cams mounted on a camshaft. The camshaft is geared directly to the crankshaft, and turns when the crankshaft turns. In Fig. 16-12 we have a cross-sectional view of a gasoline engine. Notice how the rotation of the cams opens the valves. Coiled springs close the valves after the cam projection has passed the end of the valve stem.

13. Cooling a gasoline engine. The constant series of explosions in a gasoline engine soon heats the cylinder head, the piston, and the cylinder walls. A gasoline engine does not run well until it is warmed up. But it must not get so extremely hot that the pistons expand and become tight in the cylinders. Neither must it reach such a temperature that the cylinder walls and head become distorted. To lubricate them and keep them cool, oil in the crankcase is splashed and pumped to all the moving parts.

In automobile engines the cylinder block is hollow. Water is circulated through the spaces around each cylinder by a centrifugal water pump. As the water becomes warm from the absorbed heat, it flows through connecting hoses from the top of the engine to the top of the radiator. Air, drawn through the radiator by a fan, cools the water in the radiator tubes. The cooled water returns to the lower part of the engine to absorb more heat. The temperature of the cooling water is controlled by a thermostat.

14. The Diesel engine. *Diesel* (*deez*-ul) *engines* operate on either a four-stroke cycle, as does an ordinary gasoline engine, or on a two-stroke cy-

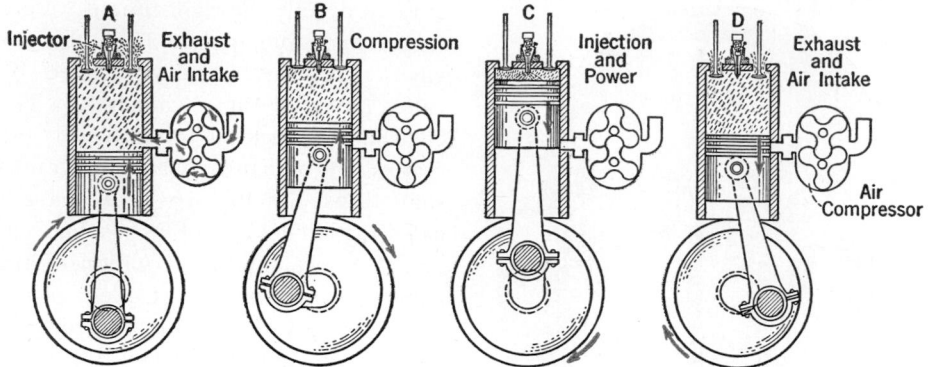

Fig. 16-15. The two-stroke cycle of a Diesel engine.

cle. The four-stroke cycle of a Diesel engine consists of an intake stroke, a compression stroke, a power stroke, and an exhaust stroke. During the intake stroke, air enters the cylinder. During the compression stroke, the air is compressed to one-sixteenth of its original volume. This high compression heats the air to about 1000° F. Just at the end of the compression stroke, a fine spray of oil is injected into the cylinder. This spray of oil injected into the highly compressed and very hot air burns immediately. The expansion of the hot gases forces the piston downward during the power stroke. The exhaust stroke pushes out the burned gases. In a Diesel engine there is no spark plug.

The two-stroke Diesel engine has only a compression stroke and a power stroke. Exhaust and intake are accomplished at the end of the power stroke and at the start of the compression stroke by using a blower. See Fig. 16-15. As the piston nears the bottom of the cylinder, it uncovers the openings from a small blower. Compressed air from the blower rapidly forces the burned gases out through the open exhaust valves at the top of the cylinder. Thus, in the short interval that the piston is at the bottom of the cylinder, exhaust gases are blown out and replaced by fresh air. As the piston starts the compression stroke, it covers the openings from the blower. The injection of the fuel occurs near the end of the compression stroke. The two-stroke cycle gives twice as many power strokes as a four-stroke cycle.

15. What is the fuel injector? This is an important part of any Diesel engine. The fuel injector must spray the desired amount of oil into the cylinder under high pressure at just the right time. See Fig. 16-16. In *A* the oil chamber has been filled and the injector is ready for an injection stroke. In *B,* as the plunger moves down, it covers the fuel inlet, trapping oil in the chamber. The pressure on the oil increases to 15,000 lb/in². This pressure now forces up the lower end of the needle valve plunger, lifting the needle valve off its seat. The oil sprays out the fine holes of the injector tip into the cylinder.

16. The advantages of Diesel engines. All Diesel engines use a fuel which is cheaper than gasoline. This

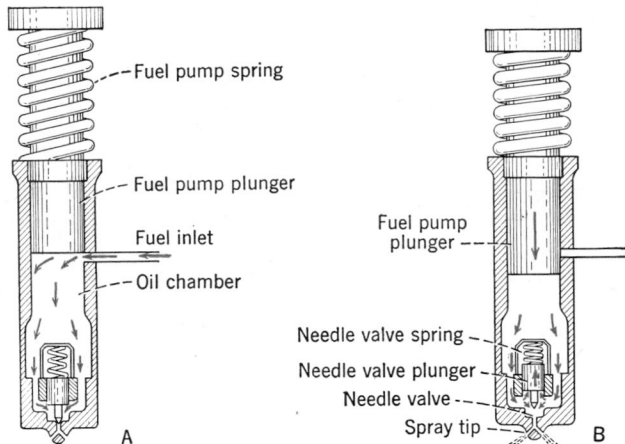

Fuel pump spring

Fuel pump plunger

Fuel inlet

Oil chamber

Fuel pump plunger

Needle valve spring

Needle valve plunger

Needle valve

Spray tip

A

B

Fig. 16-16. The injector sprays the fuel oil into the cylinder of a Diesel engine.

is fuel oil, which is similar to kerosene, but which has more heat value than the same weight of gasoline. The efficiency of a Diesel engine may be from 35 to 40%, while that of a gasoline engine is usually about 25%. At low speeds Diesel engines run more efficiently than gasoline engines. Also, they operate cooler at low speeds. You might think that the lack of a carburetor and ignition system would be an advantage in a Diesel engine. However, the absence of these parts is offset by the need for an injector. Injectors must be very precisely made. Consequently, they are expensive.

With all these advantages, why do we not use Diesel engines in automobiles and airplanes? Because Diesel engines must be strongly constructed to withstand the very high pressures produced in the cylinders. This makes a Diesel engine heavier than a gasoline engine for the amount of power produced. A Diesel engine may weigh about 15 lb/hp, while a gasoline engine used in an automobile weighs only 10 lb/hp. Air-cooled airplane

engines can deliver about 1 hp for each pound of weight.

Today we find Diesel engines used in trucks and buses. Large, ocean-going ships run on Diesel power. Also, Diesel units rapidly are replacing steam locomotives on our nation's railroads.

17. The external combustion engine versus the internal combustion engine. The efficiencies of gasoline and Diesel engines are relatively high. From 25–40% of the energy of the fuel is changed into useful work. The rest of the energy is wasted in the exhaust gases, the cooling system, and through friction. The efficiency of steam locomotives is usually from 5–8%, while that of stationary steam engines and small turbines may run from 10–20%. Higher efficiencies are attained only in very large, high pressure turbines.

Internal combustion engines can start and stop at a moment's notice. They do not waste fuel when they are stopped. A steam engine can not be started until the fuel has been burning

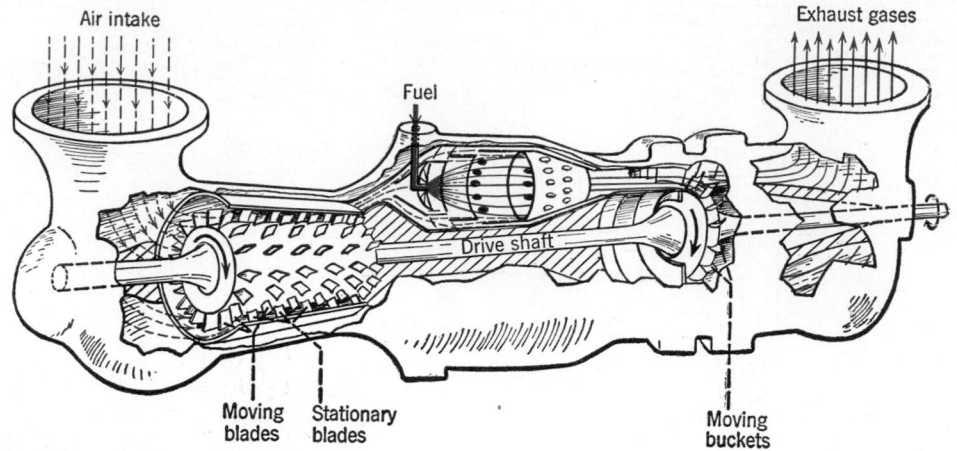

Fig. 16-17. The principle of operation of a gas turbine.

long enough to produce steam. Also, the fuel continues to burn after the engine is shut down. Internal combustion engines develop a lot of power in a small space. Steam engines take up more room for the power they produce.

18. The gas turbine. This is the newest engine which converts the heat energy of a fuel into useful work. Originally developed for airplanes, the gas turbine now shows promise in locomotives, large trucks, small ships, and in small power plant and pumping station applications.

The principle of the gas turbine is remarkably simple. A large volume of air is continually sucked into a compressor, where its pressure is increased. The compressed air then flows into the combustion chamber. Here the fuel — natural gas, gasoline, fuel oil, or powdered coal — is injected and burns. Only part of the compressed air is needed for complete combustion of the fuel. From the combustion chamber the hot, burned gases and heated air rush at tremendous speeds through the exhaust nozzle. On the way to the nozzle, the exhaust gases turn a turbine which drives the compressor. In airplane engines of this type, the thrust of the exhaust gases drives the airplane forward. In other applications, the energy from the exhaust gases is transformed into rotary motion by the turbine. Power beyond that needed to drive the compressor may be taken from the turbine-compressor shaft.

19. The turbo-jet engine. There is really only one moving part in a turbo-jet engine. This is the long shaft through the center of the engine. Attached to the front end of this shaft is the compressor; the turbine is attached at the other end. The compressor sucks air into the front of the engine and compresses it as the air moves straight through the compressor chamber. Fuel, usually similar to kerosene, is injected into the air stream just behind the compressor. Here it burns very rapidly at high temperature, and produces a tremendous pressure. The hot, high-pressure gases pass through the turbine which drives

Fig. 16-18. A rocket provides the thrust needed to launch this pilotless bomber into the air.

the compressor. The terrific unbalanced forward force exerted by the gases as they rush out through the exhaust pushes the engine forward at a terrific pace. Jet engines of 25,000 horsepower have been produced thus far.

20. How does a rocket work? A rocket works on the same principle as the jet engine. However, the difference is that a rocket carries both fuel and the oxygen needed to burn it. The jet engine carries only fuel. It gets the oxygen to burn its fuel from the atmosphere.

Since a rocket carries its own oxygen, it may go beyond the earth's atmosphere. Rockets can travel better in outer space because there is no friction from surrounding air to slow them down. Rockets have been sent up 250 miles above the earth. Also, rocket motors have been made which develop about 600,000 horsepower at top speeds. A rocket-powered airplane has traveled over 1500 miles per hour.

Summary

One British thermal unit of heat is equivalent to 778 foot-pounds of work. One calorie of heat is equivalent to 4.19 joules or 4.19×10^7 ergs of work.

We can use heat to produce steam. Then the pressure exerted by the expanding steam in the cylinders of a steam engine, or in the chamber of a steam turbine, may be used to do work. The burning of the vapor from gasoline or other flammable liquids within a cylinder or turbine chamber is another way of converting heat into work.

The four strokes of a gasoline engine are intake, compression, power, and exhaust. The valves of the engine are controlled by cams. A gasoline engine is cooled by water which is circulated between the cylinder block and the radiator by the action of a centrifugal water pump. The temperature of the cooling water is controlled by a thermostat.

Diesel engines operate on either a four-stroke cycle or a two-stroke cycle. No ignition system is necessary because the fuel-air mixture is so highly compressed that the heat of compression is great enough to kindle the fuel.

A gas turbine consists of a compressor and a combustion chamber. The compressor sucks in a large volume of air and increases its pressure. The fuel is injected into this compressed air in the combustion chamber. The hot, burned gases and heated air drive a small turbine to which the compressor is connected. In a jet airplane engine, the thrust of the exhaust gases drives the airplane forward.

Terms to Define . . .

British thermal unit	Foot-pound	Non-condensing
Calorie	Fuel injector	engine
Compression stroke	Gasoline engine	Power stroke
Condensing engine	Gas turbine	Reciprocating
Converting heat into work	Intake stroke	motion
Converting work into heat	Internal combustion engine	Rocket
Diesel engine	Jet engine	Rotary motion
Exhaust stroke	Joule	Steam engine
External combustion engine	Mechanical equivalent of	Steam turbine
Fire-tube boiler	heat	Water-tube boiler

Questions

GROUP A

1. What is the mechanical equivalent of heat in the metric system? In the English system?

2. Explain why a steam engine is an external combustion engine. Why is a gas turbine an internal combustion engine?

3. What is the function of the sliding valve in a steam engine?

4. How is the reciprocating motion of the pistons changed into rotary motion in an engine?

5. What is the function of the stationary blades of a steam turbine?

6. What are the advantages of the steam turbine over the steam engine? What are some of the advantages which the steam engine itself has?

7. Describe the movement of the piston, intake valve, and exhaust valve during the four strokes of a gasoline engine. During which stroke is the mixture of gasoline vapor and air exploded?

8. Describe the manner in which a gasoline engine kept running between successive power strokes?

9. What are the principal parts of a gas turbine? What occurs in each part when the turbine is in operation?

10. What is the difference between a jet engine and a rocket engine?

GROUP B

11. How does a condenser increase the effective steam pressure of an engine?

12. Explain the difference between fire-tube and water-tube boilers.

13. Why are the larger blades of a steam turbine near the low pressure end of the turbine?

14. What is the compression ratio of a gasoline engine? Of a Diesel engine? Why is there this difference?

15. What function besides lubrication is performed by the oil in the crankcase of an automobile?

16. Why does the thermostat in the cooling system of an automobile not open to permit full circulation of cooling fluid until the engine warms up?

17. Describe the movement of the piston, the blower, the exhaust valves, and the injector during the two strokes of a Diesel engine.

18. How does the efficiency of a gasoline or Diesel engine compare with that of a steam engine and a steam turbine?

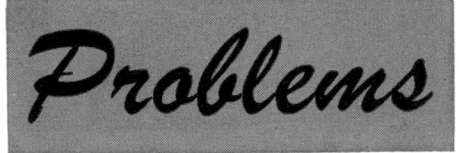

(In the Mathematics Refresher, refer to Sections 4, 6, 7, 10, and 16.)

GROUP A

1. How many foot-pounds of work are required to produce 250 Btu?

2. How many joules of work can be obtained from 10,000 cal?

3. One pound of coal furnishes 12,000 Btu. How many foot-pounds of work can be obtained from the complete combustion of 1 ton of this coal?

4. One gram of gasoline liberates 11,500 cal when it is burned. How many joules of work can be obtained from the burning of one liter of gasoline? Specific gravity of gasoline is 0.7.

5. How many Btu per hour are needed to generate 1 hp?

6. The water going over Niagara Falls drops about 165 ft. How much warmer will the water be at the bottom of the Falls?

GROUP B

7. The overall efficiency of a boiler and steam turbine is 20%. If 50 lb of coal are burned each hour in the boiler, how much work can be done by the turbine? What is the horsepower? The coal has a heating value of 10,000 Btu/lb.

8. A gasoline engine develops 200 hp with an efficiency of 25%. If gasoline has a heat of combustion of 120,000 Btu/gal, how many gallons of gasoline are consumed per hour?

● **9.** The natural gas burned in a gas turbine has a heating value of 100,000 cal/g. If 2 g of gas are burned in the turbine each second, and the efficiency of the turbine is 25%, what is the output in kilowatts?

● **10.** What must be the velocity in m/sec of a snowball at 0° C, if it is completely melted by its impact against a wall?

● **11.** A Diesel-electric locomotive burns 300 gal of fuel oil per hour in developing 2000 hp. If one gallon of fuel oil furnishes 100,000 Btu, what is the efficiency of the locomotive?

● **12.** How many tons of fuel oil are burned in one day by an ocean liner whose engines develop 10,000 hp with an efficiency of 25%? The heat of combustion of the fuel oil is 20,000 Btu/lb.

Things to Do

1. Visit a steam turbine electric generating station. Find out what fuel is used, how the water for the boilers is purified, how the spent steam is condensed, and how the turbines operate to drive the electric generators.

2. If there is a nearby plant where a gas turbine is in operation, visit this plant also.

3. Have a truck mechanic or a locomotive mechanic explain the operation of a Diesel engine to the class.

Unit 8

Sound

The small tank shown in the photograph is an ultrasonic generator which cleans metal parts in a very remarkable fashion. Beneath the tank is a quartz crystal which vibrates very rapidly when electricity is applied to it. Because the crystal vibrates at a frequency greater than that of sounds we can hear, we say it vibrates at an ultrasonic frequency. The cleaning solvent in the tank is agitated by the vibrating crystal. The technician is holding a small wire basket containing tiny precision parts used in guided missiles. These parts have just been cleaned by dipping them momentarily into the rapidly vibrating solvent.

In this unit about Sound, we are going to learn the general characteristics of sound waves. Also, we are going to discover how they are transmitted, reflected, and absorbed. We shall learn how sounds may be harmoniously combined so as to produce music. Then, too, we shall learn about discoveries with sound waves that are beyond the range of normal human hearing.

Chapter 17

Sound and
Wave Motion

1. SOUND AND WAVE MOTION

1. How are sounds produced? Suppose that we take a very thin strip of wood, or a piece of steel like a hacksaw blade, and clamp one end in a vise. When we strike this clamped material sharply, the free end vibrates to and fro, as shown in Fig. 17-1. Al- so, if we bow or pluck the wood or steel strip, like a violinist bows or plucks the strings on his violin, the free end will vibrate. If we make the wood or steel vibrate rapidly, it produces a humming sound that we can hear. The violinist, when he bows or

─────────── *Vocabulary* ───────────

BEAT. An outburst of sound followed by an interval of comparative silence.

ECHO. A repetition of a sound due to the reflection of the sound wave from some surface.

FREQUENCY. The number of cycles per second of the vibrating body which produces the sound.

INFRASONIC. Below the range of human hearing.

INTENSITY. A property of sound waves which depends on their energy. It is increased by increasing the amplitude and the area of the vibrating body.

INTERFERENCE. The superimposing of one wave on another.

LONGITUDINAL WAVE. A wave motion in which the particles vibrate to and fro along the path which the wave travels.

LOUDNESS. The effect which sounds of varying intensity have on the ear.

PITCH. The property of sound which depends on the frequency of the sound waves received by the ear.

RESONANCE (*rez*-uh-nenss). The inducing of vibrations of a natural rate in matter by a vibrating source having the same or a simple multiple frequency.

SOUND. Vibrations in matter which can be detected by our ears. Also applied to similar vibrations above and below the normal range of human hearing.

TRANSVERSE WAVE. A wave motion in which the particles vibrate at right angles to the path along which the wave itself is traveling.

ULTRASONIC. Above the range of human hearing.

WAVE LENGTH. The distance between any one particle in a wave and the particle in the next wave which is moving in a corresponding fashion.

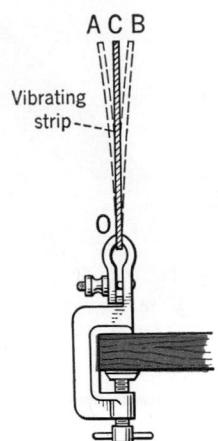

Fig. 17-1. A vibrating body produces sound waves.

plucks the strings of his instrument, causes them to vibrate. They produce sounds. Such experiments show us that *sounds are produced by vibrating matter*.

Now let us take a tuning fork. We can make the fork vibrate by striking one of the prongs with a rubber hammer. While the fork is vibrating, we can hear the sound it produces. The prongs of the fork swing back and forth so rapidly that your eye can not readily detect the movement. However, we can show that the fork is vibrating by placing it, prongs down, in a glass of water. The prongs spatter the water back and forth, as shown in Fig. 17-2. Any matter, including gases like the air itself, may vibrate rapidly enough to produce sound.

2. How do sounds get to our ears? We use the telephone to transmit sounds over longer distances than the human voice can carry. What are the parts of the telephone system? First, we have a transmitter which sets up electrical vibrations. We also have wires to carry these vibrations, and a

receiver which changes them into audible sounds again. In the same way, when we hear sounds directly, we need a vibrating body which acts as the source of the sound. We must have a receiver to pick up the sound. This is the function of our ears. Also, we need something to carry or transmit the sounds from their source to our ears.

Most of the time sounds come to us through the air. Air acts as a *transmitting medium*. At ordinary altitudes we usually have no difficulty hearing one another. However, the air on a mountain is less dense than that in the valleys, and it does not transmit sound as readily. As we might expect, dense gases are better transmitters of sound than rare gases, because the molecules are either larger or are closer together.

Try this experiment to show how air carries sound. Put an electric bell under a bell jar, as shown in Fig. 17-3. Then connect the bell to some batteries so that it starts to ring. While it is ringing, begin to pump the air out of

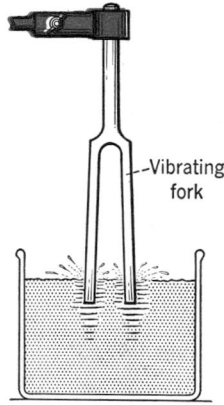

Fig. 17-2. The spattering of the water shows that the prongs of the fork were vibrating.

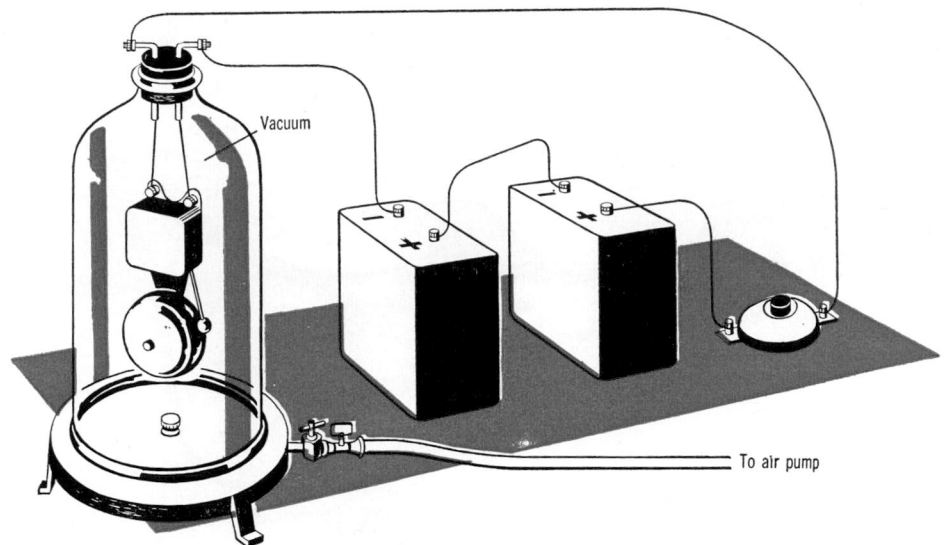

Vacuum

To air pump

Fig. 17-3. You can not hear the bell ring after the air has been removed from the bell jar because sound does not travel through a vacuum.

the bell jar. As the air gets thinner and thinner, you will find that the sound becomes fainter and fainter. When you allow air to enter again, the sound gets louder again. Thus it is evident that *sound does not travel through a vacuum, but it does travel readily through air.*

Did you ever dive to the bottom of a lake, pick up some rocks, and strike them together under water? If so, you may have been surprised to discover how clearly you could hear them being hit together. The sound of an outboard motor on a boat far out on the lake can be heard quite plainly if you listen under water. *Liquids are better transmitters of sound than air or other gases.*

Sometimes a faucet washer loosens up, and when water is drawn from the pipe the washer vibrates. The sound of this vibration usually can be heard in all parts of the house. The sound

is carried by the water pipes. A train can be heard from a greater distance by the sound which comes through the rails. Some hearing aids depend on the bones just behind the ear to carry the sound to the inner ear so that it may be heard. In general, *solids are better transmitters of sound than either liquids or gases.*

3. The ear is our receiver of sound. Let us look at a diagram of the ear, Fig. 17-4. Notice that the outer ear is shaped so that it is an efficient receiver of sound. It collects sound vibrations and conducts them through the ear canal to the *eardrum.* The eardrum is a thin membrane which separates the outer ear from the middle ear. To it are connected the small bones of the middle ear. Sound vibrations act on the eardrum and cause these small bones to vibrate. The bones really are levers which transmit sound vibrations to the *oval window.*

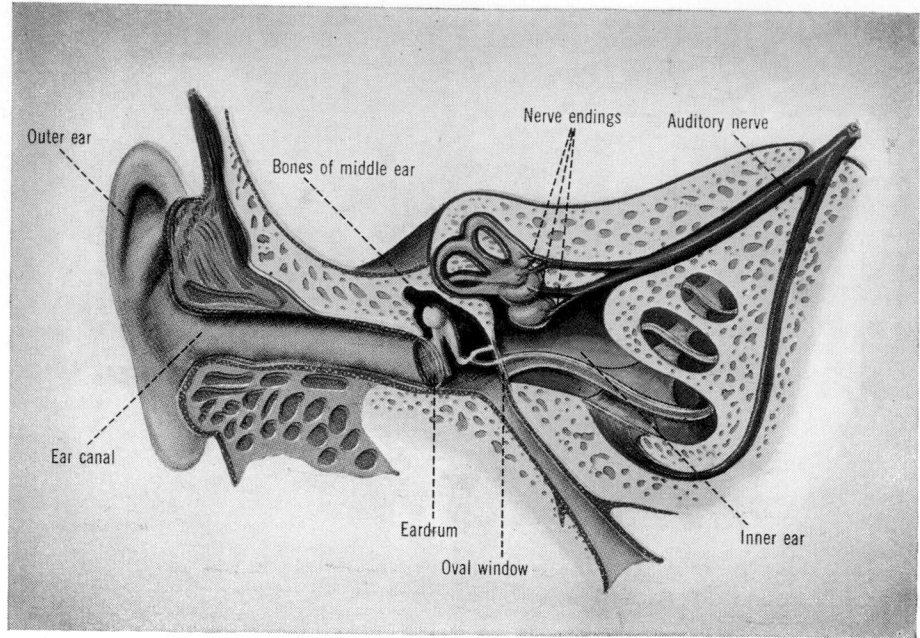

Fig. 17-4. The structure of the ear.

The oval window is a membrane which separates the middle ear from the inner ear. As this window vibrates, it sets up similar vibrations in the inner ear.

The inner ear is a small coiled tube which is filled with liquid. In this small tube there are about 30,000 nerve endings. The vibrating fluid acts on these nerve endings in a special way. Certain nerve endings are affected only by low-pitched sounds, while others are affected only by sounds of higher pitch. When the vibrating fluid stimulates these *auditory nerves,* they carry to the brain the sensation which we call sound.

4. What do we mean by sound? An age-old riddle asks: If a tree falls in a forest where there are no ears to hear it, is sound produced? In order to answer this we must explain what we mean by sound. In the *physio-logical* sense of the term, three things are necessary for the production of sound: (1) a vibrating body; (2) a medium for transmitting the sound; (3) an ear, which serves as the receiver. In the *physical* sense of the term, the word **sound** *applies just to the vibrations in matter which our ear interprets as sound. It also applies to similar vibrations above and below the normal range of human hearing.* So we see the answer to the riddle depends upon which definition we use.

5. How fast does sound travel in air? During a thunder storm it is possible to see a distant lightning flash, and then several seconds later hear the thunder. If we are at the finish line during a track meet we see the smoke from the starter's gun before we hear the report. For short distances, light travels almost instantaneously. Therefore, the time which elapses between a lightning flash and the thunder, and between the smoke of the gun and the report, must be the time required for the sound to travel from its source to our ears.

The average of a large number of trials shows that the speed of sound in air is about 1087 feet per second. For our purposes, let us use a number which is easier to remember, and which at the same time is sufficiently accurate. *The speed of sound in air at 0° C is 1090 feet per second.* As the temperature rises, the speed increases. *An increase in temperature of 1C° causes an increase in speed of about 2 feet per second.* At 15° C, for example, the speed is 1090 + (2 × 15), or 1120 feet per second. In the metric system, the speed of sound in air at 0° C is about 332 meters per second, and the increase in speed is about 0.6 meter per Centigrade degree.

6. How fast does sound travel in other materials? In 1827 two Swiss scientists measured the speed of sound in the water of Lake Geneva. Their measurements showed that the speed of sound in water is 1435 meters per second. This is about four times as fast as the speed of sound in air. More recent measurements give the speed of sound in water as 1461 meters per second, or 4794 feet per second.

In some solids, the speed of sound is even greater. In a steel rod, for example, sound may travel 16,500 feet per second — about 15 times as fast as in air. (See Table 15, Appendix B.)

7. What do we mean by vibration? In Section 1 we observed that a thin strip of wood or steel could be made to vibrate by striking, bowing, or plucking it. When one end of the strip was clamped in a vise, the other end could move to and fro, or *vibrate.* We already have learned about the vibratory movement of a pendulum. Several of the definitions which we learned then can also be applied here. The movement of the vibrating strip from A to B, Fig. 17-1, constitutes a half vibration. The movement from A to B and return is a complete vibration, or *cycle.* The *amplitude* of the vibration is the distance AC. The *period* is the time required for one cycle. The **frequency** *is the number of cycles per second of the vibrating body which produces the sound.*

8. The two kinds of vibration. (1) *Transverse.* In order to illustrate transverse vibrations, we shall need a long spiral spring. Suppose we stretch it between two supports several feet apart. When we pluck this spring *at right angles* to its length, a wave is set up which travels from one end of the spring to the other and is reflected back again. See Fig. 17-5. *A wave,* such as this one, *in which the particles vibrate at right angles to the path along which the wave travels, is called a* **transverse wave.**

Practically everyone has seen water

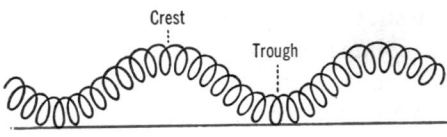

Transverse waves in a spring

Rarefaction   Condensation

Longitudinal waves in a spring

Fig. 17-5. Comparison of transverse and longitudinal waves.

waves. These are transverse waves. As the wave advances, the water rises and falls. There is very little forward movement of the water itself, except when the waves tumble onto the shore.

(2) *Longitudinal.* To illustrate *longitudinal* (lon-juh-*too*-dih-n'l) waves, we may use the same stretched spring. Let us compress several turns of the spring near one end and release them quickly. We find that this compression travels to the opposite end of the spring and returns by reflection. But if we observe closely, we find that the particles of the spring do not vibrate at right angles to the direction of the wave motion, as was the case with the transverse waves. Instead we find that *they vibrate to and fro along the path which the wave travels.* They are **longitudinal waves.**

9. Sound waves are longitudinal vibrations. Again look at Fig. 17-1. When the steel strip shown there is moving from *A* to *B,* the air immediately in front of it is condensed, or compressed. The air immediately behind it expands, or becomes rarefied. As the strip returns from *B* to *A,* the air that was compressed by the first movement expands. The air that was expanded is now compressed. While the strip continues to vibrate, a series of *condensations* and *rarefactions* is produced. In Fig. 17-6, the lines which are close together represent the

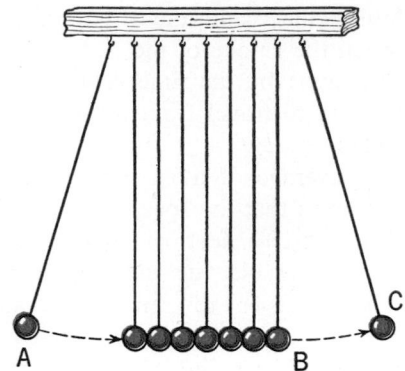

Fig. 17-7. The compression produced by ball *A* is transmitted to ball *B* without the forward movement of the other balls.

compressed air particles or condensations; the lines which are farther apart are the rarefactions. This is a *longitudinal train of waves.* The vibrating particles move back and forth along the path in which the waves are traveling.

When such waves move forward, there is little forward movement of the air. Each compression transfers its energy to the air particles ahead of it. We may illustrate how this happens by using the collision balls shown in Fig. 17-7. If we raise ball *A,* and then let it fall against the others, the impulse is transferred to each ball in turn until *C* is reached. This ball flies out, as shown in the figure, but the others remain stationary.

10. How do we measure the length of a wave? A **wave length** is the distance between any one particle in a wave, and the particle in the next wave which is moving in a corresponding fashion. We may use Fig. 17-8 to illustrate how we measure the length of transverse waves. The highest parts of the waves, *A* and *B,* are called *crests.* Since the particles at these

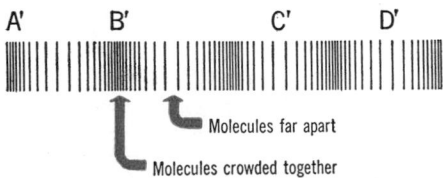

A'   B'   C'   D'

Molecules far apart

Molecules crowded together

Fig. 17-6. A longitudinal train of waves.

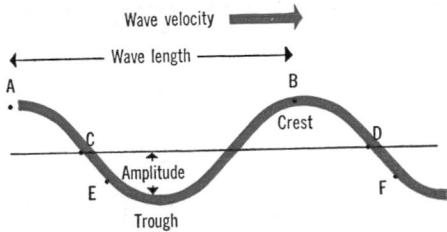

Fig. 17-8. Terms used with transverse waves.

points are performing in a corresponding fashion, the distance from *A* to *B* is one wave length. The point *E* shows a *trough* (trawf) of the wave. We could measure the wave length by finding the distance between successive troughs. Likewise, the distance from *C* to *D,* or *F* to *G* is one wave length.

To learn how we measure the length of a longitudinal wave, let us look again at Fig. 17-6. Here, the wave length is the distance between successive condensations, as from *A'* to *B'*. It is also the distance between successive rarefactions — the distance from *C'* to *D'*.

11. How can we relate speed, wave length, and frequency? Suppose we have a tuning fork which vibrates 275 times per second, and that we use it on a day when the speed of sound is 1100 feet per second. In one second the fork produces a train of waves 1100 feet long, which consists of 275 condensations and 275 rarefactions. We can find the length of one wave by dividing the speed, 1100 feet per second, by the frequency, 275 cycles per second. $1100 \div 275 = 4$. Each wave, therefore, is 4 feet long. The first wave travels 4 feet before the second wave starts, and travels another 4 feet, or a total of 8 feet, before the third one starts.

Physicists use the letter v to represent the speed. The letter f represents the frequency, or the number of cycles per second. The Greek letter λ (lambda) represents the wave length. The relationship between them is given by the formula,

$$v = f\lambda.$$

If we know any two of these quantities, we can calculate the value of the third.

Study the Sample Problem below to see how this is done.

SAMPLE PROBLEM

A tuning fork having a frequency of 320 cycles per second produces waves 3.5 ft in length. What is the speed of the sound in air? What is the temperature?

SOLUTION

From the formula, $v = f\lambda$, we know that the speed equals the product of the frequency and the wave length.

Multiplying, 320 cycles/sec $\times$ 3.5 ft = 1120 ft/sec, the speed. To find the temperature, we subtract 1090 ft/sec, the speed at 0° C, from 1120 ft/sec. The difference equals 30 ft/sec. $30 \div 2 = 15$, the number of degrees needed to cause an increase of 30 ft/sec in the speed. The temperature is therefore 15° C.

2. REFLECTION OF SOUND

12. What are echoes?   You probably have stood near a cliff or near the wall of a building and heard an *echo* when you called out loudly.   The sound waves were reflected from the cliff or wall just as a rubber ball bounces off a hard surface.   Sound waves are reflected when they strike a medium of greater density.   If the wave traveled back along the same path that it took toward the reflecting surface, then you hear the echo of the sound you made.   *An* **echo** *is a repetition of a sound due to the reflection of the sound wave from some surface.*

A reflected sound wave travels at the same speed as the original wave. On a day when the temperature is 20° C, the speed of sound is 1130 feet per second.   We would hear an echo from a cliff 1130 feet away after 2 seconds.   It takes one second for the original wave to reach the cliff, and another second for the reflected wave to return.

13. Echoes may be useful.   *Sonar,* which means *sound navigation and ranging,* is a method for using sound wave echoes to aid in the piloting of ships.   An intermittent sound wave is sent out through the water by a source mounted on the hull of a ship.   By measuring the time which elapses between sending out the sound and the time it is received back, the device indicates the depth of the water, the presence of nearby shoals, or the location of a sunken ship or a submerged submarine.   It is possible for one ship to converse with another by means of sonar.   The sound waves used are usually those *above the range of human hearing, in the* **ultrasonic** *frequency range.*

Petroleum engineers use echoes in their search for new oil fields.   They set off small dynamite explosions in holes drilled into the earth.   The vibrations in the earth, called *seismic* (*syze*-mik) *waves,* travel away from the explosions in all directions.   They are reflected back to the surface by deep layers of rock.   Receivers pick up these reflected waves.   A chart, plotted by automatic recording instruments, indicates the elapsed time be-

Fig. 17-9. A dynamite explosion being set off by a petroleum prospecting party. In the background is the truck from which the explosion was set off. In the foreground is the truck which contains the recording apparatus.

tween the initial explosions and the reflected waves. This chart may be interpreted to reveal the depth and inclination of the subsurface rock formations. Certain types of rock formations are more likely to yield petroleum. The engineer locates these formations from the charts he prepared. Wells then are drilled in the most promising locations.

14. How can we deaden noises? It is desirable to deaden the noises in offices and classrooms, since people work more efficiently under quiet conditions. In such rooms, where many typewriters or other business machines are operated, the walls and ceilings can be covered with sound insulating materials. Cork or composition floors, and the rugs in private offices also cut down the bothersome reflections of sounds. Plaster walls containing porous materials, such as vermiculite, are said to be more sound absorbent. Studios used for radio and television broadcasting are elaborately sound-proofed to shut out disturbing sounds.

15. Special conditions affect the transmission of sound waves. Sound waves ordinarily spread out in all directions from a vibrating body. We can, however, partially direct sound waves by using a *megaphone*. The sides of a megaphone tend to keep the sound waves from spreading out. Consequently, the sound is stronger in one particular direction. Other devices which direct sound waves are *automobile horns,* and the *loudspeaker* in radio and in television sets.

The *stethoscope* used by physicians to examine your heart and lungs contains a diaphragm which vibrates just like your ear drum when sound waves strike it. However, since this dia-

Fig. 17-10. Sounds in rooms and corridors are reduced when the ceilings are fitted with sound-absorbing material. Here a workman is installing perforated metal sections in a corridor ceiling to deaden the sound of footfalls and conversation.

phragm is much larger than the one in your ear, it can respond to much fainter sounds.

Sound waves may be bent by the air and concentrated at a point some distance from the source, even though they are not heard at locations in between. You sometimes find this happening on a lake on a summer evening, when the cool air near the surface of the lake is covered by a layer of warmer air.

Dome-shaped ceilings sometimes reflect sound waves so that they are focused at one particular place. This happens in the Hall of Statuary in the Capitol Building in Washington, D.C. Whispers spoken near one side of this hall are heard distinctly near the op-

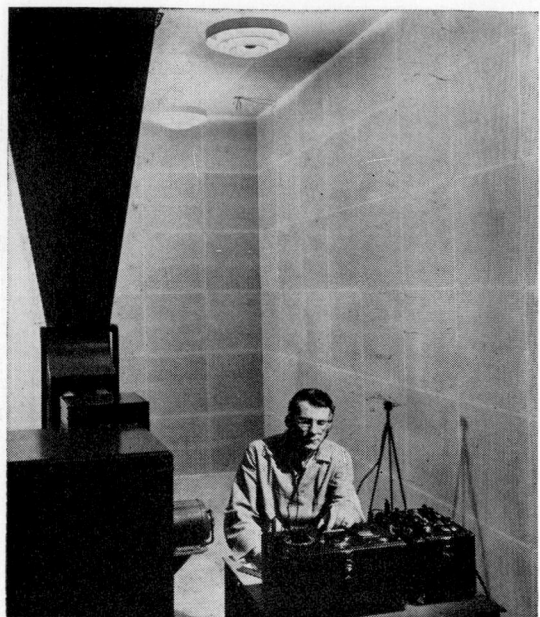

Fig. 17-11. In this sound-proofed room, a technician is determining the amount of noise produced by the motors and fans used in ventilating equipment. Notice the sound-absorbent material used on the walls and ceiling.

posite side. However, you can not hear them in the center, which is only half as far away.

16. The acoustic properties of rooms and auditoriums. Have you ever listened to a speaker whose words were mumbled and hard to understand, even though he seemed to be talking loud enough? Sometimes this difficulty in hearing is caused by echoes which a voice sets up in a large room or in an auditorium. In a large auditorium a sound may last as long as two seconds. It can be reflected from one wall to another many times before it dies out. The sound your ears receive is composed of the original wave and reflected waves of varying strengths. The result is a confusion of sound. Usually, when the auditorium is filled with people, these echoes are reduced, since the sound waves are broken up by the bodies of the audience. The auditoriums of today are designed to eliminate most of the troublesome echoes. Their walls and ceilings are covered with sound-absorbent materials to reduce the reflection of sound waves. The furniture and draperies also help since they, too, are poor reflectors of whatever sound is produced.

3. INTENSITY, LOUDNESS, FREQUENCY, AND PITCH

17. What makes sounds different? We say that a nearby clap of thunder is loud. A whisper is soft and low. A cricket has a shrill, high chirp. A bulldog has a deep growl. The voices of Eddie Fisher and Dinah Shore are pleasing; we want to hear them often. Jimmy Durante and Donald Duck capitalize on the raspiness of their voices. These examples show us that sounds do differ. Each has characteristics which we associate with that sound and with no other. Sounds differ from each other in several fundamental properties. In this section we shall discuss two properties, *intensity* and *frequency*. These are physical characteristics of sound waves themselves. Their effects on us are called *loudness* and *pitch*. Another property of sound waves, *quality,* will be discussed in the following chapter.

18. How do intensity and loudness differ? (1) *Intensity.* Any person who has tossed pebbles into a pond knows that he can make higher waves by throwing the pebbles in than he can by dropping them in gently. When we use more energy, we produce a water wave of greater height, or *amplitude.* When a violinist draws the bow across his instrument lightly, he does not transfer much energy to the string. The sound produced by the string is of low intensity. More vigorous bowing increases the amplitude of vibration of the string. The sound increases in intensity. A large tuning fork can produce stronger condensations and rarefactions than a small one. Thus it produces a more intense sound. *The intensity of a sound depends on the energy of the sound waves. It is increased by increasing the amplitude and the area of the vibrating body.* (2) *Loudness.* Sounds which are intense do not always seem loud to us. We may be a considerable distance from their source, or, again, the wind may be blowing from us toward the source of sound, making the air a poorer conductor. **Loudness** *is the property of sound determined by the effect of the energy of the sound waves on our ears; that is, it is the effect which sounds of varying intensity have on the ear.* Sound waves are given off in all directions from a vibrating body. Consequently, the waves spread out over a greater area as they advance. The areas of these concentric waves are proportional to the squares of their distances from their source. A whistle will seem only one-fourth as loud to a person one-half mile away as it does to one who is only one-fourth mile distant. *The loudness of a sound is inversely proportional to the square of the distance from the source. It depends upon the medium through which the sound is traveling.*

If we increase the intensity of a sound while the observer remains at a fixed distance from its source the sound, of course, gets louder. However, the relation between intensity and loudness is not one of direct proportion. It is more nearly a logarithmic scale. A sound must be 10 times as intense as the softest sound we can hear before it becomes twice as loud; it must be 100 times as intense before it becomes three times as loud. The degree of loudness is difficult to measure accurately, since it depends on the judgment of a listener and not on any purely physical measurement.

19. How do we measure intensity and loudness? Intensity is measured with acoustical apparatus. It does not depend upon the hearing sense of an observer. The intensity of the faintest sound we can hear, called the *threshold of hearing,* has an energy of 10^{-16} watts/cm^2. In measuring the intensity level of a sound wave, the energy of the unknown sound is compared with the energy of this faintest sound. The intensity level of a sound wave is given by the equation,

$$\beta = 10 \log \frac{I}{I_0},$$

where β (Greek letter beta) is the intensity level in decibels of a sound of energy I, measured in watts/cm^2. I_0 is the energy of the threshold of hearing, 10^{-16} watts/cm^2. The decibel is named for Alexander Graham Bell (1847–1922), the inventor of the telephone.

The intensity levels in decibels for a

number of familiar noises are given below.

Type of Sound	Decibels
Threshold of hearing	0
Whisper	10–20
Quiet Office	20–40
Automobile	40–50
Conversation	60
Heavy Street Traffic	70–80
Elevated Trains, Riveters	90–100
Thunder	110
Threshold of Pain	120

20. Pitch depends upon the frequency. If you listen carefully to the music of a concert band, you discover that a piccolo has a higher, shriller pitch than a flute. It may, however, be played more softly or louder than a flute. Women's voices are of higher pitch than men's. They may be softer or louder than men's voices, too. We see then, that the pitch of sounds may differ, even though the loudness of sounds does not.

In order to learn what property of a sound wave determines its pitch, we shall use a siren disc like that in Fig. 17-12. The siren disc has five rows of holes. The outer four rows are evenly spaced holes. The number of holes in these rows is 24, 30, 36, and 48 respectively. We mount this siren disc so that it can be rotated rapidly. While it is rotating, we shall direct a stream of air against the 24-hole row. The stream of air vibrates because it is cut off regularly by the metal between the holes of the disc. We hear a sound which has a steady pitch. If we turn the disc more rapidly, the pitch rises. When we slow down the disc, the pitch falls. Next, let us keep

Fig. 17-12. The pitch of a sound depends upon the number of vibrations per second which the ear receives.

the disc turning at a constant speed and compare the pitch of the sounds produced by directing the air stream against the 24-hole row, and then against the 48-hole row. We find this second sound has a pitch an octave higher than the first. Finally, if we direct an air stream against each of the four evenly spaced rows in turn, starting with the inner row, the notes *do, mi, sol, do'* are produced. From these experiments we discover that the pitch rises when the air stream vibrates more rapidly. The pitch falls when the rate of vibration is decreased. *The **pitch** of a sound depends upon the frequency, or number of cycles per second, which the ear receives.*

From the equation $v = f\lambda$, we readily can see that sounds of high frequency must have shorter wave lengths than sounds of low frequency. The wave length of the sound produced by a fork vibrating 512 times per second will be only half as long as that produced by a fork vibrating 256 times per second. The pitch of the first fork is an octave higher than that of the second fork because twice as many waves reach our ears per second. An increase in pitch is a result of an increase in frequency — it also means a decrease in wave length.

21. What is the Doppler effect? At one time or another you probably have stood at a railroad crossing waiting for a train to pass. As you stand by the track and listen to the steady warning horn of the Diesel locomotive coming toward you, you notice that the pitch of the horn drops abruptly as soon as the train passes you. This variation of the pitch heard from a moving source of sound is called the Doppler effect. Let us find out why we hear the pitch of the horn change, even though we know that the frequency of the sound which the horn produces does not change.

If the train is stopped down the track and the engineer sounds the horn, our ear receives the same number of vibrations per second that the horn produces. We hear a sound of steady pitch. When the horn is sounded as the train approaches us, the number of vibrations per second reaching our ears is greater than the frequency of the sound produced. *The motion of the source of sound toward us* causes us to receive the vibrations at a faster rate than they are produced. Each vibration travels at the same speed, but each successive vibration has a shorter distance to travel to reach our ears. Thus, they arrive more frequently than they are sent out. The pitch we hear is correspondingly higher than the frequency of the sound produced.

When the train goes away from us

and the horn is sounded, each successive vibration has farther to travel to reach our ears. The vibrations do not arrive as frequently as they are sent out. Thus, the sound we hear as the train goes away is of lower pitch.

22. The range of frequencies which we can hear. When we wave our hands we produce condensations and rarefactions in the air, just as a tuning fork does. However, we don't hear anything. The frequency of such vibrations is too slow to affect our auditory nerves. For most persons, a frequency of 20 cycles per second is necessary in order for them to hear an audible sound. This frequency represents the *lower limit of audibility*. Persons vary considerably in their ability to hear sounds of low pitch.

There is an *upper limit of audibility,* too. Vibrations may be so rapid that the ear does not respond to them. The highest frequency which people can hear is about 20,000 cycles per second. However, there is considerable variation between individuals concerning the highest pitch to which their ears are sensitive.

23. Sound frequencies we can not hear are useful, too. In the past few years scientists have been actively studying the properties of sound waves having frequencies both below and above those that we can hear. Sound waves which vibrate fewer than 20 times per second are in the **infrasonic** *range. They are below the range of human hearing.* Sound waves like these have been used with some success in the drilling of deep oil wells. The low-frequency vibrations break up hard rock much more easily than the conventional rotary drill bits.

Sound waves above the frequencies

we can hear, beginning at about 20,000 cycles per second, are in the **ultrasonic range.** The simplest application of these waves is a dog whistle. We can not hear the sound it makes. Your dog can because his ears are sensitive to sounds an octave or more higher than are yours. Today these ultrasonic waves can open your garage door automatically, and literally shake the dirt out of your clothing. They also are used to detect flaws in metal castings or automobile tires, and they speed the germination of seeds, as well

as increase their yield. Ultrasonic waves now show promise as insect and pest controls, as a means for a new kind of nerve surgery, and also as a means of making almost permanent emulsions of heretofore immiscible materials.

Ultrasonic waves are produced by applying a high frequency, alternating voltage to opposite faces of a quartz crystal. The electricity causes the crystal to vibrate mechanically. Frequencies as high as 500,000 cycles per second have been attained.

4. RESONANCE AND INTERFERENCE

24. Forced vibrations increase the intensity of sounds. When we strike a tuning fork with a rubber hammer we cause it to vibrate. The vibration is at a natural rate which depends upon the fork's length, its thickness, and the material of which it is made. When we strike a note on a piano, we set the strings in vibration at a natural rate, too. The only external forces which affect this rate are friction and gravitation. Suppose we set a tuning fork in vibration and then press its stem against the top of a table. The tone we hear becomes louder when the fork is in contact with the table. Why? With the stem of the vibrating tuning fork pressed against the table, the fork *forces* the table top to vibrate with the same frequency. It did this even though the natural vibration rate of the table top is undoubtedly different from that of the fork. When the tuning fork is vibrating, pulses of energy are transmitted through the stem. This vary-

ing force causes the table top to vibrate with the same frequency. Since the table has a much larger vibrating area than the tuning fork, these *forced vibrations* produce a more intense sound.

If we stretch a violin string tightly between two clamps, we find that it does not produce a very intense sound as it vibrates. When the same string is stretched across the bridge of a violin, the thin wood of the violin is forced to vibrate in response to the vibrations of the string. The intensity of the sound is increased by the forced vibrations of the violin. The sounding board of a piano acts in the same way to intensify vibrations of the strings.

25. What is resonance or sympathetic vibration? The two tuning forks shown in Fig. 17-13 have the same frequency. They are mounted on individual boxes which increase the intensity of the sound through forced vibrations. Each box has an

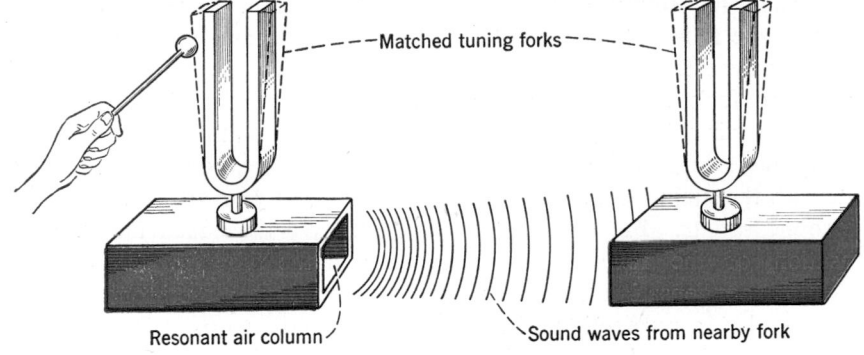

Fig. 17-13. Resonance between two matched tuning forks.

end open. Let us place one of these forks at the front of the room and the other at the rear. The open ends of the boxes must be toward each other. Now let us set the fork at the front of the room in vibration. After it has vibrated several seconds, we touch the prongs to stop them. We now find that the fork at the rear of the room is vibrating weakly. What caused this? The condensations and rarefactions of the sound waves produced in the air by the tuning fork at the front of the room acted on the second fork in a regular fashion. This caused it to vibrate. Such action is called *resonance* (*rez*-uh-nenss) or *sympathetic vibration*. A person who sings near a piano will cause the strings which produce similar frequencies to vibrate. **Resonance** *occurs when the natural vibration rates of two objects are the same. It also occurs when the vibration rate of one of them is a multiple of the other.* If we change the frequency of one of the mounted tuning forks by adding a weight to one of its prongs and repeat our experiment, no resonance is produced. Both forks must have the same frequency in order to produce sympathetic vibration.

26. Resonance in tubes. Let us hold a vibrating tuning fork over a cylinder as shown in Fig. 17-14. When we gradually add water to the tube, we find that there is a certain water

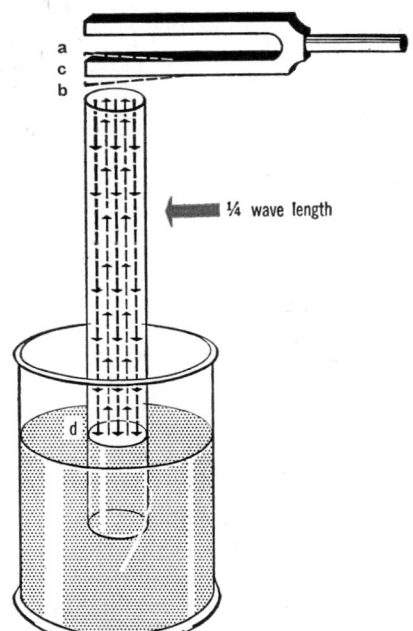

¼ wave length

Fig. 17-14. A sound wave travels the length of the tube during one-fourth of a cycle of the tuning fork. Therefore, the length of the tube is one-fourth of the wave length of the sound.

level at which the sound is loudest. The sound wave reflected by the water surface meets the direct wave produced by the tuning fork exactly in phase. This causes the air column in the cylinder to vibrate sympathetically, or to resonate with the tuning fork. A more intense sound results. Furthermore, a condensation of the reflected wave unites with a condensation of the direct wave. Also, a rarefaction of the reflected wave unites with a rarefaction of the direct wave. This uniting of two waves in phase amplifies the sound, just as the piling of the crest of one water wave upon the crest of another makes the resulting wave higher. When we have our tube adjusted so that it reinforces sound waves, it acts as a *resonator*.

In Fig. 17-14, as the prong of our tuning fork goes down from c to b, the compression it forms travels from c to d in air. This compression is reflected and reaches c just as the prong reaches c. As the prong continues to move upward to a, it produces a compression. But this compression is formed from air already somewhat compressed by the simultaneous passing of the reflected wave. The result is a much higher degree of compression than the prong of the fork alone could produce. While the prong of the fork has been moving from c to a, a rarefaction was formed *beneath it,* and this rarefaction has traveled to d. There it is reflected and returns to c just as the prong reaches c. As the prong once again moves down from c to b, a rarefaction is formed *above it*. But this rarefaction is being produced in air already rarefied by the reflected wave. The combined rarefaction is greater than what the fork prong alone

could produce. These more intense compressions and rarefactions formed above the prongs of the tuning fork sound louder to our ears.

The cycle of the tuning fork prong which produces one sound wave is from c to b to c to a and back to c again. We have seen that the sound wave in the tube travels the distance from c to d while the prong of the fork moves from c to b. When the fork is making one-fourth of a cycle, the sound wave travels the length of the tube. If the fork makes a cycle, the sound wave can travel a distance four times the length of the tube. This distance, or four times the length of the tube, is therefore the length of one sound wave. Conversely, the length of the tube is one-fourth the wave length of the sound. From our experiment we find that *a closed tube produces the best possible resonance when its length is one-fourth that of the sound wave which it reinforces.* (Actually it is slightly less than one-fourth of a wave length, because a correction must be made for the diameter of the tube.) Expressed as a formula:

$$\lambda = 4(l + 0.4d),$$

in which λ is the wave length, l is the length of a closed tube, and d is the diameter of the tube.

When a vibrating fork is held over an *open* tube, resonance is also produced. We find by experiment, however, that such a tube produces the *best resonance when its length is about one-half* the wave length of the sound it reinforces. The formula is

$$\lambda = 2(l + 0.8d),$$

in which λ is the wave length, l is the length of the open tube, and d is the diameter of the tube.

27. Sound waves can interfere with one another. If you drop two pebbles simultaneously into a smooth pond, they each set up their own set of ripples. Observe what happens where the ripples from one pebble cross those from the other one. Where two crests cross each other, the water is piled up higher than in either crest alone. Where two troughs cross each other, an even deeper trough is formed. If a crest crosses a trough, the water level is hardly disturbed. A similar thing happens to sound waves. We observed in our experiment with resonance in tubes that the meeting in phase of two sound waves produces a louder sound. If two sound waves meet out of phase they should cancel each other. Either a much quieter sound or no sound at all should be produced. We find that this happens in the " dead spots " in a large room or auditorium. Here, however, because of the number of echoes there usually is not complete silence.

When one sound wave is superimposed upon another, we have **interference** *of sound*. If, as in the resonating tube, the reflected wave is added to the effect of the direct wave, we have *constructive* interference. When two waves tend to cancel each other's effects, the interference is *destructive*.

28. Beats are produced by the interference of sound waves. Let us imagine that there are two sound waves traveling in the same direction through air, or through some other medium. One of these waves is 4 feet long. We represented it by the graph at (a) in Fig. 17-16. The other wave is 5 feet long. Its graph is given at (b). We see that at some places the two waves are in almost the same phase. In

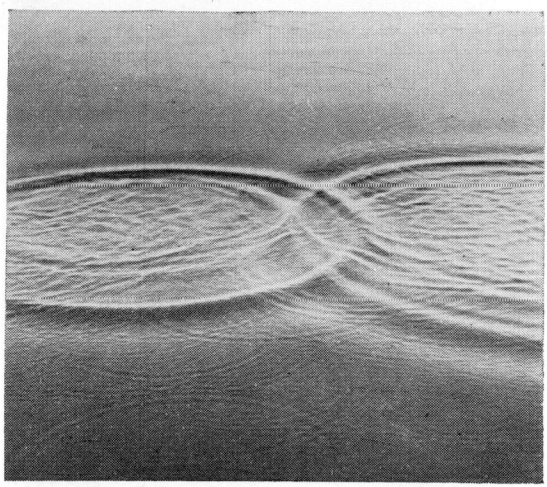

Fig. 17-15. Wave patterns formed by water when two pebbles are dropped into a still pool. Notice how the intermingled waves increase at their crests.

other places they are in almost the opposite phase. The straight line represents the mid-point of the wave motion in each case.

Now let us use another straight line and plot a composite curve, as in Fig. 17-16(c). We do this by using the resultants of all the crests and troughs of the two sets of waves. At point *C,* the crests which represent sound condensations meet and the *sound is intensified.* At point *D,* a condensation coincides with a rarefac-

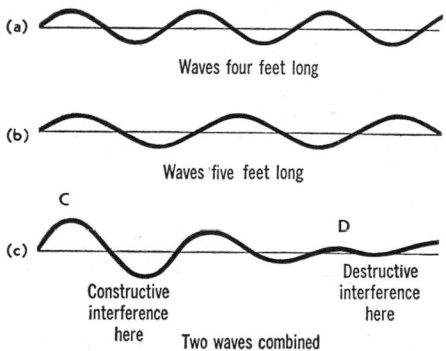

Fig. 17-16. Constructive and destructive interference of waves.

tion. The *sound is diminished,* and silence may result. When two tuning forks of unequal frequency are sounded at the same time, we find that the sound is alternately louder and softer. We have the rapidly fluctuating constructive and destructive interference that we noted in Fig. 17-16C. *This outburst of sound followed by an interval of comparative silence is called a* **beat.** The number of beats produced per second is equal to the difference between the frequencies of the two vibrating bodies. For example, if we sound tuning forks having frequencies of 256 and 260 simultaneously, we will hear 4 beats per second. We would also hear 4 beats per second if the frequencies of the forks were 256 and 252.

Summary

Sounds are produced by vibrating matter. Sound waves travel to the ear through a transmitting medium. Solids are the best media for sound transmission. Liquids are better transmitters of sound than air or other gases.

The speed of sound in air at 0° is 1090 feet per second. An increase in temperature of one Centigrade degree causes an increase in speed of sound of about two feet per second. Sound travels about four times as fast in water as it does in air. Its speed in solids is many times as great as in air.

A wave motion in which the particles vibrate at right angles to the path along which the wave travels is a transverse wave. A wave motion in which the particles vibrate to and fro along the path which the wave travels is a longitudinal wave. Sound waves are longitudinal.

Frequency and intensity are properties of sound waves. The frequency is the number of cycles per second of the vibrating source. The intensity of a sound depends on the energy of the sound waves. Pitch and loudness are effects which sound waves have on our ears. The pitch depends on the frequency of the vibration received by the ear. Loudness is a measure of the effect of the energy of the waves received on the ear. The decibel is the unit used for measuring the intensity of sounds.

When one sound wave is superimposed upon another, interference of sound results. If the two sound waves are in phase, the interference is constructive. If the two sound waves are out of phase, the interference is destructive.

Terms to Define...

Amplitude	Crest	Echo
Auditory nerves	Cycle	Forced vibration
Beat	Doppler effect	Frequency
Condensation	Eardrum	Infrasonic

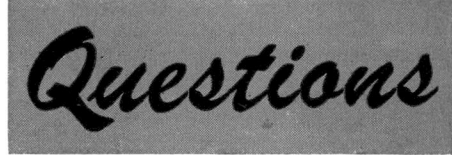

GROUP A

1. How are sound waves produced? How are sound waves usually transmitted to a person's ears?

2. Why is sound not transmitted through a vacuum?

3. Why is sound transmitted better through a liquid or a solid than it is through a gas?

4. What is the speed of sound in ft/sec at 0° C? In m/sec at 0° C? How does the speed of sound vary with the temperature?

5. Give examples of the terms "cycle," "amplitude," "period," "frequency," and "wave length."

6. What is the difference between a longitudinal wave and a transverse wave?

7. How is the speed of a wave motion related to its wave length and frequency?

8. What is an echo? How may echoes be useful? When are they distracting?

9. How does a megaphone help a cheerleader be heard?

10. Distinguish between intensity and loudness. To what property of a sound wave are they related?

11. Distinguish between frequency and pitch. Do sounds of the same pitch travel with the same speed? Give an illustration which proves the truth of your answer.

12. Why is the sound of a tuning fork louder when the stem of the fork is pressed against the top of a table?

13. What conditions are necessary in order to produce resonance?

14. How does the length of a closed tube compare with the wave length of the sound which produces the best resonance?

15. How does the length of an open tube compare with the wave length of the sound which produces the best resonance?

16. What is constructive interference of sound waves? Destructive interference of sound waves? What are beats?

GROUP B

17. Using Fig. 17-4, describe how the human ear receives sound waves and transforms them into nerve impulses which are sent to the brain.

18. Some school auditoriums, cafeterias, and typing classrooms are equipped with sound-proof ceilings. What are they? How do these ceilings help cut down noise?

19. If you sit at the rear of a large indoor theater, the motion of the lips of the actors on the screen may precede the sound of their voices. But if you sit at the rear of a drive-in theater with "in-a-car" speakers, the action of the screen and the sounds you hear are synchronized. Explain this.

20. Can you hear the approach of an airplane flying at supersonic speed?

21. Why is the intensity of sound measured on a logarithmic scale?

22. The engineer of a Diesel locomotive sounds the horn as his train approaches you. How does the pitch you hear compare with the pitch he hears?

23. What is the range of normal human hearing? What name is applied to sound vibrations below the range of hearing? Above the range of hearing?

Problems

(In the Mathematics Refresher, refer to Sections 10, 15, and 16.)

GROUP A

1. What is the speed of sound at 20° C? How long will it take for sound to travel 5000 ft at this speed?

2. What is the wave length, in feet, of the sound produced by a tuning fork which has a frequency of 320 cycles per second? The temperature is 15° C.

3. A tuning fork vibrates 256 times per second. What is the wave length, in meters, of the sound produced when the temperature is 30° C?

4. How long does it take for sound to travel 5 kilometers if the temperature is 10° C?

5. A tuning fork has a frequency of 440 cycles per second. If another tuning fork of slightly lower pitch is sounded at the same time, 5 beats per second are heard. What is the frequency of the second tuning fork?

6. At 15° C, a tuning fork produces resonance when held over a closed tube 12 in long and 1 inch in diameter. What is the wave length of the sound and the frequency of the fork?

7. What is the wave length of the sound produced by a tuning fork which resonates with an open tube 20 cm long and 2 cm across?

8. How many beats per second will be heard when a string with a frequency of 288 cycles per second is plucked simultaneously with another string whose frequency is 320 cycles per second?

9. What is the length of an open tube 1.5 inches in diameter which produces resonance with a tuning fork whose frequency is 128 cycles per second? The temperature is 20° C.

10. A tuning fork which vibrates at the rate of 384 cycles per second produces resonance with a closed tube 8 in long and 1.5 inches in diameter. What is the speed of sound?

GROUP B

11. Five seconds after a fog horn is sounded on a ship, the echo of the horn is heard. If the sound is reflected from an iceberg, how far away is the iceberg? The temperature is −10° C.

12. Find the length of a closed tube 2 inches in diameter which produces resonance with a tuning fork whose frequency is 512 cycles per second. The temperature is 25° C.

13. A man drops a stone into a mine 800 ft deep. If the temperature is 5° C, how many seconds will pass before he hears the stone strike the bottom?

14. A rifle shot is fired in a valley with parallel walls. The echo from one wall is heard in 2 sec and the echo from the other wall is heard 2 sec later. If the temperature is 20° C, how wide is the valley?

● 15. Paul throws a stone over a cliff and hears it strike the rocks at the bottom after 8 sec. Temperature is 25° C. How high is the cliff?

● 16. A Diesel locomotive approaches a crossing at 60 mi/hr. If the horn has a frequency of 288 cycles per second and the temperature is 15° C, what is the frequency of the sound heard by the watchman at the crossing?

● 17. What is the intensity in decibels of a sound which has an energy of 10^{-11} watts/cm²?

● 18. What is the energy in watts/cm² of a sound whose intensity is 30 decibels?

Things to Do

1. Stand near a railroad crossing and observe the change in pitch of a locomotive horn when it is sounded from a moving train.

2. Prepare a report on the uses of ultrasonic waves, and present your report to the class.

3. Find out what portions of your school building have sound-proof ceilings. Compare the noise level in an area which has been thus treated with an area which has not.

4. Demonstrate the phenomena of resonance with two matched tuning forks as described in Section 25.

Chapter 18

Sound and Music

★ 1. MUSIC AND NOISE

★ 1. What is the difference between music and noise? In Section 20, Chapter 17, we used a siren disc to show that the pitch of sound rises as the frequency is increased. We forced a stream of air through regularly spaced holes. The sound we produced was pleasant and of steady pitch. It was a *musical tone*. The strings of a violin produce musical tones. **Tones** *are sounds produced by an object which vibrates in regular fashion.* On most siren discs, the row of holes closest to the center is irregularly spaced. If we direct air against this row of holes, we hear an unpleasant, jarring sound. *Sound waves produced by irregular vibrations are called* **noise**. When we strike a desk with a ruler, scrape our feet across the floor, or drop glassware, we cause irregular vibrations. Such sounds are noise.

★ 2. The diatonic scale. In our earlier experiments with the siren disc, Section 20, Chapter 17, we directed a stream of air successively against the rows of regularly spaced holes. The sounds we heard corresponded to *do, mi, sol, do'* of a musical scale. If now we force the air stream through the first three of these rows of holes simultaneously, sounding *do, mi,* and *sol*

Vocabulary

CHROMATIC (kroh-*mat*-ik) **SCALE.** The diatonic scale with five half tones added.

DIATONIC (dy-uh-*ton*-ik) **SCALE.** A musical scale built up from three major chords.

FUNDAMENTAL TONE. The tone produced by an object which is vibrating as a whole.

MAJOR CHORD. The combination of tones produced by sounds whose frequencies are in the ratio of 4, 5, and 6.

NOISE. A sound produced by an object which vibrates in irregular fashion.

OVERTONE. A tone whose vibration rate is a whole number multiple of that of the fundamental.

QUALITY. A property of sound waves which depends on the number and prominence of the overtones.

TEMPERED SCALE. A twelve-note scale with a constant frequency change between successive notes.

TONE. A sound produced by an object which vibrates in regular fashion.

	do	re	mi	fa	sol	la	ti	do	re
Syllables	do	re	mi	fa	sol	la	ti	do	re
Letters	C	D	E	F	G	A	B	C'	D'
Frequency	256	288	320	341	384	426	480	512	576
Relative frequency	24	27	30	32	36	40	45	48	54
Chord (tonic)	4		5		6				
Chord (dominant)					4		5		6
Chord (subdominant)				4		5		6	

together, the combination is a *major chord,* or *major triad.* These three rows have 24, 30, and 36 holes respectively. Therefore, 24, 30, and 36 are the relative frequencies of the musical tones. Dividing these frequencies by six, we obtain the simpler ratios of 4, 5, and 6. *Any three notes whose vibration ratios are 4, 5, and 6 will produce a **major chord** when sounded together.* The major **diatonic** (dy-uh-ton-ik) **scale** *is built up of three major chords.* You can see how this is done by studying the table of frequencies at the top of the page.

Physicists use 256 cycles per second as the frequency of middle C. If your piano were tuned to this frequency, the table above shows the frequencies of tones produced by the white notes in a little more than an octave above middle C. We find that the frequencies for C, E, and G have ratios of 4, 5, and 6. They form a major chord. Another major chord is formed by the notes G, B, and D', and a third by the notes F, A, and C'.

The note C', which is one octave above middle C, has a frequency just twice that of C. If one tone has a frequency twice that of another, the first tone is an octave higher than the sec-

C D E F G A B C' D' E' Letter names
Do Re Mi Fa Sol La Ti Do' Re' Mi' Syllable names
256 288 320 341 384 426 480 512 576 640 Vibration rates
1 9/8 5/4 4/3 3/2 5/3 15/8 2 9/8 5/4 Vibration ratios

Fig. 18-1. The major diatonic scale. Key of C.

ond. Doubling the frequency raises the pitch one octave. From the table we see that the frequency of D is $\frac{288}{256}$, or $\frac{9}{8}$ times that of C. D in the table has just $\frac{1}{2}$ the frequency of D', an octave higher. The frequency of E is $\frac{320}{256}$, or $\frac{5}{4}$ that of C. F is $\frac{341}{256}$, or $\frac{4}{3}$; G is $\frac{384}{256}$, or $\frac{3}{2}$; A is $\frac{426}{256}$, or $\frac{5}{3}$; and B is $\frac{480}{256}$, or $\frac{15}{8}$. C' is $\frac{512}{256}$, or $\frac{2}{1}$. See Fig. 18-1.

In the next octave, we find that D' is $\frac{576}{512}$, or $\frac{9}{8}$ times the frequency of C'. In the same manner we can find the frequency of any note in this octave by multiplying the frequency of C' by the ratios we found in the first octave. For example, the frequency of E' is $\frac{5}{4} \times 512$, or 640. We also could have found this frequency by multiplying the frequency of E, 320, by 2, since E' is an octave higher than E.

★ **3. The chromatic scale.** Suppose we construct a scale using D, with a

	C	D	E	F	G	A	B	C'	D'
Key of C	256	288	320	341	384	426	480	512	576
Key of D		288	324	360	384	432	480	540	576

CHROMATIC SCALE		TEMPERED SCALE	
C	256	C	256
C#	266.6	C# or D♭	271.2
D♭	276.5		
D	288	D	287.3
D#	300	D# or E♭	304.4
E♭	307.2		
E	320	E	322.5
F	341.3	F	341.7
F#	355.5	F# or G♭	362
G♭	368.6		
G	384	G	383.6
G#	400	G# or A♭	406.4
A♭	409.5		
A	426.6	A	430.5
A#	444.4	A# or B♭	456.1
B♭	460.8		
B	480	B	483.3
C'	512	C'	512

Fig. 18-2. Comparison of the chromatic scale in the key of C and the tempered scale.

frequency of 288, as the first note. To find the frequencies of the notes in this scale, we multiply 288 in turn by $\frac{9}{8}, \frac{5}{4}, \frac{4}{3}, \frac{3}{2}, \frac{5}{3}, \frac{15}{8}$, and 2. The table at the bottom of page 376 shows how this compares with the C scale.

In some cases the frequencies of notes on the two scales are equal. Others vary so very slightly that the difference is not too noticeable. However, in the frequencies of F and C' there is considerable variation. This difference is so very great that two new notes, F# (F sharp) and C#, are used by a musician when he plays in the key of D.

How does the frequency of our new tone, F#, compare with that of F. By simplifying their frequency ratio $\frac{360}{341}$, we get approximately $\frac{25}{24}$. The vibration rate of F# is thus about $\frac{25}{24}$ that of F. F# is said to be a half tone higher than F. If a note in the *chro-*

matic (kroh-*mat*-ik) *scale* is to be lowered a half tone or flatted, the frequency of the flatted tone is $\frac{24}{25}$ of the original tone. Now let us build up a series of scales using each of the notes in the C scale as the first note. When we compare them, we find that at least five new notes, or tones, must be added to each octave to take care of serious variations in frequency between the scales. In other words, *the* **chromatic scale** *is the diatonic scale with five half tones added.*

★ **4. The tempered scale.** In building up the chromatic scale we found that there were five serious variations in frequency between the notes in these scales. If we compare the calculated frequencies closely, we find many cases where there is a difference of about 4 to 6 cycles per second. In the chromatic scale, too, there is a difference in frequency between C# and D♭ (D flat). C# $= \frac{25}{24} \times 256$, or 266 cycles/sec. D♭ $= \frac{24}{25} \times 288$, or 276 cycles/sec. If we build up all the possible scales using C, C#, D♭, D, D#, E♭, E, and so on, as first tones we find that we need so very many different frequencies, that an octave would have about 70 notes. How could you ever learn to play a piano or an organ having 70 keys in each octave? It would be highly impractical, if not impossible!

The scale commonly used for tuning and playing musical instruments is a compromise scale. The scale is one in which there is a constant change of frequency between successive notes. This scale comprises the eight notes from C to C', and the five additional notes that we found were absolutely necessary in the chromatic scale. This gives us a **tempered scale** *with twelve* *intervals between the successive notes.* Since the frequency of C′ must be twice that of C, we find the ratio between the frequencies of successive notes by extracting the twelfth root of 2. $\sqrt[12]{2} = 1.05946$. This means that the frequency of any note in the tempered scale can be obtained by multiplying the frequency of the preceding note by 1.05946. This equally tempered scale is used in playing most musical instruments. A skillful solo violinist, however, may produce more effective music by using the true intervals of the diatonic scale. A comparison of the two scales is given in Fig. 18-2.

★ **5. The pitch used by physicists differs from that used by musicians.** The middle C tuning forks which you use for your sound experiments in physics laboratory are tuned to 256 cycles per second. We used this basic frequency for our illustrations in calculating the frequencies for the tones in the diatonic, chromatic, and tempered scales. When C has a frequency of 256, the frequency of A above middle C is 427.

The American Federation of Musicians has adopted 440 cycles per second as the frequency of A. The actual scales used by musicians are built around this frequency. The National Bureau of Standards constantly broadcasts a musical tone of 440 cycles per second on a shortwave radio frequency of 5,000 kilocycles. If you compare a C tuning fork from the physics lab with the middle C note on the piano, you will find that the tuning fork has a lower pitch.

★ **6. How are harmony and discord produced?** Some combinations of notes we strike on the piano are pleas-

ing. We say that the tones produce *harmony.* Such a combination might be the notes C and E. However, if we strike two adjacent white keys, like C and D, the sound is not so pleasant. We say that it is *discordant.* Why do these combinations of tones produce such different reactions?

We learned earlier that beats are heard when two sounds of different frequency are produced simultaneously. The number of beats per second is equal to the difference in frequency. When C and E are sounded together, 64 beats per second result. These are so very close together that the ear does not detect them. The sound is harmonious. When C and D are struck at the same time, there are 32 beats per second. This number of beats has an unpleasant effect, and produces the worst possible discord.

We may use two singing flames to show that it is the number of beats per second which determines whether a sound will be pleasing or not. Let us connect the jet tubes to the gas supply, as shown in Fig. 18-3. We ignite the

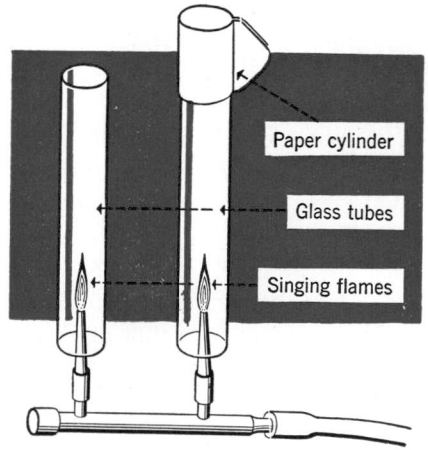

Fig. 18-3. Beats can be produced by singing flames.

gas and support two glass tubes, about 1 inch in diameter and 16 to 18 inches long, over the flames. Next we adjust the flames to the proper height to produce a singing noise. If we slide a paper cylinder over one of the tubes to change its length, the frequency of the flame will be changed. When there is only a slight difference in the frequencies, only a few beats per second are heard. The sound is not displeasing, even though you probably can detect the separate beats. By further increasing the length of one tube, we can produce about 30 beats per second. The sounds are jarring and discordant together. If we increase the number of beats to 64 or more, the sounds become harmonious. They are no longer displeasing to the ear.

2. QUALITY

7. What is the fundamental tone. Suppose that you stretch a piece of piano wire about a meter in length between two clamps. Make it tight enough so that the wire will vibrate when plucked. If you pluck it in the middle, you may be able to see that the wire vibrates *as a whole,* like the string shown in Fig. 18-4. When an *entire wire or string vibrates back and forth as a single unit,* it produces its lowest pitch. The lowest pitch is called its **fundamental tone.**

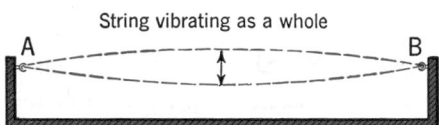

String vibrating as a whole

A   B

Fig. 18-4. A string vibrating as a whole sounds its fundamental.

Physicists have elaborated on our simple apparatus of a wire stretched between two clamps, and made it into the *sonometer* (suh-*nom*-eh-ter), shown in Fig. 18-5. The sonometer consists of two or more wires or strings stretched over a sounding board. The sounding board intensifies the sounds produced by the wires. Since the strings may be varied in diameter, tension, length, or material, the instrument is useful for testing the frequency of strings and for showing how they vibrate.

8. How are overtones produced? We have seen that a wire or string may vibrate as an entire unit. Now let us conduct an experiment which will show us other ways in which strings may vibrate. We shall divide the length of

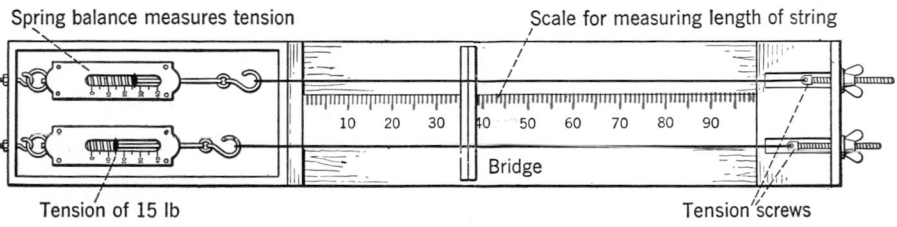

Spring balance measures tension   Scale for measuring length of string

10   20   30   40   50   60   70   80   90

Bridge

Tension of 15 lb   Tension screws

Fig. 18-5. The sonometer is used to study the laws of strings.

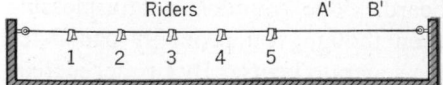

Fig. 18-6. The paper riders show that a string vibrates in segments.

a sonometer string into eight equal parts. At positions 1, 2, 3, 4, and 5, as shown in Fig. 18-6, we will put V-shaped paper riders. Now place a bridge under the string at *A*, and bow it at *B*. We find that the paper riders at positions 1, 3, and 5 are thrown off. Those at 2 and 4 are not disturbed.

Evidently the string was not vibrating as a whole, or all the riders would have been thrown off. Actually, the string was vibrating in four equal parts, or segments, as we have shown in Fig. 18-7. The places between the segments where there is no vibration are called *nodes*. Riders 1, 3, and 5 were at the mid-points of the vibrating segments and were thrown off. Riders 2 and 4 were at the nodes. We made the string vibrate in this fashion by creating the first node at *A*. This caused nodes to be formed at the other two positions. From this experiment, we conclude that when we pluck or bow a string near one end, we can cause it to vibrate in several segments.

Now let us compare the pitch of one of these vibrating segments with the fundamental produced by the string. In the experiment we just conducted, the vibrating segment was one-fourth

the length of the string. The pitch of this segment is two octaves above the fundamental. This new tone is called an *overtone*. If the string vibrates in only two segments, an overtone one octave above the fundamental is heard. *A note whose vibration rate is a whole number multiple of that of the fundamental is called an* **overtone** *or harmonic.* Let us tune a string so that when it vibrates as a whole it produces C, 256 cycles per second, as its fundamental. An *oscilloscope* (os-*sil*-oh-skohp) *picture* of a fundamental tone is shown in Fig. 18-9A. If we cause the string to vibrate in two segments, the first overtone, or second harmonic, of C, with a frequency 2 × 256, or 512, is heard. This corresponds to C′, an octave above C. See Fig. 18-9B. The second overtone or third harmonic of C, heard when the string vibrates in three segments, has a frequency 3 × 256, or 768. This is G′. See Fig. 18-9C. We produce the third overtone or fourth harmonic when the string vibrates in four segments. Its frequency is 4 × 256, or 1024; the note is *C″*. See Fig. 18-9D. The fourth overtone or fifth harmonic of C is *E″*, whose frequency is 5 × 256, or 1280.

9. What is the quality of a sound? It is not difficult to pick out the sounds produced by the different instruments of an orchestra, even though they may

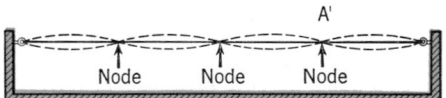

Fig. 18-7. The pattern of vibration of the string of Fig. 18-6. Notice the location of the loops and nodes.

String vibrating as a whole and in segments at the same time

Fig. 18-8. Overtones are produced when a string vibrates in two or more segments.

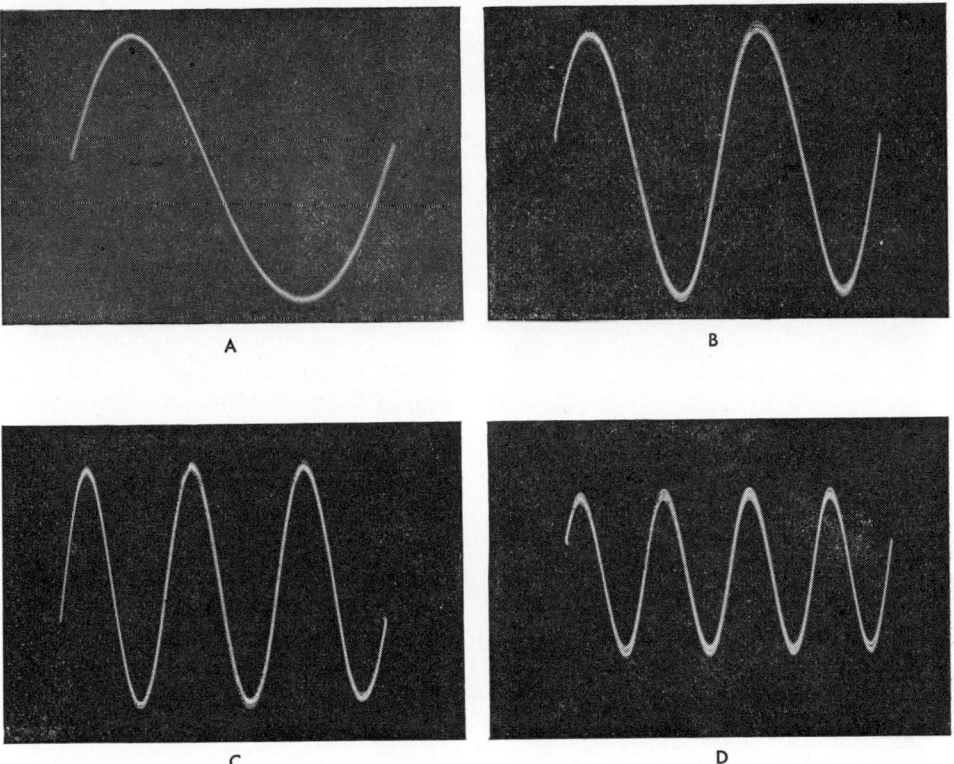

Fig. 18-9. Waveform pictures of *A* a fundamental tone, *B* the second harmonic, *C* the third harmonic, and *D* the fourth harmonic.

be playing the same note and may be playing it equally loud. The difference is a property of these sounds called *quality*.

Again let us use our sonometer and bow one of its strings near the middle. It sounds its fundamental. Now, if we touch the string *very lightly* in the middle, we can cause it to vibrate in two segments and as a whole at the same time. See Fig. 18-8. We can still hear the fundamental, but added to it is the sound of the first overtone. The combination is richer and fuller. The quality of the sound has been improved by the addition of the overtone to the

fundamental. See Fig. 18-10A. *The quality of a sound depends upon the number of overtones present and upon their prominence.* When stringed instruments are played, they are bowed, plucked, or struck near one end instead of in the middle. This produces overtones which blend with the fundamental and give a richer sound. See Fig. 18-10B.

The quality of the tones produced by orchestral instruments varies greatly. For example, a tone produced by a French horn consists of the fundamental and the second harmonic. You can readily see this by comparing these

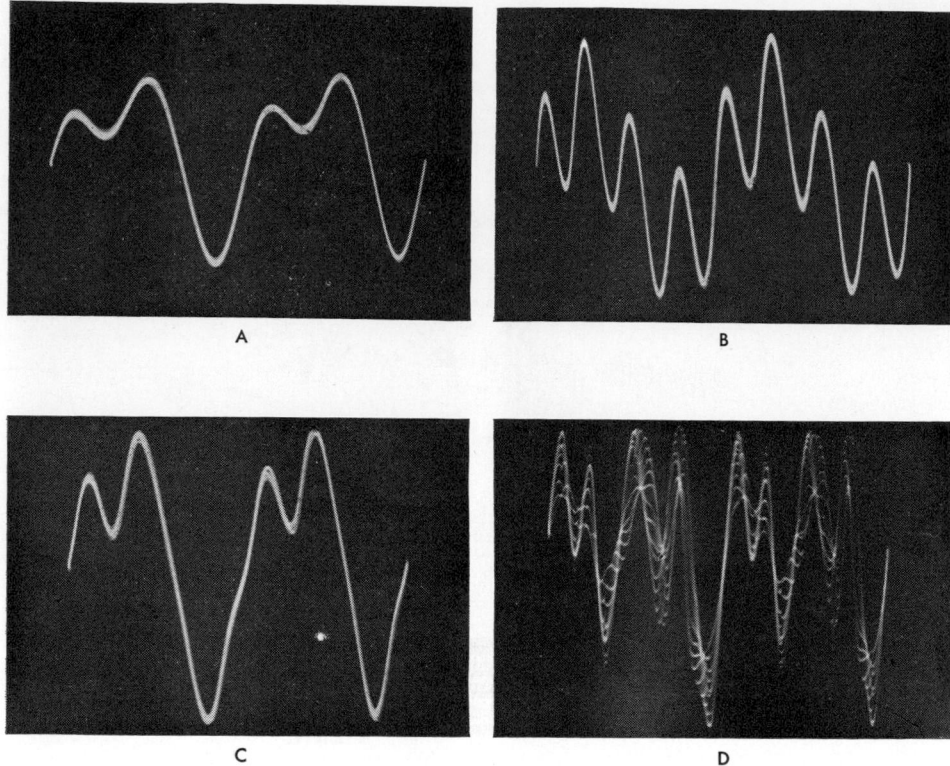

Fig. 18-10. Waveform pictures of *A* a fundamental and second harmonic, *B* a fundamental and fourth harmonic, *C* the tone of a French horn, and *D* the tone of a trumpet.

figures, Fig. 18-10A and Fig. 18-10C. In an instrument like the trumpet, however, its peculiar tonal quality is due to the high intensity of its high-frequency overtones. See Fig. 18-10D.

3. LAWS OF STRINGS

10. How does the frequency of a string vary with its length, diameter, tension, and density? The strings of a piano produce sounds with a wide range of frequencies. If we examine these strings we find that there are great differences among them. The strings which produce the low fre-quency tones are long, thick, and loose. The strings which the upper keys strike are short, thin, and tight. One string produces a loud enough tone for the low notes, but three strings are needed for the high ones.

Through the use of a sonometer, several facts have been learned about

Fig. 18-11. In a symphony orchestra, the musicians play instruments which produce sounds by means of vibrating strings, vibrating air columns, and vibrating membranes. How many instruments can you identify? How is the sound produced by each?

the conditions which affect the frequency of vibrating strings. These are sometimes called the *laws of strings*.

(1) *Law of lengths.* When a musician wishes to raise the pitch of a stringed instrument, he may shorten the length of the string. A violinist shortens the vibrating length of the A string about one inch when he wishes to produce the note B. *The frequency of a string is inversely proportional to its length, if its diameter, density, and tension remain unchanged.* See below.

(2) *Law of diameters.* In the piano, the strings which produce the higher frequencies have smaller diameters. This is true of other stringed instruments like the cello and the harp. A string with a diameter of 0.1 inch will vibrate twice as fast as a similar string 0.2 inch in diameter. *The frequency of a string is inversely propor-*

SAMPLE PROBLEM

If the D string of a violin is 12 inches long, how much must it be shortened to produce the note E?

SOLUTION

The frequency of D is 288; that of E is 320. We set up the proportion $\frac{288}{320} = \frac{x}{12}$.

Solving, $x = 10.8$ inches, the length of a string which vibrates 320 times per second. The D string must be shortened 1.2 inches to produce the note E.

Fig. 18-12. The strings of a grand piano. Notice that the longer strings at the top of the picture are not only thicker but are also wound with wire so that they can produce the lower tones.

tional to its diameter, if its length, density, and tension are constant.

(3) *Law of tensions.* When you tune a violin, you tighten the string to increase the frequency, or loosen the string to decrease it. Experiments have proved that *the frequency of a string is directly proportional to the square root of the tension on the string, if all the other factors are constant.*

(4) *Law of densities.* The heavier a string is, the slower it vibrates. The strings which produce the low frequency tones in a piano are thick. The lowest strings are even wound with copper wire to make them vibrate more slowly. *The frequency of a string is inversely proportional to the square root of its density, if other factors are constant.*

SAMPLE PROBLEM

A string stretched with a force of 9 lb produces the note C. What force must be applied to this same string to make it produce the note C′?

SOLUTION

The frequency of C is 256; that of C′ is 512. By proportion,

$$\frac{256}{512} = \frac{\sqrt{9}}{\sqrt{x}}.$$

Solving, $x = 36$ lb.

---

4. MUSICAL INSTRUMENTS

11. There are many stringed instruments. Vibrating strings produce the sounds made by a number of musical instruments. The basic part of a symphony orchestra is the string section, in which we find violins, violas, cellos, and string basses. The piano and harp, as well as the guitar and ukulele, are other stringed instruments. The vibrating strings on these instruments do not produce very intense sounds, but in each instrument there is a sounding board to vibrate and intensify the sound so that it can be heard. Strings for such instruments are made from a variety of materials, and in many lengths and thicknesses. They are mounted across the sounding board and tuned to proper pitch by adjusting the tension. If the pitch produced by a string must be varied when the instrument is played, its vibrating length is shortened by the fingers of the player.

12. How do organ pipes produce sound? The air blown into an organ pipe is usually directed against one edge of an opening in the pipe. See Fig. 18-13. This sets the air vibrating within the pipe. The wave length of these vibrations, and consequently their frequency, is determined by the length of the pipe, as we learned from our study of resonance in tubes, Section 26, Chapter 17. *A closed organ pipe produces a sound whose wave length is four times as long as the pipe itself.* A closed pipe one foot long will produce a sound wave four feet long. *An open pipe produces a sound wave which is twice the length of the pipe itself. An open pipe produces a tone an octave higher than a closed pipe of the same length.*

In constructing a set of organ pipes for the notes of an octave, the lengths of the pipes must be inversely proportional to the vibration ratios given in Section 2. They are inversely proportional because sounds of higher frequency have shorter wave lengths. The lengths of the pipes used to sound the notes of one octave, beginning with C, will have the following ratios: $1, \frac{8}{9}, \frac{4}{5}, \frac{3}{4}, \frac{2}{3}, \frac{3}{5}, \frac{8}{15}$, and $\frac{1}{2}$. *The frequency of a pipe varies inversely as its length.*

13. What overtones can pipes produce? When a pipe is blown gently, its fundamental is usually the only tone produced. Harder blowing may add

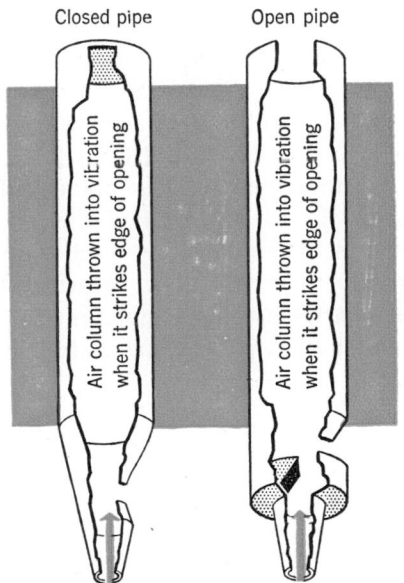

Fig. 18-13. A vibrating air column in an organ pipe produces sound.

Fig. 18-14. The pipes of a pipe organ. The different lengths, the different shapes, and the different materials of which these pipes are made cause them to produce sounds of different pitch and quality.

overtones to this fundamental. If the pipe is a closed one, there will always be a node at the closed end, and a loop at the other end. The only overtones possible with closed pipes are those whose frequencies are *odd* multiples of the fundamental. The first overtone which can be produced by a closed C organ pipe is not C′, but G′, a tone having a frequency 3 (an odd number) times that of the fundamental. The next overtone is E″, whose frequency is 5 times that of C.

With open pipes there is a node in the middle and a loop at each end. With these pipes the entire series of overtones is possible. The first overtone of an open C pipe is C′, the second overtone is G′, and the third overtone is C″.

When a hole is bored in a pipe, it produces the same effect as though the

pipe were cut off at the point. A loop is produced at the opening. Wind instruments of nearly all kinds have several holes so that the length may be varied to produce sounds of varying pitch. The opening of such holes is controlled by the fingers directly, or by keys or valves.

★ **14. How are sounds produced by a Hammond organ?** This instrument imitates electrically the effects of a pipe organ. It produces organ-like tones without pipes and vibrating air columns. The tones first are created as electric waves and then transformed into sound waves. About 90 tone wheels, each the size of a silver dollar, generate the electric waves. There is one tone wheel for each frequency which is to be produced. The tone wheels are mounted so that they all may be rotated at the same constant speed by an electric motor. On the rim of each wheel there are regularly spaced bumps similar to the teeth on a gear wheel. The number of bumps determines the frequency the wheel will produce. Near each tone wheel there is a small magnet, wound with a coil or wire. See Fig. 18-15.

As the tone wheels rotate, the bumps disturb the field of the small magnets and set up tiny electric currents in the coils. The frequency of these currents depends upon the number of bumps passing the magnet per

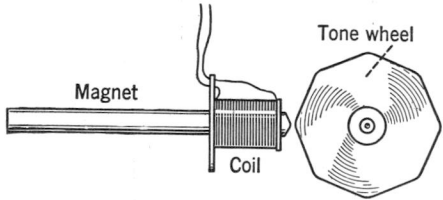

Fig. 18-15. A tone wheel, magnet, and coil in a Hammond organ.

second. If one of the wheels rotates so that 440 bumps per second disturb the magnetic field, then 440 electrical impulses are set up in the coil each second. These currents are electrically filtered to insure a pure tone, amplified by electronic tubes, and changed into sound waves by a loudspeaker. The 440 electrical impulses per second become a tone with a frequency of 440 cycles per second.

15. Producing sound in wind instruments. A vibrating air jet is the source of the sound in many wind instruments. The air jet may be produced by a vibrating reed, as in the harmonica, accordion, clarinet, and saxophone. The pitch of a harmonica or accordion is altered by setting different reeds vibrating. These instruments have a separate reed for each tone they produce. The pitch of a clarinet or saxophone depends on the length of the vibrating air column within the instrument.

In the flute, fife, and piccolo the vibrating air jet is produced in the same manner as in the organ pipe. A stream of air is directed against the edge of an opening near one end of the instrument. The pitch is regulated by the length of the vibrating air column.

In the trumpet, trombone, and other types of horn instruments, the lips of the player vibrate. The frequency of the sound produced depends upon the length of the instrument tube. This may be controlled by valves, or, as in the case of the trombone, by a slide.

16. How do vibrating membranes produce sound? In some musical instruments, the vibrating part is a membrane. The tambourine, bass drum, and kettle drum are examples. The human voice is produced by the vibration of membranes. The vocal cords are really two folds of muscular membrane which are stretched across the larynx. We control the tension on our vocal cords by muscular contraction. Changes in tension produce changes in the pitch of the voice. When we speak, we alter or modulate the sounds produced by the vocal cords by using our tongue, palate, teeth, and lips. In this way, vowel and consonant sounds are formed. The quality of the voice depends upon the overtones which are made prominent by resonance.

★ **17. How is a phonograph record made?** While there are several types of phonograph records available today which are played at different speeds and with different needles, the general method of making such records is the same. They are recorded in a room much like a radio station studio. Here the artists perform before the microphones. The microphones transform the sound waves into variations in an electric current. These electrical impulses are amplified and blended by a sound engineer in order to provide the balanced performance he wants. This original performance is usually recorded on magnetic tape so that it may be easily edited. (See Section 10, Chapter 31.) When the recording is satisfactory, it is re-recorded on a master disc by means of an electromagnetic cutting head. This cutting head contains a very sharp and accurately pointed needle that cuts zigzag grooves in the master disc to correspond to the original sound variations.

The master record is carefully inspected to make sure that the grooves are cleanly cut. Then several wax impressions are made from the lacquered master. These wax impressions are

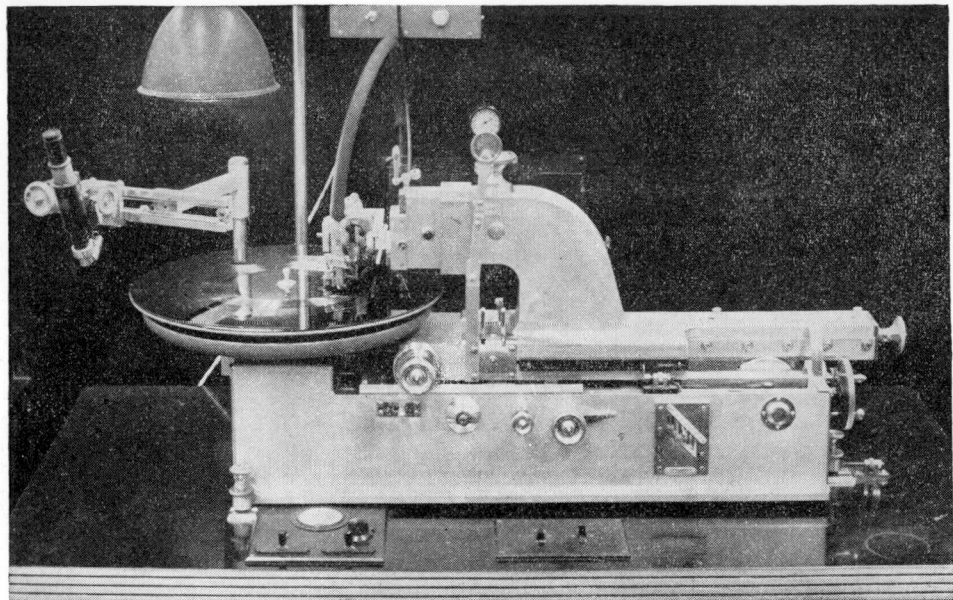

Fig. 18-16. The turntable on which the wax master record is cut.

dusted with graphite and plated with copper by means of electricity. The copper plates made in this way have the grooves of the original master as ridges on their surfaces. In other words, they are the reverse of the original master. These molds produce the final record. The mold is pressed into a record base material, which may be plastic or some other material. The impression which the mold makes is an accurate reproduction of the lacquered master record which was first cut.

★ **18. How is the sound reproduced from a phonograph record?** The phonograph record is rotated on a turntable at exactly the speed at which the master originally was cut. A needle with a properly shaped point follows the grooves cut in the record. These grooves cause the needle to vibrate. The needle transmits these vibrations to either a crystal or a small electromagnetic coil. The crystal-type pickup usually contains a Rochelle salt crystal. This material has the property of transmitting an electric current which varies with the pressure exerted on the crystal. The vibrations from the needle create this variable pressure on the crystal. As a result, a varying electric current is sent along the wire from the tone arm to the amplifying tubes in the reproducer.

In the electromagnetic type pickup, the vibrations of the needle cause corresponding variations in a magnetic field. This, in turn, produces similar variations in an electric current flowing along the wires between the tone arm and the amplifier. The electrical impulses from the pickup are made more powerful in the amplifier so that they can operate the speaker and reproduce the sound.

★ **19. What is high fidelity reproduction?** We learned that the quality of a sound depends upon the number and

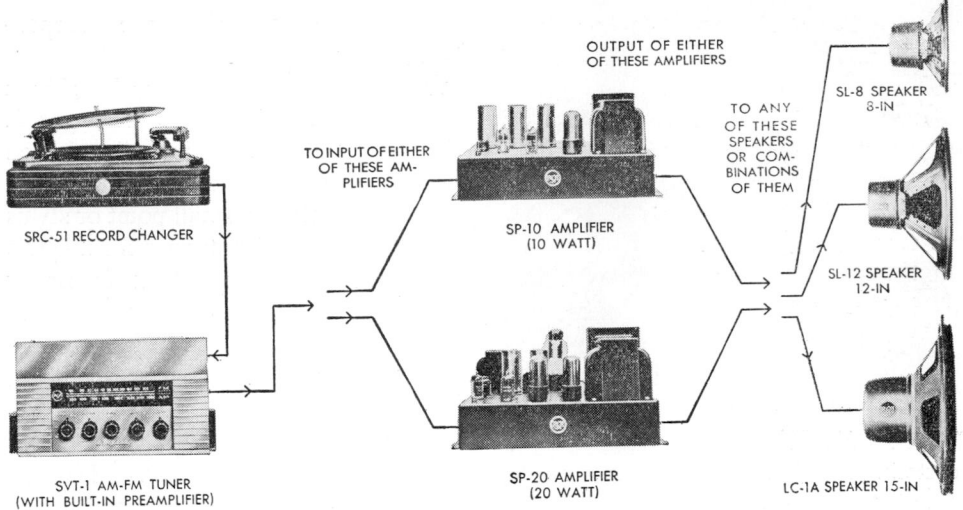

Fig. 18-17. A typical arrangement for a high fidelity phonograph system.

prominence of its overtones. In order to reproduce the sounds of musical instruments adequately, scientists generally agree that we must record and be able to get back through our loudspeaker at least the first four overtones. Putting these overtones on a record has been more successful than reproducing them. The ordinary commercial phonograph usually has a top frequency of about 6000 cycles per second. Modern records have a top frequency of about 15,000 cycles per second, so that many of the overtones they carry are lost in ordinary reproduction.

Several years ago some music and electronics enthusiasts, dissatisfied with the inferior sound reproductions they were getting, began assembling their own phonographs. Their purpose was to develop a reproducer that would transform into sound waves the entire range of frequencies pressed into a modern phonograph record. Their equipment was put together from separate parts specially manufactured to meet rigid requirements. Such phono-

graphs, with improved light-weight pickups, more responsive amplifiers, as well as properly mounted combinations of speakers, reproduce the high frequency overtones available on present recordings. The upper frequency limit on some of these *high-fidelity,* or " hi-fi," reproducers is about 20,000 vibrations per second — beyond the upper limits of average human hearing. So very popular has this type of sound reproduction become, that manufacturers are now marketing high fidelity phonographs.

★ **20. What is a dictating machine?** The dictating machine is a modification of the phonograph for office use. Rather than have a stenographer take dictation directly, an executive sitting at his desk speaks into a mouthpiece. His words are recorded by the machine on a revolving, hard wax cylinder or disc. Later, the cylinder or disc is given to a stenographer who plays it back on a reproducing machine. Through small tubes leading to her ears she listens to the speaker's words

Fig. 18-18. A business man using a dictating machine to record his reply to a letter. Later his secretary will play back the disc and type his reply.

and at the same time types the message. The advantage of the dictating machine is its convenience. The executive and the stenographer may work on dictated correspondence independently of one another.

★ **21. Sound waves may be shown graphically.** (1) The *vibrograph*. This is a device which is easily adapted for use in a high school physics laboratory. We attach a small point or stylus to one prong of a tuning fork. The stem of the tuning fork is firmly clamped and the fork set in vibration. If a piece of smoked glass, or one coated with whiting, is drawn beneath the vibrating fork, the stylus traces its vibrations on it. See Fig. 18-19.

(2) *The oscilloscope*. Modern methods of seeing sound waves utilize the cathode-ray *oscilloscope*. The sound waves to be " seen " are first transformed by a microphone into electrical impulses. These impulses trace a visual pattern on the fluorescent screen of the oscilliscope.

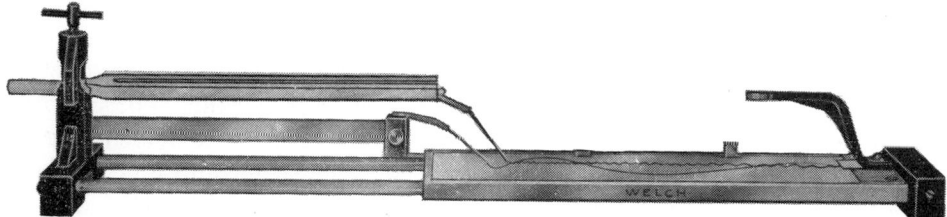

Fig. 18-19. A vibrograph can be used to measure the frequency of sound waves produced by a tuning fork.

Summary

A major chord is built up of tones whose frequencies are in the ratio of 4, 5, and 6. The major diatonic scale is built up from three major chords; it consists of eight notes in each octave for any given key. The chromatic scale has five additional half-tone notes per octave. In the equally tempered scale, the interval between notes is uniform. The ratio between the frequencies of successive notes is the twelfth root of two.

The frequency of a vibrating string is inversely proportional to its length, its diameter, and the square root of its density; it is directly proportional to the square root of the tension.

The sound waves from musical instruments generally are produced by vibrating strings or air columns. Vibrating columns of air may be set up by reeds, by the vibrations of the lips of the player, or by air striking the edge of an opening.

A closed organ pipe is one-fourth as long as the sound wave which it produces. An open pipe is one-half as long as the sound wave which it produces. In an open pipe, the whole series of overtones is possible. In a closed pipe, only those overtones whose frequencies are odd multiples of the fundamental are possible.

Sound waves may be analyzed by the vibrograph, or by an oscilloscope.

Terms to Define...

Chromatic scale	Laws of strings	Stringed instruments
Crystal pick-up	Major chord	Tempered scale
Diatonic scale	Noise	Tone
Discord	Oscilloscope	Vibrating membranes
Electromagnetic pick-up	Overtone	Wave length of sound from
Fundamental	Overtones produced by pipes	closed organ pipe
Hammond organ	Phonograph record	Wave length of sound from
Harmony	Quality	open organ pipe
High fidelity reproduction	Sonometer	Wind instruments

Questions

GROUP A

1. What is a fundamental tone? The first overtone? How do they compare in frequency?

2. How does the frequency of the fundamental compare with that of the third harmonic? With that of the fourth harmonic?

3. Why is it easy for us to distinguish between the note A on a piano and the note A as sounded on a trombone?

4. How do the strings on a harp illustrate all of the laws of strings?

5. Which law of strings is used in tuning a violin? Which in playing the instrument?

6. What is the function of the thin, wooden bridge between the strings and the sounding board of a cello?

7. Some of the pipes of a pipe organ are made of wood. Some are of metal. Why?

8. How is the vibrating air column produced in a clarinet, a trombone, and in a flute?

9. Why is it often difficult to understand the speech of a person who lost all his teeth?

10. Will a piano tuned at 68° F be in tune when the temperature is 85° F?

GROUP B

★ **11.** How do the vibrations of a source which produces a musical tone differ from the vibrations of a source which produces noise?

★ **12.** What is a major chord?

★ **13.** How is the diatonic scale built up from major chords?

★ **14.** How do the frequencies of notes an octave apart compare?

★ **15.** How is the chromatic scale constructed?

16. Explain how the tempered scale was devised. Why is it a compromise scale?

★ **17.** Why does the tone of middle C on a tuned piano not correspond with the tone of a C tuning fork used in a physics laboratory?

★ **18.** Explain how beats cause two notes which are struck simultaneously to sound harmonious or discordant.

★ **19.** Why can a Hammond organ produce very pure musical tones?

★ **20.** Describe the various steps in the production of a master phonograph record.

★ **21.** How is a phonograph record reproduced? What is hi-fi?

★ **22.** Why is a dictating machine of particular value to a busy executive?

★ **23.** Explain how the vibrograph apparatus may be used to measure the frequency of a tuning fork.

(In the Mathematics Refresher, refer to Sections 2, 8, 10, and 16.)

GROUP A

1. What is the wave length of the tone produced by an open organ pipe 4 ft long?

2. If a closed organ pipe 6 ft long is played, what is the wave length of the sound heard?

3. What is the length of a closed organ pipe which produces the note A, 440 cycles per second, when the temperature is 20° C?

4. How long must an open organ pipe be if it is to produce a tone with a frequency of 1760 cycles per second at 25° C?

5. If the A string on a violin is 10 in long, how much must it be shortened to produce C'? Assume that the violin is tuned to the physical scale, in which A = 426 cycles per second.

6. When a string is stretched with a force of 16 lb, it sounds the note C. With how much force must the string be stretched to yield the note E? Use frequencies of the physical scale.

7. Compare the frequency of one string 25 cm long and 0.5 mm in diameter with that of another string 100 cm long and 0.25 mm in diameter. The strings are of the same material and are stretched by the same force.

8. A closed organ pipe produces the note E, 320 cycles per second. What are the frequencies of the first and second overtones of this pipe? To what notes do they correspond?

9. If an open organ pipe produces the note G_1, 192 cycles per second, what are the frequencies of first and second overtones of this pipe? To what notes on the scale do they correspond?

10. What is the frequency of C' on the scale where A = 440 cycles per second?

GROUP B

11. When a string 20 inches long is stretched with a force of 50 lb, its frequency is 440 cycles per second. If the string is shortened to 16 inches and the stretching force is increased to 98 lb, what is the new frequency?

12. If a string is 15 inches long and under a tension of 64 lb, it gives *Do* on a certain scale. How much must the string be shortened to produce *Re?* If the length is not changed, by how much must the tension be increased in order to produce *Re?*

13. Calculate the frequency and the wave length of the lowest note on the piano, A_4, a little more than three octaves below middle C, when the temperature is 20° C.

14. Calculate the frequency and the wave length of the highest note on the piano, C'''', when the temperature is 20° C.

Things to Do

1. Have the members of the class who play musical instruments bring them to class. Have each one explain and demonstrate how his instrument produces sound, what its range is, and how its pitch is altered.

2. Examine the pipes of a large pipe organ. Find out how the organist controls the air flow to each pipe. How is the volume of sound produced by a pipe organ changed?

3. If you have a Hammond organ in your school, have the organist demonstrate the effects which it can produce.

4. If your school has a disc recorder, use it to make records of the voices of class members.

Unit 9 — Light

Most of the natural light we receive on earth comes to us from the sun. Light, like heat and sound, is a form of energy. Would it not be wonderful if we could change some of the light energy we receive from the sun into some other useful form of energy, such as electricity? Well, scientists have succeeded in doing just that. The device held by the scientist in the photograph is called a solar battery. It consists of strips of a special material which produces electricity when sunlight strikes it.

In our study of Light, we shall learn about the nature of light waves. We shall find that they are the same kind of waves as heat, X rays, and radio waves. We shall discover how light waves are reflected by mirrors, refracted by lenses, and dispersed into colors by prisms. We also shall study optical instruments, including cameras, microscopes, and telescopes.

Chapter 19

Light

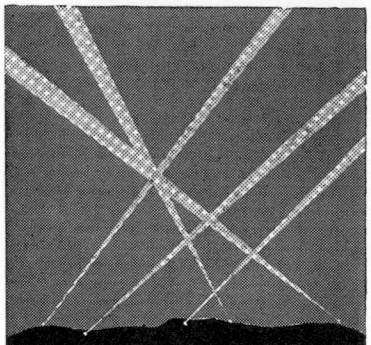

1. THE NATURE OF LIGHT

1. What is the nature of light? The light given off by the sun or by an electric lamp enables us to see our surroundings. Without such sources of light, our eyes would be useless. As important as light is to our daily lives, scientists yet do not have a complete explanation of the nature of light.

When light from the sun strikes our skin we feel the sensation of warmth. If we expose our skin to the sun's rays, we become sunburned. These observations lead us to believe that light must be a form of energy because light is so closely associated with heat. We know that heat is a form of energy. As we walk along a road or sidewalk on a bright day, we find that our body cuts off some of the light from the sun, and casts a shadow. The outlines of the shadow seem to indicate that light travels in straight lines.

Many of the properties of light can be explained on the theory that light is a transverse wave motion with both electrical and magnetic properties. This theory satisfactorily explains the variation in the velocity of light as it passes through different solids, liquids, and gases. The wave theory also explains the reflection of light. But the action of light when it strikes the sensitive cell of a photographic exposure meter calls for an explanation other

---

Vocabulary

CANDLE. Unit for measuring the intensity of a light source.

ILLUMINATED. Visible because of reflected light.

LIGHT. Electromagnetic radiation which is visible to the human eye.

LUMEN. Unit for measuring the illumination on a surface.

LUMINOUS. Visible because of emitted light.

MICRON (*my*-kron). $\frac{1}{1,000,000}$ meter.

OPAQUE (oh-*payk*). Does not transmit light.

PHOTOMETER (foh-*tom*-eh-ter). Instrument for comparing the intensities of two light sources.

TRANSLUCENT. Transmits light waves but scatters them so that objects can not be distinguished.

TRANSPARENT. Transmits light waves so that objects may be distinguished.

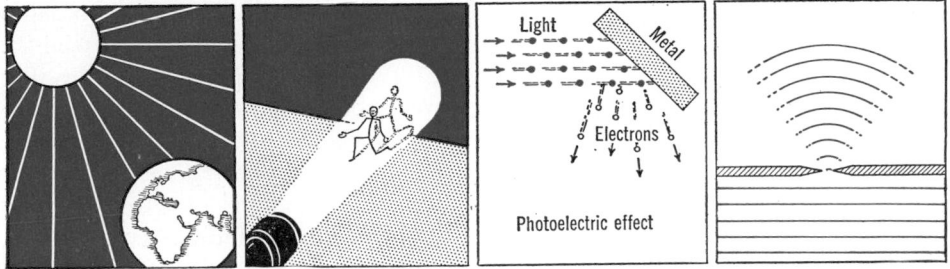

Fig. 19-1. Light is a form of energy which travels in straight lines. When it is emitted or absorbed by matter it acts as if it were a stream of particles, but when it travels from one spot to another, it acts as if it were a wave.

than that provided by the wave theory. In this case light acts as though it were a stream of fast-moving particles. Consequently, at the present time, physicists accept the idea that light has two different aspects. When light travels from one spot to another, it acts as though it were a wave. But when it is emitted by matter or absorbed by matter, it acts as though it were a stream of particles. *Light may be defined as electromagnetic radiation, which is visible to the human eye.* It is also applied to radiation having frequencies somewhat above and below the range of human sight.

2. The electromagnetic spectrum. We already have learned that a hot object may transfer heat by radiation. If we make the temperature of an object high enough, it will give out light in addition to heat. We know, too, that when a cloud cuts off the light from the sun, it cuts off the sun's heat at the same time. Observations such as these have led physicists to the conclusion that radiant heat and light have some properties in common. They both are electromagnetic waves, and they both travel at the same velocity.

Heat and light are forms of electromagnetic waves. We may detect them with our senses. Actually they are only two of many varieties of electromagnetic waves. Fig. 19-2 is a chart which shows all the known types of electromagnetic waves. They are listed in order of their frequency and wave length.

3. Light waves differ from sound waves. There are many important differences between sound waves and light waves.
(1) Light waves travel through a vacuum, but sound waves do not. Light waves are electromagnetic waves, while sound waves require matter for their transmission.
(2) Light waves are transverse vibrations, while sound waves are longitudinal.
(3) Sound waves vary in length from about 1 cm to nearly 21 m. Light waves are so short that their length is measured in millimicrons. A *micron* (*my*-kron), abbreviated by the Greek letter, μ, (mu), is $\frac{1}{1,000,000}$ m, or *10^{-6} m*. A millimicron, abbreviated mμ, is $\frac{1}{1000}$ of a micron and equals 10^{-9} m. Light waves vary in length from 400 mμ to 700 mμ.
(4) Under most conditions, light waves travel in straight lines but sound waves readily bend around corners. We can

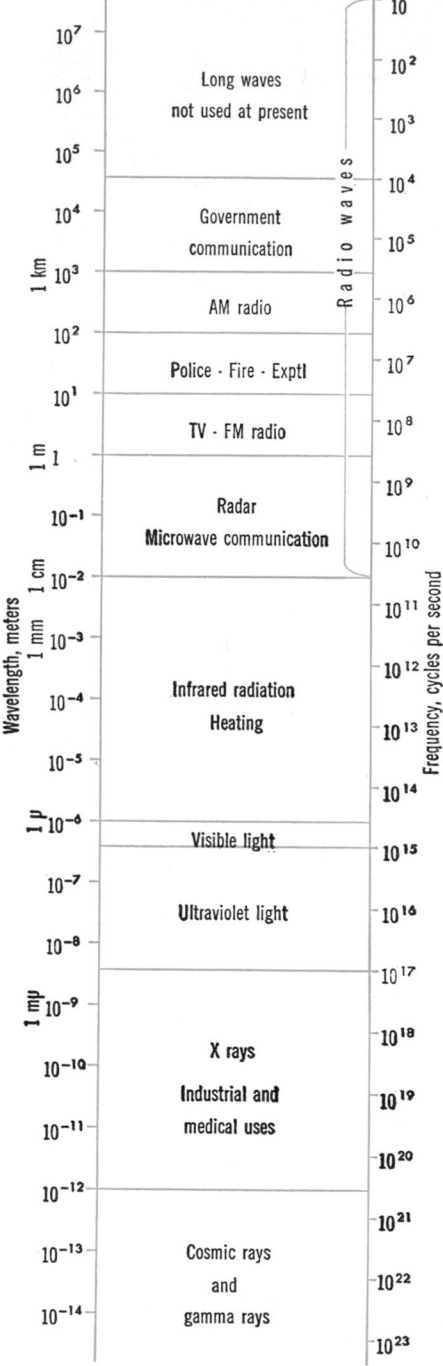

Fig. 19-2. The electromagnetic spectrum.

hear a person who stands around a corner from us, but we can not see him. (5) Light waves travel so rapidly that over short distances we consider them instantaneous. The velocity of sound is very slow compared to the velocity of light.

4. Sources of light. (1) *Natural.* Nearly all the natural light we receive comes from the sun. Moonlight is really sunlight reflected to us from the surface of the moon. Distant stars furnish us with an extremely small amount of light. (2) *Artificial.* There are several ways of producing artificial light. We may heat materials until they glow, or become incandescent. This is the way we get light from the filament of an electric light bulb. We may bombard the molecules of a gas with electrons and produce light such as we see in a neon sign. Visible light from fluorescent tubes is produced by the action of invisible ultra-violet light on chemicals with which the tube is coated. The light of a fire-fly is produced by complex chemical reactions.

5. Luminous and illuminated objects. When a platinum wire is heated, it emits waves of shorter and shorter length as its temperature rises. Soon the wire becomes incandescent. It now is a **luminous** body. The wire *is visible primarily because of the light it emits.* An object which gives off light because of the energy of its oscillating particles is said to be luminous. The sun and the stars are luminous bodies.

Just as radiant heat may be reflected, light waves may be turned back from the surfaces of bodies. Mirrors reflect some of the light that comes to them from some other source. A body that merely *reflects light which it re-*

ceives and makes itself visible is an **illuminated** *body.* We already have mentioned the moon as an example. Like a huge mirror, it reflects some of the light which it receives from the sun.

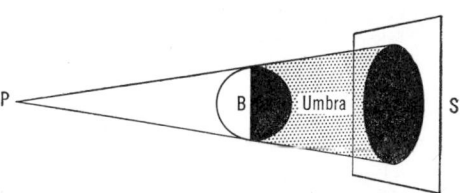

Fig. 19-3. When the source of light is a point, the shadow cast by ball *B* is of uniform intensity. This shadow is called an umbra.

6. Reflection, absorption, and transmission of light. What happens to light waves when they reach the glass of a window or the surface of a body of water? Some of them are *reflected* from the glass or the water. Some of them are *transmitted* through the glass or water. Still other light waves are *absorbed* by the glass or water.

(1) *Reflection.* Smooth water has been known as a reflector of light since prehistoric times. It makes a fairly good mirror. Panes of glass in the windows of a distant house reflect light to us. If the glass is removed, we see only dark openings. Highly polished metals are good reflectors of light.

(2) *Absorption.* Dark-colored objects absorb light readily. Black objects absorb nearly all the light they receive. When the *vertical* rays of the sun are incident upon a body of water, most of them are either *absorbed* or *transmitted.* More of the rays are *reflected* when they strike the water at an *oblique* angle. You can look at the image of the sun in the water without discomfort when the sun is directly overhead, but your eyes are dazzled by the reflected rays from the setting sun.

(3) *Transmission.* Air, glass, and water *transmit light readily.* They are said to be **transparent.** So much light is transmitted by transparent bodies that it is easy to distinguish objects through them. Other substances *transmit some light, but so much of the light is scattered or diffused by them that the*

objects seen through them can not be identified. These are **translucent** substances. Typical examples of them are frosted electric light bulbs and parchment lampshades. **Opaque** (oh-*payk*) *substances do not transmit light at all.* These are substances through which we can not see.

7. Rays, beams, and pencils of light. From a luminous point-source, light waves travel outward in all directions. If the medium through which they are traveling is of the same nature throughout, light waves travel in straight lines. We use this property of light when we aim a rifle. The light from the object at which we are aiming is reflected along the sights of the rifle. A single line of light coming from a luminous point is called a *ray.* Several parallel rays form a *beam* of light. The rays coming from the sun are so nearly parallel that we may consider them as beams. When several rays of light come from a point, they form what is called a *diverging pencil.* Rays from an automobile headlight are somewhat diverging. Several rays of light proceeding toward a point form a *converging pencil.* When the sun's rays pass through a burning glass, they are bent as they pass through the glass. They converge at a point called a *focus.*

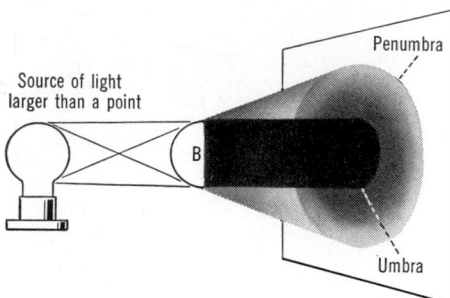

Fig. 19-4. When a source of light is larger than a point, the shadow cast by ball *B* is not of uniform intensity. All rays of light are excluded from the umbra. Also, some of the rays of light are excluded from the region of the penumbra.

8. What causes shadows? Since an opaque object absorbs light, the space behind it is in darkness. Any space from which the light is excluded by an opaque object is called a *shadow*. When the source of light is a point, as in Fig. 19-3, an opaque ball, *B,* cuts off all the rays which strike it, and produces a shadow of uniform darkness on screen *S.* If the light comes from a source which is larger than a point, the shadow varies in intensity. See Fig. 19-4. The part from which all the rays of light are excluded is called the *umbra.* The lighter part of the shadow is called the *penumbra.* The luminous source is not entirely hidden from an observer in the penumbra, but part of its rays are cut off.

9. Eclipses. (1) *Eclipse of the sun.* As the moon revolves around the earth, it periodically passes between the earth and the sun. This happens every month when the moon is at *new* moon. During most new moons, the plane of the orbit of the moon about the earth and the plane of the orbit of the earth about the sun do not coincide. Therefore, the moon does not cut off the rays of the sun. Occasionally, however, the planes of these orbits do coincide. Then the moon cuts off the sun's rays, and an eclipse of the sun occurs. During a solar eclipse there are only certain portions of the earth's surface that fall within the umbra of the moon. When the moon is at the position shown in Fig. 19-5, the sun will be totally eclipsed for an observer at any place on the earth within the umbra of the moon. For persons on the earth in the penumbra of the moon, the eclipse of the sun will be only partial.

(2) *Eclipse of the moon.* There is always a shadow stretching out from the earth on the side opposite the sun. When our portion of the earth revolves into this shadowed region, it becomes night. In its orbit around the earth, the moon sometimes passes through this shadow projected by the earth.

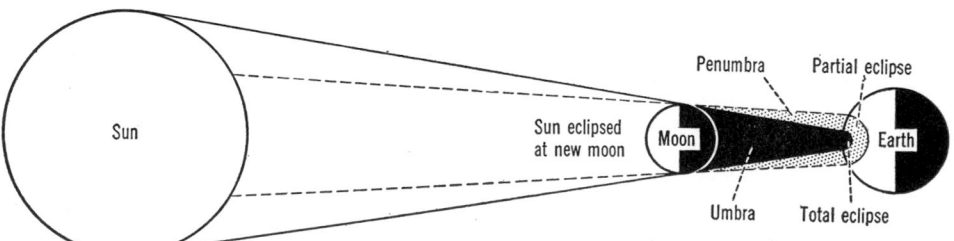

Fig. 19-5. An eclipse of the sun occurs when the moon's shadow falls on the earth.

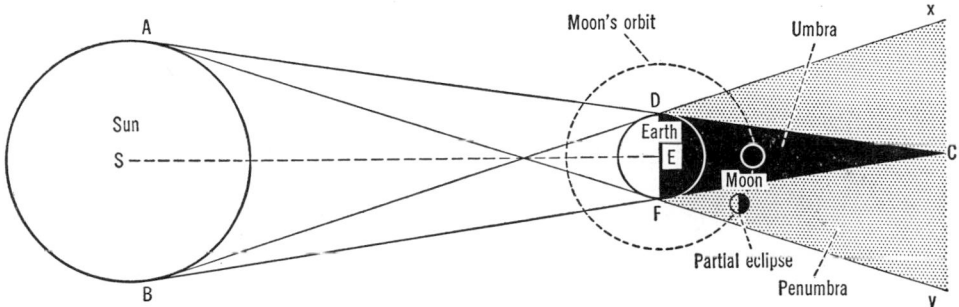

Fig. 19-6. An eclipse of the moon occurs when the moon enters the earth's shadow.

Then an eclipse of the moon occurs. Fig. 19-6 shows how the moon passes from the earth's penumbra into its umbra. Then it moves on through the umbra into the other portion of the penumbra, and the eclipse ends. The eclipse happens only during those full moons when the planes of the orbits of the moon around the earth and the earth around the sun closely coincide.

10. The speed of light. The notable modern work in measuring the speed of light was performed by Albert A. Michelson (1852–1931). Using extremely precise methods, he was able to measure the speed of light in the air and in a vacuum.

(1) *The speed of light in air.* An octagonal mirror which could be rotated very rapidly was set up on Mount Wilson in California. Both concave and plane mirrors were placed atop Mount San Antonio, about 22 miles away. At certain positions during its rotation, a ray of light could be reflected from a face of the octagonal mirror to the mirrors at Mount San Antonio. Here it was reflected back again in a parallel line to Mount Wilson. The reflected ray was observed on Mount Wilson by means of a telescope.

Using mirrors and slits, the position of the source of light sent out by the rotating mirror could be compared

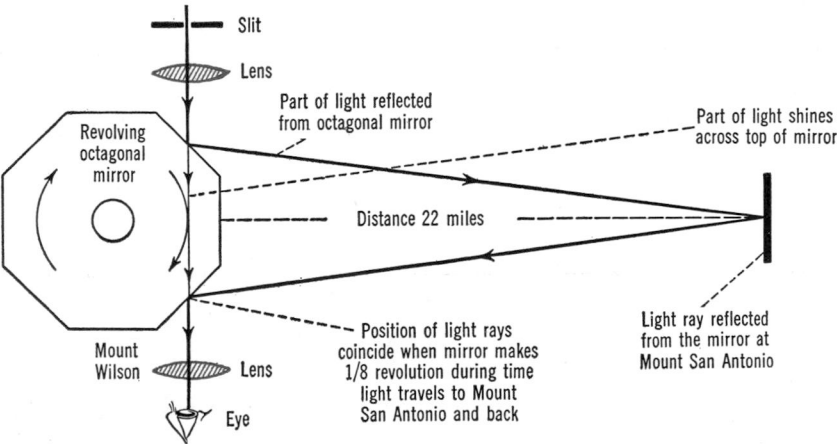

Fig. 19-7. Michelson's octagonal mirror method for measuring the speed of light.

Fig. 19-8. The mile-long vacuum tube used by Michelson to eliminate errors due to haze and variations in air density while measuring the velocity of light.

with the position of the reflected light received from Mount San Antonio. When the octagonal mirror revolved slowly, the ray of light traveled to Mount San Antonio and back before the mirror turned very far. The position of the reflected light was moved sidewise only a little. As the speed of the mirror was increased, the position of the reflected light was shifted so far that it could no longer be seen. But when the speed of the mirror was further increased, the reflected light was seen once again, but this time it moved in from the opposite side. Finally a speed was reached when the position of the source of light sent out by the rotating mirror and the position of the reflected light once again coincided. At this speed the mirror was turning one-eighth of a revolution during the time the light traveled to Mount San Antonio and back. Because the distance between the two mountains and the speed of the revolving mirror were known, Michelson was able to calculate the velocity of light in air.

(2) *The speed of light in a vacuum.* For more accurate work, Michelson constructed a mile-long vacuum tube in which the light was reflected back and forth ten times. The value he obtained using this method was 299,790 km/sec. This is believed to be accurate to within 1 km/sec. In the English system, the velocity of light in a vacuum is 186,285 mi/sec.

2. PHOTOMETRY

11. Intensity and illumination. We already have learned that an intense sound may not seem very loud to a listener who is at a considerable distance from the source. With light it is much the same. The amount of

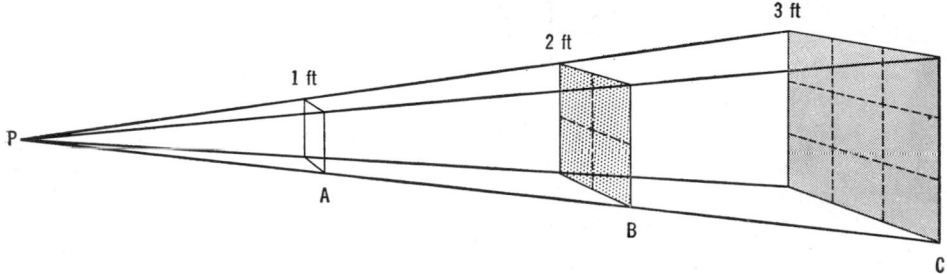

Fig. 19-9. The illumination varies inversely as the square of the distance from the source of light.

illumination we receive depends on the intensity of the source, and on our distance from that source. *The unit for measuring the illumination on a surface is a* **lumen.** Illumination is measured in *lumens per square foot* or *lumens per square meter. The intensity of a source of light* depends upon the energy produced by the luminous body. *It is measured in* **candles** *or candlepower.*

We receive twice as much illumination from a source of light whose intensity is 40 candles as we do from a source with a 20-candle intensity provided we are an equal distance from each one. We shall use Fig. 19-9 to show why illumination decreases as we move away from the source.

Light is emitted from the luminous point, *P*, and spreads out in all directions. Suppose we place the screen *A*, with an area of just 1 ft², exactly 1 foot from the light source. *B*, which is four times as large, is placed 2 feet distant; and *C*, which has nine times the area of screen *A*, is placed 3 feet away. Screens *B* and *C* are both completely shaded by the screen *A*. When screen *A* is removed, those rays of light which illuminated *A* fall upon screen *B*. But *B* has an area of 4 ft² while the area of *A* is only 1 ft². Con-

sequently, each square foot of surface at *B*, 2 feet from the light source, can receive only one-fourth as much light as a square foot of surface at *A*, only 1 foot distant. Likewise, *C* is three times as far away as *A*, and the light will be spread over nine times as much area. Thus 1 ft² of surface will receive only one-ninth as much light at *C* as at *A*.

These observations may be summarized as follows: *The illumination of a body is inversely proportional to the square of its distance from the source of light.*

12. Units for the measurement of light. There are two quantities of light that we generally wish to measure. One is the intensity of a source of light. The other is the amount of illumination on a surface.

(1) *The unit of intensity.* As was mentioned before, the intensity of a source of light is measured in candles. Originally an actual candle was used as a standard. But this was not very satisfactory because the exact intensity of a candle is not easy to reproduce. Today *the candle is defined as the intensity of the light emitted through an opening $\frac{1}{60}$ of a square centimeter in area from a hollow enclosure maintained at the temperature of solidify-*

ing platinum, about 1755° C. In practice it is convenient to use incandescent lamps which have been rated by comparison with the standard.

Incandescent lamps used for interior lighting generally have an intensity ranging from a few candles to several hundred candles. A 40-watt lamp has an intensity of about 35 candles. The intensity of a 100-watt lamp is about 130 candles. On the other hand, a 40-watt fluorescent lamp has an intensity of about 200 candles.

Let us screw an ordinary tungsten lamp into a socket mounted on a board so that the lamp burns base down. When the lamp is turned on, we observe that the amount of light given off in a horizontal direction is greater than that given off vertically. Consequently, the intensity of this lamp will depend on the direction from which we measure it. The candle power of a lamp may be measured horizontally, vertically, or from some other direction. Sometimes it is the average, or the *mean,* candle power which is given. (2) *The units of illumination.* Sup-

pose we have a 1-candle source of light placed in the center of a sphere 1 foot in radius. The inside of the sphere has been painted white. All of the light given out in all directions will strike the walls of this sphere. The light reflects from one wall to the other until the illumination on the walls is uniform. A sphere with a radius of 1 foot has an area of 12.57 square feet. In order to make the amount of light falling on each square foot of the inside of the sphere 1 lumen, the total amount of light given out by a 1-candle power source is defined as 12.57 lumens. *The amount of illumination falling on a surface 1 foot from a 1-candle power source is 1 lumen per square foot.* (This unit was formerly called the foot-candle, but the use of this term is being discontinued.) A person sitting 1 foot from a lamp with an intensity of 20 candles, receives 20 lumens/ft² of illumination. If he sits at a distance of 2 feet from such a lamp, he receives only 5 lumens/ft². The illumination E, in lumens per square foot, may be found by dividing

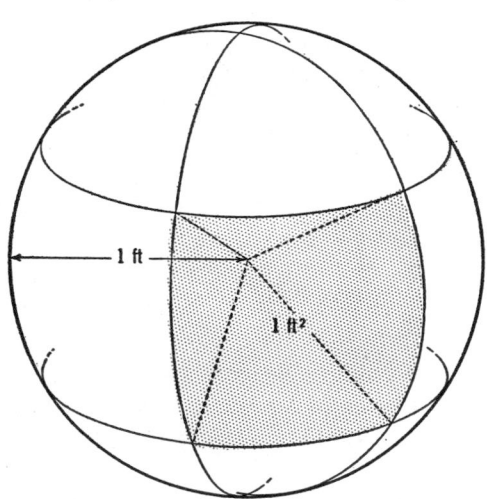

The total amount of light given out by the 1-candle power source at the center of this sphere is 12.57 lumens. Since the surface area of the sphere is 12.57 ft², the illumination on each square foot is one lumen.

Fig. 19-10. Definition of the lumen as the unit of measurement of illumination.

SAMPLE PROBLEM

What illumination will be provided on a surface 3 ft from a lamp with an intensity of 120 candles?

SOLUTION

We substitute in the equation $E = \dfrac{I}{R^2}$.

$E = \dfrac{120}{(3)^2}$.

Solving, $E = 13.3$ lumens/ft², the illumination.

the intensity of the source, I, in candles, by the square of the distance R, in square feet.

$$E = \frac{I}{R^2}.$$

If R^2 is given in square meters, the illumination E will be given in lumens per square meter. See problem above.

13. How much light do we need? The amount of illumination we need varies with the kind of work we are doing. The illumination out-of-doors from direct sunlight on a clear day is about 10,000 lumens/ft². Indoors,

we use much smaller amounts of illumination. Lighting engineers, who have studied the illumination needed for various tasks, suggest at least 30 lumens/ft² for reading ordinary print. For reading fine print, 50 lumens/ft² are needed. For sewing on dark-colored goods, 200 lumens/ft² will be needed.

14. Providing the light we need. Suppose we need 30 lumens/ft² for reading. If we do not consider reflection, we must use a 100-watt lamp with an intensity of about 130 candles, and sit slightly farther than 2 feet from

Fig. 19-11. Observe the difference which good lighting makes. An adequate lamp increases the general illumination in addition to providing sufficient illumination on the work.

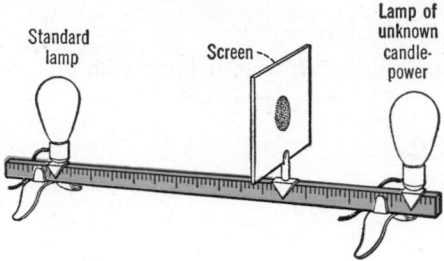

Fig. 19-12. The Bunsen, or grease-spot, photometer.

the lamp. In an actual case, however, the walls and ceilings greatly affect the amount of light reflected to our work. Lampshades likewise direct much light, that would otherwise be wasted, into more useful directions. As a result, it is possible by proper light reflection to get adequate illumination with lower candle-power lamps. See Fig. 19-11.

15. How do we measure the intensity of a source of light? We *measure the candlepower of any light source by comparing its intensity with that of a standard light source.* The *instrument used is called a* **photometer** (foh-*tom*-eh-ter).

(1) *Bunsen photometer.* This photometer is sometimes called the grease-spot photometer. If we take a piece

of paper with a grease spot in the center and hold it toward the window, the grease spot will appear lighter than the rest of the paper because it transmits light better. Again, because it is a poorer reflector of light than the paper, the grease spot will appear darker than the paper when held away from the window and seen by reflected light. The Bunsen photometer consists of such a piece of paper placed on a meter stick between a standard lamp and the lamp of unknown candle power. The paper is moved back and forth along the meter stick until it is equally illuminated on both sides. At this point the grease spot practically disappears. See Fig. 19-12. When the paper screen is properly adjusted, we measure the distance from the standard lamp to the grease-spot screen, and the distance from the lamp of unknown intensity to the screen. The intensities of the two light sources, in candles, are directly proportional to the squares of their distance from the screen. See Sample Problem below.

(2) *Joly photometer.* This is another simple photometer. It generally gives more satisfactory results than the

SAMPLE PROBLEM

A lamp with an intensity of 20 candles is used as a standard on a Bunsen photometer. The screen is equally illuminated when it is 20 cm from the standard lamp and 80 cm from the lamp of unknown intensity. What is the intensity of the unknown lamp?

SOLUTION

The unknown lamp must have the greater intensity. It provides the same illumination at 80 cm that the standard lamp provides at 20 cm. Since the illumination varies with the square of the distance from the source, the unknown lamp must be $(80)^2/(20)^2$ or 16 times as intense.

16 × 20 candles = 320 candles, the intensity of the unknown lamp.

grease-spot photometer. Essentially, it consists of two blocks of paraffin separated by a thin sheet of metal. The light from either side is transmitted by the paraffin, but is stopped by the metal. By looking at the edges of the blocks of paraffin it is easy to adjust the photometer so that both sides are equally illuminated. The distances to the lamps are then measured and calculations made in the same manner as with the Bunsen photometer.

(3) *Spherical photometer.* This accurate photometer is used commercially. The lamp to be tested is placed in the center of a large sphere which is painted white on the inside. The in-

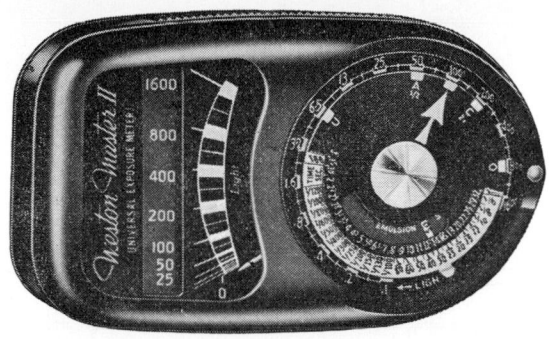

Fig. 19-14. Photographers use such meters as this to measure the amount of illumination on the subject being photographed.

tensity of the light transmitted through a window is measured by means of a photo-electric cell. The more intense the light, the stronger the current which flows through the photo-electric cell.

16. Measuring the amount of illumination. When planning lighting installations or when taking photographs, it is necessary to know the amount of illumination available. The instruments used for these purposes are called "light meters" or "exposure meters." They contain a light-sensitive cell which transforms the illumination falling on it into an electric current. The amount of illumination and the electric current produced are proportional within the range of the instrument. Consequently, a light meter can be calibrated directly in lumens per square foot, or in foot-candles. The operation of a light meter is described in Chapter 33.

Fig. 19-13. A spherical photometer being used to determine the intensity of a fluorescent tube.

Summary

Light is a form of electromagnetic radiation. When light travels from one spot to another, it acts as though it were a wave. When light is emitted by matter or absorbed by matter, it behaves as though it were a stream of particles. Light ordinarily travels in straight lines at a speed of about 186,000 miles per second.

An object is luminous if it is visible because of the light it emits. An object is illuminated if it is visible because of the light it reflects.

An object may reflect, absorb, or transmit the light which it receives. A substance that transmits light readily is said to be transparent. A substance that transmits light, but scatters it so that objects can not be distinguished, is said to be translucent. If a substance does not transmit light at all, it is said to be opaque.

The amount of light which a body receives is directly proportional to the intensity of the luminous object and inversely proportional to the square of the distance between the light source and the illuminated body.

Photometry deals with the measurement of the intensity of light. Intensity is measured in candles. The amount of illumination is measured in lumens per square foot or lumens per square meter. The Bunsen, Joly, and spherical photometers are most frequently used.

Terms to Define...

Absorption	Intensity	Penumbra
Artificial sources of light	Joly photometer	Ray
Beam	Light	Reflection
Bunsen photometer	Light meter	Shadow
Candle (unit)	Light waves vs. sound waves	Speed of light
Eclipse of the moon	Lumen	Spherical photometer
Eclipse of the sun	Luminous	The mile-long tube
Electromagnetic spectrum	Micron	Translucent
Focus	Natural sources of light	Transmission
Illuminated	Octagonal mirror	Transparent
Illumination	Opaque	Umbra

Questions

GROUP A

1. How do scientists explain the nature of light?

2. Arrange the following in order of their increasing wave length: visible light; infrared light; ultraviolet light; X rays; radio waves; cosmic rays.

3. Compare light and sound as to origin, transmitting media, length of wave, type of wave, speed of wave, and frequency of wave.

4. What is our most important source of natural light? What are our common sources of artificial light?

5. Distinguish between *luminous* and *illuminated* objects.

6. Define and illustrate the terms *transparent*, *translucent*, and *opaque* materials.

7. In what phase is the moon if a solar eclipse occurs? Explain.

8. In what phase is the moon if a lunar eclipse occurs? Explain.

GROUP B

9. In what unit do we measure the intensity of a light source? How is this unit defined?
10. In what unit do we measure illumination? How is this unit defined?
11. Why is it important to have a moderate level of illumination in a room in addition to the light concentrated on your work?
12. During the solar eclipse visible in the United States on June 30, 1954, a strip of land about 85 miles wide was in the moon's umbra, while a strip of land more than 4000 miles wide was in the moon's penumbra. Why was this?
13. By using Fig. 19-7, explain how Michelson determined the speed of light in air.

(In the Mathematics Refresher, refer to Sections 2, 8, 10, 11, and 16.)

GROUP A

1. The distance from the earth to the sun is about 92,500,000 miles. How long does it take for light from the sun to reach the earth?
2. What is the illumination on the page of a book 3 ft from a source whose intensity is 100 candles?
3. It is recommended that the illumination be 50 lumens per square foot for newspaper reading. How far from the paper should a 200-candle source be placed to provide this illumination?
4. What is the illumination 5 ft from a lamp whose intensity is 150 candles?
5. The amount of illumination thrown on a screen by two sources of light is the same when the distances from the lamps to the screen

are 3 m and 2 m respectively. If the intensity of the first lamp is 20 candles, what is the intensity of the second lamp?
6. A lamp, intensity 16 candles, is placed at the 0.0 cm mark on a meter stick. A lamp of unknown intensity is placed at the 100.0 cm mark. If a Bunsen photometer is equally illuminated when placed at the 60.0 cm mark, what is the intensity of the unknown lamp?
7. Two lamps, 30 candles and 20 candles respectively, are placed at opposite ends of a meter stick. Where must the screen of a photometer be placed so that both sides are equally illuminated?
8. The illumination on a screen located 3 ft from a source of light is 4 times as much as that on a second screen which is illuminated by the same source. The intensity of the source is 25 candles. How far is the second screen from the source?

GROUP B

9. If the intensity of a fluorescent lamp is 60 candles, at what distance does it provide an illumination of 10 lumens per square foot?
10. How far away is the nearest star if it takes 4.3 years for the light from the star to reach the earth?
11. A standard 40-candle lamp is placed at one end of a meter stick. A lamp of unknown intensity is placed at the other end. If the two sides of a photometer are equally illuminated when it is placed 70 cm from the standard lamp, what is the intensity of the unknown?
● **12.** A 100-watt lamp placed at one end of a meter stick and a 10-candle source placed at the other end equally illuminate a photometer which is 75 cm from the 100-watt lamp. How many candles per watt does the lamp supply?
● **13.** How many revolutions per second did Dr. Michelson's octagonal mirror make if light traveled 44 miles while the mirror made one-eighth of a revolution?

Things to Do

1. Use a light meter to determine the number of lumens per square foot illumination on the pupils' desks in your classroom. How does the illumination compare with the minimum of 30 lumens/ft² needed for school tasks?

2. Look up in an encyclopedia the story of Galileo's attempt to measure the speed of light. Also look up the method used by Roemer, a Danish astronomer. Report on your reading to the class.

Chapter 20

Reflection of Light

1. Several factors govern the reflection of light. *Reflection is the turning back of light waves from a surface.* The amount of light an object reflects depends upon the kind of material it is made of, how well its surface is polished, and the angle at which the light strikes its surface. Polished aluminum makes a better reflector than polished black plastic. We know that a piece of polished metal is a much better reflector than a piece of rough metal. The glare of the setting sun on the surface of water shows us that light is strongly reflected when the rays strike a surface at an oblique angle.

2. The laws of reflection. The reflection of light is similar to the reflec-

tion of sound or to the rebound of an elastic ball. The line *MN* in Fig. 20-1 represents the reflecting surface. *AD* is a ray of light incident upon the reflector at *D*. *DB* is the path of the reflected ray. *CD* is drawn perpen-

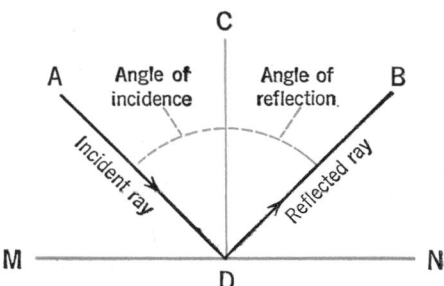

Fig. 20-1. The angle of reflection equals the angle of incidence.

Vocabulary

ANGLE OF INCIDENCE. The angle between the incident ray and the normal drawn to the point of reflection.

ANGLE OF REFLECTION. The angle between the reflected ray and the normal drawn to the point of reflection.

CONCAVE. Curved in away from the observer.

CONVEX. Curved out toward the observer.

FOCUS. A point at which light rays meet, or from which rays of light diverge.

MIRROR. A shiny surface which is used to form images by regular reflection of light.

NORMAL. A line drawn perpendicular to a line or to a plane.

REAL IMAGE. An image which is actually formed by rays of light.

REFLECTION. The turning back of light waves from a surface.

SPHERICAL ABERRATION (ab-er-*ay*-shun). Failure of rays from a single point source to be converged by a lens to form a single point image.

VIRTUAL IMAGE. Image which only appears to the eye to be formed by rays of light.

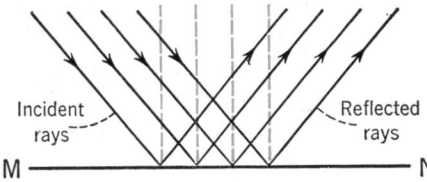

Incident rays

Reflected rays

M —————————————————— N

Fig. 20-2. Regular reflection of light.

dicular to the reflecting surface at the point of reflection, no matter whether the reflecting surface is plane or curved. The line *CD* is called a **normal**, since it is *a line drawn perpendicular to a line or plane.* The angle *ADC* is called the **angle of incidence**, *which is the angle between the incident ray and the normal drawn to the point of reflection.* The angle *BDC* is the **angle of reflection**, *or the angle between the reflected ray and the normal drawn to the point of reflection.*

By laboratory experiment it may be shown that *the angle of reflection is equal to the angle of incidence.* Furthermore, *the reflected ray lies in the same plane as the incident ray and the normal to the reflecting surface at the point of reflection.* These statements are called the LAWS OF REFLECTION.

3. What is regular reflection? Probably you have had the experience sometime or other of being the victim of someone using a small mirror to reflect sunlight into your eyes. The regular reflection of sunlight by a mirror produces a blinding glare. The rays from the sun are nearly parallel and have the same angle of incidence. They are therefore nearly parallel when reflected from the mirror. Fig. 20-2 shows the reflection of a beam of light from a polished plane surface.

4. What is diffused reflection? In Fig. 20-3 we see what happens to a beam of light which is incident upon an irregular surface. The laws of reflection hold true for each particular ray of light. But the normals to the surface are not parallel, and the light is scattered in all directions. Such scattering, or *diffusion,* of light is extremely important. If the sun's rays were not diffused by rough surfaces and by dust particles in the air, the corners of a room and the space under shade trees would be in almost total darkness. In front of the windows the glare would be dazzling.

5. How can we increase the diffusion of light? In order to avoid glare we often increase the diffusion of light by reflection or transmission.

(1) *By reflection.* Newspapers are printed on unglazed paper. They are easy on the eyes for reading because the rough surface diffuses the light. In order to have illustrations appear more clearly, books are often printed on semi-gloss paper. Semi-gloss paper is a compromise because illustrations, or half-tones, should be printed on full-gloss paper to be most effective. But words printed on full-gloss paper would be very difficult to read. Wall paper for living rooms and bedrooms is usually unglazed, so that the rough surface promotes diffusion. Glazed wall paper or high-gloss enamel paints are popular for bathrooms and kitch-

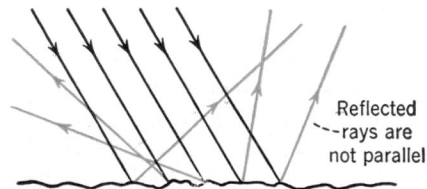

Reflected rays are not parallel

Fig. 20-3. Irregular reflection promotes the diffusion of light.

Fig. 20-4. Glass blocks promote the diffusion of transmitted light into this attractive living room.

ens mainly because they are washable. (2) *By transmission.* Practically all electric light bulbs are now frosted on the inside to promote diffusion and prevent glare. Also, some lamps are made for use in unshaded fixtures. These have such a shape and color that their direct rays do not produce glare. Lampshades of cloth and semi-transparent paper soften the light by increasing diffusion. Glass blocks and roughened plate glass are frequently used in windows to admit light and yet prevent glare.

6. What is a mirror? *Any highly polished surface which can be used to form images by the regular reflection of light may be called a* **mirror.** The most frequently used mirrors are those which consist of *plane* pieces of plate glass which are silvered on one surface

so that they reflect a large amount of light. The efficiency of an ordinary silvered mirror is about 70%.

For special purposes, *curved* mirrors are used. Such curved surfaces may form part of a sphere, a cone, or a cylinder. Curved mirrors are either *concave* or *convex.* When the outside surface of a sphere is the reflecting surface, the mirror is **convex,** *which means curved outward toward the observer.* The inside of a hollow sphere forms a mirror which is **concave,** or *curved inward away from the observer.*

7. There are two kinds of images. Rays of light are sometimes reflected from a curved mirror in such a manner that they meet in front of the mirror to form an image of the object from which the light comes. Such a picture or visual counterpart of the object may

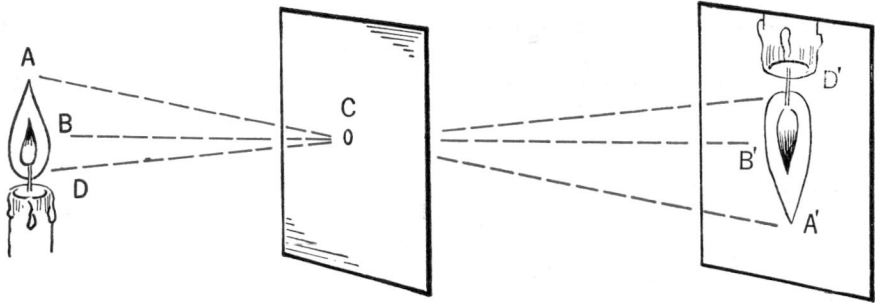

Fig. 20-5. Tiny openings may be used to form images. Note that the image here is inverted.

be thrown upon a screen. *An image of this kind, which is formed by actual rays of light, is called a **real image**. Real images are always inverted, and they may be either larger or smaller than the object.*

When you look at yourself in a plane mirror, the rays of light appear to come from behind the mirror. Of course, we know that the rays of light are really reflected from the surface of the mirror. But they seem to meet behind the mirror to form the image. *An image of this kind, which only appears to the eye to be formed by rays of light, is called a **virtual image**.* Of course, such an image can not be thrown upon a screen. *Virtual images are always erect. They, too, may be enlarged or reduced in size.*

8. Images may be formed through small openings. In a darkened room on the sunny side of the house, let us punch a pinhole through a black shade which covers the window. If we hold a piece of white paper a foot or more from the opening, a small image of the sun will be produced on it. In a dark room we can also form an excellent image of a candle flame on a white screen by letting the rays from the candle pass through a small opening,

or aperture. See Fig. 20-5. Since light travels in straight lines, a ray of light from A, the tip of the candle, will pass through the opening to form an image of the tip of the flame at A'. From D a ray of light will fall upon the screen at D'. Rays from B form an image at B'. If the opening is very small, the image will be sharp and well-defined, although not very bright. When we increase the size of the opening, the image becomes brighter, but less distinct. The pinhole camera is an application of this method of forming images.

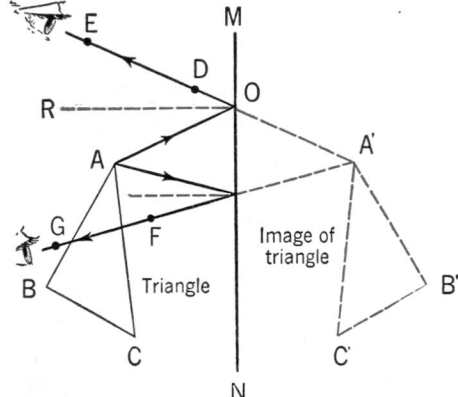

Fig. 20-6. The method of constructing the image of an object as formed by a plane mirror.

SAMPLE PROBLEM

An object 6 ft tall is 8 ft from an aperture which forms an image on a screen placed 4 inches from the opening. What is the size of the image?

SOLUTION

We have the equation, size of object : size of image = object distance : image distance.

Changing all the dimensions to inches and substituting in this equation, 72 in : X = 96 in : 4 in.

Solving, X = 3 in, the size of the image.

In Fig. 20-5, the triangles ABC and $A'B'C$ are similar. Therefore, $AB : A'B' = BC : B'C$. But, AB equals one-half the size of the object, and $A'B'$ equals one-half the size of the image. BC is the distance of the object from the aperture, and $B'C$ equals the distance of the image from the aperture. Therefore, we see that *the relative sizes of the object and image are proportional to their relative dis-*

Fig. 20-7. A room showing the decorative use of mirrors. The mirrors here tend to make the room look larger.

tances from the opening. If we increase the distance of the object from the aperture, we reduce the size of the image. But moving the screen farther from the opening will increase the size of the image. See problem above.

9. The images formed by plane mirrors. When you look at yourself in a plane mirror, you find that your image is neither enlarged nor reduced. It is erect; it is virtual, since the rays seem to come from behind the mirror; and it is as far behind the mirror as you are in front of it. Because the image is formed on the extension of the normal behind the mirror, it will be reversed. Your right hand will appear as the left hand of your image, and vice versa.

By experiment it is possible to construct the image of an object as it is formed by a plane mirror. Let us use for the object a triangle, *ABC*, drawn upon a sheet of paper. See Fig. 20-6. The mirror is placed on the line *MN*. A pin is then placed at the vertex *A* of the triangle. By looking at the image of this pin in the mirror, you can arrange two pins, *E* and *D*, in line with the image of the pin at *A* as seen in the mirror. Since light travels in straight lines, the image of the pin will

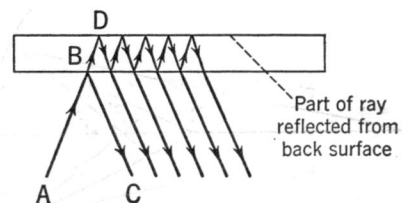

Fig. 20-8. Light is reflected from both the front and rear surfaces of a mirror.

be on the line *ED* produced or extended behind the mirror. In the same manner we may set two other pins *G* and *F,* in line with the image of the pin at *A.* The image is also on this line produced. Since *A',* the point of intersection of the two sight lines, is the only point common to both lines, the image of *A* must be at the point *A'.* By the same method, we may locate the image of the point *B* at *B',* and of the point *C* at *C'.* In all these cases *the image is found to be as far behind the mirror as the object is in front.* By joining the points and measuring the lines *A'C', A'B',* and *C'B',* we prove that *the image is the same size as the object.*

This method of constructing images verifies the laws of reflection of light. As we look along *ED,* we see the ray of light coming from *A.* It is incident upon the mirror along line *AO.* From point *O* it is reflected along *ED.* When we erect a perpendicular or normal to the mirror at *O,* we bisect the angle *AOE.* The angle *EOR,* which is the angle of reflection, is equal to the angle of incidence *AOR.* The incident ray *AO,* the reflected ray *OE,* and the normal *OR* all lie in the same plane.

10. The uses of plane mirrors. From earliest times, mirrors have been used by people in order to see themselves. We use them in our homes also

for their decorative effect. Large mirrors give an illusion of depth to small rooms. Automobiles, trucks and busses are equipped with side and rearview mirrors to enable the operator to see the other vehicles around him.

11. What is multiple reflection? Sound waves bound and rebound between parallel cliffs or walls and produce echoes and re-echoes. In a similar fashion, light waves reflect back and forth between parallel mirrors, or mirrors set at an acute angle, and form multiple images. The image formed in one mirror acts as the object which forms an image in the second mirror. Another image of this image may then be formed. Because some light is absorbed each time, each succeeding image is fainter than the one producing it.

A thick plate-glass mirror also shows multiple reflection because both surfaces are reflectors. Fig. 20-8 shows how the ray of light *AB* is partially reflected at *B,* forming the reflected ray *BC.* The unreflected part of ray *AB* passes through the glass to *D,* the back of the mirror, where it is reflected by the silvered surface. The path this ray may take is shown by the arrowheads. When it reaches the

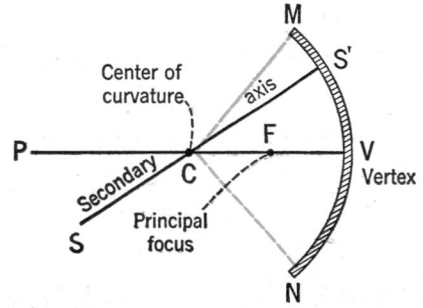

Fig. 20-9. A diagram used in defining terms used with curved mirrors.

front surface, it is divided. Part of the ray enters the air and part is reflected to the silvered surface again. In such a mirror a series of images of a bright object may be seen.

12. Terms used with curved mirrors. Before we can understand how images are formed by curved mirrors, we must define several terms that we are going to use. We first must assume that the curved mirror we are going to use is part of the surface of a sphere. On paper we represent the mirror by the arc of a circle. Fig. 20-9 will help us understand the following definitions.

(1) The *center of curvature, C,* is the center of the sphere of which the mirror forms a part.

(2) The *aperture* is the angular portion, *MCN,* of the sphere that is included by the mirror. Generally, only a few degrees of the total surface are used as the reflecting surface.

(3) The *vertex, V,* is the center of the mirror itself.

(4) The *principal axis* is the line *PV* drawn through the center of curvature and the vertex.

(5) Any other line drawn through the center of curvature, *SS'* for example, is called a *secondary axis.*

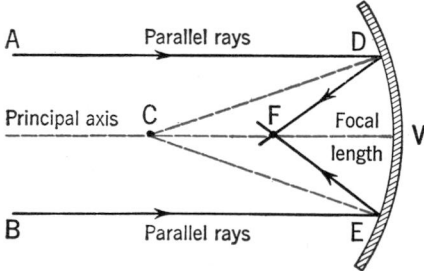

Fig. 20-10. Parallel rays of light are reflected by a concave mirror and meet at the principal focus.

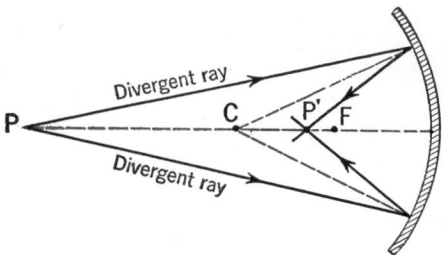

Fig. 20-11. The reflection of divergent rays by a concave mirror.

(6) The *normal* to the surface of a concave mirror is the radius drawn from the point of incidence. (The radius is perpendicular to the tangent to the surface drawn through the point of incidence.) In a convex mirror, the normal is the radius produced; that is, extended through the mirror.

13. How are light rays focused? Let us draw two lines *AD* and *BE* to represent rays of light parallel to the principal axis. They are both incident upon a concave mirror as shown in Fig. 20-10. From the points of incidence, we draw the normals *CD* and *CE.* By construction, we make the angles of reflection *CDF* and *CEF* exactly equal to the angles of incidence *ADC* and *BEC,* respectively. When we do this we find that these parallel rays are reflected from the mirror to meet at the point *F. A point such as this, where rays meet, is called a* **focus.** *With a convex mirror, the reflected rays are divergent,* but they seem to meet at a point behind the mirror. Such a point is called a *virtual focus.* If the aperture of the mirror is small, rays of light parallel to the principal axis will meet or appear to meet at the *principal focus.* The principal focus is a point *halfway between the center of curvature and the vertex.* The dis-

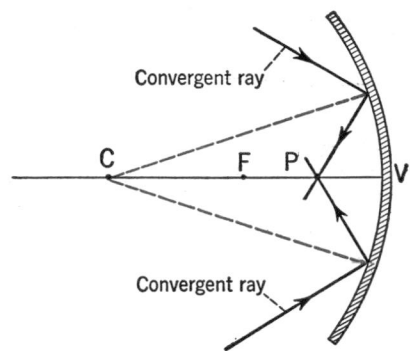

Fig. 20-12. The reflection of convergent rays by a concave mirror.

tance *FV* from the principal focus to the vertex is called the *focal length of the mirror.*

Diverging rays coming from a point *P* on the principal axis will be brought to a focus on the principal axis, but the focus will be nearer to the center of curvature than it is to the mirror. See Fig. 20-11. Converging rays are also focused by curved mirrors. Fig. 20-12 shows an example where such converging rays are focused upon the principal axis between the vertex and the principal focus.

14. Constructing the image of a point in a spherical mirror. Let us look at Fig. 20-13. We wish to find the image of point *P* that is formed by a concave mirror. First we draw the principal axis. Now, because light is given off in all directions from point *P*, we may draw *any two lines* from *P* to represent rays of light which fall upon the mirror. Then we find where they intersect after reflection from the mirror. In all of our construction work we must make the angles of incidence and reflection equal. We will find the construction easier if we select the secondary axis for *one line*. A ray following this path is incident upon the

mirror at an angle of 90° and will be reflected directly back upon itself. So we draw the secondary axis *PS* from *P* to the mirror. Then the image of the point *P* must lie at some point on the line *PS*. To find its exact position, we draw another line from *P*. For this other line representing a ray of light from *P*, we choose the line *PB*, which is parallel to the principal axis. We choose this line because we know that all rays parallel to the principal axis are reflected through the principal focus, *F*. From the point of incidence of this ray upon the mirror at *B*, it is reflected back through *F*. The point *P'*, where this reflected ray crosses secondary axis, must be the image of point *P*. *P'* is the only point common to the reflections of the two rays of light we traced from *P* to the mirror. To prove that *PB* passes through *F* when reflected, we may draw the normal *BC*, and show that the angle of incidence *PBC* equals the angle of reflection *CBF*.

15. How are images formed by concave mirrors? We may construct the image of an object that is formed by a concave mirror by locating the images of enough different points. If the object is an arrow, we can locate the entire image by finding the posi-

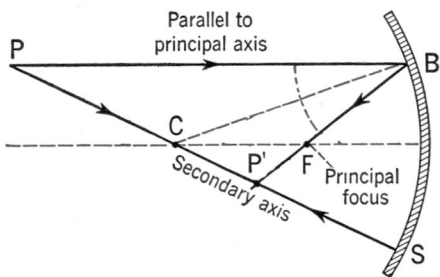

Fig. 20-13. The formation of the image of a point in a concave mirror.

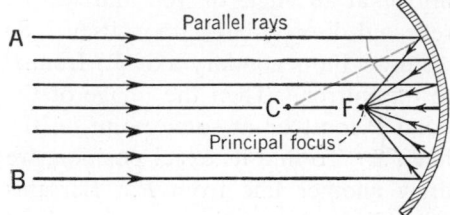

Fig. 20-14. The image formed when parallel rays of light are reflected by a concave mirror is a point at the principal focus.

tions of the image of the head and the image of the tail of the arrow.

Case 1. Object at an infinite distance. If we could have an object at an infinite distance from the mirror, all the incident rays would be parallel. All of them would be reflected back to the principal focus, as shown in Fig. 20-14. We therefore conclude that *the image formed by a concave mirror when an object is at an infinite distance is a point at the principal focus.*

Case 2. Object at a measurable distance beyond the center of curvature. This case is illustrated in Fig. 20-15. We wish to locate the image of the arrow *AB*. We find the image of *A* by the method we learned in Section 14.

We draw the secondary axis *AE* and the parallel ray *AD*. *AD* is reflected back through *F* to form the image of *A* at the point *A'*. In the same fashion we locate the image of *B* at the point *B'*. The construction lines used to locate the image of *A* are all numbered 1; those used to locate the image of *B* are numbered 2. From the diagram, we see that *the image in this case is real, inverted, smaller than the object, and is formed between the center of curvature and the principal focus.* The nearer the object approaches the center of curvature, the larger the image becomes.

Case 3. Object at the center of curvature. When the object is at the center of curvature, as shown in Fig. 20-16, we find that the image of *A* is formed at *A'*, a point coincident with *B*. The image of *B* is at *B'*, a point coincident with *A*. To show the secondary axes in this case, we would need to make the aperture of the mirror 180°. *When the object is at the center of curvature, the image is real, inverted, the same size as the object, and located at the center of curvature.*

Case 4. Object between the center of curvature and principal focus. This

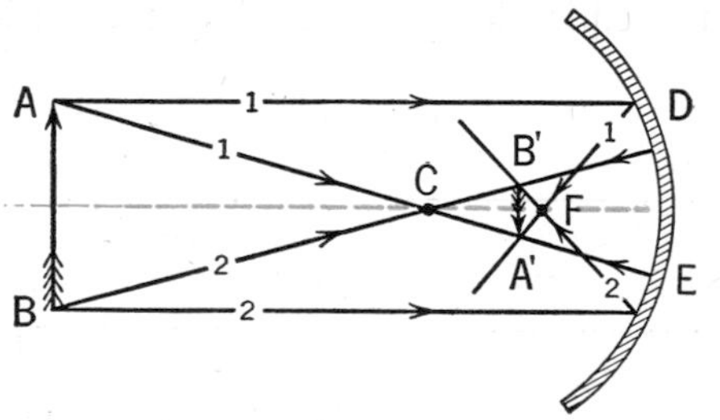

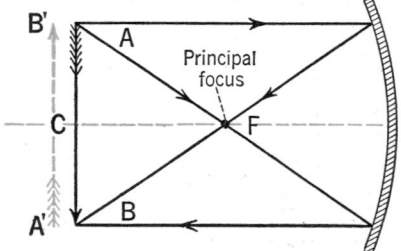

Fig. 20-15. When the object is beyond the center of curvature, a smaller, inverted, real image is formed between the center of curvature and the principal focus on the same side of the mirror.

Fig. 20-16. When the object is at the center of curvature, an inverted, real image, the same size as the object, is formed at the center of curvature on the same side of the mirror.

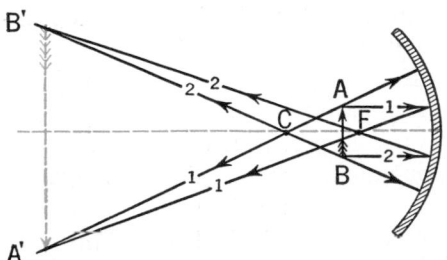

Fig. 20-17. When the object is between the center of curvature and the principal focus, a larger, inverted, real image is formed beyond the center of curvature on the same side of the mirror.

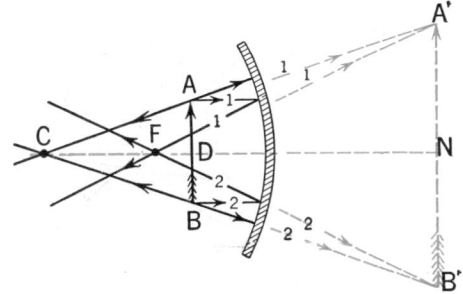

Fig. 20-19. When the object is between the principal focus and the mirror, a larger, erect, virtual image is formed behind the mirror.

case is the converse of Case 2. As shown in Fig. 20-17, we use the same method of finding the image that we have used before. We observe that in this case *the image formed is real, inverted, larger than the object, and formed beyond the center of curvature.* The nearer the object approaches the principal focus, the larger the image becomes.

Case 5. Object at principal focus. This case is the converse of Case 1. When we try to construct the image as in other cases, we find that the rays that are reflected from the mirror are parallel. See Fig. 20-18. When the object is at the principal focus, no image is formed.

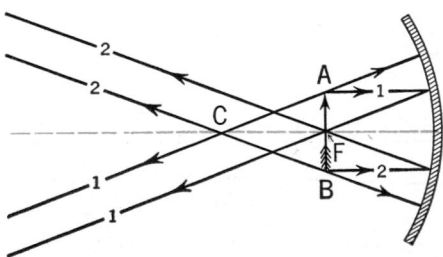

Fig. 20-18. The rays of light from an object at the principal focus are reflected by the mirror parallel to one another. No image is formed.

Case 6. Object between principal focus and mirror. When we attempt to construct the image as we did in other cases, we find that the reflected rays which leave the mirror are *divergent.* They can never meet to form a real image. They *appear to meet behind the mirror,* however, to form a virtual image, as shown in Fig. 20-19. In this case, *the image is virtual, erect, enlarged, and situated behind the mirror.*

16. How are images formed by convex mirrors? When we look into a convex mirror of the type used as an outside rear view mirror on some trucks, we see a small, erect image of reduced size. The diagram shown in Fig. 20-20 may be used to show how such an image is formed. *AB* represents the object. The secondary axes are the *radii produced.* The parallel rays are reflected from the surface of the mirror and made divergent. When these reflected rays are extended behind the mirror, they *appear* to meet at the principal focus. With a convex mirror, *all images formed are virtual, erect, smaller than the object, and located between the mirror and the principal focus.* The size of the image is

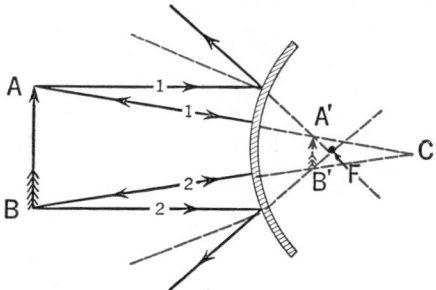

Fig. 20-20. The only image which can be formed by a convex mirror is smaller than the object, erect, and virtual.

increased by bringing the object closer to the mirror, but it can never become as large as the object itself.

17. Uses of curved mirrors. Curved mirrors are used in amusement parks to form fantastic images. The convex rear view mirror sometimes used by automobile and truck drivers gives a wide field of vision. Unfortunately, a driver can not judge the distance of a car approaching from the rear by the size or position of the image in the mirror. Some drivers use both a convex and a plane mirror, because in a plane mirror the image seems to be as far behind the mirror as the object is in front of the mirror.

Concave mirrors are used as reflectors of light. They are also used for forming images. We may use Cases 1 and 3 to find the focal length of a concave mirror. Since the focal length is just half the radius, we may double the focal length to find the radius of curvature. We may use Cases 2 and 4 to form images on a screen. Case 2 gives a bright image of reduced size, while Case 4 gives an enlarged image. When an enlarged image is formed, it always loses brightness. The concave shaving mirror is an application of Case 6. Your dentist uses a small mirror of this type when examining your teeth.

If we place an electric lamp at the principal focus of a concave mirror, its rays will be reflected from the mirror along almost parallel lines. When the lamp is placed a little nearer the mirror than the principal focus, the rays will be slightly divergent, as shown in Fig. 20-21. Such a reflector is used in some types of lanterns and in the headlights of locomotives. Searchlights and spotlights may contain a concave mirror, but lenses are generally used with these devices to concentrate the light rays on a distant object.

18. What is spherical aberration? If we use a mirror of *large aperture,* the parallel rays of light which strike the mirror near its edge are not reflected through the principal focus. They are focused at a point nearer the mirror, as shown in Fig. 20-22. Only those parallel rays which are incident upon the mirror near its vertex are reflected to the principal focus. *The failure of rays from a single point to be converged by a lens to form a single point image is called* **spherical aberration** (ab-er-*ay*-shun). Spherical aberration causes the distorted images produced by spherical mirrors of large aperture.

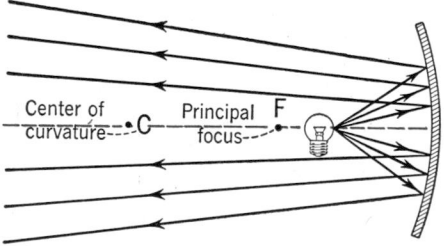

Fig. 20-21. In order to produce a slightly divergent beam of light, the lamp is placed a little nearer a concave mirror than its principal focus.

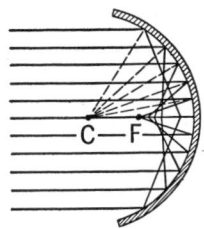

Rays do not all
focus at one point

Fig. 20-22. The parallel rays of light which are reflected from near the edge of a concave mirror are not reflected exactly through the principal focus because of spherical aberration.

There are several ways in which we may reduce spherical aberration. First, if the aperture of the mirror can be kept as small as 10° or 12°, the distortion of the image is negligible. Second, a mirror of larger aperture may be used to collect more light rays. But a ring-shaped diaphragm of some opaque material must be used with it to cut off those rays near the edge which would cause distortion. A third method of reducing spherical aberration calls for the use of a mirror whose surface is not spherical, but has the curve of a parabola. Fig. 20-23 shows how parallel rays are all focused at a point by such a mirror. Automobile headlights are generally fitted with parabolic reflectors. Large reflecting telescopes also use parabolic reflectors to collect the light rays and focus them.

19. How do the relative sizes of the object and image compare? In Section 8 we found that the relative size of the object and the image depended upon their respective distances from the aperture. We used similar triangles to prove this. In the same manner, we can prove that the sizes of the object and the image formed by a curved mirror depend upon their relative distances from the center of curvature. See Figs. 20-15, 20-16, 20-17, 20-19, and 20-20. For mirrors of small aperture, it is possible to show that *the relative sizes of the object and image depend on their respective distances from the mirror.* We may state this as a proportion — size

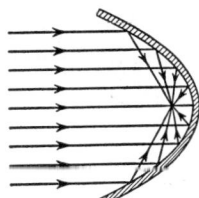

Rays all meet
at a point

Fig. 20-23. There is no aberration when a parabolic mirror is used.

SAMPLE PROBLEM

An object 8 in high is placed 3 ft from a concave mirror. The image is formed on a screen 18 in from the mirror. How high is the image?

SOLUTION

Since the image distance is given in inches, we must first convert the object distance from 3 ft to 36 in.

Then we substitute in the formula, $S_o : S_i = D_o : D_i$. $8 : S_i = 36 : 18$.

Solving, $S_i = 4$ in, the height of the image.

of object (S_o) : size of image (S_i) = distance of the object from the mirror (D_o) : distance of image from the mirror (D_i). Or,

$$S_o : S_i = D_o : D_i.$$

Of course, when an object is magnified or reduced in size, both the length and breadth are changed proportionally. See the Sample Problem, page 419.

20. The distance of the object and image in terms of the focal length. There is a definite mathematical relationship between the distance of the object, the distance of the image, and the focal length of a curved mirror. While its derivation is beyond the scope of secondary school work, we can still use the formula for solving problems dealing with curved mirrors. If we use D_o to represent the distance of the object from the mirror, D_i to represent the distance of the image from the mirror, and f to represent the focal length, then,

$$\frac{1}{D_o} + \frac{1}{D_i} = \frac{1}{f}.$$

This formula may be used in all cases utilizing concave mirrors. When D_i is a negative quantity, the image is virtual.

For convex mirrors, both $\frac{1}{D_i}$ and $\frac{1}{f}$ are negative.

Fig. 20-24. A cutaway view of a sealed-beam automobile headlight showing the parabolic reflector.

SAMPLE PROBLEM

An object is 6 ft from a mirror whose focal length is 8 in. Find the distance from the mirror at which the image is formed.

SOLUTION

We substitute the data given in the problem in the formula $\frac{1}{D_o} + \frac{1}{D_i} = \frac{1}{f}$. (Note that we must convert 6 ft to 72 in, so that all the distances given in the problem will be in inches.) $\frac{1}{72} + \frac{1}{D_i} = \frac{1}{8}$.

In order to clear fractions, we multiply each term by the lowest common multiple of the denominators, $72D_i$.

This gives $D_i + 72 = 9D_i$. $8D_i = 72$. $D_i = 9$ in, the distance from the mirror at which the image is formed.

Summary

The amount of light reflected from an object depends upon the kind of material of which it is made, how well its surface is polished, and the angle at which the light strikes its surface. The angle of reflection equals the angle of incidence. These angles both lie in the same plane.

Images are real or virtual. A real image is inverted; it can be thrown upon a screen. Virtual images are erect; they can not be thrown upon a screen.

Images formed by plane mirrors are erect, virtual, the same size as the object, and as far behind the mirror as the object is in front.

A focus is a point where rays of light meet or from which rays of light diverge. Rays parallel to the principal axis are reflected to a point on the principal axis, midway between the center of curvature and the vertex. This point is the principal focus. Its distance from the vertex is the principal focal length. It equals half the radius of curvature of a concave mirror.

The sizes of the object and image and their distances from the mirror are given by the formula $S_o : S_i = D_o : D_i$. The formula which relates object distance, image distance, and focal length, is $\dfrac{1}{D_o} + \dfrac{1}{D_i} = \dfrac{1}{f}$.

Terms to Define...

Angle of incidence	Image in convex mirror	Real Image
Angle of reflection	Image in plane mirror	Reflection
Aperture	Inverted	Regular reflection
Center of curvature	Laws of reflection	Secondary axis
Concave mirror	Mirror	Size of object vs. size of image
Convex mirror	Multiple reflection	
Diffused reflection	Normal	Spherical aberration
Erect	Plane mirror	Vertex
Focal length	Principal axis	Virtual focus
Image in concave mirror	Principal focus	Virtual image

Questions

GROUP A

1. What three factors determine the amount of light an object will reflect?
2. What are the two laws of reflection?

3. When you look in a plane mirror, do you see yourself as others see you? Why?
4. Draw a diagram to illustrate the following: center of curvature; vertex; principal axis.
5. Which mirror produces a real image?
6. In what three ways may spherical aberration in mirrors be reduced?

GROUP B

7. Suppose we paint on a mirror with white paint the word "paint." Now, when we place

this mirror in a beam of sunlight, the reflection of the sunlight on a smooth wall consists of a bright area in which the letters of the word "paint" appear dark. Why?

8. What kind of trick mirror produces a short, fattened image? a tall, thin image?

9. What kinds of mirrors could be used and where should the object be placed to produce (1) an enlarged real image? (2) a small real image? (3) a real image the same size as the object? (4) an enlarged virtual image? (5) a small virtual image?

10. Draw a ray diagram to show the formation of an image by a concave mirror when the object is at a measurable distance outside the center of curvature. What are the characteristics of the image (1) on the same or the opposite side of the mirror from the object? (2) closer to the mirror or farther from the mirror than the object? (3) erect or inverted? (4) smaller than the object or larger than the object? (5) real or virtual?

11. Draw a ray diagram to show the formation of an image by a concave mirror when the object is between the principal focus and the center of curvature. What are the characteristics of the image? See Question 10.

12. Draw the ray diagram which shows the formation of an image by a convex mirror. What are the characteristics of this image? See Question 10.

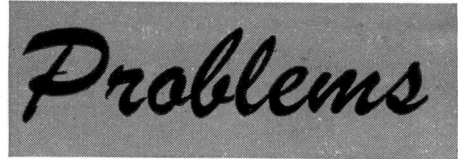

(In the Mathematics Refresher, refer to Sections 8, 9, 10, and 16.)

GROUP A

1. A concave mirror has a focal length of 10 cm. What is its radius of curvature?

2. If the radius of curvature of a curved mirror is 8 in, what is its focal length?

3. While you are looking at the image of your feet in a plane vertical mirror, you see a scratch in the glass of the mirror. How far is the scratch from the floor? Assume that you are 5 ft 8 in tall.

4. A boy 5 ft tall stands 20 ft from the opening of a small pinhole camera. If the camera is 6 in deep, how large is the boy's image?

5. The light from a distant star is collected by a concave mirror. If the radius of curvature of the mirror is 5 ft, how far from the mirror is the image formed?

6. An object is placed 25 cm from a concave mirror whose focal length is 5 cm. Where will the image be located?

7. An object 10 in high is located 36 in from a concave mirror. If the focal length of the mirror is 6 in, where is the image located and how large is it?

8. An object placed 21 in from a spherical concave mirror gives a real image 14 in from the mirror. What is the radius of curvature of the mirror? If the image is 12 in tall, what is the height of the object?

GROUP B

9. An object and its image in a concave mirror are the same size when the object is 15 in from the mirror. What is the focal length of the mirror?

10. An object is placed 5 cm from a concave mirror whose focal length is 15 cm. Where is the image located? If the object is 2 cm high, what is the size of the image?

● **11.** A man 6 ft tall stands in front of a mirror. What is the smallest vertical mirror that will allow him to see his full image? If the mirror makes an angle of 30° from the vertical toward him, what must be the minimum length?

● **12.** An object 2 in tall stands at the 0.0 cm mark on a meter stick. If a convex mirror of 25 cm focal length is placed at the 50.0 cm mark, where is the image and how tall is it?

───────── *Things to Do* ─────────

1. Observe the changes in your image as you walk toward a large concave mirror. Do the same with a large convex mirror.

2. Construct a model periscope, using two pieces of plane mirror for the reflecting surface.

3. Find out your state's regulations concerning the adjustment of automobile headlights. How must they be adjusted? How often?

Chapter 21

Refraction of Light

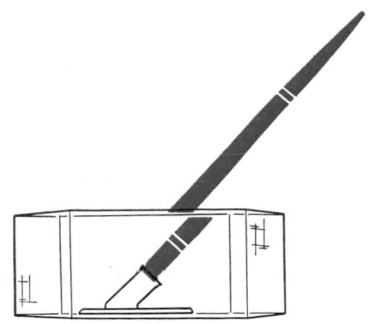

1. REFRACTION OF LIGHT

1. The refraction of light. In shooting at a target with a rifle, we make use of the fact that light travels in straight lines. We line up the bull's-eye with the two sights on the rifle. However, if we use the same procedure in shooting at a fish swimming beneath the surface of the water, we would very likely miss. The fish just isn't where he appears to be. Light travels in straight lines only when the medium through which it travels is of the *same optical density* throughout. **Optical density** *is a property of a transparent substance which is a measure of the speed of light through the substance.* Light rays are *bent out of their course* as they pass from water to air, or from air to water. *The bending of light rays as they pass obliquely from one medium into another of different optical density is called* **refraction.** Because of refraction, fish appear higher in the water than they really are. Consequently, when we aim a rifle at the spot where the fish appears to be and fire, the shot passes harmlessly over it. See Fig. 21-1.

A stick or a teaspoon placed in a tumbler of water appears to be bent or broken at the surface. Suppose we let *MN* of Fig. 21-2 represent the surface of a body of water. *AO* represents the path of a ray of light traveling

---

Vocabulary

ANGLE OF REFRACTION. The angle between the refracted ray and the normal drawn to the point of refraction.

CRITICAL ANGLE. That angle of incidence at which the refracted ray makes an angle of 90° with the normal.

INDEX OF REFRACTION. The ratio of the speed of light in a vacuum to its speed in a given substance; the ratio of the sine of the angle of incidence to the sine of the angle of refraction.

LENS. A portion of a transparent substance bounded by two polished, non-parallel, curved surfaces, or by one polished plane and one polished curved surface.

OPTICAL DENSITY. A property of a transparent substance related to the speed of light through it. Light travels more slowly through media of higher optical density.

REFRACTION. The bending of light rays as they pass from one medium into another of different optical density.

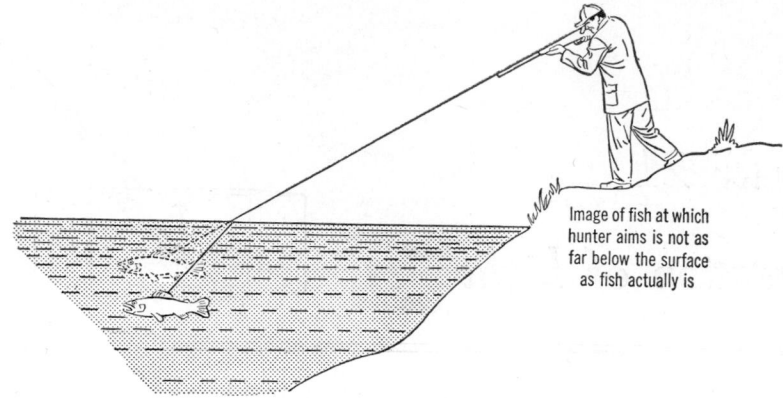

Image of fish at which
hunter aims is not as
far below the surface
as fish actually is

Fig. 21-1. The bending of light as it leaves the water causes us to see the fish higher in the water than it actually is.

through the air and striking the water at *O*. Some of the light will be reflected along the path *OE*. But the light entering the water, instead of continuing along *OF* in a straight line, is bent as it passes from air into water. It actually takes the path *OB*.

The incident ray *AO* makes the angle *AOC* with the normal. This angle is called the *angle of incidence*. The *refracted ray OB* makes the angle *DOB*

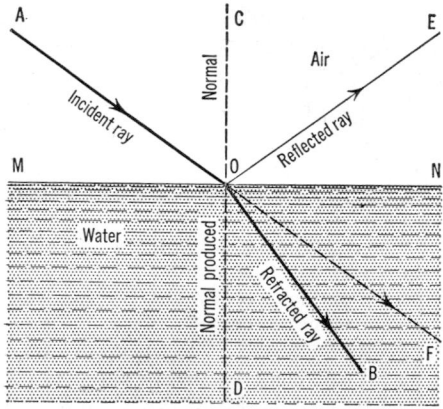

Fig. 21-2. When light strikes water at an acute angle, some of it is reflected. That which enters the water is bent out of its course, or refracted.

with the normal produced. *This angle between the refracted ray and the normal drawn to the point of refraction* is called the **angle of refraction.** The angle *BOF* is called the *angle of deviation*. A ray of light passing obliquely from one medium into another of different optical density is refracted. If the ray of light traveling through the first medium strikes the second medium *at right angles, or along the normal, the ray of light is not refracted at all.*

2. The variation of the speed of light in different media causes refraction. Suppose you are driving in your automobile along a straight, level road. Suddenly the right front wheel of the car accidentally slips off the hard pavement onto the shoulder. The car swerves to the right because the increased friction of the soft earth for the tire retards the right front wheel. Notice how the slower speed of the right side of the car alters the direction in which the car moves.

A column of men is marching five abreast along a hard road. The position of their successive footsteps is shown in Fig. 21-3. The line of march,

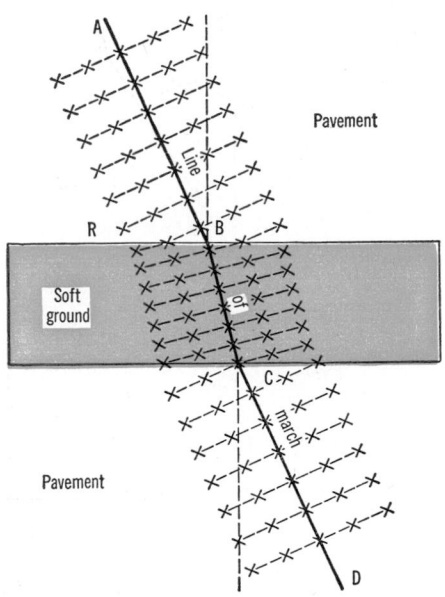

Fig. 21-3. The refraction of light may be likened to a column of men marching over pavement and soft ground.

AB, carries them over a strip of marshy ground where their speed is retarded. The man at *R* enters the marshland first, and is the first to be retarded. Because it is more difficult to move over the soggy ground, this man must take shorter steps in order to keep up the cadence. Meanwhile, the other men keep up their original speed until they enter the marshy ground, and the line of march now takes the direction *BC*. In the marshy ground all the men are equally retarded. Their steps are uniformly shorter than they were on hard ground. Finally the man *R* reaches harder ground, and he can step out with his original speed again. The line of march now takes the direction *CD*. You will observe that as the speed decreases, the line bends *toward* the perpendicular, or normal. An increase in speed on entering a new medium causes the line to bend *away*

from the normal. If the line of march were along the perpendicular, all the men would enter the marshy land at once. Their speed would be cut down simultaneously, and the line of march would not be bent.

Light travels more slowly in water than it does in air. Consequently, a ray of light from the air striking the surface of water behaves like the column of men marching into marshy ground. The edge of the ray which first strikes the water is the first to be retarded. The ray is therefore bent out of its course. Bending toward the normal occurs when the light enters a medium of greater optical density, in which the speed is retarded. The bending occurs in the opposite direction if the speed of light is greater in the new medium. Light rays incident upon the medium at an angle of 90° are all retarded or accelerated equally. Consequently, in such cases there is no bending.

3. The index of refraction. We learned in Chapter 19 that the speed of light in a vacuum is approximately 186,000 miles per second. The speed of light in water is almost 140,000 miles per second, just about $\frac{3}{4}$ as fast as in a vacuum. The speed of light in ordinary glass is about 124,000 miles per second. This is about $\frac{2}{3}$ the speed of light in a vacuum. *The ratio of the speed of light in a vacuum to its speed in another substance is called the* **index of refraction** *for that substance.* For example,

index of refraction (glass) =

$$\frac{\text{speed of light in vacuum}}{\text{speed of light in glass}}.$$

The value for glass is $\frac{3}{2}$, or 1.5. Since the speed of light in water is only three-fourths as great as in a vacuum, the index of refraction of water is $\frac{4}{3}$, or 1.333. The index of refraction of a few common substances is given in Table 16, Appendix B.

The speed of light in air is only slightly different from the speed of light in a vacuum. Therefore, without much error, we can use the index of refraction for cases where light travels *from air* into another medium.

★ The index of refraction is also defined as the ratio of the sine of the angle of incidence to the sine of the angle of refraction. If we let μ represent the index of refraction, θ_i (theta sub i) represent the angle of incidence, and θ_r represent the angle of refraction,

$$\mu = \frac{\sin \theta_i}{\sin \theta_r}.$$

We shall use Fig. 21-4 to define the sine of an angle. In the right triangle *ABC,* the sine of the angle *BAC* is defined as the ratio of the length of side *a,* opposite the angle *BAC,* to the hypotenuse, *c.* Enlarging the triangle without changing the size of the angle *BAC* does not affect this ratio, since the quotient of a'/c' equals the quotient a/c. (Triangles *ABC* and *AB'C'* are similar. Therefore, corresponding

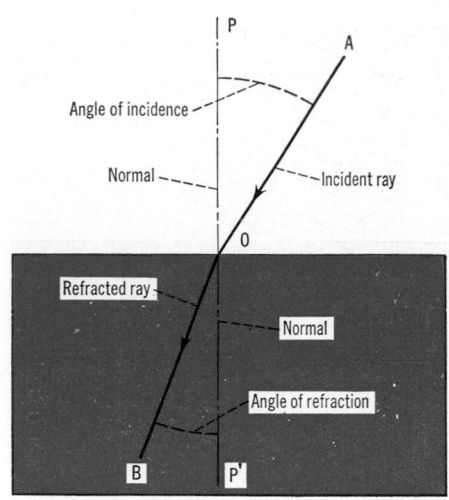

Fig. 21-5. The index of refraction equals the sine of the angle of incidence divided by the sine of the angle of refraction.

sides are proportional.) The sines for the angles from 0° to 90° are given in Table 18, Appendix B.

★ In Fig. 21-5, the line *AO* represents a ray of light traveling through the air and incident upon a glass plate at *O.* This ray is refracted as it enters the glass and moves along the path *OB.* To find the index of refraction, we first draw the normals *OP* and *OP'.* The index of refraction between the air and the glass equals the sine of the angle *AOP,* the angle of incidence, divided by the sine of the angle *BOP',* which is the angle of refraction.

4. How is the index of refraction of a substance used? The index of refraction of a pure, transparent substance is a constant quantity which is a definite physical property of the substance. Consequently, we can identify substances by measuring their index of refraction. We also can check their purity by this method. An instrument called a *refractometer* (ree-frak-*tom-*

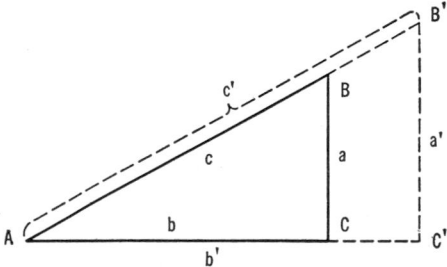

Fig. 21-4. The sine of an angle is the ratio of the length of the side opposite the angle to the length of the hypotenuse.

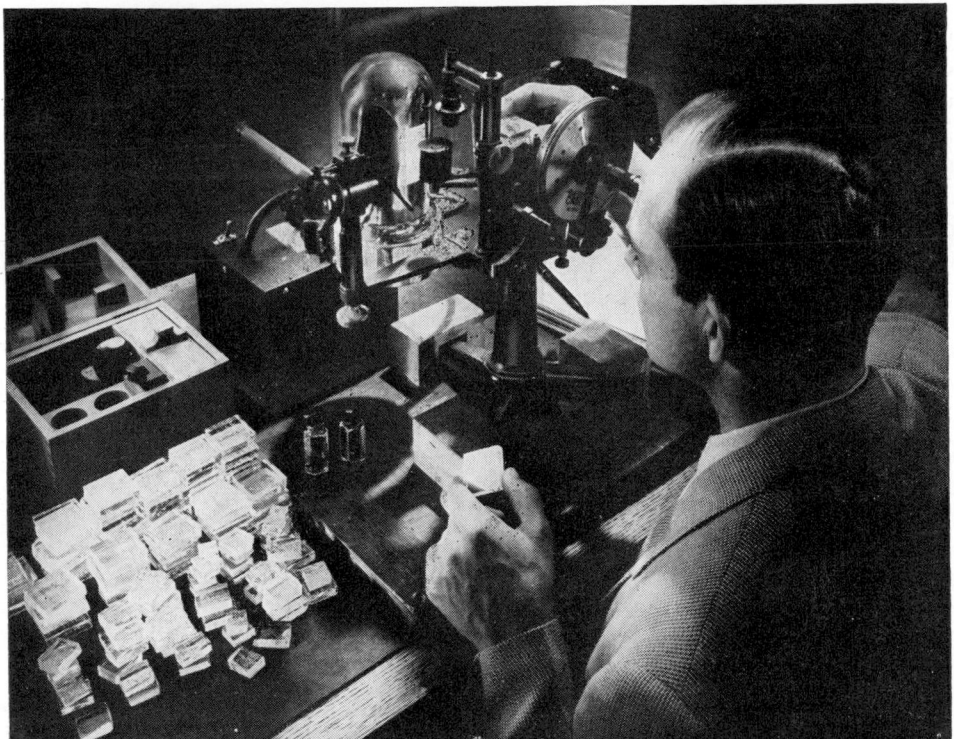

Fig. 21-6. A refractometer being used to determine the refractive index of glass for optical instruments.

eh-ter) is used to measure the index of refraction of a substance quickly and accurately. For example, butter fat and margarine have different indexes of refraction. One of the first tests made in a food-testing laboratory to determine whether butter has been adulterated with margarine is the measurement of the index of refraction. The exceedingly high index of refraction of a diamond furnishes one of the most positive tests for its identification.

5. The laws of refraction. Some of the facts which we have learned about refraction may be summarized in the LAWS OF REFRACTION.

Law 1. When a ray of light passes obliquely from a medium of lesser to one of greater optical density, it is bent toward the normal. Conversely, a ray of light passing obliquely from an optically denser to a rarer medium is bent from the perpendicular to the surface.

Law 2. The angle of refraction lies in the same plane as the angle of incidence and the normal to the surface at the point of incidence.

Law 3. The index of refraction for any two media is constant, no matter what the angle of incidence.

6. Tracing a ray of light through a glass plate. If we know the index of refraction of a transparent substance, it is possible to trace the path that a ray of light will take in passing through the substance. In Fig. 21-7,

ABCD represents a piece of plate glass, and *EO* represents a ray of light incident upon it. From *O* as a center let us describe two arcs having the ratios 3 and 2, the index of refraction of glass. Draw the normal *OF*. Then draw the line *GH* parallel to *OF*, but passing through the point where the incident ray intersects the smaller arc. The line *OP* which is determined by the points *G* and *O* marks the path taken by the refracted ray as it travels through the glass.

If the ray were not refracted as it leaves the glass, it would go out along the line *PK*. To show how it is refracted, we use *P* as a center and draw arcs having the same ratio, 3 to 2, as before. Draw the normal *PL*, and a line parallel to the normal. This time we draw the parallel line through the point where the *larger* arc is intersected by the refracted ray produced. The line *PM* shows the path which the refracted ray takes as it leaves the glass.

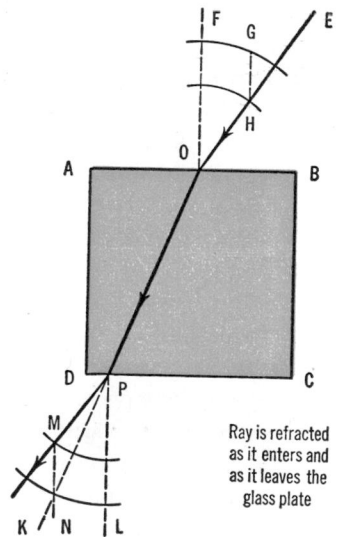

Fig. 21-7. The method of tracing a ray of light through a glass plate.

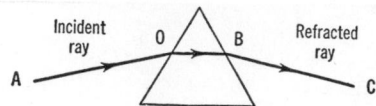

Fig. 21-8. The path that a ray of light takes as it passes through a prism.

If the ray of light *AO* is incident upon a triangular glass prism, as shown in Fig. 21-8, it is bent toward the perpendicular and travels along the line *OB*. As the light leaves the prism, it is refracted from the perpendicular along the line *BC*.

7. The refraction of the atmosphere. We know that light travels slightly faster in a vacuum than it does through air. As light approaches the earth from the sun or the stars, it is refracted as it enters the earth's atmosphere. But since the light enters an atmosphere which gradually increases in density, a ray of light coming from the sun or a star follows a path similar to the curve shown in Fig. 21-9. The refraction is gradual, instead of one distinct bend at the interface between two media.

Because of atmospheric refraction, we do not see the sun or the stars in their true positions except when they are directly overhead. We see the sun in its true position at noontime if its rays are vertical. In the figure, we see the setting sun at *S'*, instead of in its

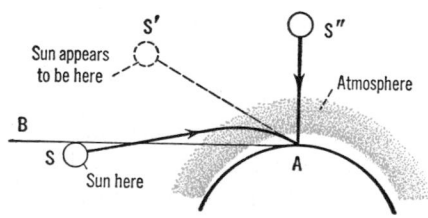

Fig. 21-9. The refraction of the atmosphere causes the sun to appear higher in the sky at sunset than it actually is.

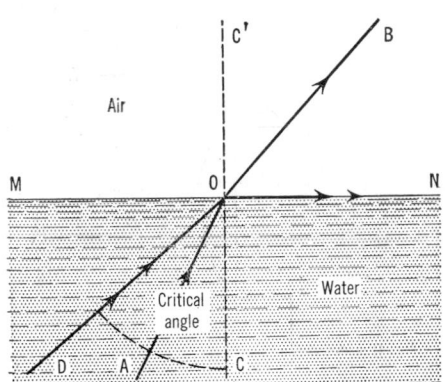

Fig. 21-10. The angle of incidence at which the refracted ray makes an angle of 90° with the normal is called the critical angle.

true position at *S*. The refraction of light by the earth's atmosphere makes the sun at this time appear about one diameter higher than it really is. Since the index of refraction from outer space to air is only 1.00029, the diagram is greatly exaggerated in order to show the bending.

8. What is a mirage? Sometimes when you are driving along a smooth, black-top road on a hot, dry summer day, you see what looks like pools of water on the road ahead. But when you get to the spot where you have seen them, the road is quite dry. The wet spots just are not there.

When the road is actually wet, light from the sky is reflected from the surface of the road. Seeing this reflection, we judge that the road is wet. We make this interpretation because on other occasions when we have seen similar reflections, the road has been wet. But sometimes we are fooled. On a hot day the layer of air nearest the road has a lower density. *Light from the sky entering this layer of air of lower density is refracted upward,*

away from the road. It is this refracted light from the sky that we sometimes see. Such an optical illusion is called a *mirage* (mer-*ahzh*). Our eyes can not distinguish between light from the sky which is reflected from water to our eyes and light from the sky which is refracted by warm air to our eyes. As a result, we think we see pools of water, when actually there are none.

9. What is the critical angle? A ray of light which passes from a medium of higher optical density into one of lower optical density is bent from the perpendicular or normal. Suppose we have an incident ray of light, *AO*, traveling from water into air and bent from the perpendicular along the line *OB*, as shown in Fig. 21-10. What will happen to this refracted ray, *OB*, as we increase the angle of incidence, *AOC*? When the angle of incidence increases, the angle of refraction becomes larger, too. The refracted ray emerges from the water along a path that comes closer and closer to the water surface. As we continue to increase the angle of incidence, we finally reach a point where the refracted

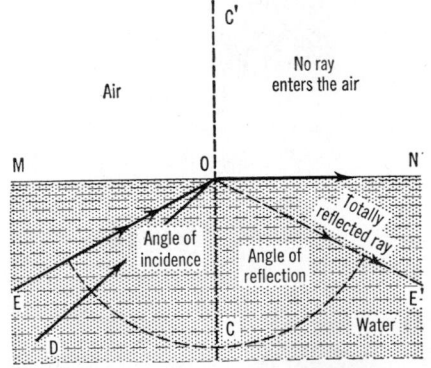

Fig. 21-11. When the angle of incidence exceeds the critical angle, total reflection occurs.

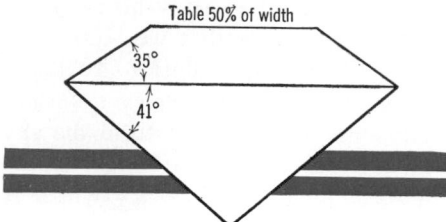

Fig. 21-12. Proper cutting enhances the brilliance of a diamond by permitting the maximum amount of reflection.

ray *does not enter the air at all* but takes the path *ON,* along the water surface. The angle of refraction has become 90°. *That particular angle of incidence at which the refracted ray makes an angle of 90° with the normal is called the* **critical angle.** The critical angle for water occurs when the incident ray *DO* makes an angle of 48.5°

Fig. 21-14. The light-piping effect of a rod made of Lucite acrylic resin. The source of light is at the bottom right. Note how brightly the instruction chart is lighted, while the man holding it is in almost total darkness.

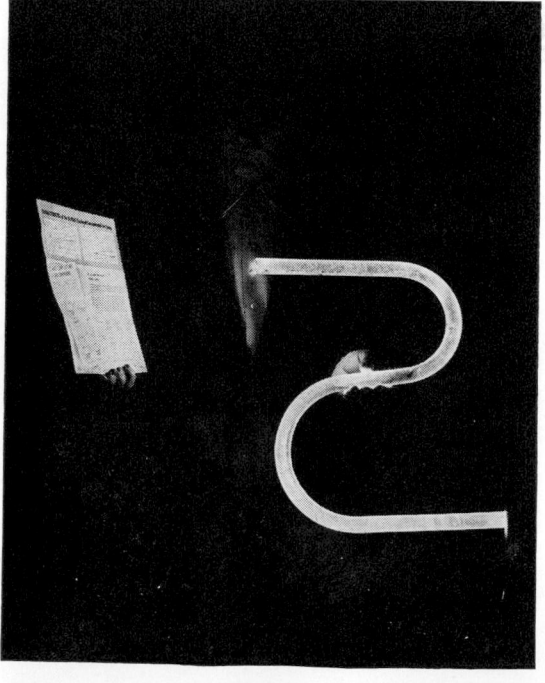

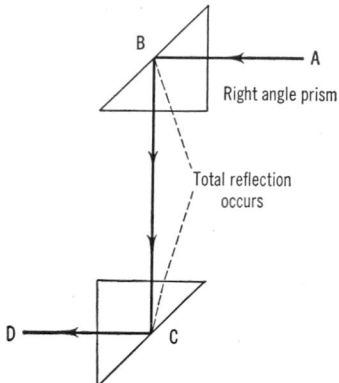

Fig. 21-13. Total reflection occurs in the prisms within a periscope.

with the normal. The critical angle for crown glass is 42°, while the critical angle for diamond is only 24°.

10. What is total reflection? It is possible to increase the angle of incidence of a ray of light passing from water into air beyond the critical angle. What happens to the refracted ray if this is done? It disappears. No part of the incident ray enters the air. It is *totally reflected* from the water surface. In Fig. 21-11, *EO* represents a ray of light which makes an angle of incidence with the water surface which is greater than the critical angle. The angle of incidence, *EOC*, is greater than the critical angle, *DOC*. The ray of light is reflected back into the water medium along the line *OE'*. This case is simple reflection in which the angle of incidence *EOC* equals the angle of reflection *E'OC*. *Total reflection always occurs when the angle of incidence exceeds the critical angle.*

11. Applications of total reflection. Since the index of refraction of a diamond is high, its critical angle is rather small, only 24°. As a result, much of the light which enters a cut diamond is totally reflected and emerges only from the top of the diamond. This makes the diamond a very brilliant gem.

When a ray of light enters a right-angle glass prism like that shown in Fig. 21-13, it is totally reflected. The periscope of a submarine has two such prisms. The observer at *D* sees objects along the line *AB*. The light rays are reflected down the tube by the first prism, and then reflected at right angles by the second prism. The right-angle prisms are much more effective than two mirrors would be if set in the same position, because a mirror reflects only about 70% of the light it receives.

In high-grade binoculars, right angle prisms are used to give a wider range of vision. Sometimes they are used to reinvert an image and make an inverted image erect. Right-angle prisms are also used in reflecting telescopes and in range finders on war ships.

Rods of clear, colorless plastic are sometimes used for transmitting light. Rays of light entering one end of such a rod are totally reflected by the walls of the rod. They emerge only from the other end of the rod, even though the rod is curved or bent into an unusual shape. This effect is illustrated by Fig. 21-14.

2. REFRACTION OF LIGHT BY LENSES

12. What is a lens? A lens can be made from almost any transparent substance. But in order for a portion of a transparent substance to act as a **lens,** *it must be bounded by two non-parallel, curved surfaces, or by one plane surface and one curved surface. These surfaces must be smoothly polished.* Lenses are nearly always made of glass. They are of two kinds.

(1) *Converging.* Some converging lenses are shown in Fig. 21-15. Notice that they are thicker in the middle than they are at the edges. Lenses like these tend to bend rays of light so that they converge and form a real focus. Lenses *A* and *B* in the figure are *flat* lenses. *C* is a *meniscus* lens. (2) *Diverging.* When a lens is thicker at the edges than it is in the middle, it tends to make rays of light more divergent. The double concave lens and the plano-concave lens of Fig. 21-16 are *flat* lenses. The convexo-concave lens is a *meniscus* lens.

13. How do lenses affect light? A ray of light which strikes the center of a lens passes through it without be-

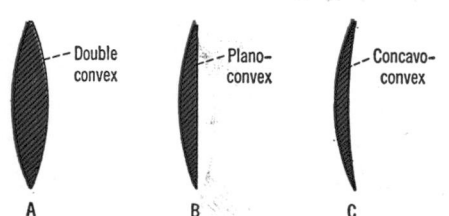

Fig. 21-15. Converging lenses are thicker at the center.

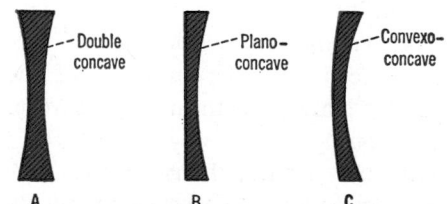

Fig. 21-16. Diverging lenses are thicker at the edges.

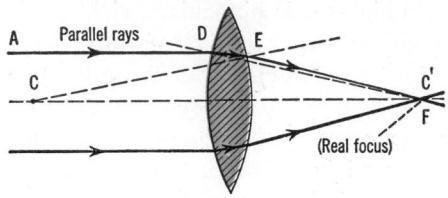

Fig. 21-17. Parallel rays of light are brought to a real focus by a converging lens.

ing appreciably refracted. A ray of light will be bent out of its course if it passes through any other part of a lens. In Fig. 21-17, the ray *AD,* parallel to the principal axis, is bent toward the normal as it enters the lens at *D.* When it leaves the lens at *E,* it is bent away from the normal. *Parallel rays of light are refracted by converging lenses in such a way that they meet at a point called the principal focus.* If converging rays of light strike such a lens, they are made more convergent, and are brought to a focus at a point nearer the lens than the principal focus. Diverging rays which are incident upon such a lens are made less divergent.

Fig. 21-18 shows that diverging lenses tend to scatter rays of light. Parallel rays are made divergent. They appear to meet at a point called a *virtual focus.* This is shown by the dotted lines. Converging rays are made less convergent by such lenses, and diverging rays are made still more divergent.

14. Terms used with lenses. Before we can study the formation of images by lenses, we must learn several definitions.

In many lenses, there are two *centers of curvature.* These are the points *C* and *C'* in Fig. 21-19. They are the centers of the intersecting spheres

which form the lens. The *principal axis* passes through the centers of curvature. The ray of light *AB,* parallel to the principal axis, is refracted and passes through the *principal focus, F.* The *secondary axes* pass through the *optical center* of a lens. The *optical center O* practically coincides with the *geometrical center* of the lens. The ray *AOA'* travels along the secondary axis drawn from *A.* Rays of light passing through the optical center of a lens are *not appreciably refracted.*

In a fashion similar to curved mirrors, lenses refract parallel rays so that they meet at the principal focus. But this focus is not midway between the lens and the center of curvature. Its position on the principal axis will depend upon the index of refraction of the lens. With a double convex lens of crown glass, the principal foci and the centers of curvature almost coincide. With such a lens, the radius of curvature and the principal focal length are almost equal. Increasing the index of refraction shortens the focal length. The thicker a lens is, the shorter its focal length will be.

15. Forming images with lenses. We can learn how images are formed by lenses through studying Fig. 21-19 again. *C* and *C'* represent the centers of curvature of the lens *L.* We are going to show how the image of point *A* is formed. Just as we did with im-

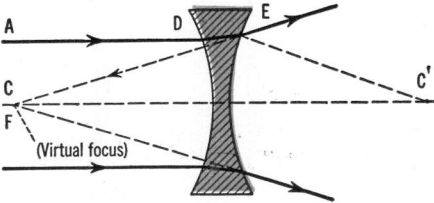

Fig. 21-18. Parallel rays of light are spread out by a diverging lens.

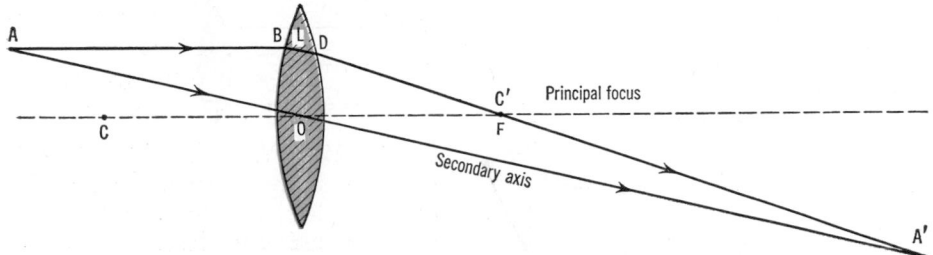

Fig. 21-19. A ray of light parallel to the principal axis is refracted by a converging lens so that it passes through the principal focus. A ray of light passing through the optical center of a lens is not appreciably bent out of its course.

age formation in mirrors, we use two rays coming from point *A*, and see how they are focused by the lens. One of the rays of light we choose goes along the secondary axis. It will not be appreciably refracted as it passes through the optical center of the lens, *O*. For the other ray, we select one traveling toward the lens parallel to the principal axis. This ray, *AB*, will be refracted as it enters the lens at *B* and leaves the lens at *D*. It passes through the principal focus, *F*, which is the same point as *C'*. Thus we locate the image of *A* at *A'*, where the ray refracted through the principal focus meets the secondary axis, *AA'*.

There are several differences between lenses and mirrors.

(1) Secondary axes pass through the optical center of a lens and not through either of its centers of curvature.

(2) The principal focus is at or near the center of curvature, depending on the refractive index of the glass from which the lens is made. This makes the focal length of a lens practically equal to its radius of curvature. The focal length of a mirror is one-half the radius of curvature.

(3) Since the image produced by a lens is formed by rays of light which ac-

tually pass through the lens, a *real* image is formed on the side of the lens opposite the object. This is just the reverse of what we learned for mirrors. *Virtual images* that are formed by lenses appear to be on the same side of the lens as the object.

(4) Convex lenses form images in almost the same manner as concave mirrors. Concave lenses are like convex mirrors in the manner in which they form images.

16. How are images formed by convex lenses? We shall consider six different cases of image formation.

Case 1. Object at infinite distance. You have all used a small burning glass to focus the sun's heat rays upon a point. Light rays focus in the same manner. While the sun is not at an infinite distance, it is so far away that its rays are nearly parallel. When an object is at an infinite distance so that its rays are parallel, *the image formed is a point at the principal focus.* The following method may be used to find the focal length of a lens. When the sun's rays are focused on a white screen, the distance from the screen to the lens is the focal length of the lens. See Fig. 21-20.

Case 2. Object at a distance from

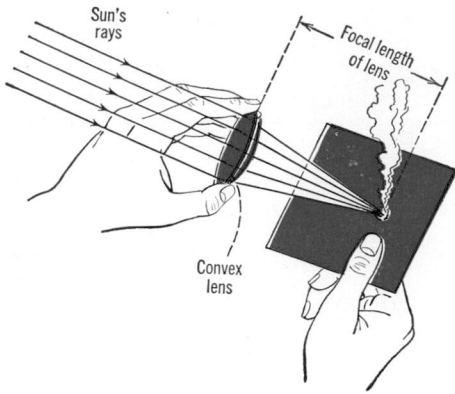

Fig. 21-20. The image formed when parallel rays of light pass through a converging lens is a point at the principal focus.

the lens more than twice the focal length. We have illustrated Case 2 in Fig. 21-21. The secondary axes are drawn from *A* and from *B*. Light traveling along these paths is not appreciably refracted as it passes through the lens. Rays parallel to the principal axis are also drawn from *A* and from *B*. These rays are refracted and pass through the principal focus. They meet the secondary axes at *A'* and *B'* to form the image *A'B'*. In this case, *the image is real, inverted, smaller than the object, and distant from the lens more than once and less than twice the focal length.* The lenses of the eye, the camera, and the telescope are all applications of this case.

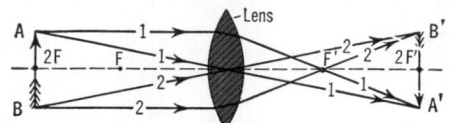

Fig. 21-22. When the object is at *2F*, an inverted, real image, the same size as the object, is formed at *2F* on the opposite side of the lens.

Case 3. Object at a distance equal to twice the focal length. We construct this image in the same manner as before. The construction is shown in Fig. 21-22. In Case 3, *the image is real, inverted, the same size as the object, and at a distance from the lens equal to twice the focal length.* This case is used to invert an image without changing its size, as in the field telescope.

Case 4. Object at a distance more than once and less than twice the focal length. This case is the converse of Case 2. From Fig. 21-23 we see that *the image is real, inverted, enlarged, and distant more than twice the focal length of the lens.* The compound microscope, the stereopticon, and the motion picture projector are all applications of a lens used in this manner.

Case 5. Object at the principal focus. This case is the converse of Case 1. If you draw a diagram, you will find that the rays of light are paral-

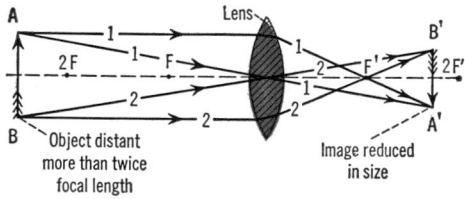

Fig. 21-21. When the object is beyond *2F*, a smaller, inverted, real image is formed between *F* and *2F* on the opposite side of the lens.

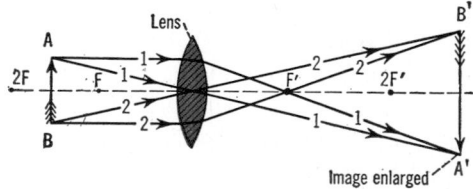

Fig. 21-23. When the object is between *2F* and *F*, a larger, inverted real image is formed beyond *2F* on the opposite side of the lens.

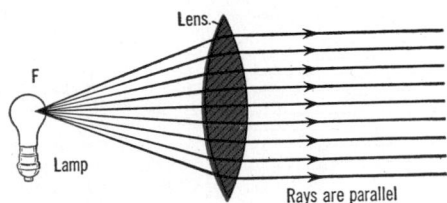

Fig. 21-24. The rays of light from an object at F are refracted by the lens and emerge parallel to one another. No image is formed.

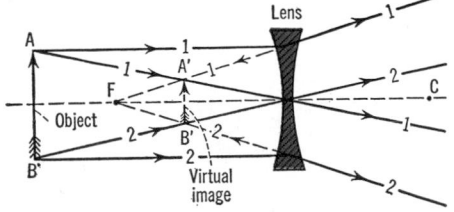

Fig. 21-26. The only image which can be formed by a concave lens is smaller than the object, erect, and virtual.

lel as they leave the lens. *No image is formed.* If a lamp is placed at the principal focus of a lens, as shown in Fig. 21-24, its rays leave the lens as a beam of light. A lighthouse and a searchlight are applications of Case 5.

Case 6. Object at a distance from the lens less than one focal length. Look at Fig. 21-25. Notice that the rays are divergent as they leave the lens. Consequently no real image can be formed on the side of the lens opposite that of the object. If you place your eye close to the lens on the side opposite the object, you can see a *virtual, erect, enlarged image on the same side of the lens as the object.* This image can not be thrown on a screen. Yet the simple magnifier and the eyepieces of microscopes and telescopes

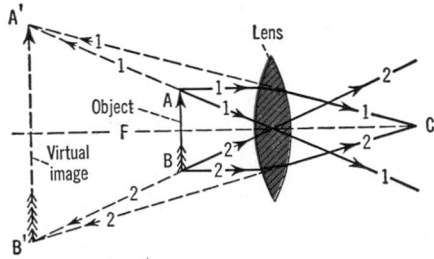

Fig. 21-25. When the object is between F and the lens, a larger, erect, virtual image is formed beyond F on the same side of the lens.

all make use of this method of forming images.

17. How are images formed by concave lenses? Concave lenses tend to scatter light rays. Consequently, the only kind of an image that can be formed by a concave lens is one that is *virtual, erect, and reduced in size.* Such lenses are used to neutralize the effect of a convex lens, or to reduce, to some extent, the converging effect of convex lenses. See Fig. 21-26.

18. Spherical aberration in lenses. When using a camera on a bright day, we close the diaphragm almost entirely, so that light passes through only the central part of the camera lens. The image that is produced when we use only the central part of the lens is very well-defined. If the day is cloudy, we must admit more light to the camera in order to expose the film satisfactorily. But in this case the image produced by some lenses may not be so distinct and clearcut. In opening the diaphragm, we permitted light to enter the camera through parts of the lens nearer its edge. These light rays do not focus at exactly the same point as the rays passing through the center of the lens. This defect of a spherical lens is called spherical aberration.

The diaphragm used in optical in-

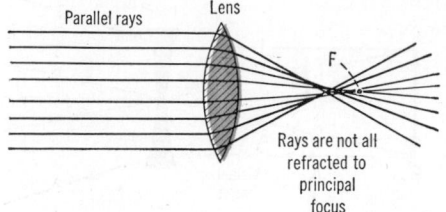

Fig. 21-27. When parallel rays of light pass through a lens, the rays passing through the edge of the lens are not refracted to the principal focus.

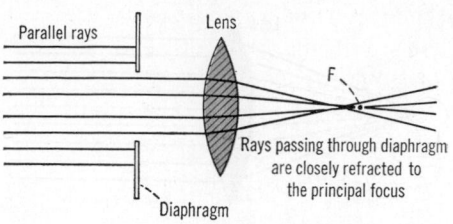

Fig. 21-28. The diaphragm cuts off the parallel rays which would not be refracted to the principal focus and insures the formation of a sharper image.

struments to remedy the defect of spherical aberration in lenses does not actually correct the defect. It merely masks out the rays of light which would not be properly refracted.

19. The relative sizes of an object and its image formed by a lens. We use exactly the same formula to find the relative sizes of an object and its image with respect to their distances from a lens that we did for curved mirrors. The letters S_o and S_i in the following formula represent the sizes of the object and the image. D_o and D_i represent the distances respectively of the object and the image from the optical center of the lens. This is the formula:

$$S_o : S_i = D_o : D_i.$$

20. How are the distance of the object and the distance of the image related to the focal length of a lens? Again we use exactly the same formula that we used with curved mirrors to find the distances of the object and image from a lens in relation to its focal length. We use D_o to represent the distance of the object from the lens. D_i represents the distance of the image from the lens. The focal length of the lens is represented by f. The formula is:

$$\frac{1}{D_o} + \frac{1}{D_i} = \frac{1}{f}.$$

When the image is virtual, D_i is negative. For concave lenses, both $\frac{1}{D_i}$ and $\frac{1}{f}$ are negative.

Summary

Refraction is the bending of light rays as they pass obliquely from one medium into another of different optical density. When a ray of light is passing into a more highly refractive medium, it is bent toward the normal. When a ray of light is passing into a medium of lower optical density, it is bent away from the normal.

The index of refraction of any substance is the ratio of the speed of light in a vacuum to its speed in that substance. The index of refraction may also be defined as the ratio of the sine of the angle of incidence to the sine of the angle of refraction.

That particular angle of incidence at which the refracted ray makes an angle of 90° with the normal is called the critical angle. Total reflection occurs when the angle of incidence exceeds the critical angle.

Convex lenses form images in a manner similar to concave mirrors. Concave lenses are similar to convex mirrors in this respect.

Spherical aberration in lenses may be remedied by using a diaphragm.

The formula for finding the relative sizes of object and image in terms of their relative distances from a mirror may also be used for lenses. The formula relating the object distance, image distance, and focal length of a mirror may also be used for lenses.

Terms to Define...

Angle of deviation
Angle of incidence
Angle of refraction
Center of curvature
Converging lens
Critical angle
Diverging lens
Erect image
Flat lens
Focal length
Focus

Images formed by concave lenses
Images formed by convex lenses
Index of refraction
Inverted image
Laws of refraction
Lens
Meniscus lens
Mirage
Optical center

Optical density
Principal axis
Principal focus
Real image
Refraction
Refraction of atmosphere
Secondary axis
Spherical aberration
Total reflection
Virtual focus
Virtual image

Questions

GROUP A

1. Define *refraction, angle of refraction, angle of deviation*, and *index of refraction*.

2. What property of a transparent substance causes the refraction of light rays which strike it at an oblique angle?

3. What are the three laws of refraction?

4. What is meant by the terms "critical angle" and "total reflection"?

5. What causes spherical aberration in lenses? How may it be remedied?

GROUP B

6. What practical use is made of the index of refraction of a substance?

7. When we see a mirage, we usually think that the substance we see is water. Why?

8. You are looking diagonally down at a fish in a pond. To the fish, does your head appear higher or lower than it actually is?

9. Explain why we see the sun before it actually rises above the horizon in the morning, and why we see it after it has dropped below the horizon in the evening.

10. What kinds of lenses could be used and where should the object be placed to produce (1) an enlarged real image? (2) a small real image? (3) a real image the same size as the object? (4) an enlarged virtual image? (5) a small virtual image?

(In the Mathematics Refresher, refer to Sections 8, 9, 10, and 16.)

GROUP A

1. The speed of light in chloroform is 123,000 mi/sec. What is the refractive index?

2. What is the speed of light in a diamond whose refractive index is 2.42?

3. A penny at the bottom of a glass cylinder is 30 cm from the eye. If water is poured into the cylinder to a depth of 16 cm, how much closer does the coin appear?

4. A double convex lens has a focal length of 20 cm. If it is placed 50 cm from an object, at what distance from the lens will the image be?

5. If an object is 10 in from a double convex lens of 5-inch focal length, how far from the lens will the image be formed?

6. The focal length of the lens in a box camera is 10 cm. The fixed distance between the lens and the film is 11.0 cm. If an object is to be clearly focused on the film, how far must it be from the lens?

7. An object 3 in tall is placed 20 in from a double convex lens. If a real image is formed 10 in from the lens, what is the focal length of the lens and the size of the image?

8. If an object 30 cm from a double convex lens forms a real image 60 cm from the lens, find the focal length of the lens. What is the size of the image if the object is 5 cm high?

GROUP B

9. Make a drawing which shows the path of a ray of light passing from a medium of refractive index 1.33 into a medium of refractive index 1.5. The angle of incidence is 45°.

10. An object 3 cm tall is placed 16 cm from a double convex lens with a focal length of 24 cm. Find the location and size of the image.

11. When an object 2 in tall is placed 8 in from a convex lens, an image is produced on the same side of the lens as the object, but 24 in away from the lens. What is the focal length of the lens and the size of the image?

● **12.** An optical bench pointer 1 cm tall is placed at the 55 cm mark on the meter stick. When a double convex lens is placed at the 0 cm mark, an image is formed at the 5 cm mark. What is the focal length of the lens? What is the size of the image?

● **13.** If the angles of incidence and refraction of a ray of light passing from air into water are 60° and 41°, what is the index of refraction of the water?

● **14.** Calculate the critical angle for carbon tetrachloride.

Things to Do

1. Place a spoon in a tumbler half full of water. Observe the spoon diagonally and from directly above. Also look at the spoon from the side and through the bottom of the tumbler. Notice the varying amount of refraction.

2. Experiment with the various shaped pieces of glass which are part of the equipment of an optical disc. Discover how their surfaces refract rays of light which are incident upon them.

Chapter 22

Color

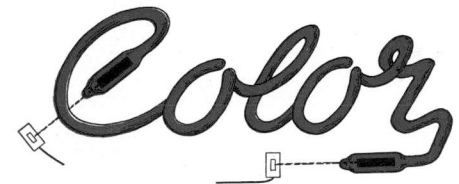

1. Light may be dispersed by a prism. Suppose we take a glass prism and let a narrow beam of sunlight fall upon it through a slit in the window shade of a darkened room. If the light which leaves the prism now strikes a white screen, we do not see on the screen a narrow beam of white light which has been bent out of its path by refraction through the prism. Instead we see a band of colors, with one shade blending gradually into another. *This band of colors produced when sunlight is dispersed by a prism is called a* **solar spectrum.** The dispersion of sunlight into several colors was first demonstrated by Newton. He divided the spectrum of sunlight into seven bands of color: red, orange, yellow, green, blue, indigo, and violet.

Newton's experiments showed that sunlight is actually complex because it is composed of several colors. *Light which consists of several colors is called* **polychromatic light.** If *light consists of only one color, it is called* **monochromatic light.**

The dispersion of light by a prism shows us that the angle of refraction for red light is not so great as the angle of refraction for violet light. The angle of refraction of other colors lies between these two. See Fig. 22-1. As a result, the index of refraction of a substance is not the same for light of different colors. If we wish to be very exact in measuring the index of refraction of a substance we must use monochromatic light. And in giving our value we must indicate the par-

---

Vocabulary

ABSORPTION SPECTRUM. A continuous spectrum interrupted by dark lines.

CHROMATIC ABERRATION. The non-focusing of light of different colors.

COLOR. A property of light waves which depends upon their wave length or frequency.

COMPLEMENTARY COLORS. Two colors which combine to form white light.

CONTINUOUS SPECTRUM. An unbroken band of colors.

DIFFRACTION. The bending or spreading of a light wave after passing through a very narrow opening.

INTERFERENCE. Effect produced by super-imposing two beams of light on one another.

LINE SPECTRUM. A spectrum consisting of distinct and separate colored lines.

MONOCHROMATIC LIGHT. Light consisting of only one color.

POLARIZED LIGHT. Light whose waves vibrate in only one plane.

POLYCHROMATIC LIGHT. Light which is composed of several colors.

PRIMARY COLORS. Red, green, and blue-violet.

PRIMARY PIGMENTS. Peacock blue, magenta, and yellow.

SOLAR SPECTRUM. The band of colors produced when sunlight is dispersed by a prism.

439

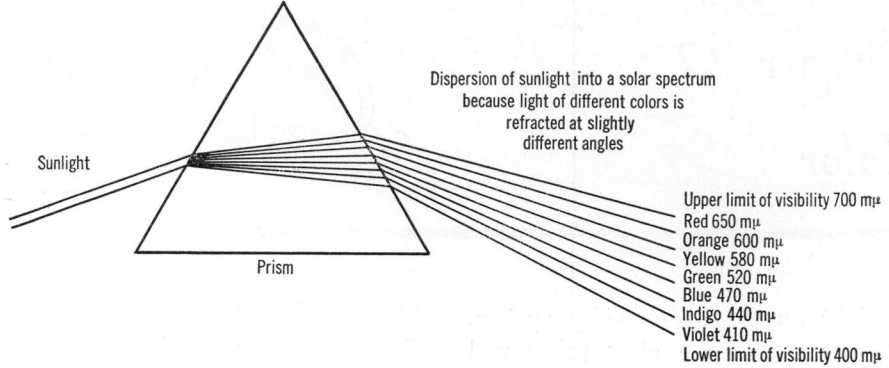

Fig. 22-1. A prism disperses sunlight into the colors of a solar spectrum.

ticular color of light that we used in our determination.

2. What determines the color of light? The color of light depends upon the number of cycles which reach the eye per second. *Color is a property of light waves which depends upon their wave length or frequency.* Color bears the same relation to light that pitch does to sound.

Suppose we have a clear glass, tungsten-filament light bulb mounted in a socket. We have the bulb connected with wires to a device which enables us to control the amount of electricity flowing through the lamp. When we permit only a small amount of electricity to flow through the filament, we can not see any change in its appearance. But as we gradually increase the electric current, the filament begins to glow with a very dark red color. To produce this color, the electrically-charged particles in the atoms of tungsten must be vibrating fast enough to produce light with a wave length of 700 mμ. You remember that a millimicron, mμ, is a very small unit of length which equals 10^{-9} m. Even before the lamp filament glows with visible light, experiments show that it

emits longer waves which we detect as heat. These are called *infrared rays*. As we continue to allow more electricity to flow through the lamp filament, it gives off orange light, then yellow light, and finally white light. A photographer's tungsten-filament flood lamp operates at a very high temperature. If we pass through a prism the rays given off by such a lamp, we can obtain a band of colors which is almost like the solar spectrum.

The shortest waves which the eye can see are those produced by violet light. These waves are only 400 mμ in length. Shorter waves are known, such as those of *ultraviolet light* and X rays, but the human eye is not sensitive to them.

From the wave lengths of various colors given in Fig. 22-1, we see that our eyes are affected by a range of wave lengths equivalent to only about one octave. The wave length of the light at the upper limit of visibility is about twice as great as the wave length of the light at the lower limit of visibility. *Color is a property of light waves which depends entirely upon their length.*

The formula,

$$c = f\lambda,$$

relates the velocity of light, c, to the frequency, f, and the wave length, λ (lambda). The velocity of light is about 300,000,000 m/sec. If we divide this number by the wave length for pure violet, 410 mμ, we find that the frequency of the wave motion of violet light is 7.3 × 10¹⁴, or 730 trillion cycles per second.

3. What determines the color of objects? Color is a property of the light waves which reach our eyes. It is not a property of the objects we see. The property which objects have is that of absorbing certain wave lengths from the light incident upon them and reflecting others. Let us take a piece of cloth which we say is blue when we look at it in sunlight. Suppose we hold it in the red portion of a solar spectrum in a darkened room. The cloth now seems black. If we place a piece of red cloth in the blue portion of the solar spectrum, it also appears black. *The color of an opaque object depends upon the kind of light which it is capable of reflecting to the eye.* If an object reflects all the sunlight colors which it receives, we say that it is *white.* We call an object black if it absorbs all the light rays that fall upon it. An object is called red if it absorbs all other colors and reflects only red light. Of course a piece of blue cloth will appear black in the red portion of the spectrum. There is no blue light there for it to reflect, and it absorbs all other colors. For the same reason, a red cloth will appear black in the blue portion of the spectrum. *The color of an opaque object also depends on the color of the light which shines upon it.*

The color of transparent objects depends upon the color of the light waves which they transmit. Ordinary window glass, which transmits all colors, is said to be colorless. Red glass absorbs all colors but red, which it transmits. The stars of the United States flag would appear red on a black field if viewed through red glass.

4. Combining colors to produce white light. If polychromatic light can be dispersed into its simple colors, it seems reasonable to suspect that we can combine simple colors to form polychromatic light. There are three ways in which this may be done.

(1) If we place a prism in the path of the solar spectrum formed by another prism, the different colors will recombine to produce white light. See Fig. 22-2. Other colors may be compounded in the same manner.

(2) If we have a disc which has the spectral colors painted on it, as shown in Fig. 22-3, we may combine the colors by rotating the disc rapidly. The light from one color forms an image which persists on the retina of the eye until each of the other colors in turn has been reflected to the eye. We really see them all at one time. If pure spectral colors are used in the

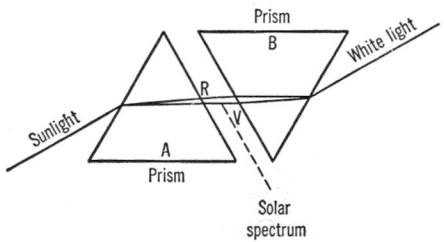

Fig. 22-2. A second prism may be used to recombine the colors of a solar spectrum and produce white light again.

proper proportion, they will blend to produce white light.

(3) In Section 6 we will learn how three colored beams of light may be combined to produce white light.

5. What are complementary colors? Let us once again use the prisms shown in Fig. 22-2. But this time, instead of permitting all of the colors produced by dispersion from the first prism to enter the second prism, we shall cut off the red light from the first prism. The remaining spectral colors combine as they pass through the second prism. The color of the light emerging from the second prism is blue-green. By subtracting red light from white light, we produce blue-green light. We might now predict that red light and blue-green light combine to produce white light. And we can show that this is true by means of the rotating color disc. *Any two colors which combine to form white light are said to be* **complementary.**

In similar fashion, we can show that blue and yellow are complementary colors. White goods acquire a yellow color after continued laundering. Blueing, or a bluish dye added to soap or detergents, is used to neutralize the yellow color and make the wash white. If iron is present in sand used for making glass, it gives a green color to the glass. Manganese gives glass an amethyst, or purplish-red color. However, if these two elements are present in the right proportion the glass will be colorless.

6. The primary colors. We have seen that sunlight is composed of seven basic colors which can not be further dispersed. These seven colors are sometimes called *elementary colors.* They combine to produce white light.

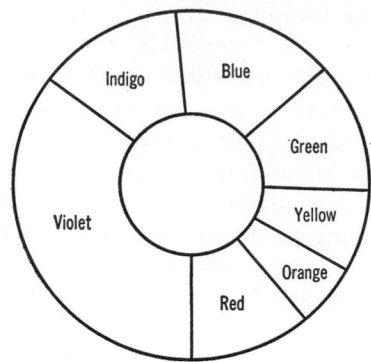

Fig. 22-3. When a disc that is colored as indicated is rotated, white light is seen.

Two complementary colors will also combine to produce white light.

Experiments with beams of different colored lights have shown that any color can be described in terms of any three other different colors. Many times the original color can be duplicated by combining the three colors in varied amounts. In some cases, one or two of the three colors must be combined with the first color. Then a match may be secured between this combination and those remaining. The three colors which can be used most successfully in color matching experiments of this sort are *red, green, and blue-violet.* Consequently, these have been called the **primary colors.**

By using Von Nardroff's color apparatus, we can see how several simple color matching experiments work out. A beam of light from a projector is thrown on a screen through three circular openings in the color apparatus. In each opening we place a colored glass slide. Over one opening we place a red glass slide. Over another, we place a blue-violet glass slide. Over the third we place a green glass slide. These are the three primary colors.

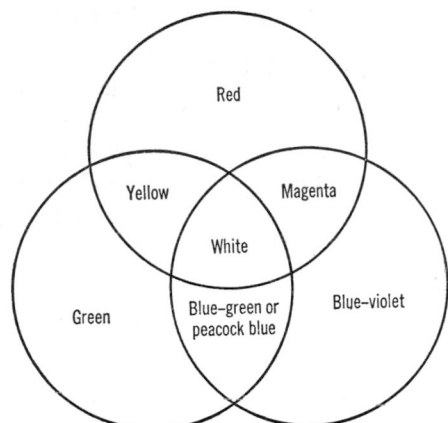

Fig. 22-4. The overlapping of beams of light of the primary colors produces the complementary colors and white.

The slides may be moved in this apparatus so that the beams of light passing through them will overlap on a screen, as shown in Fig. 22-4. Where the three primary colors overlap, they combine to produce white light. The overlapping of the green and red produces yellow. Where the red and blue-violet overlap, the color is magenta. The blue-violet and green combine to give blue-green. If we use the blue-violet and yellow together we have white light, since these colors are complementary. Taking yellow from white will leave blue-violet, which is the color shown in Fig. 22-4. In the same manner, taking red light from white leaves blue-green. And taking green from white leaves magenta.

7. The mixing of pigments. When we *add* blue-violet light and yellow light, we produce white light. If we mix a blue-green pigment with a yellow pigment, we do not produce white, but green instead. Each pigment *subtracts* certain colors. For example, the yellow pigment subtracts, or absorbs blue-violet light and reflects red and

green. The blue-green pigment absorbs red light and reflects blue-violet and green. Green is the only color that is reflected by both pigments. As a result the mixture of these two pigments is green.

When we mix pigments, each one always subtracts certain colors from white light. The color which results depends upon the light waves that are not absorbed. The **primary pigments** are the complements of the three primary colors. They are, respectively, a blue-green called *peacock blue* (the complement of red), *magenta* (the complement of green), and *yellow* (the complement of blue-violet). When the three primary pigments are mixed, all the colors are subtracted from white light, and the mixture is black.

★ **8. The four-color printing process.** In the four-color printing process, four negatives of the same subject are made. Three negatives are made through colored filters, each stained the color of one of the three primary pigments. The fourth, for making the plate for printing with black ink, is not filtered. Half-tone plates are then made from these negatives in the usual manner. Each of the colored plates is printed on white paper, first with yellow ink, then with magenta ink, then peacock-blue, and finally with black. The accuracy of the color reproduction depends on the selection of the proper shades of ink.

★ **9. Color photography.** There are a number of types of film available for taking colored still and motion pictures. While they differ slightly in the physical composition of the film and in the method of development and color fixing, they reproduce colors by essentially the same process.

Color film consists of several layers. The top layer contains an emulsion which is sensitive only to blue-violet light. Beneath this layer is a yellow filter layer which absorbs blue-violet light, but transmits red and green light to the layers of film below. The middle layer of emulsion is sensitive only to green light. The lower layer of emulsion is sensitive only to red light. Beneath these three layers of emulsion is a black layer which prevents reflection of light back through the emulsion layers. Beneath this light-absorbing layer is the film base.

During the development and processing of the film, the portions of the blue-violet-sensitive emulsion *which were not affected by light* are dyed yellow. The portions of the green-sensitive emulsion *which were not affected by light* are dyed magenta. And the portions of the red-sensitive emulsion *which were not affected by light* are dyed blue-green. The sensitive silver compounds on which the images are originally recorded, and the silver formed during the development of the film, are removed during the final processing. This leaves only the colored dye images on the film.

★ **10. Infrared photography.** Photographs can be taken using electromagnetic waves which are just beyond the range of human visibility. Infrared waves reflected by objects are not affected by clouds, fog, and other atmospheric conditions which produce a haziness in photographs taken with visible light. Consequently, much clearer long-distance photographs may be taken with a camera equipped with an infrared filter and using infrared sensitive film. In Fig. 22-5 the picture on the left was taken by the usual method with light that is visible to

Fig. 22-5. The photograph on the left was taken with ordinary film. That on the right was taken through an infrared filter on infrared sensitive film. Note the greater clarity of the distant clouds in the infrared photograph.

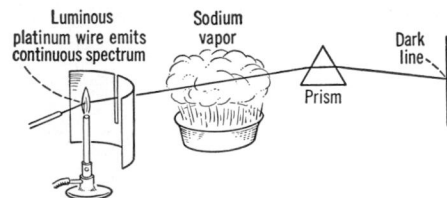

Fig. 22-6. Non-luminous sodium vapor absorbs yellow light of the same wave length as that emitted by luminous sodium vapor.

the eye. The same scene was photographed at the same time with an infrared filter and infrared film. The picture on the right shows the photograph obtained by this method.

11. There are different kinds of spectra. We have seen how the sun's rays are separated into colors by a prism to form a solar spectrum. Light from other sources may be analyzed in the same manner. There are three kinds of spectra.

(1) *Continuous spectra.* A platinum wire held in the colorless flame of a burner produces a spectrum that consists of an *unbroken band of seven colors.* Since the seven *colors form one unbroken band,* this spectrum is called a **continuous spectrum.** *Continuous spectra are produced by incandescent solids, liquids, and gases under extremely high pressure.*

(2) *Line spectra.* Suppose we dip a platinum wire into a solution of common table salt, sodium chloride. When we hold the wire in the flame, it gives off a bright yellow light produced by the vaporization of the salt. If this bright yellow light is passed through a slit and then through a prism, the spectrum consists of two bright-yellow lines, spaced very closely together. *Luminous gases or vapors under atmospheric pressure produce bright-line*

*spectra. A **line spectrum** consists of distinct and separate colored lines.*

(3) *Absorption spectra.* We may produce a continuous spectrum by heating the platinum wire in the flame of a burner as we did before. Then we place an iron pan containing sodium chloride between the slit and the prism, as in Fig. 22-6. When the pan is heated enough to vaporize the sodium chloride, but not hot enough to make it luminous, two dark lines appear in the continuous spectrum produced by the incandescent wire. These dark lines appear in the spectrum just where the two yellow lines on a sodium bright-line spectrum appear. The yellow light waves have been absorbed by the sodium chloride vapor. Such spectra are called *absorption spectra. An **absorption spectrum** is a continuous spectrum interrupted by dark lines.* Gases or vapors can absorb light waves of the same length they would produce themselves if they were heated to incandescence.

★ **12. The Fraunhofer lines.** In 1802 the English scientist William Hyde Wollaston (1766–1828) noticed that certain dark lines appear in the spectrum produced by passing sunlight through a narrow slit and then through a prism. About ten years later, these dark lines were discovered independently by Joseph von Fraunhofer (*frown*-hohf-er) (1787–1826), a German physicist. With apparatus which he constructed himself, Fraunhofer charted the position of a number of these dark lines. He observed that they always appear in the same positions in the spectrum. Furthermore, their positions are the same as those occupied by the bright lines caused by the luminous vapors of different elements. Since about 600 of these lines were charted by Fraunhofer, they are known as *Fraunhofer lines*.

By studying Fig. 22-7 we can understand why the sun produces absorption spectra. The photosphere consists of highly compressed gases, which would form continuous spectra if the sun had no atmosphere. The chromosphere consists of luminous gases under less pressure. They would produce bright-line spectra, if they could be examined alone. In the outer portions of the sun's atmosphere, there are undoubtedly non-luminous vapors which absorb the waves that might produce bright-line spectra.

★ **13. How is a rainbow produced?** When sunlight strikes drops of falling water a solar spectrum may be produced. Water disperses light the same way a glass prism does, but reflection and refraction are also important in forming a rainbow. Fig. 22-8 shows the path that a ray of sunlight takes in passing through a drop of water. As the ray enters the drop at *A* it is both refracted and dispersed. The red ray is totally reflected at *R* and the violet ray is totally reflected at *V*. When they leave the drop at *B,* both rays are again refracted. The angle which these

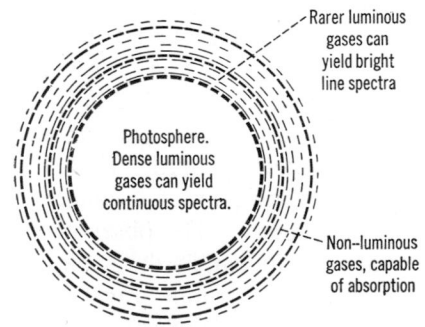

Fig. 22-7. The sun's atmosphere causes it to emit an absorption spectrum.

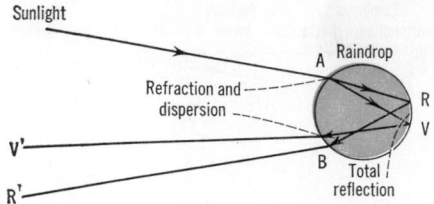

Fig. 22-8. A rainbow is produced by refraction, total reflection, and dispersion of light.

refracted rays make with the horizon of an observer as he stands with his back to the sun is 40° for the violet and 42° for the red rays. In the actual bow which we see, the red rays come from drops of water at an angle of 42° and the violet rays come from those at an angle of 40°. The other colors are formed by drops between these angles. A rainbow is an arc because the eye of the observer is at the tip of a cone from which he sees the colored rays refracted from drops in all directions at angles of from 40° to 42°.

Sometimes a larger secondary bow is seen above the primary. The colors are reversed in the secondary bow, with the violet being on the outside. The light is refracted from drops of water at an angle of from 51° to 54°. It enters the lower part of the drop and is refracted and dispersed as in the primary bow, but it is twice totally reflected before it leaves the drop. For this reason more light is absorbed, and the secondary bow is always fainter than the primary bow.

14. What is chromatic aberration? In our experiment with the prism we learned that light waves of different colors have different indexes of refraction. As a result, light is also dispersed when it passes through a lens. Since violet light is bent more than the

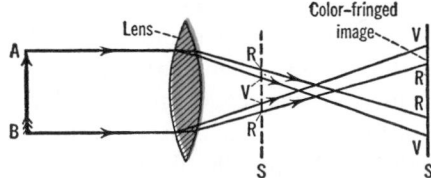

Fig. 22-9. Chromatic aberration is caused by unequal refraction of the different colors.

other colors, it is brought to a focus by a double convex lens at a point nearer the lens than other colors. Because red is refracted the least, the focus for the red rays is farthest from the lens. See Fig. 22-9. A screen placed at S shows a disc of white light surrounded by a ring of colors. The innermost color in the ring is violet, and it is surrounded by the other colors. If the screen is moved to the position S', the innermost color in the ring will be red. Images formed by ordinary spherical lenses are always fringed with spectra colors. *The non-focusing of light of different colors is called* **chromatic aberration.**

15. How may chromatic aberration be remedied? The fringe of colors around the image formed by an ordinary lens is a nuisance. It was a serious hindrance to the successful use of telescopes and microscopes until the latter part of the eighteenth century. Then John Dollond (1706–1761), an English optician, discovered that chromatic aberration could be remedied by using a combination of lenses. A double convex lens made of crown glass used with a plano-concave lens made of flint glass, corrects the dispersal of light without preventing refraction and image formation. A lens combination of this type is called an *achromatic* (without color) *lens.*

16. Interference of light waves. We have learned that sound waves may interfere with one another and produce a sound of fluctuating intensity, which we call beats. Light waves show a similar phenomena, called **interference,** *which is the effect produced by superimposing two beams of light on one another.* This is one of the strongest pieces of evidence in support of the wave theory of light. If we clamp together two circular plates of glass, one of them *plane* and the other *very slightly convex,* we shall have between them a wedge-shaped film of air. Near the actual point of contact, the film of air is about as thick as the length of a light wave. If light from a sodium vapor lamp, which gives only yellow light, strikes this device, alternate yellow and dark bands of light are reflected. Reflection occurs at both surfaces of the glass. The wedge-shaped film of varying thickness causes some of the reflected waves to meet in the same phase, while others meet in opposite phase. Where they meet in the same phase, we see *yellow bands.* Where they meet in opposite phase, they inter-

Fig. 22-10. Newton's rings are produced by interference of light waves.

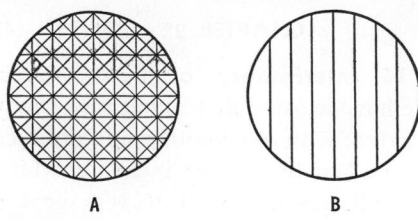

Fig. 22-11. *A.* Possible appearance of the end of a beam of light. *B.* Appearance of the end of a beam of polarized light.

fere and produce *dark bands*. See Fig. 22-10. When sunlight strikes this device, we see a band of colors. The wedge-shaped air film causes different colors of *different wave lengths* to interfere at different positions. The color we observe at a particular point is the complement of the color removed by interference.

17. Diffraction of light waves. According to the wave theory of light, light waves should bend around corners. Our common experience with light shows that it travels in straight lines. However, under some conditions light waves do bend out of their straight course. *When light waves pass through an opening which is small in comparison with the lengths of light waves, they spread out and produce*

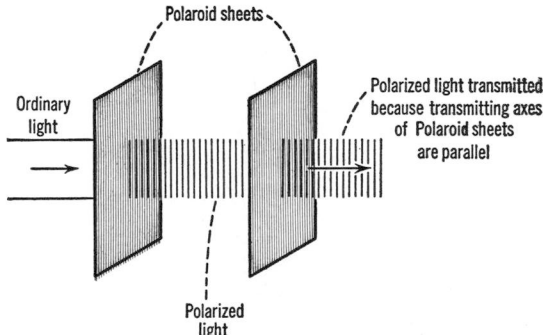

Fig. 22-12. Light is transmitted when the axes of the Polaroid sheets are parallel.

spectral colors as they interfere with one another. This phenomena is called the **diffraction** of light. It may also be produced by the reflection of light from a surface which is covered with exceedingly fine parallel lines.

By means of a diamond point, 15,000 to 30,000 lines to the inch have been ruled on glass, or on special metallic surfaces. These ruled plates are called *diffraction gratings*. With a glass grating, light is transmitted through the narrow space between the lines and spreads out, or is diffracted. A grating is much better than a prism for examining spectra because the colors are spread out and the spectrum which is produced may be several feet in length.

18. The polarization of light. If we could look at the end of a beam of light we would probably see some of its transverse waves vibrating from side to side, some up and down and others at various angles represented in Fig. 22-11*A*. Certain crystals, such as tourmaline, and a man-made material called *Polaroid, transmit light waves which vibrate in only one plane.* When light passes through such materials, the light which emerges is said to be **polarized**. See Fig. 22-11*B*.

Suppose we have two pieces of Polaroid arranged with their transmitting axes parallel, as shown in Fig. 22-12. A complex beam of light is polarized as it passes through the first sheet of Polaroid. Since the transmitting axis of the second sheet is parallel to that of the first, the polarized light from the first sheet passes through the second one also. Suppose, however, that we now turn the transmitting axis of the second sheet of Polaroid through an angle of 90°, as shown in Fig. 22-13.

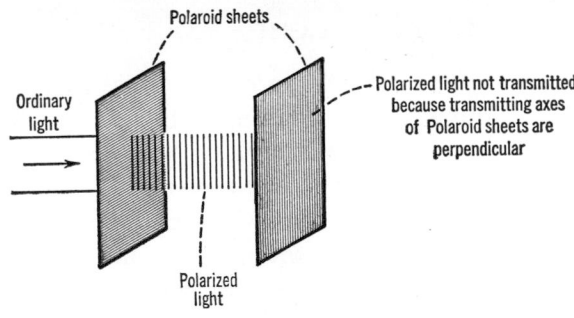

The light that is polarized by the first sheet of Polaroid can no longer pass through the second sheet. As a result, no light passes through two pieces of Polaroid oriented in this fashion. In this position, the sheets of Polaroid are said to be *crossed*.

In order to explain how Polaroid acts, let us study Fig. 22-14. We can make a rope vibrate in an up-and-down direction through a picket fence. But we can not make it vibrate from side to side through such a fence. Through horizontal slots we can make the rope vibrate from side to side but not up and down. In a similar way, the first sheet of Polaroid permits only light waves vibrating in one plane to pass through. If the transmitting plane of the second sheet is oriented in the same direction as that of the first, the light waves pass on through, just as the vibrations of the rope pass through the second set of pickets in Fig. 22-14A. But when we cross the sheets of Polaroid, the vibrating light waves are stopped by the second sheet of Polaroid, just as the second set of pickets stops the vibrations of the rope in Fig. 22-14B.

Fig. 22-13. Light is not transmitted when the axes of the Polaroid sheets are perpendicular.

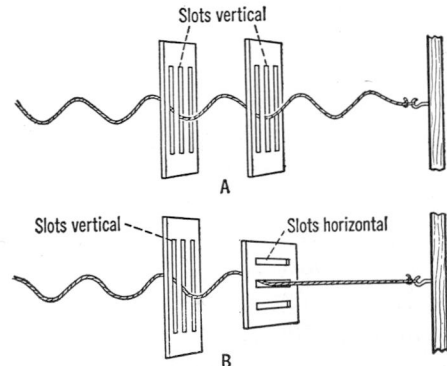

Fig. 22-14. A. When the slots are both vertical, the vibrations passing through the first slots also pass through the second slots. B. When the slots are at right angles to each other, vibrations passing through the first slots are stopped by the second slots.

Summary

Sunlight may be dispersed by a prism into a continuous band of colors called the solar spectrum because the angle of refraction varies slightly for light of different colors. Light which is composed of several colors is called polychromatic light. Light consisting of only one color is called monochromatic light.

The color of light depends upon the frequency or the wave length of the radiation which reaches our eyes. Rays of a slightly longer wave length than we can see are called infrared rays. Rays of a slightly shorter wave length than visible light are called ultraviolet rays.

The color of an opaque object depends upon the color of the light which shines upon it and upon the kind of light which it is capable of reflecting to the eye. The color of a transparent object depends upon the color of the light waves which it transmits.

Any two colors which combine to form white light are said to be complementary. The seven basic colors of the solar spectrum are called elementary colors. The three colors which can be used most successfully in color matching experiments are red, green, and bluish-violet. These are called the primary colors. The primary pigments are the complements of the three primary colors.

Color photographic film contains three layers of emulsion, each of which is sensitive to one of the three primary colors. In developing this film the portions unaffected by light are dyed with the complementary color.

Incandescent solids, liquids, and gases under extremely high pressure yield continuous spectra. Luminous gases under atmospheric pressure produce bright-line spectra. Gases absorb light waves of the same length they would emit if heated to incandescence.

Sunlight can be dispersed by drops of falling water, such as rain, producing a rainbow.

The non-focusing of light of different colors is called chromatic aberration. It may be remedied by using a lens combination made from two or more kinds of glass of differing refractive index.

Light waves show interference and diffraction. Light which vibrates in only one plane is said to be polarized.

Terms to Define . . .

Absorption spectra	Crossed polarizers	Mixing pigments
Achromatic	Diffraction	Monochromatic light
Chromatic aberration	Diffraction grating	Polarized light
Color	Elementary colors	Polaroid
Color of an opaque object	Four-color printing	Polychromatic light
Color of a transparent object	Fraunhofer lines	Primary colors
Color photography	Infrared light	Primary pigments
Combining colors	Infrared photography	Prism
Complementary colors	Interference	Rainbow
Continuous spectra	Line spectra	Solar spectrum
	Millimicron	Ultraviolet light

GROUP A

1. Why does a prism disperse sunlight into a band of colors?

2. What property of light determines its color?

3. What name is given to electromagnetic waves which are slightly longer than visible light? What name is given to those which are slightly shorter than visible light?

4. If a black object absorbs all the light rays incident upon it, how can we see it?

5. What is the apparent color of a red dress in a closed room which is illuminated only by green light?

6. What will be the apparent color of a yellow flower if viewed through a piece of blue glass?

7. What would you expect to see if you looked at the United States flag through a piece of red glass? Through a piece of blue glass?

8. What are the primary colors? Name the complement of each primary color. What is a complementary color?

9. Why is it impossible to make white paint from orange paint by adding a pigment of another color?

10. Define and give examples of line, absorption, and continuous spectra.

11. How could you prove that a piece of white-hot iron is giving off red light?

12. What is chromatic aberration in lenses? How may it be remedied?

13. If automobile headlight lenses and windshields were of Polaroid, how should they be arranged to reduce headlight glare?

14. How do sunglasses of Polaroid reduce the glare of bright sunlight?

GROUP B

15. Why is a blue dye added to some detergents to whiten clothes?

16. Why does the appearance of a person's complexion change when seen under the blue-green light of a mercury vapor lamp? Under the bright yellow of a sodium vapor lamp?

17. Why do the following appear red? (1) glowing charcoal; (2) a cherry; (3) a neon sign; (4) the sunrise; (5) the world "through rose-colored glasses."

18. How do the colors of a soap bubble originate?

19. Why do we say that light *usually* travels in straight lines?

★ **20.** Why are the inks used in the four-color printing process the complements of the three primary colors?

★ **21.** What are the advantages of photographing a broad landscape with infrared-sensitive film?

★ **22.** What is the origin of the Fraunhofer lines?

Things to Do

1. Procure samples of paper or cloth of various colors. View them through pieces of glass or cellophane of various colors. How do the color of the sample and the color of the glass or cellophane affect the apparent color you see?

2. Make a color wheel based on Fig. 22-3. What color appears when it is rotated?

3. Report to the class on the uses of infrared and ultraviolet light.

4. Using small Polaroid discs, demonstrate some of the properties of polarized light to the class. Under what circumstances would a Polaroid filter placed in front of a camera lens result in clearer photographs?

Chapter 23

Optical Instruments

1. What optical instruments do we most frequently use? In order to read this page, you are using the most important optical instruments in existence, the human eyes. To enable your eyes to receive more light and see objects at greater distances, you would use a telescope. To help you examine very small objects in detail, you would use a microscope. Eyeglasses correct imperfections in the optical system of our eyes. Many optical instruments have a combination of lenses to remedy aberration. In describing optical instruments in this chapter, for the sake of simplicity we shall mention only single lenses. In the drawings, the path of only a few rays of light through these lenses will be shown.

2. The structure of the human eye. The eye is a remarkable optical instrument. Fig. 23-1 is a diagram which shows eye structure. The eye consists of several parts.

(1) *The white coat.* This is the hard, tough, outer coat of the eyeball. It preserves the shape of the eyeball and protects the eye.

(2) *The middle coat.* This coat contains a black pigment. Its purpose is to absorb stray rays of light and to prevent the blurring of images by reflection from the walls.

(3) *The inner coat, or retina.* This covers only the rear portion of the eyeball. *The nerves of the eye spread through the* **retina,** *forming a light-sensitive screen to receive images.*

(4) *The crystalline lens.* This double convex lens forms on the retina a *real image* of the object at which we are looking.

Vocabulary

ASTIGMATISM (uh-*stig*-muh-tizm). A defect of vision caused by an irregularly curved cornea or lens.

COLOR BLINDNESS. A defect of the eye which causes confusion of two or more colors.

DURATION OF VISION. The retention of an image on the retina for a short time after the removal of the object causing the image.

FARSIGHTEDNESS. A defect of vision caused by too short an eyeball or too flat a lens.

NEARSIGHTEDNESS. A defect of vision caused by too long an eyeball or too convex a lens.

POWER OF ACCOMMODATION. The ability to change the curvature of the lenses of the eyes.

RETINA. The inner coat of the eye which contains light-sensitive nerve endings.

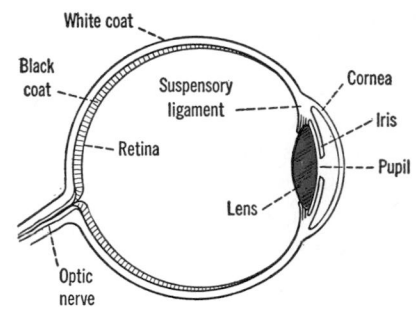

Fig. 23-1. The structure of the eye.

(5) *The iris.* This is the colored portion of the eye. It serves as a diaphragm to cut off rays of light from the edge of the lens. The hole in the center of the iris is called the *pupil.* In a dark room, the pupil becomes larger to admit more light. In bright sunlight, it contracts to reduce the amount of light admitted. See Fig. 23-2. This action protects the retina from damage by exposure to too intense light.

The eye is filled with watery and jelly-like materials which aid in the formation of images. The eyelids act as shutters to screen out the light, and, in general, to protect the eye.

3. How does the eye form images? The objects that we see clearly are those which always are distant from our eyes more than twice the focal length of the lenses in our eyes. As a result, each lens forms an image of these objects on the retina which is real, *inverted,* and *smaller* than the object. Fig. 23-3 shows how this image is formed. It is bright and well-defined.

Our eye lenses have considerable **power of accommodation.** They are supported by muscles which *can change the curvature of the lenses when necessary.* If the muscles increase the convexity of the lenses, the focal length is decreased. This makes our eyes *self-focusing.* If an object is brought close, our eye muscles contract. Then the increased convexity of the lenses makes it possible for a sharp image to be formed on each retina, and we see nearby objects clearly. In normal eyes, the lenses can be made convex enough so that the person can see clearly objects which are only 10 in or 25 cm away. This distance is known as the *nearest distance for distinct vision.*

4. How do we see colors? Scientists still do not know exactly how our eyes react to light waves of different lengths so that we see colors. The most generally accepted theory of color vision is one proposed by Thomas Young (1773–1829), an English physician and scientist. It was later elaborated on by Hermann Helmholtz (1821–1894), a great German physicist. According to the YOUNG-HELMHOLTZ COLOR VISION THEORY, *the ret-*

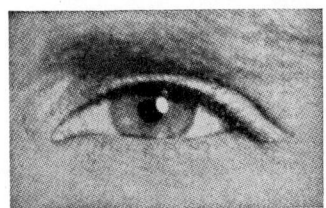 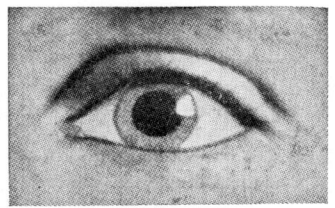

Fig. 23-2. The pupil at the left is contracted in strong light. That on the right is expanded in subdued light.

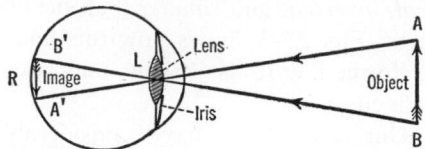

Fig. 23-3. The lens of the eye forms a smaller, real, inverted image on the retina.

ina of the eye is provided with three sets of nerves. Each set of nerves is sensitive to one of the three primary colors.

If all three sets of nerves are equally stimulated, we receive the sensation of white. No stimulation gives us the sensation of darkness, or blackness. When red waves enter the eye, they stimulate *chiefly* the nerves that produce the sensation of red, and we see that color. If only those nerves that are sensitive to green are stimulated, the sensation of green is produced in the brain. When yellow light enters the eye, both the red and green sets of nerves are stimulated and we see yellow. The brain identifies purple if the nerves sensitive to red and bluish-violet are stimulated. Thus all colors and shades are produced by the proper stimulation of one, two, or three sets of color nerves.

★ **5. What is color blindness?** *Color blindness is a defect of the eye which causes some persons to confuse two or more colors which others can readily distinguish.* About 6 to 7% of men and less than 1% of women are color blind. The defect is usually inherited, but certain diseases and large doses of certain drugs may produce temporary color blindness. Most color-blind persons can not distinguish between reds, greens, and yellows, or between blue-greens, blues, and violets. The first group of colors appears to them as shades of yellow. The second group seems to be shades of blue. This type of color blindness is explained by the Young-Helmholtz theory as resulting from a lack of one of the three sets of nerves required for complete color vision. Other, rarer, forms of color blindness seem to be caused by the lack of two or even three sets of color nerves. In extreme cases, a person's eye may be sensitive only to lights and shadows.

★ **6. Retinal fatigue.** Suppose that we suspend a bright red disc against a white background in strong sunlight. Let us look intently at the disc for about one minute. Now, if the red disc is removed, we will see on the white screen a blue-green spot the size of the disc. This phenomenon is due to *retinal fatigue.* The retina of the eye tires of red and refuses to be stimulated by it any longer. The other six colors reflected by the white background combine to produce the blue-green color. Red and blue-green are

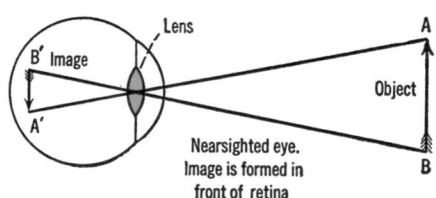

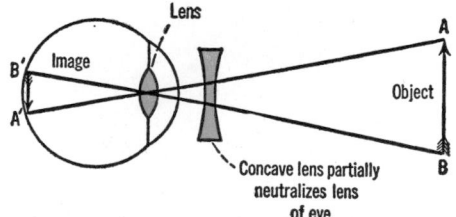

Fig. 23-4. A concave lens may be used to correct nearsightedness.

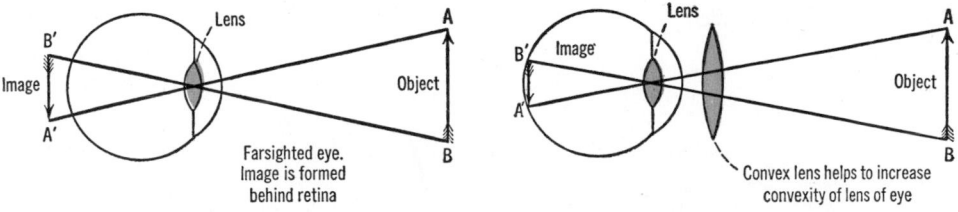

Fig. 23-5. A convex lens may be used to correct farsightedness.

complementary colors. When we repeat the experiment, using a blue disc instead of a red one, the spot that appears after the eye tires of blue is yellow.

7. Correcting defects of the eye. A normal eye is self-focusing, since the muscles of the eye can change the shape of the lens enough to make the image fall upon the retina whether the object is nearby or remote. However, some persons are either *nearsighted* or *farsighted*. Persons who are **nearsighted** *have eyeballs that are either too long, or the lenses of their eyes are so convex, that the image is formed in front of the retina.* Only when the object is brought very close to the eye, so that its rays are diverging when they reach the lens, will such an eye give distinct vision. See Fig. 23-4.

The defect called nearsightedness can be corrected by wearing glasses which partially neutralize the abnormal convexity of the lens of the eye. Such eyeglasses have concave lenses which make the rays of light more divergent before they enter the eye.

If the eyeball is too short, or if the lens is too flat, **farsightedness** *will result.* In order to have the lens form the image on the retina, instead of behind it, an object must be held unusually far from the eye. See Fig. 23-5.

In order to correct farsightedness, glasses with convex lenses are pre-scribed. Such glasses make the light rays more convergent before they enter the eye. Then the lens of the eye can form the image on the retina. Glasses with double lenses, called *bi-focals,* are sometimes used to enable a person to read with one set of lenses and to see more remote objects clearly with the other set.

The *cornea* is the somewhat bulging front portion of the eyeball. If its surface is not perfectly curved, or if the lens itself is somewhat irregular, then all parts of an object will not be in focus at the same time. To an eye having such a condition, the lines of Fig. 23-6 do not all appear equally distinct at one time. This *defect in vision caused by an irregularly curved*

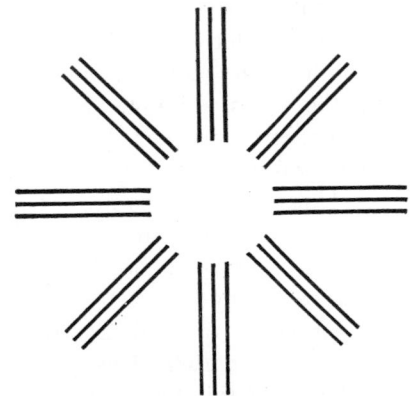

Do all the lines appear equally distinct?

Fig. 23-6. The lines are not all equally distinct if the eye has astigmatism.

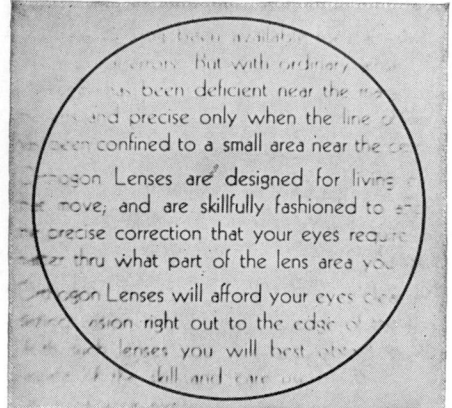

Fig. 23-7. Flat lenses form distinct images through their centers. Objects at one side are blurred.

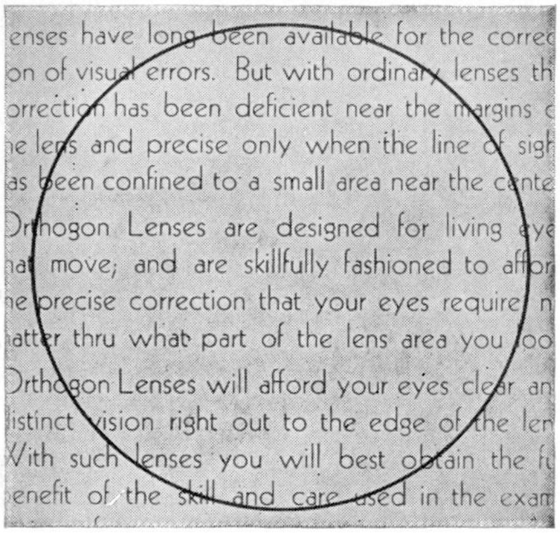

Fig. 23-8. A meniscus lens gives a fairly distinct image, even from an angle.

cornea or lens is know as **astigmatism** (uh-*stig*-muh-tizm). To correct the defect, glasses are worn which have been specially ground to counteract these irregularities.

8. Why are meniscus lenses used? If the flat lenses of Fig. 21-15 and 21-16 were used in eyeglasses, you would not get a clear image unless you looked through the center of the lens. Thus you would be forced to turn your head from side to side or up and down in order to see objects clearly. The letters in the center of Fig. 23-7 are in focus with such a lens, but those around the edges are not. Such flat lenses present another drawback. Their center is nearer the eye than their edges. Unless the glasses are set farther from the eyes than they should be, your eyelashes would brush against them and cause annoyance.

The lenses *C* of Fig. 21-16 and 21-17 are both *meniscus* lenses. With curved lenses of this type, you have a fairly wide range of vision without having to turn your head to see clearly. See Fig. 23-8. Meniscus lenses con-

form to the shape of the eyeball much better than flat lenses.

9. How do we judge size? We all know that a man a quarter of a mile away appears so small that we may mistake him for a boy. A half dollar held at arm's length seems as large as does the sun, which actually is at a distance of over 92,000,000 miles. From Fig. 23-9 we see that the image of *AB* that is formed on the retina is larger than the image of *A'B'*. When we know how far away an object is, we can estimate its size. But we need a great deal of experience before we can estimate both size and distance. A baby reaches for the moon and cries because he can not get it. Later he learns to estimate its distance by means of objects which are between him and the moon.

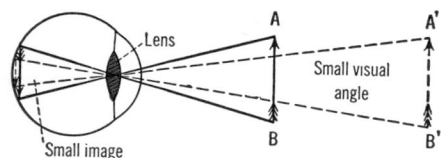

Fig. 23-9. We judge the size of an object from the size of the visual angle.

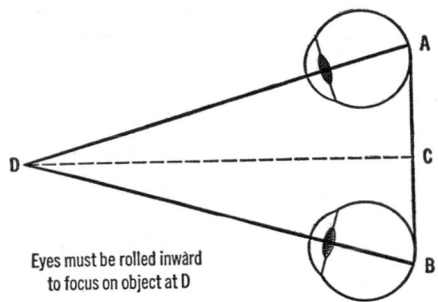

Fig. 23-10. We judge the distance of an object by the amount of muscular effort required to focus both eyes on the object.

10. How do we estimate distance?
We learned that we judge the size of an object from the size of the visual angle. Our judgment of size depends upon our knowledge of the object's distance, too. Consequently, if we know the size of an object, we can estimate its distance. To show that the method of estimating distance by the size of the visual angle is not especially accurate, try the following experiment. Suppose a teacher stands in front of a blackboard in the front part of the schoolroom and extends his arm. Then a pupil directly in front of him, but in the back part of the room, can not judge how far the teacher's hand

is from the blackboard, provided the pupil keeps one eye closed. With both eyes open, he can judge fairly accurately. In binocular vision, we see a little more of the right side of a three-dimensional object with our right eye, and a little more of the left side with our left eye. In this way we get depth of vision, or perspective.

From Fig. 23-10, we see that our eyes roll inward to some extent when we focus both eyes upon the point *D*. A certain amount of muscular effort is used in such a case. By experience we learn to estimate the distance *CD* by the angles *CAD* and *CBD*. The distance between the eyes is the base line from which we learn to estimate distance by the amount of muscular effort needed to roll the eyes inward until both are focused on the object.

11. A camera is similar to the eye.
If we compare Fig. 23-11 with the diagram of the eye, Fig. 23-1, we find that the photographic camera and the eye are similar. The sensitive emulsion on the film or plate corresponds to the retina, and receives the image. The camera lens, or combination of lenses, acts like the crystalline lens of the eye. It forms an image on the film

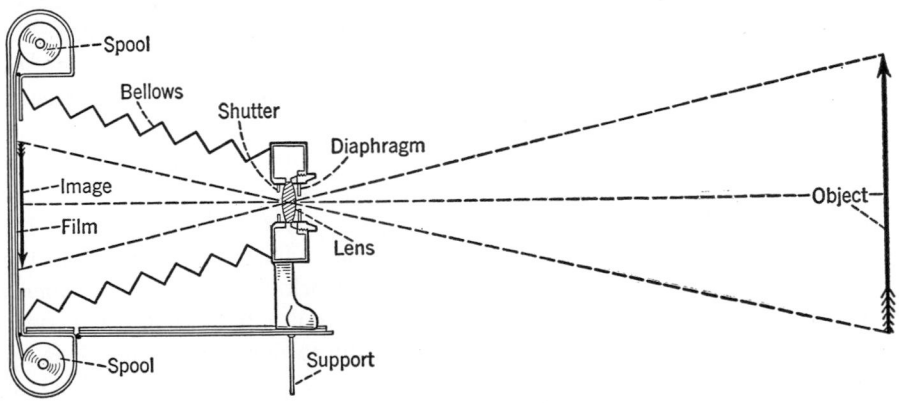

Fig. 23-11. A diagram to show how a camera forms images.

or plate that is real, inverted, and smaller than the object. The diaphragm regulates the amount of light which enters the camera just as the iris regulates the amount of light entering the eye through the pupil. The shutter of the camera also excludes light just as the eyelids do. The interior of the camera is blackened to absorb stray rays of light.

In several ways, however, your eyes are superior to a camera. First of all, they are self-focusing, whereas the lens of a camera must be moved nearer the plate or film, or farther away, depending on the distance of the object from the camera. The iris of the eye automatically regulates the amount of light needed to form clear images. For best results, a photographer has to use an exposure meter to measure the amount of light reflected from the object that is to be photographed. He then adjusts the diaphragm of his camera so that enough light enters to record a clear picture on the film. With your two eyes you get distance and perspective. A single photograph does not show depth.

On the other hand, the camera has some advantages over your eyes. A camera provides a picture of all the details of the object. With the eye some of the details of an image formed on the retina are so feebly impressed that they are either ignored or quickly forgotten. A photograph gives us a picture of an object at a certain instant in a given position. The image received through the eye may be a composite picture of several successive images in different positions. Each image persists for about $\frac{1}{20}$ of a second before another that is distinct from the first may be formed. Thus we remember a

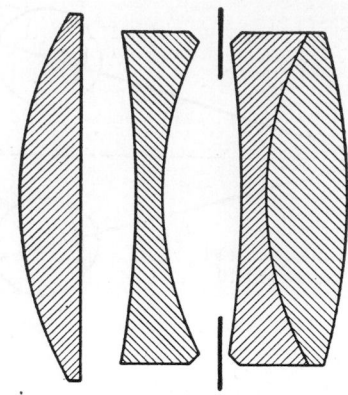

Fig. 23-12. An anastigmat lens consists of a combination of several lenses of different refractive indexes. Such a lens can produce a large, clear image.

composite picture which may have been formed by the blending of several images.

★ **12. Anastigmat and rectilinear lenses.** When ordinary lenses are used and the diaphragm of a camera is opened wide, the image on the film is generally sharp and well-defined at the center but blurred near the edges. Rays of light from horizontal and vertical lines in a plane in the object are not focused in the same plane on the edges of the image. This defect of lenses is known as astigmatism. By using a combination of lenses of suitable refractive indexes and focal lengths an *anastigmat* lens which gives good definition over a wide area can be made. See Fig. 23-12.

Lenses that can be used with a large aperture are said to be *fast* because they let a lot of light into a camera quickly. They are used for high-speed work. The *effective aperture* of a lens is equal to the diameter of the camera diaphragm when it is open as wide as possible. The speed of a lens depends upon the ratio of its focal

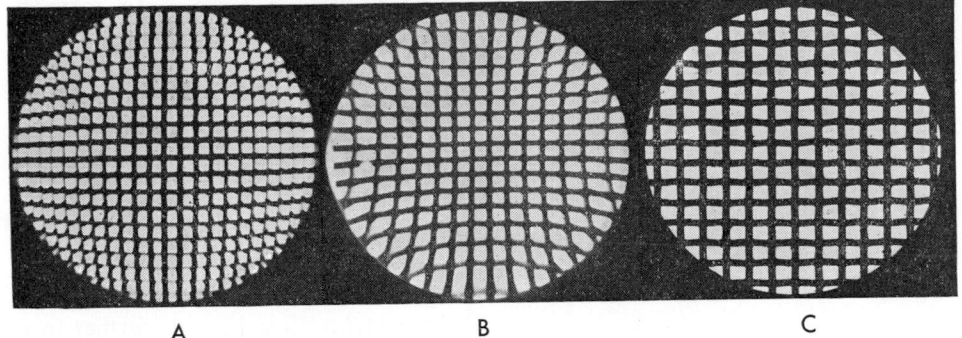

Fig. 23-13. *A.* "Barrel" distortion produced by a plano-convex lens, flat side toward a wire screen. *B.* "Pin cushion" distortion produced by a plano-convex lens, curved side toward a wire screen. *C.* The image formed by a corrected lens.

length to the effective aperture. This ratio is called its *relative aperture*. In an f-4 lens, the focal length is 4 times the effective aperture. Such a lens is 4 times as fast as an f-8 lens, and 16 times as fast as an f-16 lens. The speed ratios are proportional to the squares of the relative apertures.

If a plano-convex lens is placed in a camera with the flat side toward the object, the image that is formed is distorted. For example, a wire screen has the appearance shown in Fig. 23-13*A*. When the lens is turned so its convex side faces the object, the opposite effect is produced. Fig. 23-13*B*. Distortion is produced by all single lenses, but this effect is especially noticeable in pictures of buildings with straight lines. This defect may be remedied by using two lenses with their corresponding curves facing in opposite directions and with the diaphragm between the lenses. Such a combination is a *rectilinear lens*. See Fig. 23-13*C*.

13. The simple magnifier. A double convex lens of rather short focal length may be used as a simple magnifier. The lens is held a little nearer the object than one focal length. The

eye is placed close to the lens on the opposite side. This is a practical example of Case 6; the image is enlarged, virtual, and erect. See Fig. 23-14. As the object is near the principal focus, approximate magnifying power of a simple magnifier equals

$$\frac{\text{the least distance for distinct vision}}{\text{focal length of the lens}}.$$

In centimeters, this becomes $\dfrac{25 \text{ cm}}{f}$, since 25 cm is the least distance for distinct vision. In inches, the magnifying power is $\dfrac{10 \text{ in}}{f}$. In each case f is the focal length of the lens. To give a magnification of 5, we use a lens of 5 cm or 2 inches focal length.

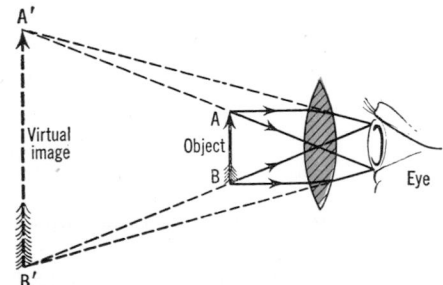

Fig. 23-14. The formation of an image by a simple magnifier.

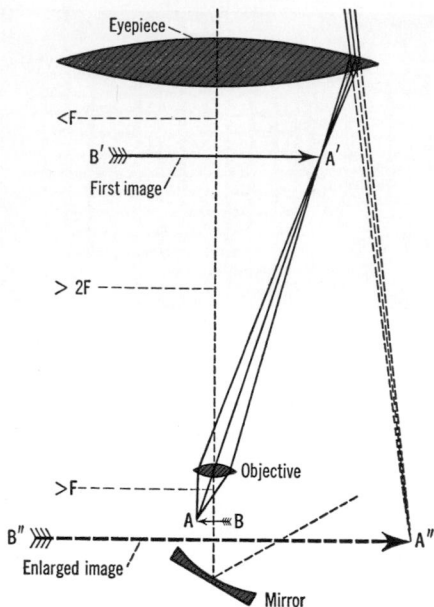

Fig. 23-15. The compound microscope forms a real image by Case 4 and then magnifies that image by Case 6.

14. The compound microscope. This microscope probably was invented by Zacharias Janssen, a Dutchman, about the year 1590.

A compound microscope forms an enlarged image by means of one lens. This image is then magnified by a second lens. Because the first image must be real in order for it to be magnified

further, we use Case 4 to form it. Case 6 is then used to magnify this first image. The two lenses we need are mounted at opposite ends of a brass tube whose length is adjustable. That lens near the object is called the *objective*. The lens near the eye is called the *eyepiece*.

In Fig. 23-15 we see that a converging lens is used as the objective. The object *AB* is placed a trifle farther from this lens than its focal length. At *A'B'*, a distance slightly more than twice the focal length of the objective lens, an enlarged real, inverted image is formed. The eyepiece acts as a simple magnifier to enlarge this image. A mirror reflects strong light upon the object.

The magnifying power of the objec-

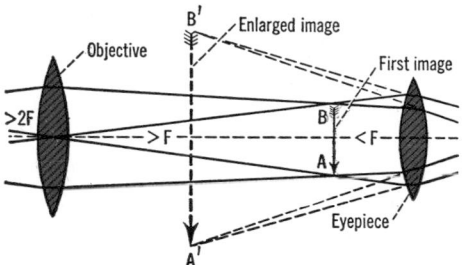

Fig. 23-16. The refracting telescope forms a real image by Case 2 and then magnifies that image by Case 6.

SAMPLE PROBLEM

The tube of a microscope is 16 cm long. The focal length of the objective is 0.5 cm, and the focal length of the eyepiece is 2.5 cm. What is the magnification of the objective, of the eyepiece, and of the microscope?

SOLUTION

The magnification of the objective equals $\frac{L}{f_o}$, 16 cm ÷ 0.5 cm = 32. The magnification of the eyepiece equals $\frac{25}{f_e}$, 25 ÷ 2.5 = 10.
The magnification of the microscope equals 32 × 10 or 320.

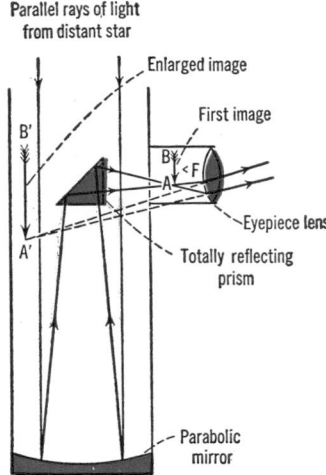

Parallel rays of light
from distant star

Enlarged image

First image

B'

B

A

< F

Eyepiece lens

Totally reflecting
prism

A'

Parabolic
mirror

Fig. 23-17. Formation of an image in a reflecting telescope.

tive is approximately equal to the length of the tube L, divided by the focal length, f_o of the objective, or $\dfrac{L}{f_o}$. The magnifying power of the eyepiece, acting as a simple magnifier, equals $\dfrac{25}{f_e}$, when f_e, the focal length of the eyepiece is given in centimeters. The total magnification is equal to the product of the two, $\dfrac{25\,L}{f_e\,f_o}$, if the measurements are all given in centimeters. See Sample Problem on page 460.

15. The refracting telescope. A refracting telescope has two lens combinations. The objective lens is of large diameter so that it will admit large quantities of light. The objects to be viewed in telescopes are always distant more than twice the focal length of the objective lens. As a consequence, the image that is formed is smaller than the object, but it is exceedingly bright. The eyepiece magnifies the real image which is produced by the objective lens. See Fig. 23-16. The magnifying power is approximate-

ly equal to the focal length of the objective, f_o, divided by the focal length of the eyepiece, f_e, or f_o/f_e.

16. The reflecting telescope. The largest telescopes in the world are reflecting telescopes. In order to collect light, a reflecting telescope uses a large concave mirror instead of an objective lens. Because it is easier to make a large mirror than it is to make a lens of the same size, a reflecting telescope can be made much larger than a refracting telescope.

Since the objects being viewed with a reflecting telescope are at a finite distance beyond the center of curvature of the mirror, Case 2 applies. The image produced is real, inverted, and located near the principal focus of the mirror. This real image is reflected

Fig. 23-18. A reflecting telescope is being used here in tracking a guided missile during flight for photographic purposes. The operator is using a refracting telescope to keep the missile in the field of view covered by the camera.

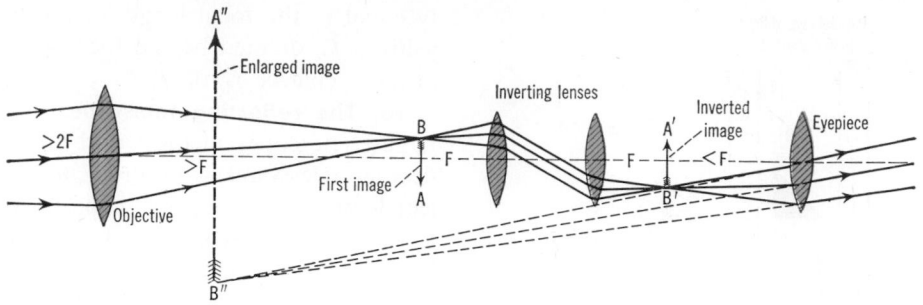

Fig. 23-19. The terrestrial telescope forms the first image by Case 2. This image is inverted by two lenses using Case 5. The inverted image is magnified by Case 6.

out of the path of the rays of light incident on the mirror and can be viewed with an eyepiece. See Fig. 23-17.

The image formed by astronomical telescopes and microscopes is inverted and reversed.

17. A terrestrial telescope. The objective lens and eyepiece of an ordinary field telescope form images, just as their counterparts do in the refracting astronomical telescope. It would be very awkward, however, to see ob-

Fig. 23-20. The reinverting of the image in binoculars is done by a pair of totally reflecting prisms.

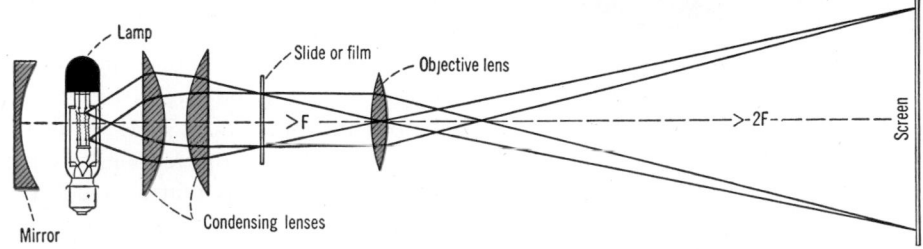

Fig. 23-21. The optical system of a projector.

jects inverted and reversed in a field telescope. For that reason, another lens system is used to reinvert the real image formed by the objective. Thus the final image is erect. See Fig. 23-19. So that this additional lens system merely inverts and does not magnify the image, this lens system must be placed exactly its own focal length from the image formed by the objective.

The prism binocular is actually a double field telescope. However, two sets of totally reflecting prisms are used to make the final image inverted, rather than a third lens system as in the field telescope. This method of reinverting the first image shortens the distance between the objective and eyepiece. Consequently binoculars are more compact and convenient to carry than field telescopes.

18. Projecting an enlarged real image on a screen. The same optical system is applied in many common projection instruments. Film strip projectors, slide projectors, and motion picture projectors all produce a projected image on a screen by the same optical method. The object is usually a brightly illuminated, transparent film or glass slide. (Some instruments will also project images of opaque objects.) The objective lens is a combination of converging lenses which acts as a sin-

gle lens. The object is placed a trifle farther from the lens than one focal length. The screen on which the image is to be formed is placed at a distance considerably more than twice the focal length of the objective. Because the image is real, inverted, and enlarged, the film or slide must be placed upside down in the projector. Then the image appears erect on the screen.

19. Duration of vision makes motion pictures possible. One airline company has a red and blue stripe painted near the tip of each propeller blade on all its airplanes. When these propellers are spinning, a complete red and blue circle is visible. This happens because an image formed on the retina of the eye persists for about $\frac{1}{20}$ of a second after the object causing the image has been removed. The red and blue stripes on the propeller blades form complete circles because the image of a blade in one position does not fade out during the time required for the next blade to move into the same position. *This retention of an image on the retina of the eye for a short time after the object causing the image has been removed, is called* **duration of vision.** This particular property is utilized in the viewing of motion pictures.

In preparing film for a sound mo-

Fig. 23-22. A strip of motion picture film. Notice the successive poses of the two football players in each film frame.

Fig. 23-23. A modern portable sound motion picture projector for home, school, or industrial use.

tion picture, 24 separate pictures, or frames, of the moving object are taken per second. Each frame showing the object is slightly different from the one before it. See Fig. 23-22. The pictures are then projected on a screen at the same rate as that at which they were taken. Because our eye retains the image of one picture until the next one takes its place, we get the illusion of continuous motion. Slow-motion films are taken at a more rapid rate and then projected at 24 frames per second. This has the effect of extending the motion over a longer time. In stop-motion photography the pictures are taken at a slower rate and then projected at normal speed. We use this type of photography to show in a short time a process which normally takes much longer, such as the opening of a flower.

20. Projecting motion pictures. A motion picture projector produces a real image on a screen by the method described in Section 18. The enlarged, inverted image is produced by an objective lens placed farther from the film than one focal length. Condensing lenses concentrate light on the film so that the projected image will be as bright as possible. The mechanism for running film through a projector is somewhat complex. An electric motor drives sprocket wheels which pull the film from one reel, run it between the condensing lenses and the objective lens, move it over a sound pick-up mechanism, and finally feed it to another reel upon which it is wound. The film moves at a constant speed through all parts of the projector except through the film gate. The film gate consists of two metal strips which guide the film into the proper position

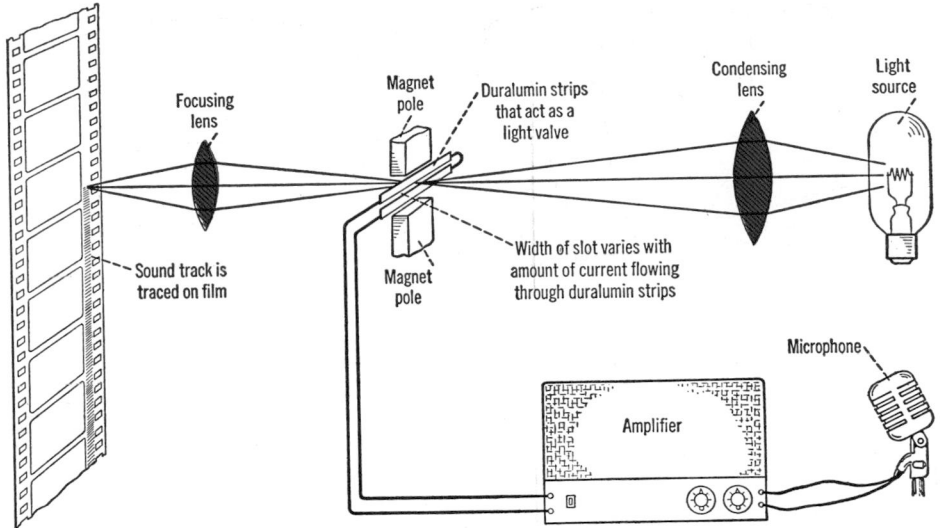

Fig. 23-24. One method of recording a sound track on motion picture film.

between the condensing lenses and the objective lens. The film must repeatedly come to a complete stop in the film gate. When a part of the film stops, the individual picture is centered in the opening in the film gate between the illuminating lamp and the projector lens. A revolving shutter cuts off the light to the picture while the film is pulled through the gate from one frame to the next.

★ **21. The motion picture sound track.** Sounds which are to accompany the projection of a motion picture may be registered photographically on a small strip paralleling the individual pictures on the film. The pictures and the sound track are photographed first on separate strips of film. These later are combined into one film when the final print is made.

In recording sound on film, the sound is picked up by a high-fidelity microphone. The microphone changes the sound waves into a varying electric current. In one process this cur-

rent is amplified and passed through a *light valve.* The light valve consists of thin strips of metal placed about 0.001 inch apart between the poles of a powerful magnet. As the amplified current flows through these strips, they are attracted and repelled by the poles of the magnet. As a result, the width of the slit between them varies in proportion to the strength of the current produced by the sound waves. A beam of light passes through the narrow slit of the light valve and is focused upon the edge of the film. The variations in the width of the slit cause variations in the amount of light passing through the valve. When the film is developed, there will be light and dark bands on the sound track which correspond to the sound waves that entered the microphone.

In order to reproduce the sound, a beam of light passes through a narrow slit and then through the sound track on the edge of the film. Because of the variations in intensity of the sound

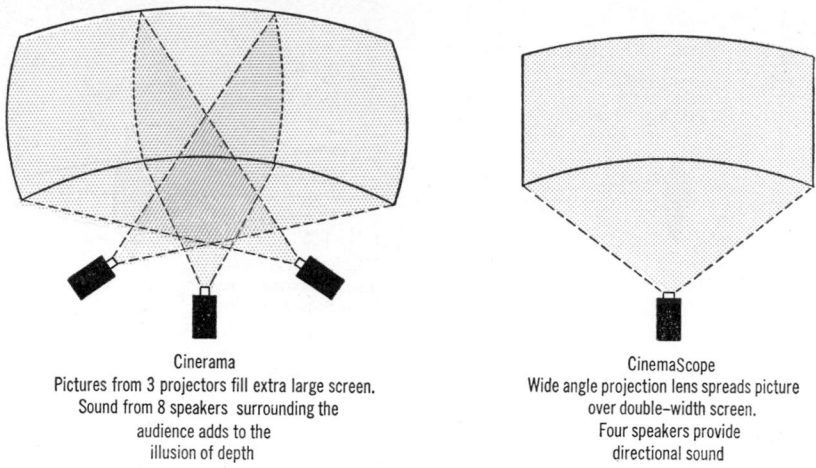

Cinerama
Pictures from 3 projectors fill extra large screen.
Sound from 8 speakers surrounding the
audience adds to the
illusion of depth

CinemaScope
Wide angle projection lens spreads picture
over double-width screen.
Four speakers provide
directional sound

Fig. 23-25. The essential features of Cinerama and CinemaScope.

track, the light which has passed through it varies in brightness. This light then strikes the sensitive surface of a photoelectric cell. The variations in the light falling on this cell cause corresponding variations in the electric current which the cell produces. The variable electric current is amplified and then conducted to a loudspeaker which converts the electric current back into sound waves, which then are heard by the audience. Another process of recording sound on film uses a magnetic sound track. This method is explained in Section 10, Chapter 31.

22. Giving depth to motion pictures. Two recent developments attempt to give an illusion of depth to projected motion pictures. These are Cinerama and CinemaScope.

(1) *Cinerama.* The illusion of depth produced by Cinerama is a result of making the audience feel that it is a part of the projected picture. In order to do this, the Cinerama screen is made very large and curved. Pictures for Cinerama are taken by a camera with three different lenses and three separate strips of film. The lenses are placed in the camera with an angle of 40° between them. The projection of Cinerama requires three different synchronized projectors. The picture from the left projector forms the right side of the projected image. The picture from the right projector produces the left portion of the image on the screen. The center projector produces the central part.

Sound effects aid the illusion of depth. Five speakers are placed behind the screen, and three more at the sides and in the rear of the theater.

(2) *CinemaScope.* CinemaScope utilizes a wide-angle curved screen. It is the same height as an ordinary motion picture screen, but twice as wide. Only one projector fitted with a special wide-angle lens is required. CinemaScope uses regular theater-size motion picture film. However, the lens of the camera which photographs the scene compresses the width of the picture. See Fig. 23-26 and Fig. 23-27. When the film is shown, a special lens on the

projector spreads the image out again so that it appears in normal proportion.

23. The spectroscope. The *spectroscope* is an optical instrument used for examining spectra. It consists of a prism mounted on a circular protractor. See Fig. 23-28. The *collimator tube* receives light through a narrow slit, and transmits it through the lens so that the rays are parallel as they strike the prism. A small telescope magnifies the spectrum which is produced by the prism. Crosshairs in the telescope may be focused on any line in the spectrum. Both the collimator tube and the telescope are mounted on a circular protractor so that the angular position of any line can be carefully measured.

★ **24. Uses of the spectroscope.** A spectroscope can be used for several purposes. We already have learned that various kinds of spectra are produced by matter. A spectroscope is used to study the characteristics of the light emitted or absorbed by matter, whether in solid, liquid, or gaseous form. By studying spectra, we can

Fig. 23-26. A single frame from the motion picture HELEN OF TROY, which was filmed in CinemaScope.

learn about the structure of atoms and molecules. A spectroscope reveals many characteristics of the distant stars. The most familiar use of a spectroscope is to identify the kinds of atoms and molecules in a given sample of material. It also is possible to make an estimate of the quantities of each kind of atom or molecule.

★ **25. The polariscope.** This instrument has a polarizing film at one end of a tube two feet or more in length.

Fig. 23-27. The same film frame after it has been projected through an anamorphic lens onto a theatre screen.

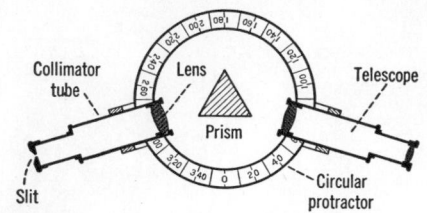

Fig. 23-28. Diagram of a simple prism spectroscope.

Monochromatic light is polarized as it passes through this film. At the opposite end of the tube — the end through which you look — there is a similar film called the analyzer. It is mounted in a rotating disc so that it may be completely turned. Some chemical compounds have the ability to twist or turn the plane of polarized light. Glucose and some other organic substances have this property.

Suppose we turn the analyzer so that it does not transmit any light. Now let us place a sugar solution in the tube between the polarizer and the analyzer. It twists the plane of the polarized light and permits some of it

to pass through the analyzer. Now let us turn the analyzer so that once again it does not transmit light. By measuring the number of degrees through which we have turned the analyzer, we can calculate the percentage of sugar in the solution. The amount of rotation of the plane of polarized light varies with the substance and with the strength of the solution.

★ **26. Other uses of polarized light.** In addition to using polarized light to analyze sugar and other chemicals, a chemist may use polarized light to identify tiny crystals. Manufacturers of automobiles and machine parts are using polarized light to examine materials to learn how they behave under applied stress. The strains in the material show clearly under polarized light. Building materials, too, can be tested in the same way. The polarized light transmitted by certain types of sun glasses eliminates the annoying glare when bright sunlight is reflected from the surface of a road or by the water of a smooth lake.

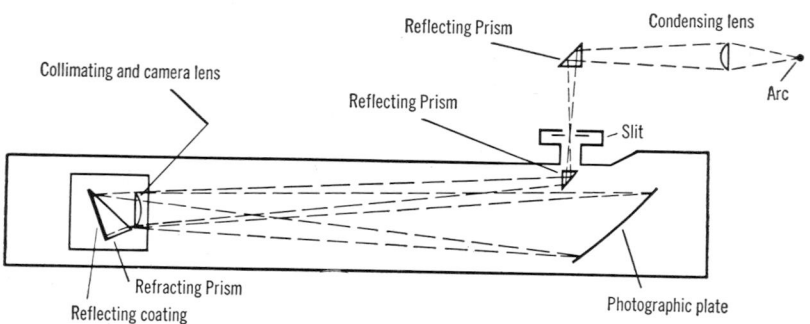

Fig. 23-29. A prism spectroscope used for analytical purposes.

Summary

The eye is the most frequently used optical instrument. It has a lens which forms a real, inverted image on the retina. According to the Young-Helmholtz color vision theory, the retina of the eye contains three sets of optical nerves, each of which is sensitive to one of the three primary colors.

The camera is very similar to the eye. The camera forms a real image upon a sensitive film or plate by means of a lens system.

In astronomical telescopes, either a large lens or a concave mirror is used to collect large quantities of light to form a bright, real image of the distant object. The image is then magnified by means of a powerful eyepiece. A terrestrial telescope contains a third lens system which reinverts the image so that it is erect with respect to the object.

The same optical system is applied in many common projection instruments. Condensing lenses are used to focus rays of light upon a transparent slide or film. The image of this brightly illuminated object is formed on the screen by a lens system utilizing Case 4.

The spectroscope is an instrument for examining spectra. The polariscope utilizes polarized light for experimental purposes.

Terms to Define...

Anastigmat lens	Formation of images by the eye	Reflecting telescope
Astigmatism	Iris	Refracting telescope
Binocular vision	Least distance for distinct	Relative aperture
CinemaScope	vision	Retina
Cinerama	Meniscus lens	Retinal fatigue
Color blindness	Nearsightedness	Simple magnifier
Compound microscope	Objective	Sound motion pictures
Cornea	Polariscope	Sound track
Duration of vision	Power of accommodation	Spectroscope
Effective aperture	Projecting an enlarged real	Structure of the eye
Estimating distance	image	Terrestrial telescope
Eyepiece	Pupil	Young-Helmholtz color vi-
Farsightedness	Rectilinear lens	sion theory

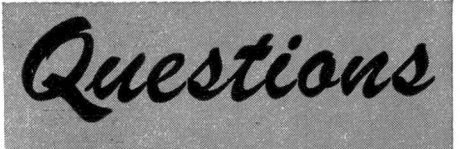

Questions

GROUP A

1. Identify and give the function of the following parts of the eye: (1) retina; (2) lens; (3) pupil; (4) iris; (5) eyelid.

2. Is the image formed by the eye real or virtual? Erect or inverted? Smaller or larger than the object? Closer to the lens or farther from the lens than the object? On the same or opposite side of the lens from the object?

3. How do scientists believe the eye sees colors?

4. What type of lens is used to correct nearsightedness? Why? What type of lens is used to correct farsightedness? Why?

5. What causes astigmatism?

6. Why does the sun appear larger at sunrise and sunset than it does at noon?

7. How do our eyes enable us to see three-dimensional images?

8. Compare the functions of the following parts of a camera with the corresponding parts of the eye; (1) film; (2) diaphragm; (3) shutter; (4) lens; (5) blackened interior.

9. What advantages does the camera have over the eye? What advantages does the eye have over the camera?

10. Of which case of convex lenses is the simple magnifier an application?

11. Explain the lens system and image formation of a compound microscope in terms of the lens cases used.

12. Explain the lens system and image formation of a refracting telescope in terms of the lens cases used.

13. What applications of reflection and refraction are found in the reflecting telescope?

14. How does a terrestrial telescope compare with a refracting astronomical telescope?

15. Are motion pictures actually in motion? Explain why we see the image we do.

GROUP B

16. What is the "power of accommodation" of the eye?

17. What are bi-focals?

18. Why do meniscus lenses produce clearer images than flat lenses when used in eyeglasses?

19. Explain how the illusion of depth is produced in (1) Cinerama; (2) CinemaScope.

20. When the distance between a projector and the screen is increased, what adjustment must be made in the distance between the film and the objective lens to bring the image back into focus?

★ **21.** How is color blindness explained by the Young-Helmholtz theory?

★ **22.** If you stare at a piece of bright green paper for about a minute and then look away, what color is the image of the paper which remains on the retina?

★ **23.** What is an anastigmat lens? A rectilinear lens? What is the relative aperture of a lens?

★ **24.** How does a beam of light help reproduce the sound track on motion picture film?

★ **25.** What are some industrial applications of the spectroscope?

★ **26.** Give several examples of practical uses of polarized light.

Problems

In the Mathematics Refresher, refer to Sections 8, 9, 10, and 16.)

GROUP A

1. What is the focal length of the lens in your eye when you read a book 14 inches from your eye? Distance from lens to retina is 0.75 in.

2. What is the focal length of the lens in your eye when you are looking at a person standing 50 ft away? The distance from the lens to the retina is 0.75 in.

3. What is the magnifying power of a simple magnifier whose focal length is 4 in?

4. Calculate the magnifying power of a compound microscope when it is equipped with a $10 \times$ eyepiece and a $25 \times$ objective.

5. What is the magnifying power of a sky telescope which has an objective, focal length, 8 ft, and an eyepiece, focal length, 1 in?

6. The focal length of a camera lens is 2 in. How far must the lens be from the film to produce a clear image of an object 10 ft away?

GROUP B

7. The objective lens of a compound microscope has a focal length of 0.5 cm. The eyepiece has a focal length of 2 cm. If the lenses are 15 cm apart, what is the magnifying power of the microscope?

8. The dimensions of the picture on a standard lantern slide are $2\frac{1}{2}$ by 3 in. This slide is to be projected to form an image 5 ft by 6 ft at a distance of 30 ft from the objective lens of the projector. What focal length objective lens must be used? What is the distance from the slide to the objective lens?

9. The tube of a microscope is 160 mm long. If the focal length of the eyepiece is 3 cm and the focal length of the objective is 5 mm, find the magnifying power.

● **10.** What is the distance between the objective lens and the eyepiece lens of a terrestrial telescope when viewing an object 1 mile away? Focal length of objective, 5 in. Focal length of inverting lens system, 1 in. The two lenses are 2 inches apart. Focal length of eyepiece, 2 in.

Unit 10

Electricity

Of all the forms of energy, electricity is the most useful. What would your home life be like if suddenly all the electrical appliances were removed? You would have no electric lights, no radios, no television sets. You would have no motors to drive the fans or pumps which help circulate the heat through your home in winter.

Electricity is useful because it can readily be changed into other forms of energy. It promotes certain chemical changes. We use it to produce heat and light. We use it to transmit sounds and pictures over wires or through the air. By means of motors we convert it into mechanical energy.

Because electricity is so very important to our way of living in the United States, vast dams and power supply projects have been built both by the government and by private industry to supply our ever-growing need for electricity. The photograph shows the dam and powerhouse at Grand Coulee — the largest man-made structure ever built.

Chapter 24

Static Electricity

1. Static electricity was discovered many centuries ago. Thales (*thay-leez*), a wise man of ancient Greece, is believed to be the first person to have discovered some effects of *static* electricity. About 600 B.C., he found that by rubbing amber with flannel it could be made to attract bits of paper or thin shavings of wood. (Amber is the fossilized resin from prehistoric soft-wood trees.)

Many years later, William Gilbert (1540–1603), an early English scientist, made an additional discovery. He learned that many different kinds of materials act the same way that amber does. When they are rubbed they acquire the property of attracting other lightweight objects. Gilbert gave the name *electricity* (from the Greek word for amber, *elektron*) to this phenomenon.

2. Friction produces static electricity. Have you ever noticed a crackling sound when you stroke a cat's back in dry, cold weather? During the winter months you can shuffle around over a rug or carpet and easily acquire enough static electricity by friction to make a spark when you touch the metal part of an electric lamp or light switch. If you try to comb dry hair with a plastic comb, the hair flies out in all directions. Also, the electrified comb will attract bits of paper. *Stationary electric charges* are termed *static electricity.*

To detect the presence of static electricity we may use an *electroscope* like that shown in Fig. 24-1. It consists of a lightweight ball of wood pith suspended by means of a silk thread. Sometimes the pith ball is coated with metallic paint to make its surface a better conductor. Suppose that we electrify a glass rod by rubbing it with silk. Now, when we hold the electrified rod near the ball, we find that it

---

Vocabulary

CAPACITOR. A combination of conducting plates separated by insulators.

CONDUCTOR. A material through which an electric charge can readily travel.

ELECTROSCOPE. A device for detecting the presence of an electric charge, determining its sign, or measuring its intensity.

INSULATOR. A material through which an electric charge does not readily pass.

ION. An atom or a group of atoms which has an excess of electrons or a deficiency of electrons.

STATIC ELECTRICITY. Stationary electric charges.

472

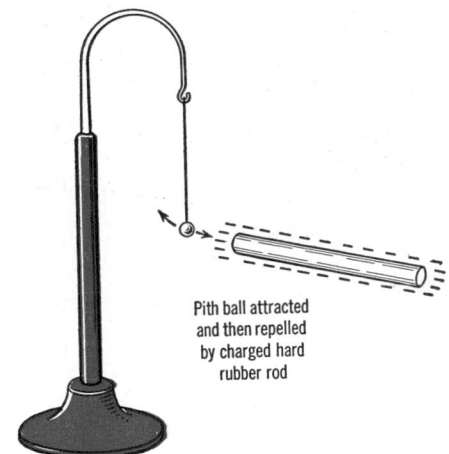

Fig. 24-1. The behavior of a pith ball electroscope when a negatively-charged hard rubber rod is brought near.

is first attracted to the rod, and then repelled. The same effect is produced if we rub a rod of hard rubber with flannel or catskin and then hold the rod near the electroscope. Also, we find that the silk, flannel, and catskin show signs of electrification when tested with the electroscope.

3. There are two kinds of electric charges. Let us electrify a glass rod by rubbing it with silk and then suspend it by a silk thread, as shown in Fig. 24-2. If we bring near it a second glass rod electrified in the same manner, the rods repel each other. If we bring the suspended glass rod near a piece of hard rubber which has been electrified by rubbing it with catskin, we find that the two rods attract. In a similar fashion we can show that one electrified hard-rubber rod is repelled by a second similarly electrified hard-rubber rod. However, an electrified hard-rubber rod is attracted by a glass rod which has been electrified by rubbing it with silk. From such experiments we conclude that there are two

ways in which bodies may be electrified, or *charged*. The names given to the two types of electrification, or charges, are *positive* and *negative*. These terms were introduced by Benjamin Franklin (1706–1790).

The type of electric charge produced on a glass rod by rubbing the rod with silk is called a *positive charge*. The electric charge produced on a hard-rubber rod by rubbing it with a piece of catskin is called a *negative charge*. From the experiments we performed with electrified rods, we conclude that: *Like electrical charges repel each other; unlike electrical charges attract.*

4. What is an electroscope? When a charged rod is brought near an electroscope, Fig. 24-1, the lightweight pith ball is first attracted to the rod, and then repelled. While the rod and pith ball are in contact, some of the charge from the rod spreads out over the ball. When the pith ball becomes sufficiently charged with the same kind of electricity as the rod, it is repelled.

A more sensitive electroscope is shown in Fig. 24-3. It consists of a brass rod with a brass ball or disc at one end. The rod passes through a rubber stopper which fits the mouth of a glass flask. Two strips of gold leaf or aluminum foil are attached to the

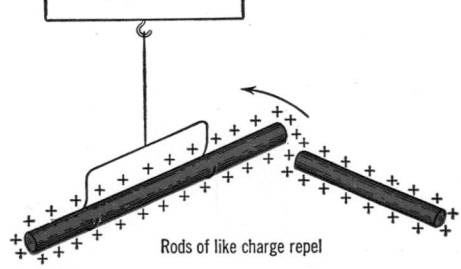

Fig. 24-2. Rods with like charges repel each other.

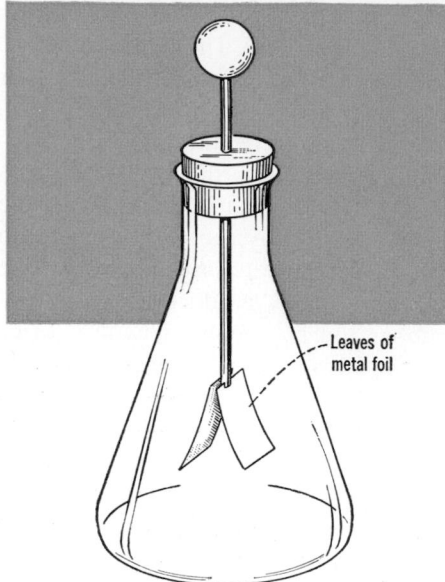

Fig. 24-3. A simple electroscope with leaves of metal foil.

lower end of the rod. If an electric charge is applied to the ball or disc, it spreads down over the rod to the leaves or foil. This charges both leaves with

electricity of the same kind, and as a result, they repel one another.

If we apply too intense a charge to an electroscope, the leaves are so strongly repelled that they may be torn. In order to prevent this from happening we may use a *proof plane*. This device can be made by cementing a penny to a glass or hard-rubber rod. To use a proof plane, we first touch the penny to the charged object and then to the knob of the electroscope. An efficient **electroscope** of the type shown in Fig. 24-4 may be used *to detect the presence of an electric charge, to determine its sign, or to measure its intensity.* Such an electroscope may be used for studying radioactive materials.

5. Conductors and insulators. Let us support the ball *B* of Fig. 24-5 by a silk thread and then join the ball to the knob of an electroscope by means of a copper wire. If the ball *B* is then charged electrically, the leaves of the electroscope diverge. Apparently, the

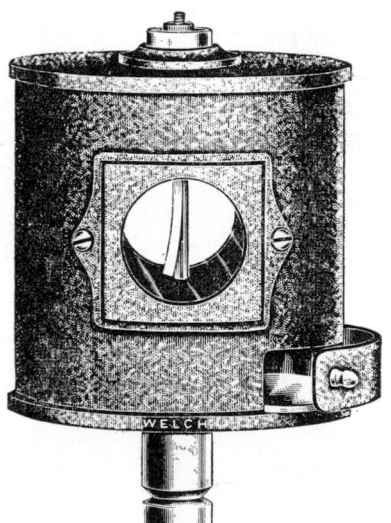

Fig. 24-4. The Hoag electroscope is used to detect radioactivity.

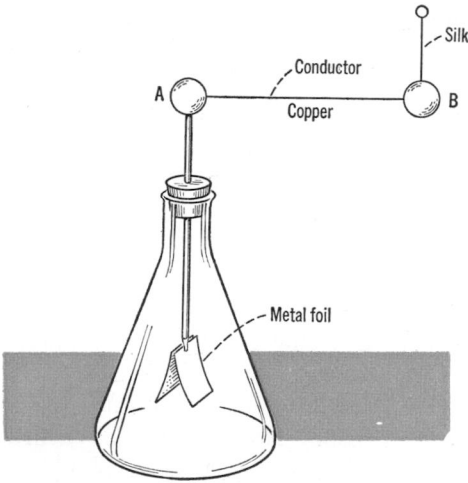

Fig. 24-5. Copper is a conductor because electric charges readily travel along it.

charge which is placed on *B* can travel through the copper wire to the electroscope. Let us repeat the experiment. This time, however, we connect the ball to the knob of the electroscope by means of a silk thread. Now we find that the charge which is applied to the ball *B* does not travel to the electroscope. It does not make the leaves of the electroscope diverge.

A material through which an electric charge can readily travel is called a **conductor.** Metals are good conductors. Silver is the best known conductor. Copper and aluminum also are very good conductors.

Materials through which an electric charge does not readily pass are called **insulators.** Some of the best insulators are mica, rubber, Bakelite, paraffin, shellac, oils, silk, wool, sulfur, and dry hair.

6. Some particles of matter are electrically-charged. In our study of the structure of matter in Chapter 1, we learned that atoms are composed of electrically-charged particles — protons and electrons — and neutral particles — neutrons.

On the basis of this theory of the structure of matter, we shall explain what happens in a familiar type of chemical reaction, and what happens in producing static (stationary) electric charges.

7. Applications of the theory of the structure of matter. (1) *To a chemical reaction.* The sodium atom, represented in Fig. 24-6, has eleven protons in its nucleus. Each proton has a single positive electric charge. There are eleven electrons revolving in orbits about the nucleus. Each electron has a single negative charge. There are two electrons in the first, or

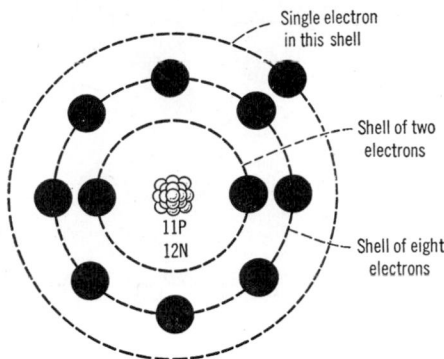

Fig. 24-6. The sodium atom has a tendency to give up the single electron in its outer shell.

innermost, orbit, eight in the second, and a single electron in the third, or outermost orbit. Since the number of protons equals the number of electrons, this atom is electrically neutral. However, a sodium atom has a tendency to give up its outer electron. When a sodium atom loses this outer electron it becomes a sodium *ion,* with one unbalanced positive charge. Using the chemical symbol Na for sodium and e^- for electron, we may write an equation to show this change:

$$Na - e^- = Na^+.$$

Fig. 24-7 represents an atom of chlorine with seventeen protons in the nucleus and seventeen electrons in orbits about the nucleus. Seven electrons are in the outermost orbit. The chemical symbol for chlorine is Cl. The chlorine atom has a tendency to take another electron. In this way it acquires a negative charge and becomes a chloride ion:

$$Cl + e^- = Cl^-.$$

When the positive sodium ion, Na^+, unites with a negative chloride ion, Cl^-, common table salt, NaCl, is formed.

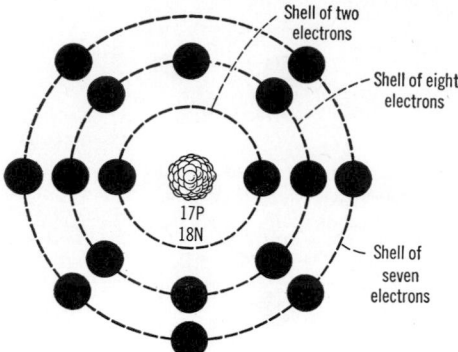

Fig. 24-7. The chlorine atom has a tendency to take another electron in its outer shell.

See Fig. 24-8. Many chemical changes occur in a similar manner.

(2) *To the production of electrostatic charges.* A glass rod is made up of atoms composed of protons and electrons. We believe that protons occupy rather fixed positions in solids, but that the electrons have some freedom of movement. If the number of electrons in the glass rod equals the number of protons, the glass rod has *no unbalanced electrical charges.* When we rub the glass rod with silk, some electrons are scraped off the glass and adhere to the silk. The glass is

now *deficient in electrons;* it has a *positive charge.* The silk, however, has an *excess of electrons;* it has become *negatively-charged.* When we rub a hard-rubber rod with catskin, electrons are rubbed off the catskin by the hard rubber. In this way the hard rubber becomes negatively charged, and the catskin becomes positively charged.

8. Two methods of producing electrification. (1) *The contact method.* Suppose we have a negatively-charged hard-rubber rod. Since it is negatively-charged, *it has an excess of electrons.* Now let us touch the rod with a proof plane, as shown in Fig. 24-9. While the rod and proof plane are in contact, some electrons from the rod move onto the proof plane. The rod *shares* its excess electrons with the proof plane. The proof plane has been charged by *contact,* or by *conduction.*

If we touch a positively-charged glass rod with the proof plane, some electrons flow from the proof plane to the glass rod to help equalize the deficiency of electrons. Both the rod and the proof plane will now have a positive charge. See Fig. 24-10. *An object which is charged by contact always*

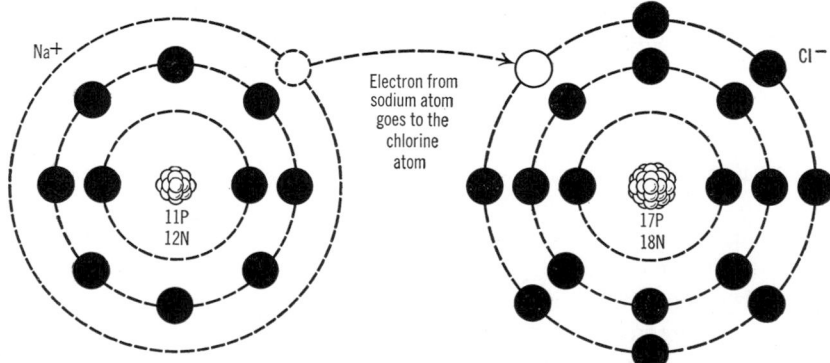

Fig. 24-8. In forming table salt, the sodium atom transfers its outer electron to the chlorine atom.

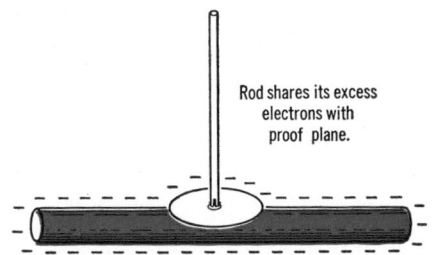

Fig. 24-9. The proof plane becomes negatively charged by contact with the rod because some of the electrons which are on the rod flow onto the proof plane.

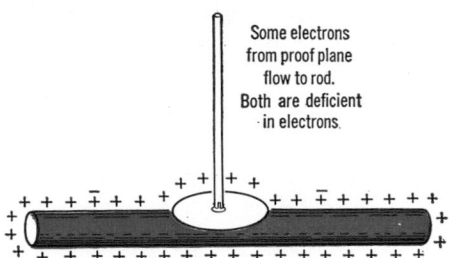

Fig. 24-10. The proof plane becomes positively charged by contact because some of its electrons flow onto the positively-charged rod, and leave the proof plane with a deficiency of electrons.

acquires a charge of the same sign as the object which touches it.

(2) *The induction method.* Let us next see what happens when we bring a charged rod *near* a conductor, but do not touch it. The conductor *AB*, Fig. 24-11, is insulated from the earth. It has an equal number of electrons and protons. It is electrically neutral. Suppose we bring a *negatively-charged* rod, *C*, near *AB*. Immediately, some of the electrons of *AB* are repelled. They move toward the far end of the conductor. When the rod is removed, the electrons spread over the conductor as before. Let us next bring a *positively-charged* rod near the conductor. Now the electrons are attracted to the near end of the conductor. The far end has a deficiency of electrons.

A charged rod brought near a conductor induces electricity of the same sign in the far end of the conductor. It induces electricity of the opposite sign in the near end of the conductor.

9. An electroscope may be charged by induction. Fig. 24-12*A* shows an uncharged electroscope. It has neither an excess nor a deficiency of electrons. If you hold a negatively-charged rod near the knob of the electroscope,

Fig. 24-12*B*, the electrons are repelled to the opposite side of the knob and to the leaves. Since both leaves are now negatively charged, they diverge widely. Next touch the knob with your finger, as in Fig. 24-12*C*. Some electrons are now repelled through your body, which is a fair conductor, to the earth. And since electrons have been driven from both the knob and the leaves, these parts of the electroscope

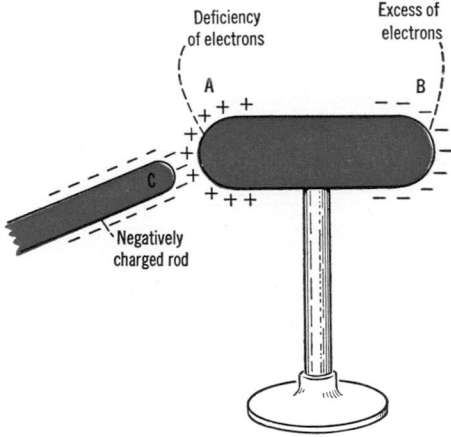

Fig. 24-11. A charged rod brought near a conductor induces electricity of the same sign in the far end of the conductor. It induces electricity of the opposite sign in the near end of the conductor.

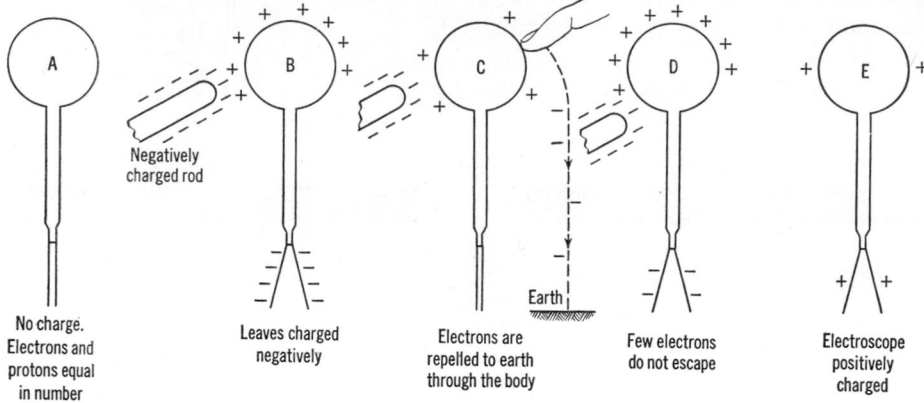

Fig. 24-12. The steps in the method of charging an electroscope by induction.

are left with unbalanced positive charges.

Remove your finger from the knob. See Fig. 24-12D. The electrons which were repelled to the earth through your body can not return easily. The electroscope now is charged *positively,* as shown in Fig. 24-12E. Eventually, enough electrons will return to the electroscope through the air to discharge it.

You also can charge an electroscope with negative electricity. To do this, hold a positively-charged glass rod near the knob, touch the knob, remove your finger, and then remove the rod.

By using a charged electroscope, you can determine the sign of an unknown electric charge. For example, you may touch a proof plane to a charged object of unknown sign. Then bring the proof plane in contact with the knob of a *positively-charged* electroscope. If the sign of the object of unknown charge is positive, the divergence of the leaves will be increased; if the sign is negative, the divergence will be diminished.

10. Where do electric charges reside? Michael Faraday used a silk bag of conical shape, like that of Fig. 24-13, to show the location of the charges on an electrically-charged object. When he gave the bag an electrical charge and then tested it, he found that the charges were on the *outside* of the bag. By pulling the string, Faraday turned the bag inside out. But when he tested it, he found that the charges were again on the outside. The inside of the bag showed no electrification.

Fig. 24-14 represents a hollow metal

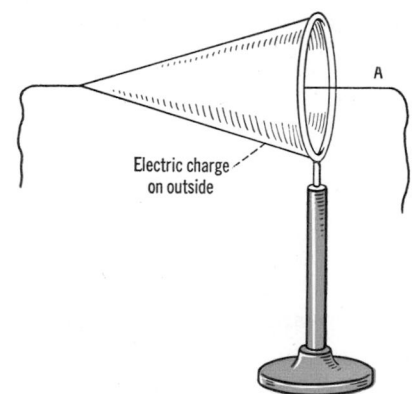

Fig. 24-13. The type of conical silk bag used by Faraday to demonstrate that electric charges reside on the outside.

tube mounted on an insulated stand. Two pith balls are suspended from a hook placed on the outside of the cylinder, and two pith balls are hung from a loop on the inside. If the cylinder is connected by means of a chain or wire to an electrical machine, the pith balls on the outside will diverge when the machine charges the cylinder. But the pith balls inside are not affected. This experiment shows us that electric charges reside on the outside of a conductor.

11. The effect of the shape of a conductor. Suppose we electrify an egg-shaped conductor like that shown in Fig. 24-15. When we test it with a proof plane, we find that all parts of the conductor are not equally charged. The density of the charges is greater at the small end than it is at the large end. If we increase the curvature at the small end by making it more pointed, the density of the charges in-

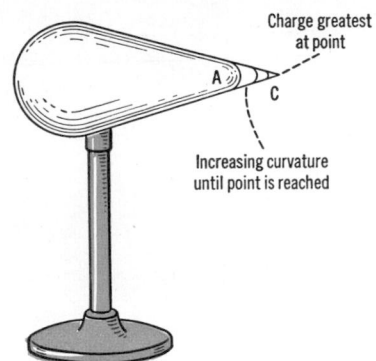

Fig. 24-15. The electrical density is greatest at the point of greatest curvature.

creases, too. *The electrical density, or the quantity of charge per unit area, is greatest at the point of greatest curvature.*

12. The discharging effect of points. Suppose we make the egg-shaped conductor of Fig. 24-15 still more pointed. The electrical density at the pointed end increases, too. Finally, the density of the charges becomes so great that the air surrounding the point becomes *ionized*. *An* **ion** *is defined as an atom or a group of atoms that has an excess or deficiency of electrons.* If gas molecules in the air lose electrons, they form positive ions; when the gas molecules gain electrons, they form negative ions. If a conductor, shown in Fig. 24-15, is positively charged, the gas near the point becomes positively charged, too. Because the strong positive charge of the conductor strips some electrons from them, the gas molecules become positively charged. The positively-charged gas ions are then repelled from the conductor with sufficient velocity to produce an *electrical wind.* The electrons torn from the gas molecules by the positively-charged conductor are attracted to the

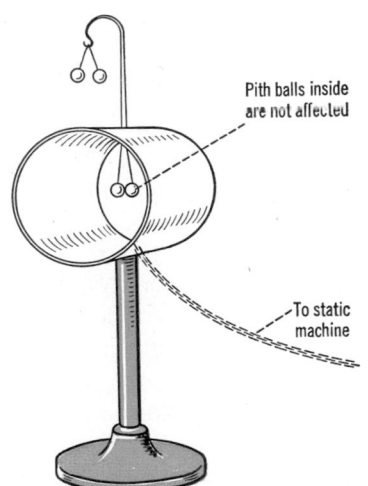

Fig. 24-14. When the metal cylinder is charged by the static machine, the pith balls outside diverge, while those inside are not affected. What does this tell us about the location of the charge?

Fig. 24-16. An artificial lightning discharge produced by a 2,400,000 volt impulse generator. This impulse generator is used for testing large power transformers.

conductor and tend to neutralize its charge. As a result, *a pointed conductor loses its charge rapidly*. This leakage of electricity from points on the surface of a charged object is called the *discharging effect of points*.

A charged electroscope may be discharged rapidly if we hold a needle a few inches from the knob. The point of the needle becomes charged by induction. Electrons pass between the needle and the knob and neutralize the charge on the electroscope.

13. How is an electric spark produced? We are all familiar with the sparks produced in some electrical machinery. We can produce sparks, too, by stroking the fur on a cat's back, or by shuffling across a rug and touching

the metal part of an electric lamp. Air is normally an electrical insulator because the gas molecules composing it are electrically neutral. We have seen, however, that strongly-charged bodies may strip electrons from gas molecules and change them into charged ions.

If a gas ion is near a charged body, considerable attractive or repulsive force may be exerted on the ion. This force will give the ion a high velocity. Its velocity may become great enough to enable the ion to break off an electron from a gas molecule with which it collides. This forms two ions. These may again collide with other molecules forming four ions. These in turn may form eight ions, and so on. Since there are large numbers of molecules in the gas, many ions may be formed almost immediately by this process. The formation of ions makes the air a conductor. Electrons then move through the air and the strong charges which originally produced the ions are neutralized. We see this movement of electrons as an electric spark. Air is heated and expanded by the spark. We hear a sharp crack as the air cools and rushes together again. The entire process takes only about a millionth of a second. See Fig. 24-16.

14. What is lightning? You no doubt know the story of Benjamin Franklin and his kite. See Fig. 24-17. When Franklin flew his kite in a thunderstorm, he succeeded in drawing sparks from a key fastened to the string of the kite. This was how Franklin proved that a lightning flash and an electric spark are identical.

Sometimes a lightning discharge takes place between two clouds. In other cases it occurs between a cloud and the earth. Perhaps because of the

Fig. 24-17. Franklin's famous experiment which proved that lightning and electricity were the same. This was a very dangerous experiment. It is a wonder that Franklin was not killed by a stroke of lightning.

rapid condensation of its water vapor a cloud becomes electrically charged. Suppose an electric charge much higher than that of the earth is built up. Then a violent electrical discharge may occur between the cloud and an object on the earth. When this happens, we say that the object has been " struck " by lightning. The air, which is normally an insulator, " breaks down " under the exceedingly high charge, and permits the discharge to take place.

★ **15. Lightning rods furnish some protection.** The lightning rod was invented by Franklin to protect buildings from the destructive effects of lightning. We believe that this is how they work. A pointed rod which extends above a building becomes charged inductively when a cloud passes over it. The rod helps to discharge the cloud quietly in much the same manner that the pointed end of a needle discharges an electroscope.

Lightning rods are frequently used on isolated buildings, like farmhouses, barns, and fire towers. Power lines, power stations, and other electrical structures are usually protected against damage by lightning.

16. What is a capacitor? Let us connect the insulated metal plate, *A*, to an electroscope as shown in Fig. 24-19. Now let us charge this plate. As we increase the intensity of the charge, the leaves of the electroscope

Fig. 24-18. A house equipped with a lightning rod protection system.

diverge more widely. But suppose we have a second plate, *B*, which is connected with the earth, or grounded. When we bring this grounded plate *B* near plate *A*, the leaves of the electroscope begin to fall together. The quantity of charge on *A* has not been decreased. But the distribution of electrons on *A* is no longer uniform. If we add more charges to plate *A*, we find its *capacity* is decidedly greater. Several times as much charge must be added to *A* to produce the same divergence of the leaves as before.

A combination of conducting plates separated by insulators is known as a **capacitor,** *or condenser.* In our ex-

periment above, the air gap between the plates acts as the insulator. If we shove a glass plate down between the two metal plates, the leaves of the electroscope collapse to some extent. The glass plate increases the capacity of plate *A* still more, because glass is a better insulator than air. Mica is one of the best insulators for a capacitor. If we use larger plates, we increase the amount of charge which may be held by the capacitor. From our experiments, we conclude that *the amount of charge held by a capacitor increases with the size of the plates, increases as the distance between the plates is decreased, and depends upon the insulator, or dielectric.*

17. Operation of a capacitor. Suppose plate *A* of Fig. 24-19 has a negative charge, and that we keep adding to the charge. Finally, the charge reaches a certain capacity at which electrons leak away to the air as fast as they are supplied. When plate *B* is brought opposite *A*, it becomes charged by induction. Its electrons are repelled to the far side of the plate and away to the earth through the

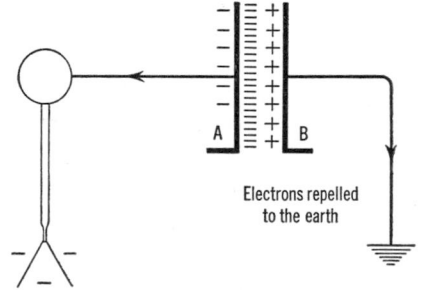

Electrons repelled to the earth

Fig. 24-19. The principle of the operation of a capacitor.

ground wire. The unbalanced positive charges remaining upon *B* " bind " the electrons on *A*. Consequently we can increase the number of electrons on *A* many times before the leaves of the electroscope diverge to their original position. Capacitors are used extensively in radio work.

The unit of electrical capacity is the *farad,* abbreviated f. But since the farad is such a large unit, the *microfarad,* μf, is more often used. A microfarad is one-millionth of a farad.

⭐ **18. The Leyden jar is a capacitor.** The Leyden-jar capacitor was made at the University of Leyden, Holland, as early as the middle of the eighteenth century. It consists of a glass jar, coated with metal foil about halfway up, both inside and outside. A knobbed brass rod extends through the stopper. The lower end of the rod is connected to the inner surface of the jar by means of a brass chain. See Fig. 24-20.

To charge a Leyden jar, we connect the knob with one terminal of an elec-

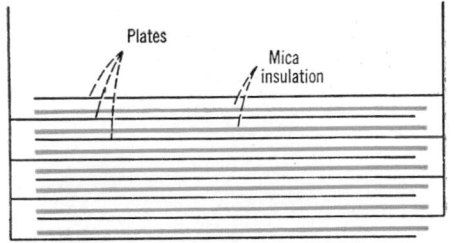

Fig. 24-21. The mica capacitor.

trical machine. The outer coating may be connected to the other terminal of the machine, or it may be grounded by holding the jar in your hand. The charge being applied to the inner surface is bound by the opposite charge induced on the outer coating. You may discharge the jar by touching the two surfaces simultaneously, or by touching the knob when the jar stands on the table. It may also be discharged by placing one end of a bent conductor in contact with the outer surface and then bringing the other end close to the knob of the Leyden jar.

19. There are several types of commercial capacitors. Capacitors having a *fixed capacity* may be made in several ways. The mica capacitor consists of a number of small metal plates separated by thin mica sheets. See Fig. 24-21. The assembled plates are

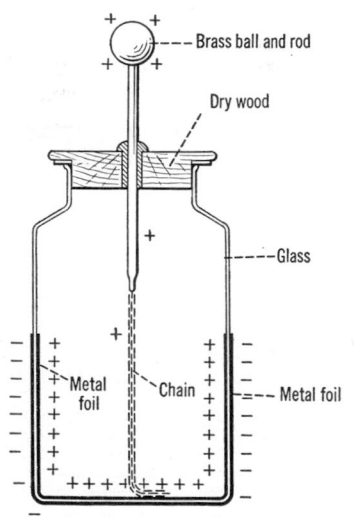

Fig. 24-20. The Leyden jar capacitor.

Fig. 24-22. A common type of capacitor.

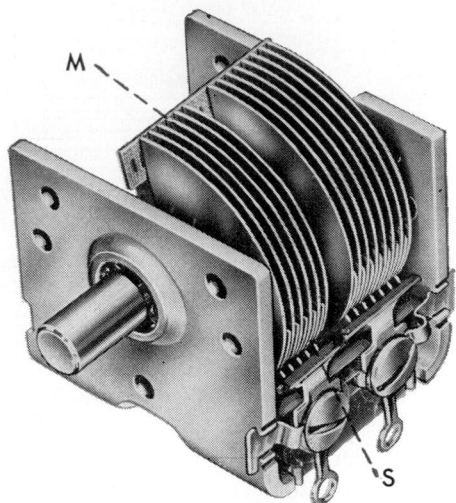

Fig. 24-23. The capacity of a variable capacitor is changed by varying the amount by which the movable plates overlap the fixed plates.

usually covered by an insulating material like Bakelite, as in Fig. 24-22. Some capacitors use waxed paper as the dielectric. These consist of two strips of metal foil separated by wax paper. The strips are rolled to form a cylinder and then coated with wax to keep out moisture and air. Electrolytic capacitors consist of plates of aluminum foil alternated with pieces of gauze which have been saturated with borax solution. When the capacitor is operated, a thin film of aluminum oxide and oxygen forms on the surface of the aluminum foil. The aluminum foil forms one plate of the capacitor; the borax solution the second plate. The aluminum oxide and oxygen act as the dielectric.

Variable capacitors are used in radio receivers. We use them to select the particular station to which we wish to listen. A variable capacitor consists of several sets of stationary metal discs, *S*, Fig. 24-23, which have about half the surface of the disc cut away. Similar metal plates are mounted on an axis. When the axis is turned, these metal plates, *M*, slide between adjacent fixed plates. The two sets of plates are insulated by the air. They do not touch one another. As more of the surfaces of the plates overlap when we turn the axis, the capacity is increased.

★ **20. What is an electrophorus?** The electrophorus (eh-lek-*trof*-er-us), shown in Fig. 24-24, was invented by Alessandro Volta (1745–1827). The bed, *A*, is composed of hard rubber, or some other insulating material. *B* is a metal disc which has an insulated handle. When you rub the hard-rubber bed with a piece of catskin or other

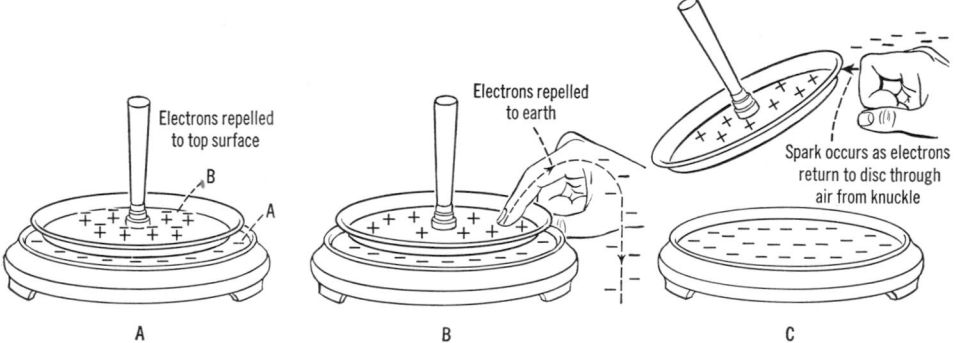

Fig. 24-24. The charging and discharging of the disc of an electrophorus.

fur, it becomes negatively charged. Now place the disc upon the hard-rubber bed. It is not charged appreciably by contact, since it touches the surface of the insulating material at only a few points. *It may be strongly charged by induction.* Electrons are repelled to the upper surface of the disc, as shown in Fig. 24-24*A*. If you touch the disc with a finger, the electrons are repelled to the earth, and the disc becomes positively charged. See Fig. 24-24*B*.

If you lift the disc and hold the knuckle of a finger near the edge, a short electric spark may be drawn from the disc. See Fig. 24-24*C*. By returning the disc to the bed, touching it a second time with a finger, and then lifting it, another spark may be obtained. You may repeat this procedure several times without recharging the bed of hard rubber.

★ **21. How do induction machines work?** There are several machines that generate static charges by induction. One of these is the Wimshurst machine. When the terminals of this device are separated and the crank turned, a difference of charge is built up between the terminals. When the difference of charge becomes sufficiently great, the air becomes ionized and an electric spark jumps between the terminals. Static or induction machines may produce a spark several inches long.

22. Electrostatic devices collect dust particles. The Cottrell apparatus may be used to remove smoke and dust particles from flue gases. In the apparatus of Fig. 24-26 the wires are highly charged. Then the dust particles, which become charged with electricity of the same sign, are repelled toward the opposite terminal. In this

Fig. 24-25. When the large glass discs are rotated, the Wimshurst machine generates static electricity by induction.

way valuable material can be recovered and the dust nuisance eliminated at the same time.

In order to remove dust particles from the heating and ventilating air circulated through homes and offices, elec-

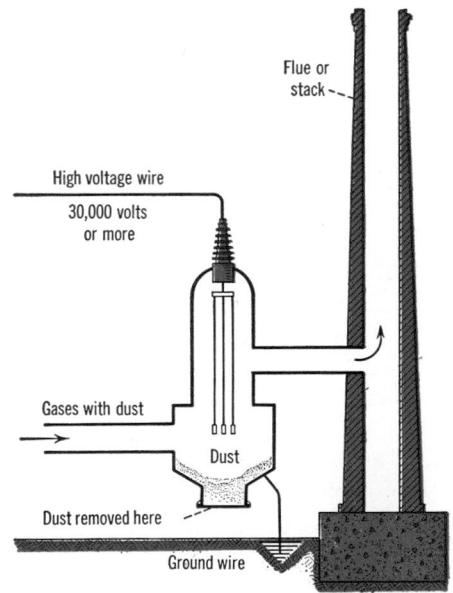

Fig. 24-26. The Cottrell apparatus electrostatically precipitates dust and dirt.

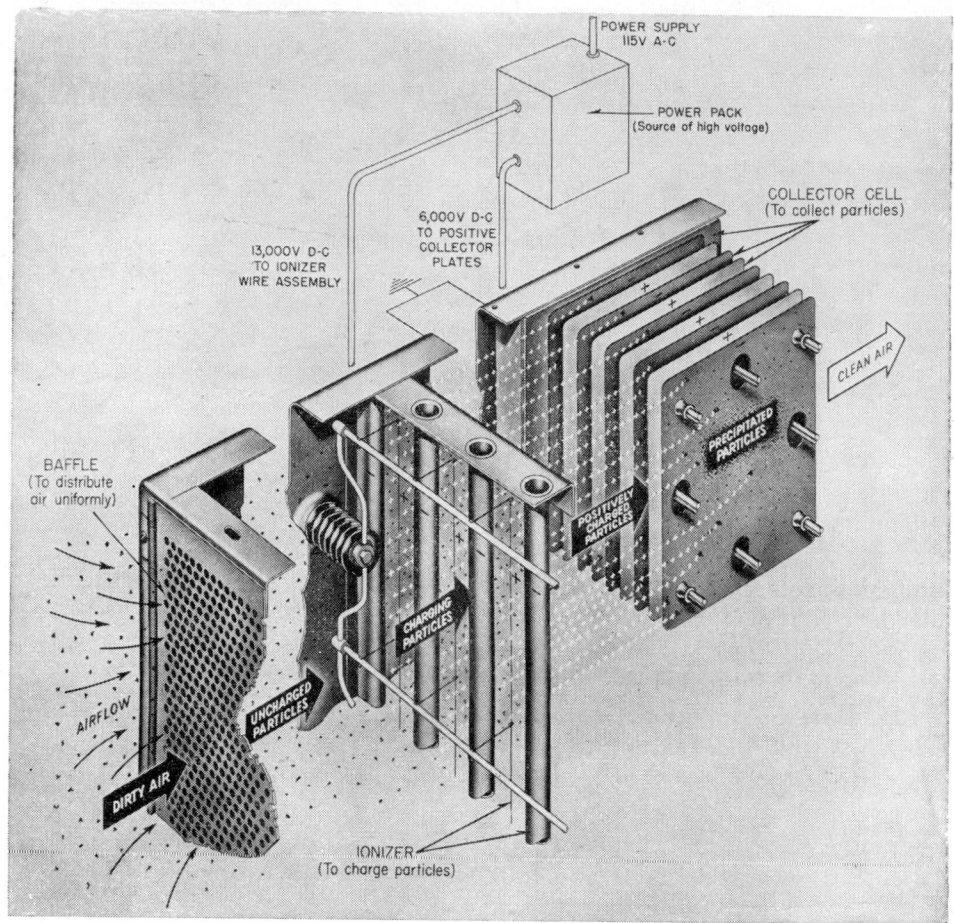

Fig. 24-27. Diagram showing the operation of an electronic dust precipitator. The dust particles are first given a positive charge by the ionizer. Then they are attracted to the negatively-charged collector plates.

tronic air cleaners have been developed. One such device, shown in Fig. 24-27, first gives the dust particles passing through it a positive charge. These positively-charged particles are then attracted to negatively-charged collector plates. The dust is held firmly on these plates by an adhesive coating. The plates are washed periodically to remove accumulated dust. Such cleaners remove 90% of the dust from the air passing through them.

23. Overcoming the hazards of static electricity. The spark produced during a static electric discharge may be hot enough to ignite flammable cleaning fluids. Extreme care should be exercised when using these fluids, or an explosion and fire may result. Modern hospital operating rooms are equipped with conducting floor surfaces. All equipment is grounded. Physicians and nurses must wear special shoes with conducting soles. These precautions are necessary to prevent explosive anesthetic vapors igniting from a spark of static electricity.

Conducting belting is used for power and conveyor belts. Ordinary belting accumulates electric charges as it moves over the various wheels. Sparks from the discharge of this belting may injure workers and equipment. An automobile becomes charged from the continuous flexing of the tires and tubes as well as from the motion of the tires on the road. Powdered carbon black, a conductor, is used in some inner tubes to prevent the accumulation of charges. The small wire sticking up from the road near toll booths on a super highway draws off the charge from your automobile. Then you and the toll collector do not get shocked as you exchange money. On days when the relative humidity is about 80%, we do not experience shocks from static electricity. Then the charge leaks off on the water molecules in the air.

Fig. 24-28. This wire sticking up from the roadway draws the static electric charge from the automobile as it approaches a toll booth on a super highway.

Summary

Static electric charges may be produced on an object by friction. There are two kinds of electric charges, positive and negative. Like electrical charges repel each other; unlike electrical charges attract.

An electroscope is used to detect the presence of an electric charge, to determine its sign, or to measure its intensity.

Conductors transmit electric charges readily. Insulators, or dielectrics, are poor transmitters.

Electrically-charged particles make up the atoms of which all matter is composed. A positively-charged object is deficient in electrons. A negatively-charged object has an excess of electrons.

Objects can be electrified by contact with a charged object. They may also be electrified by induction. An electric charge resides on the outside of a conductor. It has its greatest density where the curvature is greatest. A pointed conductor loses its charge rapidly.

An electric spark is produced when the air becomes ionized and permits the passage of electrons. Lightning is a violent electrical discharge. Metal rods are often used to protect buildings against lightning.

A capacitor is a combination of conducting plates separated by insulators. The amount of charge held by a capacitor increases with the size of the plates, increases as the distance between the plates is decreased, and depends upon the insulator.

Electrostatic devices are used to collect dust particles. Special conducting devices frequently are used to overcome the hazards of static electricity.

Terms to Define...

Capacitor	Electrostatic dust precipita-	Lightning rod
Charging by contact	tors	Location of charge on a con-
Charging by induction	Excess of electrons	ductor
Conductor	Farad	Microfarad
Deficiency of electrons	Fixed capacitor	Negative charge
Discharging effect of points	Hazards of static electricity	Positive charge
Electrical density	Insulator	Proof plane
Electric spark	Ion	Static electricity
Electrophorus	Leyden jar	Variable capacitor
Electroscope	Lightning	Wimshurst machine

Questions

GROUP A

1. What happens to the electrons on the surface of a glass rod when we rub it with a silk cloth? What charge does the rod acquire? What charge does the silk cloth acquire?

2. What happens to the electrons on a piece of cat's fur when we use it to rub a hard-rubber rod? What charge does the cat's fur acquire? What charge does the rod acquire?

3. Explain why a pith ball is attracted to a charged hard-rubber rod. If the pith ball touches the rod, it is suddenly repelled. Why?

4. What rule governs the attraction and repulsion of charged bodies?

5. Why do the leaves of an electroscope separate if a charged rod is brought near? Does it make any difference whether the rod is charged negatively or positively?

6. What is a conductor? What is an insulator? Give several examples of good conductors and good insulators.

7. Explain how an electroscope is charged by contact. How does the charge put on the electroscope compare with the charge on the charging body?

8. How is an electroscope charged by induction? How does the charge put on the electroscope compare with the charge on the charging body?

9. Why does the charge reside *only on the outside* of a charged body?

10. Explain how the charge is distributed on the surface of an egg-shaped body.

11. Why is an electroscope easily discharged by bringing a needle near its knob?

12. What is lightning?

13. What is a capacitor? What determines the amount of charge which may be held by a capacitor?

14. Explain how a capacitor holds a larger

charge on a conductor than the conductor normally could hold.

15. Why do you sometimes feel a spark when you touch the door handle of an automobile after sliding across the plastic seat covers?

16. Why are equal quantities of both positive and negative charges produced at the same time?

GROUP B

17. How may an electroscope be used to determine whether a body is positively or negatively charged?

18. Why are the occupants of a modern steel-frame building not harmed when such a building is struck by lightning during a severe thunderstorm?

19. Why is it impossible to perform static elec-tricity experiments when the relative humidity is high?

20. The two knobs of an electrostatic machine are placed one inch apart. Explain what happens as the knobs acquire opposite charges by the rotation of the machine.

21. Describe three types of fixed capacitors. How is a variable capacitor made?

22. How do electrostatic dust precipitators remove dust particles from the air? Why are they more effective than filters?

★ **23.** How do lightning rods offer protection to a building?

★ **24.** The disc of an electrophorus may be discharged several times before the bed must be recharged. What is the source of the energy which produces the electric spark which jumps to your knuckle when the disc is discharged?

Things to Do

1. Write a report on modern uses of static electricity and on the ways in which static electricity is controlled to prevent dangerous explosions.

2. Several members of the class may visit an industrial or residential dust precipitator instal-lation and report to the class on its operation.

3. Perform static electricity experiments at home. A comb will serve as the hard-rubber rod. A piece of wool or flannel can be used in place of the cat's skin. Small bits of paper can substitute for pith balls.

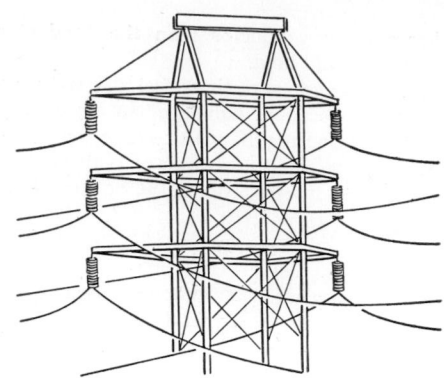

Chapter 25

Current Electricity

1. Comparison of static electricity and current electricity. In Chapter 24 we studied the properties of static charges of electricity. We found that they flowed from one charged body to another of different charge if the bodies were connected by a conductor. This is the way we discharged a Leyden jar capacitor. We also saw how objects of greatly different charge might ionize the air, temporarily cause it to become a conductor, and allow charges to pass between the objects. Electric sparks and lightning are examples of this type of moving charges.

But such moving charges are either too small to be of any practical value, or they are too great, and are thus destructive. They can not be produced and controlled with sufficient ease to light our homes, iron our clothes, or refrigerate our food.

If we compare the flow of electrons through a conductor with the flow of water through a pipe, it will help us in our first study of moving electric charges.

In Fig. 25-1 we see similar hydraulic and electrical systems. In the hydraulic system, the water is first raised

---

Vocabulary

AMMETER. The instrument used for measuring the rate of flow of electricity.

AMPERE. The unit for measuring the rate of flow of electricity.

CONDUCTANCE. The reciprocal of resistance.

DIRECT CURRENT. That type of electric current in which the electrons move continuously in one direction through the conductor.

ELECTRIC CURRENT. The flow of electrons along a conductor.

MIL. 0.001 inch.

OHM. The unit for measuring electrical resistance.

PARALLEL. That method of connecting electrical equipment with separate paths for the current through the various devices.

RESISTANCE. The opposition of a conductor to the flow of electrons.

RESISTIVITY. Resistance of a mil-ft of wire.

SERIES. That method of connecting electrical equipment so that all the current must flow through each device in turn.

SOURCE OF ELECTROMOTIVE FORCE. A device which furnishes electrons of increased potential energy.

VOLT. Unit of potential difference.

VOLTMETER. The instrument used for measuring difference of potential.

490

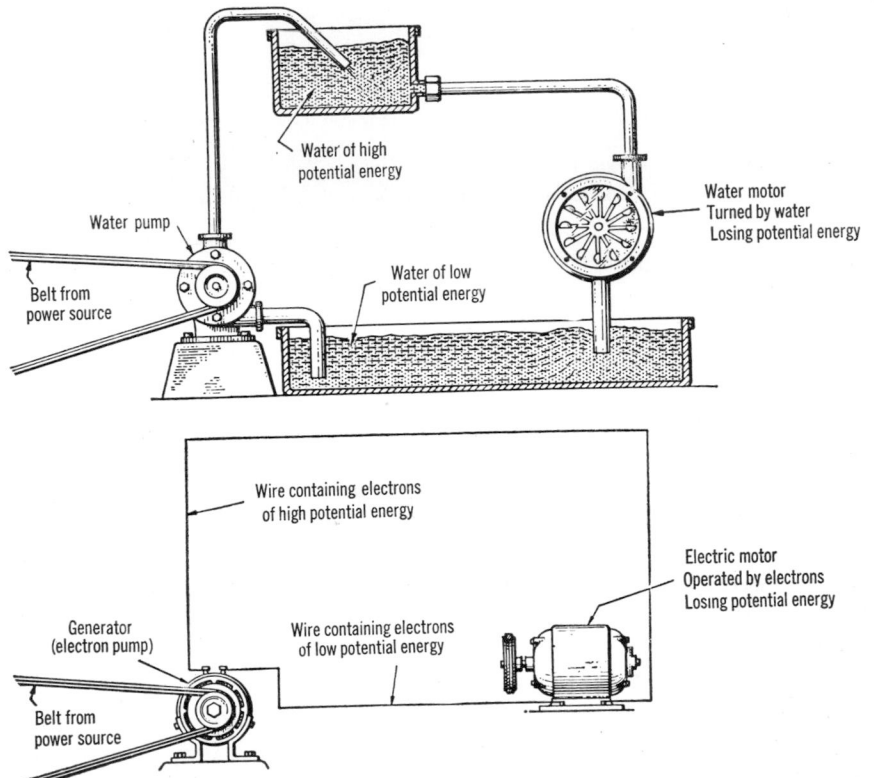

Fig. 25-1. The flow of water through the hydraulic circuit shown at the top and the flow of electrons through the electric circuit, bottom, are very similar.

to an elevated tank by a water pump. The pump is driven by an external power source. Raising the water increases its potential energy. The water may then flow from the tank and drive a water motor. The water loses potential energy driving the motor, and returns to its original elevation.

In similar fashion, an electric generator, serving as an " electron pump," raises the potential energy of the electrons passing through it. These electrons give up their increased potential energy when they operate an electric motor. *The flow of the electrons along the wire is what we call an* **electric current.**

2. How can we maintain the flow of electrons? In the hydraulic system described in Section 1 we needed a water pump to raise the potential energy of the water so that it could drive the water motor. Similarly, in an electrical system, we must have an " electron pump " to raise the potential energy of the electrons so that they may do useful work in driving an electric motor.

The water pump increases the potential energy of drops of water. The " electron pump " increases the potential energy of electrons. When the potential energy of the drops of water is being changed to kinetic energy, a

Fig. 25-2. Sources of electromotive force. From left to right, a flashlight battery, a dry cell, an automobile storage battery, and an automobile generator.

current of water is produced. When the potential energy of the electrons is being changed to kinetic energy, an electric current is produced. The more generally accepted term for what we have been calling an " electron pump " is a **source of electromotive force,** or *source of emf.* *This is a device which furnishes electrons of increased potential energy.* There are several such sources. One of these is an electric generator. Others are dry cells used in flashlights and storage batteries used in automobiles. All of these devices furnish electrons of increased potential energy at the expense of mechanical or chemical energy.

3. Some common electrical units. There are several units used by physicists to measure the characteristics of electric currents. Let us refer again to Fig. 25-1.

Because of the difference in level, the water flows from the upper tank, through the water motor, and into the lower reservoir. With electricity, the characteristic which is like *difference in level* is called **difference of potential,** or **potential difference.** *The unit in which difference of potential is measured is called the* **volt.** *The electrical instrument for measuring difference of potential is a* **voltmeter.**

We might measure the rate at which water flows through pipes in some unit such as gallons per second. *The rate of flow of electricity,* is called the **current,** and *is measured in a unit called the* **ampere.** *The instrument for measuring the rate of flow of electricity is an* **ammeter.**

The pipes through which water flows will offer some resistance to its passage. This is caused by friction between the walls of the pipe and the water molecules. Similarly, even the best *conductors* like silver and copper *offer some opposition, or* **resistance** *to the passage of electrons. We measure electrical resistance in a unit called the* **ohm.** Several methods for measuring resistance are described later in this chapter.

4. What is Ohm's law? We know that the amount of water flowing through a pipe will increase if the water pressure is increased. Also, that the amount of water which flows decreases if the resistance offered by the pipe increases. In a similar fashion, we might expect that the amount of current flowing in an electric circuit increases if the voltage is increased, and decreases if the resistance of the circuit is increased. Experiments show that this idea is correct. Georg Simon Ohm (1787–1854), a German physicist, was the first to express these observations in the form of a definite law. See Fig. 25-3. OHM'S LAW may be stated as follows: *The current flowing in a circuit, in amperes, is directly proportional to the potential difference, in volts, and inversely proportional to the resistance of the circuit, in ohms.*

current (amperes) =

$$\frac{\text{potential difference (volts)}}{\text{resistance (ohms)}}$$

The letter I is used to represent the current in amperes. V is used to represent the potential difference in volts. R is used to represent the resistance of the circuit in ohms. Ohm's law, stated algebraically, is

$$I = \frac{V}{R}.$$

See the Sample Problem below.

5. The laws of resistance. Various substances offer different amounts of

Fig. 25-3. Georg Simon Ohm (1787–1845) was a German physicist. He discovered the relation between electrical potential, current flow, and resistance, and formulated Ohm's law.

SAMPLE PROBLEM

What current, in amperes, will flow through a conductor with a resistance of 30 ohms if the potential difference is 120 volts?

SOLUTION

Ohm's law formula is $I = \frac{V}{R}$. In the problem I is the quantity we are asked to find. V equals 120 volts and R equals 30 ohms.

Substituting in the formula, $I = \frac{120 \text{ volts}}{30 \text{ ohms}}$.

Solving, $I = 4$ amperes, the current which will flow.

SAMPLE PROBLEM

In an electric circuit, what potential difference in volts is required to cause a current of 10 amperes to flow through a resistance of 4 ohms?

SOLUTION

Substituting in the formula, $I = \frac{V}{R}$, we obtain 10 amperes $= \frac{V}{4 \text{ ohms}}$.

Solving, $V = 40$ volts, the potential difference which is required.

resistance to the passage of an electric current. Some materials are good conductors. Others have a very high resistance. There are several factors which affect the resistance of a conductor.

(1) *Law of lengths.* If 1 foot of water pipe offers a certain amount of friction to a current of water flowing through it, we would expect 10 feet of pipe to offer 10 times as much friction. Using similar reasoning, we would expect 10 feet of wire to have 10 times as much resistance as 1 foot. Experiments prove that this is true. Therefore we conclude that *the resistance of a conductor is directly proportional to its length.*

(2) *Law of diameters.* Everyone knows that a 6-inch pipe will carry a larger current of water than a 1-inch pipe, assuming that the pressure is the same in both cases. We encounter much more friction when we force water through a pin-hole opening than when we force water through a larger opening. In the same manner, a small wire offers more resistance to the flow of electrons than does a large wire. Experiments show that a wire 1 mm in diameter has *four times* as much resistance as the same length of wire 2 mm in diameter. The wire of 2-mm diameter has *four times* as much cross-sectional area as the wire 1-mm in diameter. *The resistance of a conductor is inversely proportional to the square of its diameter, or to its cross-sectional area.*

(3) *Effect of temperature.* More current flows through the coils of an electric iron when the coils are cold than after they become hot. *The resistance of a metallic conductor increases with the temperature.*

(4) *The resistance depends upon the material.* Copper is the metal most often used as a conductor of electricity. Its resistance is lower than that of any other metal except silver. If we let the Greek letter ρ (rho) represent a *constant* which depends upon the material, the LAWS OF RESISTANCE for round wires may be summarized by the following formula:

$$R = \frac{\rho l}{d^2}.$$

The constant ρ is called the *resistivity* — it depends only on the material and the temperature; l is the length of the conductor in feet; and d is the diameter of the wire in *mils*. *A **mil** equals 0.001 inch.* Engineers sometimes measure the cross-sectional area of a round wire in *circular mils.* The area in circular mils equals the square of the diameter expressed in mils. If a wire has a diameter of 0.025 in, then its diameter equals 25 mils. Its cross-sectional area will be $(25)^2$, or 625 circular mils. The constant ρ represents the resistance in ohms of one foot of wire whose diameter is 0.001 in; or, **resistivity** *is the resistance of one mil-foot of wire.* Table 19, Appendix B, gives the value of ρ at 20° C for a few of the most used conductors. Table 20, Appendix B, gives certain properties of copper wire.

See Sample Problem, page 495.

6. Some everyday electrical terms. Before we can apply Ohm's law and the laws of resistance to electrical circuits, there are some terms we must learn to use. Sources of electromotive force like dry cells and automobile batteries have two terminals. One is marked *positive* (+) and the other *negative* (−). Joining these two ter-

SAMPLE PROBLEM

Find the resistance of 150 feet of No. 24 copper wire.

SOLUTION

First we must obtain some data from Appendix B. From Table 18, we find that for copper, $\rho = 10.37$. From Table 19 we find the diameter of No. 24 wire is 20.1 mils.

Substituting in the formula, $R = \dfrac{\rho l}{d^2}$, we obtain $R = \dfrac{10.37 \times 150}{(20.1)^2}$.

Solving, $R = 3.85$ ohms, resistance.

SAMPLE PROBLEM

What length of No. 36 nichrome wire must be used in making a resistance of 10,000 ohms?

SOLUTION

From Table 19, Appendix B, we learn that No. 36 wire is 5.00 mils in diameter. From Table 18, Appendix B, we find that ρ for nichrome is 602.

Substituting in the formula $10,000 = \dfrac{602\, l}{(5.00)^2}$. Squaring the denominator and cross-multiplying, $250,000 = 602\, l$.

Solving, $l = 415.3$ ft, the length of wire needed.

minals with a conductor is called *making,* or *closing* the circuit. When we disconnect the conductor we say we are *breaking* the circuit; the cell or battery is then on *open circuit.* We frequently use a *conventional diagram* to represent a cell. This is not an actual diagram showing all the parts of the cell, but merely a symbol showing the two terminals of the cell. In such a diagram, as in Fig. 25-4, a long, thin line represents the positive terminal, and a short, thick line the negative terminal.

Chemical action within a cell maintains a good supply of electrons of higher potential energy at the negative terminal. When the cell is on closed circuit these electrons stream through the *external circuit* toward the positive terminal. This *type of electric cur-* *rent in which the electrons move continuously in one direction through the conductor is called a **direct current.*** In this book, diagrams of direct current circuits show *the direction of electron flow from negative to positive in the external circuit.* We first shall study the simpler laws which govern the flow of direct current. Later on we shall learn about the more complex nature of alternating current.

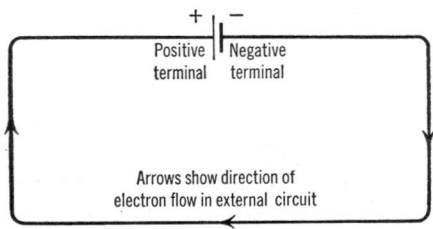

Fig. 25-4. Conventional diagram of a cell on a closed circuit.

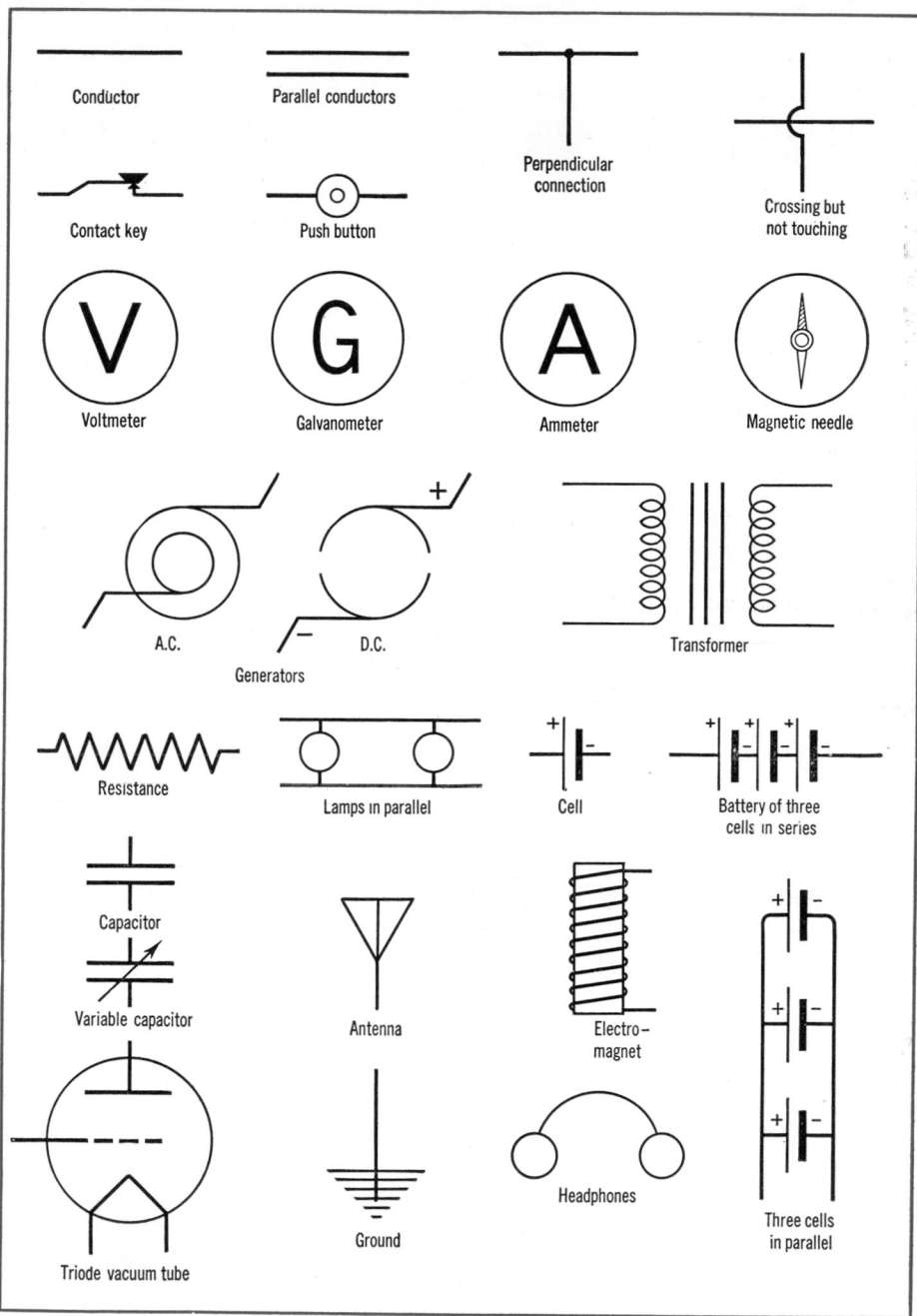

Fig. 25-5. Conventional symbols used in electrical wiring diagrams.

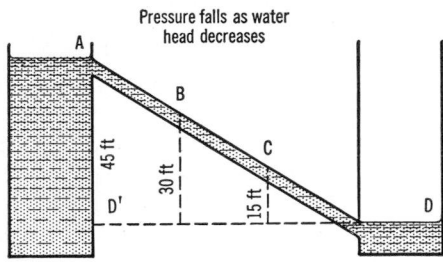

Fig. 25-6. Fall in pressure is directly proportional to the length of the pipe.

7. Conventional electrical diagrams. Many pieces of electrical apparatus are so very complicated that only an artist could make wiring diagrams if attempts were made to give a real picture of them. Consequently, electricians use many conventional diagrams to represent instruments and appliances. On page 496 you will find the ones most frequently used. Refer to them from time to time in your study. You should always use them when making electrical wiring diagrams for class or laboratory use.

8. The fall of potential along a conductor. Suppose we have two water tanks, A and D, which are connected as shown in Fig. 25-6. The difference in pressure between the two tanks is represented by a water head of 45 feet. At point B in the connecting pipe the pressure has fallen until it is represented by a water head of 30 ft. The difference of pressure between point C and the surface of the water in tank D is represented by a water head of 15 ft. There is a continuous fall of pressure along the connecting pipe. This fall of pressure is directly proportional to the length of the pipe.

In a similar manner, there is a fall of potential along a conductor when an electric current flows through the conductor. Suppose we have a stor-

age battery whose terminals A and B are joined by a uniform wire 12 ft long, as in Fig. 25-7. Let us use a voltmeter to measure the differences in potential between various points on the conductor. The wires which connect such an electrical instrument are large enough so that we may neglect their resistance. When we connect the voltmeter directly across the terminals of the storage battery, we find that the difference of potential is 6 volts. If this is the difference of potential between the two terminals of the battery, then the drop of potential along the 12-ft wire connected to these terminals must also be 6 volts.

Now let us keep one terminal of the voltmeter connected to B, and connect the wire from the other terminal to point C, 6 feet from B. The difference in potential between B and C is just 3 volts. If we connect the negative terminal of the voltmeter to the wire at C and the positive terminal at

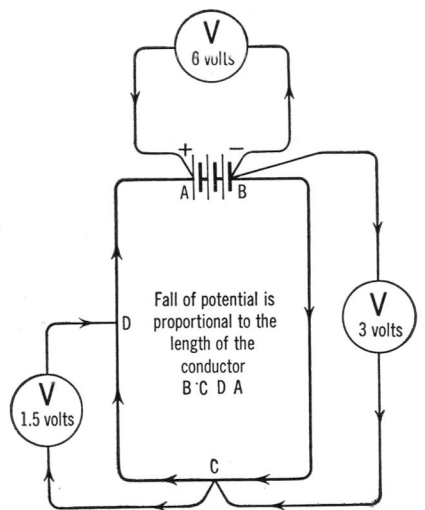

Fig. 25-7. Fall of potential along a wire of uniform resistance is directly proportional to the length of the wire.

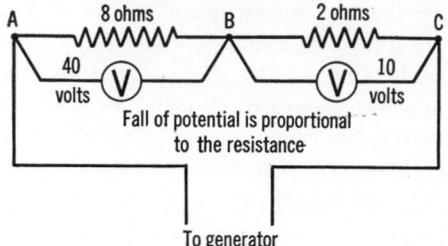

Fig. 25-8. If the resistance of the conductor is not uniform, the fall of potential is proportional to the resistance in each part of the circuit.

D, just 3 feet away, the voltmeter shows a reading of 1.5 volts. From this experiment we conclude that *the fall of potential along a wire of uniform resistance is directly proportional to the length of the wire.*

If the external resistance is not uniform, a fall of potential occurs that is not uniform, either. Suppose we have a generator which maintains a constant potential difference of 50 volts between *A* and *C,* Fig. 25-8. *AB* has a resistance of 8 ohms; the resistance of *BC* is 2 ohms. The total resistance is 10 ohms. From Ohm's law we know that a current of 5 amperes will flow through the circuit. In order for this current of 5 amperes to flow through *AB,* 8 ohms resistance, the potential difference between *A* and *B* must be 40 volts. The potential difference between *B* and *C* must be 10 volts to send a current of 5 amperes through 2 ohms resistance. From these examples, we learn that *the fall of potential is directly proportional to the resistance.*

9. Connecting resistances in series. When we *connect several pieces of electrical apparatus in* **series,** *the current flows successively through one after another.* Suppose we have eight

lamps connected in series with a 112-volt generator, as shown in Fig. 25-9. Each lamp *L* has the same resistance, 100 ohms. Then the total resistance of the circuit is 800 ohms, *the sum of all the separate resistances.* The amount of current flowing through the circuit will equal 112 volts ÷ 800 ohms, or 0.14 amperes. This current flows through each lamp. If we connect a voltmeter across the terminals of each lamp, we find a fall of potential of 14 volts. This fall of potential is proportional to the resistance.

There are certain disadvantages to series wiring. If one of the lamps in Fig. 25-9 burns out, the others will not light. This is because the circuit has been broken. Sometimes it is necessary to have more current flow through one appliance than through another. This is impossible with appliances wired in series. Each *adds* its resistance to that of every other appliance in the same series circuit.

(1) *The total resistance in a series circuit is equal to the sum of all the separate resistances.*

(2) *The current in all parts of a series circuit is the same.*

(3) *The fall of potential in a series circuit is proportional to the resistance.*

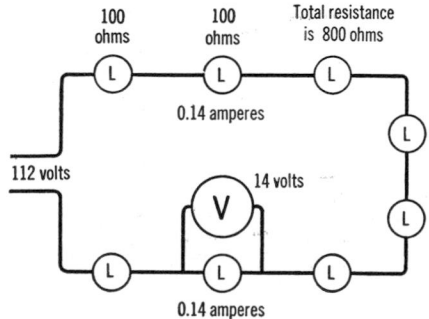

Fig. 25-9. A circuit containing eight lamps connected in series.

10. Resistances connected in parallel. Let us assume that there are two equally good and parallel roads between St. Louis and Kansas City. Under normal conditions each road carries half the traffic. The congestion, or resistance, is less than what we would find if all the traffic were forced to travel over one road. What happens, then, when we have two *parallel* wires through which an electric current can flow? *Parallel wiring is that method of connecting electrical equipment so that there are separate paths for the current through the various devices.* Look at Fig. 25-10. The electron current from *A* divides. Part of it flows through branch *C* to *B*, and the rest flows through branch *D* to *B*. Suppose each branch of the divided circuit has a resistance of 10 ohms. Then each branch will carry one-half the current. *The total resistance of both branches is one-half that of each branch.*

It may surprise you that the total resistance of a *shunt or divided circuit* is less than that of any branch. But remember that two parallel water pipes can carry more water than a single pipe. Also that more traffic can move in a given direction over several parallel roads than over just one.

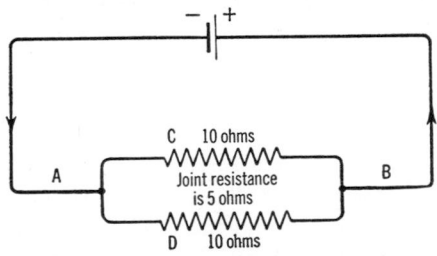

Fig. 25-10. When each branch of a divided circuit has the same resistance, the joint resistance is only one-half that of a single branch.

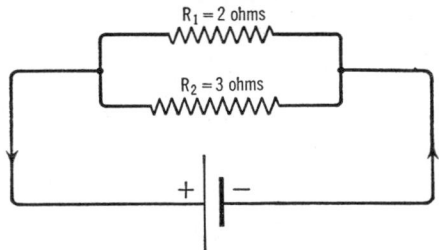

Fig. 25-11. The total conductance equals the sum of the separate conductances.

11. Finding the total resistance of parallel conductors. If each of two or more parallel conductors has the same resistance, then their total resistance is that of a single conductor divided by the number of conductors. For example, four wires of 8 ohms resistance each are joined in parallel. Their *total resistance* is one-fourth that of a single wire, or 2 ohms.

Suppose, however, that we have two wires joined in parallel in a circuit, as in Fig. 25-11. The resistance, R_1, of one branch is 2 ohms, and the resistance, R_2, of the other branch is 3 ohms. *The **conductance** of a wire is defined as the reciprocal of its resistance.* We wish to find the joint resistance, R, of both branches. The total conductance is $1/R$; the conductance of branch R_1 is $1/R_1$; the conductance of branch R_2 is $1/R_2$. Since the total conductance equals the sum of the separate conductances, we may write the formula,

$$\frac{1}{R} = \frac{1}{R_1} + \frac{1}{R_2}.$$

Substituting the known values, we have

$$\frac{1}{R} = \frac{1}{2} + \frac{1}{3}.$$

Solving, $R = 1.2$ ohms.

SAMPLE PROBLEM

Find the joint resistance of three wires joined in parallel. One has a resistance of 2 ohms; another a resistance of 3 ohms; and the third a resistance of 6 ohms.

SOLUTION

Substituting in the formula, $\frac{1}{R} = \frac{1}{R_1} + \frac{1}{R_2} + \frac{1}{R_3}$, we obtain $\frac{1}{R} = \frac{1}{2} + \frac{1}{3} + \frac{1}{6}$.

Clearing of fractions, $6 = 3R + 2R + R$. Solving, $R = 1$ ohm, the joint resistance.

12. The current carried by each branch of a divided circuit. If there are two exits of equal width from a building, we would expect the same number of persons to leave through each exit. Similarly, if the two conductors of a divided circuit have the same resistance, each will carry one-half the current.

Suppose we have three parallel water pipes leading from a reservoir. All are connected to the same water main, as represented in Fig. 25-12. The number of gallons of water per minute flowing through the main equals the total number of gallons per minute discharged by the three pipes.

If we have two or more conductors,

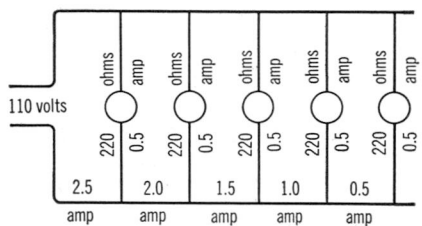

Fig. 25-13. A circuit containing five lamps connected in parallel.

and each has the same resistance, the current flowing through each branch equals $1/n$th of the total current. Fig. 25-13 represents 5 lamps wired in *parallel*. Each lamp has a resistance of 220 ohms. They operate on a 110-volt circuit. Their total resistance is $1/n$th, or $\frac{1}{5}$, of 220 ohms, or 44 ohms. Therefore, from Ohm's law, the amount of current that will flow in the main circuit is 110 ÷ 44, or 2.5 amperes. Each lamp carries $\frac{1}{5}$ of the current, or 0.5 ampere.

Just as more people can pass through a *wide* door, so more current in a divided circuit flows through the branch with *less* resistance. If one of two parallel roads between two cities is 50 ft wide, and the other is only 25 ft wide, we would expect the broad road, with less resistance, to carry $\frac{2}{3}$ of the traffic. In Fig. 25-11, let us assume that the current in the main cir-

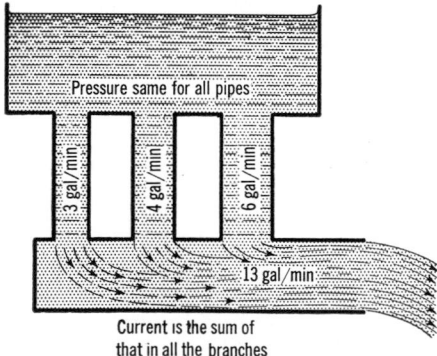

Fig. 25-12. The current in the main pipe equals the sum of the currents in all the branches.

SAMPLE PROBLEM

The two branches of a parallel circuit have resistances of 1 and 9 ohms, respectively. If a current of 30 amperes flows through the main circuit, what current will flow through each branch?

SOLUTION NO. 1

We may solve this problem by logical reasoning. The branch that has a resistance of 1 ohm will carry $\frac{9}{10}$ of the current, or 27 amperes. The 9-ohm branch will carry $\frac{1}{10}$ of the current, or 3 amperes.

SOLUTION NO. 2

Using Ohm's law, substituting in $\frac{1}{R} = \frac{1}{R_1} + \frac{1}{R_2}$, we obtain $\frac{1}{R} = \frac{1}{1} + \frac{1}{9}$.

Solving, $R = 0.9$ ohm, the joint resistance.

Substituting in $I = \frac{V}{R}$, we obtain 30 amperes $= \frac{V}{0.9 \text{ ohm}}$. Solving, $V = 27$ volts, the potential drop across each resistance. By substituting in Ohm's law for each resistance, we obtain, $I_1 = \frac{27 \text{ volts}}{1 \text{ ohm}}$, and $I_2 = \frac{27 \text{ volts}}{9 \text{ ohms}}$.

Solving, $I_1 = 27$ amperes, and $I_2 = 3$ amperes.

SAMPLE PROBLEM

Three appliances are connected in parallel on a 110-volt circuit. Their resistances are 22, 44, and 55 ohms, respectively. See Fig. 25-14. Find the amount of current flowing through each appliance. Find the current in the main circuit. What is the joint resistance?

SOLUTION NO. 1

The difference of potential across the terminals of each appliance is 110 volts. Using Ohm's law, the current through appliance A equals 110 volts ÷ 22 ohms, or 5 amperes. The current through B equals 110 volts ÷ 44 ohms, or 2.5 amperes. The current flow through C equals 110 volts ÷ 55 ohms, or 2 amperes.

The current in the main circuit equals 5 amperes + 2.5 amperes + 2 amperes, or 9.5 amperes.

By Ohm's law, the joint resistance equals 110 volts ÷ 9.5 amperes. Solving, we obtain 11.6 ohms.

SOLUTION NO. 2

As an alternate solution, we first find the combined resistance by substituting in $\frac{1}{R} = \frac{1}{R_1} + \frac{1}{R_2} + \frac{1}{R_3}$. We obtain $\frac{1}{R} = \frac{1}{22 \text{ ohms}} + \frac{1}{44 \text{ ohms}} + \frac{1}{55 \text{ ohms}}$.

Solving, $220 = 10R + 5R + 4R$, and $R = 11.6$ ohms, the joint resistance.

By Ohm's law, the current in the main circuit is 110 volts ÷ 11.6 ohms, or 9.5 amperes. The current through each appliance is then found as in Solution No. 1.

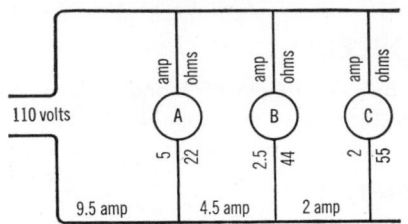

Fig. 25-14. Three appliances connected in parallel on a 110-volt circuit.

cuit is 5 amperes. Three-fifths of the current flows through branch R_1 having 2 ohms resistance. Only $\frac{2}{5}$ of the current flows through branch R_2, whose resistance is 3 ohms. Note that:

(1) *The voltage across the terminals of all the appliances in a parallel circuit is practically the same.*

(2) *The current flowing in each branch of a two-branch circuit is inversely proportional to the resistance of that branch.*

(3) *The total current in the circuit equals the sum of the currents in the separate branches.*

(4) *The resistance in each branch and the total resistance in the circuit may be found by Ohm's law.*

See Sample Problems, page 501.

13. Why do we generally use parallel wiring? Some strings of Christmas tree lights consist of small bulbs that are wired in series. When one lamp in the string burns out, the circuit is broken and none will light. It is bothersome to screw a new lamp into one socket after another in order to find the burnt-out lamp. You can see that it would be most unsatisfactory for all our lamps to be wired in series. We would have to turn them all on, or have none at all. When electric lamps are wired in parallel, however, we can turn on *one or more* at any time.

If the receptacles or outlets in your

house wiring system were wired in series, every lamp and every appliance you use would receive the same amount of current. But you may need only a fraction of an ampere for your small lamps and 5 or more amperes for a toaster or an iron. By having the outlets wired in parallel, you can plug into one of the receptacles a floor lamp that draws only 0.5 ampere from a 120-volt circuit, and at the same time plug into another receptacle an iron that takes 5 amperes. On a parallel circuit you can use several appliances, regardless of the fact that each one draws a different amount of current. Fig. 25-14 shows the amount of current flowing through each of several appliances connected in parallel on a 110-volt circuit. It also shows the amount of current in the main circuit. A tributary of a river adds to the volume of water in the river. Each branch of a parallel circuit adds to the number of amperes flowing in the main circuit.

14. The measurement of resistance. There are several ways to measure the resistance of a conductor.

(1) *Voltmeter-ammeter method.* Let us look at Fig. 25-15. Here we wish to measure the resistance of the conductor *AB*. To do this we connect an

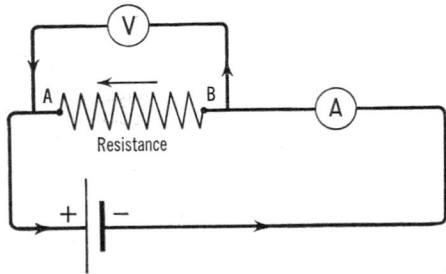

Fig. 25-15. The voltmeter-ammeter method of measuring resistance.

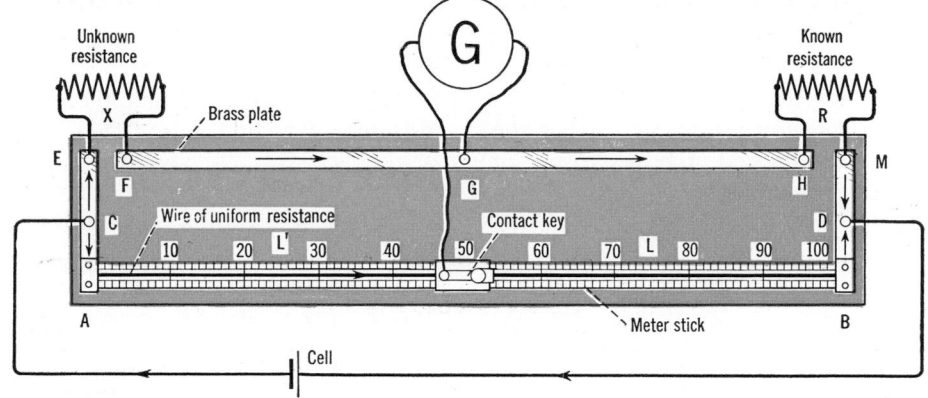

Fig. 25-16. The Wheatstone bridge method of measuring resistance.

ammeter *in series* with the resistance and a cell, and find the number of amperes I flowing through the resistance. A voltmeter connected *in parallel* across the ends of the conductor enables us to find the potential difference V in volts. Then, by Ohm's law,

$$R = \frac{V}{I}.$$

(2) *Wheatstone bridge method.* A Wheatstone bridge consists of a board a little more than a meter in length and about 15 centimeters wide. See Fig. 25-16. We mount rather heavy strips of brass across each end of the bridge and along one side. The brass strip along the side has a gap near one end where we insert a conductor of *unknown resistance, X.* There is a gap near the opposite end to permit us to insert a known resistance, *R.* We stretch a wire of uniform resistance, *AB,* over the meter stick on the opposite side of the bridge. Every unit length of that wire has the same resistance as any other unit length. We connect one terminal of a *galvanometer,* a sensitive instrument which measures small currents and indicates their di-

rection of flow, to the binding post, *G.* We attach the other terminal to the contact key. This key can be moved along the wire, and can make contact with it at any point. The current of electrons from a cell flows to the binding post *C,* where it divides. Some of the electrons flow along the wire. The rest of them flow along the opposite side of the bridge through both the unknown resistance *X* and the known resistance *R.* The two branches unite at *D.* Then the electrons flow back to the cell to make the circuit complete.

Will any current flow through the galvanometer? If the electrical potential in the wire at the contact point is exactly equal to that at the binding post *G,* no current will flow through the galvanometer. If the potential at the point of contact is higher than it is at the point *G,* electrons will flow in one direction through the galvanometer. If the potential at *G* is higher, then the electrons flow in the opposite direction through the galvanometer. When using the bridge, you slide the contact key along the wire until you find a point where no current flows through the galvanometer. You can tell when you have reached this point because the needle of the galvanometer will not be deflected as you press the contact key against the wire. This is called *balancing the bridge.* When the bridge is balanced, the resistance of wire L' : resistance X = resistance of wire L : known resistance R. But the resistances of L and L' are proportional to their lengths, and their lengths can be read from the meter stick. Suppose L' is 30 cm, L is 70 cm, and the known resistance R is 35 ohms. Then,

$$30 \text{ cm} : X = 70 \text{ cm} : 35 \text{ ohms.}$$

Solving, $X = 15$ ohms.

Summary

The flow of electrons along a conductor is called an electric current. A source of electromotive force, such as a generator or battery, raises the potential energy of electrons so that they may do useful work when they flow along a conductor. The difference in the potential energy of the electrons, or potential difference, is measured in volts. The rate of flow of electricity is measured in amperes. The resistance of a conductor to the flow of electrons is measured in ohms. Ohm's law states that the current flowing in a circuit, in amperes, is directly proportional to the potential difference, in volts, and inversely proportional to the resistance of the circuit, in ohms.

In a direct-current circuit, the direction of electron flow is from the negative terminal to the positive terminal in the external circuit.

When we connect pieces of electrical apparatus one after another in a circuit, they are connected in series. The same current flows through each part of a series circuit. When resistances are connected in series, the total resistance is the sum of the separate resistances.

When we connect pieces of electrical apparatus so that part of the current flows through each piece of apparatus, they are connected in parallel. When resistances are connected in parallel, the reciprocal of the total resistance equals the sum of the reciprocals of the separate resistances.

Terms to Define...

Ammeter	Fall of potential	Resistance
Ampere	Laws of resistance	Resistances in parallel
Breaking the circuit	Mil	Resistances in series
Closed circuit	Negative terminal	Resistivity
Closing the circuit	Ohm	Series wiring
Conductance	Ohm's law	Sources of emf
Conventional diagram	Open circuit	Volt
Direct current	Parallel wiring	Voltmeter
Electric current	Positive terminal	Voltmeter-ammeter method
External circuit	Potential difference	Wheatstone bridge method

GROUP A

1. What is an electric current?

2. Give some examples of sources of electromotive force.

3. What is the unit of potential difference? What instrument is used to measure potential difference?

4. In what unit do we measure the rate of flow of electricity? What instrument do we use for measuring the rate of flow of electricity?

5. What is the unit of electrical resistance? In what ways may resistance be measured?

6. State Ohm's law in words. Then give the formula for Ohm's law and explain the meaning of each term in the formula.

7. The resistance of a conductor depends upon what four factors?

8. What is resistivity? What is a mil? A circular mil?

9. What names are given to the two terminals of a dry cell or storage battery? Which terminal supplies electrons of higher potential energy?

10. Draw a conventional diagram for a cell. Label the parts of your drawing.

11. What do we mean by the term "open circuit"? By the phrase "closing the circuit"?

12. Explain how electrons flow in the external circuit when the circuit is connected to a source of direct current.

13. If three equal resistances are connected in series, how does the combined resistance compare with the value of a single resistance? How does the current through each resistance compare with the current through the entire circuit?

14. If three equal resistances are connected in parallel, how does the joint resistance compare with the value of a single resistance? How does the current through each resistance compare with the total current through the external circuit?

GROUP B

15. What change in the energy of an electron is produced by a source of emf? What change in the energy of an electron occurs when it passes through an electric motor?

16. Explain how the resistance of a conductor varies with its length, its diameter, its temperature, and with the material of which it is made.

17. What determines the rate at which the potential difference drops as it flows through a conductor?

18. Why are electrical appliances usually connected in parallel rather than in series?

19. What is the conductance of a wire?

20. Explain how the voltmeter-ammeter method is used for measuring resistance.

21. Explain why no current flows through the galvanometer in Fig. 25-16 when the Wheatstone bridge is balanced.

22. Will more current flow through the heating coils of an electric toaster when the coils are cold than when they are hot?

23. Will more current pass through a circuit if lamps are connected in parallel than if the same lamps are connected in series?

24. Houses generally are wired so that the lights in the halls may be operated either from upstairs or downstairs. Study Fig. 25-17 and explain how the lamp L may be controlled from either switch A or switch A'.

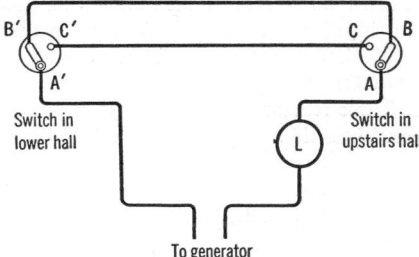

Fig. 25-17. Wiring diagram for a single lamp controlled by each of two switches.

(In the Mathematics Refresher, refer to sections 2, 8, 9, 10, and 16.)

GROUP A

1. An electric iron uses 8 amperes on a 120-volt circuit. What is its resistance?

2. The resistance of an electric light bulb is 230 ohms. If a potential difference of 115 volts is applied to the bulb, what current will flow through it?

3. What voltage must be applied to a resistance of 25 ohms in order that a current of 0.5 ampere will flow through it?

4. A wire 100 ft long has a resistance of 30 ohms. What will be the resistance of 300 ft of this wire?

5. A piece of wire with a diameter of 0.04 inch has a resistance of 20 ohms. What will be the resistance of a piece of wire of the same length and the same material if the diameter is reduced to 0.01 inch?

6. A wire, 0.05 inch in diameter, has a resistance of 3 ohms per 100 ft. What will be the resistance of 500 ft of this wire if the diameter is reduced to 0.01 inch?

7. What is the resistance of 400 ft of copper wire which has a diameter of 10 mils? ($\rho = 10.37$)

8. If the wire which is mentioned in Problem 7 is made of platinum, what is its resistance? ($\rho = 602$)

9. How many feet of nichrome wire, 0.003 inch in diameter, are required to make a 10,000-ohm resistance? Here again use: ($\rho = 602$)

10. Three resistances of 6 ohms each are connected in series. What is the combined resistance?

11. If the three resistances in Problem 10 are connected in parallel, what is the joint resistance?

12. A 5-ohm and a 10-ohm resistance are connected in series. If a potential difference of 1.5 volts is applied, what current flows through each resistance? What is the potential difference which is found to exist across each resistance?

13. A 6-ohm and a 3-ohm resistance are connected in parallel. A potential difference of 3.0 volts is applied to their terminals. What is the joint resistance? What current flows through each resistance?

14. Three resistances of 10 ohms each are connected in series. What voltage must be applied to cause a current of 5 amperes to flow through these resistances?

15. If the three resistances which are mentioned in Problem 14 are connected in parallel, what voltage must be applied to cause a total current of 5 amperes to flow through the joint resistance?

GROUP B

16. What is the joint resistance when a 5-ohm, a 10-ohm, and a 20-ohm resistance are connected in parallel?

17. What is the joint resistance when a 2-ohm, a 6-ohm, and an 8-ohm resistance are connected in parallel?

18. Two resistance coils of 9 and 12 ohms, respectively, are connected in parallel with an 18-volt battery. Calculate the joint resistance. What current flows in the main circuit? What current flows through each resistance?

19. What is the resistance of 5000 ft of No. 24 copper wire?

20. What is the resistance of 5000 ft of No. 27 copper wire? How does this resistance compare with that found in Problem 19?

21. A 6-ohm, a 9-ohm, and an 18-ohm resistance are connected in parallel. What is the joint resistance? What current flows through each resistance if the combination is connected to a source of emf of 6 volts? What is the total current flow?

● 22. How much greater must be the diameter of aluminum wire to have the same resistance as a piece of No. 18 copper wire? Compare the weights of 1000 ft of each of these wires. Why is aluminum replacing copper in long high-voltage transmission lines?

● 23. An electric toaster uses a current of 5 amperes on a 120-volt circuit. What is the resistance of the heating coils? If they are made of nichrome wire, 20 mils in diameter, how many feet of wire are needed?

● 24. Calculate the specific resistance of aluminum. A spool of No. 18 aluminum wire, 1000 ft long, has a resistance of 10.4 ohms.

25. In the voltmeter-ammeter method of measuring resistance, Fig. 25-15, the voltmeter reads 1.4 volts and the ammeter reads 0.28 ampere. What is the value of the resistance?

26. In the Wheatstone bridge method of measuring resistance, Fig. 25-16, a total of 60 ohms has been put in the circuit as known resistance from a resistance box. The galvanometer indicates no deflection when the contact is made at 55 cm on the slide wire. What is the value of the unknown resistance?

● 27. What length of No. 24 manganin wire would make a resistance coil of 100 ohms?

● 28. The heating coils of an electric ironer use 12 amperes on a 120-volt circuit. What is their resistance? If these coils are to be 25 ft long, what diameter of nichrome wire must be used?

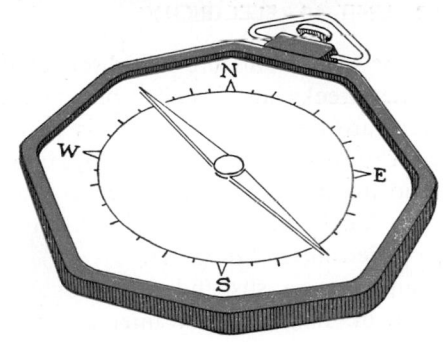

Chapter 26

Magnetism

1. THE NATURE OF MAGNETISM

1. Magnetism and electricity are closely related. The operation of many types of electrical apparatus depends on both magnetism and electricity. Without a relationship between these two phenomena, we would not have huge generators to produce the vast quantities of electricity that we use. Nor would we have electric motors to transform electrical energy into mechanical energy.

Before we can learn how these and many other electrical devices operate, we first must learn about magnetism. We need to know about the magnetic properties of certain metals and the magnetic properties of the earth. Then, too, we must discuss the beliefs now held as to how magnetism is produced.

2. Natural magnets. In a section of Turkey, formerly called Magnesia, there are deposits of an iron ore which has the property of attracting bits of

---

Vocabulary

DOMAIN. A group of atoms which have their magnetic fields more or less permanently aligned.

INDUCED MAGNETISM. Magnetism produced in a magnetic material by the presence of a magnet.

MAGNETIC DECLINATION. The deviation between true north and north as indicated by a compass needle.

MAGNETIC FIELD. The space permeated by magnetic lines.

MAGNETIC INCLINATION. The deviation between the equilibrium position of a compass needle mounted on a horizontal axis and true horizontal.

MAGNETIC LINE. The path an independent, north-seeking pole would take in moving from the N-pole to the S-pole of a magnet.

MAGNETIC POLE. The region of a magnet where the magnetic force appears to be concentrated.

NORTH–SEEKING POLE. The pole of a magnet which is attracted toward the North Magnetic Pole of the earth.

PERMANENT MAGNET. A magnet which retains its magnetism.

PERMEABLE. Readily gathers in magnetic lines.

SOUTH–SEEKING POLE. The pole of a magnet which is attracted toward the South Magnetic Pole of the earth.

TEMPORARY MAGNET. A magnet which loses nearly all its magnetism in a very short time.

TRANSPARENT. Permits the passage of magnetic lines.

iron or steel. This ore was discovered by the Greeks, and is called *magnetite.* There are other deposits of this black iron ore in the Adirondack Mountains of northern New York and in certain other localities. Pieces of such ore are called *natural magnets.*

Suppose we suspend an elongated piece of magnetite by means of a thread so that it is free to rotate in any direction. When it comes to rest, we find that the ends of the magnetite point nearly north-and-south. For this reason natural magnets were called *lodestones* (leading stones). About the twelfth century, men began to use lodestones to indicate directions in much the same manner as we now use a magnetic compass.

3. How to make a magnet. Many centuries ago, men learned how to magnetize a piece of iron by rubbing it on a lodestone. We do not use lodestone for this purpose any more because *artificial magnets,* which are much better than natural magnets, can be made very easily. As a laboratory experiment in the making of a magnet, we may start with a thin, steel rod. Half of a steel knitting needle works satisfactorily. With the knitting needle held in one hand, we use the other hand to stroke it with *one end of a magnet.* We always begin each stroke at the same end of the needle.

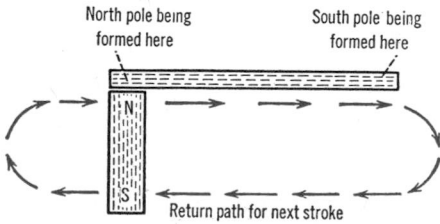

Fig. 26-1. The bar is stroked as indicated in order to form a magnet.

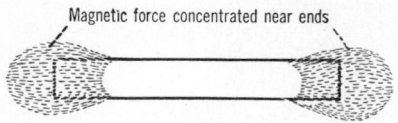

Magnetic force concentrated near ends

Fig. 26-2. The filings are clustered around the poles.

At the end of a stroke, the magnet is brought back through the air to the starting position, as shown in Fig. 26-1. If we stroke the knitting needle in this fashion 15 to 20 times, the needle becomes magnetized sufficiently to attract a small quantity of iron filings.

4. A few materials are magnetic. Everyone knows that a magnet will attract bits of iron and steel. Consequently, these substances are called *magnetic materials.* There are two other metals, *nickel* and *cobalt,* which are attracted by a magnet. But they are not nearly so strongly attracted as are iron and steel. Some alloys are attracted by a magnet, too, but we generally think of iron and steel as the most important magnetic materials.

5. Most materials are nonmagnetic. Most common substances, wood, copper, and glass, for example, are only very, very slightly attracted by a magnet. They are said to be *paramagnetic.* A few substances, such as zinc and bismuth, are *feebly* repelled by a magnet, and are said to be *diamagnetic.* Both paramagnetic and diamagnetic substances are often called *nonmagnetic* materials.

6. What is magnetic polarity? Let us sift some iron filings on a sheet of paper and lay a bar magnet in the filings. When we lift the magnet, we find that the filings cling to the magnet *at or near the ends only.* See Fig. 26-2. *The magnetic force appears to be concentrated at or near the ends of*

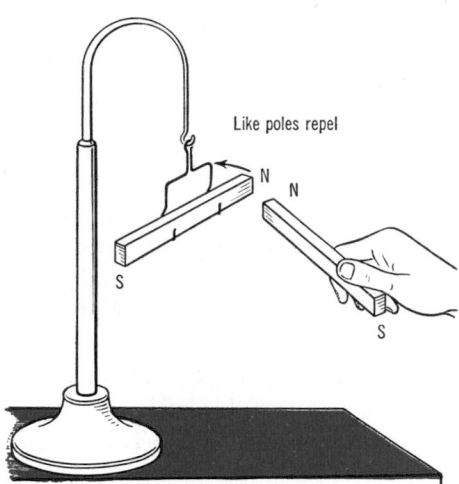

Fig. 26-3. Like poles repel. Unlike poles attract.

the magnet. These areas are called the **poles of the magnet.**

Let us suspend a bar magnet so that it can turn freely, as in Fig. 26-3. When it comes to rest, we find that the magnet points in a nearly north-and-south direction. There are two kinds of magnetic poles. *The pole of a suspended magnet which points toward the north is called a* **north-seeking pole;** it is sometimes called merely a north pole, or N-pole. The other pole is the **south-seeking pole,** *because it is attracted to the earth's south,* and is sometimes called a south pole, or S-pole.

7. Attraction and repulsion between magnetic poles. Suppose we again use a bar magnet suspended as in Fig. 26-3. When we bring the north-seeking pole of a second bar magnet near the north-seeking pole of the suspended magnet, we find that the *two poles repel each other.* If we bring the south-seeking pole near the south-seeking pole of the suspended magnet, we find that these poles repel each

other also. We conclude that *like magnetic poles repel.*

Now let us bring the south-seeking pole of the magnet near the north-seeking pole of the suspended magnet. We find that they attract. We also find that there is attraction between the north-seeking pole of the magnet and the south-seeking pole of the suspended magnet. We conclude that *unlike poles attract.* We may summarize the results of our experiments with the statement: *Like magnetic poles repel; unlike poles attract.* Physicists have found by experiment that the force of attraction between magnets is directly proportional to the strengths of the magnetic poles. It also is inversely proportional to the square of the distance between them. A magnetic pole is of unit strength when it repels an exactly similar pole one centimeter away with a force of one dyne.

8. Uses of the magnetic compass. We have seen that a magnet which is free to rotate will finally come to rest in a nearly north-and-south line. If we mount a magnetized needle on a pivot, we may use it as a compass to show directions. See Fig. 26-4. After the invention of the mariner's compass, sailors felt much safer when sailing into uncharted seas. Of course, a compass needle is not an infallible guide. It is affected by the metal parts of ships. Later, we shall find that the north-seeking pole of a compass does not point even approximately north in some regions.

9. There are both temporary and permanent magnets. (1) *Temporary.* Pieces of soft iron or of silicon steel are easily magnetized, but *they lose nearly all their magnetism in a very short time.* We say that such magnets

Fig. 26-4. A small, pocket-type magnetic compass.

pouring the mixture of molten metals into sand molds. After the metal hardens, the rough castings are removed from the sand and smoothed on a grinding machine. Other magnets are made by mixing very finely powdered alloying metals in the correct proportion. Then the mixture of metal powders is placed in a die and subjected to high pressure. This high pressure fuses the powders into a solid piece of metal having the shape of the die.

These cast or molded pieces of alnico must now be magnetized. This is done by placing them for a short time in contact with strong electromagnets. When alnico has been magnetized in

have little *retentivity*. They are called **temporary magnets.** While temporary magnets lose most of their magnetism quickly, nearly all of them retain a small amount for a much longer time. This retained magnetism is called *residual magnetism.*

(2) *Permanent.* It is difficult to magnetize a piece of hard steel, but when steel is magnetized it retains its magnetism well. Steel may be used for making **permanent magnets** *because its retentivity is high.* Steel which contains the metal tungsten alloyed with iron makes good permanent magnets, too. But *alnico* magnets, made from an alloy of iron with aluminum, nickel, and cobalt, are more powerful. They can lift about 50 times their own weight.

10. How are permanent magnets made? Most of the small, powerful, permanent magnets being manufactured today are of the alnico type. They are made in one of two ways, depending on the size and shape of the desired magnet. Some magnets are made by

Fig. 26-5. A small, alnico magnet is strong enough to support the weight of a standard typewriter.

such a fashion, it retains its magnetism almost indefinitely.

11. Uses of permanent magnets. Permanent magnets are used in a variety of commercial applications. Many of their uses depend on their ability to separate magnetic materials from non-magnetic materials. Permanent magnets are used to remove stray pieces of iron from flour, textile fibers, chemicals, stoker coal, and many other materials. Some machine shops use permanent magnets to remove metal chips from the cooling oil used in metal machining operations. Magnets are also used to separate steel sheets from a stack when the sheets are to be fed into forming machinery. Still other permanent magnets are used to hold metal parts together in the proper position for assembly.

12. How can steel be demagnetized? If we break a piece of magnetized knitting needle, we do not destroy its magnetism. We have two more poles formed. Even if we break the needle into several pieces, each piece will always have two poles, a north-seeking pole and a south-seeking pole. Fig. 26-7 shows what happens when we break a magnet into two or more pieces. Let us hold a piece of the magnetized needle in the flame of a burner until it is red hot. Then we place it in an east-west direction and let it cool. When we try to pick up some iron filings, we find that the needle has lost nearly all its magnetism. We conclude that *heating a magnet destroys its magnetism.*

A magnet will lose nearly all its magnetism if we hold it in an east-and-west line and tap it repeatedly with a hammer. For this reason we should avoid dropping, jarring, or pounding magnets. It is also possible to demag-

Fig. 26-6. An industrial application of permanent magnets. Two magnetic alarms are installed on the rubber reclaiming line ahead of sizing screens. When tramp iron among the rubber scraps accumulates so that it weakens the magnetic field, an alarm is sounded to inform the operator.

netize objects by using alternating currents of electricity.

13. Magnetizing by induction. If we hold a bar magnet *near* or *in contact with* a soft iron nail, as shown in Fig. 26-8, the nail becomes a magnet by *induction*. The nail retains its magnetism as long as the magnet is held

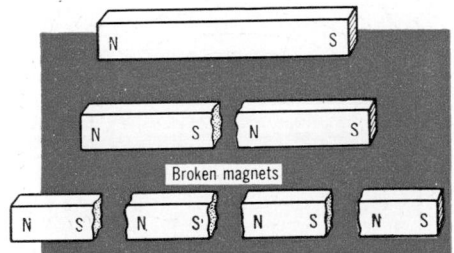

Fig. 26-7. When a magnet is broken, each piece becomes a separate magnet.

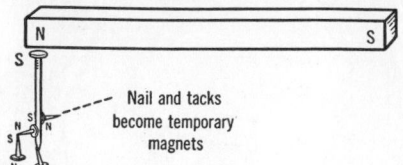

Fig. 26-8. The nail becomes a magnet by induction. What about the tacks?

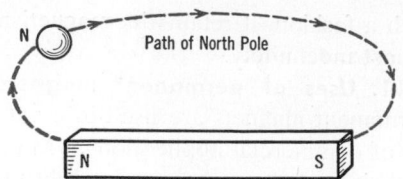

Fig. 26-10. The path that an independent north-seeking pole takes in moving from the N-pole to the S-pole of a magnet is a magnetic line.

near it or in contact with it. It will even pick up several tacks. But it loses its magnetism as soon as the magnet is removed. *Magnetism produced in this manner by the presence of a magnet is called* **induced magnetism.**

We can use a small compass needle to show that the nail has polarity while the magnet is held near it. Each tack held by the nail has also become a magnet by induction. The end of the nail near the north-seeking pole of the magnet becomes a south-seeking pole. The other end becomes a north-seeking pole. When iron filings cling to a magnet, each filing becomes a temporary magnet by induction. In fact, any piece of iron brought near a magnet becomes a temporary magnet.

14. What are magnetic lines? Suppose we place a smooth piece of cardboard over a bar magnet and sprinkle iron filings evenly over the cardboard. When we tap the board gently, the filings arrange themselves

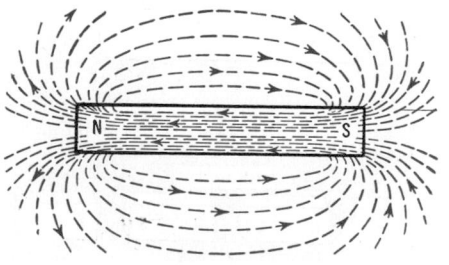

Fig. 26-9. Magnetic lines about a permanent magnet.

along curved lines, as shown in Fig. 26-9. These curved lines are called *magnetic lines* or *lines of force.* Let us imagine that we have an independent north-seeking pole — one without the south-seeking pole. When we place it at the north-seeking pole of a strong bar magnet, it moves in a curved path from the north-seeking pole to the south-seeking pole, as shown in Fig. 26-10. This happens because our imaginary independent north-seeking pole is repelled by the north-seeking pole of the magnet and attracted by the south-seeking pole. In each case the forces are inversely proportional to the squares of the distances between them. *The path that an independent north-seeking pole would take in moving from the N-pole to the S-pole of a magnet is known as a* **magnetic line.**

We know, of course, that it is impossible to get an independent north-seeking pole. But we can use a Mayer's floating magnet, which consists of a magnetized sewing needle thrust through a bit of cork large enough to float the needle, and can get a fair approach to the theoretical condition. We place a bar magnet beneath the trough of water in which the needle floats. See Fig. 26-11. Since the S-pole of the needle is so much farther from the magnet than the N-pole, the path taken by the floating magnet is es-

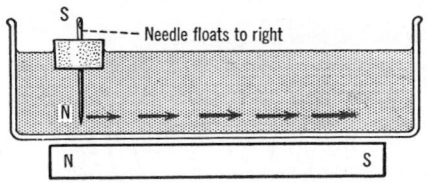

Fig. 26-11. The path taken by a floating magnet is essentially along a magnetic line.

sentially a curve similar to that of Fig. 26-10.

15. What is a magnetic field? When we wish to use a compass needle to establish a north-south direction, we must move all pieces of iron at least a meter away. Magnetic lines extend some distance out from a magnet. *The space permeated by magnetic lines is called a* **magnetic field.** A magnetic field is influenced by any magnetic material brought within it. The field has an inductive effect upon the magnetic material.

16. Mapping a magnetic field. We can make a permanent chart of a magnetic field by pinning blueprint paper over a magnet which rests in a grooved board so that the paper will lie flat. We must do this in subdued light. We then sift iron filings lightly and evenly over the surface of the paper. When the board is tapped gently, the filings arrange themselves in the direction of the magnetic lines. After the paper has been exposed to the light for a few minutes, the filings are poured off and the print is developed by submerging it in water. Fig. 26-9 shows the magnetic field about a single bar magnet. If two magnets are used with their like poles adjacent, the flexibility of magnetic lines is clearly indicated. See Fig. 26-12. Magnetic lines repel each other. They really act like elastic bands which are stretched from one pole of the magnet to the other. When we have two magnets with unlike poles adjacent, the magnetic lines appear to pass from the north-seeking pole of one magnet to the south-seeking pole of the other. See Fig. 26-13.

17. What are the properties of magnetic lines? From our study of magnetic lines we may summarize their properties as follows:

(1) According to the concept held by physicists, magnetic lines are *closed curves.* They extend from the north-seeking pole of a magnet, through the air, to the south-seeking pole. They return through the magnet.

(2) They do not cross one another; they repel one another. As a result, they are farther apart opposite the center of the magnet.

(3) Magnetic lines are concentrated at the poles of a magnet; they show that the magnetic field is much stronger at

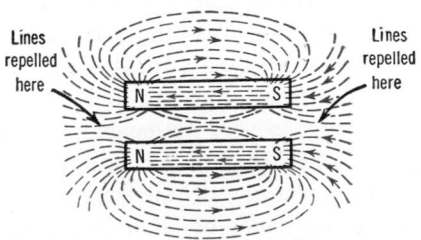

Fig. 26-12. Magnetic lines about two bar magnets with like poles adjacent.

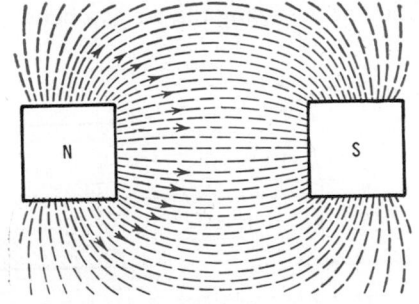

Fig. 26-13. Magnetic lines between two adjacent unlike magnetic poles.

or near the poles. They indicate the direction in which the magnetic force acts.

While the concept of magnetic lines may seem to you to be imaginative, you will find that they are important not only in magnetism, but also in practical electricity.

18. Magnetic transparency and magnetic permeability. In Section 16 we learned that a magnet can affect iron filings *through* blueprint paper. Let us repeat the experiment, covering the magnet with sheets of various materials in turn. We find that magnetic lines pass readily through copper, tin, lead, zinc, wood, glass, aluminum, and various other substances. The filings seem to be affected as readily as though the substances were not present. We conclude that these substances are *transparent* to magnetism because *they permit the passage of magnetic lines,* just as glass is transparent to light. All the materials we used for this experiment were nonmagnetic.

Now let us use a sheet of iron, a magnetic material, between the magnet and the filings. We find that the iron is not transparent to magnetism. Magnetic lines do not *cross* iron; they enter iron readily and follow a path within the iron itself. Fig. 26-14 shows magnetic lines crossing the air gap between

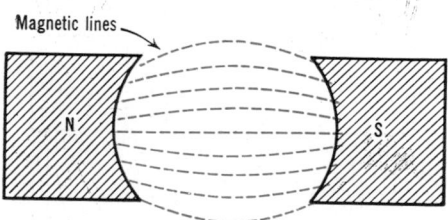

Fig. 26-14. Magnetic lines cut across the air gap between the poles of a magnet.

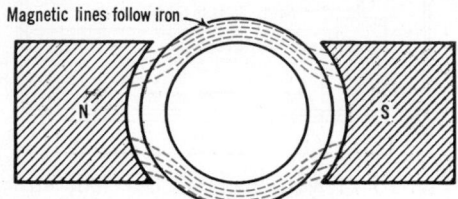

Fig. 26-15. Magnetic lines follow the soft iron ring because the ring is more permeable.

the poles of a horseshoe-shaped magnet. In Fig. 26-15, we see what happens when we place an iron ring between the poles. The magnetic lines pass through the iron rather than cut directly across the shorter air gap. Iron is very **permeable,** since it *readily gathers in magnetic lines* and affords an excellent path for their transmission.

19. Is the shape of a magnet important? Some magnets are made in the form of straight steel bars. If we bend such a bar around until it is shaped like a horseshoe, the two poles will be closer together. This reduces the air gap between them. Making a magnet horseshoe-shaped concentrates the magnetic lines and makes the magnetic field more intense. Compare the concentration of magnetic lines about a bar magnet, Fig. 26-9, with that of the horseshoe magnet, Fig. 26-16A. When a horseshoe magnet is not in use, a small piece of steel called the *armature* is placed across the poles of the magnet, as in Fig. 26-16B. Few magnetic lines enter the air, because the soft steel is so very permeable.

★ **20. The theory of magnetism.** From our study of the structure of matter, we remember that atoms consist of a central nucleus surrounded by rapidly moving and spinning electrons.

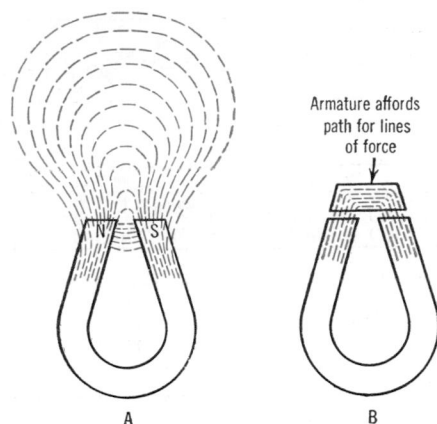

Fig. 26-16. *A.* Magnetic lines about the poles of a horseshoe magnet. *B.* The effect of an armature on the path of magnetic lines.

The structure of the three magnetic elements, iron, cobalt, and nickel, is shown in Fig. 26-17. Notice that they all have two electrons in their outermost, or N orbit, and that they have differing numbers of electrons, 14, 15, and 16, in the next-to-the-outside orbit, the M orbit.

The rotation of an electron about the nucleus of an atom sets up a tiny magnetic field about the electron. The spinning of an electron on its own axis sets up another magnetic field about the electron. In groups of electrons which form completely filled orbits, these magnetic fields neutralize each other. The electrons in the incomplete outer orbit of one atom interact with electrons in the incomplete outer orbits of other atoms to form molecules. This interaction of outer-orbit electrons to form chemical bonds between like or unlike atoms also neutralizes their individual magnetic fields.

It is only in those chemical elements which have incomplete inner orbits of electrons that the magnetic fields of these electrons may combine and produce a large, strong, magnetic field. But in most elements having incomplete inner orbits of electrons, there are strong forces between the atoms which *prevent* the magnetic fields produced by these electrons from being lined up. In just three elements, iron, nickel, and cobalt, do the forces between the atoms *assist* in lining up the magnetic fields produced by these M-orbit electrons. That is why these three elements have very strong magnetic properties. Only in the elements iron, nickel, and cobalt is it possible to line up the magnetic fields of the atoms and produce a large, strong, magnetic field.

Physicists believe that in the magnetic metals *there are groups of atoms*

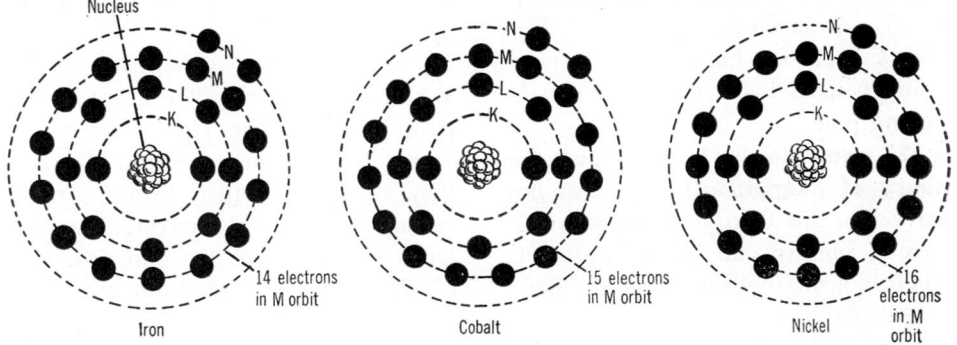

Fig. 26-17. The structure of iron, cobalt, and nickel atoms.

which have their magnetic fields more or less permanently lined up. These groups of atoms are called **domains.** In an unmagnetized bar of iron, the tiny domains are probably all in a haphazard arrangement, as represented in Fig. 26-18*A*. The small rectangles in the figure represent the domains, and the blackened ends represent their north-seeking poles. We know that two bar magnets laid side by side with unlike poles adjacent will each nullify the effect of the other. Consequently, a bar of iron in which the domains are all in a miscellaneous grouping will have no polarity.

Now let us move a magnet along the bar, stroking it from left to right with the north-seeking pole. It attracts the south-seeking poles of the domains. Each time we stroke the iron bar with the magnet, some of the domains will be twisted around in the bar so that they tend to arrange themselves in the position shown in Fig. 26-18*B*. The bar now is partially magnetized, and it shows some polarity.

Suppose we continue to stroke the iron bar in the same manner. In time, most of the domains will be arranged with their south-seeking poles toward the right, and their north-seeking poles at the left. The domains will have the orderly arrangement shown in Fig. 26-18*C*. The left-hand end of the newly magnetized bar will be the north-seeking pole.

★ **21. How do the facts support the theory of magnetism?** We can not prove that this theory of magnetism is correct, but we can list several facts which indicate that our ideas are likely to be right.

(1) The theory is in agreement with the way we make a magnet. In making

A Unmagnetized

B Partially magnetized

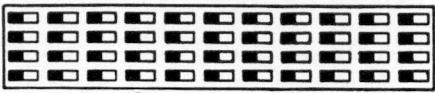
C Magnetized

Fig. 26-18. *A. Molecules in an unmagnetized bar. B. The bar is partially magnetized. C. The bar is saturated.*

a magnet, we always stroke the bar in the same direction. If we stroke the bar in the opposite direction, we reverse the polarity. If we stroke back and forth, we disarrange the domains and there is no polarity.

(2) When we break a magnet we do not destroy its magnetism. We have only separated it into two smaller groups of lined-up domains. Each of these groups of domains acts as a magnet. Even if we break a magnet up into very small pieces, we can not break it up into small enough pieces to actually break apart the atoms which make up the domains.

(3) We know that we can demagnetize a magnet by heating it red hot, or by pounding it. The high temperature makes the domains more mobile, and they swing into other positions more readily. Pounding or jarring a magnet tends to disarrange the domains.

(4) If we fill a glass tube with iron filings and stroke it carefully with one end of a bar magnet, we find that it has acquired polarity. Each filing becomes

a magnet by induction. If we shake the tube and disarrange its filings, we destroy its polarity. It seems reasonable to suspect that groups of atoms in a piece of iron form independent magnets.

(5) The theory helps to explain induction. When a magnet is brought near a piece of iron, it pulls enough of the domains around into an orderly arrangement to produce polarity. Most of them swing back to their original positions when the magnet is removed.

(6) The domains in a piece of soft iron are probably much more easily turned around than they are in hard steel. We know that iron is easily magnetized. However, since the domains are more mobile, they are more easily jostled out of their regular position. Consequently, soft iron is easily magnetized. But it loses its magnetism easily, too. Steel is actually rather difficult to magnetize, but it retains its magnetism.

(7) Let us magnetize a knitting needle and then heat it red hot at a spot about two inches from one end. Now, if we grasp the ends with pliers and twist sharply, we can distort the needle at the spot where it was heated. After the needle has cooled, we find that the iron filings will cling not only at the ends of the needle but also on either side of the spot that we heated. These *consequent poles* are developed by disarranging the domains at some spot in the magnet.

2. TERRESTRIAL MAGNETISM

22. The earth is a magnet. About 1600 A.D., William Gilbert, whose experiments with static electricity we described earlier, fashioned out of lodestone a small sphere which he called " terrella," or " little earth." When he placed small, pivoted magnetic needles at different positions on this sphere, he found that their behavior was quite similar to that of magnetized needles at corresponding places on the earth's surface.

In its effect upon magnetized objects and magnetic materials, the earth acts as though it were a huge magnet. Its magnetic lines appear to be concentrated at the earth's magnetic poles. The magnetic pole of the northern hemisphere has been discovered at about 76° North Latitude and 102° West Longitude. This is a point approximately 2000 miles due north of Bismarck, North Dakota. It is about 1100 miles from the North Geographic Pole. The South Magnetic Pole of the earth has been discovered at about 68° South Latitude and 146° East Longitude. This is a point on the Antarctic plateau about 2300 miles due south of Melbourne, Australia. The earth's magnetic lines may be considered magnetic meridians extending from one magnetic pole to the other.

We must not be confused by the terms North pole and South pole. The north-seeking pole of a magnet points toward the North Magnetic Pole of the earth. We know that this pole is not located exactly at the North Geographic Pole. Since the North Magnetic Pole attracts the north-seeking pole of a magnet, the North Magnetic Pole must actually be similar to the south-seeking pole of a magnet.

Similarly, the south-seeking pole of a magnet points toward the South Magnetic Pole of the earth. Therefore the South Magnetic Pole must actually be of the same nature as the north-seeking pole of a magnet.

23. What is magnetic declination? If the earth's North Magnetic Pole coincided exactly with its North Geographic Pole, the north-seeking pole of a compass needle would always point *true north*. But the North Magnetic Pole is actually about 1100 miles south of the North Geographic Pole. All north-and-south lines, or meridians, pass through the North Geographic Pole. *But the north-seeking pole of a compass points to the North Magnetic Pole.* For that reason, *in most localities the compass needle varies from true north, and we have* **magnetic declination.** The angle between true north, and north as shown by the compass needle, is called *angle of declination, or compass variation; it is the angle of deflection from the true north.*

On the map, Fig. 26-19, we see that there is a line of *zero declination* which passes through Canada, Michigan, Ohio, eastern Kentucky and Tennessee, and South Carolina. At places on the earth's surface through which this line passes, a compass needle points to true north. This line is called an *agonic* line. Lines drawn through places which have the same declination are called *isogonic* lines. Places east of the agonic line have *west declination,* since the compass needle points west of north. Places west of the agonic line have *east declination.*

24. What is magnetic inclination or dip? Suppose we place a small compass on top of a bar magnet and slide it from one end to the other. Near the middle of the magnet, the compass needle stands in a horizontal position. The needle dips when placed at either end of the magnet.

A compass needle mounted on a horizontal axis so that its dip may be measured is given the name of a *dipping needle.* At certain places on the earth's surface, almost midway between the magnetic poles, the dip is zero and the needle is horizontal. A line drawn through the places on the earth's surface which have zero dip is called the *magnetic equator.* It is the *aclinic line.* Lines drawn through places having the same *dip* are called *isoclinic lines.* At the magnetic poles the needle stands at an angle of 90°, or vertically. *Dip, or deviation between the equilibrium position of a compass needle mounted on a horizontal axis and true horizontal, is called* **magnetic inclination.**

25. The inductive action of the earth. Pieces of iron which have been lying in contact with the earth for some time usually show signs of polarity. We are most likely to find this situation in pieces of iron which lie parallel to the earth's magnetic meridian. Since the earth acts as if it were a huge magnet, magnetic materials in contact with it are *magnetized by induction.* Let us hold an iron rod in the direction of the earth's meridian with the north end slanting down at an angle of about 65°. If we strike the rod a few blows with a hammer, it will be found to have polarity when tested. Now let us reverse the rod and strike it as before. When we test it again for magnetism,

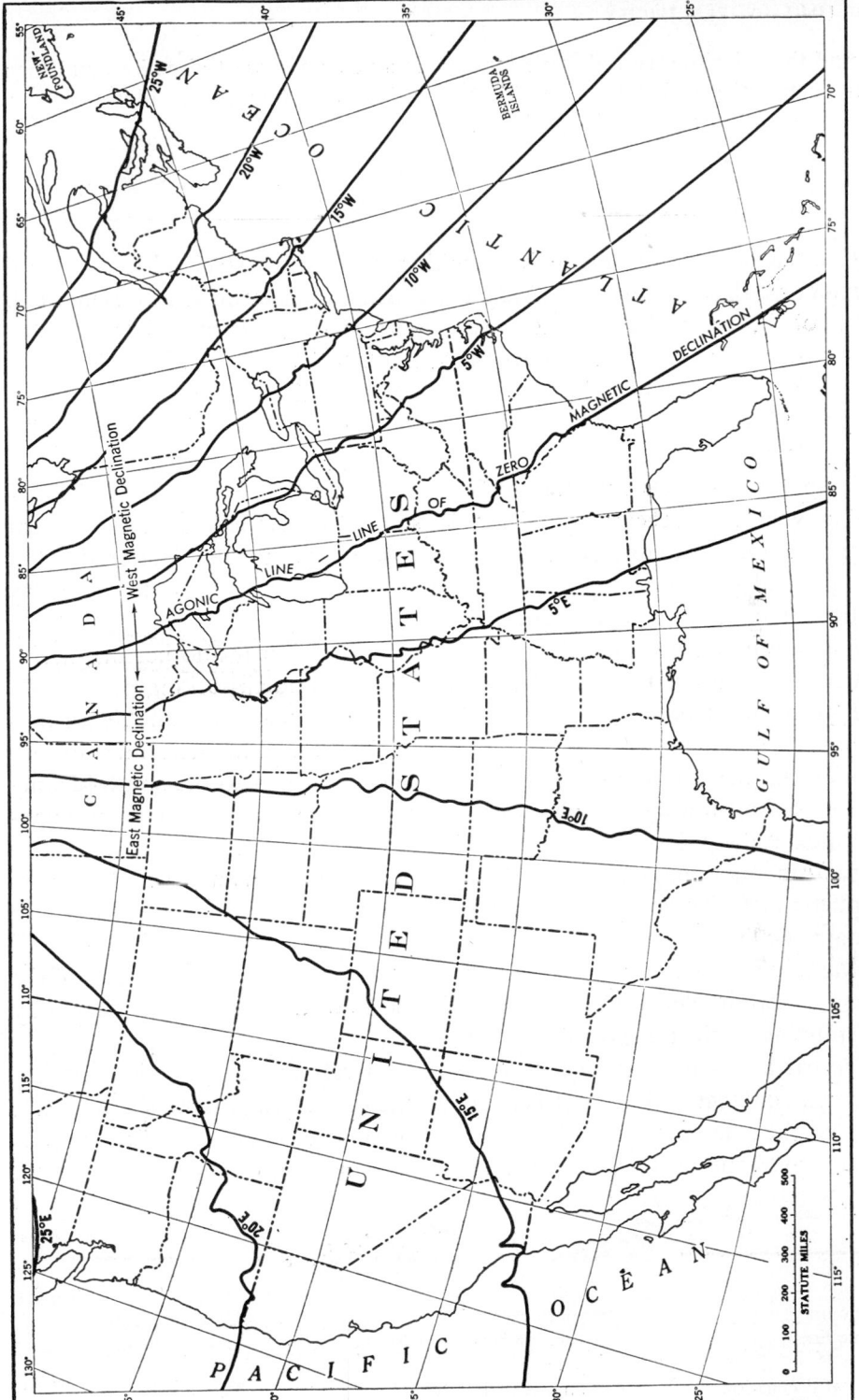

Fig. 26-19. A map of the United States showing magnetic declination.

we find the polarity reversed. We may demagnetize the rod if we hold it at right angles to the magnetic meridian, in an east and west direction, and then strike it a few sharp blows with a hammer.

──────────────, *Summary* ────────

A magnet can be made by stroking a piece of steel with a natural magnet or with a steel magnet. Magnets also are made by an electrical method. Iron, cobalt, and nickel are the most important magnetic materials.

The magnetic force appears to be concentrated at or near the ends of a magnet at regions called the poles. The north-seeking pole of a suspended magnet points to the North Magnetic Pole. Like magnetic poles repel; unlike poles attract.

Temporary magnets are those which readily lose their magnetism. Permanent magnets retain their magnetism well, some almost indefinitely. Permanent magnets are used commercially in applications where magnetic materials must be separated from nonmagnetic materials. Magnetism can be destroyed by heating, pounding, or by electric currents.

Magnetism can be induced in a magnetic material near another magnet.

A magnetic line is the path that an independent, north-seeking pole would take in moving from the N-pole to the S-pole of a magnet. The space permeated by magnetic lines is called a magnetic field. Magnetic lines extend through the air from the north-seeking pole of a magnet to the south-seeking pole. They do not cross each other; they repel one another. They are concentrated at the poles of a magnet. Nonmagnetic materials are transparent to magnetism since magnetic lines readily pass through them without change. Magnetic materials are permeable to magnetism because they readily gather in magnetic lines.

Magnetism is believed to be produced by lining up the magnetic fields of the atoms of certain elements. The magnetic fields of these atoms are set up by the spinning of their electrons.

The earth is a huge magnet. It acts inductively upon magnetic materials near or in contact with it, and magnetizes them. A compass needle does not point to the true north in all localities. The angle of deflection of a compass needle from true north is called magnetic declination, or compass variation.

──────── *Terms to Define....* ────────

Aclinic line	Armature	Consequent poles
Agonic line	Attraction between magnetic	Demagnetizing a magnet
Alnico	poles	Diamagnetic
Angle of declination	Compass variation	Dip

Dipping needle
Domain
East declination
Induced magnetism
Inductive action of the earth
Isoclinic line
Isogonic line
Lodestone
Magnetic equator
Magnetic field
Magnetic inclination

Magnetic lines
Magnetic material
Magnetic permeability
Magnetic transparency
Magnetite
Mapping a magnetic field
North Magnetic Pole
North-seeking pole
Paramagnetic
Permalloy
Permanent magnet

Poles of a magnet
Properties of magnetic lines
Repulsion between magnetic
  poles
Residual magnetism
South Magnetic Pole
South-seeking pole
Temporary magnet
Theory of magnetism
Uses of permanent magnets
West declination

GROUP A

1. What is a lodestone? Why is it sometimes called a natural magnet?

2. Describe how you can magnetize a large nail by using a permanent bar magnet. What method was used in magnetizing the permanent bar magnet?

3. What three metals are the most important magnetic materials? Name an alloy which can be strongly magnetized.

4. Where is the magnetic force of a magnet concentrated?

5. Name the two types of magnetic poles. Why are they given these names?

6. State the rule which describes the attraction and repulsion of magnetic poles.

7. Define the terms "temporary magnet," "retentivity," "residual magnetism."

8. What are some of the important industrial uses of permanent magnets?

9. Why is it important that the permanent magnets used for physics laboratory work be handled carefully, so that they are not dropped, jarred, or pounded?

10. Describe an experiment which illustrates the production of induced magnetism.

11. What is a magnetic line? Describe two ways in which we may determine the path of a magnetic line.

12. What properties of magnetic lines do we discover when we study a magnetic field?

13. What is the advantage of making a magnet in the shape of a horseshoe? What is the function of a horseshoe magnet armature?

14. Differentiate between "north-seeking pole," "North Magnetic Pole," "south-seeking pole," and "South Magnetic Pole."

15. What is the angle of declination, or compass variation?

16. What is an agonic line? An isogonic line? West declination? East declination?

17. From Fig. 26-19 determine what direction the north-seeking pole of a compass would point if at (1) New York; (2) Atlanta; (3) Fort Worth; (4) Los Angeles.

18. What is a dipping needle? The aclinic line? An isoclinic line?

GROUP B

19. How can you prove that a piece of steel is magnetized? Is attraction a conclusive test?

20. What are paramagnetic materials? What are diamagnetic materials? Why are these sometimes called nonmagnetic materials?

21. Describe how an alnico magnet is made.

22. What does the expression "transparent to magnetism" mean? What is the meaning of the expression "iron is very permeable"?

23. If two bar magnets are held together with unlike poles adjacent, they show little attraction for magnetic materials. If, however, they are held with like poles together, they show increased attraction. Explain.

24. Briefly describe the magnetic properties of the earth.

25. Why is a magnetic compass not an entirely dependable guide to direction?

26. Which direction must you take from the North Geographic Pole to reach the North Magnetic Pole?

27. Explain how magnetic materials imbedded in the earth may acquire magnetic properties.

★ **28.** What probably is the reason for magnetic properties of iron, cobalt, and nickel?

Chapter 27

Magnetic Effects of Electricity

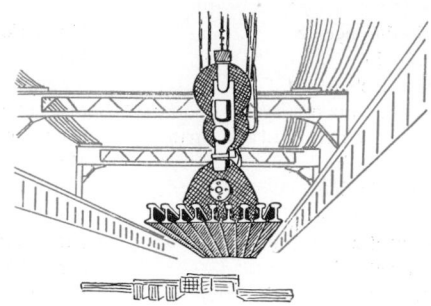

---

1. Oersted's discovery. In 1819 Hans Christian Oersted (*Er*-stet) (1777–1851), a Danish physicist, made an important discovery. He found that a small compass needle is deflected when it is brought near a conductor through which an electric current is flowing. He also found that the compass needle is deflected because the electric current sets up a magnetic field around the conductor. See Fig. 27-1.

2. Finding the direction of the magnetic field. Let us repeat Oersted's experiment. First we connect the terminals of a loop of wire to a cell. Then we place a compass needle *below* the wire where the plane of the loop runs north-and-south, as shown in Fig. 27-2. When electrons flow from *south to north,* the north-seeking pole of the compass needle is deflected toward the *east.* When the flow of electrons is reversed, the north-seeking pole is deflected toward the *west.* Fig. 27-3 shows how the deflections appear when you look down on the apparatus. If you know the direction in which the

electrons are flowing, you can predict the direction in which the needle will be deflected. If you watch how the needle is deflected, you can tell the di-

Fig. 27-1. Hans Christian Oersted (1777–1851) was a Danish physicist. In 1819 he made his famous discovery of the relationship between electricity and magnetism.

Vocabulary

ELECTROMAGNET. An iron bar or core wrapped with a large number of turns of insulated wire.

HELIX. A conductor which has been wound into a spiral coil.

SOLENOID (*soh*-luh-noyd). A long helix.

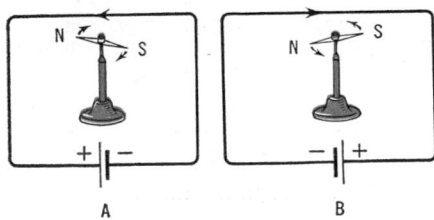

Fig. 27-2. *A.* When electrons flow from south to north, the north-seeking pole of the compass needle below the conductor is deflected toward the east. *B.* When electrons flow from north to south, the north-seeking pole of the compass needle below the conductor is deflected toward the west.

rection in which the electrons are flowing. The following left-hand rule will help you remember this relationship.

> *Left-hand rule No. 1. If you grasp the wire with the thumb of your left hand pointing in the direction in which the electrons flow, the fingers beneath the wire will point in the direction in which the north-seeking pole is deflected.* The needle will be deflected in the *opposite* direction if it is placed *above* the wire through which the electrons are moving.

3. Magnetic lines circle a conductor. From Oersted's experiments we know that an electric current produces a magnetic field about a conductor. The magnetic lines of this field circle the conductor. Suppose we pass a vertical wire through a piece of cardboard about 6 inches square. At each of the four corners of the cardboard we place a small magnetic compass. When current flows through the wire, the compass needles are deflected until they become nearly tangent to the magnetic lines about the conductor. When the

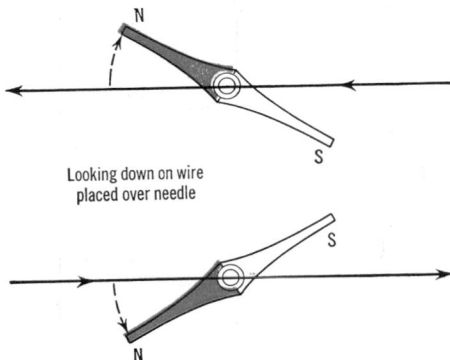

Looking down on wire placed over needle

Fig. 27-3. Looking down upon the magnetic needles.

electrons flow *upward,* the magnetic lines circle the conductor in a *clockwise* direction, Fig. 27-4*A.* When the electrons flow *downward,* the magnetic lines circle *counterclockwise.* Fig. 27-4*B.*

> *Left-hand rule No. 2.* This rule, which is similar to No. 1, applies to vertical conductors. *Grasp the conductor with your left hand so that your thumb points in the direction in which the electrons flow. Your fingers then will circle the wire in the direction of the magnetic lines.*

4. What is a helix or solenoid? If you make a loop in a wire through which a current is flowing, *the faces of*

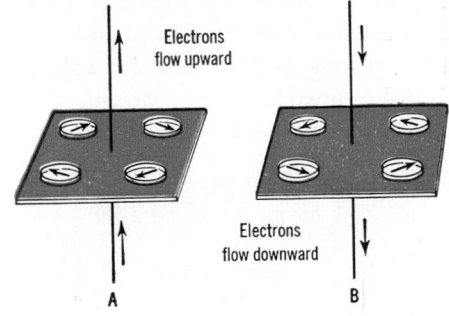

Electrons flow upward

Electrons flow downward

Fig. 27-4. The magnetic lines circle a conductor.

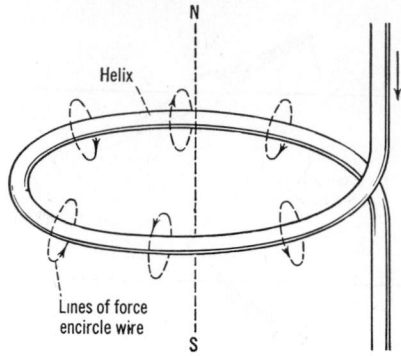

Fig. 27-5. The faces of a loop of wire carrying a current show polarity.

the loop will show polarity. You readily can see why this happens by studying the direction of the magnetic lines about the wire, as shown in Fig. 27-5. Inside the loop all the magnetic lines are directed upward. On the outside of the loop all the magnetic lines are directed downward. The face of the loop toward you becomes the *north-seeking pole* when the electrons flow *clockwise* through the loop. If you reverse the direction of the electron flow, you reverse the polarity.

You can increase the polarity by winding several loops of wire in the form of a spiral. See Fig. 27-6. Now each loop becomes a magnet, and the whole spiral acts like a row or pile of disc magnets with their unlike poles adjacent. Such *a conductor wound into a spiral coil is called a* **helix**. In turn, *a long helix is called a* **solenoid** (*soh*-luh-noyd).

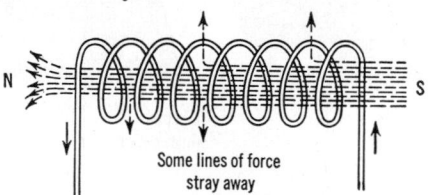

Fig. 27-6. The ends of a helix are magnetic poles.

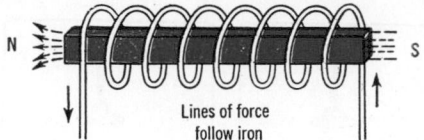

Fig. 27-7. The iron bar in the helix concentrates the magnetic lines.

5. The electromagnet. From Fig. 27-6 we see that many magnetic lines tend to stray between the loops of the helix. This scatters and weakens the magnetic force. To prevent this weakening, we can place an iron bar in the helix. Since iron is extremely permeable, the bar affords an excellent path for the magnetic lines. See Fig. 27-7. This *helix with an iron core is an* **electromagnet**. Joseph Henry (1797–1878), an American physicist, made the first practical electromagnets.

The core of an electromagnet is made from soft iron or silicon steel. Both these metals have great permeability, and are easily magnetized and demagnetized. A large number of turns of insulated wire are wound on this core. The wire may be held in place by a coating of shellac. Insulated wire is used so that the current does not short circuit from one coil to the next, or through the iron core.

When we connect the ends of the wire to a cell, current flows through the coils and forms a temporary magnet. When the circuit is broken, the electromagnet loses nearly all its magnetism. However, the core does retain a trace of residual magnetism.

6. Upon what does the strength of an electromagnet depend? Since each coil of wire which carries a current has its own magnetic lines, we can increase the strength of an electromagnet *by increasing its number of coils* *or turns.* We also can increase the strength by sending more current through the coils. Because current strength is measured in amperes, we may combine both statements to read: *The strength of an electromagnet depends upon the number of ampere-turns.*

7. Finding the polarity of an electromagnet. We can use two methods to find the polarity of an electromagnet. (1) We can test the poles of the magnet with a compass needle. The pole which repels the north-seeking pole of the needle is the north-seeking pole of the magnet. The pole which repels the south-seeking pole of the needle is the south-seeking pole of the magnet. (2) We can use the direction of the magnetic lines, just as we did with the helix. This gives us a third left-hand rule.

> *Left-hand rule No. 3. Grasp the magnet with your left hand. Let your fingers circle the magnet in the direction in which the electrons flow. Then your extended thumb will point to the north-seeking pole of the magnet.*

In Chapter 26 we learned that permanent magnets are made in the shape of a horseshoe to bring the poles closer together and thus increase the intensity of the magnetic field. We can do this same thing with electromagnets. In such cases, a coil of wire is wound around each pole of the magnet. The wire is wound in a clockwise direction around one pole; it is wound in a counterclockwise direction around the other pole. If we look down upon the poles of a horseshoe-shaped electromagnet, we find that the electrons flowing

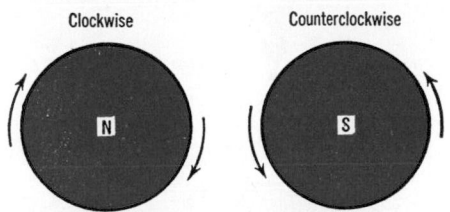

Fig. 27-8. Looking down upon the poles of an electromagnet.

around one pole in a *clockwise* direction make it a *north-seeking pole.* The electrons flowing in a *counterclockwise* direction around the other pole make it a *south-seeking pole.* See Fig. 27-8.

8. Uses of electromagnets. While large blocks of magnetized alnico alloy make very strong permanent magnets, we can not control this magnetic attraction in a useful fashion. But the magnetic attraction of strong electromagnets may be easily controlled by varying the current through the windings. Such electromagnets are used in handling scrap iron and steel. They can lift several tons at a time. See Fig. 27-9.

Surgeons use electromagnets for removing small splinters of steel from a person's eyeball or from other parts of his body. An electromagnet is used in the automatic cut-off valve of some gas furnaces.

Many electrical instruments contain electromagnets. The electric bell, the telegraph, the electric generator, and the electric motor are important examples. Some measuring instruments also use an electromagnet, either directly or indirectly. The recording of sound and television on tape or wire is done by means of electromagnets.

9. Construction of an electric bell. Fig. 27-10 shows the construction of an electric bell. A small electromag-

Fig. 27-9. An electromagnet being used to load scrap metal into boxes at a steel mill.

net is permanently mounted on an iron base. One end of the wire with which the magnet is wound is attached to a binding post, *D,* which is insulated from the base. The other end is attached to an adjustable contact screw. A flexible spring, which is bent over to make contact with the contact screw, is also fastened to the base. The soft iron armature which carries the hammer is fastened to this spring. As the spring vibrates back and forth, the hammer strikes a series of blows upon the gong.

10. How does an electric bell work? Suppose we attach several dry cells in series to the binding posts, *B* and *D,* so that the electrons will enter the bell at *D.* They flow through the coils of the magnet to the contact screw, then along the spring, and through the iron base of the bell to *B.* As they flow through the magnet coils,

they energize the magnet, which then attracts the armature strongly, so that the hammer strikes the gong. But when the armature is pulled over toward the magnet, the bent end of the spring is pulled away from the contact screw. This breaks the circuit. The magnet loses its magnetism and no longer attracts the armature. Because of its elasticity, the spring returns the armature and hammer to their former position. The circuit is now closed, and the current re-magnetizes the magnet. The whole operation is repeated. The spring alternately " makes " and " breaks " the circuit; the magnet is magnetized and then demagnetized in succession. This causes the hammer to vibrate rapidly.

11. The electric door chime. Electric door chimes have replaced door bells in many homes. This device contains a solenoid and a soft-steel plunger which can slide up and down

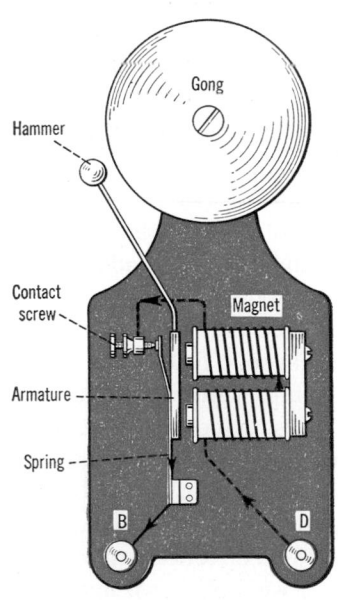

Fig. 27-10. The construction of an electric bell.

in the center hole of the solenoid, as shown in Fig. 27-11. When the switch is closed to complete the circuit, the electrons flowing through the solenoid coils produce a north pole at the top of the solenoid, and a south pole at the bottom of the solenoid. Remember that a permanent magnet induces magnetism in nails or tacks brought near it. Likewise, the magnetic field of the solenoid induces magnetism in the soft-steel plunger. The N-pole at the top of the solenoid induces an S-pole at the top of the plunger. The S-pole at the bottom of the solenoid induces an N-pole at the bottom of the plunger. Because unlike poles attract, the plunger is pulled up into the center of the solenoid. The wooden tip on the rod attached to the plunger strikes the chime bar and produces a musical tone. When the circuit is broken, the plunger drops down from the center of the solenoid.

12. The wiring of electric bells and door chimes. Sometimes it is desirable to have one bell or chime in the front hall and another in the kitchen, and to have both operated by one push

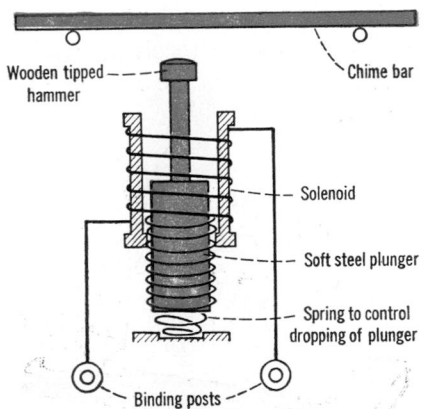

Fig. 27-11. The construction of a door chime.

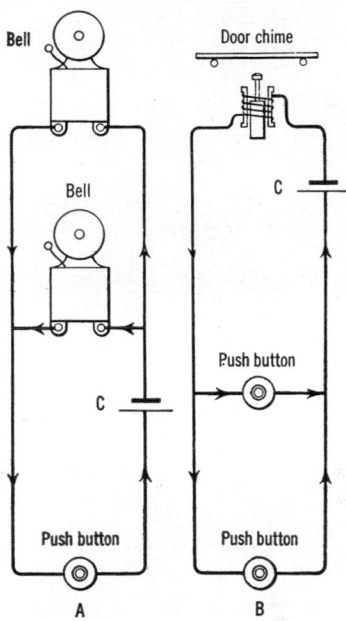

Fig. 27-12. A. Two bells wired in parallel. B. Two push buttons in parallel.

button. In such a case we wire the two appliances in parallel, as shown in Fig. 27-12A.

If we wish to have a door bell or chime operated by either one of two push buttons, we wire it as shown in Fig. 27-12B. The battery must be placed between the bell or chime and the first push button.

For the sake of simplicity we have shown electric bells and chimes operated by dry cells or batteries. Usually, though, they are powered by current from a small transformer which is connected to the household electric lines.

13. The telegraph. Samuel F. B. Morse (1791–1872) invented the telegraph in 1837. The first practical message was sent from Washington to Baltimore on May 24, 1844. See Fig. 27-13. For the successful operation of a telegraph system, these essential

Fig. 27-13. Samuel F. B. Morse (1791–1872) was an American inventor. Here he is shown during the historic moment when he sent his first message by telegraph from Washington to Baltimore.

parts and appliances are needed: the *line wires,* the *batteries,* the *key,* the *sounder,* and the *relay.*

The telegraph key is used to open and close the circuit. This key is more carefully designed than an ordinary contact key or push button. See Fig. 27-14.

The sounder, which produces an audible signal, is used as a receiver. An electromagnet is mounted on the base of the sounder. A lightweight aluminum lever, pivoted at *A,* Fig. 27-15, holds an iron armature a fraction of an inch above the poles of the magnet. A coiled spring keeps the lever in this position. When a cell is attached to the binding posts, *B* and *C,* and the circuit is closed, the electromagnet is energized. It attracts the iron armature and pulls the lever down. A small setscrew near one end of the lever strikes the metal shoulder, *D,* producing a sharp click. When the operator releases the key and breaks the circuit, the magnet is de-energized and loses its magnetism. The spring will then push the armature up and completely away from the magnet, thus breaking the contact.

14. What is the Morse code? When a telegraph key is pressed and released quickly, the sounder gives a short, sharp click known as a " dot." When the key is held down for a slightly longer time, the sound is somewhat prolonged, and produces what is called a " dash." Samuel Morse devised a system of dots and dashes to represent the different letters of the alphabet. Operators who are receiving read the message by ear from the clicking of the sounder.

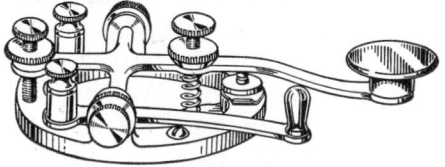

Fig. 27-14. A telegraph key.

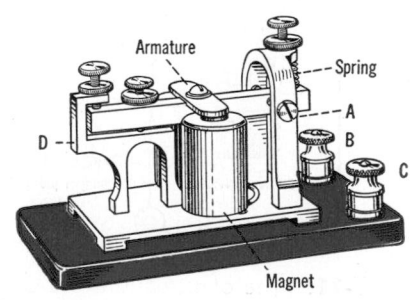

Fig. 27-15. A telegraph sounder.

15. The telegraph relay. Since a telegraph line may be many miles long, the resistance of the wire may become so great that the current strength is reduced to a small value. It may even become so very feeble that the click of the sounder can barely be heard. To prevent this situation, we use a relay.

The relay opens and closes the circuit containing the sounder and a local battery. It consists of an electromagnet which has a large number of turns of fine wire. This magnet is connected to the line wires. See Fig. 27-16. When current enters the relay through the binding posts, *A* and *B*, it energizes the electromagnet. By means of a pivoted armature the relay alternately " makes " and " breaks " the local sounder circuit. One end of the armature is connected to the local circuit through the binding post *C*. The other end is connected through the binding post *D* when the end of the armature is in contact with the end of the screw *E*. Screw *F* has a tip of insulating material.

16. Connecting telegraph instruments together. Fig. 27-17 shows how the key, sounder, and relay are connected at one end of a telegraph line. The electromagnet of the relay is connected to the line wire through the switch or key. The line battery supplies current to the line wire. The

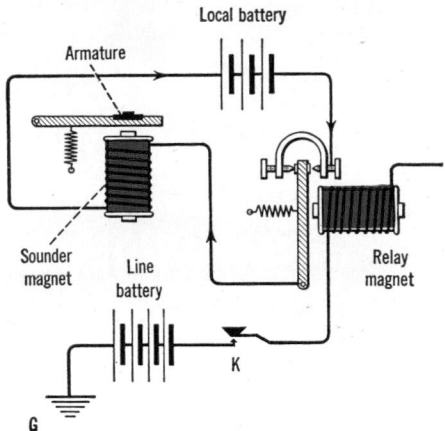

Fig. 27-17. A diagram of a local telegraph system showing key, sounder, relay and batteries.

armature of the relay makes and breaks the local battery circuit which operates the sounder. At the opposite end of the line the instruments are connected in the same manner.

When the operator at the *far* end of the line is sending a message, the key at the *near* end must be kept closed, and vice versa. This can be done by means of the slide lever provided for that purpose, or by the operator himself.

17. The Teletypewriter system. Most commercial telegraph work today is carried on by teletype. A Teletypewriter circuit consists of two typewriter-like devices connected by telegraph wire. It is possible both to send and receive a typewritten message on the same instrument, although some are designed only for receiving. The keyboard on the sending machine has three rows of keys. These keys print capital letters, punctuation marks, and numerals, and control the operation of the machine.

When a key is pressed on the trans-

Fig. 27-16. A telegraph relay.

Fig. 27-18. A modern Teletypewriter machine used for both sending and receiving messages.

mitter, a set of signals goes over the wires to the receiver. The signals are interpreted by the receiver, and the letter struck on the keyboard of the transmitter is printed automatically by the receiver on a sheet of paper or paper tape.

In addition to its use for transmitting telegrams, Teletypewriter systems are used for relaying news rapidly to newspapers, radio, and television stations. The police quickly obtain and spread information about criminals by Teletypewriter. Hotels, airlines, and railroads use the Teletypewriter system to make and confirm travel reservations.

18. The telephone transmitter changes sound into a varying electric current. The invention of the telephone is generally credited to Alexander Graham Bell (1847–1922).

The modern telephone uses a handset of the type shown in Fig. 27-19. The handset contains two important units, the transmitter and the receiver. They are mounted in a plastic handle which fits the ear and mouth. For purposes of better illustration, we have shown these two units separately in Fig. 27-20, which represents a simple circuit. A cross-section view of a transmitter is shown in Fig. 27-21. It consists of a small box filled with particles of granular carbon. The back of the box consists of a fixed carbon plate. The front of the box is a plate attached to the vibrating diaphragm. Wires are connected to these plates so that current may pass through the carbon particles. When a sound wave condensation presses the carbon particles closer together, they touch at more points and the total resistance becomes less. Thus more current flows through the transmitter. When a rarefaction occurs, the pressure on the carbon particles becomes less, and as a result a smaller current flows. The variation in the resistance of the carbon granules varies the strength of the current flowing through the wires of the circuit. These current variations correspond electrically to the sounds picked up by the transmitter.

19. How does the receiver work? The construction of a receiver is shown in Fig. 27-22. Fine, insulated wire is

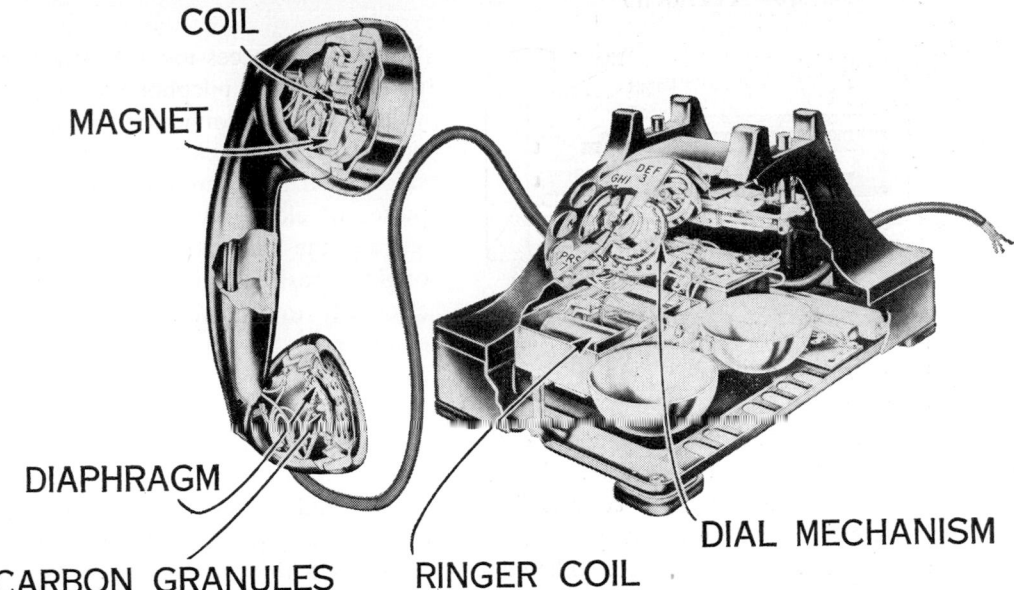

COIL

MAGNET

DIAPHRAGM

CARBON GRANULES   RINGER COIL

DIAL MECHANISM

Fig. 27-19. A cutaway view of a modern telephone handset.

wound around the poles of the horse-shoe magnet. A soft iron diaphragm is mounted so that it is near the poles of the magnet. When the current variations from the telephone line reach the coils, they vary the magnetic field. This causes the diaphragm to be attracted and repelled in a corresponding fashion. Its vibration reproduces the sounds sent over the line from the transmitter.

20. Dialing a telephone number. In many communities it is possible to connect one telephone with any other

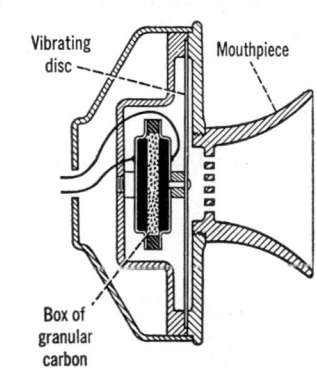

Fig. 27-21. A cross-section of a telephone transmitter.

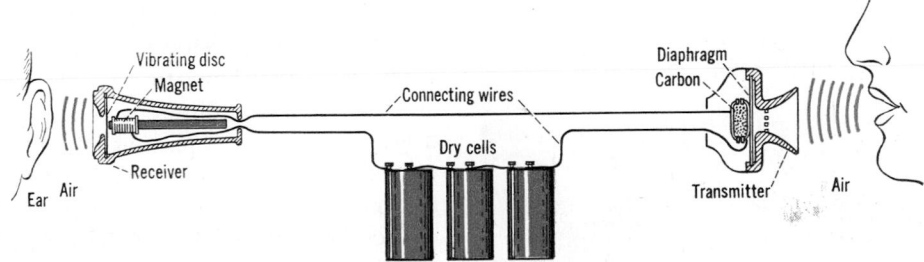

Fig. 27-20. A simple telephone circuit which can be used easily for laboratory demonstrations.

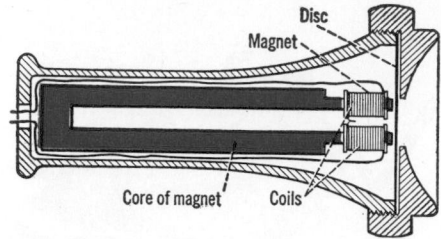

Fig. 27-22. A cutaway view of a telephone receiver showing the permanent magnet, the coils, and the disc diaphragm.

local telephone automatically by dialing the appropriate number. When you lift the receiver, you complete an electrical circuit between your telephone and the central office. The current flowing through this circuit causes automatic switching equipment to be connected to your telephone. When the connection has been established, you hear a humming signal, which is called the dial tone. It means that the equipment now is ready to receive further signals from your telephone.

Fig. 27-23. The switching mechanism for dial telephones in a modern central office.

You dial in succession the letters and numbers of the telephone with which you wish to be connected. The rotation of the dial back to its original position each time sends out a series of pulses of electricity. When you dial a " 1," the return of the dial to its original position sends one pulse of electricity to the automatic switching equipment. If you dial " 4," the returning dial sends out four pulses of electricity.

In a modern central office, these dialed electrical pulses are first received and stored in an apparatus called a *sender*. The sender activates other switching equipment. As this equipment operates, it sends impulses back to the sender. The switching equipment moves from contact to contact until the pulses it returns to the sender match those which were dialed to the sender. Then the two telephones are automatically connected, and the sender is cut out of the circuit so that it may be used to complete other calls entering the central office. Other signals transmitted to the calling telephone indicate whether the called telephone is ringing or is busy.

In many cities throughout the United States and Canada, long distance calls may be dialed directly by the long-distance operator. The equipment used for such long-distance dialing is similar in principle to that already described. However, long-distance calls may have to pass through as many as eight different central offices. The sender apparatus in the first central office stores the dialed numbers and makes the connection to the second central office. When the connection is completed, it passes the dialed numbers along to the second central office. Here these numbers are used again by automatic switching equipment to make the connection with the third central office, and the dialed numbers are again sent on. Finally the central office which serves the called number is reached, and the last connection is made.

Summary

An electric current sets up a magnetic field around the conductor through which it is flowing. If you grasp the conductor with the thumb of your left hand pointing in the direction in which the electrons flow through the conductor, your fingers will encircle the conductor in the direction of the magnetic lines.

A wire spiral through which current is flowing acts as a magnet. It is called a helix, or solenoid. If we insert an iron bar in a helix, we produce an electromagnet. The strength of an electromagnet depends upon the number of turns and the amount of current flowing through it. If you grasp an electromagnet with your left hand, and let your fingers circle the magnet in the direction in which the electrons flow, your extended thumb will point to the north-seeking pole of the electromagnet.

Many electrical instruments and appliances contain electromagnets. Among these are electric bells, telegraph relays and sounders, and telephone receivers.

Terms to Define . . .

Dialing a telephone number	Long-distance dialing	Telegraph relay
Direction of a magnetic field about a conductor	Polarity of an electromagnet	Telegraph sounder
	Residual magnetism	Telephone receiver
Electric bell	Sender	Telephone transmitter
Electric door chime	Solenoid	Teletypewriter
Electromagnet	Strength of an electromagnet	Uses of electromagnets
Helix	Telegraph key	Wiring bells and chimes

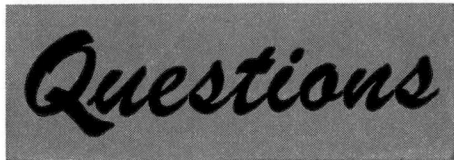

GROUP A

1. What important discovery was made by the Danish physicist, Oersted?

2. If electrons flow through a conductor from north to south, in which direction will the north-seeking pole of a compass needle placed above the conductor be deflected? In which direction will the compass needle be deflected if the electrons flow through the conductor from south to north?

3. State the left-hand rule for the direction of deflection of the north-seeking pole of a compass which is placed near a horizontal conductor through which electrons are flowing.

4. In which direction will the north-seeking pole of a compass needle be deflected if the compass is placed near a vertical conductor through which electrons are flowing upward? How will such a compass needle be deflected if the electrons are flowing downward instead of upward?

5. State the left-hand rule for the direction of deflection of the north-seeking pole of a compass which is placed near a vertical conductor through which electrons are flowing.

6. What is a solenoid?

7. In which direction must electrons flow through the coils surrounding the north pole of an electromagnet?

8. Why must insulated wire be used for the windings of an electromagnet?

9. Upon what factors does the strength of an electromagnet depend?

10. State the left-hand rule for finding the polarity of an electromagnet when we know the direction in which electrons flow through the windings.

11. What are some practical uses of electromagnets?

12. How is an electric bell constructed and operated?

13. How is an electric door chime constructed and operated?

14. How does the telephone transmitter vary an electric current in response to the sound waves which enter it?

15. How does a telephone receiver convert the variations in an electric current into sound waves?

GROUP B

16. How would you make an electromagnet from a soft-steel rod six inches long and a piece of insulated wire four feet long?

17. What is meant by the "residual magnetism of an electromagnet"?

18. How is a horseshoe-shaped electromagnet made?

19. Explain why the faces of a loop of wire through which an electric current is flowing show polarity.

20. Draw a diagram which shows how two electric bells are connected to a battery if they both are to be controlled by a single push button.

21. Draw a diagram which shows how an electric bell is connected to a battery so that it may be controlled by each of two push buttons.

22. What are the parts of a simple telegraph circuit, and how are they connected?

23. How are messages sent by Teletypewriter?

24. What are the parts of a simple telephone circuit, and how are they connected?

25. How does the dial on a telephone enable us to connect one telephone to another local telephone?

26. How is automatic long-distance dialing accomplished?

Things to Do

1. Make an electromagnet out of a short piece of soft-steel rod and a piece of insulated wire several feet long. See how many small carpet tacks you can pick up with your electromagnet when it is connected to a dry cell.

2. Make a horseshoe-shaped electromagnet.

3. Visit the telephone office in your community to observe how calls are put through from one telephone to another.

4. Visit your local telegraph office or railroad station to observe how telegraph instruments or Teletypewriter machines are used for the transmission of messages.

5. Demonstrate to the class the methods of connecting two door bells with batteries and two push buttons so that (1) each push button operates both bells; (2) each push button operates a separate bell.

Chapter 28

Electrical Measurements

1. Definitions of electrical units. We now are ready to give a more complete explanation of the electrical units we have been using. We also shall include several other frequently used electrical units.

(1) *The ampere.* If we have a current passing through an elongated loop of wire, as shown in Fig. 28-1*A,* a magnetic field will be set up around the wire. The direction of this field can be determined by the left-hand rule. Since the two sides of the loop of wire are near each other, the magnetic fields set up will overlap. Because these magnetic fields are in the same direction inside the loop, they repel one another. If the wires are not too stiff and are free to move, they will be spread apart. If we pass a current through the branched circuit shown in Fig. 28-1*B,* the magnetic fields set up around each branch will be in opposite directions to each other inside the loop. This produces an attractive force between the wires, and the wires will

Vocabulary

AMPERE. Unit of current strength. One ampere of current flowing through each of two long parallel wires one meter apart causes a magnetic force of 2×10^{-7} newton on each meter of each wire.

COULOMB. Unit of electric charge. One coulomb of electricity passes a given section of a conductor in one second when the conductor carries a constant current of one ampere.

GALVANOMETER (gal-vuh-*nom*-it-er). Instrument for measuring small currents.

KILOWATT–HOUR. 1000 watt-hours.

OHM. Unit of resistance. The resistance of a conductor in ohms is the ratio of the potential difference between its ends measured in volts and the current flowing through it measured in amperes.

VOLT. Unit of potential difference. The difference in potential between two points in a circuit is one volt if one joule of work is done by electrical forces in moving one coulomb of charge between the two points.

WATT. Unit of power. One watt is the power supplied when a current of one ampere is driven through a circuit by a potential difference of one volt.

WATT–HOUR. Unit of energy. If the potential difference in a part of a circuit is one volt, a current of one ampere flowing continuously through this part of the circuit for one hour will furnish one watt-hour.

535

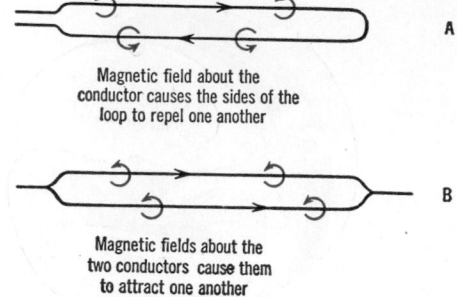

Fig. 28-1. Attractive and repulsive forces between current-carrying conductors.

be drawn together. These attractive and repulsive forces between current-carrying conductors are directly proportional to the current flow which we measure in amperes. A measure of these forces would therefore provide an exact definition of the ampere. Physicists have been able to make such measurements. *The ampere is defined as that amount of current flowing through each of two long, parallel wires one meter apart, which causes a magnetic force of 2×10^{-7} newton on each meter of each wire.*

(2) *The coulomb.* Earlier we mentioned that the ampere designated the rate of current flow, much as gallons per second might measure the rate of flow of water. Let us now see what unit is used to measure the quantity of electricity, much as the gallon is used to measure the quantity of water. The *coulomb is the unit which designates the quantity of electricity. The coulomb is the quantity of electricity which passes a given section of a conductor in one second when the conductor carries a constant current of one ampere.* The ampere and the coulomb are related by the equation $Q = It$, where Q is the amount of charge in coulombs, I is the current in

amperes, and t is time in seconds. The coulomb is the unit which measures the number of electric charges, usually electrons, which pass a given point in an electric circuit. The charge of one electron has been measured very carefully. It is 1.6019×10^{-19} coulomb. One coulomb, then, equals the combined charge on 6.242×10^{18} electrons.

(3) *The volt.* The unit of potential difference, the volt, is measured in terms of the work required to move electric charges. Specifically, *the difference in potential between two points is one **volt** if one joule of work is done by electrical forces in moving one coulomb of charge between the two points.*

(4) *The ohm.* Transforming the Ohm's law formula, $I = V/R$, to $R = V/I$, we have a definition of resistance. *The resistance of a conductor in **ohms** is the ratio of the potential difference between its ends measured in volts, and the current flowing through it measured in amperes.*

(5) *The watt.* In Section 4, Chapter 10, we learned the relationship between the horsepower and the watt as units of power. The watt also is used in electricity. *One **watt** is the power supplied when a current of one ampere is driven by a potential difference of one volt.* Thus $P = IV$, where P is power in watts, I is current in amperes, and V is potential difference in volts. We may derive another useful equation for calculating electric power by substituting $V = IR$ (Ohm's law) in $P = IV$, and obtaining $P = I^2R$.

(6) *The kilowatt-hour.* If the potential difference in a part of a circuit is one volt, a current of one ampere flowing continuously through it for one hour will furnish one **watt-hour** of

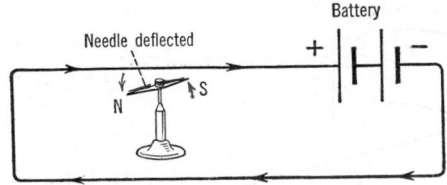

Fig. 28-2. A current flowing through a loop of wire affects the magnetic needle.

electrical energy. You as a consumer buy electrical energy at a certain price per watt-hour or per kilowatt-hour. *One kilowatt-hour equals 1000 watt-hours.* An electric iron operating on a 120-volt circuit may use 5 amperes of current continuously for one hour. It thus consumes 600 watt-hours (120 × 5 × 1) of electrical energy, or 0.6 kilowatt-hour. These calculations of electric power apply to the use of *direct current. They also will apply to alternating current circuits which contain only resistances.* Power calculations in other types of alternating current circuits will be explained in Chapter 32.

2. What is a galvanoscope? We learned that a current flowing through a wire sets up a magnetic field around that wire. Let us wind the wire into a loop and place a compass needle in the center of it. When a current flows through the loop, the needle is deflected, as shown in Fig. 28-2. If we increase the number of turns in the loop, we increase the deflection. By using a large number of turns, we can cause even a feeble current to produce a marked deflection of the needle.

A device similar to that in Fig. 28-3 may be used to show how an increase in the number of turns in the coil increases the deflection of the needle. It is called a *galvanoscope* (gal-*van*-uh-skohp). *It may be used to detect the*

presence of an electric current or to determine its direction.

3. Construction of a galvanometer. Sometimes it is necessary to do more than to detect the presence of a current or to determine its direction. Often we need to measure its strength or to find the voltage. For these purposes we use a calibrated measuring instrument called a **galvanometer** (gal-vah-*nom*-it-er), *which measures the strength of a weak electric current.*

Let us examine Fig. 28-4, which shows the essential parts of a galvanometer. A coil of wire is pivoted on jeweled bearings between the poles of a permanent horseshoe magnet. It is really a helix which becomes magnetized when current flows through it. Thus we have two magnets: (1) a permanent horseshoe magnet which is fixed on the base of the instrument; (2) an electromagnetic helix, which is free to turn upon its axis. Electrical connections to the helix are made through the two control springs. These springs hold the coil in such a position that the pointer shows a zero reading when no current is flowing through it. In a galvanometer the zero mark is at the mid-point of the scale.

Fig. 28-3. A simple galvanoscope.

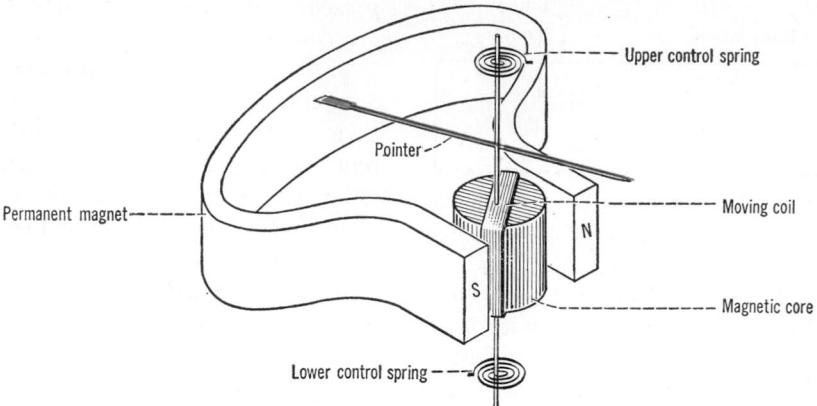

Fig. 28-4. Magnet and moving coil of galvanometer, ammeter, or voltmeter.

When current flows through the helix, its faces acquire polarity and they are attracted and repelled by the poles of the permanent magnet. A small, lightweight pointer attached to the coil moves along a graduated scale whenever the coil turns on its axis. If we increase the strength of the current flowing through the coil or helix, we increase the strength of its magnetism.

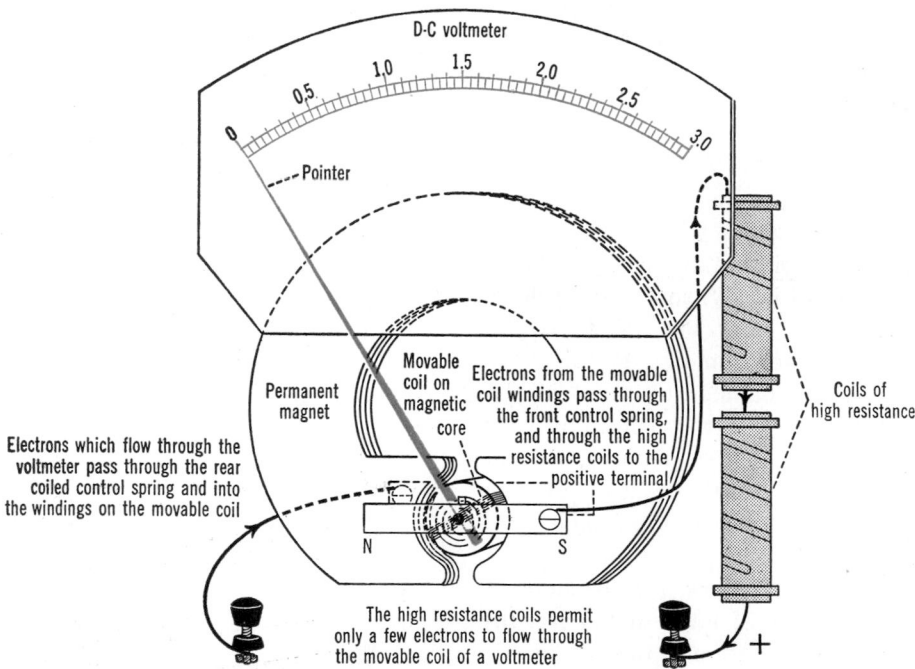

Fig. 28-5. The construction of a D–C voltmeter, showing the high resistance coils in series with the windings on the movable coil.

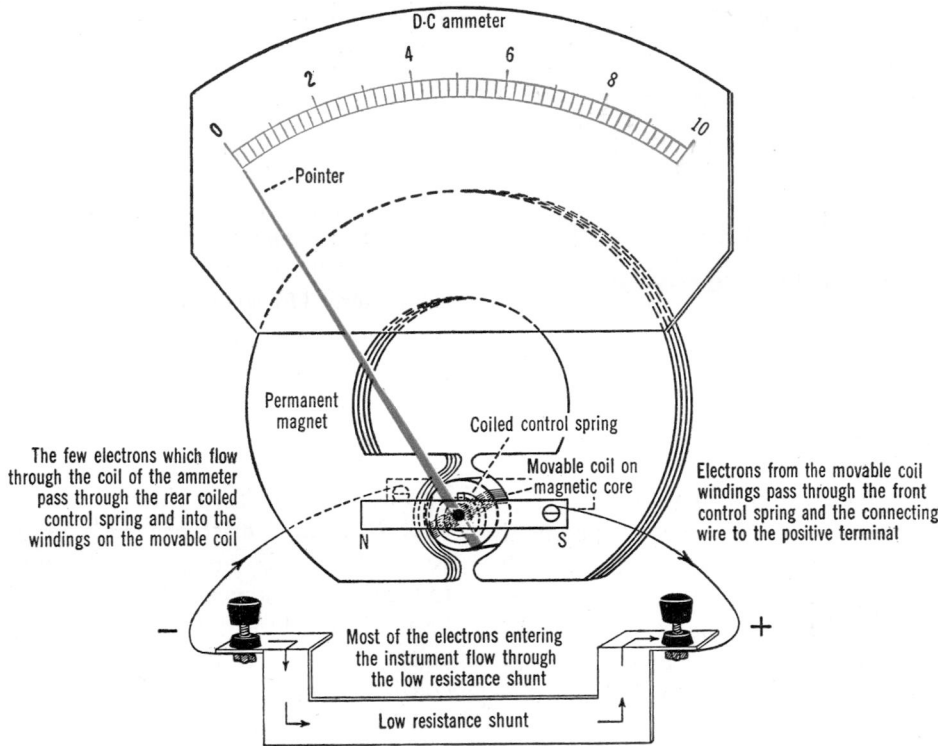

Fig. 28-6. The construction of a D–C ammeter, showing the low resistance shunt in parallel with the windings on the movable coil.

The coil exerts more force against the control springs and, as a consequence, its deflection is greater. If current flows through a galvanometer in one direction, the needle will be deflected to the left. If the current direction is reversed, the needle will be deflected to the right.

4. How does the voltmeter work? Many voltmeters are similar to galvanometers. The zero point on the scale is at the left. They are so graduated that they read potential difference directly in volts.

A voltmeter must measure difference of potential between two points in an electrical circuit without appreciably changing this potential difference. Therefore, only a very small current is permitted to flow through the instrument. To keep the current flow small, a coil of high resistance is connected in series with the movable coil. Then just enough current flows through the coil to magnetize it slightly and cause deflection of the needle. There is not

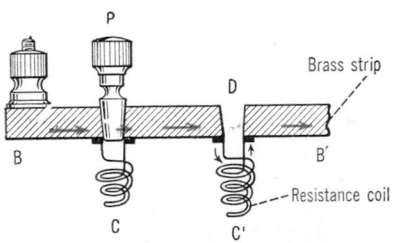

Fig. 28-7. The total resistance offered by the coils of a resistance box depends on which plugs are removed.

Fig. 28-8. A resistance box showing the construction and arrangement of the coils.

enough current flowing to lower significantly the difference of potential while readings are being taken. *All voltmeters are high-resistance instruments*. They are connected in *parallel* across a circuit to any two points between which we wish to find the difference of potential.

5. How is an ammeter used? An ammeter does not really differ much in construction from a galvanometer. It is a *low-resistance* instrument. Since

Fig. 28-9. Watt-hour meter for use with alternating current.

it is used to measure the amount of current flowing in a circuit, it must be connected in *series* in that circuit. It must not offer more than a small amount of resistance. Otherwise it would reduce the amount of current flowing in the circuit because of its own resistance. The winding of the coil is usually the same as that used for a voltmeter. However, instead of having a high-resistance coil in series with the movable coil, a *low-resistance shunt* is connected across its terminals. In that way, the resistance of the ammeter becomes negligible. Nearly all the current flows through the shunt.

6. How are resistance coils used? Resistance boxes are sometimes used to measure resistance. They also may be used to reduce the voltage in a circuit or to decrease the current. They consist of coils of high resistance wire which usually are made from an alloy whose resistance does not change a great deal with changes in temperature. They are constructed in such a way that one or more of the coils can be connected in series. Then we can vary the total resistance as desired. For example, in Fig. 28-7, current will flow through the brass strips, *BB'*, when the brass plug, *P*, is inserted, instead of flowing through the coil *C*. Since there is no plug inserted at *D*, current will flow through the coil *C'*. It can be made to flow through coil *C* by removing the plug. Each coil has a different resistance, and a wide variation is possible by removing different plugs or different combinations of plugs. See Fig. 28-8.

The standard of resistance maintained at the National Bureau of Standards in Washington, D.C., consists of 10 one-ohm coils of manganin alloy wire. The resistance of these coils has been determined with great accuracy.

7. What is a rheostat? The name, rheostat (*ree*-oh-stat), is given to any device that is used to vary the flow of current by means of a variable resistance. It usually consists of a coil of wire wound on some refractory material, like porcelain. One end of the coil is attached to one terminal of the circuit. The other terminal is connected to a sliding contact. As we move the contact across the coils, we can place as many coils in the circuit as we wish.

8. The watt-hour meter. In order to measure the electrical energy used in a circuit, we can connect a voltmeter across the terminals of the circuit. We must also connect an ammeter in series with the circuit. Then the reading of the voltmeter in volts multiplied by

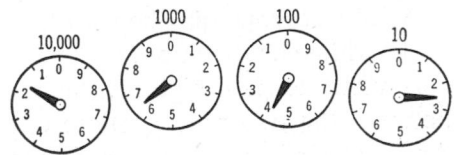

Fig. 28-10. Kilowatt-hour meter dials.

that of the ammeter in amperes equals watts. But this is too cumbersome a method for commercial measurement. Electric *watt-hour meters* are made to give readings directly in kilowatt-hours. Different types of watt-hour meters are used for alternating and for direct current. See Fig. 28-9.

The right-hand dial of Fig. 28-10 reads by kilowatt-hours from 0 to 10; the next dial reads by tens from 0 to 100; the third dial reads by hundreds from 0 to 1000. The left-hand dial reads by thousands. The reading shown here is 1642 kilowatt-hours.

--------------------------------- *Summary* ---------------------------------

The important electrical units are defined in this chapter.

(1) The ampere is that amount of current flowing through each of two long, parallel wires one meter apart which causes a magnetic force of 2×10^{-7} newton on each meter of each wire.

(2) The coulomb is the quantity of electricity which passes a given section of a conductor in one second when the conductor carries a constant current of one ampere.

(3) The difference in potential between two points is one volt if one joule of work is done by electrical forces in moving one coulomb of charge between the two points.

(4) The resistance of a conductor in ohms is the ratio of the potential difference between its ends measured in volts and the current flowing through it measured in amperes.

(5) One watt is the power supplied when a current of one ampere is driven by a potential difference of one volt.

(6) If the potential difference in a part of a circuit is one volt, a current of one ampere flowing continuously through it for one hour will furnish one watt-hour of electrical energy. One kilowatt-hour equals 1000 watt-hours.

A galvanoscope may be used to detect the presence of an electric current or to determine its direction.

A voltmeter is a high resistance galvanometer. It is connected in parallel between the two points whose difference of potential we wish to measure. An ammeter is a very low resistance galvanometer. It is connected in series in a circuit.

Resistance boxes contain coils of wire of known resistance which may be used singly or in series.

——————— *Terms to Define...*———————

Ammeter	Joule	Rheostat
Ampere	Kilowatt-hour	Volt
Charge on an electron	Newton	Voltmeter
Coulomb	Ohm	Watt
Galvanometer	Ohm's law	Watt-hour
Galvanoscope	Resistance box	Watt-hour meter

Questions

10. Describe the construction and use of a resistance box.
11. How does a rheostat differ from a resistance box?
12. What property of an electric current is measured by a watt-hour meter?

GROUP A

1. What is an ampere?
2. What is the unit of potential difference? Define this unit.
3. In what unit is the resistance of a conductor measured? How is this unit defined?
4. What is the unit in which electric power usually is measured? Give two formulas by which electric power may be calculated. What are the limitations of these formulas?
5. In what units is electric energy measured? Define these units.
6. How must a voltmeter be connected in a circuit? Why must this be done?
7. Why must a voltmeter be a very high resistance instrument?
8. How must an ammeter be connected in a circuit? Why must this be done?
9. Why must an ammeter be a very low resistance instrument?

GROUP B

13. What is a coulomb of electrical charge? What is the charge of an electron?
14. How is a galvanoscope used to detect the presence of an electric current or to determine its direction?
15. How is a galvanometer made? What magnetic and elastic forces are acting when a galvanometer is operated?
16. How is a voltmeter similar to a galvanometer? In what ways is a voltmeter different from a galvanometer?
17. Compare an ammeter with a galvanometer.
18. What characteristics must the wire have that is used in resistance box coils?
19. What several examples show the relationship of electrical units to mechanical units?
20. A magnetic compass may not indicate north in the vicinity of electrical measuring instruments. Why?

Problems

(In the Mathematics Refresher, refer to Sections 9, 10, 15, and 16.)

GROUP A

1. If a current of 0.5 ampere flows through a circuit for 15 sec, how many coulombs of charge have passed a given point in the circuit?

2. In order that 100 coulombs of electricity pass through a circuit in 5 minutes, what current strength must be used?

3. If the current is 0.6 ampere, how long will it take for 30 coulombs of electricity to pass through a circuit?

4. If the potential difference between the ends of a conductor is 30 volts, and the current flowing through the conductor is 0.4 ampere, what is the resistance of the conductor?

5. What power in watts is consumed by an electric lamp which draws a current of 0.75 ampere on a 120-volt line?

6. What current in amperes flows through a 1000-watt electric iron when it is operated on a 110-volt circuit?

7. An electric iron is rated at 750 watts. How many kilowatt-hours of energy are supplied to this iron if it is operated for 15 hours? At 4 cents per kilowatt-hour, how much does it cost to operate this iron for 15 hours?

8. An electric toaster draws 5 amperes when operated on a 120-volt line. How many watts of power is this? If the toaster is used for 10 minutes, how many kilowatt-hours of electricity are consumed?

GROUP B

9. Two parallel wires two meters long are placed one meter apart. If the total magnetic force between the two conductors is 1.6×10^{-6} newton, what current in amperes flows through each wire?

10. What is the total charge in coulombs on one billion electrons?

11. What current will a 300-watt lamp use when operated on a 120-volt circuit? What is the resistance of the filament? If this lamp is used for 15 hours, how many kilowatt-hours of electricity are consumed? At a price of 5¢ per kilowatt-hour, how much does it cost to operate this lamp?

12. A coffee percolator contains a heating coil which has a resistance of 20 ohms. The percolator is used on a 120-volt circuit for 20 minutes per day. At 3¢ per kilowatt-hour, what will be the cost of operation for a month based on 30 days?

● **13.** What current is used by a 200-watt lamp operated on a 120-volt circuit? What is the resistance of this lamp? If three of these lamps are used in series, what will be the combined resistance? What current will flow? If the three lamps are connected in parallel, what is the joint resistance? What current will flow in the main circuit now?

● **14.** An ammeter, which has a resistance of 0.01 ohm, is connected in series in a circuit through which a current of 10 amperes is flowing. If a shunt, whose resistance is 0.001 ohm, is connected across the terminals of the ammeter, what is the new reading of the ammeter?

Things to Do

1. Under your instructor's supervision, examine the construction of a D.C. galvanometer, a D.C. ammeter, a D.C. voltmeter, and a resistance box. Make a report on your findings to the class.

2. If there is a member of the class who is interested in electricity or radio as a hobby and has a combination voltmeter-ammeter-ohmmeter, ask him to demonstrate it to the class.

3. Read the dials of your electric meter on the same day that it is read by the meter reader. When he returns, read them again. Using the scale of charges of the electric company, calculate your electric bill.

Chapter 29

Chemical Effects of Electricity

1. Electricity and chemistry. Chemical changes in matter are closely related to electricity. In Section 7, Chapter 24 we learned how compounds can be formed from chemical elements by the transfer of electrons. In this chapter we shall learn about the chemical changes an electric current produces. The electroplating of metals is one such change. We also shall discover that some chemical changes can produce electricity. An example is the storage battery which furnishes electricity to start an automobile.

2. What is electrolysis? All chemical compounds are made up of two or more elements. We know, for instance, that ordinary table salt is the compound called sodium chloride (NaCl). It is composed of two elements, sodium (Na) and chlorine (Cl). The compound we call water (H_2O) is made up of hydrogen and oxygen. Some compounds are broken up or decomposed by the action of sunlight. Some are decomposed by the use of heat. Certain compounds which dissolve in water and some compounds which can be melted easily may conduct an electric current. This passage of electric current may change or decompose the compound through which it passes. *The conduction of electricity through a solution or through a molten compound together with the resulting chemical changes is called* **electrolysis** (ch-lck-*trol*-uh-sis).

3. What are the parts of an electrolytic cell? The vessel or tank in which electrolysis occurs is known as an *electrolytic cell*. Fig. 29-1 shows an electrolytic cell. Here we have two *electrodes. The electrode connected to the positive terminal of a source of current is called the* **anode.** The anode is positively charged. The other electrode is called the **cathode.** Since *the cathode is joined to the negative terminal* of a generator or battery, it is negatively charged. Thus the electrons enter the cell by way of the cathode and leave by way of the anode. *The solution or liquid through which the current flows in the cell is known as the* **electrolyte** (eh-*lek*-truh-lyte).

4. The electrolysis of water. When we try to pass an electric current through pure water, we find that the water is a poor conductor. Water ionizes very slightly to form positively charged hydrogen ions (H+) and negatively charged hydroxide ions (OH−). However, not enough of these ions from water are present to conduct an appreciable current from one electrode to the other. But a little sulfuric acid added to the water makes a solution which is a much better conductor. Sulfuric acid (H_2SO_4) is a compound made up of hydrogen, sulfur, and oxygen. When sulfuric acid is dissolved in water, a molecule of the acid breaks up into two hydrogen ions, (H+), each having a positive electric charge, and

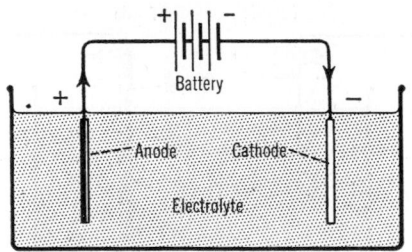

Fig. 29-1. An electrolytic cell, which consists of an anode and a cathode connected to a source of current and immersed in an electrolyte.

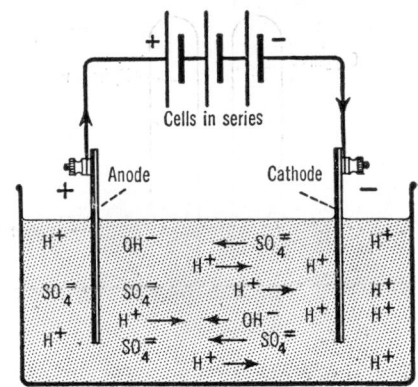

Fig. 29-2. The movement of the ions in the electrolyte during electrolysis of water.

one sulfate ion, ($SO_4^=$), which has two negative charges of electricity.

Suppose we put into this solution of sulfuric acid and water two electrodes made of platinum. We connect them to the terminals of a battery, as in Fig. 29-2. In this solution we have positively charged hydrogen ions from the water and the acid. We also have negatively charged hydroxide ions from the water and negatively charged sulfate ions from the acid. Since charges of unlike sign attract, the cathode will attract the hydrogen ions, and the anode will attract both the sulfate ions and the hydroxide ions.

When the hydrogen ions reach the cathode, they take electrons from it and become bubbles of neutral hydrogen gas, which escape from the solution. Four hydrogen ions take four electrons from the cathode to form four hydrogen atoms or two hydrogen molecules,

$$4H^+ + 4e^- = 2H_2\uparrow.$$

(Cathode reaction)

At the anode there are two possible reactions. Either the sulfate ions or the hydroxide ions can be discharged

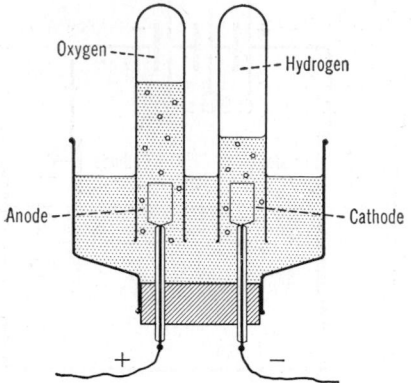

Fig. 29-3. During the electrolysis of water, oxygen is liberated at the anode while hydrogen is liberated at the cathode.

and give up their electrons. Since the sulfuric acid ionizes almost completely, and water ionizes only very slightly, there will be many more sulfate ions near the anode to be liberated than there will be hydroxide ions. However, even though the sulfate ions outnumber the hydroxide ions, less voltage is needed to discharge the hydroxide ions. Consequently it is these ions which are liberated. Four liberated hydroxide ions produce two molecules of water and one oxygen molecule. This oxygen gas bubbles from the solution.

$$4OH^- = 4e^- + 2H_2O + O_2 \uparrow .$$

(Anode reaction)

If we combine this equation with that for the cathode reaction, we see that the net change is

$$2H_2O = 2H_2 \uparrow + O_2 \uparrow ,$$

for every four electrons passing through the circuit.

If we use an apparatus of the type shown in Fig. 29-3, we can collect the two gases. The hydrogen accumulates in the tube above the cathode, and the oxygen bubbles into the tube above the anode.

5. The plating of metals. As an illustration we shall use copper plating. The reaction is carried on in an electrolytic cell or vat. A slightly acid solution of copper sulfate ($CuSO_4$) in water is used as the electrolyte. This electrolyte contains copper ions (Cu^{++}), sulfate ions, ($SO_4^=$), hydrogen ions, (H^+), and from the ionization of water, a very few hydroxide ions, (OH^-). *The object to be plated is suspended from the cathode. The anode is a bar of pure copper.* See Fig. 29-4.

When we turn the current on, the copper ions are attracted to the cathode where they take on electrons and become copper atoms. The copper atoms are deposited in an even layer on the object to be plated. At the anode three possible reactions may occur to furnish electrons. Sulfate ions may be discharged, hydroxide ions may be discharged, or copper atoms may form copper ions. The formation of copper ions from copper atoms takes place at the lowest voltage of the three possible reactions. Therefore this is the re-

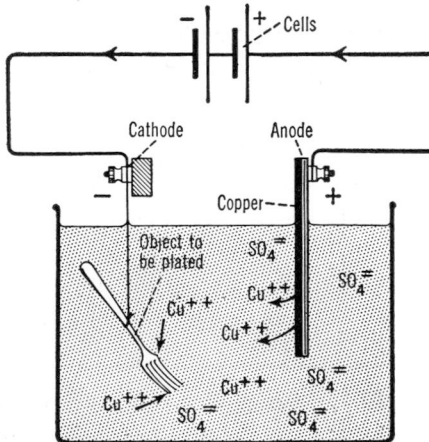

Fig. 29-4. An electrolytic cell used for copperplating.

action which occurs. As a copper ion plates out on the cathode, a copper atom from the anode forms a copper ion in the electrolyte. This action keeps the concentration of copper ions in the electrolyte nearly constant.

In general, *the object to be plated is made the cathode; a bar of the pure metal with which the object is to be plated is made the anode; a salt of the metal is used as the electrolyte.*

★ **6. Books are printed from electrotypes.** In making an electrotype, the page may be set in type in the usual way, either by hand or by machine. Then an impression of the type is made by covering it with a special wax which is pressed down into the type to fill all the depressions. The wax is then removed and the face is covered with graphite in order to make it a conductor. Next it is attached to the cathode of a copper-plating cell. When a firm layer of copper has been deposited by electrolysis, the electrotype is removed from the plating solution. The wax is melted away and the copper sheet is backed with tin foil and enough lead to make it thick and rigid so that it will not bend in the printing press. To lengthen its life, an electrotype may be plated with nickel, which increases its hardness. See Fig. 29-5.

7. Extracting metals by electrolysis. Many metals may be extracted from their ores by heating such ores in the presence of coke or carbon. There are some metals, however, with which this process does not work. Among these is aluminum. About seventy years ago a method of extracting aluminum by electrolysis was developed by Charles M. Hall (1863–1914).

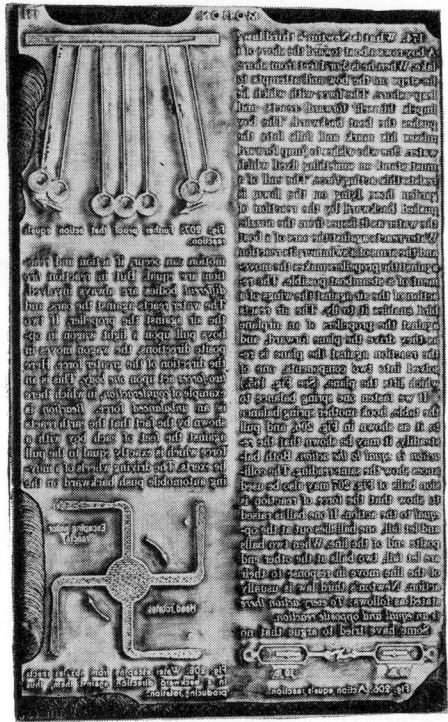

Fig. 29-5. An electrotype used for printing a textbook page, in this case, for the 1951 edition of MODERN PHYSICS. The three figures separated from the type are illustrations.

The chief ore of aluminum is bauxite, which consists largely of aluminum oxide, Al_2O_3. After the aluminum oxide is freed of impurities, it is dissolved in melted cryolite, sodium aluminum fluoride. It is then decomposed by electrolysis.

In the Hall process, an iron box of the type shown in Fig. 29-6 is used as the cathode. The anode consists of several carbon rods which dip down into the electrolyte, which is a solution of aluminum oxide in melted cryolite. The negative oxygen ions migrate to the carbon rods. The aluminum ions migrate to the cathode where they are

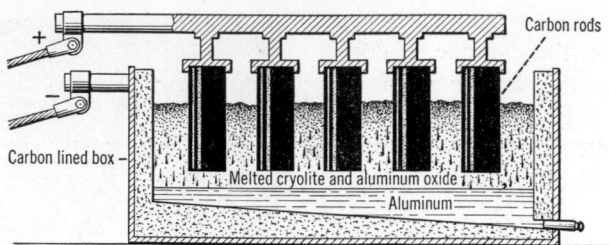

Fig. 29-6. Producing aluminum by the electrolysis of melted aluminum oxide.

neutralized to form atoms of aluminum. The molten aluminum collects in the bottom of the box, from which it is withdrawn from time to time.

Other metals, such as sodium, magnesium, and potassium, are extracted from their ores by electrolysis. The non-metal chlorine is also prepared by the same method. Either a solution of common salt in water, or the fused salt itself may be used as the electrolyte. Chlorine is set free at the anode. See Fig. 29-7.

Certain metals are *refined* by electrolysis. Copper, for example, is purified by using a bar of impure copper as the anode of an electrolytic cell, and a thin sheet of very pure copper as the cathode. When the current is turned on, the impure copper goes into solution at the anode, and highly refined copper is plated upon the cathode. The impurities collect at the bottom of the tank as a kind of " mud," from which gold and silver, which are often found in small quantities in copper ores, are recovered. They are separated from each other, and can be refined by electrolysis. See Fig. 29-8.

8. What are the laws of electrolysis? Faraday formulated three LAWS OF ELECTROLYSIS. He found that a current that deposits half a pennyweight of silver in ten minutes will deposit one pennyweight of silver in

twenty minutes.   In general, we may say:

Law 1. *The amount of any metal that is deposited by an electric current is directly proportional to the length of time the current flows.*

From experiment it can be shown that a current of one ampere will deposit by electrolysis exactly 0.001118 g of silver per second. A current of ten amperes will deposit exactly ten times as much per second. Stated in general terms:

Law 2. *The amount of any metal deposited during electrolysis is directly proportional to the strength of the current in amperes.*

Some elements are deposited by electrolysis much faster than others. For example, a current which will liberate 1 g of hydrogen can, in the same time, liberate 8 g of oxygen, or 35.5 g of chlorine. The same current that will deposit 107.88 g of silver in a given time will deposit 31.8 g of copper, or only 9 g of aluminum, in the same time. We see that 1 g of the element hydrogen is equivalent to 8 g of oxygen, to 9 g of aluminum, and to 107.88 g of silver. The law may be stated as follows:

Law 3. *The amount of an element deposited in a given time by a current of one ampere is directly proportional to the electrochemical equivalent of the*

Fig. 29-7. In these cells, chlorine is being prepared by electrolysis of a concentrated solution of common salt.

element. *The **electrochemical equivalent** is the number of grams of a material which will be deposited by the passage of one coulomb of charge.* (See Table 17, Appendix B.)

We may combine these three laws in the equation $m = zIt$, where m is the mass of material deposited in grams, z is the electrochemical equivalent, I is the current strength in amperes, and t is time in seconds.

★ **9. The silver coulombmeter.** Faraday's laws give us a precise method of measuring the amount of charge which flows through a circuit. If we know the length of time the electricity flows, we may determine the average current strength. Let us connect a platinum

dish with the negative terminal of a source of current of about 2 volts potential. We may then fill the dish partly full of a solution of some silver salt. A platinum spiral rod is connected to the positive terminal of the source of current and dipped into the silver solution.

One coulomb of electricity (one ampere of current for one second) flowing through such a silver solution will deposit on the walls of the dish 0.001118 g of silver. If an average current of one ampere flows through the solution for one hour, $1 \times 60 \times 60$, or 3600 coulombs, will have deposited 4.025 g of silver. By weighing the amount of silver deposited, the number

Fig. 29-8. Lifting a load of copper cathodes from the electrolytic cells in the tankhouse of a copper refining plant. These are the sheets of purified copper which have been prepared by electrolysis.

of coulombs of electricity is easily and accurately determined.

10. What is a voltaic cell? We have been studying electrolytic cells in which the passage of electricity through a solution produced chemical changes at the electrodes. *Voltaic cells,* on the other hand, are devices in which chemical reactions at the electrodes produce electricity. In such

Platinum
dish
cathode

Platinum spiral
anode

Solution of a
silver salt

Fig. 29-9. A silver coulomb-meter is used to measure the number of coulombs of electricity passing through a circuit.

cells, chemical energy is transformed into electrical energy.

In 1790 Luigi Galvani (1737–1798), an Italian scientist, made an interesting discovery. He was experimenting with a frog which was suspended by means of a copper wire attached to its leg. When the muscle of the frog's leg was touched with a scalpel, it twitched vigorously. Galvani erroneously believed that the twitching was due to electricity in the frog's leg. Alessandro Volta learned of Galvani's discovery and carried on a series of experiments which led to the invention of the voltaic cell. The volt and the voltaic cell are both named in honor of Volta.

Suppose we dip a zinc strip and a carbon rod into a vessel of water. In order to make the water a better conductor, we may add a substance like sulfuric acid. We did this in the electrolysis of water. The carbon rod and zinc strip are the electrodes. The conducting solution is the electrolyte.

Now let us connect the electrodes externally by a conductor, as in Fig. 29-10. If we test this cell, we find that electrons are flowing in the conductor from the zinc strip to the carbon rod. However, instead of hydrogen bubbles being evolved at the zinc strip, as might be expected from the interaction of the zinc and the sulfuric acid, they are evolved at the carbon rod. By means of chemical energy the carbon rod is maintained at a higher potential than the zinc. Since the chemical action goes on continuously, the difference of potential between the electrodes is maintained. The current continues to flow through the wire as long as the chemical action goes on. The voltaic cell we have just constructed is a kind of electrical pump which acts to build up and maintain a difference of potential. *A voltaic cell consists of two dissimilar conducting materials immersed in a fluid which is also a conductor.*

Dozens of different types of voltaic cells have been devised. Zinc is the most frequently used metal for the negative plate of a voltaic cell. Many different elements have been used for the positive plate, including carbon, copper, gold, silver, and even platinum. However, carbon is the element most frequently used. Also, various solutions have been used in different types of voltaic cells.

11. The theory of action in a voltaic cell. Let us refer again to the simple voltaic cell in which the two elements, carbon and zinc, are dipped into dilute sulfuric acid.

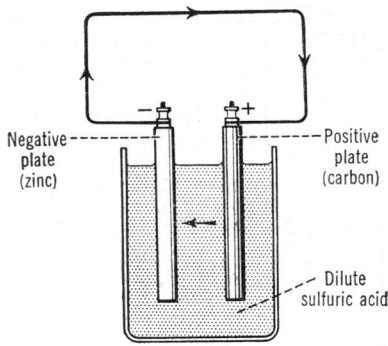

Fig. 29-10. Diagram of a voltaic cell.

The atoms forming the zinc strip have a strong tendency when immersed in an electrolyte to lose two electrons each and form zinc ions,

$$Zn = Zn^{++} + 2e^-. \text{ (Cathode reaction)}$$

These positively charged zinc ions go into the solution, but the electrons remain on the zinc strip. This causes the zinc strip to become negatively charged. In the electrolyte we have other positive ions. Of these only H^+ hydrogen ions from water and from the addition of acid need be considered. The excess of plus zinc ions being formed around the negative plate will repel the plus hydrogen ions and drive them over toward the neutral carbon rod or plate. There hydrogen ions (H^+) take electrons from the carbon rod. The hydrogen ions have their charges neutralized and escape from the solution as neutral bubbles of hydrogen gas.

$$2H^+ + 2e^- = H_2 \uparrow. \text{ (Anode reaction)}$$

On *open circuit,* this chemical action continues until the plus charges on the carbon rod exert enough back pressure to repel the similarly charged hydrogen ions with a force exactly equal to their repulsion by the plus zinc ions. This

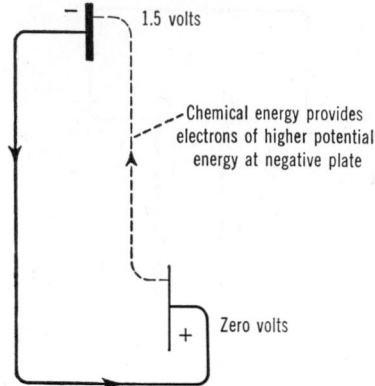

Fig. 29-11. A voltaic cell provides electrons of higher potential energy because of chemical action in the cell.

occurs in the case of carbon and zinc when the difference of potential between the two plates of the cell is about 1.5 volts. Different combinations of elements and different solutions give somewhat different voltages. Copper and zinc give about 1.1 volts.

On *closed circuit,* there is a fall of potential along the conductor. This happens because there is a stream of electrons from the negatively charged zinc strip flowing through the conductor and tending to neutralize the excess positive charge on the carbon rod. The chemical action goes on all the time, continuously building up a difference of potential between the two plates. It stops only when the zinc is completely used up. We conclude, therefore, that *a voltaic cell is a device which transforms chemical energy into electrical energy.*

12. Two common defects of voltaic cells. (1) *Local action.* Carbon or coal is used in extracting zinc from its ores. Commercial zinc usually has some carbon particles distributed through it. As such zinc forms zinc

ions, these small particles of carbon are set free. Some of them adhere to the surface of the zinc and some remain suspended in the electrolyte. They become positively charged in the same manner as the positive plate. Then they set up miniature circuits within the cell itself, as shown in Fig. 29-12. This results in wasted energy, because the small circuits do not contribute anything to the flow of electrons in the *external circuit.* Chemical action within a cell which produces only wasted energy is called *local action.*

We may prevent local action by using pure zinc, but zinc which is entirely free from carbon is expensive. We may also prevent local action if we amalgamate the zinc plate by rubbing its surface with mercury. The mercury dissolves the zinc and brings it to the surface. The carbon impurities do not dissolve, but remain covered by the mercury. Local action thus is prevented.

(2) *Polarization.* The term *polarization,* when applied to voltaic cells, has no relation to the polarization of light or to magnetic polarity. *It is a defect in cells caused by the accumulation of hydrogen bubbles on the positive plate.*

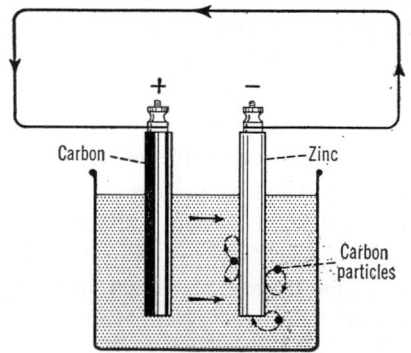

Fig. 29-12. Local action in a voltaic cell.

Let us connect a simple voltaic cell with a voltmeter, as shown in Fig. 29-13. At first the voltmeter probably will show a reading of about 1.5 volts. If we let this cell stand on closed circuit for several minutes, we will notice a gradual drop in voltage. If we examine the plates of such a cell, we find that the positive plate is covered with an accumulation of tiny bubbles of hydrogen gas. A plate of hydrogen has been virtually substituted for the carbon plate with which we started. The cell is said to be *polarized*.

13. How can polarization be prevented or remedied? Since polarization lowers the voltage which a cell gives, it is undesirable. It also increases the internal resistance of the cell. Several different methods have been used to prevent or remedy polarization.

(1) *Mechanical.* If we lift the positive plate of a polarized cell from the solution, wipe off the hydrogen bubbles, and then put it back into the acid solution, the voltage will again rise practically to normal. Such a remedy is neither convenient nor practical, and its effect is only temporary.

(2) *Chemical.* A polarized cell is shown in Fig. 29-13. Suppose we add to it a small crystal of potassium dichromate, or some other chemical substance which readily reacts with hydrogen. We soon find that the voltage has again risen to nearly normal. Potassium dichromate is a compound which is a vigorous *oxidizing agent*. It reacts with the hydrogen bubbles, oxidizing them and forming water. Consequently, an oxidizing agent can be used to remove hydrogen and remedy polarization.

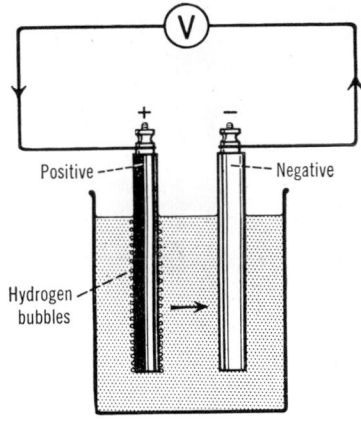

Fig. 29-13. Polarization of a voltaic cell is caused by the accumulation of hydrogen bubbles on the positive plate.

(3) *By the discharge of metallic ions at the positive electrode.* The use of a different chemical reaction at the positive electrode, one which does not produce hydrogen, is another method of preventing polarization. In the Daniell cell, zinc forms the negative plate, but a copper strip is used as the positive plate. The electrolyte near this plate is copper sulfate. Copper ions from the solution take electrons from the copper strip and become copper atoms,

$$Cu^{++} + 2e^- = Cu.$$

The copper sulfate solution is kept separate from the zinc ions in solution either by its greater density, as in the gravity type cell, or by means of a porous cup.

14. How is a dry cell made? The *negative plate* of a dry cell is a zinc cylinder lined with porous cardboard. This forms the walls and bottom of the cell. The *positive plate* is a carbon rod, placed in the center of the cylinder, and surrounded with a thin layer of manganese dioxide and powdered carbon. Instead of a liquid electro-

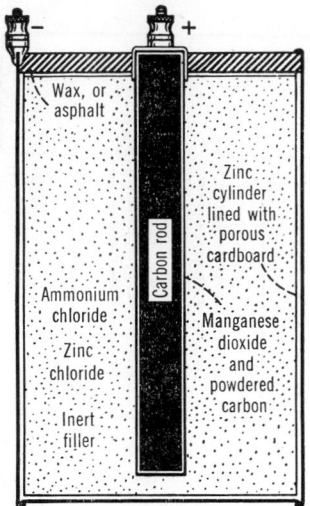

Fig. 29-14. Sectional view of a dry cell, showing the various parts.

lyte, the dry cell uses a paste of ammonium chloride, zinc chloride, some inert filler, and a little water. This paste fills the space between the manganese dioxide layer and the zinc outer cylinder. The top is covered with wax or asphalt to prevent loss of water by evaporation.

When this cell is operating, zinc atoms from the negative plate form zinc ions. At the positive carbon rod, ammonium ions gain electrons, forming ammonia gas and hydrogen. The ammonia gas is taken up by the zinc chloride. The hydrogen reacts with the manganese dioxide, which is present as a depolarizer. Inert materials added to the paste may help reduce the internal resistance.

A dry cell gives an electromotive force of about 1.5 volts. Under long, hard usage it may polarize, but it recovers when it stands on open circuit. Its internal resistance is so very small that it may give a current of from 30 to 40 amperes.

★ **15. The Weston standard cell.** Certain voltaic cells have been devised which maintain a very constant electromotive force, provided only very small currents are drawn from them. The Weston standard cell is one of the most frequently used. At 20° C it has an emf of 1.018 volts. Such a cell may be used as a secondary standard of voltage.

16. Upon what does the emf of a cell depend? To find the answer to this question, we may connect a voltmeter to the terminals of a *non-polarizing* cell, and note the reading. If we move the plates of the cell nearer together, the emf is not affected. If we lift one or both of the plates, the voltmeter reading remains the same as long as the plates touch the liquid. If we use a cell with smaller plates, the emf remains the same. We conclude from these observations that the emf of a cell does not depend upon the size of the plates, the distance between them, or the depth to which they are immersed in the solution. It can be shown by further experimentation that the *electromotive force of a cell depends upon the materials used in its construction.* This refers to the metals used as plates and also to the kind of liquid used in the solution. Temperature has a slight effect on the emf of a cell.

17. Measuring the resistance of a voltaic cell. We will need a voltmeter and an ammeter. If we connect the voltmeter across the terminals of the cell on open circuit, we can find the electromotive force, ε, between the two plates. See Fig. 29-15. We then disconnect the voltmeter. Now we connect an ammeter in the cell circuit with a coil of resistance wire, R_e. The ammeter tells us the rate of current flow through the circuit. This current, in amperes, is represented by the symbol I. In a cell circuit, we must consider two resistances: (1) the external resistance, R_e; (2) the internal resistance, R_i, which is offered by the solution or paste in the cell itself. The total resistance, R, is equal to the sum of the external resistance, R_e, and the internal resistance, R_i. Applied to a voltaic cell, Ohm's law is stated:

$$I = \frac{\mathcal{E}}{R_e + R_i}.$$

The voltmeter gives us the reading $\mathcal{E}$; the ammeter gives the reading I; if we use a wire of known resistance, R_e, we can calculate internal resistance R_i. See the Sample Problem below.

18. Voltaic cells vary in resistance. If we measure the internal resistances of different types of cells by the method used in the preceding section, we find that they vary widely. A gravity cell or a Daniell cell will show an internal resistance of from 1 to 6 ohms. Since their voltage is only 1.1, such cells seldom furnish even one ampere of current. On the other hand, the internal resistance of a new dry cell of

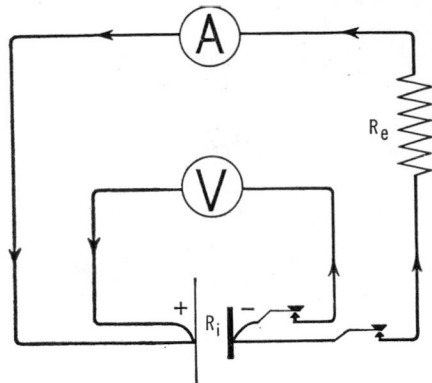

Fig. 29-15. A voltmeter and ammeter may be used to measure the internal resistance of a cell.

standard size is approximately 0.05 ohm. When the external resistance is zero, a cell whose voltage is 1.5 and whose resistance is 0.05 ohm can furnish 30 amperes of current.

Let us use a non-polarizing cell with an ammeter. If we move the plates farther apart, we find that the ammeter reading drops. If we lift one or both of the plates so that they are not so deeply immersed, we again find that the ammeter reading drops. In both cases, we increased the internal resistance of the cell. In the first case, we made the

---

SAMPLE PROBLEM

A dry cell gives a reading of 1.5 volts; an ammeter in circuit with a coil whose resistance is 0.2 ohm shows a reading of 5 amperes. Find the internal resistance of the cell.

SOLUTION

We have given the following: $\mathcal{E} = 1.5$ volts; $I = 5$ amperes; $R_e = 0.2$ ohm; R_i is to be found. Substituting the values given in the cell formula, we get

$5 = \dfrac{1.5}{0.2 + R_i}$. To solve for R_i, we first cross-multiply, $5(0.2 + R_i) = 1.5$. Then we remove the parentheses, $1 + 5R_i = 1.5$. Transposing, $5R_i = 1.5 - 1$, and dividing, $R_i = 0.1$ ohm, internal resistance.

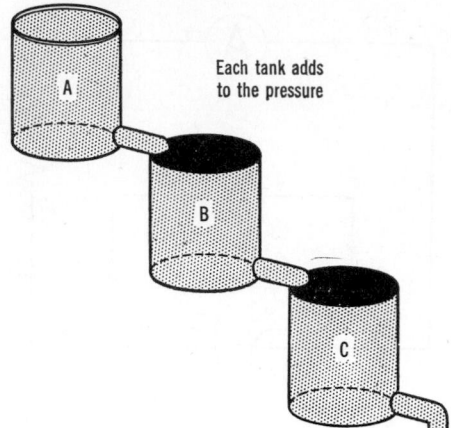

Fig. 29-16. Water analogy for series grouping of cells.

current flow across a longer liquid path; and in the second case we reduced the cross-sectional area of the liquid path. In order to reduce internal resistance, *we must use large plates and place them as close together as possible.*

19. The grouping of cells. Sometimes a single cell does not give sufficient voltage or enough current for our needs. It is possible to group two or more cells in such a manner that we can get more voltage, more current, or both. Of the several methods used to group cells, we shall discuss only two: (1) *series grouping,* and (2) *parallel grouping.*

(1) *Series grouping.* If a single tank of water does not furnish enough pressure, we can increase the " water head " by placing more tanks above it, as shown in Fig. 29-16. Each tank increases the water pressure by increasing the depth. With three tanks, the pressure is three times as great. In a similar manner, we may group cells *in series* by joining the positive plate of one cell to the negative plate of a second, and so on, as shown in Fig. 29-17.

Then we find that *each cell added increases the voltage.* If a single cell has an emf of 1.5 volts, then three cells will have an emf of 4.5 volts. When n represents the number of cells, then the total voltage of n cells becomes $n\varepsilon$.

The water in the three tanks must flow through each of the tanks in turn. As a result, the water meets three times as much resistance as it did in flowing through a single tank. For the same reason, the *total internal resistance* of three cells grouped in series is just three times that of a single cell. For any number of cells, n, the internal resistance is nR_i. Naturally, the external resistance, R_e, is not affected by changes in cell grouping. For cells grouped in series, we modify the formula for Ohm's law as follows:

$$I = \frac{n\varepsilon}{R_e + nR_i}.$$

Some rules which apply to cells *in series:*

(a) Ohm's law applies to series circuits.

(b) The *voltage* across the terminals of *all* the cells in a *series* circuit is equal to the *sum* of all the separate voltages. Hence we multiply ε, the voltage of a single cell, by n, the number of cells.

(c) The total *resistance* of a *series* cir-

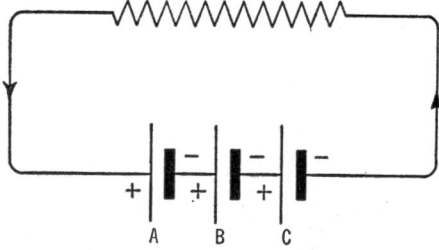

Fig. 29-17. How cells are grouped in series.

cuit is equal to the *sum* of all the separate resistances. Hence we multiply R_i, the resistance of a single cell, by *n*, the number of cells.

(*d*) The amount of current is the same in every part of a *series* circuit.

(2) *Parallel grouping.* Suppose we have three tanks of water all the same level, as in Fig. 29-18. Connecting them all to the same external pipe does not increase the pressure. No matter how many water tanks of the same depth we have in parallel grouping, there is no increase in pressure. In a similar manner we may group two or more cells *in parallel* by joining all the positive plates with one wire and all the negative plates with another wire. See Fig. 29-19.

In this system of grouping, *there is no increase in voltage,* no matter how many cells are used.

Since only one-third of the water flows from each of the three tanks in parallel, the resistance offered is only one-third that of a single tank. In a similar manner, one-third of the current will flow through each of the three cells connected in parallel. The *total internal resistance* of three cells in parallel is only one-third that of a single cell. Grouping cells in parallel does not increase the voltage. Yet in some cases we can get much more current

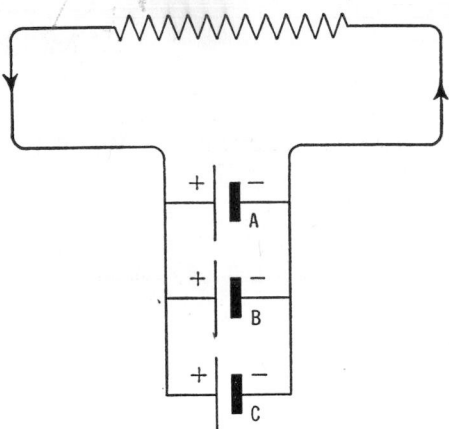

Fig. 29-19. How cells are grouped in parallel.

by such grouping because the internal resistance of any number of cells, *n*, is equal to $1/n$ the resistance of a single cell. For parallel grouping, we modify the formula for Ohm's law as follows:

$$I = \frac{\varepsilon}{R_e + \dfrac{R_i}{n}}.$$

Some rules which apply to cells in parallel:

(*a*) Ohm's law applies to the entire circuit or to any branch of the circuit.

(*b*) The *total voltage* across the terminals of all the cells is the *same* as that for a single cell. Adding cells in parallel does not raise the voltage.

(*c*) The *total internal resistance* of any number of cells in parallel is only *1-nth* that for a single cell.

(*d*) The *total current* furnished by the group is equal to the *sum* of the currents in all the separate parts.

20. Which grouping is more useful? We easily can perform some laboratory experiments to test these two methods of grouping cells. The formulas given above were derived from the results of such experiments. By

Pressure same in each case

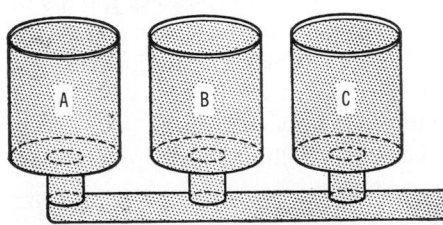

Fig. 29-18. Water analogy for parallel grouping.

SAMPLE PROBLEM

We have 20 dry cells, each with a voltage of 1.5 volts and an internal resistance of 0.1 ohm. What current will a single cell send through an external resistance of 500 ohms? What current will 20 cells give if they are grouped in series? What current will they produce if they are grouped in parallel?

SOLUTION

(a) *Single cell.* By substitution in the formula for Ohm's law, we get:

$$I = \frac{1.5}{500 + 0.1} . \text{ Solving, } I = 0.0030 \text{ ampere.}$$

(b) *Series.* Substituting the values given in the formula, we have:

$$I = \frac{20 \times 1.5}{500 + (20 \times 0.1)} . \text{ Solving, } I = 0.059 \text{ ampere.}$$

(c) *Parallel.* Substituting in the formula for cells in parallel, we obtain the following:

$$I = \frac{1.5}{500 + \dfrac{0.1}{20}} . \text{ Solving, } I = 0.0030 \text{ ampere.}$$

solving problems involving the methods of grouping cells, it is easy to find out which method gives the more useful results. See above Sample Problem.

When we analyze the results, we find that 20 cells in series give *nearly 20 times as much current* as a single cell does in this particular case. We observe, too, that the 20 cells in parallel give almost *the same current* as a single cell in this problem, in which the external resistance is large. But this problem illustrates only what happens when the external resistance is large. For a problem in which the external resistance is small, see page 559.

From this problem, we might infer that parallel grouping is superior to series grouping, since 20 cells in series furnish only a trifle more current than a single cell. In our first problem, the external resistance was very large com-pared to the total internal resistance. In this problem the external resistance was smaller than the internal resistance. If the maximum current is desired we always use such a method of grouping cells that the *external* and *total internal* resistances are as nearly equal as possible. If the *external resistance is large, use series grouping. When the external resistance is small, use parallel group-ing.* It is possible to have cells in *mixed* grouping. For example, it is possible to have two parallel groups of three cells each connected in series.

21. The principle of the storage cell. In our study of the voltaic cell we found that two dissimilar conductors immersed in a fluid that is also a con-ductor may be used to produce an elec-tric current. Such a *primary* cell transforms chemical energy into elec-trical energy. It also is possible to start

SAMPLE PROBLEM

Suppose we have the same 20 cells to be used with a small external resistance of only 0.005 ohm. What current will a single cell furnish? What current will the cells produce if grouped in series? What current will flow if they are joined in parallel?

SOLUTION

(a) *Single cell.* By substitution, we have,

$$I = \frac{1.5}{0.005 + 0.1}.$$ Solving, I = 14.3 amperes.

(b) *Series.* By substitution,

$$I = \frac{20 \times 1.5}{0.005 + (20 \times 0.1)}.$$ Solving, I = 14.9 amperes.

(c) *Parallel.* By substitution,

$$I = \frac{1.5}{0.005 + \dfrac{0.1}{20}}.$$ Solving, I = 150 amperes

---

with two plates more or less similar and make them dissimilar by means of electrolysis. Thus we use electrical energy to produce a chemical change. We transform electrical energy into chemical energy. Such a *storage cell,* or *secondary cell,* is then used just like a voltaic cell to produce an electric current. When the storage cell is being charged it uses electricity. As it is being discharged, the stored chemical energy is used to produce electricity.

22. How does the lead storage cell work? Let us immerse two lead plates in a water solution of sulfuric acid. When these two plates are connected to the terminals of a direct current generator or some cells in series, electric current decomposes the water indirectly in a manner just like that described in Section 4. The hydrogen escapes at the cathode, but the oxygen does not escape when *lead plates* are used. See

Fig. 29-20. The oxygen unites chemically with the lead anode to form lead dioxide, PbO_2. In this way, the two plates are made dissimilar. One of the lead plates has been changed at the

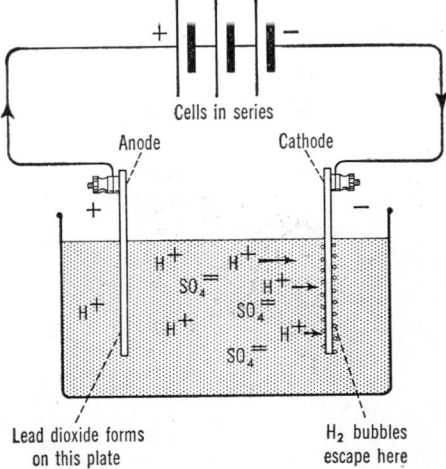

Fig. 29-20. The chemical action that occurs during the charging of a storage cell.

Fig. 29-20.

Fig. 29-21. Positive and negative plates of a lead storage cell. On the left are the positive plates, in the center the separators, and on the right, the negative plates.

surface into lead dioxide, a reddish-brown deposit which can be seen if we look at the anode carefully. The other plate is gray and somewhat spongy.

Next let us connect the cell, which we have just charged, to a voltmeter. This voltmeter may show an emf between the two plates of about 2.2 volts.

Fig. 29-22. Cutaway view of a 12-volt lead storage battery.

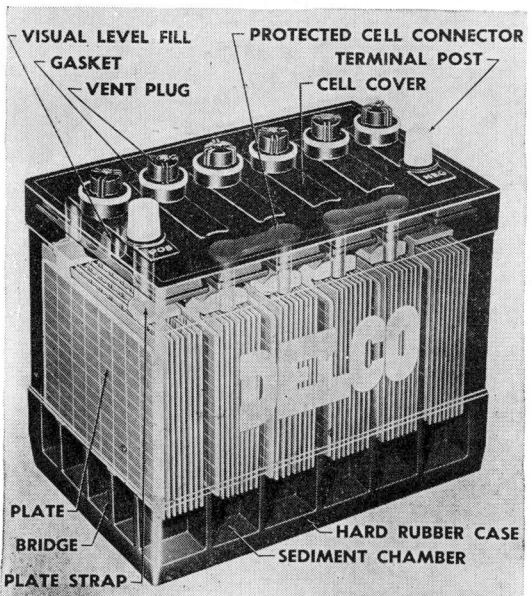

VISUAL LEVEL FILL — PROTECTED CELL CONNECTOR
GASKET — TERMINAL POST
VENT PLUG — CELL COVER

PLATE
BRIDGE — HARD RUBBER CASE
SEDIMENT CHAMBER
PLATE STRAP

The lead dioxide plate is the positive plate. While the cell is discharging, the lead dioxide is converted into lead sulfate and water is formed. The lead plate is also changed to lead sulfate. When the surfaces of both plates become coated with lead sulfate, they are chemically similar. No more current can flow from the cell.

Fortunately the process can be reversed by charging the cell again. The equation which represents the chemical action follows:

$$\text{Discharging} \rightarrow$$
$$PbO_2 + Pb + 2H_2SO_4 \rightleftarrows 2PbSO_4 + 2H_2O$$
$$\leftarrow \text{Charging}$$

The specific gravity of concentrated sulfuric acid is a little more than 1.800, and that of water is 1.000. Suppose we have a cell that is fully charged. Its electrolyte, a mixture of water and sulfuric acid, has a specific gravity of 1.300. Since water is formed when a cell is being discharged, the specific gravity may drop to 1.150. It rises again when we recharge the cell, since water is decomposed and sulfuric acid is formed. For this reason we can use a hydrometer to determine whether a storage battery needs recharging.

23. How is the commercial lead storage cell constructed? Usually, the commercial cell does not differ from the experimental cell discussed in Section 22. The chemical action is the same, but the plates are more efficient. The positive plate, Fig. 29-21, has a large number of grids packed with lead dioxide. This distributes the active lead dioxide through the plate as well as at its surface. The negative plate has a large number of small cells, or pockets, filled with spongy lead to increase the amount of surface of the plate. Separators of rubber, treated wood, or glass fiber are kept between the plates so that they may be placed very close together without touching. By using large plates and placing them close together, we may make the internal resistance very low.

24. How is the Edison storage battery constructed? Thomas Alva Edison (1847–1931) devised a lightweight, strong, durable storage battery. In the cells of this battery the positive plate consists of nickel-plated, perforated iron tubes filled with nickel flake and hydrated nickel oxide. See Fig. 29-23. The negative plate consists of nickel-plated, perforated iron cells, or pockets, filled with iron oxide. The electrolyte is potassium hydroxide. The cells are enclosed in a strong nickel-plated steel container. The chemical action is too complex to be explained here.

25. Batteries are rated in ampere-hours. In accordance with Faraday's laws, the amount of chemical energy stored up in a battery depends upon the amount of current used to charge the battery and upon the time the current flows. The *capacity* of a storage cell is usually rated in *ampere-hours*. To illustrate this, a battery which has a capacity of 90 ampere-hours can supply a current of 1 ampere for 90 hours, 2 amperes for 45 hours, 3 amperes for 30 hours, and so on. Thus we see that it is possible for a battery to deliver a small quantity of electrical energy for a long time, or a larger amount of electrical energy for a shorter time.

26. The advantages and disadvantages of storage cells. The lead storage battery is heavy, and its basic construction is weak. Under ideal conditions, its efficiency is about 75%. Be-

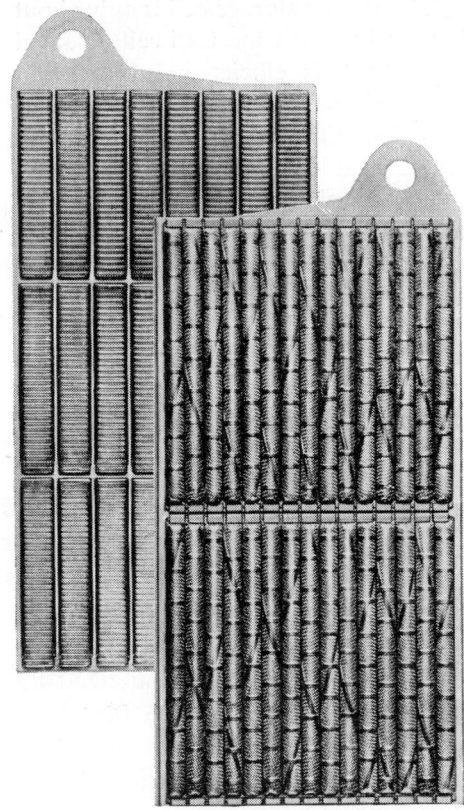

Fig. 29-23. Positive and negative plates of an Edison cell.

cause of its very low internal resistance it can supply a very large amount of current for short periods of time. This makes the lead storage battery extremely useful for operating the self-starters on automobiles. However, the lead cell must not be completely discharged. It also is injured by charging it too rapidly, or by drawing too large currents from it and discharging it too fast. When fully charged, it should show a voltage of about 2.2, and the specific gravity of the electrolyte should be about 1.300. Distilled water must be added to the battery at frequent intervals to replace the water that is lost during the operation of the cell.

The Edison storage cell is only about half as heavy as the lead cell of equal capacity. Its efficiency is somewhat less, and its internal resistance is higher. The Edison cell is mechanically strong, and is not so readily injured by rapid charging or discharging. The maximum voltage of the Edison cell is about 1.25; hence five Edison cells in series will furnish about the same voltage as three lead cells joined in series.

27. What are some uses of storage cells? The primary use of storage cells is to furnish current to the electrical systems of automobiles, trucks, airplanes, and trains.

Storage cells are also used for telephone work. In physics laboratories they may be used to provide direct current for electrical experiments. Some delivery trucks use storage batteries for their motive power.

Summary

The conduction of electricity through a solution or through a molten compound, together with the resulting chemical changes, is called electrolysis. The vessel in which electrolysis occurs is called an electrolytic cell. In the cell there are two electrodes: the positive electrode is called the anode, the negative electrode is the cathode. The solution, or liquid, through which the current flows in the cell is the electrolyte.

Faraday's LAWS OF ELECTROLYSIS state: The amount of any metal that is deposited by an electric current is directly proportional (1) to the length of time the current flows, (2) to the strength of the current in amperes, and (3) to the electrochemical equivalent of the element.

A voltaic cell consists of two dissimilar conducting materials immersed in a fluid which is also a conductor. A voltaic cell is a device for transforming chemical energy into electrical energy. The two common defects of a voltaic cell are local action and polarization. Local action may be prevented by amalgamating the zinc plate with mercury. Polarization may be remedied by using an oxidizing agent as a depolarizer or by having metallic ions discharged at the positive electrode.

Storage cells are voltaic cells from which electrical energy may be obtained. The chemical change which takes place in such cells, however, enables us to recharge them by passing electricity through the discharged cell. Well-known storage cells include the lead storage cell and the Edison cell.

Terms to Define . . .

Advantages and disadvantages of storage cells	Anode	Closed circuit
Ampere-hour	Capacity of a storage cell	Depolarizer
	Cathode	Dry cell

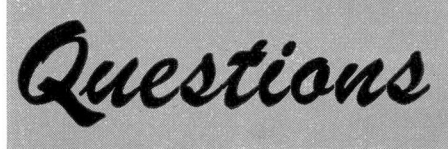

15. How does a storage cell differ from a voltaic cell? How are they alike?

16. What factors in the construction of a lead storage cell reduce its internal resistance?

17. How is the Edison storage cell constructed?

18. For what purposes are storage cells used?

GROUP A

1. What is electrolysis? What effect may the passage of electricity have on a molten compound or on the solution of a compound?

2. Define (1) electrolytic cell; (2) electrode; (3) anode; (4) cathode; (5) electrolyte.

3. Why is sulfuric acid added to water before it is electrolyzed?

4. How is impure copper refined by electrolysis? What by-products often pay the cost of the refining process?

5. State Faraday's laws of electrolysis. What is the electrochemical equivalent of an element?

6. What is a voltaic cell? What energy change occurs in a voltaic cell?

7. Describe the difference in action in a voltaic cell when it is on open circuit and when it is on closed circuit.

8. What are two common defects of voltaic cells, and how may each be remedied?

9. What is the emf of an ordinary dry cell? What maximum current can it deliver?

10. A flashlight was used for such a long time that the batteries weakened and the bulb gave off only a feeble light. Yet when the flashlight was turned on the next day, the lamp glowed brightly again. Explain.

11. Upon what does the emf of a cell depend?

12. Upon what factors does the internal resistance of a cell depend?

13. What are the advantages to the series grouping of cells? What are the disadvantages?

14. What are the advantages to the parallel grouping of cells? What are the disadvantages?

GROUP B

19. During the electrolysis of water, which ion is discharged at the cathode? Which ion is discharged at the anode? Write the electrochemical equations for these reactions.

20. How would you proceed to electroplate a metallic object with copper? What reactions occur at each electrode?

21. Describe the method by which aluminum is produced from aluminum oxide by electrolysis.

★ **22.** What device may be used to measure precisely the amount of charge which flows through a circuit in a given time?

23. Explain why a zinc-carbon voltaic cell is a source of emf.

24. What are the functions of the following parts of a dry cell? (1) The zinc can; (2) the carbon rod; (3) manganese dioxide; (4) zinc chloride; (5) wax or asphalt covering.

25. What effect do each of the following conditions have on the quality of an electroplating job? (1) Low current strength; (2) agitating the electrolyte; (3) concentrated solution of metallic salt as the electrolyte; (4) high voltage.

26. Describe a method of measuring the internal resistance of a voltaic cell by using a voltmeter and an ammeter.

27. When should a series grouping of cells be used? When should a parallel grouping of cells be used?

28. Describe what happens to the plates in a lead storage cell as it is being discharged. As it is being recharged. What happens to the electrolyte during each of these processes?

29. How do we rate the capacity of a storage battery?

30. Compare the lead storage battery with the Edison storage battery.

(In the Mathematics Refresher, refer to Sections 9, 10, and 16.)

GROUP A

1. How many grams of silver will be deposited by an electric current of 0.5 ampere in 8 minutes?

2. When a certain current flows through an electroplating bath for 10 minutes, it deposits 0.600 g of copper. What is the average current strength?

3. How many grams of oxygen will be liberated from water by the passage of a 0.3-ampere current for 2 hours?

4. What is the current strength that will be required to liberate 20 g of aluminum in 1 hour?

5. The emf of a single dry cell is 1.5 volts and its internal resistance is 0.1 ohm. When connected to an external resistance of 50 ohms, what current will flow?

6. A storage battery has an emf of 6.0 volts and an internal resistance of 0.25 ohm. What current flows through a 100-ohm resistance connected across the terminals of the storage battery?

7. Two cells, 1.5 volts each, are connected in series. They each have an internal resistance of 0.15 ohm. What current will flow if they are connected to an external resistance of 3.2 ohms?

8. If the cells in Problem 7 are joined in parallel and then connected to the external resistance, what current will flow?

9. A voltaic cell has an emf of 1.5 volts; its internal resistance is 0.2 ohm. What current can five such cells in series yield if the external resistance is 25 ohms?

10. What current will the five cells of Problem 9 furnish when joined in parallel?

11. What current will the five cells of Problem 9 furnish if they are joined in series with an external resistance of 0.05 ohm?

12. What current will the five cells of Problem 9 furnish if they are joined in parallel and the external resistance is 0.05 ohm?

GROUP B

13. A sheet of pure copper weighing 5 kg is to be prepared by electrolysis. If the current strength to be used is 100 amperes, how many hours will it take to deposit this amount of copper?

14. A storage battery is made up of three cells connected in series. Each cell has an emf of 2.0 volts and an internal resistance of 0.1 ohm. What is the total emf of the battery? What current will flow when this particular battery is connected to an external resistance of 30 ohms?

● **15.** A voltaic cell has an emf of 1.2 volts, and an internal resistance of 0.05 ohm. What current will six such cells joined in series yield if the external resistance is a piece of nichrome wire that is 5 ft long and is also 20 mils in diameter?

● **16.** A battery consists of four cells in series. Each cell has an emf of 2.0 volts and an internal resistance of 0.1 ohm. The battery is connected to three resistances, 9 ohms, 10 ohms, and 15 ohms, in parallel. Find the total emf of the battery, the total internal resistance of the battery, the total external resistance, the total current through the external circuit, and the current through each resistance. Draw a diagram of this circuit before you attempt to solve the problem.

● **17.** Draw a diagram showing a battery of three cells in series connected with an external circuit consisting of two resistances connected in parallel and these connected in series with a third resistance. Each cell of the battery has an emf of 1.5 volts and an internal resistance of 0.5 ohm. The two resistances connected in parallel are 10 ohms and 15 ohms. The resistance connected in series with them is 7.5 ohms. Find the total emf of the battery, the total internal resistance of the battery, the combined resistance of the external circuit, the total current flowing in the external circuit, and the current through each resistance in the external circuit.

Chapter 30

Heating and Lighting Effects of Electricity

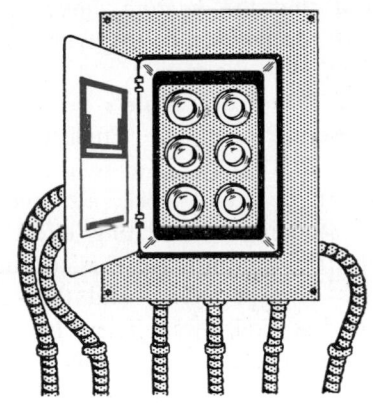

1. Electricity may be used to produce heat. Suppose we screw three binding posts, *A, B,* and *C,* into a piece of wood 8 in × 5 in × ½ in, and connect them with the terminals of one or two dry cells, as shown in Fig. 30-1. Let us place a piece of Gauge No. 30 copper wire between *A* and *B*. We connect *B* and *C* with an equal length of

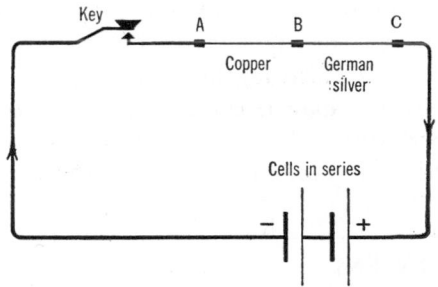

Fig. 30-1. Heating effect of the electric current.

No. 30 German silver wire. No. 30 wire is rather small, as it is only 0.01 inch in diameter. When we complete the circuit by closing the switch, the German silver wire will become red hot, and probably will melt. The copper wire will get warm too, but it is not likely to melt. Since the amount of current flowing through both wires is the same, we conclude that, if other conditions are the same, the *heating effect of an electric current is greater in the wire which has the greater resistance.*

Now let us connect a single piece of No. 28 copper wire from *A* to *C.* If we pass the current from a single cell through the wire, it may glow feebly. If the current from two or three cells in series is passed through the wire, it will probably melt. We

---

Vocabulary

CARRYING CAPACITY. The amount of current in amperes which a conductor may safely carry.

OVERLOAD. Forcing a conductor to carry a current which is greater than its carrying capacity.

SHORT CIRCUIT. A circuit through a *small* resistance.

THERMOCOUPLE. Two dissimilar metallic conductors joined at their ends and used for measuring temperature.

WELD. To melt metal parts together.

find that the *heating effect increases with the number of amperes of current flowing in the circuit.*

2. What are Joule's laws? James Prescott Joule, the English physicist who first studied the relationship between heat and work, also pioneered in studying the heating effect of an electric current. He carried out a series of experiments and then formulated several laws. These laws enable us to calculate the amount of heat developed in a conductor when a current is flowing through it. The following statements are known as JOULE'S LAWS:

(1) *The amount of heat produced in a conductor is directly proportional to its resistance in ohms.*

(2) *The amount of heat produced is directly proportional to the square of the current in amperes.* For example, a current of two amperes flowing through a conductor will produce four times as much heat as a current of one ampere.

(3) *The amount of heat produced is directly proportional to the time the current flows.*

We may combine these three laws in the formula,

$$W = I^2Rt. \quad \text{(in joules)}$$

W is the energy produced, in joules; I is the current strength, in amperes; R is the value of the resistance, in ohms; and t is the time the current flowed, in seconds.

In order to convert the energy W into calories, we must use the conversion factor 0.24. (There are 0.24 calories per joule.) The formula then is

$$W = 0.24I^2Rt. \quad \text{(in calories)}$$

See the Sample Problem below.

3. There are many electrical heating appliances. We all are familiar with irons, toasters, percolators, grills, ranges, and deep fryers which are heated by electricity. In the majority of electrical heating appliances, coils of high resistance nichrome wire are used.

If two pieces of wire are placed end to end and a high current is passed through them, the heat developed at the point of contact may be sufficient to melt them and **weld** *them into one piece.* Sometimes, metal plates used for construction work are riveted together. The edges of metal plates may also be welded together electrically.

4. Too high a current overloads a conductor. In the experiment described in Section 1 we found that the

---

SAMPLE PROBLEM

The heating coil in a coffee percolator has a resistance of 22 ohms and uses 5 amperes of current. How long will it take to heat one liter of water from 20° C to the boiling point, 100° C, in such a percolator?

SOLUTION

One liter of water weighs 1000 g. To heat this amount of water from 20° C to 100° C requires $1000 \times (100 - 20) \times 1$, or 80,000 calories. Substituting in the formula, $W = 0.24 I^2Rt$, we have $80,000 = 0.24 \times 5^2 \times 22 \times t$. Solving, $t = 606$ seconds, or 10.1 minutes, the time required.

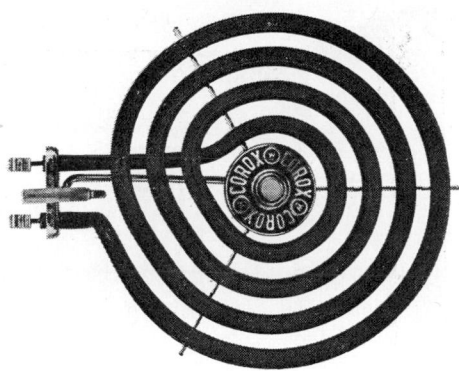

Fig. 30-2. A view showing construction of the heating element of an electric range.

Fig. 30-3. Cutaway showing the heating coils in an electric toaster.

current from a couple of dry cells joined in series is sufficient to melt a short piece of No. 28 copper wire. Suppose we send the same amount of current through a short piece of wire of the diameter used for house wiring, No. 14. We find that this wire is heated, but it is not likely to melt. No. 14 wire has a greater carrying capacity. *The* **carrying capacity** *of a wire is the amount of current in amperes which it can carry safely. If we try to force more current through a wire than it can carry safely, we have an* **overload.** An overloaded wire may melt, and it may set fire to any flammable material near it.

There are two likely ways in which a person may cause an overload in the wiring circuit in his home.

(1) *By putting too many appliances on one circuit.* Suppose your house wiring can safely carry 17 amperes. In order to prepare refreshments for a party, you plug in two sandwich toasters and a coffee percolator. Each of these appliances takes 5 amperes of current. Then you turn on the deep fryer, which uses at least 5 amperes

more current. You now have appliances which draw 20 amperes of current from a line which can carry safely only 17 amperes. This overload may blow the fuses or melt the wires.

(2) *By a short circuit.* Suppose you have a floor lamp with a worn, kinked electric cord. The insulation has bro-

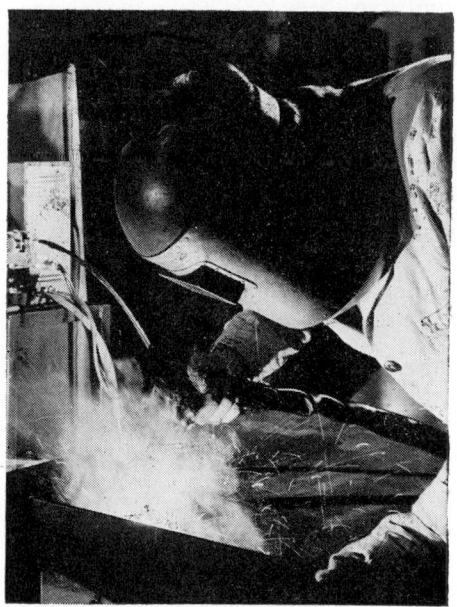

Fig. 30-4. Welding metals together by a consumable electrode, inert gas, arc welding process.

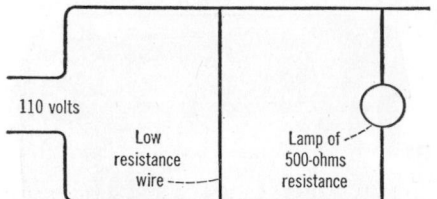

Fig. 30-5. The greater part of the current flows through the low-resistance wire, producing a short circuit.

ken away in places. If someone steps on the cord, he may press the two wires together so that they touch. *This circuit through a small resistance forms a* **short circuit.** To show why a short circuit causes an overload, let us assume that we have a lamp which has a resistance of 500 ohms operating on a 110-volt circuit. The current which flows through the lamp is 0.22 ampere (Ohm's law). If we scrape the insulation from the wires and join them by a heavy piece of low resistance wire, we have a short circuit. See Fig. 30-5. To make our calculations simple, let us also assume that the resistance of the wire producing the short circuit is exactly one ohm. The current through the one-ohm resistance is 110 amperes. Now let us compare the heating effect in the second case with that of the first.

$$\frac{I^2R}{I^2R}, \quad \text{or} \quad \frac{110 \times 110 \times 1}{0.22 \times 0.22 \times 500} = 500.$$

From our calculation we see that the amount of heat produced when the wires are short-circuited is 500 times as much as when the current goes through the lamp. It is to be expected that the wires will melt.

5. Fuses protect electrical circuits against overload. We know that overloaded wiring may cause a fire.

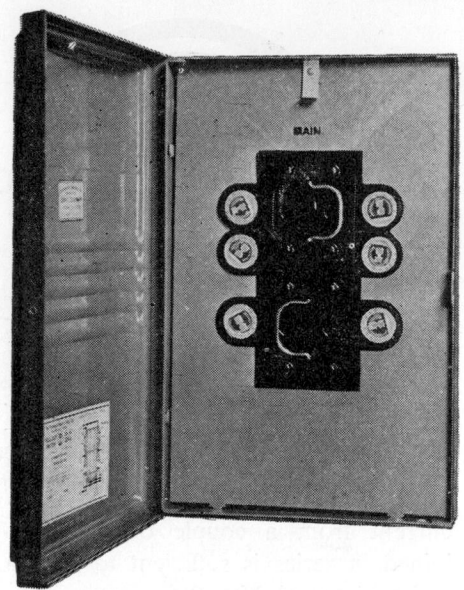

Fig. 30-6. A modern fusebox commonly found in many homes.

Even if the overloaded wires do not actually set fire to a house, they may melt at any place within the walls or ceiling. To prevent such an occurrence, fuses or circuit breakers are used in wiring circuits. In ordinary house wiring the fuses are placed in metal boxes, usually installed in the basement. See Fig. 30-6. The fuse plugs of Fig. 30-7 frequently are used. The contact points are shown in the sectional view. They consist of fusible wire surrounded by insulating mate-

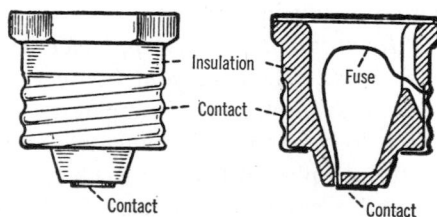

Fig. 30-7. Plug-type fuses. The fusible metal is surrounded by non-flammable material.

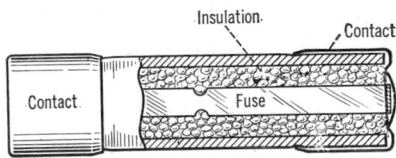

Fig. 30-8. A cutaway view of a cartridge fuse.

rial. When an overload occurs, the fuse wire melts and breaks the circuit. It is easy to replace a fuse after the cause of the overload has been removed. Sometimes cartridge fuses are used in certain circuits. See Fig. 30-8. A circuit breaker is an electromagnetic switch, a thermal device, or a combination of the two which turns off automatically if too high a current passes through it.

6. Edison made the first incandescent lamp. About seventy-five years ago Thomas Edison invented the incandescent lamp. One of the problems which confronted him was the choice of material for the lamp filament. It was necessary for the filament to have a high electrical resistance; it must not be too brittle; its melting point had to be very high; it had to be enclosed in an evacuated bulb so that it would not burn or unite with the oxygen from the air. After several years' search, Edison finally succeeded in using a carbon filament made by heating bamboo fiber. See Fig. 30-9.

The finding of a satisfactory filament did not solve the entire problem. The ends of the filament had to be connected to two short pieces of wire that could be sealed in glass. However, if the metal expanded more than the glass upon heating, it would contract more upon cooling, and the seal would not

be perfect. Platinum was found to have the same coefficient of expansion as glass. Consequently, two pieces of platinum wire were used in the early carbon lamps. The other ends of the platinum wires were connected by copper wires, one to a brass disc and the other to a threaded cylinder. Both the disc and cylinder made connections with the terminals of the lighting circuit when the bulb was screwed into the socket.

7. Today's incandescent lamps have tungsten filaments. Men of science are never satisfied. An extensive search was undertaken to find a better filament material than carbon. Today, the filaments of our incandescent lamps are made of tungsten. Tungsten is used because it has a very

Fig. 30-9. Thomas Alva Edison (1847–1931) was one of our most prolific American inventors. He is best known for his invention of the incandescent lamp in 1879. He is also the inventor of the phonograph, a motion picture projector, and the Edison storage cell.

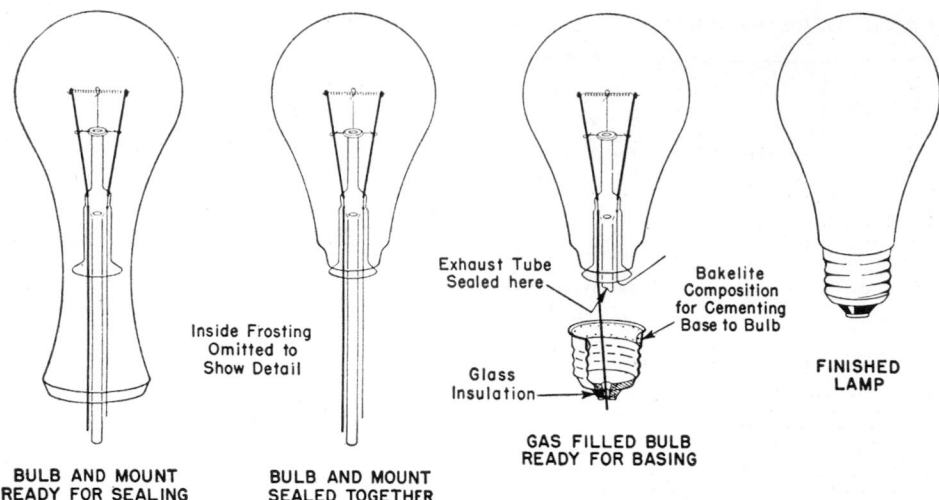

Inside Frosting Omitted to Show Detail

Exhaust Tube Sealed here

Bakelite Composition for Cementing Base to Bulb

Glass Insulation

FINISHED LAMP

GAS FILLED BULB READY FOR BASING

BULB AND MOUNT READY FOR SEALING

BULB AND MOUNT SEALED TOGETHER

Fig. 30-10. Steps in the final assembly of an electric lamp.

high melting point and a high resistance; it is not too brittle; and because it evaporates very slowly even at a high temperature. The filament in modern tungsten lamps is a coiled coil the ends of which are fastened to the ends of supports connected with " lead-in " wires. See Fig. 30-10. The bulb is frosted on the inside to prevent glare from the hot filament. In addition, some lamps have a milky-white coating inside the glass to provide greater dif-

Fig. 30-11. The pair of photoflood lamps gives the extra-bright illumination needed for taking motion pictures indoors.

Fig. 30-12. A photoflash attachment for your camera provides the illumination needed for taking pictures anywhere, anytime.

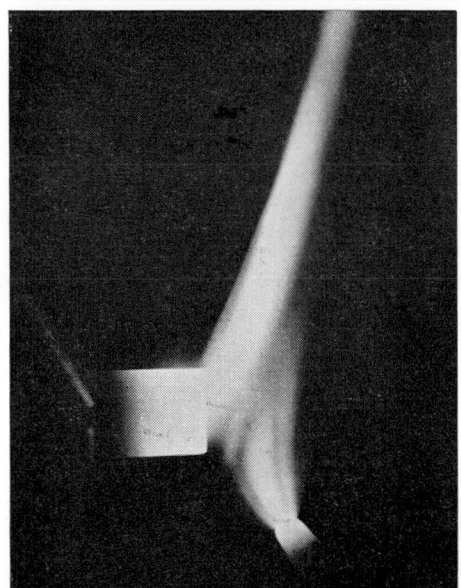

Fig. 30-13. A direct-current high intensity arc used to provide the illumination needed for motion picture projection.

fusion and a softer light. New, indirect lamp bulbs give such diffused light that they can be used without shades in older-type ceiling fixtures. Lamp bulbs are filled with a mixture of nitrogen and argon. This mixture of inert gases reduces evaporation of the filament, permits a higher filament temperature, and produces a whiter light. An alloy, consisting largely of nickel and iron, has been made to take the place of platinum as material for " lead-in " wires.

8. Infrared lamps are used in industrial heating processes. Infrared lamps are similar in construction to ordinary tungsten lamps. However, they operate at a much lower filament temperature. Under these conditions very little light is produced, but strong, infrared, radiant heat rays are emitted. This radiant heat is used in baking

paint finishes on automobile bodies, in drying printing inks, and in many other baking, drying, and heating applications.

9. Photoflash and photoflood lamps provide light for photographers. In order to insure adequate and controlled amounts of light for picture taking, photographers may use two special types of lamps. (1) The photoflood lamp operates at a much higher temperature than an ordinary tungsten lamp, and thus provides much more light. The filament temperature is about 3100° C. The life of such lamps is from three to ten hours. The lamps use from 250 to 1000 watts. (2) The photoflash lamp, or " flash bulb," is filled with aluminum wire or foil, and oxygen. When current passes through the filament it ignites the aluminum, which burns almost instantaneously in the trapped oxygen. The filament may be heated by flashlight batteries or, in some cases, by a 115-volt house circuit. The temperature of the flash is about 3500° C, and it lasts for about three- to four-hundredths of a second.

10. How does an arc lamp work? An arc lamp consists of two carbon

Fig. 30-14. A small, laboratory-type electric resistance furnace. The front of the furnace and the door have been removed to show the heating coils.

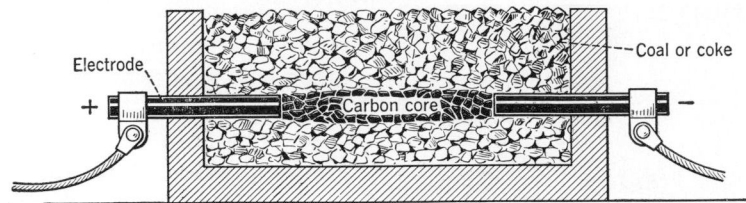

Fig. 30-15. The carbon core offers resistance in this furnace for making graphite. Furnaces of this type are also used for making silicon carbide.

rods which are connected to the terminals of an electric circuit. When these rods are brought together momentarily, the heat produced at the point of contact is great enough to vaporize some of the carbon and produce an intensely bright light. If the carbon rods then are separated about a quarter of an inch, the circuit is not broken because the carbon vapor continues to conduct the current from one rod to the other, as shown in Fig. 30-13. The light comes from the incandescent positive carbon electrode, and not from the vapor. A clutch mechanism is used to lower gradually the upper carbon rod and to regulate the distance between the two carbon rods.

Arc lights usually are operated on a line where the difference of potential between the carbon rods is about 50 volts. They use from 10 to 25 amperes of current. Arc lamps are used in commercial motion picture projectors, as well as in spotlights and searchlights.

11. Electric furnaces give high temperatures. There are two common types of electric furnaces.
(1) *Resistance furnaces.* In one type of resistance furnace, an electric current is passed through a coil of wire made of platinum, nichrome, tungsten, or molybdenum which is wound upon a refractory material. The substance to be heated is placed inside the coil. A resistance furnace can produce a temperature of from 1000° C to nearly 2000° C.

In another type of resistance furnace, heat is produced by the electrical resistance of the material in the furnace itself. The furnaces used for making silicon, silicon carbide, and artificial graphite are of this type. See Fig. 30-15.
(2) *Arc type furnaces.* Exceedingly high temperatures can be obtained in arc type electric furnaces. Their temperature is estimated to be about 3500° C. An electric arc is formed between two carbon rods in a refractory crucible. The material to be heated is placed in this crucible. An electric furnace used for making steel is a combination of the arc and resistance type. See Fig. 30-16.

12. Electricity can be produced from heat. Let us twist or solder together the ends of two different pieces of wire — for example, copper and iron — to form a loop. If the two metal joints are maintained at different temperatures, a current will flow through the loop. We can detect this current by placing a sensitive galvanometer in the circuit, as in Fig. 30-17.

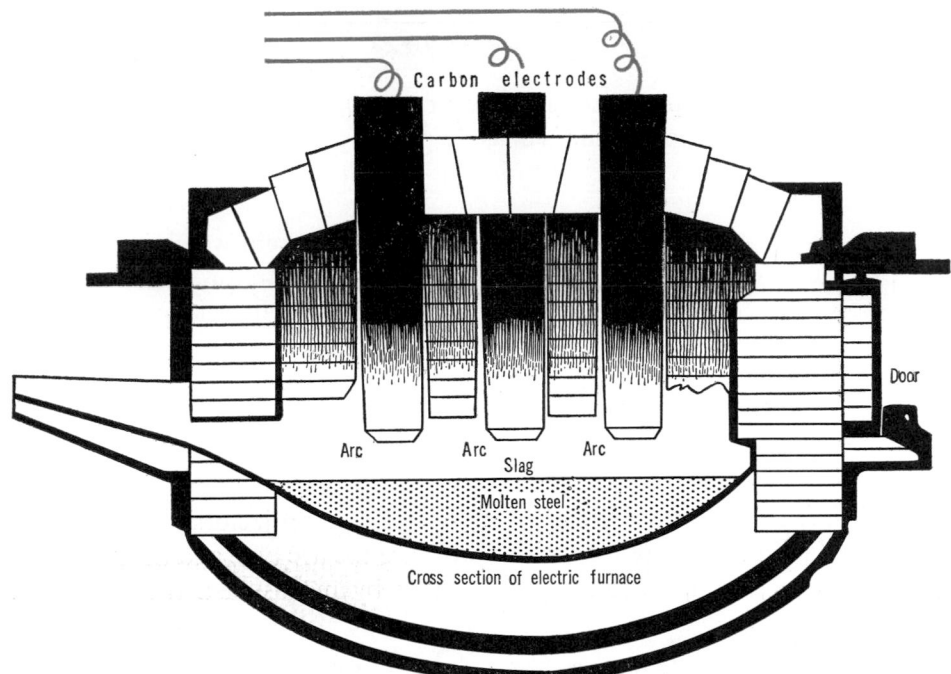

Fig. 30-16. Sectional view of an electric furnace for making steel.

At ordinary temperatures the electrons flow from iron to copper at the hot junction, and from copper to iron at the cold junction. The current through the circuit varies with the difference in temperature between the junctions.

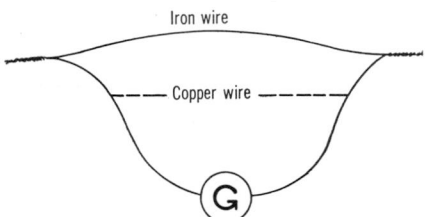

Fig. 30-17. When the junctions of the two wires are at different temperatures, current flows through the galvanometer.

When two such dissimilar metallic conductors joined at their ends are used to measure temperatures, the device is called a **thermocouple.** If a sensitive voltmeter, calibrated to read temperatures directly, is used in place of the galvanometer, the device becomes a *thermoelectric thermometer,* or *pyrometer* (py-*rom*-eh-ter).

Since the current produced by only one set of junctions is rather small, we can connect several in series. In this way the currents add to one another. Such a *thermopile* (*ther*-moh-pyl) may register temperature changes of one one-hundred-millionth of a degree. Using similar instruments, astronomers have measured the heat of stars.

Summary

Joule's laws deal with the heating effect of an electric current: The amount of heat produced in a conductor is directly proportional (1) to its resistance in ohms, (2) to the square of the current in amperes, and (3) to the time the current flows.

The carrying capacity of a wire is the amount of current which it can safely carry. If we force a conductor to carry more current than this, we overload it. An overload may cause a conductor to heat up so that it melts or sets fire to nearby flammable material.

The incandescent lamp was invented by Edison. Today's lamps are greatly improved over Edison's original design. Infrared lamps are used for industrial heating or baking processes. Photoflash and photoflood lamps are used by photographers to supply the necessary light for picture taking. Arc lamps are used in searchlights and in large motion picture projectors.

The two familiar types of electric furnaces are the arc type and the resistance type. We can produce electricity from heat by means of a thermocouple.

Terms to Define...

Arc lamp	Incandescent lamp	Pyrometer
Arc-type furnace	Infrared lamp	Resistance furnace
Carrying capacity	Joule's laws	Short circuit
Cartridge fuse	Overload	Thermocouple
Circuit breaker	Photoflash lamp	Thermopile
Fuse plug	Photoflood lamp	Welding

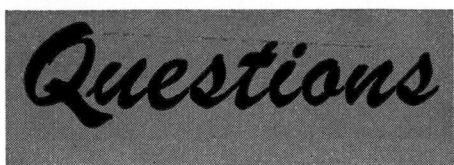

GROUP A

1. A piece of silver wire and a piece of iron wire of the same length and same gauge number are connected in series with a dry cell. Which wire becomes hotter? Why?

2. One piece of platinum wire is connected across the terminals of a single dry cell. A second piece of platinum wire, identical with the first, is connected across the end terminals of two dry cells connected in series. Which piece of platinum wire becomes hotter? Why?

3. How is the heating effect of a circuit changed by keeping the current strength constant and cutting the resistance in half?

4. How is the heating effect of a circuit changed by keeping the resistance constant and doubling the current strength?

5. What are the causes of an overloaded circuit?

6. What size fuse should be used generally to protect home wiring? Why not use a 30-ampere fuse?

7. How does a fuse protect against an overloaded circuit? What other device sometimes is used?

8. What are the advantages of tungsten filaments? Inside-frosted bulbs? Gas-filled lamps?

9. For what purposes are infrared lamps used?

10. How are photoflood and photoflash lamps used in taking photographs?

GROUP B

11. How is the heating effect of a circuit changed by keeping the voltage constant and cutting the resistance in half?

12. Describe some of the problems faced by Edison when he developed the electric lamp.

13. What is the source of the light used for projecting motion pictures in theaters?

14. Describe types of electric furnaces.

15. What is a thermocouple? A pyrometer?

(In the Mathematics Refresher, refer to Sections 6, 10, and 16.)

GROUP A

1. How many calories will be liberated by a resistance of 55 ohms through which a current of 2 amperes flows for 10 minutes?

2. An electric heater draws 10 amperes when operated on a 120-volt circuit. How many calories will be liberated by this heater if it is operated for one-half hour?

3. The resistance of an electric iron is 24 ohms. It draws a current of 5 amperes. How many calories of heat will be developed if the iron is used for 40 minutes by a housewife who is ironing clothes?

GROUP B

4. A coffee percolator has a heating coil of 20 ohms resistance. How many calories of heat does it liberate per second when connected to a 120-volt circuit? If the percolator contains 500 g of water at 20° C, how long will it take to heat this water to 100° C, assuming that no heat is lost?

● **5.** An electric iron weighs 1.5 kg. The heating element consists of a coil of No. 24 nichrome wire 6 ft long. The iron is operated on a 115-volt circuit. The specific heat of iron is 0.1. How long will it take for the iron to be heated from 20° C to 150° C, assuming that no heat is lost?

● **6.** An electric hotplate draws 10 amperes on a 120-volt circuit. In 7 minutes this hotplate can heat 600 g of water at 20° C to boiling, and boil away 60 g of water. What is the efficiency of the hotplate?

Things to Do

1. Report to the class on the life and work of Edison.

2. Make a list showing which lights and wall outlets are protected by each fuse in your home wiring installation.

3. As a class or demonstration experiment, determine the efficiency of a hotplate or coffee percolator. See how long it takes to bring a weighed quantity of water from room temperature to boiling. From the voltmeter and ammeter readings and the elapsed time, find the amount of heat input. From the weight of water and the temperature change, find the heat output. Divide the output by the input and multiply by 100%. How is heat wasted in this experiment?

4. Have a member of the class who is an amateur photographer demonstrate the use of photoflash and photoflood lamps in picture taking.

5. Arrange for two members of the class to visit the projection booth of a local motion picture theater, and report on the operation of the arc lamp which furnishes the light for projection.

Chapter 31

Electromagnetic Induction

1. INDUCED CURRENTS

1. What is electromagnetic induction? We learned how Oersted discovered that an electric current flowing through a conductor sets up a magnetic field around the conductor. About 1831, Michael Faraday began some experiments in which he tested the effect of a magnetic field upon a conductor moving through the field. He also tried the opposite condition of moving a magnetic field so that its lines cut through the conductor.

Suppose we repeat one of Faraday's experiments. Let us connect the terminals of a spool of insulated wire to a sensitive galvanometer, as shown in Fig. 31-2. When we push one end of a strong bar magnet down into the spool, the galvanometer needle is deflected. This shows that a current is induced in the wire by the magnet. When the bar magnet is withdrawn from the spool, an induced current is set up in the opposite direction. We can induce a stronger current by thrusting the magnet more quickly into the spool or withdrawing it more quickly. When the magnet is at rest in the spool, no current is induced. If we use the opposite pole of the magnet, the current directions are just reversed.

Faraday's experiments proved that *an emf is produced in a conductor when a magnet is moved so that its mag-*

Vocabulary

ALTERNATING CURRENT. A current in which the movement of the electrons is to-and-fro in the conductor.

GENERATOR. A device for converting mechanical energy into electrical energy.

INDUCTION. Producing an emf in a conductor by moving the conductor with respect to a magnetic field.

MOTOR. A device for converting electrical energy into mechanical energy.

PRIMARY COIL. The coil of wire through which current from an external source passes.

SECONDARY COIL. The coil in which an emf is induced by current variations in the primary coil.

SELF–INDUCTION. A property of coiled conductors whereby the magnetic field of one turn induces an emf in the next turn.

TRANSFORMER. A device for changing the voltage of an alternating current.

Fig. 31-1. Michael Faraday (1791–1867) was a distinguished physicist and chemist. Faraday liquefied certain gases, formulated the laws of electrolysis, and discovered the principle of electromagnetic induction.

netic lines are cut by the conductor. This is a phenomenon which is called *induction*.

2. Inducing current in a moving conductor. In the experiment described in Section 1, we moved a magnet so that its magnetic lines were cut by one or more conductors. Let us modify the experiment and push a coil or loop of wire down over one of the poles of a horseshoe-shaped magnet.

See Fig. 31-3. As the coil moves down past the pole of the magnet, it cuts or intersects magnetic lines and an induced emf is set up in the coil. If the ends of the coil are connected to the terminals of a galvanometer, then we have an induced current set up in the coil. This is shown by the deflection of the galvanometer needle. As we remove the coil, the induced current flows in the opposite direction. *An induced current is always set up in a closed circuit when a conductor in that circuit is cutting magnetic lines.* It makes no difference whether the conductor moves across the magnetic lines, or whether the magnet moves past the conductor. One or the other must be in motion to produce an induced current.

We must distinguish between an induced emf and an induced current. If the ends of a coil, as in Fig. 31-3, are not connected, and the coil is on open circuit, then an *induced emf* is set up in the coil as it moves across the magnetic lines. With an open circuit, no current can flow. When we close the circuit by connecting the coil to a galvanometer, we obtain an *induced current.* An induced emf has poten-

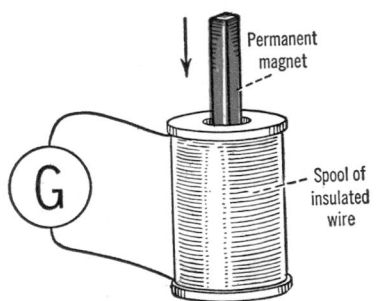

Fig. 31-2. When the magnet is lowered into the coil, its magnetic lines are cut by the conductor and induce an emf in it.

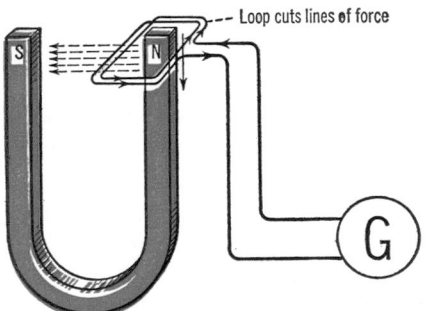

--- Loop cuts lines of force

Fig. 31-3. An emf is also induced by moving a coil through the magnetic lines of a permanent magnet.

tial energy; when the circuit is closed, its energy becomes kinetic, and an induced current flows through the circuit.

3. How can we use one current to produce another? The secondary coil shown in Fig. 31-4 consists of a large number of turns of fine, insulated wire wound on a large wooden spool. Its terminals are connected to a simple galvanometer. Let us place a primary coil inside this secondary coil. The primary coil has a few turns of insulated wire wound on a small spool, and is connected in series with a contact key and a dry cell.

When we press the key and close the circuit, a current flows through the primary coil. We also find that the galvanometer needle is deflected, showing that a current is induced in the secondary coil. The magnetic lines produced by the current flowing in the primary coil are cut by the wires of the secondary coil and set up an induced current in the secondary. If the key is kept closed, the induced current soon stops flowing. When we release the key and break the circuit, the galvanometer deflection is in the opposite direction. A current is induced in the secondary coil, but in the opposite direction.

Upon closing the circuit, the magnetic field caused by the current flowing through the primary coil rises to maximum strength, and the magnetic lines threading across the secondary turns cause the induced current. When the circuit is broken, the strength of the magnetic field quickly falls to zero and an induced current flowing in the opposite direction is set up. In both cases, the induced current stops when the magnetic lines stop

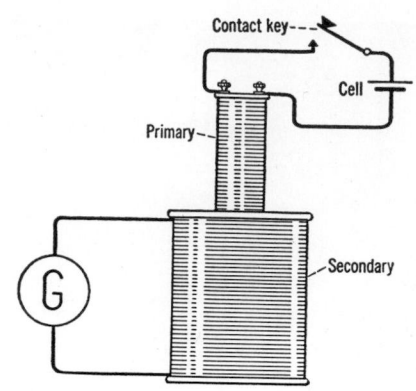

Fig. 31-4. Varying the current in the primary induces an emf in the secondary coil.

changing. *Increasing or decreasing the number of magnetic lines in a magnetic field induces an emf in a conductor present in that field.* If the circuit of the secondary is closed, as it is by the galvanometer, an induced current is produced. The induced emf and the induced current exist only while *the strength of the magnetic field is varying.*

4. The direction of the induced current. When a wire is moved between the poles of a horseshoe magnet, as shown in Fig. 31-5, an induced emf is set up in the wire. If we close the circuit, an induced current flows. By connecting the ends of the wire to a sensitive galvanometer, it may be shown that the current flows in one direction as the wire is moved *down* between the poles of the magnet, and in the reverse direction as it is moved *up* through the magnetic field between the two poles. Cutting magnetic lines in one direction sets up a current in a conductor; when the conductor cuts magnetic lines in the opposite direction, the current is reversed. When the conductor moves parallel to the

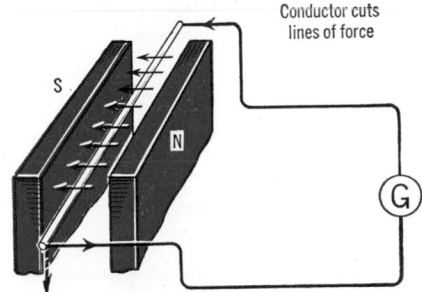

Conductor cuts
lines of force

Fig. 31-5. Verify the direction of the induced current using the left-hand rule.

magnetic lines, no current is induced because no lines are cut.

The direction in which the induced electron current flows may be found by the *left-hand rule, or generator rule: Let the forefinger of the left hand point in the direction of the magnetic lines; turn the hand so that the extended thumb points in the direction the conductor is moving; the middle finger, bent at right angles to both the thumb and forefinger, will then point in the direction in which the electrons flow through the conductor.* Applying this rule to Fig. 31-5, we find that the electrons flow through the wire toward the observer as the wire moves down between the poles of the magnet; they flow from him as the wire moves up between the poles of the magnet.

5. What is Lenz's law? In Section 2 we learned that an induced current is set up in a coil of wire as it moves down over the pole of a magnet if the coil is connected to a closed circuit. The coil then becomes a magnet. The induced current flows in such a direction that the magnetic pole of the moving coil opposes the field of the stationary magnet. If the coil is brought down toward the N-pole of a magnet, the coil current flows in such

a direction that the end of the coil which approaches the N-pole will also become an N-pole. The two N-poles repel each other, and tend to prevent the coil from being lowered over the pole of the magnet. Work is done in overcoming this force of repulsion.

If we reverse the motion, the current reverses and an S-pole is formed; this S-pole tends to prevent the removal of the coil by attracting the N-pole of the magnet. Therefore, work is done again in removing the coil. *A current induced in a moving conductor always flows in such a direction that it forms a magnetic field which opposes the motion of the conductor.* This is called LENZ'S LAW.

Similarly, if we push the coil down over the S-pole of the magnet, the current that is induced will flow in such direction that the face of the coil approaching the magnet becomes an S-pole and opposes the motion. Mechanical energy is changed into electrical energy.

6. What is the strength of the induced emf? A higher emf is induced when a conductor is moved through a magnetic field more rapidly and cuts magnetic lines faster. If we use a stronger magnet, there will be more magnetic lines to cut and, again, we will get a higher emf.

When we double the number of turns in the coil, we double the number of conductors that cut magnetic lines. We also can increase the induced emf by increasing the number of turns. All this may be summarized with one statement: *The strength of the induced emf depends upon the number of magnetic lines cut per second.*

To build up a high voltage by induction, *we may increase the strength of the field magnet, increase the speed of the coil through the field, or increase the number of loops or turns in the coil.* In each of these ways, we increase the number of magnetic lines cut per second.

7. Self-induction opposes current flow. Connect a small lamp in series with a switch and a dry cell and close the switch. The lamp lights up almost immediately. It goes out quickly when the switch is opened. But now let us put a coil like that shown in Fig. 31-2 into the circuit, also in series. When we close the switch, we find that the lamp does not light up as quickly. Upon opening the switch, we find also that the lamp stays lighted longer than it did when we opened the switch before, and that it grows dim slowly rather than quickly.

This demonstrates what is known as *self-induction.* It was discovered by an American physicist, Joseph Henry, Fig. 31-6. Let us see how it affected our experiment. Each time we closed the switch and then opened it, the current built up and then died down, and the magnetic field about the wires did the same. In the second case, however, the presence of the coil changed the speed with which the current increased and decreased. In the second case, when the current was building up, the magnetic lines were not just cutting space about the wires in the circuit. In the coil, they were intersecting the adjacent wires. Since moving magnetic lines in a primary coil can induce a current in an adjacent secondary, it seems reasonable that the field about one loop of coil will also induce a current in the adjacent loops of the same coil. In other words, **self-induction** *is a phenomenon in coiled conductors*

Fig. 31-6. Joseph Henry (1797–1878), who was an American physicist, discovered self-induction and developed the electromagnet.

whereby the magnetic field of one turn induces an emf in an adjacent turn. By Lenz's law, too, a current induced in this manner opposes the motion of the current. That is why the lamp did not light up as rapidly in the second half of the experiment. Self-induction opposed the building up of the current strength. It also kept the light from going out as quickly by opposing the dying out of the electric current.

8. How does an induction coil work? Instead of having to joggle a contact key up and down, as we did to induce a current in Section 3, it is much more convenient to substitute a vibrating contact like that in an electric bell. This will automatically " make " and " break " the circuit of the primary, and give us the essentials of what is called a *spark coil,* or an *induction coil.*

In Fig. 31-7, when the current flows

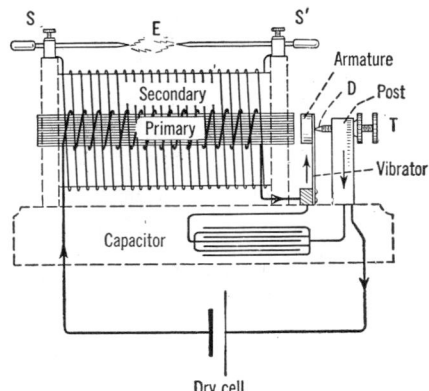

Fig. 31-7. An induction coil will increase the voltage of an intermittent direct current.

through the few turns of insulated wire in the primary, the core made of a bundle of iron wires becomes an electromagnet and attracts the armature. The circuit is broken when the armature is pulled away from the contact screw, *T*. The magnetic field in the primary collapses rapidly, and a strong emf is induced in the secondary, which is composed of thousands of turns of fine insulated wire. However, the core of the primary has lost its magnetism; therefore the armature is released and closes the circuit. As the magnetic field in the primary increases again, an emf is induced in the secondary in the opposite direction. Thus an alternating emf exists in the secondary. A spark may be produced at *E*.

A capacitor is used regularly with an induction coil. It is connected so that the current break is between its terminals. When the break occurs, the energy that ordinarily would tend to spark across the gap at *D* has an easier path into the capacitor. The break itself then becomes more sudden, the magnetic field collapses faster, and a larger emf is induced. This is seen in

a stronger spark at *E*. The break becomes so sudden that actually the induced current then is about 10,000 times as strong as at the make. A strong, pulsating direct current is in effect produced. The capacitor also helps demagnetize the core in readiness for the next cycle of operation by discharging back through the primary coil after the contact is broken.

9. The ignition system of an automobile. In the operation of a gasoline engine, the spark must occur at just the right time to ignite the explosive mixture of gasoline vapor and air. It must also occur in the proper cylinder. To accomplish this, a *timer* and *distributor* are used. A battery system with an induction coil produces the spark needed for ignition.

In Fig. 31-8, one terminal of the battery is connected to the metal frame and to the engine; the other terminal is connected by means of the switch with the primary of an induction coil. The timer is used to break the circuit in the primary and thus induce a high voltage in the secondary coil. One terminal of the secondary coil is grounded and the other terminal is connected to the rotor, a part of the distributor. As this rotor makes contact with the metal segment, the induced voltage is high enough to cause a spark to leap across the gap between the two terminals of the spark plug in cylinder 2.

The diagram shows how each of the four cylinders will fire in turn. As the cam, *A,* of the timer rotates, it will break the circuit four times during one revolution. The fiber ring is made of insulating material, but each one of the metal segments is connected with a spark plug. As the rotor turns in the

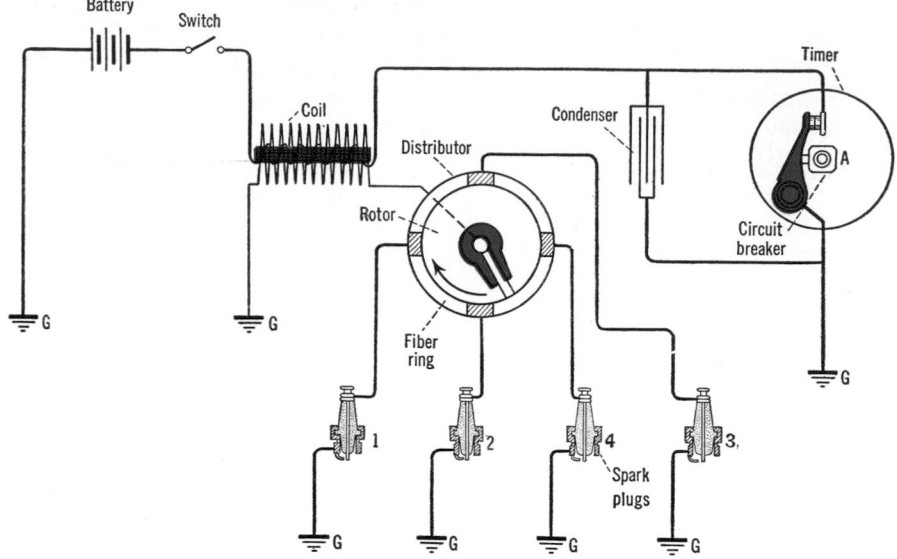

Fig. 31-8. A diagram of the ignition system, showing the timer, coil, and distributor.

direction shown by the arrow, a spark will be produced in spark plugs numbered 2, 1, 3, and 4 in turn as it makes successive contact with the metal segments. Both the timer and the distributor are geared with the engine so that the timing will be perfect.

10. What is tape recording? The recording of sound, as well as black-and-white and color television on tape is an application of the principles of electromagnets and electromagnetic induction. In magnetic recording, a steel wire, or film or narrow tape coated with powdered iron, is moved at constant speed past an electromagnet in the *recording head*. The electromagnet is connected electrically with a microphone. The variations in the electric current caused by sound entering the microphone produce corresponding changes in the current energizing the electromagnet. As the tape, film, or wire moves past the electromagnet, the variations in the strength of the magnet induce magnetism of varying amounts in it.

When the tape is played back past a *reproducing head,* which may actually be the same electromagnet used for recording, the magnetic variations in the tape induce corresponding variations in the current through the electromagnet. The current variations are amplified and converted to sound waves by the loudspeaker. Thus sounds recorded on the tape are reproduced.

By adapting this same principle to a wider tape, enough signals can be recorded to reproduce both the picture and sound for television. For Cinema-Scope motion pictures, four separate sound tracks are recorded magnetically on the film. One of the outstanding advantages of this type of recording is the ease with which the induced magnetism on the tape, wire, or film can be removed. High-frequency alternating currents are used. Afterward, a new recording may be placed on the tape.

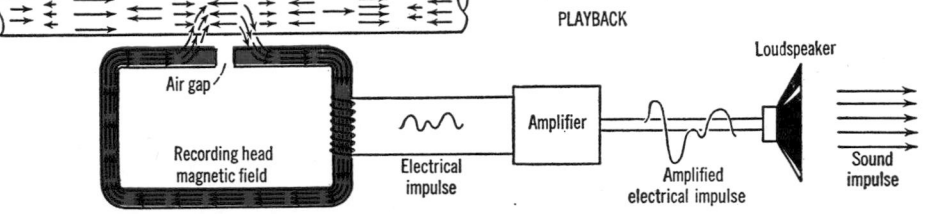

Fig. 31-9. The principle of the wire recorder.

2. GENERATORS

11. What is a simple generator?
Moving a loop of wire up and down in a magnetic field is not a convenient method for producing an induced current. Fig. 31-10 shows a single loop of wire mounted on an axis so that it may be rotated by hand between the

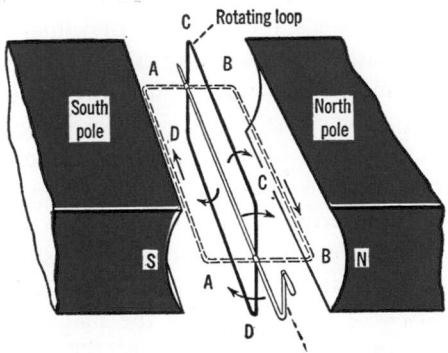

Fig. 31-10. A simple generator mounted between the poles of a horseshoe magnet.

poles of a horseshoe field magnet; thus it cuts magnetic lines. Such an arrangement is a simple *generator*. The *field magnet* furnishes the magnetic lines. The rotating loop, which we call the *armature,* cuts the magnetic lines. A **generator** *converts mechanical energy into electrical energy.*

When the crank is turned, one wire of the loop moves down past the N-pole of the field magnet as the other wire moves up past the S-pole. By applying the left-hand rule, we find that the electron flow circles the loop in one direction during one half-revolution and goes in the opposite direction during the other half-revolution. The complete revolution is known as a *cycle.* The current in the armature of our generator is *alternating.*

A current that flows in one direction during part of a cycle and in the oppo-

site direction during the rest of the cycle is called an **alternating current.** This is the type of current usually furnished by light and power companies. When a current flows in one direction only, it is called a *continuous* or *direct current.* This is the type of current that is produced by dry cells and storage batteries.

With this revolving loop, the emf rises to a maximum in one direction as one wire of the loop moves up past one pole. The emf is a maximum when the wire is right at the pole, because it is then cutting the maximum number of magnetic lines. The emf starts decreasing as the wire moves away from the pole, and falls to zero when the wire is moving parallel with the magnetic lines. As the wire moves down past the other pole, it cuts magnetic lines in the opposite direction, and the emf rises to a maximum in the other direction. The emf reaches a maximum when both wires of the loop are cutting a maximum number of magnetic lines, as at *AB,* Fig. 31-10. When the loop reaches the position shown at *CD,* no magnetic lines are being cut, and the emf is zero. As a result, the induced emf during one complete revolution varies as shown in Fig. 31-11.

For simplicity of discussion, we have used a one-turn loop for our armature. The induced emf in a single turn is very

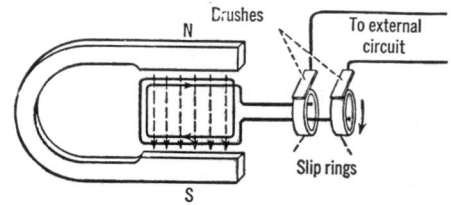

Fig. 31-12. Alternating current is taken from the armature and transmitted to the external circuit by means of slip rings and brushes.

small. Practical generators contain coils consisting of many turns of wire to provide more useful voltages. Also, many coils may be mounted around the rotating shaft to form the armature of a generator.

12. How is current taken from the armature? If we were to connect the ends of a revolving loop or coil directly to some instrument, the wires would be twisted off after a few revolutions. To make a practical generator circuit, the ends of the loop are soldered to two brass rings, called *slip-rings,* which are mounted on the same shaft as the armature. These rings are insulated from each other. Two metal strips or carbon blocks, called *brushes,* rest lightly on the slip-rings as they revolve with the loop, as in Fig. 31-12. The brushes are stationary, but they make continuous contact with the rotating slip-rings. The ends of the wires that lead to the external circuit are connected to the brushes, which take current from the slip-rings and transmit it to the external circuit.

13. What is a magneto? The simple generator we have discussed consists of a coil rotated in the magnetic field of a permanent magnet. To obtain a greater electrical output we may use a larger coil and rotate it in the field of several permanent magnets.

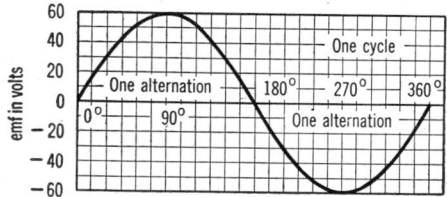

Fig. 31-11. Graph showing the output of a laboratory generator during one cycle.

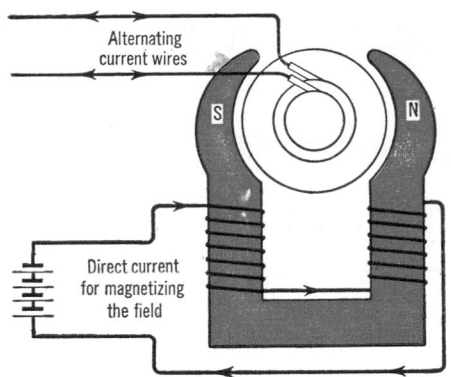

Fig. 31-13. The field of an alternating current generator is produced by an electromagnet.

Such a machine is called a *magneto* (mag-*nee*-tow). When its output is connected to a spark coil, the sparks produced ignite the gasoline vapor and air mixture inside the engines on outboard motors, lawn mowers, motorbikes, and in some airplanes.

14. The commercial alternating current generator. Using permanent magnets for the magnetic field limits the amount of electrical power produced. An electromagnet can create a much stronger magnetic field than can a permanent magnet, and it is used in large alternating current (A.C.) generators.

The A.C. generator has three essential parts:

(1) The *field electromagnets* that produce magnetic lines.

(2) The *armature,* which consists of an iron core wound with a large number of coils of insulated wire. The armature revolves between the poles of the field magnet so that the armature coils cut magnetic lines.

(3) The *slip-rings* and *brushes.*

Alternating current is generated in the armature exactly as in the case of the single rotating loop in the magneto.

When this current is taken from the armature by the brushes which rest on the slip-rings, the current in the external circuit is also alternating; that is, it flows through the external circuit first in one direction, and then in the opposite. There are two alternations for each cycle. Since many commercial machines have a frequency of 60 cycles per second, the number of alternations is 120 per second.

15. How is the field magnet magnetized? In the magneto, permanent magnets are used to furnish the magnetic lines. In A.C. generators, however, we use electromagnets instead of permanent magnets, as indicated in Fig. 31-13. In larger generators, such as that in Fig. 31-14, a small, direct-current generator, called an *exciter,* is used to magnetize the field. By this means the current through the field is

Fig. 31-14. A workman applying insulating tape to the coil ends of the stator for a 135,000 kilowatt turbine generator. Notice the size and complexity of its construction.

kept constant. Voltage does not vary if the A.C. generator speed is constant.

16. Stationary armatures are used in large A.C. generators. If high voltages are produced in generators with rotating armatures, such armatures have to be well insulated. The slip-rings tend to spark and produce short circuits. Therefore, engineers have developed A.C. generators with stationary armatures, called *stators* (*stat*-erz). The field magnet turns inside the armature, and is called the *rotor*. Magnetic lines are still cut by the armature, so that an induced emf is produced.

The current is taken from the stator without the use of slip-rings and brushes. This eliminates many of the difficulties of insulation. Voltage applied to the rotor is small enough so it is easy to use slip-rings and brushes to lead the current to the rotor.

★ **17. How does the direct-current generator work?** In only one essential does the *direct-current* generator differ from that used for alternating current. The terminals of the armature are not connected to slip-rings, but instead to metal segments of a *commutator*. The commutator changes the alternating current of the armature into a current which flows in one direction only into the external circuit. This is a *direct current,* which is abbreviated, D.C. In its simplest form, the commutator consists of a ring of brass which has been split into two semicircular segments, well insulated from each other. The terminals of the armature coil are each soldered to one segment, as shown in Fig. 31-15. Brushes resting on these segments take current from them just as they do from the slip-rings of the A.C. generator.

As the coil of Fig. 31-15 rotates so

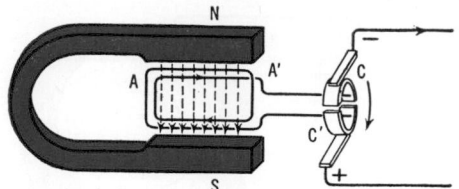

Fig. 31-15. The commutator segments change from one brush to the other at the same instant the electron current reverses in the armature. The alternating current in the armature becomes a direct current in the external circuit.

that the top wires *A A'* move away from you, the electrons flow out of the coil to the commutator segment *C*. The brush making contact with this segment is receiving electrons, hence it is considered negative. As the armature rotates more, the wires *A A'* of the loop get closer to the S-pole and begin to cut magnetic lines in the opposite direction. The electron flow then reverses itself and comes out of the coil to segment *C'*. But during this rotation of the coil or loop, the segment *C'* has also moved until it is now in contact with the negative brush. Therefore the brush marked " minus " always rests on that segment to which the electrons from the armature are flowing. Thus the current is *alternating* in the armature, but continuous in the external circuit. The brushes are adjusted so that the commutator segments change from one brush to the other at the same instant that the electron current reverses in the armature.

When only one coil is used in the armature, the emf is pulsating, or intermittent. See Fig. 31-16. To secure a more constant voltage, many coils are used in a commercial generator.

The output emf of a three-coil armature is shown in Fig. 31-17. This

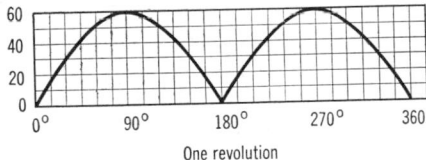

Fig. 31-16. The curve of the pulsating output of one coil producing direct current.

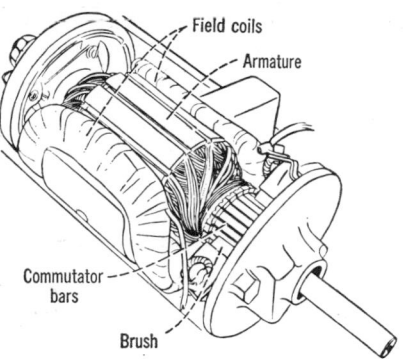

Fig. 31-18. An automobile generator has many armature coils so that its output is quite constant.

armature has two commutator bars for each coil, or a total of six bars. These are arranged so that each set of bars contacts the brushes during the time that the corresponding coil is passing through the greatest number of magnetic lines. Thus coil *1* in Fig. 31-17 supplies its output to the brushes for the first 60 degrees of rotation and is then cut out of the circuit, while coil *2* cuts in. The emf produced by coil *1* after it has been cut out is represented by the dotted lines. Since this emf is not conducted to the brushes, it appears only at the open ends of the coils, and, in a sense, it is wasted. The output of emf is brought back to its peak value by coil *2,* again decreases slightly, but is raised again by coil *3* when it is cut into the circuit by its commutator bars. The heavy line shows that the output emf never decreases to zero as does that of the single rotating coil. A fairly constant output results. Additional coils would produce still less variation in output.

A cross-section view of an automobile generator, in which several coils are used, is shown in Fig. 31-18.

★ **18. Direct-current generators are self-exciting.** Most D.C. generators use all or part of the induced current in the armature to energize the field. Therefore they are called self-exciting. They may be *series-wound, shunt-wound,* or *compound-wound.* In a series-wound generator all the armature current energizes the field magnet, the wire from one of the brushes passing around the core of the field before passing to the external circuit. In the

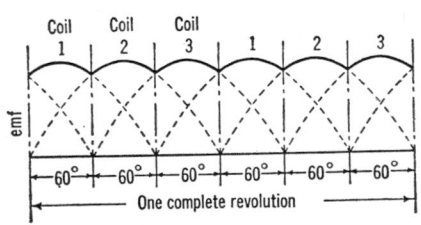

Fig. 31-17. A three-coil armature produces a more constant emf.

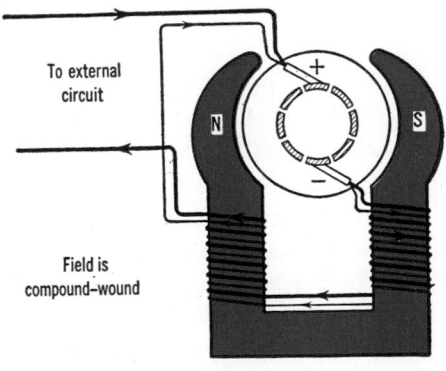

Fig. 31-19. A compound-wound generator. What is the effect of changing the resistance in the external circuit?

shunt-wound, a separate wire, using only a part of the induced current from the armature, energizes the field. The compound-wound generator is a combination of both types, as in Fig. 31-19. An increase in the resistance of the external circuit reduces the current in the series coils, but increases it in the shunt coils. This means that with the proper number of each type of coil, a constant field strength can be maintained, even under varying loads.

3. MOTORS

19. What are the parts of an electric motor? The simple D.C. motor does not differ essentially from the generator. It has one electromagnet which serves as the field magnet. Another electromagnet serves as the armature. There is a commutator, and brushes also are used. *The purpose of the electric* **motor** *is to transform electrical energy into mechanical energy.* Current from a generator, or from some other source, is led to the electric motor. There it produces two magnetic fields, one in the field magnet and the other in the armature. The poles of the field magnet mutually attract and repel those of the armature with sufficient force to cause the armature to rotate rapidly.

20. What makes a motor run? To understand the principle of the electric motor, let us mount an electromagnet on an axis so that it is free to rotate between the poles of a horseshoe magnet, as in Fig. 31-20. If we pass current through the electromagnet in such a direction that the pole at the top of the figure is an S-pole, it will be attracted by the N-pole of the stationary field magnet and repelled by the S-pole. Its N-pole at the opposite end is attracted by the S-pole of the field magnet and is at the same time repelled by the N-pole.

All these forces are working together to turn the electromagnet which serves as an armature in a counter-clockwise direction. It would stop when the two sets of opposite poles are nearest each other if it were not for its inertia. Inertia carries the N-pole, for example, slightly beyond the S-pole of the magnet. If *at that particular instance* the direction of the current flow in the rotating magnet is reversed, then its poles will be reversed. See Fig. 31-21. The stationary poles of the field will then continue to drive the rotating magnet through a second 180° of rotation by their attraction and repulsion. Another change in the direction of the current and another reversal of the poles will turn the armature through another

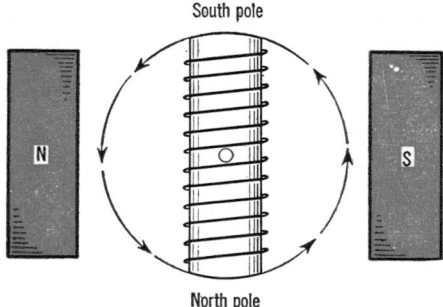

South pole

North pole

Fig. 31-20. The poles of the armature are attracted by the opposite poles of the permanent magnet and cause the armature to rotate in a counter-clockwise direction.

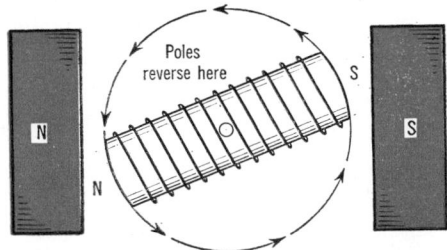

Fig. 31-21. Reversing the direction of the electron current through the armature changes its polarity and causes it to be rotated another 180°.

half-circle. A commutator and brushes are used to change the direction of the current flow at just the right instant.

The commutating action is shown in Fig. 31-22. As the electrons flow through the armature loop in a clockwise direction, the loop becomes a magnet with its N-pole facing you, and its S-pole is on the far side of the loop. The N-pole of the field magnet repels the N-pole of the loop and attracts its S-pole. The S-pole of the field magnet at the same time attracts the N-pole of the loop and repels its S-pole. The two forces of attraction and the two forces of repulsion all work together to turn the loop in the direction shown by the arrow. If the electrons continue to flow in the same direction, the loop will stop rotating as soon as its poles are opposite the corresponding unlike poles of the field magnet. However, at about the time that point is reached, the commutator reverses the direction of the electron current in the loop and its polarity is reversed. Then the attraction and repulsion continue as before. Inertia carries the poles past the points of dead center.

The direction of rotation may be found by use of the *right-hand rule,* or *motor rule. Extend the forefinger of*

the right hand in the direction of the magnetic lines; turn the middle finger, bent at right angles to both the thumb and forefinger, so that it points in the direction of electron flow. The extended thumb then points in the direction of rotation.

The *torque* or twisting force that produces rotation of a motor armature depends upon *the strength of the current, the number of windings in the armature, the number of turns in each winding, and the strength of the magnetic field* through which the armature rotates. The strength of this magnetic field depends on the number of ampere-turns in the field coils.

★ **21. There are two kinds of direct-current motors.** Such direct-current motors may be *shunt-wound* or *series-wound.* In a shunt-wound motor, the windings of the field magnet and those of the armature are connected in parallel. A shunt-wound motor's speed is not much affected by varying loads.

On the other hand, the torque of a series-wound motor is much greater at starting than that of a shunt motor. A series motor is used when the motor must start under a heavy load.

22. What types of alternating-current motors are there? Series motors may run on alternating as well as

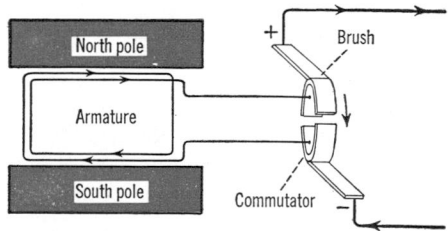

Fig. 31-22. The commutator reverses the direction of the electron current in the armature of a motor.

on direct current. The current reverses at the same time in both the field and the armature. Series motors are used for fans, vacuum cleaners, sewing machines, and so on.

Induction motors operate only on alternating current. They have two parts. One is the *stator,* which differs little from the stator of an A.C. generator in the manner in which it is wound. The other is the *rotor,* which is built of copper bars laid in slotted, laminated iron cores. In the type known as the *squirrel-cage rotor* all the copper bars are connected at each end to copper rings. See Fig. 31-23. When an alternating current passes through the winding of the stator, a rotating magnetic field is set up by the current. The rotor is not connected to the stator or to the electrical supply in any way, but the rotating magnetic field produces a current in the rotor by induction. The magnetic field set up in the rotor by this induced current is dragged after the rotating magnetic field in the stator. Thus the rotor turns very rapidly on its axis. Induction motors are made in all sizes; their advantage lies in their simplicity.

23. Back emf is developed by a motor. Suppose that we connect an incandescent lamp in series with a small motor. If the motor armature is held so that it can not rotate, the lamp lights. When the armature is released, the light grows dimmer as the motor comes up to full speed.

The voltage from the lighting circuit is impressed upon the motor. When the armature of the motor rotates in the magnetic field of the motor, it is cutting magnetic lines and producing an emf. From Lenz's law we know that this emf produced by the motor

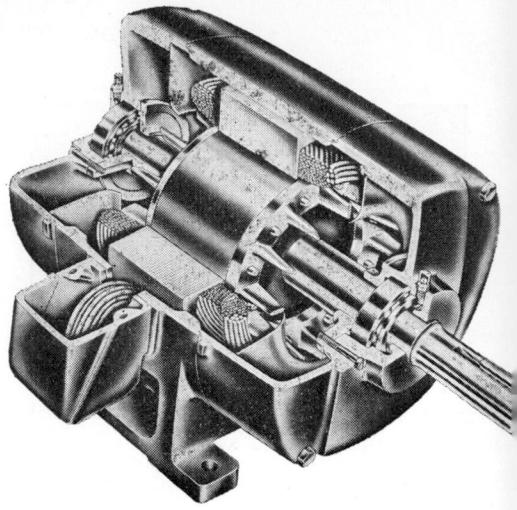

Fig. 31-23. A cutaway view of an induction motor.

must be a *back emf* or a *counter emf.* The back emf opposes the impressed emf. The effective voltage which drives the motor is equal to the *difference* between the impressed emf and the back emf. When running, every motor is also a generator.

If a motor whose measured resistance is only 5 ohms is attached to a 110-volt circuit and its armature shaft clamped in a vise to prevent it from turning, 22 amperes of current will flow through the armature. If the same armature, when running at full speed, cuts magnetic lines fast enough to produce a counter emf of 100 volts, then the effective voltage is equal to $110 - 100$, or 10 volts. The resistance does not change, but now only 2 amperes of current flow through the armature of the motor.

The back emf of a motor which is running without load will be almost equal to the impressed emf. Just enough current flows through the motor to overcome friction. If the armature slows down under load, then the back emf falls and more current flows

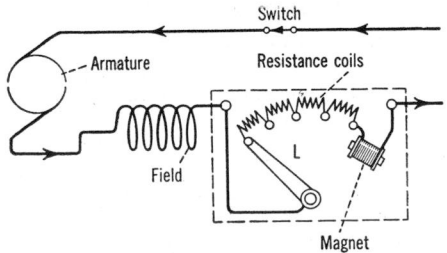

Fig. 31-24. The starting box wiring for a series-wound motor.

through the armature. In this way a motor adjusts itself to a varying load.
★ 24. How should we start motors? The resistance of a motor armature is very low. For that reason, current rushes through a motor armature when it is turned on suddenly. Small motors have so little inertia that they come up to speed quickly. They can carry without injury the temporary overload that occurs before the armature is brought up to speed and develops a back emf. The armatures of large motors come up to speed slowly. They are likely to "burn out" if the full current is turned on without first bringing the motor up to speed.

In starting the large D.C. motors, rheostats are generally used to protect the armature. Several coils of resistance wire are connected in series with the motor, as shown in Fig. 31-24. As

the speed of the motor increases, the resistance is cut out gradually. Fig. 31-24 shows a starting box which can be used to cut one coil after another out of the circuit by shoving the lever *L* to the right. The electromagnet holds the lever in place for full-speed operation. When the switch is opened, no current flows through the electromagnet, and the lever is pulled to the left by a spring.

In starting a *shunt-wound* motor, the resistance in the field is increased as the resistance in series with the armature is gradually reduced. In Fig. 31-25, if the lever *L* is moved to the right one coil after another is cut out of the armature circuit and added to the field circuit. Both operations increase the

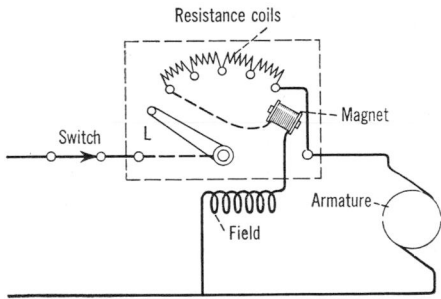

Fig. 31-25. The starting box wiring for a shunt-wound motor.

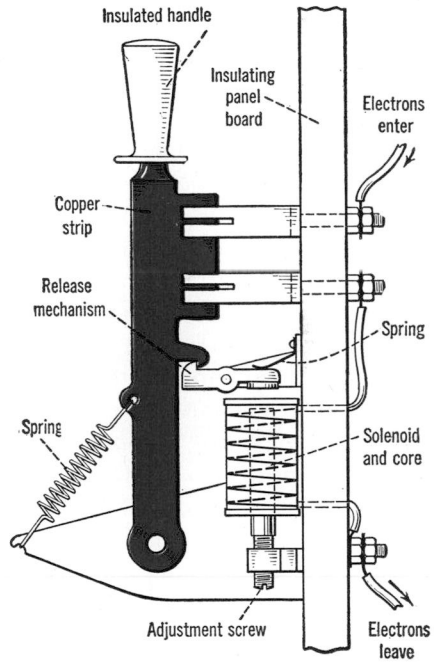

Fig. 31-26. If too much current flows through the coil, the iron core is pulled up into the coil. It then hits the release mechanism, and the spring pulls the switch to the left to break the circuit.

amount of current flowing through the armature, and thus increase the speed of the motor.

25. What are circuit breakers? Sometimes an overload may decrease the speed of a motor suddenly. If that happens, an abrupt rush of current through the armature may ruin it. To prevent injury, an automatic circuit breaker opens the circuit when such an overload occurs. When too much current flows through the coil of Fig. 31-26, which is shown at the bottom of page 591, the iron core is pulled up-ward into the coil to release the catch and break the circuit.

Underload circuit breakers also are in use. In an automobile a small electric generator driven by the car engine is used to charge the storage battery. An underload circuit breaker is used to disconnect the storage battery from the generator until the generator voltage rises to such a point that it is greater than the back voltage of the battery. Thus the underload circuit breaker prevents the battery from discharging back through the generator.

4. THE TRANSFORMER

26. How does a transformer operate? In its simplest form, which is shown in Fig. 31-27, a *transformer* consists of two coils wound around a core of thin iron sheets or laminations. *An external source of alternating current is connected to the terminals of the primary winding, AB, or* **primary coil.** The alternating current, in rising to a maximum in one direction and then falling to zero, varies the strength of the magnetic field around the primary. *These current variations in the primary induce an emf in the secondary winding, or* **secondary coil.** Then it rises to a maximum in the opposite direction and later drops to zero, thus introducing an opposite emf in the secondary. In this way *a* **transformer** *changes the voltage of an alternating current.*

The emf's in the primary and in the secondary of a transformer have nearly the same ratio as the relative number of turns of wire in the coils. For example, if there are 20 turns in the secondary for every turn in the primary, the emf in the secondary will be almost twenty times as high as that in the primary. Such a transformer connected to a 110-volt A.C. line will produce a voltage of about 2200 at the secondary. A transformer which raises the voltage in such a manner is called a *step-up transformer.* By reversing the primary and secondary, we have a *step-down transformer.* For example, if 110 volts A.C. is connected to the secondary of the transformer just described, then the voltage in the primary is reduced to only 5.5 volts, a 20-to-1 step down.

There is no gain in energy in a trans-

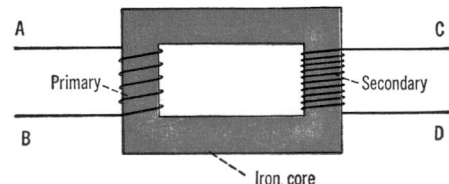

Fig. 31-27. A transformer has two or more coils wound about thin iron sheets.

former because the current strength is reduced as the voltage is increased. Actually, a small amount of energy is lost as heat. In a commercial transformer, the two coils generally are concentric. Fig. 31-28 shows the coils of a commercial transformer being lowered into the transformer housing.

27. Why is alternating current used in power transmission? Because it is easy to change the voltage of an alternating current by means of a transformer, it is much cheaper to transmit electrical power as alternating current than as direct current. To illustrate this, suppose we wish to transmit 1200 kilowatts of electrical energy a distance of 100 miles. If it is to be transmitted at a potential of 12,000 volts, then 100 amperes are required. ($12,000 \times 100 = 1,200,000$ watts, or 1200 kilowatts.) If the voltage were increased to 60,000 then only 20 amperes of current would be required. If we assume that the resistances of the transmission wires are the same, let us see how the heating effects would compare in the two cases. Transmitting at 100 amperes in one case, and at 20 amperes in the second case, we find that the heating effects are proportional to $(100)^2$ and to $(20)^2$. The ratio is 25:1. In other words, the heating effect is 25 times as great at 100 amperes as at 20 amperes. More energy

Fig. 31-28. The coils of a commercial transformer being lowered into their housing.

is thus wasted in transmitting at low voltage and high current than at high voltage with low current.

High-voltage transmission means lower current strength, and thinner wires can be used for A.C. transmission lines than for high-current D.C. at lower voltage.

The voltage of *direct current* can not be varied without tremendous losses. Hence, it is customary to use *alternating current* when electrical energy is to be

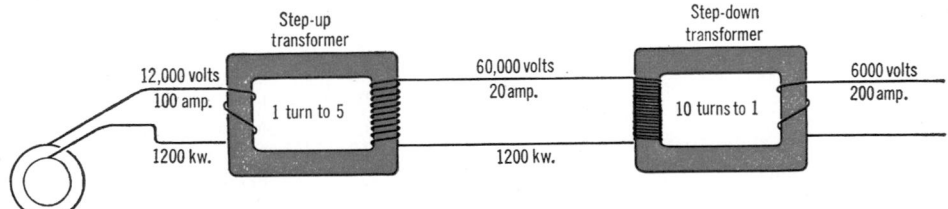

Fig. 31-29. Transformers vary the voltage of an alternating current.

transmitted long distances. The practice is to use an A.C. generator to produce current, step up the voltage by means of a transformer, and then transmit the energy at high voltage to some distant station. There it is stepped down to the voltage needed to operate the appliances for which it is intended.

Summary

An *emf* is induced in a conductor when a magnet is moved so that its magnetic lines cut through the conductor. An induced *current* is always set up in a closed circuit when a conductor in that circuit is cutting magnetic lines. Increasing or decreasing the number of magnetic lines in a magnetic field induces an emf in a conductor present in that field.

The direction of an induced electron current is given by the left-hand rule. Let the forefinger of the left hand point in the direction of the magnetic lines; turn the hand so that the extended thumb points in the direction the conductor is moving; the middle finger, bent at right angles to both the thumb and forefinger, will then point in the direction in which the electrons flow through the conductor.

Lenz's law states that a current induced in a moving conductor always flows in such a direction that it forms a magnetic field which opposes the motion of the conductor.

An electric motor is a device which transforms electrical energy into mechanical energy. It consists of a field magnet and an armature. The armature is so supplied with electricity that its poles become alternately North and South and are continually attracted and repelled by the poles of the field. A motor when running also acts as a generator and produces a back emf. The direction of rotation of a loop conductor in a magnetic field is given by the right-hand rule: Extend the forefinger of the right hand in the direction of the magnetic lines; turn the middle finger, bent at right angles to both the thumb and forefinger, so that it points in the direction of electron flow. The extended thumb then points in the direction of rotation.

Terms to Define...

Alternating current	Direction of induced current	Induction
Armature		Induction coil
Back emf	Direction of rotation of a motor	Induction motor
Brushes		Lenz's law
Circuit breaker	Distributor	Magneto
Commutator	Exciter	Motor
Compound-wound	Field magnet	Primary coil
Cycle	Induced current	Recording head
Direct current	Induced emf	Reproducing head

Rotor
Secondary coil
Self-induction
Series motor
Series-wound
Shunt motor

Shunt-wound
Slip-rings
Spark plug
Squirrel-cage rotor
Starting a motor
Stator

Step-down transformer
Step-up transformer
Strength of induced emf
Tape recording
Timer
Torque

GROUP A

1. What are the conditions under which an emf is induced in a conductor?

2. What is the difference between an induced emf and an induced current?

3. How does an increase or decrease in the number of magnetic lines in a magnetic field affect a conductor present in that field?

4. State the left-hand rule which helps us remember the direction in which an induced electron current flows.

5. How can we increase the strength of an induced emf?

6. What is the difference between direct and alternating current?

7. How is the induced current taken from the revolving loop in an A.C. generator? ★ In a D.C. generator?

8. Explain how the armature of an electric motor is made to turn continuously.

9. State the right-hand rule to find the direction of rotation of an electric motor.

10. Name the two main types of A.C. motors.

11. What is meant by back emf? How is it induced in electric motors?

12. What is the function of the circuit breaker in the electrical system of an automobile?

13. How is the voltage of an alternating current raised or lowered?

14. Why is alternating current used for long distance power transmission?

GROUP B

15. What is Lenz's law?

16. Describe an experiment which illustrates self-induction.

17. Explain how an induction coil operates.

18. How does an automobile storage battery produce the spark between the points of the spark plugs in order to ignite the gasoline vapor-air mixture in the cylinders?

19. In what form are sound waves recorded on wire or tape?

20. Why is the armature of a large commercial A.C. generator stationary, while the field magnets rotate?

21. For what purposes are magnetos used?

22. Upon what factors does the torque of an electric motor depend?

★ **23.** Why can an alternating current generator never be self-exciting? Why may a direct current generator be self-exciting?

★ **24.** Describe how large, series-wound and shunt-wound D.C. motors should be started.

Things to Do

1. Study a diagram of the electrical system of an automobile and see how many applications of the use of electricity you can find. You should be able to find the battery, generator, motors, lights, induction coil and spark plugs, horn, and so on.

2. Construct a small electric motor using nails, wire, a piece of wood, thumb tacks, and so on. You should be able to procure instructions for

making such a motor from your local electric company.

3. Visit the power plant which generates the electricity used in your community.

4. Take apart an old bell transformer and examine its construction.

5. Examine various types of A.C. and D.C. motors to learn how they are constructed and how they operate.

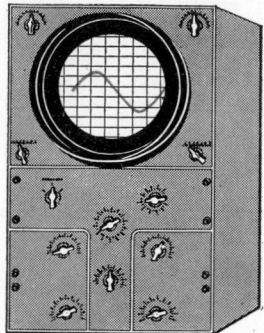

Chapter 32

Alternating Current

1. Alternating-current circuits differ from direct-current circuits. In Chapters 25 and 28, we studied Ohm's law and power calculations for D.C. circuits. We said then that the formulas we developed for those circuits also could be applied to A.C. circuits which contained *only resistance*. Now we are ready to learn about the action of capacitors and inductances when used in A.C. circuits.

2. Action of a capacitor in an A.C. circuit. In Chapter 24 we studied the capacitor and its ability to store electrons when connected to a source of direct voltage. However, since an alternating voltage rises to a peak and

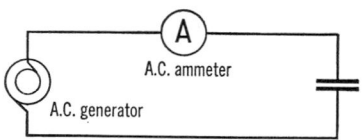

Fig. 32-1. Current from the generator flows into and out of the capacitor.

then decreases on each alteration, it *charges* and *discharges* a capacitor when applied to it. Electrons flow into the capacitor when the voltage rises, and flow out of the capacitor back to the generator when its output decreases. The net effect is that alternating current flows through the ammeter in the circuit as shown by Fig. 32-1. Although the alternating current does not flow through the capacitor itself, it flows into and out of it.

Capacitors are widely employed in the starting mechanisms of A.C. motors, and for filtering pulsating direct current so that the current is essentially constant at all times. They also are used for by-passing resistances and other units in radio equipment so that direct current can flow through them readily but alternating current will flow around them.

3. The resistance of a capacitor on direct current. The insulating mate-

---

Vocabulary

CAPACITIVE REACTANCE. The opposition of a capacitor to the flow of alternating current.

IMPEDANCE. The total opposition of a load circuit to the flow of alternating current.

INDUCTIVE REACTANCE. The opposition of a coil to the flow of alternating current.

POWER FACTOR. The ratio between the actual wattage and apparent wattage of an alternating current circuit.

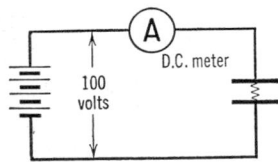

Fig. 32-2. Only a very small amount of direct current flows through a capacitor.

rial, or dielectric between the plates of a capacitor has a high resistance. The dielectric in most capacitors, such as paper, mica, and ceramic material, has a resistance of millions of ohms. Now let us assume that the capacitor in the circuit of Fig. 32-2 has a resistance of one million ohms. By applying Ohm's law to this D.C. circuit, the current flow is 100 ÷ 1,000,000 or 0.0001 ampere.

4. How do we find capacitive reactance? If a capacitor is connected to a source of alternating current at 100 volts, we find that the current is much higher than the value we found for the capacitor in the D.C. circuit. The meter in the circuit of Fig. 32-3 will show a reading of about 0.04 ampere. The capacitor is permitting more current to flow in the circuit than its D.C. resistance will allow. Some other property of the capacitor must be involved.

The charging and discharging action taking place in the circuit is dependent upon the *capacity* of the capacitor. Just as in Chapter 24 when a D.C. charge on a capacitor was discussed, its capacity depends upon *the area of the plates, the distance between the plates, and the quality of the dielectric between the plates.* Increasing the area of the plates increases the capacity. Decreasing the distance between the plates increases the capacity. Inserting a better dielectric between the plates increases the capacity.

Although the unit of capacity is the *farad,* there are no capacitors of this size in regular use. A one-farad capacitor would need to be the size of a room. Instead, one-millionth of a farad, the *microfarad,* abbreviated *μf,* is the unit mainly used in electrical and radio work. Most of the capacitors in a radio receiver are much smaller than a microfarad. Their capacity is only a few millionths of a microfarad, expressed as a few *micromicrofarads* and abbreviated *μμf.*

The capacity of a capacitor determines its opposition to the flow of alternating current. If the capacity is small, little current flows. If it is large, a high current flows. In the circuit of Fig. 32-3, a current of 0.04 ampere exists. If the capacitor is ten times as large, or 10 microfarads, then ten times as much current, or 0.4 ampere, will flow.

The opposition of a capacitor to the flow of alternating current is expressed in ohms, and *is called **capacitive reactance.*** The formula for calculating capacitive reactance is:

$$X_C = \frac{159,000}{fc},$$

where f is the frequency in cycles, and c is the capacitance in microfarads. Using this formula, the capacitor of Fig. 32-3 has a capacitive reactance of $\frac{159,000}{60 \times 1}$, or 2650 ohms.

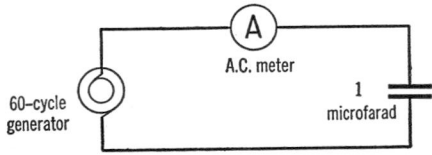

Fig. 32-3. More alternating current flows through this circuit than the resistance of the capacitor would indicate.

Note that the frequency of the applied alternating current is required in this equation. Solving some simple problems using different frequencies shows that the capacitive reactance increases if the generator produces a lower frequency. It decreases at higher frequencies.

5. What is an inductance? In Section 7, Chapter 31, we studied the property of coils called *self-induction.* It is sometimes called *inductance.* We learned that when there is a varying magnetic field in a coil, inductance opposes a change of current taking place. With alternating current, however, the magnetic field is always changing with the current, so that inductance is always taking place when a coil is in an A.C. circuit.

The *henry* is the unit of inductance. A coil has an inductance of one henry when an inducing current varying at the rate of one ampere per second produces a counter emf of one volt. The most common type of inductance, having a value ranging from one to 20 henrys, is the iron-core " choke " coil found in many radio receivers. Smaller values also are found in radio sets. These values are given in *millihenrys,* which are thousandths of a henry, and in *microhenrys,* which are millionths of a henry.

6. Inductive reactance of a coil. We have seen that the back voltage or counter emf of *a coil offers opposition to the flow of alternating current.* This is **inductive reactance.** The amount of opposition depends upon its inductance and can be expressed in ohms for a given frequency, just like capacitive reactance. The equation for inductive reactance is:

$$X_L = 2\pi f L,$$

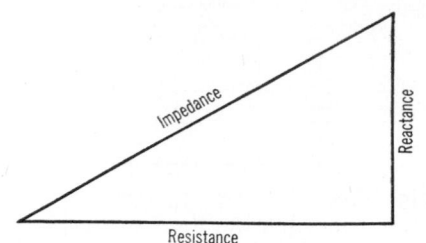

Fig. 32-4. How resistance and reactance are related to the impedance.

where f is again the frequency in cycles, and L is the inductance in henrys.

7. Impedance. To compute the *total opposition* or **impedance** *of a load circuit to the flow of alternating current* it is necessary to consider and combine three factors — *the resistance of the circuit, the capacitive reactance,* and *the inductive reactance.* The values of each of these can not be added directly because the reactive effects are not taking place exactly alike relative to time. They can be combined, however, by use of a triangle, as shown in Fig. 32-4. Resistance and reactance form the sides, and impedance in ohms is the hypotenuse. A resistance of 4 ohms and a reactance of 3 ohms combine to form an impedance of 5 ohms. The following formula uses Z for representing impedance, R for resistance, X_L for inductive reactance, and X_C for capacitive reactance.

$$Z = \sqrt{R^2 + (X_L - X_C)^2}$$

8. Ohm's law for alternating current. Impedance is substituted for resistance in using Ohm's law for A.C. circuits. Thus,

$$I = \frac{V}{Z} \quad \text{or} \quad current = \frac{voltage}{impedance}.$$

9. Practical uses for inductance. The impedance that a coil presents to

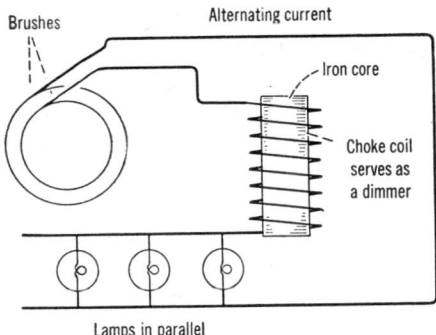

Fig. 32-5. The variable inductance of an iron core choke coil may be used to provide smooth control to dim lights.

alternating current provides a convenient method for controlling current. Suppose a coil having a movable iron core has an impedance of 240 ohms when the core is fully inserted in the coil. Its resistance is 4 ohms. It is connected in the circuit, Fig. 32-5, in series with several lamps in parallel. With the core inserted, the inductance of the coil is high and the lamps are dimly lit — if at all — because of the high impedance. As the core is withdrawn slowly from the coil, the lamps light to nearly full brilliance. The coil has decreased in inductance while the core was withdrawn, and therefore lessened in reactance. When the core is completely out of the coil its inductance may be so low that its value of impedance approaches that of the D.C. resistance, or 4 ohms. Moving the core in and out provides a smooth control of lighting that is useful in a theater for producing dramatic lighting effects.

10. How can we calculate alternating current power? Because inductive reactance opposes the flow of current, it has a retarding effect which makes the current in an A.C. circuit lag behind the emf. Fig. 32-6 illus-trates both the voltage and current curves of a circuit containing inductance. The current lags behind the voltage and does not reach its maximum so quickly. Capacitive reactance produces the opposite effect, where the voltage lags behind the current. However, the voltage and current reach a maximum at the same time in a resistance. Because of these different effects it is necessary to use the triangle to find impedance.

Because the current and voltage do not reach their maximum at the same time, alternating current power can not be found simply by multiplying volts and amperes, as was the case for direct current. We must multiply volts times amperes times *a power factor*. The power factor varies with each circuit, but it is always less than one and is expressed as a percentage.

The *apparent wattage* (the product of volts and amperes) of an A.C. circuit is always more than the actual wattage when there is reactance present. *The* **power factor** *is the ratio between the actual wattage and the apparent wattage of an alternating current circuit.* If there is only resistance in the circuit, such as an incandescent lamp, the power factor is 100%, or unity. We then can multiply A.C. volts by A.C. amperes, which will give us the true power.

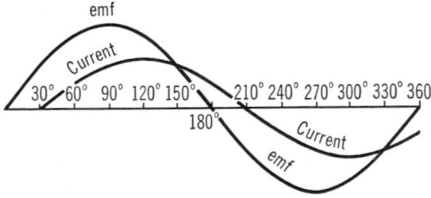

Fig. 32-6. The current lags behind the voltage in a circuit containing inductance.

11. The uses of alternating current and direct current. Direct current is used for heating, lighting, electroplating, charging storage batteries, electromagnets, and for almost any other kind of electrical work. Its big disadvantage lies in the fact that there is no practical way to raise its voltage, and its voltage can not be lowered without introducing resistance and wasting power. Alternating current can not be used for electroplating or for any other kind of electro-chemical work. It may be used for running motors and for heating and lighting. Its one great advantage is that its voltage can be changed easily using a transformer, and with little loss of energy. Thus, alternating current is used for long-distance transmission of electricity.

12. How is alternating current changed to direct current?
(1) *The motor-generator.* This consists of an A.C. motor and a D.C. generator, both mounted on the same shaft. The motor uses alternating current to turn the generator, and the generator produces direct current.

(2) *The rotary converter.* The armature of the rotary converter takes current from an alternating-current line by means of slip-rings. Such current turns the armature as a motor. Coils in a magnetic field are connected to a commutator mounted on the other end of the armature, and direct current from the commutator is fed to the external circuit.

(3) *Dry-disc rectifier.* Some metals can be treated to form an oxide surface or layer on one side that permits electric current to flow from the oxide to the metal, but not readily in the opposite direction. Such a device changes alternating current to direct current, hence it is called a rectifier.

(4) *The electronic tube.* One of many functions which a vacuum tube can perform is the changing of alternating current to direct current. Its action will be discussed in the following chapter.

Summary

Alternating current charges and discharges a capacitor. The extent of this action varies with the capacity of the capacitor. The capacity of a capacitor depends upon the area of the plates, the distance between the plates, and the quality of the dielectric between the plates. The unit of capacity is the farad, but practical capacitors are rated in much smaller units, microfarads and micromicrofarads. The opposition of a capacitor to the flow of alternating current is expressed in ohms, and is called capacitive reactance.

The total opposition or impedance of a load circuit to the flow of alternating current depends upon three factors: the resistance of the circuit, the capacitive reactance, and the inductive reactance. In A.C. circuits, the current in amperes equals the potential difference in volts divided by the impedance in ohms.

Alternating current power is the product of volts times amperes times a power factor which depends upon the type of circuit. The power factor is one or less than one.

────────── *Terms to Define...* ──────────

Alternating current power
Capacitive reactance
Choke coil
Dry-disc rectifier
Electronic tube

Farad
Henry (unit)
Impedance
Inductance
Inductive reactance

Motor generator
Ohm's law for alternating
current
Power factor
Rotary converter

GROUP A

1. How does the action of a capacitor on an A.C. circuit differ from its action on a D.C. circuit?

2. What factors are there that will determine the capacity of a capacitor? Also, in what units are the capacities of capacitors ordinarily given?

3. What is capacitive reactance? How may it be calculated?

4. What is inductance? In what units is it measured?

5. What is inductive reactance? How may it be calculated?

6. How is the impedance of an alternating-current circuit determined?

7. State Ohm's law for alternating current circuits.

8. How can we calculate the actual power consumption in an alternating current circuit?

9. What are the advantages of alternating current? Of direct current?

10. In what ways is it possible for alternating current to be changed to direct current?

(In the Mathematics Refresher, refer to Sections 2, 10, 11, and 16.)

GROUP A

1. An A.C. motor consumes 200 watts when operated on a 120-volt line. Power factor is 0.9. What current flows through the motor?

2. A 115-volt A.C. motor draws a current of 5 amperes. If the power factor is 0.85, what is the power consumption in watts?

3. A coil inserted in an A.C. circuit has a resistance of 5 ohms. Its inductive reactance is 12 ohms. What impedance has the coil?

GROUP B

4. What is the inductive reactance of a coil with an inductance of 500 millihenries if the frequency is 60 cycles per second?

5. Calculate the capacitive reactance of a 0.5 μf condenser on a 120-cycle line.

● **6.** A condenser and a coil are connected in series to a 115-volt A.C. line. The capacitive reactance of the condenser is 200 ohms. The coil has a resistance of 25 ohms and an inductive reactance of 100 ohms. What current flows through the circuit?

────────── *Things to Do* ──────────

1. Have one of the pupils in the class who makes radio his hobby bring in some resistors, capacitors, and inductances for the class to see.

2. Perhaps your physics laboratory is supplied with direct current from a motor-generator set, or from a dry-disc rectifier. Have your instructor show you these devices which change alternating current into direct current.

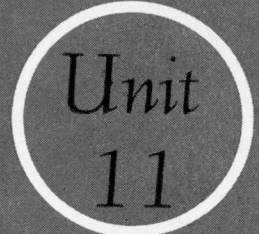

Unit 11

Modern Physics

The photograph shows the newest and largest "atom smasher," the Bevatron, at the University of California. Perhaps the glamor and novelty of such devices, along with other discoveries like color television, have attracted you to physics. And you no doubt have wondered why it has been necessary to study Mechanics, Heat, Sound, Light, and Electricity before we learn about these intriguing devices of Modern Physics.

Just as we learned arithmetic before we could understand algebra, or we studied the early history of the United States in order to better understand current events, we had to lay a background of earlier discoveries in physics before we were ready to fully understand and appreciate the advances being made today. But now we are ready. In the final chapters of this book we shall learn about present-day physics.

Perhaps as you finish this year's work, you will be challenged by the yet undiscovered frontiers of science! Investigate the possibilities of an exciting career for yourself in further study and discoveries in the realm of physics!

Chapter 33

Electronics

1. HOW ELECTRONIC TUBES WORK

1. Edison discovered the first electronic tube. The most important unit in all electronic equipment is the vacuum tube. This device was discovered by Edison in 1883 while he was improving the incandescent lamp. He observed that many lamps burned out at the end of the red-hot filament. In an effort to correct this condition, Edison sealed a metal plate inside the bulb and connected it to a battery and ammeter as in Fig. 33-1. The meter pointer flipped up-scale, showing that current was flowing through the vacuum. Edison knew this had to be so, because the meter would read only if current was flowing around a complete electric circuit. The vacuum between filament and plate was in this circuit, so some-

how the current was getting across the space.

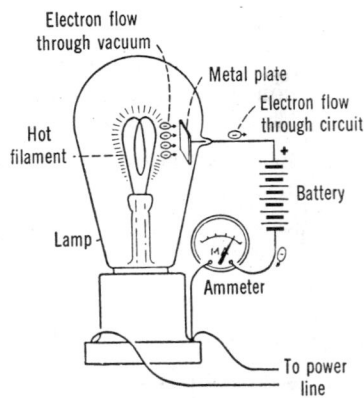

Fig. 33-1. Electrons will flow from the filament to the plate as shown when the plate is positive, but not when it is negative.

Vocabulary

CATHODE. The negative electrode in an electronic tube.

DIODE (*dy*-ohd). An electronic tube containing two elements, a cathode and a plate.

GRID. A wire coil whose charge controls the passage of electrons from the cathode to the plate.

PLATE. Positive electrode of electronic tubes.

TRANSISTOR. A device containing germanium which can be used in place of an electronic tube for controlling an electric current.

TRIODE (*try*-ohd). An electronic tube containing three elements, a cathode, a plate, and a grid.

X RAY. Invisible electromagnetic radiation of great penetrating power.

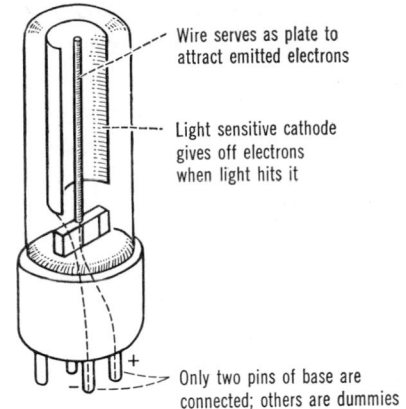

Wire serves as plate to attract emitted electrons

Light sensitive cathode gives off electrons when light hits it

Only two pins of base are connected; others are dummies

Fig. 33-3. When light strikes the sensitive cathode of this phototube, the cathode emits electrons. (Photoelectric effect)

metal points *A* and *B* will cause electrons to be pulled out of the point that is negative at the moment. These electrons will travel the short distance through air to the other point, which is positive. When the evacuated tube is connected, the same action occurs but over a much longer gap between *A'* and *B'* because electrons travel much more readily through a vacuum.

★ **4. Heaters for cathodes.** In some tubes, particularly those used in battery-operated, portable radios, the heated filament itself gives off the electrons, just as in Edison's lamp. This is shown at *A* in Fig. 33-5, and the corresponding filament symbol used inside the tube circle on diagrams appears at *A'*. More often used, however, is the indirectly heated type of cathode shown at *B*. The source of heat here is a coiled filament of tungsten wire, called the heater, inside a spaghetti-like ceramic rod. Around the ceramic is a metal sleeve covered with a coating of the oxides of rare-earth elements. When heated by the heater

element inside, this oxide coating gives off electrons much more efficiently than a bare wire itself. The cathode has its own lead in these heater-type tubes, and ordinarily is not even connected to the heating-current leads. This cathode symbol is shown at *B'*.

★ **5. What kinds of envelopes are used for tubes?** Early tubes used glass bulbs or *envelopes* like those of lamps. Electrode leads were brought out through the glass to metal pins molded into a plastic base. Connections were made to the tube through a socket into which the tube was plugged. Most tubes are still made essentially this same way today but some have a metal envelope instead of glass. The trend now is to leave off the base and let the leads serve as pins that plug into a socket.

6. How gas-filled diodes work. After all the air is pumped out of a tube, a small amount of gas is sometimes admitted before sealing off the tube. Mercury vapor, argon, neon, helium, and xenon are some of the gases used in electronic tubes. The molecules of gas, which are thousands of times larger than electrons, get in

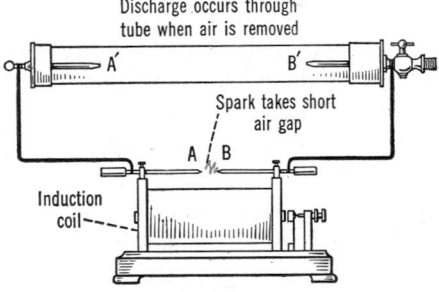

Discharge occurs through tube when air is removed

Spark takes short air gap

Induction coil

Fig. 33-4. A high voltage is used here to pull electrons out of metal. Both the spark and the discharge through the tube are examples of cold cathode emission.

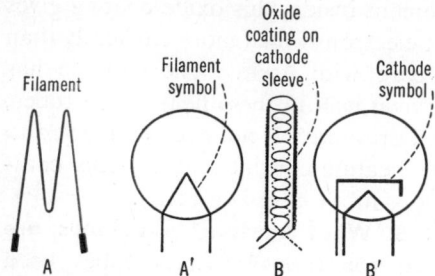

Fig. 33-5. Filament and cathode constructions and symbols.

the way of electrons traveling at high speed from cathode to plate, and cause collisions. At each collision, the electron splits the gas molecule into two parts called *ions,* one of which is positive and the other negative. The negative ion, usually just an electron, travels on to the plate together with the first electron to give increased current. More important, however, is the positive ion. Since unlike charges attract and the cathode is negative, the positive ion travels backward to the cathode and helps make more electrons come out. Here is how this occurs:

Electrons boiled out of a cathode do not immediately flash over to the plate. Instead, they hover just outside the cathode to form a highly negative space charge that repels other electrons which might be trying to break out of the cathode. The positive ions crash into these electrons and break up the gathering, combining with some of them to form gas molecules again. This ionizing action and the resulting recombination of molecules result in a visible glow not seen in high-vacuum tubes. The gas in the tube also serves to lower the effective resistance of the path in space between the cathode and the plate, so that much more current can be passed by the tube.

7. How do Tungar rectifiers charge storage batteries? One example of a gas-filled diode is the *Tungar rectifier* used for charging storage batteries from an A.C. power line. Argon gas is used in the tube. A transformer lowers the A.C. power line voltage to the correct value. The circuit is shown in Fig. 33-6. On the half-cycle, when point *A* on the secondary of the transformer is positive, the **plate** (also called the *anode*) *is also positive,* and point *B* and the cathode are negative. This is the required condition for electron flow through the tube. The complete path is from cathode to anode, through the variable resistance that controls charging rate, through the storage battery to point *A,* through the secondary to point *B* and through one lead to the cathode. Heating current for the cathode is provided by a third winding on the transformer.

When the polarity of the secondary winding reverses on the next half-cycle of the A.C. power line, the anode becomes negative and repels electrons, so there is no electron flow through the

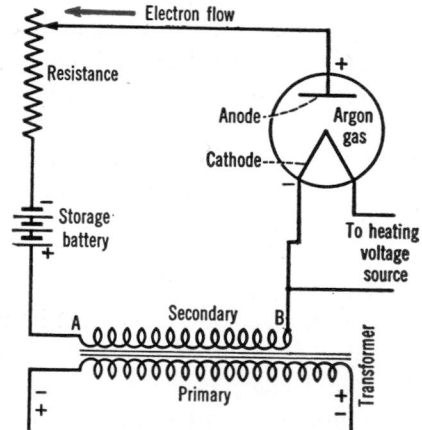

Fig. 33-6. The basic circuit of a Tungar rectifier used for charging storage batteries.

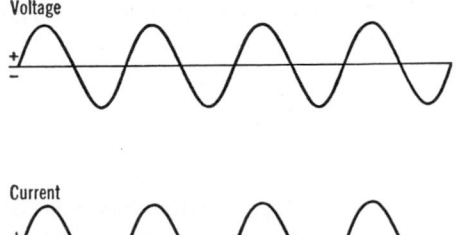

Fig. 33-7. A diode rectifier allows a pulsating direct current to pass when an alternating voltage is applied to it.

tube. This entire process is repeated for each succeeding cycle, so that current is forced through the battery only in the correct direction for charging it. The action is illustrated in Fig. 33-7, which shows the A.C. voltage waveform for the secondary of the transformer and the resulting current pulses through the charging circuit. These curves apply to all diodes.

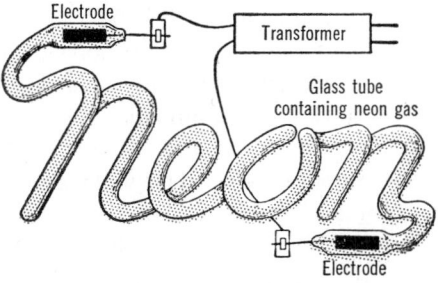

Fig. 33-8. Neon signs operate from high-voltage transformers. The glow is produced by electrons combining with the gas ions inside the tubing.

8. Getting useful light from gas tubes. A *neon* sign is a stretched-out gas-filled diode having an A.C. voltage of about 10,000 volts applied between its two electrodes, as in Fig. 33-8. Each electrode acts as a cathode on one-half of each A.C. cycle and as an anode on the other alternation. The high voltage pulls the electrons out of the cold cathode. Since there is no heater, this is sometimes called cold-cathode lighting. The amount of gas in the tube is such as to give a glow throughout the entire length of tubing. Neon gas gives a red glow. Mercury vapor in blue glass gives blue. Mercury vapor in yellow glass tubing gives green. Helium gives a yellow-white color. Each other gas has its own characteristic color produced when the positive ions of gas combine with electrons to replace those knocked out by collision.

9. What makes fluorescent lamps flicker? Another example of electronic lighting is the *fluorescent* (floo-er-*ess*-ent) lamp in Fig. 33-9. This differs from neon tubing in two ways. It has a heater to supply electrons for starting, hence it operates on much lower voltage. Also, it has a coating of fluorescent material inside the tube to produce white light, as required for illumination. Once ion formation by collision has started, enough slow-

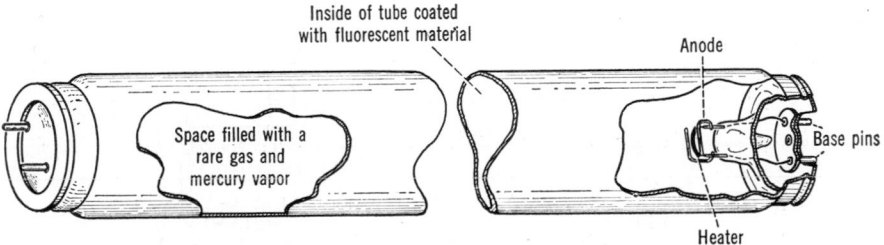

Fig. 33-9. The construction of a fluorescent lamp.

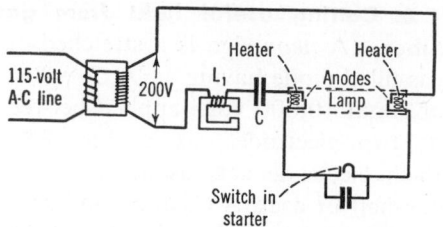

Fig. 33-10. One type of fluorescent lamp circuit.

moving ions are stuck in the space between the electrodes to start action again after the line voltage has reversed its polarity each half-cycle. The filament is thus needed only when the lamp is first turned on. To conserve filament life, a starter switch is used to disconnect the filament as soon as the light comes on.

The light that you see from a fluorescent lamp is not the glow of the gas inside but instead is the characteristic glow of the fluorescent chemicals in the coating inside the glass. These chemicals glow when illuminated by ultraviolet light from the ionized mercury vapor inside the tube. Colored glows for decorative purposes arc obtained by changing the chemicals.

Sun lamps for producing a healthful tan are essentially fluorescent lamps

without the fluorescent coating. The resulting ultraviolet light is harmful to the eyes, and should not be viewed except through protective goggles.

A typical fluorescent lamp circuit is given in Fig. 33-10. A small power transformer steps up the line voltage slightly. The iron-core choke coil L_1 limits the lamp current to a safe value, since the lamp alone would act practically as a short-circuit across the transformer once ionization started. Usually the transformer and choke are combined into one unit called a *ballast*. Condenser C is not essential to get light, but serves to make the circuit act more like a resistance than an inductance, thus improving the power factor.

10. How can we make electrons move in tubes? The two methods of making electrons go where we want them to are with an electrostatic field and with a magnetic field.

An *electrostatic field* is produced by applying voltage between electrodes, as you have learned already. This action is reviewed in Fig. 33-11 for a diode vacuum tube. The voltage may be obtained from a battery or any other D.C. source. When the plate or anode is made negative with respect to

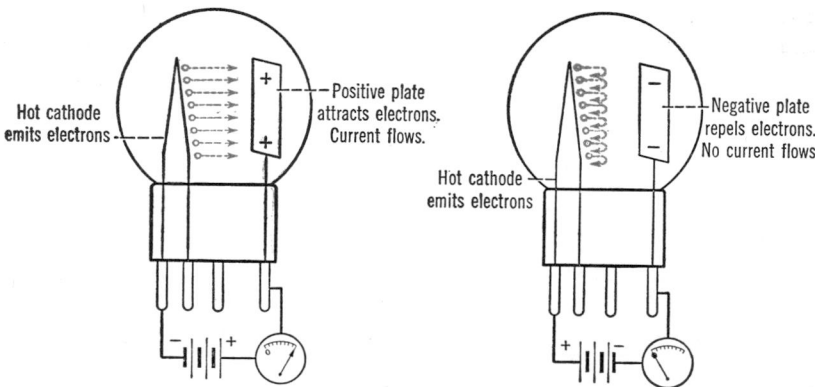

Fig. 33-11. The meters show that current flows only when the plate is positive.

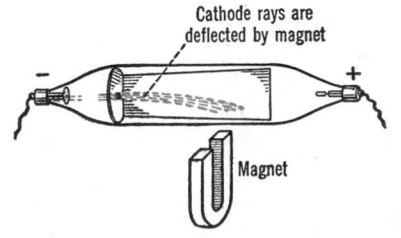

Fig. 33-12. An electron beam is deflected by bringing a magnet near it.

the cathode, the electrons that are boiled out simply turn around and go right back.

The action of a *magnetic field* on electrons is illustrated in Fig. 33-12, which shows a tube made especially for demonstrating this phenomenon. When a high D.C. voltage is applied between the electrodes at the ends with the polarity shown, electrons are pulled out of the negative electrode (cathode) by the voltage. A mask with a small hole in the center forms these electrons into a beam, and a surface coated with fluorescent material shows the path that this electron beam takes from the mask to the anode. Without the magnet, the beam goes straight across to the anode.

When a magnet is brought near the tube in Fig. 33-12 the beam is bent, and its new, curved path shows clearly on the fluorescent screen inside. Ei-

ther a permanent magnet or a electromagnet will produce the same action. Use of electromagnet coils for this purpose is illustrated in Fig. 33-13, which shows how the electron beam is moved up and down on the screen of a modern television picture tube. Similar coils above and below the neck of the tube would deflect the beam from side to side.

The direction in which an electron beam is bent depends on two things — (1) the direction of electron flow, and (2) the direction of the magnetic lines. The variation of the familiar right-hand rule in Fig. 33-14 is an easy way of finding out which way the beam will bend.

11. The most famous tube of all — DeForest's triode. Though diodes are useful in rectifying alternating current and producing light, they would not alone have made radio and all the newer electronic developments possible. What was needed was a way to boost the strength of weak radio signals. In 1906 Lee DeForest (1873–   ) achieved this *amplifying action* by placing another electrode between the cathode and the plate. *Since this made three electrodes in all,* the new tube was called a **triode** (*try*-ohd). The new electrode was a winding or grid of fine wire, hence it was called the

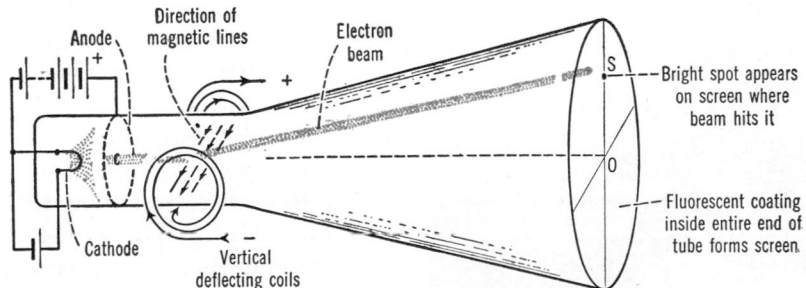

Fig. 33-13. Coils deflect the electron beam in a television picture tube.

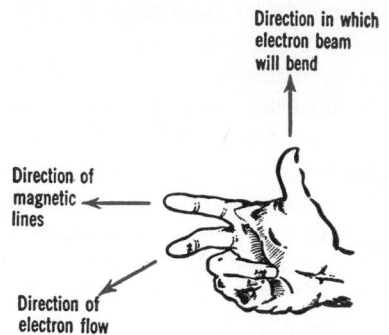

Fig. 33-14. The right-hand rule for determining the way an electron beam will be deflected. Try it on Fig. 33-13.

grid. The first DeForest triode is shown in Fig. 33-15, and construction of a modern version is shown in Fig. 33-16.

The addition of the grid immensely increases the uses to which vacuum tubes can be put. The **grid** *provides an easy way of controlling the electron flow from the cathode to the plate.* All that we need to do is vary the polarity and strength of the voltage that is applied between the grid and cathode to vary the charge on the grid, as shown in Fig. 33-17.

Fig. 33-15. The first DeForest triode.

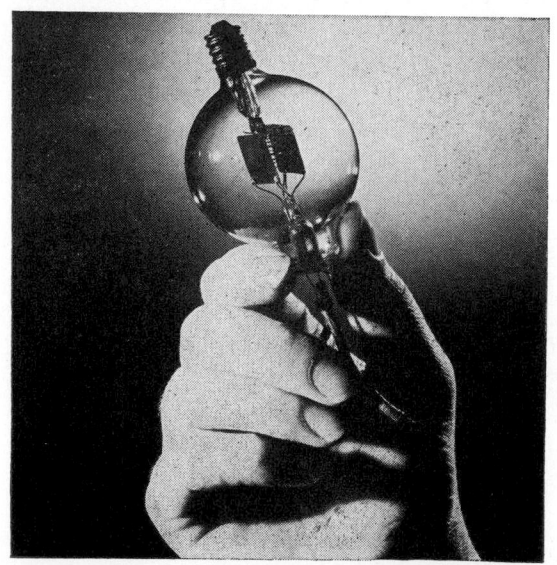

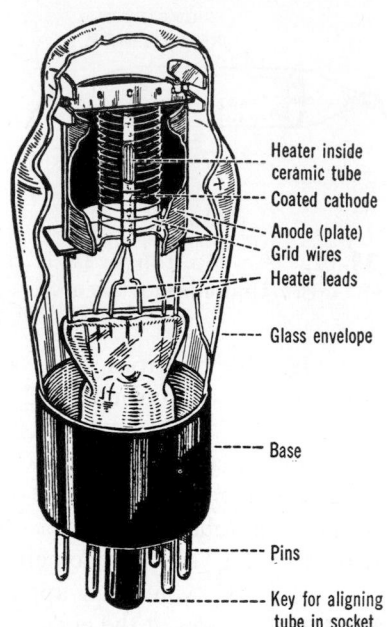

Fig. 33-16. The drawing above shows the construction of a modern glass-envelope triode.

When the grid is positive, it actually helps pull electrons from the cathode toward the plate. Some electrons will land on the grid, but because of its open construction and the much stronger charge on the plate, most of the electrons will pass between the turns of the grid and go on to the plate.

When the grid is negative it repels the electrons back to the cathode. Then no current flows. Even with the plate highly positive, it takes only a small negative charge on the grid to block the electrons, because the grid is so much closer to the cathode.

12. How the grid controls plate current. The graph in Fig. 33-18 gives a better picture of what happens to plate current in a triode when we vary the grid voltage. When the grid

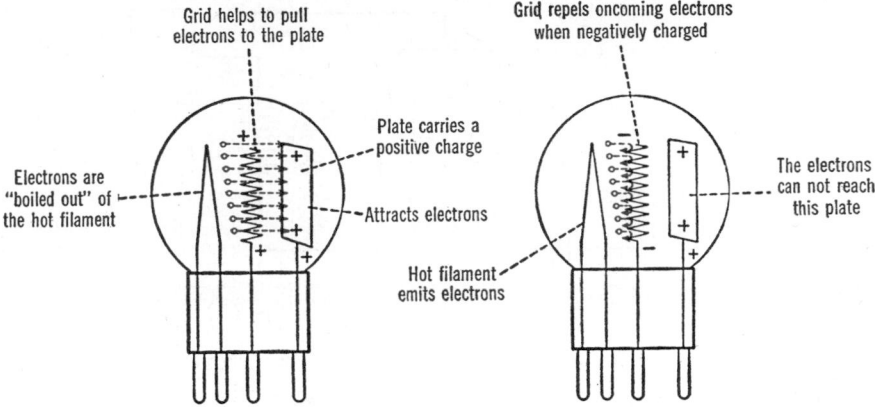

Fig. 33-17. How the grid controls the flow of electrons to the plate in a triode.

voltage is highly negative, as at point *a*, plate current is zero because all electrons are blocked by the grid. As the negative charge on the grid is reduced, we reach a point, marked *b*, where a few electrons can get through the grid wires to form a small plate current. Reducing grid voltage still more now makes plate current increase rapidly, as at *c* and *d*. When the grid voltage is zero, which means that it is the same voltage as the cathode, plate current is high just as though the grid were not there, as at point *e*. Increasing the

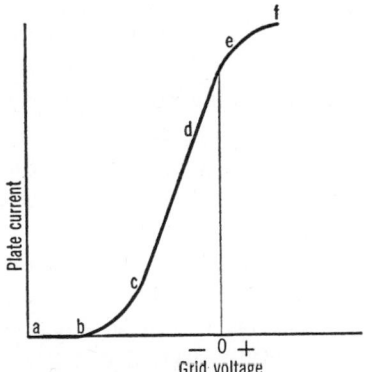

Fig. 33-18. How plate current through a triode changes when the grid voltage is varied.

voltage in a positive direction now makes plate current go higher than for a diode because the grid is pulling electrons out, too. But there is a tapering-off effect, and at point *f* the plate current reaches maximum. Further increases in positive grid voltage then have no effect on plate current.

13. How can we amplify without distorting? To increase voltages, the portion of the plate current curve that we use most often is the section between *c* and *d* in Fig. 33-18. In this straight-line region we can amplify without changing the characteristics of the weak signal coming in. Since the voltage to be increased is alternating voltage as a rule, we try to operate halfway between points *c* and *d*, along the linear portion of the curve. Then positive swings will not swing up beyond *d* where the curvature can cause distortion, and negative swings will not go beyond *c* where curvature again exists to cause distortion. To achieve this ideal condition, the grid is operated with a small constant negative charge called the *grid bias* voltage.

★ **14. What is grid bias?** A triode amplifier circuit is shown in Fig.

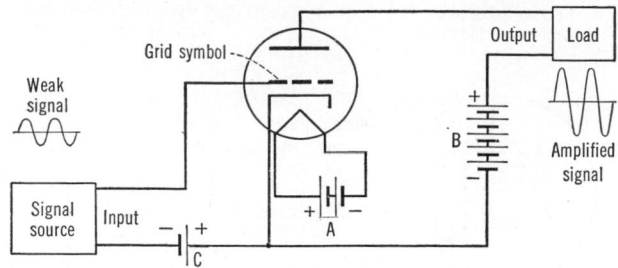

Fig. 33-19. Triode amplifier circuit, with batteries serving as voltage sources.

33-19. Note the use of the dotted-line symbol to represent the grid in the tube circle. The **A** battery provides the current for the heater. The **B** battery supplies the plate voltage that places the positive charge on the plate. It connects between cathode and plate, not just to the plate. This is essential to make the plate positive with respect to the cathode.

The third battery, placed in the grid circuit to make the grid slightly negative with respect to the cathode, is called the **C** battery. Sometimes for this reason the grid bias voltage is called the **C** bias. With these three voltages, the triode is capable of boosting the strength of a weak input signal, so that a much stronger signal is sent to the load in the plate or output circuit. This output signal has exactly the same waveform as the input signal, because we get amplification without distortion when the linear part of the plate current curve is used.

15. Using a triode as a detector. By deliberately operating a triode on the curved part of its plate current curve, such as at point *b* in Fig. 33-18, we can get both rectifying and amplifying action out of one tube. This is a highly useful characteristic for detecting weak radio signals. Each half-cycle of the input signal that swings in

the positive direction up the curve gets amplified, and alternate half-cycles that swing in the other direction have no effect because plate current is already zero at *b* and can go no lower. We will learn later that this resulting *pulsating direct current* can easily be amplified still more as an audio signal and then converted into sound waves that can be heard.

★ **16. Using a triode as an oscillator.** If a triode is connected into an amplifier circuit so that its plate is coupled back to the grid by a coil or through a condenser, *oscillation* (oss-ih-*lay*-shun) will take place. This means that the circuit itself will produce alternating current at a frequency determined primarily by the sizes of the coils and condensers in the circuits. One example of such an oscillator circuit is given in Fig. 33-20. By adjusting the tuning condenser, the frequency of the oscillation can be changed. This type of oscillator has been widely used in superheterodyne radio and television receivers.

17. Why crystal oscillators do not drift. Another widely used triode oscillator circuit, shown in Fig. 33-21, uses a carefully ground quartz crystal in the grid circuit. This crystal has the property of vibrating at a definite rate and generating a definite frequency

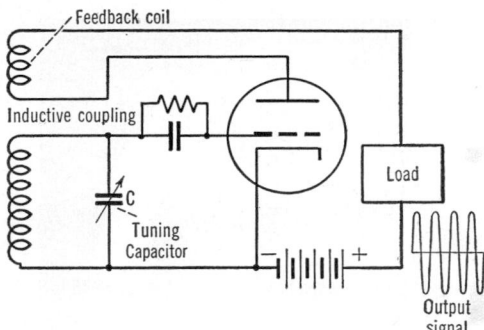

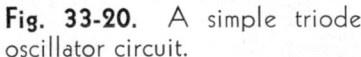

Fig. 33-20. A simple triode oscillator circuit.

of A.C. voltage when used in this circuit. The frequency is related to the thickness of the crystal slab; the thinner the slab, the higher is the frequency. By using special techniques, crystals have been ground as thin as paper, and produce frequencies as high as 100,000,000 cycles per second.

A crystal oscillator has the ability to maintain a constant frequency, whereas other types of oscillator circuits may drift or vary in frequency. For this reason, crystal oscillators are extensively used in broadcast, commercial and amateur radio transmitters, as well as in television transmitters and other precise electronic equipment requiring a constant frequency. A natural quartz crystal is shown in Fig. 33-22, and a finished slab in Fig. 33-23.

★ **18. Using crystals as diodes.** One relic of radio's younger days that can still be found in radio stores is the *crystal detector,* used in crystal receivers to rectify the incoming radio signal. An adjustable sharp-pointed wire, called a *catwhisker* was generally provided for finding a sensitive rectifying spot on the silicon or galena mineral crystal. This early crystal detector was replaced by vacuum tubes in commercial radio receivers. Improved crystal diodes came into use during World War II in radar receivers. These look like a small resistor, and require no adjusting because the catwhisker is fixed and welded at a good spot on a small crystal of silicon or germanium. See Fig. 33-24. Many television receivers contain a modern crystal diode like that illustrated.

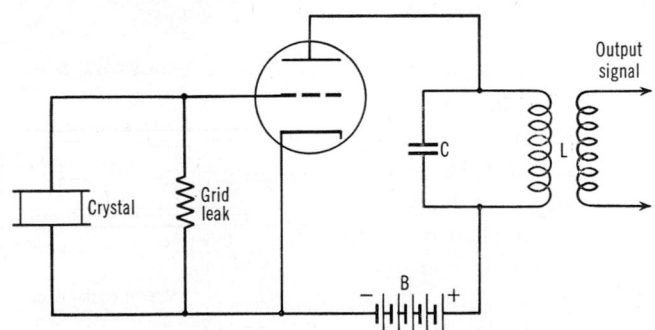

Fig. 33-21. A crystal oscillator circuit that is used in transmitters.

Fig. 33-22. Natural quartz crystal as it is found in Brazil.

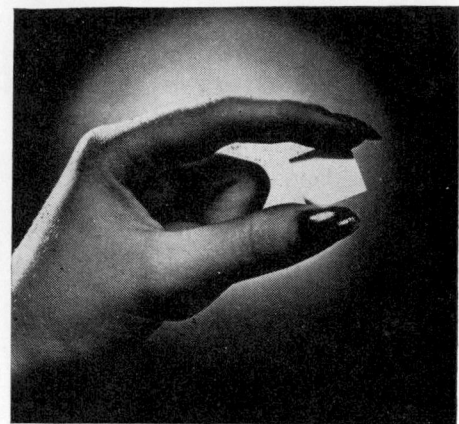

Fig. 33-23. A finished crystal slab ready for mounting in a holder.

★ **19. Other types of tubes.** There are many more complex types of radio tubes besides the diodes and triodes already covered, but we need take up only a few of them in order to understand how radio and television transmitters and receivers work.

The *tetrode* contains four elements or electrodes, one more than the triode. The additional electrode, called a *screen grid,* is a wire spiral or screen placed between the first grid and the plate. It is operated at a positive charge with respect to the cathode, and serves as an *electrostatic screen* between grid and plate. This permits the tube to work better in amplifying signals.

The *pentode* is a five-element tube, having still another grid called the *suppressor grid.* This always is located between the screen grid and the plate, and serves to repel or drive back to the plate any electrons knocked out of the plate by electrons coming from the cathode. The suppressor grid thus suppresses secondary emission of electrons from the plate. Symbols for

tetrodes and pentodes are shown in Fig. 33-25.

20. What are transistors? A few years ago engineers hailed a new crystal development that promised to replace the electron tube. Called a *point-contact* **transistor,** *the device consists of a tiny piece of germanium crystal and two very fine catwhiskers*

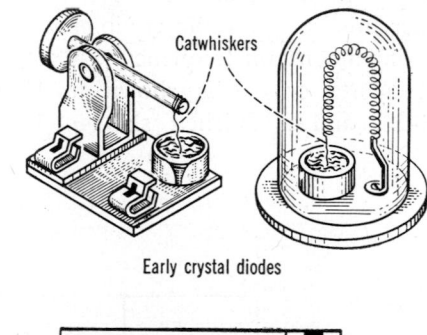

Early crystal diodes

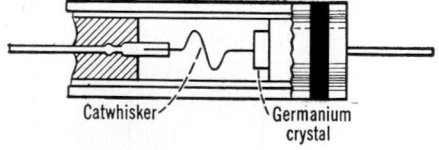

Modern crystal diode

Fig. 33-24. The old and new in crystal diodes.

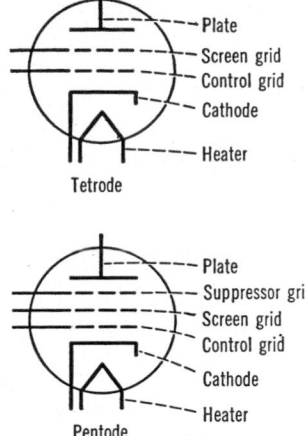

Fig. 33-25. The symbols for tetrode and pentode tubes.

in contact with it. Extreme care and microscopic tools are necessary in assembling the unit and adjusting the contacts to fixed positions. The germanium *base* and the two contacts, the *emitter* and the *collector,* form a triode that provides amplification in a manner similar to that of a triode tube. Construction of a point-contact transistor is shown in Fig. 33-26.

Another type of transistor employs a sandwich type of construction using layers of germanium material. Connections are made to each layer instead of catwhiskers. This is a junction transistor and its construction is illustrated in Fig. 33-27. Both types usually are encased in plastic for protection.

21. How do transistors operate? Germanium is one of several materials that are classed as semiconductors; they act as insulators under certain conditions and as conductors under other conditions. In a pure state germanium acts like an insulator. However, when the proper impurities are added to it, it becomes a conductor. A surplus of electrons is provided that can migrate through it. At the same time the impurities provide a deficiency of electrons that leaves vacancies or " holes " in the crystal structure. Movement of the " holes " and the electrons, both to neutralize one another and to the electrodes, determines the ability of the transistor to amplify. It does so by dealing with current changes, just the opposite of vacuum tube operation, which deals with voltage changes. The current changes take place between the three elements of the transistor: the emitter, the base, and the collector. A typical circuit of a transistor amplifier is shown in Fig. 33-28. Note the similarity to the triode vacuum tube circuit of Fig. 33-19. The input signal feeds to the emitter in place of a tube grid, and the output signal is taken from the collector instead of from a tube plate. In this circuit, the base corresponds to the cathode of the tube.

The tiny size of transistors makes them particularly useful in small, port-

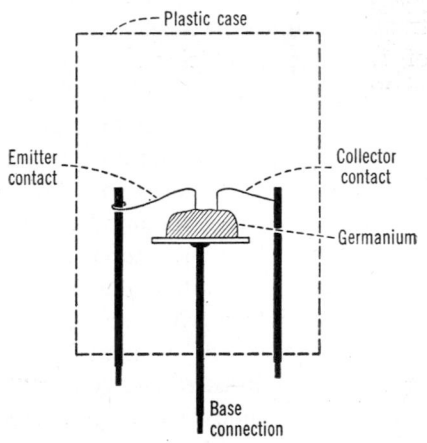

Point contact transistor

Fig. 33-26. Point-contact transistor.

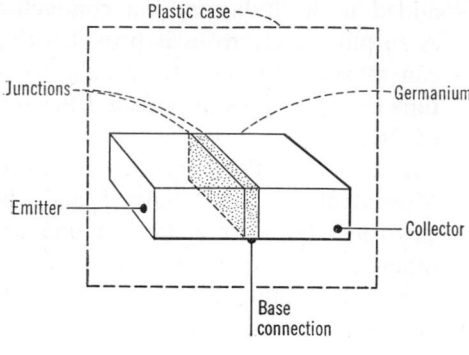

Junction transistor

Fig. 33-27. Junction transistor.

able equipment. Their low battery requirements permit even greater reduction in the size of such units. For this reason nearly all the transistors that have been commercially produced so far have been used in hearing aids.

22. Advantages of a transistor. There is no filament in a transistor, so that no battery or transformer is required for heating. The very small amount of current needed is readily obtained from a tiny battery. The battery does not need to be so large as that required by a electronic tube for the plate voltage supply. For some transistor circuits, a single pen-light cell of 1.5 volts is sufficient.

23. How do cathode-ray tubes work? In ordinary tubes the electrons emitted from the cathode flow outward in all directions to the surrounding cylindrical metal plate or anode. However, in the cathode-ray tube shown in Fig. 33-29, the emitted electrons are compressed into a wire-like stream or beam that normally is aimed at the center of a fluorescent screen on the inside of the tube face. This screen glows wherever the electron beam hits it.

Starting from the left in Fig. 33-29,

the heater provides the heat that makes the cathode emit electrons. The control grid determines the number of electrons that get into the beam. A highly negative voltage on the grid cuts off the electron beam entirely as required for black portions of a television picture, while a less negative grid voltage lets electrons go out into the beam to produce the bright spots of a picture. The focusing anode works together with the small hole in the control grid to focus the electrons to a small point at the screen. The accelerating anode requires a high voltage, often over 10,000 volts for tele-

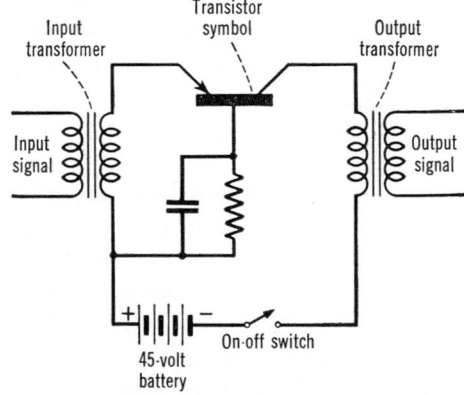

Fig. 33-28. Transistor amplifier circuit.

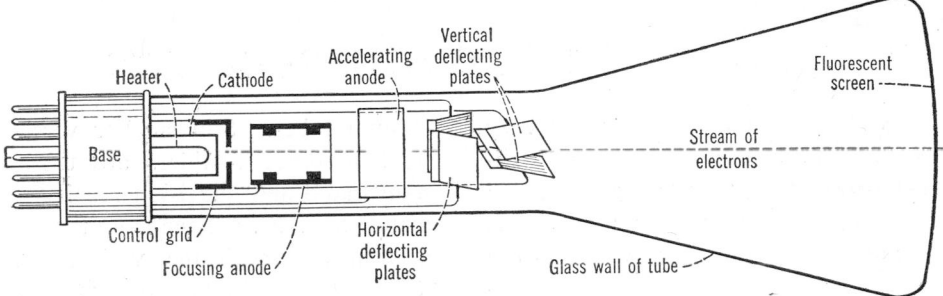

Fig. 33-29. The construction of a cathode-ray tube having electrostatic deflecting plates.

vision picture tubes, to give the electrons in the beam enough speed to produce the desired bright spot on the screen.   Together, the electrodes that have just been described are called the *electron gun*.

Outside the electron gun in the tube shown in Fig. 33-29 are two pairs of *deflecting plates*.   When voltages are applied to these, the electron beam is bent, or deflected.   Thus, with an alternating voltage applied to the plates that are above and below the beam, the electrons are alternately deflected upward and downward to form a vertical bright line on the screen.   Alternating voltage which is applied to the other two plates will form a horizontal line.

24. What are cathode-ray tubes used for?   In cathode-ray oscilloscopes, a special alternating voltage is applied to the horizontal deflecting plates of the cathode-ray tube to sweep the beam back and forth horizontally. A voltage to be studied can be applied to the vertical plates.   The result is that the wave form of the voltage is traced on the screen, as is shown in Fig. 33-30.

As you learned earlier, an electron beam can be deflected by a magnetic field as well as by an electrostatic field. Practically all television picture tubes in use today use magnetic fields to deflect the beam.   These fields are produced by coils surrounding the neck of the tube, there being no deflecting plates inside.   Another coil, used alone or in conjunction with a permanent magnet, serves to aid the internal anode in focusing the electron beam so as to give a clear picture on the screen. You will learn more about picture tubes when you study about television in Chapter 34.

Fig. 33-30. A cathode-ray oscilloscope showing wave-form patterns on the screen. The lower pattern is of an alternating voltage. The upper pattern shows the voltage after passing through a rectifier.

2. INDUSTRIAL ELECTRONICS — X RAYS

25. What is the most efficient way to convert alternating current to direct current? In many industries, one of the most important uses for tubes is in converting alternating current to the direct current required for electrochemical plants, aluminum refining plants and magnesium production. For this work, special metal-envelope tubes called *ignitrons* (ig-*ny*-tronz) are used. These use a pool of mercury as a cathode, which you see shown in Fig. 33-31. An ignitron has no filament or heater. Instead, conduction is started by applying a voltage between a small igniter electrode and the mercury pool to get a spark that starts the ionization process. Industrial ignitrons look more like metal tanks than tubes, as shown in Fig. 33-32.

The D.C. voltage required for operating radio stations and industrial electronic equipment generally is obtained from diodes, as in Fig. 33-33. These may be either gas-filled or high-vacuum tubes. Still smaller versions of these diode rectifiers are used in many radio and television receivers to change the A.C. voltage from the power transformer to the various D.C. voltages required by the other tubes.

★ **26. How motors can be controlled with tubes.** Special industrial gas-filled triode tubes called *thyratrons* (*thy*-ruh-tronz) are used to furnish the current for a D.C. motor when instant control of forward and reverse speeds is required. This arrangement, shown in Fig. 33-34, permits operating the D.C. motor from an A.C. power line. It provides the high-starting torque advantages of D.C. motors in plants not having D.C. power. Speed may be changed at any time merely by turning a small, conveniently located knob.

The thyratrons used for motor control serve first of all as rectifiers, to convert the A.C. voltages of the power transformers to the direct current re-

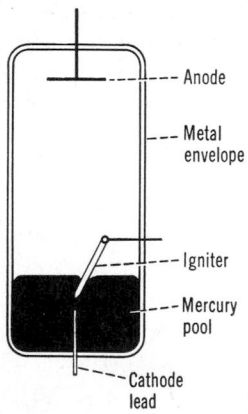

Fig. 33-31. The construction of an ignitron.

Fig. 33-32. An installation of ignitron rectifiers used to furnish direct current for the production of aluminum.

Fig. 33-33. Diode rectifiers that change A.C. to D.C. for a radio transmitter.

quired by the armature and field of the motor. But because of the grid in each, thyratrons are more than rectifier tubes. The amount of current passed by a thyratron during its half-cycle or alternation of conduction is controlled entirely by the grid, but not in the same way as in vacuum triodes. Once a thyratron starts passing current, the grid loses control because the gas in the tube becomes ionized and furnishes its own electrons. What we do is use the grid to delay the starting or firing of the tube during the conducting alternation, by applying a high negative bias through the electronic control circuits. If we delay firing until half of the alternation has passed, the motor gets only half as much cur-

rent and it slows down accordingly. Turning the speed-control knob changes the time in each cycle when the negative bias is removed from the grid, thereby changing the speed. Pushing the stop button makes all grids highly negative, cutting off both armature and field current, and thereby stopping the motor.

27. How to heat without heat by electronics. There are two ways of using radio-frequency energy to heat an object from within and yet not touch the object.

One way is by dielectric heating, which works only for dielectric materials like wood, textiles, plastics, and anything else that does not conduct electricity. The other way is by induction heating, which works only on metals.

Dielectric heating requires only a pair of metal plates to transfer radio-frequency energy from an electronic generator to the object being heated. These plates, also called electrodes, are connected by wires to the generator, which is much like a radio transmitter. Instead of feeding the radio-frequency power to an antenna, however, it is applied to the metal plates, as in Fig. 33-35, in order to form an intensely strong alternating electric field. When any nonmetallic material is placed between the plates, its molecules are pulled back and forth so rapidly that friction between them produces the desired heat.

Industrial and commercial uses for dielectric heating include setting glue

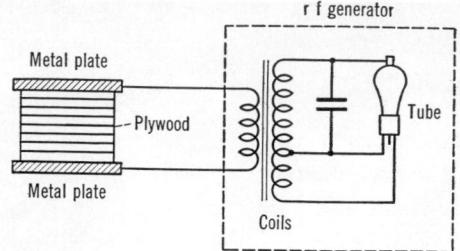

Fig. 33-35. A simplified diagram of dielectric heating. The power source for the tube is not shown.

in furniture and in plywood products, preheating plastic powders before they go into molding presses, defrosting frozen foods quickly, sterilizing grains and packaged foods, dehydrating food, curing rubber, and drying textiles.

In electronic *induction heating*, the same radio transmitter is used. Instead of the metal plates, however, a coil consisting of a few turns of copper tubing transfers the r-f energy to any metallic object placed inside its turns. Electrical induction then causes the object to heat rapidly by creating electric currents that flow in circular paths inside the object and make it red hot. Water usually is pumped through the tubing to keep the tubing cool during operation, because the high current circulating through it otherwise would melt the coil.

Induction heating has become popular for heat-treating of metals because it can heat the region to be hardened without affecting the rest of a metal object. Thus it can heat the surface of a shaft, the teeth of a gear (Fig. 33-36), or the inside of a ring-shaped object. It even can heat metal parts inside glass enclosures without softening the glass, because the r-f energy goes right through the glass.

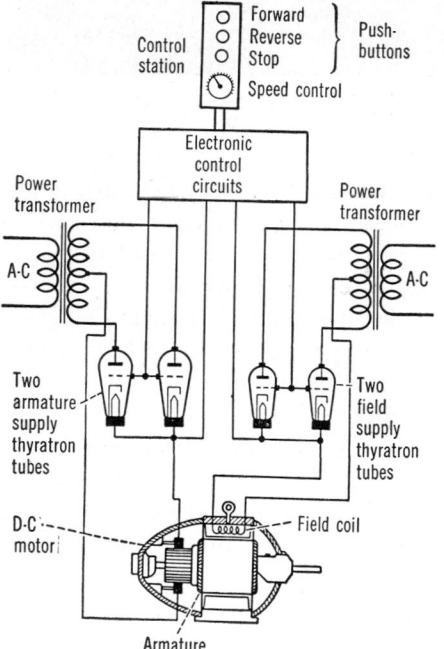

Fig. 33-34. A circuit used to operate a D.C. motor from an A.C. line and to control its speed electronically.

28. Photoelectric applications in industry. As you already learned, the phototube is simply a two-electrode tube like that used by Fleming, with a light-sensitive cathode taking the place of the filament. Light shining on the cathode causes emission of electrons from its coating of cesium, and these electrons flow through the evacuated space within the tube to the metal rod or ring that serves as the anode. When a battery is connected into the circuit, as in Fig. 33-37, to make the anode positive with respect to the cathode, emitted electrons are attracted to the anode and an output current results that is proportional to the light. A phototube thus acts like a switch that turns on an electric circuit when light is shining, and turns off the current flow when the tube is dark. The greater the intensity of the light, the greater is the current passed by the tube, up to its maximum. One or more amplifier tubes must be used to build up the current sufficiently in strength to cause operation of a relay that turns on or off the machine being controlled.

Sorting is one major industrial job for phototubes. Here a beam of light is directed on the product being examined, and the phototube is positioned to pick up the reflected light, which varies with the color and nature of the surface of the product. The control can be designed either to open or close a switch when the light is reduced or interrupted. In sorting beans, a good, white bean reflects maximum light and is allowed to pass while a dark, inferior bean reduces the light enough to operate a relay that causes an electric solenoid device to flip the bean into a discard bin.

Accident prevention is another pho-

Fig. 33-36. The teeth of this gear are being heated by electronic induction. Then they will be quickly cooled with water to increase their hardness.

toelectric control job. In the application shown in Fig. 33-38 a light source directs a beam of light across the front of the punch press to the phototube. The hammer of the press cannot drop down to punch a hole in the sheet metal while the operator's hands block the light beam. When his hands are drawn safely back out of the danger area, the press can operate.

Another type of photoelectric device in everyday use is the photovoltaic

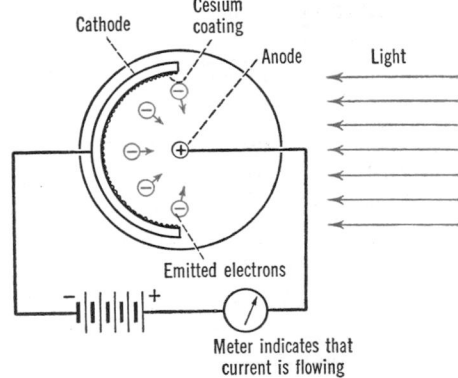

Fig. 33-37. A simple phototube circuit showing how light energy is converted into an electric current.

Fig. 33-38. When the operator's hand is in the path of the light beam, the phototube and its associated controls keep the press from descending.

cell, also called a photocell. This is used in photographic exposure meters. It can generate enough current of its own to operate the meter when light falls on the light-sensitive surface, hence no outside voltage source is needed. In one form, the photovoltaic cell is simply a sheet of copper covered with a thin layer of copper oxide that in turn is covered with a thin, semi-transparent layer of silver. See Fig. 33-39. When light shines on this sandwich, electrons flow from the copper oxide to the copper and then through the circuit that is completed by the indicating meter.

29. What are X rays? Tubes in which X rays are produced differ little from the tubes already studied. If a tungsten or platinum disc is placed in

a cathode-ray tube in such a position that the electron beam is concentrated on it, a different type of invisible radiation is produced, as indicated in Fig. 33-40. These radiations are called X rays, or they sometimes are called Roentgen (*rent*-gen) rays in honor of their discoverer. X rays are produced when high-speed electrons strike a solid, as in the more modern type of X-ray tube shown in Fig. 33-41.

X rays *are a type of electromagnetic radiation,* like light and radio waves. The only difference is in their wave length. They have many properties similar to light.

(1) X *rays are invisible.* Since the eye is sensitive only to the electromagnetic radiation we call light, other types of electromagnetic radiation of different wave length are invisible. The wave length of X rays is less than one thousandth of the length of the shortest waves of visible light.

(2) X *rays move in straight lines.* This property, together with the property of affecting photographic plates, makes it possible to take pictures using X rays.

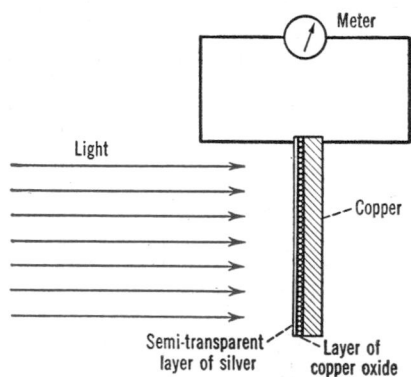

Fig. 33-39. The operating principle of a photovoltaic cell.

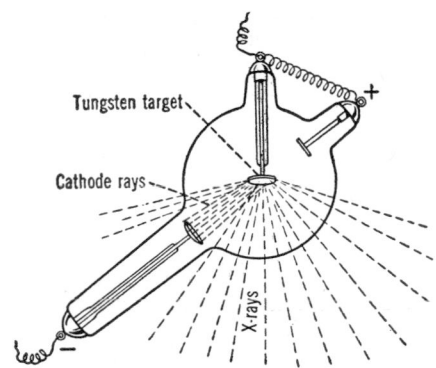

Fig. 33-40. The construction used in early X-ray tubes.

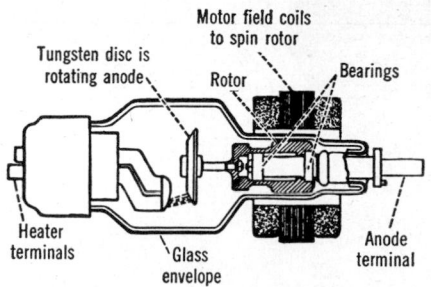

Fig. 33-41. A modern rotating-anode X-ray tube. The motor coils are outside the glass tube, and the armature is inside. The magnetic field acts through the glass to turn the armature, which keeps a cool part of the target disc in front of the beam at all times.

(3) X *rays are not affected by magnetic or electrical fields.* This shows that X rays are not charged particles.

(4) X *rays may be reflected, refracted, and polarized* by using suitable materials, such as mirrors, lenses, and polarizers.

(5) X *rays move with the velocity of light.* This is true of all electromagnetic radiations, and is the one property which characterizes them all.

(6) X *rays affect photographic plates.* X rays react with the sensitive emulsion of a photographic plate in much the same way that light does.

(7) X *rays can produce fluorescence and phosphorescence.* This property makes possible the fluoroscope and the new, portable X-ray cameras. The greater the intensity of the X rays striking the sensitive screen, the more brilliant the fluorescence.

(8) X *rays are differentially absorbed by matter.* Materials composed of light elements, such as hydrogen, carbon, oxygen, and nitrogen, are easily penetrated by X rays. Materials composed of heavier elements, such as iron, calcium, and potassium, are less readily penetrated. Consequently, when X rays are passed through a person's body in taking an X-ray photograph, the bones appear light against a darker, shadowy background, as shown in Fig. 33-42.

(9) X *rays are able to stimulate or kill living matter.* X rays are used in the treatment of cancer, since they have a greater tendency to kill the diseased tissue than the healthy tissue.

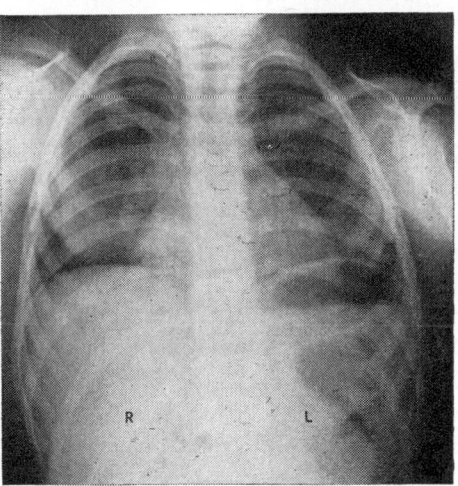

Fig. 33-42. An X-ray photograph of a human chest. The letters mark the left and right sides as you see them from the front.

Fig. 33-43. Chest X-ray machine using 4″ × 5″ film to reduce costs in mass chest examinations.

(10) X *rays produce spectra.* Just as substances give off characteristic visible light when burned or heated, forming the visible spectrum, they also give off X-ray spectra when bombarded with cathode rays. These spectra can be detected by photographic plates. They are characteristic of the material used.

30. Medical and industrial uses for X rays. With an X-ray fluoroscope, a physician can watch the action of the internal organs. He can see internal structure immediately without waiting for films to be developed. The fluoroscope uses a screen coated with a material like platinum-barium cyanide, which is sensitive to the fluorescent effects of the X rays. If one holds his hand between the fluoroscope screen and an X-ray tube, the bones of the hand can be clearly distinguished.

X-ray photographs can be taken for more extensive study than is possible with the fluoroscope. Sometimes these are direct shadow photographs, taken full size. More often, today, they are small pictures of a fluoroscope image using equipment like that in Fig. 33-43.

X rays are being used more and more frequently by industry to detect the presence of imperfections in forgings and castings, which could not otherwise be examined internally. Equipment like that in Fig. 33-44 is used. Fig. 33-45 gives an example of the kind of internal flaw that can be detected.

31. How an electron microscope shows things too small to see otherwise. The electron microscope is another application of thermionic emission of electrons. The source of electrons is a heated cathode in an electron gun, located at the top of a long, evacuated metal tube and aimed downward, as in Fig. 33-46. The electrons are accelerated downward to pass through the object being examined. The electrons then are deflected or spread out by the electromagnetic coils shown to form an enlarged image of the object on the fluorescent screen or photographic plate at the bottom of the microscope. The dotted lines in the figure show how the electron paths are deflected, much as a lens refracts light rays, to form the image. In industrial and medical research, the electron microscope goes far beyond the powers of optical microscopes. It is used to make visible the crystalline structure of metals and the shapes of particles as fine as talcum powder or dust. In medicine, it has revealed bacteria and viruses never before seen.

32. How does a radio compass work? A portable radio with a loop antenna has directional qualities. If you rotate the set until a signal is loudest and then sight along the loop, you will be looking directly at or directly

Fig. 33-44. Positioning an engine block for X-ray with a 1,000,000-volt X-ray machine.

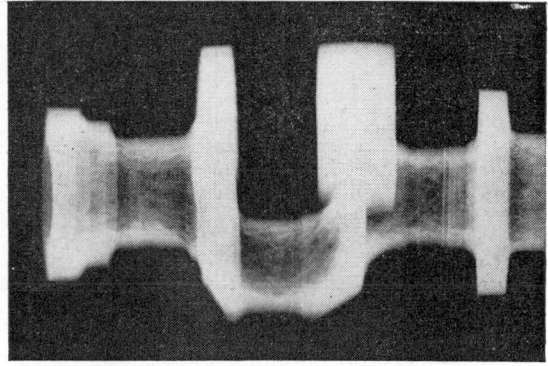

Fig. 33-45. An X-ray photograph shows that the metal has run out of this casting of a crankshaft, leaving it hollow.

away from the radio station. This is the same principle used in the modern radio compass.

Radio compasses are maintained at stations along the coast by the United States Navy Department to help ships determine their position. A message from the ship may be picked up by three or four of these shore stations. Each station measures the angle at which the ship's radio message arrives. From the positions of the stations, the distances between them, and the angles of the arriving signals at each, the location of the ship can be calculated by the master shore station, and broadcast back to the ship.

33. How is radar used? Radio waves are reflected from various solid materials much as light waves are. The idea of radar as a detector and locator of distant objects arose from this

fact. The word *radar* comes from the words *ra*dio *d*etection *a*nd *r*anging. The radar instrument contains the following elements: (1) a microwave transmitter which is turned alternately on and off almost instantaneously, sending out a radio wave which strikes any object in its path and then is re-

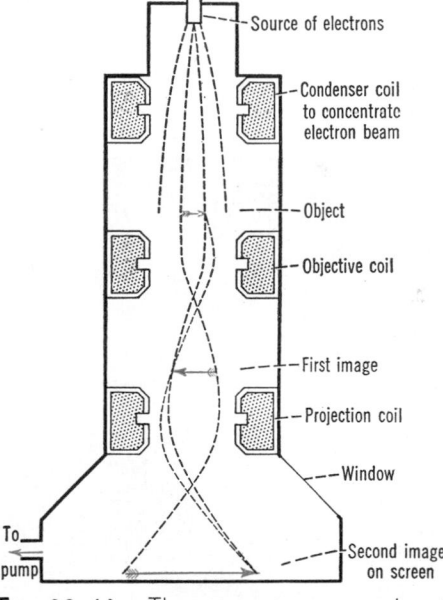

Fig. 33-46. The operating principle of the electron microscope.

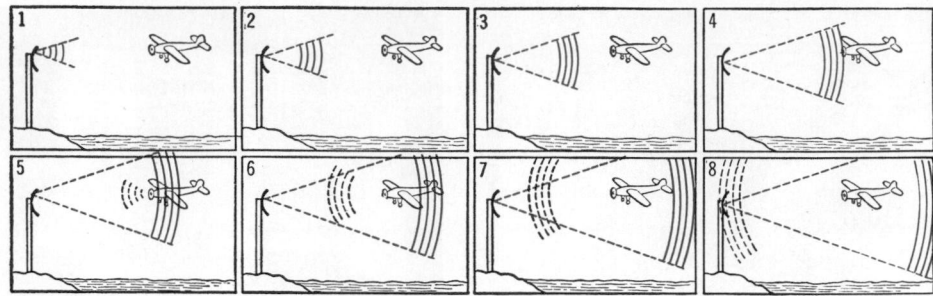

Fig. 33-47. Steps in detecting an approaching airplane by radar.

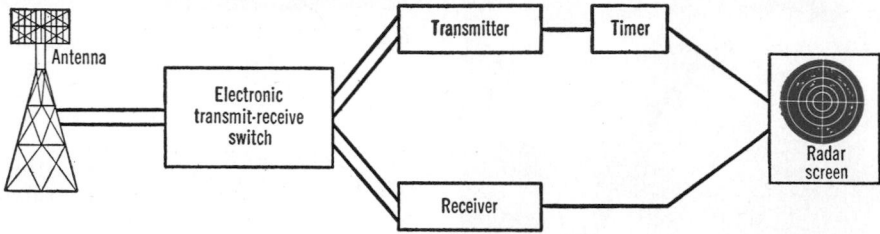

Fig. 33-48. A block diagram of a radar system.

flected back in a few millionths of a second; (2) a receiver which receives the reflected wave and measures the time it takes the wave to travel to and from the object; and (3) the antenna used for both transmitting and receiv-

Fig. 33-49. Pattern on a radar screen as a ship goes around a bend of a river.

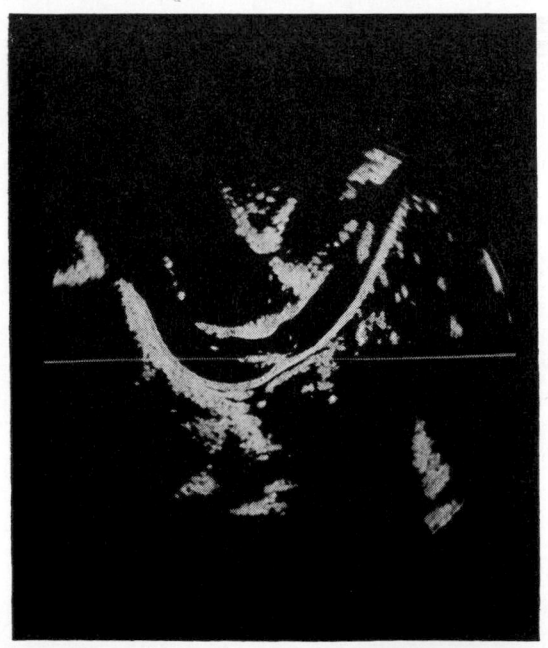

ing. The antenna is rotatable. It sends and receives waves only in the direction in which it is pointed. By knowing the direction in which the antenna is pointed, and the range, or distance which is measured by the receiver, it is possible to determine the accurate position of object or target.

In modern radar installations the reflected radio waves trace a picture of the objects sighted on the cathode-ray tube. Such a type of radar is especially important in finding targets when flying over clouds or at night. Radar is used widely as an aid to marine navigation under conditions of poor visibility because the radio waves are not disturbed by darkness, fog, or clouds. The pilot aboard the ship watches a radar screen and sees a pattern like that in Fig. 33-49. Radar installations at airports are used to guide pilots onto the runway when the limited visibility does not permit other types of landing.

Summary

Electrons can be produced by thermionic emission from heated filaments, by electrostatic attraction, by ionization of a gas, and by photoelectric emission when light strikes sensitive metallic coatings. Applications of these phenomena are neon signs, fluorescent tubes, the Tungar rectifier, cathode-ray oscilloscopes, the electron microscope, and photoelectric cells.

Electronic tubes containing a cathode, a plate, and a grid are called triodes. Slight variations in the grid voltage control the flow of electrons through the tube from the cathode to the plate. Triodes may be used as amplifiers, detectors, or oscillators. Crystal oscillators maintain a more constant frequency, however.

Electronic tubes are used throughout industry for converting alternating current to direct current, for electronic heating, and in many other ways.

Transistors are tiny crystals of semiconducting material which amplify like tubes do. They are particularly useful where small size, light weight, and compactness are important.

X rays are high energy electromagnetic radiations produced when high speed electrons strike a solid. They have important physiological effects which make them useful in medicine, and they are used in industry also.

Terms to Define...

Amplification	Fluorescent lamps	Proximity fuze
Cathode	Grid	Radar
Cathode-ray tube	Grid bias	Radio compass
Detection	Ignitron	Rectification
Dielectric heating	Induction heating	Thermionic emission
Diode	Neon sign	Thyratron
Edison effect	Oscillation	Transistor
Electromagnetic field	Photoelectric effect	Triode
Electron microscope	Phototube	Tungar rectifier
Electrostatic field	Plate	X rays

Questions

GROUP A

1. What is the "Edison effect"?
2. What use did Fleming find for the "Edison effect"?

3. Describe four ways in which electrons may be emitted. Give a practical example of each method of emission.
4. How is light produced in a neon sign?
5. How is light produced by a fluorescent lamp?
6. How are electrons controlled by an electrostatic field? By a magnetic field?
7. What is the purpose of a grid in a vacuum tube? How does it function when a tube is used as an amplifier? How does it function when the tube is used as a detector?

8. What is the advantage of a crystal oscillator over other types of oscillators?

9. What are the two main types of transistors? How do they operate?

10. Describe two types of electronic tubes which efficiently convert alternating current to direct current.

11. How are dielectric heating and induction heating used by industry?

12. List several applications of the use of phototubes.

13. For what purposes are X rays used today?

14. How is an electron microscope superior to an optical microscope?

15. How does radar aid in airplane navigation during cloudy and stormy weather?

GROUP B

16. A horizontal beam of electrons enters a magnetic field from the east. If the magnetic lines run horizontally from south to north, in which direction is the beam of electrons deflected?

17. What are the principal parts of a cathode-ray tube? What is the function of each part?

18. Explain the operation of a phototube.

19. What are the properties of X rays? What are some of the effects they can produce?

20. What is the function of the starter in a fluorescent lamp circuit? Why is a condenser included in a fluorescent lamp circuit?

21. Draw a circuit diagram and explain how a Tungar rectifier may be used to charge a storage battery.

★ **22.** What is a directly heated cathode? An indirectly heated cathode?

★ **23.** What is grid bias? How does it affect the operation of a triode tube?

★ **24.** What is the function of a screen grid in a tetrode? What is the function of the suppressor grid in a pentode?

★ **25.** Explain how a thyratron tube can be used to control the speed of a D.C. motor.

Things to Do

1. Visit your local hospital and have a technician show you and explain the operation of the X-ray equipment. If this is not possible, a local dentist or physician having X-ray equipment may let you see his installation.

2. Examine some worn-out radio tubes and observe their construction. Identify the cathode, plate, and various grids.

3. Set up and demonstrate to the class the circuit required for the operation of a neon tube and a fluorescent lamp.

4. A member of the class may be able to bring in some transistors. Ask him to explain their use.

5. The entrance doors to some stores are controlled by phototube installations. Ask the manager to show you the various parts of such an installation.

6. Visit the physics laboratories of a nearby college or university and see their X-ray equipment, electron microscope, cathode-ray oscilloscopes, and so on.

Chapter 34
Radio and Television

1. Broadcasting for entertainment. When radio or television signals are sent out in many directions from a transmitter for reception on home radio sets, we call it *broadcasting*. The other type of radio is *point-to-point communication,* where a message is placed on the air for reception by one or a limited number of persons.

The three distinct types of radio broadcasting in use today are regular *amplitude-modulation broadcasting* or *AM, frequency-modulation broadcasting* or *FM,* and *television broadcasting* or *TV.* Each has its own band of frequencies in the radio spectrum, as shown in Fig. 34-1.

2. What are kilocycles and megacycles? It is awkward to write strings of zeros after numbers as we go up in frequency. We therefore use two larger units in place of cycles.

Kilocycles means thousands of cycles. Kilocycles is abbreviated as kc.

One kilocycle is equal to 1,000 cycles. The standard AM broadcast band extends from 550,000 cycles to 1,600,000 cycles, but for convenience we express this as 550 kc to 1,600 kc. *Megacycles (meg-uh-sy-kuls)* are abbreviated as mc. One megacycle is equal to 1,000,000 cycles. Also, one megacycle is equal to 1,000 kilocycles. The FM band goes from 88,000 kilocycles to 108,000 kilocycles, which is more easily stated as 88 mc to 108 mc. Television broadcasting is done on three bands. Two of these bands, 54 mc to 88 mc and 174 mc to 216 mc, are on both sides of the FM band. These are called the vhf (very high frequency) bands. The third television band, from 470 mc to 890 mc, is called the uhf (ultra high frequency) television band. A total of 82 channels or frequency bands is used for television broadcasting. Each station is allowed to occupy a 6-megacycle

Vocabulary

AMPLITUDE MODULATION, AM. The method of broadcasting in which the strength or amplitude of the carrier signal is changed by combining it with an audio signal.

ANTENNA. A device which changes a radio wave into an alternating electric current.

CARRIER SIGNAL. The radio-frequency signal needed to carry an audio signal through space.

DETECTOR. A tube or crystal which separates the audio signal from an amplitude-modulated carrier signal.

DISCRIMINATOR. A tube which separates the audio signal from a frequency-modulated carrier signal.

FREQUENCY MODULATION, FM. The method of broadcasting in which the frequency of the carrier signal is changed by combining it with an audio signal.

IMAGE ORTHICON. A TV camera tube.

LOUDSPEAKER. Device for changing variations in electric current to sound waves.

MICROPHONE. A device for changing sound waves into variations in an electric current.

Frequency values in cycles, kilocycles and megacycles

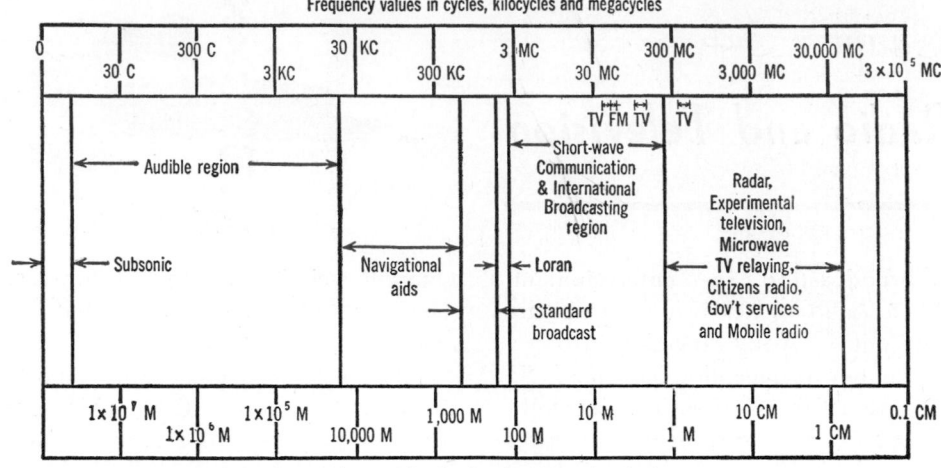

Fig. 34-1. The lower end of the electromagnetic spectrum, showing audio frequencies and the frequencies used for radio, television, and radar.

channel. Thus a station on channel 2 has a " width " in frequency of 6 mc, from 54 to 60 mc.

3. Changing frequencies to wave lengths. The mathematical relationship between frequency and wave length is the same for radio waves as for sound, except that for radio waves you use the speed of light, which is about 300,000,000 meters per second. The formula, you will recall is

$$v = f\lambda, \text{ or } f = \frac{v}{\lambda}, \text{ or } \lambda = \frac{v}{f},$$

where v is the speed of the wave in meters per second, f is the frequency in cycles per second, and λ is the wave length in meters.

4. The AM broadcasting system. The major units of an AM broadcasting system are shown in Fig. 34-2. When someone speaks before the microphone in the studio, or when an orchestra plays, sound waves are produced.

A microphone works very much like one of our own ears. It has the same membrane or diaphragm that vibrates back and forth when a sound wave hits it. Instead of nerves, however, a microphone has an electrical unit that changes movements of the diaphragm into a corresponding electrical signal.

The unit inside the microphone may be a crystal, a coil moving between the ends of a permanent magnet, or simply a corrugated metal ribbon moving between the poles of a permanent magnet. All types of **microphones** produce the same result — they *change the sound waves into the electrical equivalent of sound, an alternating current known as an audio signal.*

5. What the audio amplifier does. The audio signals coming from a microphone need to be strengthened thousands of times before they can be sent through miles of wires to the transmitter outside the city. This electrical strengthening process, called *amplification,* is done with radio tubes and radio parts in an *audio amplifier* located in the control room next to the studio. There the control operator watches a meter that shows the strength of the audio signals. He adjusts a volume control from time to time to keep the signal strength nearly constant, even though the singer or speaker in the studio moves around a lot.

6. How an AM transmitter works. From the control room the strengthened audio signal travels over private wires to the transmitter building.

At the transmitter, the audio signal is boosted in strength some more by an amplifier that is called the *modulator,* as indicated in Fig. 34-3. From here *the signal is combined with the special radio-frequency signal needed to carry it through space.* This signal is known as the **carrier signal,** and has the frequency that was assigned to the station in the United States by the Federal Communications Commission.

7. Why a carrier frequency is needed. An audio signal, no matter how strong, would not travel more than a few hundred feet through space if fed to an antenna. The audio signal must be combined with a higher frequency signal that is capable of traveling great distances through space.

The high frequency signal is known as the carrier signal because it *carries* the audio signal through space. The carrier signal is generated by a crystal oscillator and fed to a buffer amplifier that builds up its strength or power. Next, both audio signal and carrier signal are fed into the same final r.f. (radio frequency) amplifier tube and

Fig. 34-2. The illustration on the right shows you the complete AM broadcasting system, from microphone to loudspeaker.

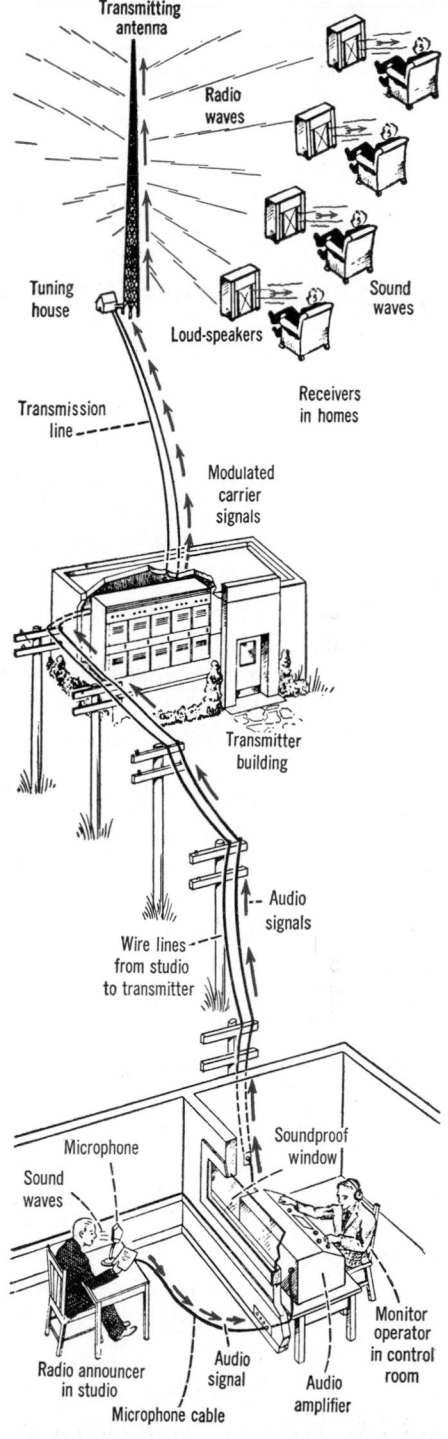

Transmitting antenna

Radio waves

Tuning house

Sound waves

Loud-speakers

Transmission line

Receivers in homes

Modulated carrier signals

Transmitter building

Audio signals

Wire lines from studio to transmitter

Microphone

Soundproof window

Sound waves

Monitor operator in control room

Radio announcer in studio

Audio signal

Audio amplifier

Microphone cable

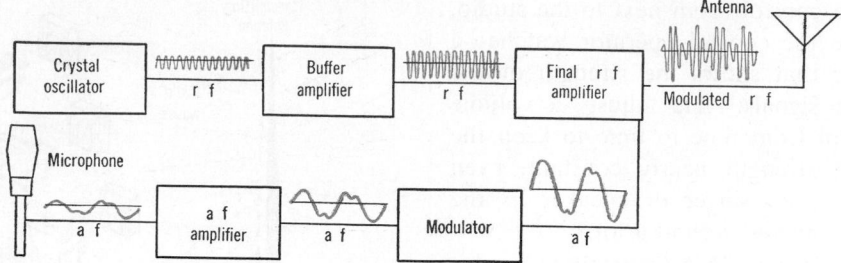

Fig. 34-3. Steps in producing an r.f. carrier signal and combining it with the amplified a.f. signal to produce the modulated r.f. output signal that is put on the air by the antenna of an AM broadcast transmitter.

combined. The result is known as the *modulated r.f. carrier signal.*

8. Getting the signal on the air. The modulated carrier signal coming out of the transmitter building is still an alternating electric current, so it travels through wires to the transmitting antenna. These wires can be one inside the other to give what is known as a coaxial cable. Occasionally the two wires are side by side, forming a transmission line.

Many different kinds of antenna towers are used by AM broadcast stations. The height of the tower for an AM station is chosen to match the frequency assigned to the station. The higher the assigned frequency the shorter is the tower needed.

9. Producing radio waves. The purpose of the transmitting antenna

tower is to send radio signals into space so they can be picked up by listeners for miles around. These radio waves travel with the speed of light (186,000 miles per second). Some radio waves travel away from the tower parallel to the ground, as from *A* to *E* in Fig. 34-4. These are called *ground waves,* and provide the most reliable source of waves for listening. They get weaker as they get farther away from the station. The higher the power of the station, the farther away its ground waves can be picked up by receiving antennas. However, fifty miles is about the farthest for reliable year-round day-and-night reception of ground waves from any AM broadcast station.

Radio waves also travel upward into the sky from a transmitting tower.

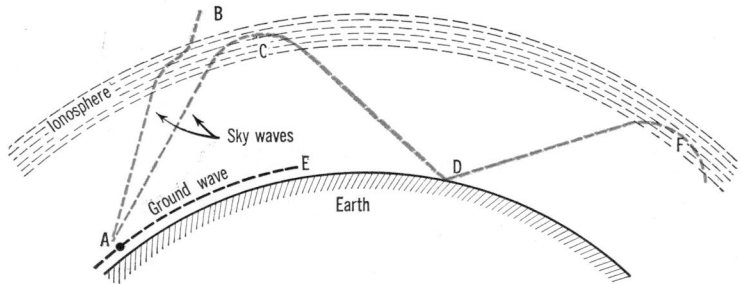

Fig. 34-4. How radio waves travel as ground and sky waves.

These are known as *sky waves*. In the daytime most AM sky waves keep right on going into space, as from *A* to *B* in Fig. 34-4, and are never heard from again. At night, however, the sky waves are bent and reflected back to earth along the path from *A* to *C* to *D* by an invisible, ionized layer of particles somewhere between 50 and 200 miles up. The radio waves may be reflected earthward hundreds, or even thousands, of miles away from the station. This is why you can hear more distant stations at night.

The reflecting layers in the sky are called *ionosphere layers*. They are formed when ultraviolet rays of the sun hit the upper layers of air in our atmosphere. These ultraviolet rays electrify or ionize the air particles. Such particles have the ability to bend radio waves back to earth.

10. Skip distance. The ionosphere layers and the earth both act like mirrors for radio waves. A sky wave from a transmitting station strikes an ionosphere layer, reflects back to the earth, and bounces off the earth up into the sky again, as from *D* to *F* in Fig. 34-4. It can be reflected several more times between sky and earth like this before the energy in the radio waves has died out. This process enables radio waves to travel halfway around the earth, or even farther.

Reception of a particular station will be good at all areas where its sky wave is hitting the earth, but poor in between these points. The distance between points of good reception is called the *skip distance*. Since the ionosphere layers move up and down from hour to hour as the action of the sun changes, the skip distance changes also from hour to hour.

11. Causes of fading. Often the program of a distant station fades in and out every minute or so. This occurs because the ionosphere layers shift up or down slightly about once a minute. If you happen to be near the region where the sky wave comes back to earth, the wave may hit your antenna one minute and pass right over it the next minute. In other words, during fading the sky wave can be sweeping back and forth across your antenna.

Fading also occurs whenever both the ground wave and sky wave of a station are bringing the program to a receiver. The ground wave travels over the shortest path, but the sky wave goes 70 miles or more up and then back again to reach the receiving antenna. The sky wave thus travels farther. Since travelling takes time even when at the speed of light, the sky wave arrives just a little later than the ground wave. Technically, we say that the two waves are out of phase. They then either help each other or partly cancel each other, depending on how much they are out of phase.

12. Types of AM receiving antennas. No matter what a receiving **antenna** looks like, it has just one job. That is, *to change the radio wave back into an alternating electric current.* This *carrier signal current* is exactly like that which flowed up the transmitting antenna tower, though much weaker. Receivers build up the strength of this weak signal current, then remove the audio signal from the carrier and change it back to sound.

Most AM broadcast sets today have built-in loop antennas. In table model receivers, this loop usually is wound or mounted on a sheet of cardboard

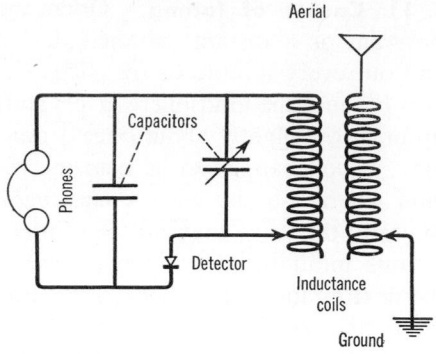

Fig. 34-5. The crystal receiver shows how a coil and a condenser are used together to tune in a desired station.

that serves as the back for the cabinet. In large floor model sets, the loop is made larger and mounted separately.

A loop antenna has directional qualities. This means that currents produced in it by a particular station are strongest when the loop is lined up with that station. Signal currents are weakest when the loop is at right angles to the path of the radio waves from that station.

The directional action of a loop antenna is most noticeable in battery-powered portable sets. Here the entire set has to be rotated for maximum volume. If this directional effect is not very pronounced in your set with a built-in antenna, the set may contain a new type of ferrite (iron powder) coil instead of a loop as the antenna.

13. What is the simplest radio receiver? The crystal receiver circuit shown in Fig. 34-5 uses no tubes and has only a few parts, hence makes a good starting point for studying receivers. It has an *antenna,* or *aerial,* for picking up radio waves. It has coils and a *variable condenser* for tuning. *It has a crystal* **detector** *for removing the audio signal from the carrier.* Finally, it has headphones for changing the audio signal back into sound.

Crystal sets need a strong signal current. This means that they usually require a long outdoor antenna.

14. The trf receiver. Another radio set that once was popular but today is disappearing is the tuned radio frequency set, usually abbreviated trf. The general arrangement of this set is shown in Fig. 34-6.

The trf set may use a diode or other tube to separate the audio signal from the carrier signal. Such a tube is called the *detector* because it does exactly the same job as a crystal detector. If you connect headphones to the detector tube in any set, you will hear programs just as in a crystal set.

15. Why tuning circuits are needed. If the antenna were connected directly to the detector, all the signal currents in the antenna would reach the detector. You would hear all the programs at once, because each station in your

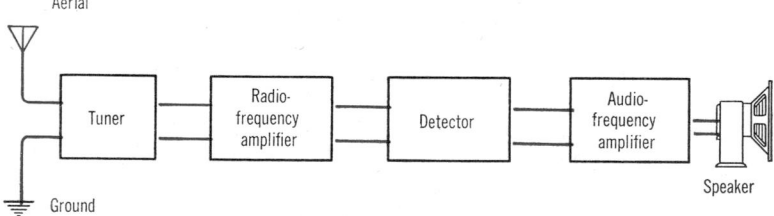

Fig. 34-6. The two amplifiers in the diagram are needed to produce sufficient signal strength in the trf receiver.

vicinity produces its own carrier signal current in your receiving antenna.

Tuning circuits are necessary to block out undesired carrier signals. A coil and a variable condenser together serve quite well as a tuner. When fully open (plates not meshed), the variable condenser tunes or responds to the high-frequency end of the broadcast band. When fully closed (fully meshed), the condenser tunes to the low-frequency end.

16. What the r.f. amplifier does. To boost the strength of the weak signal coming from the antenna, a trf receiver uses *amplifier tubes.* These tubes are located in between the tuning circuits. Each combination of a tuning circuit and amplifier tube is called a *tuned radio frequency amplifier stage.* Together these stages form the radio-frequency amplifier, commonly called the *r.f. amplifier.*

The r.f. amplifier tubes boost the strength of the desired radio-frequency carrier signal. Its tuning circuits block out undesirable r.f. carrier signals.

The r.f. amplifier feeds a strong modulated r.f. signal (an r.f. carrier mixed with the audio signal) to the detector of the trf set. The detector stage separates these by throwing away the r.f. carrier and allowing only the audio signal to pass on.

17. What the audio amplifier does. The audio signal must be boosted in strength to operate a loudspeaker. This is done with more amplifier tubes that form the audio-frequency amplifier, abbreviated *a.f. amplifier.*

The a.f. or audio amplifier may have one or more stages. The first tube in the a.f. amplifier is called the first a.f. stage, and the last is called the a.f. *output stage* or *power stage.*

An output transformer is connected between the output stage and the loudspeaker. This transformer matches the output stage to the loudspeaker, so that we get maximum volume and clearest tone.

18. Changing audio signals to sound. The *loudspeaker* is nothing more than the reverse of a microphone. A microphone produces an audio signal current when sound waves make its diaphragm move back and forth. A **loudspeaker,** on the other hand, *moves its diaphragm back and forth to produce sound waves when an audio signal is fed into it.* We thus get back the original sounds produced in the studio.

Two types of loudspeakers are in everyday use. They operate on the same principle, and differ only in the way the magnetic field is produced. One uses a permanent magnet. The other, as shown in Fig. 34-7, uses an electromagnet energized by direct current obtained from the D.C. power supply of the receiver. In both types the moving element is a small coil called the voice coil. It is attached to the center of a cone-shaped diaphragm having a flexible rim. Because it is positioned in the air gap of the magnetic field, this coil moves in and out alternately when the a.f. output signal of the receiver is sent through it, causing the diaphragm to move in and out correspondingly and to produce the desired sound waves.

19. Getting the right voltages for tubes. In the early days of radio, batteries provided the voltages required to operate the tubes. When engineers learned how to make radio sets operate directly from power lines, batteries for this use disappeared.

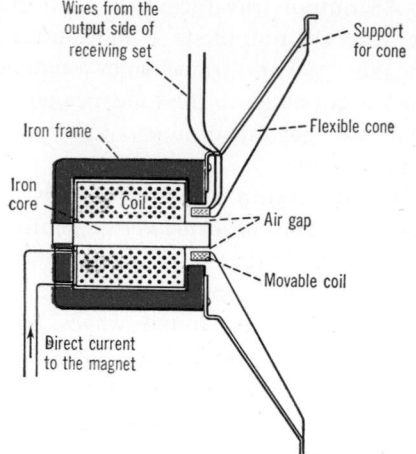

Fig. 34-7. In an electrodynamic loud-speaker, the a.f. current passes through the movable coil attached to the cone.

Most radio receivers in homes operate from the 115-volt A.C. power line. Power packs are built directly into the receivers for changing the A.C. line voltage to higher and lower values. The power pack also changes the A.C. voltage to the different D.C. voltages needed by the tubes.

20. How does a superheterodyne receiver work? Practically all AM sets in use today are *superheterodyne receivers,* usually called superhets or supers. These use the arrangement shown in Fig. 34-8. The second detector, audio amplifier and loudspeaker are exactly the same for the trf set. Between the antenna and the second detector, however, is an entirely differ-

ent arrangement for boosting the strength of the modulated r.f. carrier signal.

The superhet has an r.f. oscillator that generates its own r.f. signal. The circuits are arranged in such a way that the frequency of this r.f. oscillator signal is always higher than the frequency of the radio station to which the receiver is tuned, for example, 455 kc higher. The first detector combines the desired incoming radio station with the oscillator signal to produce a new signal whose carrier frequency is 455 kc. This new frequency is called the *intermediate frequency* or *i.f. value.* It is modulated just like the signal received from the station.

21. What the i.f. amplifier does. Most of the amplification in a superhet is done in the i.f. amplifier after the carrier signal has been changed to 455 kc. A much better job of boosting signal strength can be done in an amplifier that is built to handle only one frequency value like this. Superhets are therefore more sensitive than trf sets. The second detector separates the audio signal from the i.f. carrier just as it did in the trf receiver. From here to the loudspeaker the circuits are the same in both types of receivers.

22. The FM broadcasting system. In recent years an entirely new system of radio broadcasting, called *frequency*

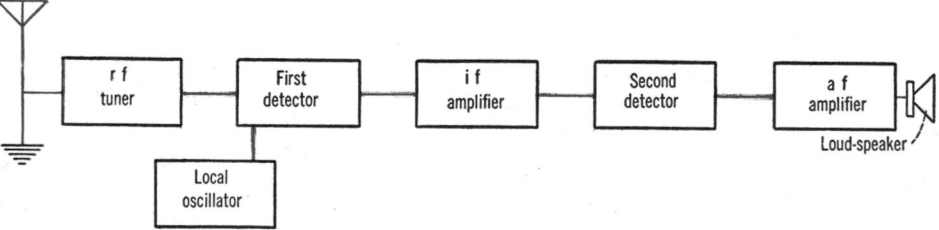

Fig. 34-8. Block diagram of an AM superheterodyne receiver.

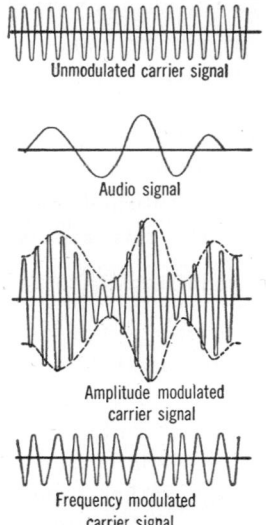

Unmodulated carrier signal

Audio signal

Amplitude modulated carrier signal

Frequency modulated carrier signal

Fig. 34-9. A comparison of AM and FM carrier signals having the same audio signal.

modulation, or simply FM, has been introduced.

The technical difference between FM and AM is shown by Fig. 34-9. *When the audio signal is combined with the carrier signal in an AM transmitter, the strength or amplitude of each carrier cycle is changed but the frequency is unchanged, giving an **amplitude-modulated** signal. In a **frequency modulation** or FM transmitter the opposite action takes place; the amplitude of the carrier is unchanged, but the frequency varies from instant to instant in accordance with the changes in the audio signal.*

Frequency-modulation broadcasting stations operate in the frequency band between 88 and 108 megacycles. This is a very much higher frequency than ordinary all-wave AM receivers tune to, so that special short antennas are needed for FM. Also, at these frequencies the sky waves usually go right on up through the ionosphere without bending back to earth. Only ground waves can be received, and therefore FM signals can not ordinarily be heard farther than about 50 miles from a station.

23. Why is FM broadcasting better? Within the service radius of an FM station, the signal obtained is almost entirely free from static. Also, the signal usually is better in fidelity (naturalness) than that of an AM station. An FM station can legally broadcast a much wider range of audio frequencies than AM broadcast stations are allowed to do. Of course, FM receivers must be better technically to take advantage of this higher fidelity.

24. The FM transmitter. Up to the point where the audio signal arrives at the transmitter building, FM and AM systems differ only in quality of equipment. Higher quality amplifiers and microphones are used in the FM studio to provide the higher fidelity program. Now let us see how FM really differs from AM.

In an AM transmitter, the process of modulation (mixing the carrier signal with the audio signal) is done in such a way that the *strength* of the carrier signal is varied by the audio signal. In FM, however, it is the frequency of the carrier signal that is varied or modulated by the audio signal. That is why it is called frequency modulation. The strength of the FM carrier remains constant.

25. The FM receiving antenna. Antennas for FM receivers are quite different from those for AM sets. The most common FM antenna is the *folded dipole* shown in Fig. 34-10. This can be located inside the attic of a house. A two-wire cable is run be-

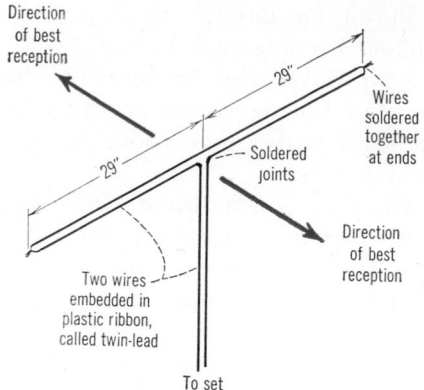

Fig. 34-10. This folded dipole is the commonest antenna used with FM receivers.

tween the walls from the antenna to the receiver location. More often, however, the folded dipole FM antenna is simply tacked to the back of the radio cabinet.

26. The FM receiver. Except for just one stage, an FM receiver is fundamentally the same as a superheterodyne AM receiver. This different stage is the *discriminator,* shown in Fig. 34-11, which replaces the second detector.

The job of the **discriminator** *is to remove the audio signal from a carrier* *signal that is swinging back and forth in frequency at an audio rate.* The discriminator delivers the desired audio signal to the audio amplifier, just as does the second detector of an AM receiver. From there on, FM and AM receivers are identical in operation.

27. Why FM sets are static-free. There usually are more i.f. amplifier tubes in FM receivers than in AM receivers. Sometimes the last i.f. amplifier tube is called a *limiter.* This means that the tube flattens out or limits undesired variation in signal strength. This limiting action is what removes static crashes from FM programs. It works so well that lightning can strike the building next door and produce nothing more than a weak click in the FM receiver.

28. The television broadcasting system. Television is a combination of the two broadcasting systems we have just studied, along with some new techniques. Television uses FM to bring in the sound portion of a program, and uses AM for the picture portion.

The reliable reception range of television signals is limited to about 50

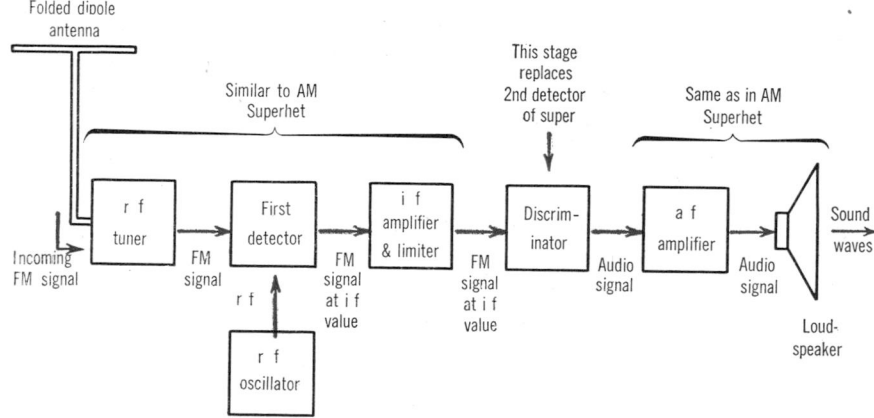

Fig. 34-11. Block diagram of a typical frequency modulation receiver.

miles because of the high frequencies involved. This is much the same as for FM. In hilly country, the range is even less if hills block the straight line-of-sight path between transmitting and receiving antennas.

29. Television requires two transmitters per station. A television station has one transmitter for sound and one for the picture. In a television studio, the microphone is hung on a boom over the performers to pick up sounds and convert them to audio signals. These are amplified and fed to the FM transmitter that broadcasts the sound portion of the program. The sound thus is handled very much as in standard FM broadcasting. This transmitter operates at the high-frequency end of the 6-megacycle-wide channel assigned to that television station. The picture transmitter operates at the low-frequency end of the channel.

30. The television camera. The picture portion of a television program starts at the television camera. There lenses focus the desired scene onto a coated plate inside *a large, television camera tube. This tube is known as the iconoscope,* the *orthicon,* or the **image orthicon,** depending on which particular type is used. Construction

of the latest image orthicon, sensitive enough to work even by candlelight, is shown in Fig. 34-12.

Light from the object being televised is focused on a light-sensitive photoelectric surface inside the image orthicon. This surface contains thousands of tiny photoelectric cells, each of which emits electrons from its back surface in proportion to the amount of light falling on it. These electrons flow from the back of the photoelectric surface through the vacuum to a special target in response to the attraction of a positively charged mesh or grid just in front of the target. A magnetic field also is used to help control the direction taken by these electrons. As the flying electrons strike the target, they each knock a larger number of electrons off the target face. This, in effect, creates a pattern of remaining electrons that corresponds to a photographic negative.

Near the base of the image orthicon is an electron gun that produces an electron beam which sweeps back and forth, line by line, across the entire back of the target. When the beam hits the target at a point that has not lost electrons, the beam curves right around and goes back to the base of the tube. When the beam hits a point

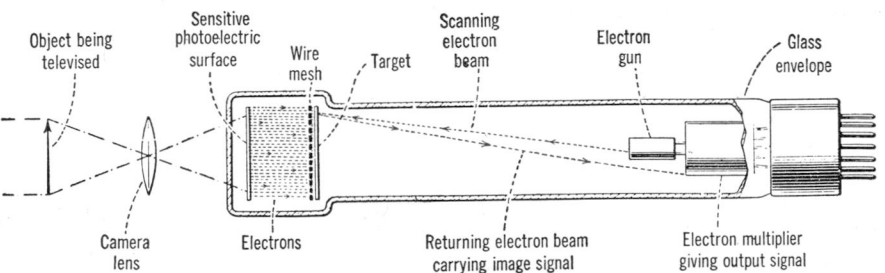

Fig. 34-12. The operation of the image orthicon, newest type of television camera tube.

that has lost electrons, it deposits enough electrons on the back of the target to make up for the loss. The returning beam thus has a gap at that instant, corresponding to a darker part of the picture. The electrons in the returning beam at each instant thus depend on how bright or how dark is the tiny object area being transmitted at that instant.

The electron multiplier at the base of the tube serves to amplify the variations in electron beam strength thousands of times, giving the camera the ability to transmit a comparatively strong signal from weakly illuminated objects. Older iconoscope camera tubes are used in studios because they give better image detail, but they require much more light on the scene. Whenever the cameraman has no control over lighting, he chooses the image orthicon.

31. What interlaced scanning means. A black-and-white television picture in the United States is transmitted as 525 separate horizontal lines. The complete process is repeated 30 times a second, which means that 30 complete snapshots of the scene are transmitted per second. The human eye sees these 30 glimpses of the scene as a continuously moving picture. Actually the picture is scanned 60 times a second, with every other line being scanned on one downward sweep. The remaining lines are scanned on the next downward sweep of the beam to complete one picture, as shown in Fig. 34-13. This process is called interlaced scanning, and serves to reduce flicker in the received picture.

32. Television studio control room. From the television camera the picture signal goes to the master control desk

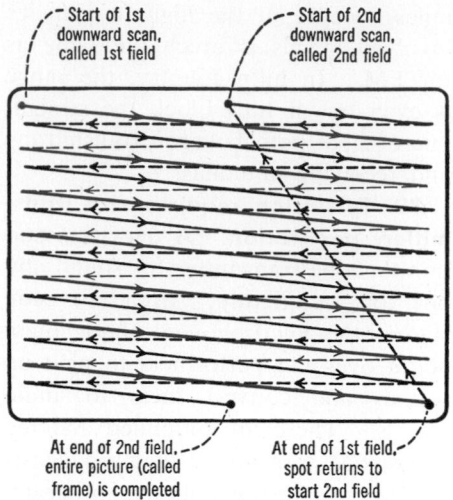

Fig. 34-13. How interlaced scanning works.

in an adjoining room. Here operators watch viewing tubes and make corrections on the signal. They also switch from one camera to another as called for by the program director, who watches all the viewing tubes and the studio as in Fig. 34-14.

The picture signal must be accompanied by various synchronizing signals that will keep receivers in step with the transmitter. These synchronizing signals are broadcast along with the picture signal. They are sent out during the intervals when the screen is momentarily dark after the end of each line and after the end of each complete picture.

33. Transmitting the picture signal. There actually is only one tiny dot of brightness on a television receiver screen at any given moment. This bright dot is varying continually in brightness. It moves along the lines of the screen so very fast, however, that our eyes see only the complete picture.

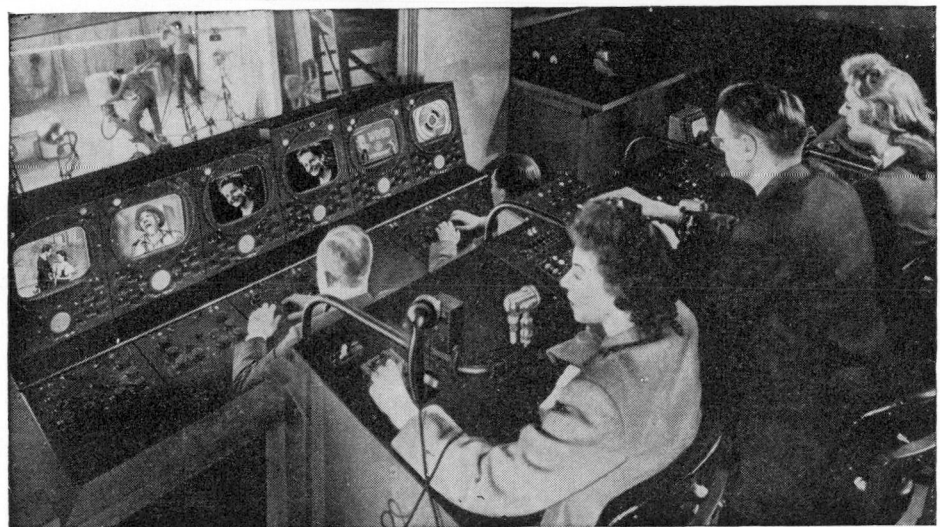

Fig. 34-14. The control room of a television station.

From the control room, the picture signal goes to the picture transmitter in another room nearby. Here the picture signal is amplified and then combined with its carrier signal.

After more amplification, the resulting modulated carrier signal travels over another cable to the transmitting antenna high on top of the building. This antenna serves for both the sound and picture for transmitters.

34. How to figure the range of a television station. The effective range of a television transmitting antenna is the straight-line or line-of-sight distance from the antenna to the horizon. This range is easily figured from the formula

$$D = 1.23\sqrt{H},$$

where D is in miles and H is in feet. Raising the receiving antenna extends the range still more, as indicated in Fig. 34-15. For this reason, high masts are used at locations just beyond the horizon to get the receiving an-

tenna up into the path of the waves. The same formula gives the added range obtained from the receiving antenna height.

As an example, the Empire State Building antenna structure in New York City provides a height of about 1,100 feet for one of its television stations. The horizon distance for this height is

$$D = 1.23\sqrt{1100},$$

which is about 40 miles. A typical home rooftop antenna is about 30 feet high, and for this

$$D = 1.23\sqrt{30} \quad \text{or} \quad 6\tfrac{3}{4}\ \text{miles.}$$

Adding this to 40 gives about 47 miles as the effective radius of the service area in level country using an ordinary receiving antenna installation. This, of course, assumes that there are no hills, buildings, or other obstructions in the way.

35. Television receiving antennas. The same receiving antenna serves for

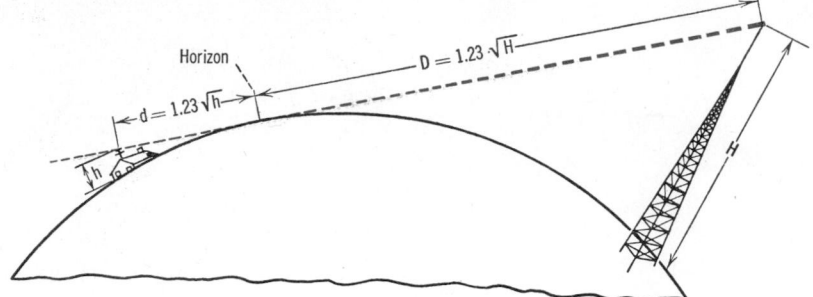

Fig. 34-15. How antenna height affects the distance at which a television station can be received.

both the sound and picture portions of a television program. In locations close to television stations a folded or plain dipole much like that for FM receivers can be used. However, a more complicated antenna arrangement usually is needed.

In radio, interference between ground and sky waves causes fading. In television, however, interference be-

Fig. 34-16. A standard dipole and reflector antenna being installed. This antenna is for use on Channels 2 through 13 in medium and high-signal level areas.

tween waves arriving over different paths gives an effect called *ghosts*. There is a faint outline or ghost image of a person a short distance to the right of the brighter image on the receiver screen. Very directional antennas, aimed away from the path of the most troublesome reflected wave, help solve the ghost problem in television.

A television antenna that is cut to the correct length for one of the 82 channels may not give a good picture for other channels. Also, an antenna that is aimed to get a good picture on one channel might not bring in properly a signal coming from another direction. For these reasons, two or more antennas are often mounted on the same mast. The ideal arrangement would be a separate antenna for each of the 82 channels, but due to cost this is impractical.

36. Getting acquainted with a television receiver. Modern television receivers use a superheterodyne circuit, as shown in Fig. 34-17. The picture signal picked up by the antenna is therefore boosted in strength and tuned in much as for an ordinary AM receiver. Because of the higher frequencies involved, the circuits and parts look a little different as shown in

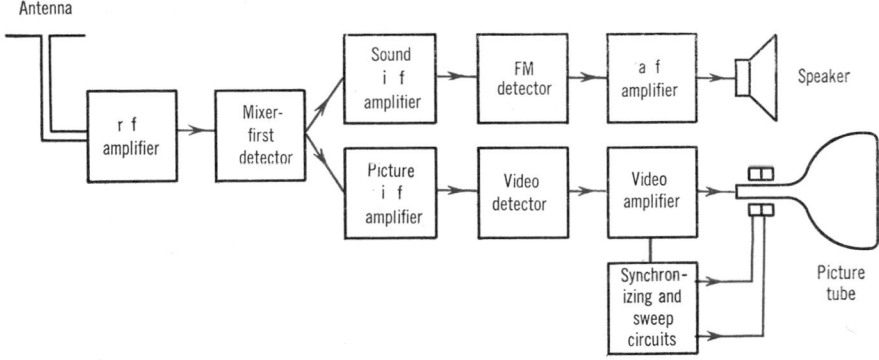

Fig. 34-17. Block diagram of a typical television receiver.

Fig. 34-18, but they work in the same way.

The second detector in a television receiver is called the *video detector* because it separates the picture or video signal from the picture carrier. This video signal is boosted in strength by the video amplifier tubes and fed to the television picture tube. There it causes the spot on the screen to vary in brightness from instant to instant.

The *synchronizing signals,* produced at the camera location and transmitted to keep receivers in step, also emerge from the video detector. These " sync " signals are used to drive horizontal and vertical sweep circuits. The horizontal sweep makes the spot on the screen move back and forth over each of the 525 horizontal lines into which the picture is divided. The vertical sweep makes the spot move down for the next scanning line when it reaches the end of one line. The vertical sweep also makes the spot move up to the top of the screen for another start each time it reaches the bottom of the picture.

37. How color pictures are transmitted. Broadcasting of color programs employs the same basic equip-

ment as black and white transmissions. Color broadcasts are received satisfactorily on black and white receivers as black and white pictures. However, additional optical and electronic equipment are needed to handle the color information and add it to the transmitted signal. Light from the scene being televised is focused by the camera lens into a series of mirrors as shown in Fig. 34-19. Two of these mirrors are made of specially treated glass which reflects one color while passing all other colors. The first of these mirrors reflects red light, but permits blue and green light to pass through. The second mirror reflects blue, but passes green light. Three images, one in each

Fig. 34-18. A compact television receiver results from use of a rectangular-face picture tube and vertical chassis.

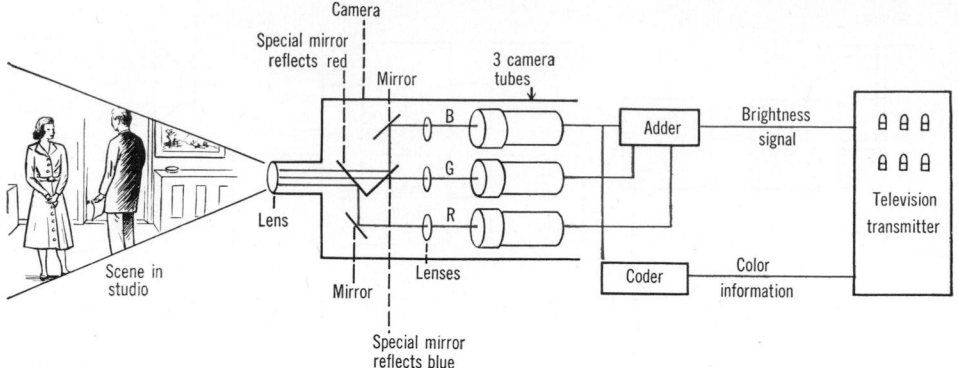

Fig. 34-19. Colors in the original scene are separated into the three primary colors of red, green, and blue at the television camera.

primary color, are thus created. Regular mirrors reflect the three primary images to lenses that focus red, blue, and green images on the faces of three image orthicon camera tubes.

The electron beam in each camera tube (Fig. 34-12) scans the image formed on the camera tube target. The three primary color signals from the three camera tubes are processed in electronic circuits and fed to an electronic adder which combines them to make the brightness signal. Samples of the three primary signals are also fed to another unit which combines them to produce a signal carrying the color information. This signal is then combined with the brightness signal to form the complete color television signal that is fed to the transmitter and then to the station antenna.

38. How the color receiver works. Many of the stages in a color receiver are the same as those in a black and white receiver. To recognize and properly utilize the color information signals, additional tubes and circuits are required. Some of these are identified in Fig. 34-20, which shows, in simplified form, the functions of tubes han-

dling color information signals required by the color picture tube. The output of the color-handling circuits provides three separate signals for the primary colors, red, green and blue.

In one type of color picture tube there are three electron guns, a mask consisting of a metal plate having thousands of tiny holes, and a phosphor screen. See Fig. 34-21. The screen may be mounted just inside a clear-glass face plate or the phosphor may be deposited on the inside surface of the face plate. The neck of the picture tube contains the three electron guns and each gun is fed one of the three color signals. The electron beams from all three guns are aimed at the mask so that they come together and pass through each tiny hole in the mask, separating into three beams again on the far side of the mask. The screen of the tube is formed of spots that are composed of three phosphor dots, one for each color. If each gun is properly aimed and focused upon one hole in the mask, the glowing spot on the phosphor screen will be found to be composed of three colored dots, red, green, and blue. The

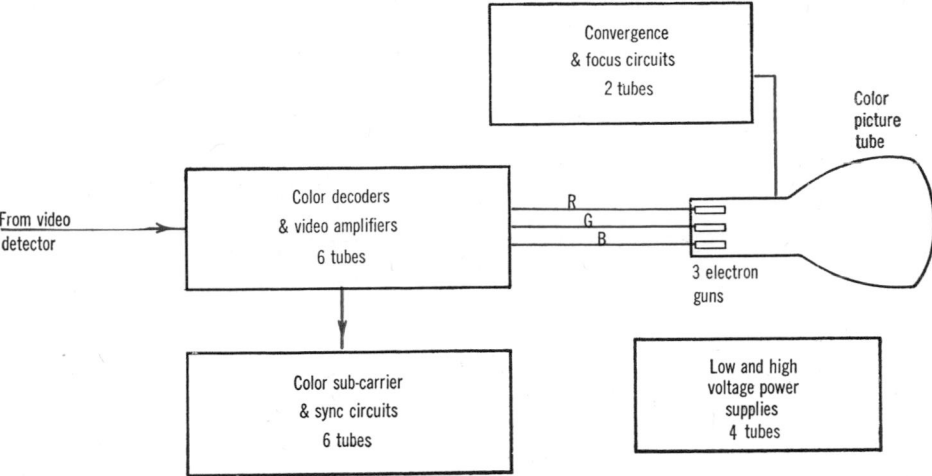

Fig. 34-20. Some of the circuits that handle the color information signals in the receiver.

strength of each color signal fed to the electron gun for a particular color determines the brightness of the dot of that color.

Scanning of the three electron beams is done just as it is in the black and white receiver, except that the three beams move together like a single beam. In addition, the scanning lines followed by the beams must align with the lines of holes in the mask. This is difficult, since there are thousands of tiny holes through which the three beams must pass in succession. For example, if there are 200,000 holes in the mask, then there are 600,000 phosphor dots on the screen. All of these must be properly activated in sequence

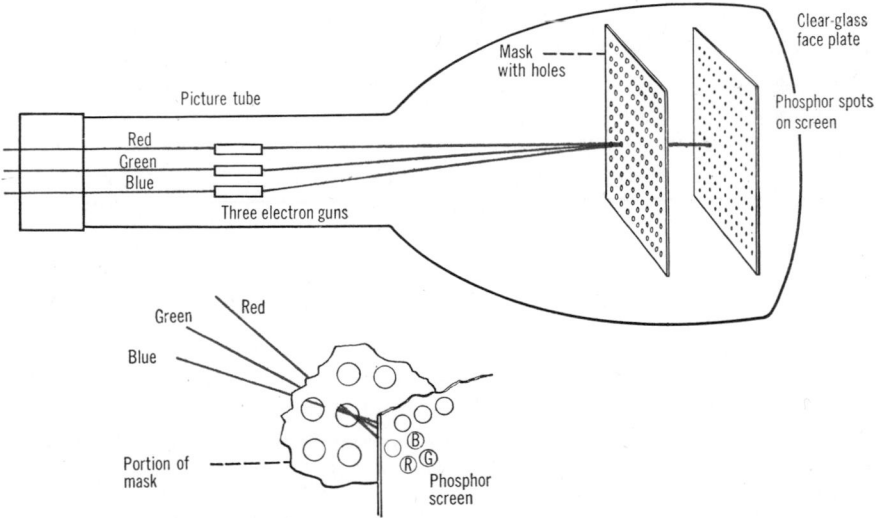

Fig. 34-21. Basic construction of color picture tube using a mask to guide the beams.

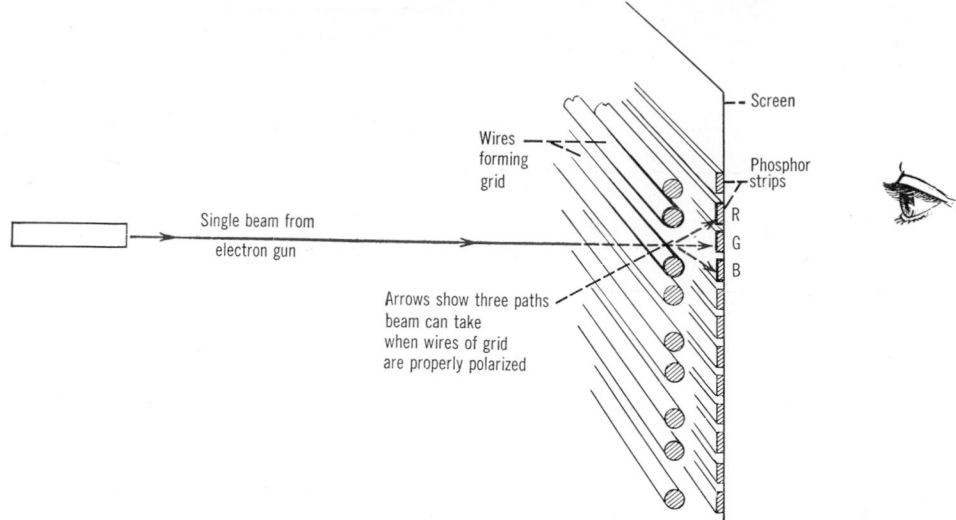

Fig. 34-22. A grid of thin wires can be polarized to bend the beam to its proper phosphor.

in one-thirtieth of a second to form one color picture. Thirty complete color pictures per second are required to make them move.

Another type of color picture tube contains phosphor strips instead of dots. Strips for red, green, and blue are arranged horizontally on the screen, as shown in Fig. 34-22. A grid of thin parallel wires is mounted close to the screen. Each pair of wires of the grid is positioned next to every set of three phosphor strips. In the simplified diagram of Fig. 34-22, a cross-section view of two grid wires and three strips is illustrated. A single electron gun can be aimed between the wires so that its beam passes between the two wires and strikes the green phosphor, causing it to glow. To excite the red or blue phosphor, the proper electrostatic charge is placed on the grid wires in order to bend the beam.

Summary

Radio waves are electromagnetic radiations, differing from light and heat only in wave length. In radio broadcasting, a carrier signal is first generated by a crystal oscillator, then modulated by an amplified voice signal. The combination may be further amplified and then delivered to the antenna. The radio waves travel from the transmitter either as ground waves or as sky waves. In radio reception the radio signal is first amplified, then rectified to a pulsating direct-current signal. After again being amplified, it is sent to the speaker, where it is transformed into sound waves.

Television camera tubes now in use are image orthicons and iconoscopes.

They transform the picture focused on them to a stream of electrical impulses which can be broadcast as a type of radio wave. The picture tube takes this stream of electrical impulses and recreates the picture from them. Additional circuits are required for color television.

Terms to Define...

AM
Antenna
Audio-frequency amplifier
Carrier signal
Detector
Discriminator
FM
Ground waves

Image orthicon
Interlaced scanning
Intermediate frequency
    amplifier
Ionosphere layers
Kilocycle
Loudspeaker
Megacycle

Microphone
Modulator
Radio-frequency amplifier
Sky waves
Superheterodyne receiver
Synchronizing signals
TV
Video detector

Questions

GROUP A

1. What are the three types of radio broadcasting in use today? In what frequency bands does each operate?

2. What is a kilocycle? A megacycle? How are the frequency and wave length of radio waves related?

3. What are the parts of an AM broadcasting system? What is the function of each part?

4. What is the purpose of a receiving antenna?

5. What is the function of the r.f. amplifier? Of the detector? Of the a.f. amplifier?

6. Explain how a loudspeaker converts an audio-frequency output signal into sound waves.

7. How does a superheterodyne radio set give higher sensitivity and selectivity?

8. What is the reliable reception range of a television station? What factors may increase or decrease this distance?

9. How does an image orthicon operate to "take" a television picture? How does the picture tube reproduce it?

10. What are the principal parts of a television receiver? What is the function of each part?

11. How is color television photographed and broadcast?

12. How does a color television receiver reproduce the color picture? What types of color television picture tubes are in use?

GROUP B

13. How are radio waves propagated through space? Explain skip distance and fading.

14. Draw a diagram of a simple crystal receiver and explain the function of each part.

15. Why are tuning circuits necessary in a radio receiver?

16. What are the advantages of frequency modulation over ordinary amplitude modulation radio reception?

17. How does an FM receiving set differ from an AM receiving set?

18. What is interlaced scanning?

19. Why are the antennas for television stations usually mounted at the top of tall buildings or on top of the highest hills near a city?

20. Why are television receiving antennas usually very complicated-looking devices?

Chapter 35

Radioactivity and
Nuclear Energy

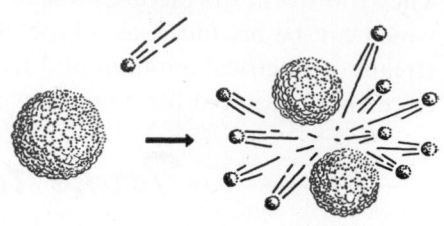

1. ATOMIC STRUCTURE

1. There are several types of particles in an atom. In Chapter 1 we learned that matter is made up of tiny particles called molecules. We also learned that these molecules are made up of even smaller particles called atoms.

The hydrogen atom is the simplest atom we know. It is composed of only two particles, a proton and an electron. A proton is about two-fifths the size of an electron, but it has a mass 1836 times as great. Consequently the proton accounts for almost all the mass of a hydrogen atom. The electron contributes very little mass. These particles, you remember, have electrical charges. The proton has a sin-

gle positive charge. The electron has a single negative charge.

Atoms which are more complex than the hydrogen atom contain other parti-

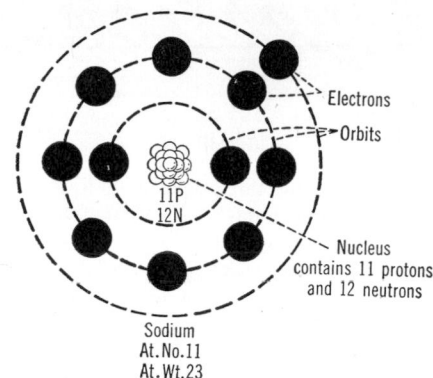

Fig. 35-1. The sodium atom.

Labels on figure: Electrons, Orbits, 11P 12N, Nucleus contains 11 protons and 12 neutrons, Sodium At.No.11 At.Wt.23

Vocabulary

ALPHA PARTICLE. A charged particle composed of two protons and two neutrons.

BETA (*bay***-tuh) PARTICLE.** An electron.

CHAIN REACTION. A reaction in which the material or energy which starts the reaction is also a product.

COSMIC RAYS. High energy particles coming from outer space.

CYCLOTRON (*sy***-kloh-tron).** An electromagnetic and electrostatic particle accelerator.

DEUTERON. Nucleus of a deuterium atom. Consists of a proton and a neutron.

FISSION. The disintegration of an atom into two nuclei of more or less equal mass.

FUSION. The process of building up more complex atoms from simple ones.

GAMMA RAYS. High energy X rays.

MESON (*mee***-son).** Charged particles with a mass about 200 times that of an electron.

POSITRON. A particle with the mass of an electron but having a positive charge.

RADIOACTIVITY. The spontaneous, uncontrollable breakdown of the nucleus of an atom with the emission of particles and rays.

cles. One of these particles is the neutron. The neutron has a mass 1838.5 times that of an electron — about the same mass as a proton. Neutrons have no electrical charge; they are electrically neutral. *A combination of two protons and two neutrons is often found.* Such a combination is called an **alpha particle.** During some changes which can be produced in the structure of an atom, *a particle with the mass of an electron but having a positive electric charge has been observed.* This particle is called a **positron.** It exists in nature for only a very short time.

An atom is not just a bunch of these particles arranged in random fashion. In Chapter 1 we learned that an atom consists roughly of two parts — the nucleus and the orbits, as in Fig. 35-1. The nucleus is the dense central part of the atom and contains the protons and neutrons. The electrons rotate about this nucleus in more or less definite orbits or energy levels. Some electrons have orbits near the nucleus. Other electrons rotate at a greater distance from it. Each atom has an equal number of protons and electrons.

A type of particle about which we know very little is the *meson (mee-*

son). There are several types of mesons. Some have a positive charge of electricity, while others have a negative charge. **Mesons** *have a mass about 200 times that of an electron.* It is believed that they hold the protons and neutrons together in the nucleus. Outside the atom they have an extremely short life, about one or two millionths of a second.

The number of protons in the nucleus of an atom is called its *atomic number.* For instance, hydrogen, with one proton in its nucleus, has an atomic number of one. A more complex atom, like copper, with 29 protons in its nucleus, has an atomic number of 29. The number of protons identifies the nucleus as belonging to a certain element.

The actual weights of atoms are very small decimal numbers that would be very difficult to work with. The actual weight of a hydrogen atom is 0.00000000000000000000000167 g-wt. As a result, a relative weight scale for the atoms has been developed. Atoms are given weights which indicate their weight in relation to one another. The standard for this relative weight scale is the oxygen atom. It was given the weight 16. An atom of sulfur, which is twice as heavy as an

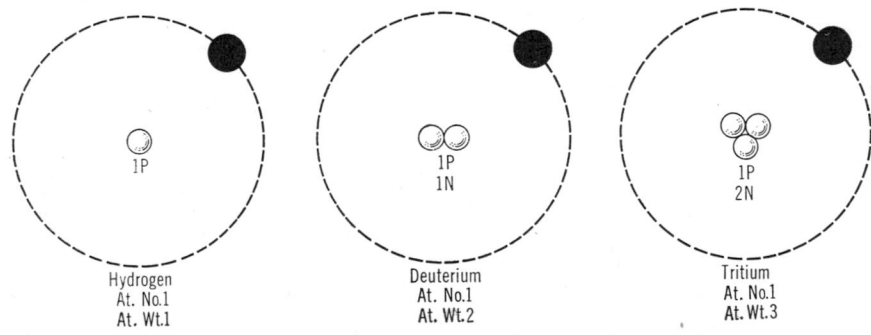

Hydrogen
At. No.1
At. Wt.1

Deuterium
At. No.1
At. Wt.2

Tritium
At. No.1
At. Wt.3

Fig. 35-2. The three isotopes of hydrogen: hydrogen, deuterium, and tritium.

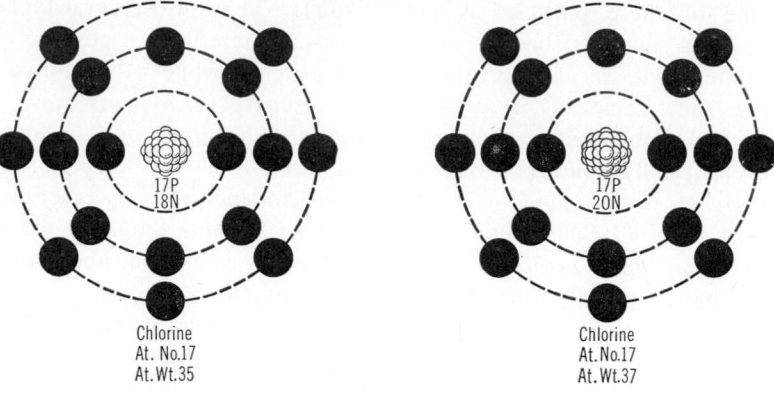

Fig. 35-3. The isotopes of chlorine differ only in the number of their neutrons.

oxygen atom, has an *atomic weight* of 32. Helium atoms have an atomic weight of 4. On this relative scale protons and neutrons each have a weight of approximately one. Electrons have a negligible atomic weight.

The atoms of some elements exist in different forms, called *isotopes.* The nuclei of isotopes of the same element all have the same number of protons. The nuclei differ, however, in the number of neutrons they contain. For example, there are three known isotopes of hydrogen. Their atomic structure is shown in Fig. 35-2. Ordinary hydrogen has one proton in the nucleus. *Heavy hydrogen, or deuterium, has a nucleus containing one proton and one neutron.* This nucleus is called a **deuteron.** *Tritium,* a third isotope, has a nucleus consisting of one proton and two neutrons. Each of these nuclei has only one electron revolving about it. Chlorine is another example of an element which has isotopes. Cl-35 has 18 neutrons in the nucleus, while Cl-37 has 20. These isotopes are shown in Fig. 35-3. They both are atoms of chlorine, since the nucleus contains 17 protons. Seventeen electrons rotate about the nucleus. The isotopes of an element all have the same chemical properties. However, they do differ slightly in mass because of the different number of neutrons.

2. RADIOACTIVITY

2. The discovery of radioactivity. Henri Becquerel (1852–1908), a French scientist, discovered radioactivity in 1896. He found that the uranium ore, pitchblende, darkened a photographic plate, even though the plate was wrapped in opaque paper. He concluded that the ore must have given off penetrating radiations. We now know that such radiations pass through some substances which are opaque to ordinary light. They are stopped, however, by dense materials like bones and metal. *The spontaneous, uncontrollable breakdown of the nucleus of an atom with the emission of particles and rays is called* **radioactivity.**

3. The discovery and properties of radium. Soon after this discovery by Becquerel, Pierre Curie (1859–1906) and his wife Marie (1867–1934) began a series of experiments to determine whether other elements showed radioactivity. Of the elements known at that time, thorium, an element then used in making Welsbach gas mantles, was the only one beside uranium that exhibited this property. Mme. Curie (Fig. 35-4) did find, however, that pitchblende, the mineral from which uranium is extracted, is four times as active as pure uranium. She concluded, therefore, that pitchblende must contain some other element more active than uranium itself. She patiently worked over several tons of pitchblende and succeeded in isolating a few milligrams of the bromide of an element that is more than 1,000,000 times as active as uranium. She named the element *radium.* Radium is most frequently used in the form of its salts: the chloride or bromide, for example. In 1910 Mme. Curie succeeded in isolating metallic radium. Both the metal and its salts are radioactive. Because of its radioactivity it has unusual properties.

(1) *It affects a photographic plate,* even through opaque substances like paper, wood, and thin sheets of metal.

(2) *Radium salts produce fluorescence* with certain salts, just as X rays do. A mixture of a very small quantity of radium bromide and zinc sulfide is luminous in the dark.

Fig. 35-4. Marie Sklodowska Curie.

(3) *Radium is active chemically;* it decomposes water, changes oxygen to ozone, and gives glass a purple color.

(4) *Radium produces important physiological changes.* It can destroy the germinating power of seeds, kill bacteria, or even destroy small animals. Radium produces frightful burns that require a long time to heal.

(5) *The salts of radium glow in the dark,* producing a pale phosphorescence. In ordinary daylight they resemble common table salt in appearance. The phosphorescence is not bright enough to be seen in daylight.

(6) *Radium gives off enough heat every hour* to melt 1.5 times its weight of ice, or about 120 calories per gram. This heat is given off continuously. Radium loses only one-half its energy in the first 1600 years, one-half of what remains in the next 1600 years, and so on.

(7) *Radium is rare and expensive.* The present price of radium is about

$20,000 per gram. Rich deposits of uranium ore occur in northern Canada and also in the Belgian Congo.

4. What is the nature of the radiation from radium and other radioactive materials? The radiation from radioactive materials consists of:

(1) *Alpha particles.* We already have learned that these consist of two protons and two neutrons. They are the same as the nuclei of helium atoms. They have two positive electrical charges. Their mass is about four times that of the hydrogen atom. They have a velocity of about 20,000 miles per second. However, their penetrating power is not very great. They can be stopped by a thin piece of aluminum foil or a thin sheet of paper. They are very efficient in ionizing gas molecules in the air.

(2) **Beta** (*bay*-tuh) **particles.** *These are electrons,* just as we discovered cathode rays to be. They have a negative electrical charge, but are only about 1/1836 the mass of a hydrogen atom. They have much greater penetrating power than alpha particles, since their velocity is from 60,000 to 180,000 miles per second.

(3) **Gamma rays.** *Gamma rays seem to be high energy X rays.* They are much more penetrating than either alpha or beta particles. They can produce phosphorescence, and they affect a photographic plate.

Fig. 35-5 shows the effect of a powerful magnetic field on the radiation from a small amount of radioactive material. The heavy alpha particles are deflected slightly in one direction; the lighter beta particles are deflected more markedly in the other direction; the gamma rays are not deflected at all. By the use of such a magnetic

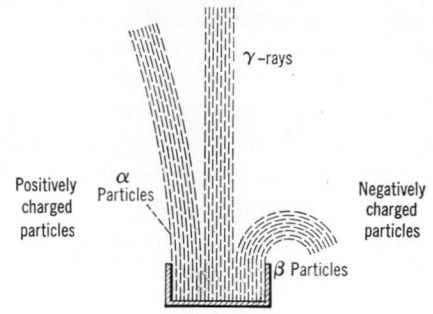

Fig. 35-5. How a magnetic field affects the different radiations.

field, Ernest Rutherford (1871–1937) learned the nature of the radiation from radioactive materials.

5. How can radiation be detected? The particles given off by radioactive materials have the property of ionizing substances through which they pass. When ionization takes place, an atom or group of atoms loses or gains one or more electrons. From a *neutral atom,* it is changed into a *charged ion.* Alpha and beta particles can produce ionization. One of the methods for studying the ionization they produce was devised by C. T. R. Wilson (1869–   ). Let us look at Fig. 35-6. The lower part of the inverted cone and rubber bulb is filled with water which is dyed black. In the upper compartment of the apparatus there is a tiny bit of the radioactive material being studied, such as a bit of radium, in a glass capsule. An emf of 100 volts or more is maintained across the air space in the upper compartment, which is artificially illuminated.

When the rubber bulb is squeezed, the air is compressed. As it is released, the air expands and tracks of alpha particles can be seen through the glass, reflected from the dark background. See Fig. 35-7. They be-

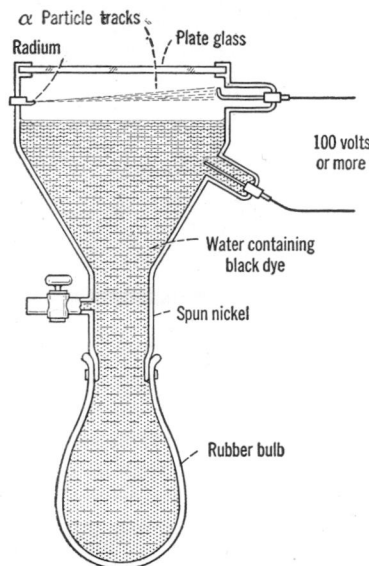

Fig. 35-6. The Wilson cloud chamber is used to study radioactive materials.

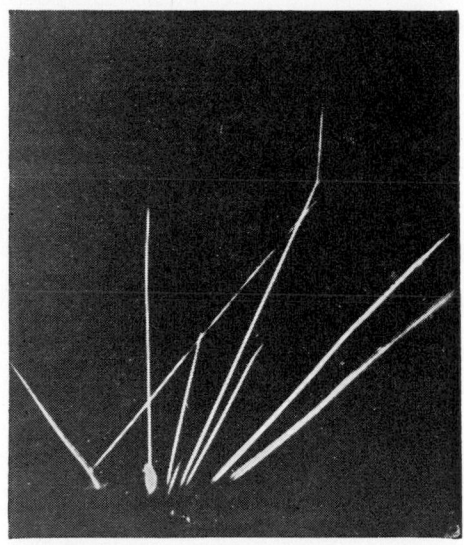

Fig. 35-7. Tracks of alpha particles photographed in a Wilson cloud chamber.

come visible because they ionize the gas molecules in the air and particles of fog condense upon them. The alpha particle tracks come out from the tip of the capsule in which the radioactive material is enclosed. By means of such a cloud chamber, physicists can identify the fragments of atoms from the particles produced when the atoms disintegrate.

An electroscope becomes discharged when ions in the air pick up or leave electrons on the electroscope knob. The rate at which an electroscope is discharged, then, is a measure of the number of ions in the air near the electroscope. Since radioactive materials produce ions in proportion to their radioactivity, their effect on an electroscope is one way in which radioactivity may be measured.

A newer method of measuring radiation is the Geiger counter, Fig. 35-8. This consists of a metal cylinder, which acts as one electrode, surrounding a thin wire, which is the other electrode. By using glass caps, the two electrodes may be insulated from one another. The voltage is adjusted so that it is almost great enough to produce a discharge. When a particle produced by radioactivity passes through the counter, it ionizes the gas in the tube. This lowers the resistance between the two electrodes, and current momentarily passes. This passage may be registered as a " click " in a loudspeaker.

6. The disintegration of a radium atom. The nuclei of radium and other radioactive elements are continually disintegrating. The alpha and beta particles which they emit are products of this atomic disintegration. The change goes on spontaneously, with certain heavy atoms breaking down into slightly lighter atoms. After an average life of 2500 years, for example, a radium atom disintegrates. This atom is 226 times as heavy as a

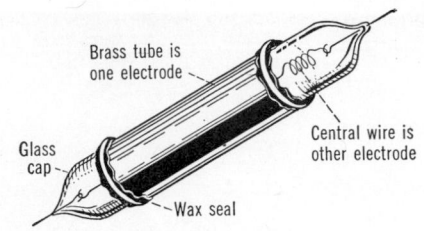

Fig. 35-8. The Geiger counter is used to detect radioactive material.

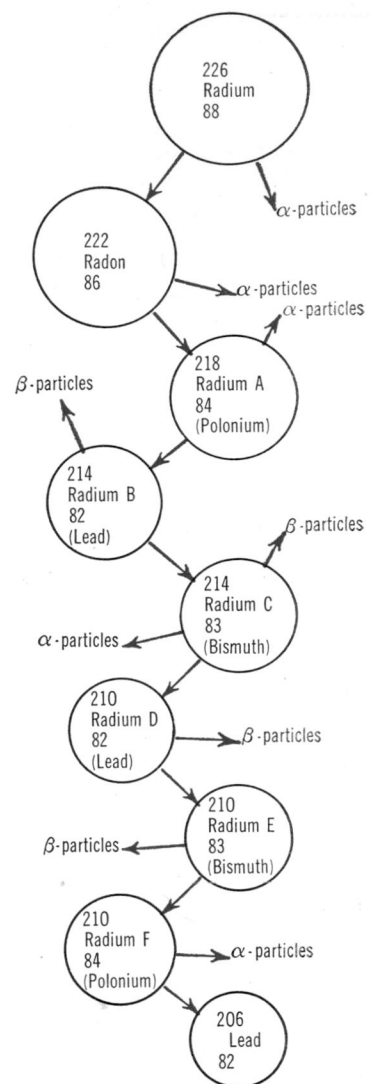

Fig. 35-9. The products of the disintegration of radium atoms.

hydrogen atom. When it disintegrates, it loses an alpha particle, which becomes a neutral helium atom upon picking up two electrons. This helium atom weighs four times as much as the hydrogen atom. The remainder of the atom, 222 times the weight of the hydrogen atom, is a gas known as radon. Thus two gases, *helium* and *radon,* are formed when an atom of radium disintegrates. The nuclear equation representing this change is:

$$_{88}Ra^{226} \rightarrow {}_{86}Rn^{222} + {}_2He^4.$$

Only the nuclei are represented in this equation. *The superscript is the atomic weight of the nucleus. The subscript is the atomic number,* the *number of protons in the nucleus.* Alpha particles, since they are helium nuclei, are represented as $_2He^4$.

Radon atoms are much less stable than radium atoms. Half of the radon atoms will disintegrate in a little less than four days. When radon disintegrates, it forms *polonium,* which also is radioactive. As polonium breaks down by emitting alpha particles, *Radium B,* an isotope of lead, is formed. This can emit beta particles to produce *Radium C,* an element with an atomic weight of 214 and an atomic number of 83. This makes it an isotope of bismuth. Both alpha and beta

particles are emitted by this isotope in forming *Radium D.* Further similar changes, as shown in Fig. 35-9, finally result in an element which has atomic number 82, and atomic weight 206. This is an isotope of lead. While radium is formed from uranium, it finally disintegrates to form lead.

3. NUCLEAR ENERGY

7. The first artificial atomic transformation. About 1919, Rutherford tried several experiments to discover if it was possible to add more particles to the nuclei of atoms and thus produce new atoms. In one experiment he bombarded nitrogen with alpha particles from radium. He found that hydrogen and an isotope of oxygen were produced. This was the first example of an artificial change or transmutation in an element.

8. Atom smashers produce artificially radioactive materials. Alpha particles from radium are not very effective in bringing about changes in the nuclei of atoms. They have little penetrating power. Consequently scientists looked for a new source of particles with which to bombard the nucleus. They wanted particles that would have greater velocity and more energy. One of the devices constructed to secure such particles was the Van de Graaff generator.

From Fig. 35-10, we see that a Van de Graaff generator is a kind of escalator for electrons. Electrons are put on the moving, insulated belt by repulsion from a strongly negative electrode. They travel up the belt to the top of the generator. Here they are picked off by a collector and transferred to the top terminal. In this way a large negative charge can be built up on the top terminal. The large difference of potential thus obtained can be used to accelerate charged particles, electrons or protons, making them effective atomic bullets. Since the high charge on a Van de Graaff generator can leak off into the atmosphere if the air is humid, such generators are sometimes built under a large, pear-shaped shell like that in Fig. 35-11. This can be filled with dry air under pressure to keep the charge on the top terminal.

By bombarding atoms with protons, deuterons, or neutrons, they can be made to give off radiation similar to that of the natural radioactive elements. They can be made *artificially radioactive*. Radioactive isotopes of all known elements have been prepared.

Dr. E. O. Lawrence (1901–) of the University of California, invented an atom smasher which operates on a different principle than the Van de

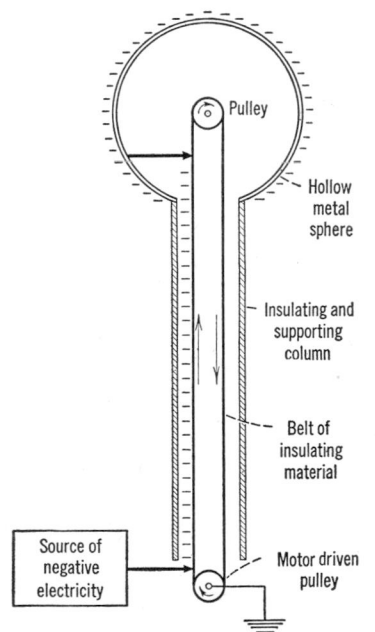

Fig. 35-10. The construction of a Van de Graaff generator.

Fig. 35-11. The pear-shaped dome covering a Van de Graaff generator used for atomic research.

take a spiral course. They move faster and faster as they near the outside of the box, acquiring more and more energy. When they reach the outer rim of the box, they are deflected toward the target. The energy of the particles accelerated in a cyclotron may reach 15,000,000 electron-volts. This is the energy an electron would have if it were accelerated across a potential difference of 15,000,000 volts. By means of the cyclotron, scientists have learned much about the structure of the atom, and about the disintegration products formed when atoms break up.

But physicists were still not satisfied with the energy of the bullets from a cyclotron. They wanted particle accelerators which would give more energy to the protons. The highest prac-

Graaff generator. He called it a *cyclotron* (*sy*-kloh-tron). See Fig. 35-12. *The* **cyclotron** *consists of a large cylindrical box,* shaped like a pill box, *placed between the poles of a huge electromagnet and used for accelerating charged particles.* The box is exhausted until a very high vacuum exists inside. The protons or deuterons which are used as bullets are fed into the center of the box. Inside the box are two hollow, D-shaped electrodes, called *dees.* These are connected to a source of very high voltage through an oscillator. When the cyclotron is in operation, the charge on these dees is reversed very rapidly by the oscillator. The combination of the high voltage alternating potential and the action of the field of the electromagnet causes the bullets inside to

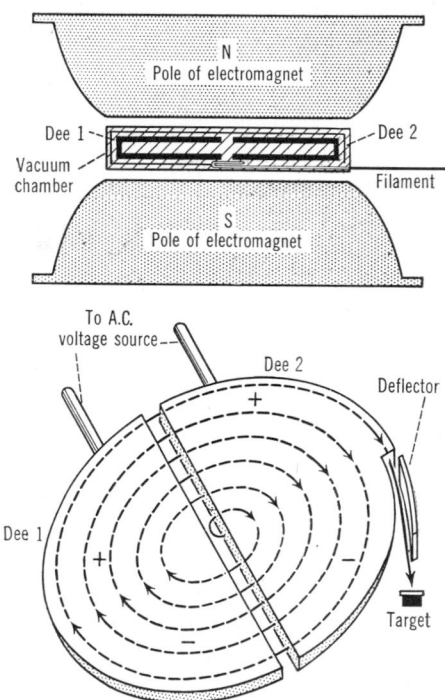

Fig. 35-12. The cyclotron produces "atomic bullets" of very high energy.

Fig. 35-13. The Cosmotron at the Brookhaven National Laboratory. In the foreground is the control room, while in the background you see the plastic-covered, 2200 ton ring-shaped magnet of the cosmotron.

tical energy which a cyclotron could provide was about 15,000,000 electron volts. When physicists tried to make the particles go faster to give them more energy, the mass of the particles increased. (See Section 9, Chapter 10.) This increased mass slowed them down to such an extent that they could not reach the gap between the dees when the oscillating voltage reversed. The first change in design to overcome this difficulty was to make the oscillator of variable frequency. Then, as the mass of the particles increased and their velocity dropped off, the frequency of the oscillator could be reduced. The changes in the voltage of the field were timed to coincide with the slower acceleration of the more massive particles. This type of machine is called a *synchro-cyclotron*. With a synchro-cyclotron, the energy of the particles can be boosted to about 600,000,000 electron volts.

The newest type of particle accelerator is the *synchrotron*. It also operates on the principle of accelerating particles by making them move in a circular path with increasing velocity. But by making both the oscillating voltage and the magnetic field variable and controllable, the path of the particles can be in a narrow circle of large diameter. The Cosmotron at the Brookhaven National Laboratory, Upton, New York, and the Bevatron at the

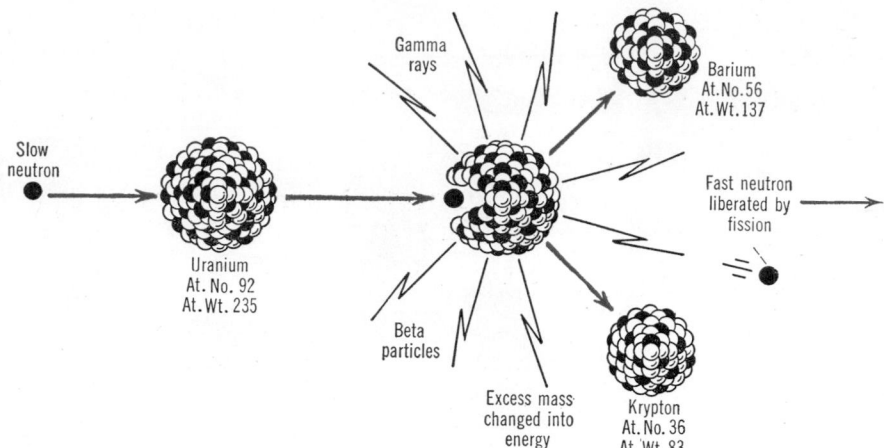

Fig. 35-14. Neutrons from the fission of one U-235 atom, when slowed down by a reaction possible.

University of California are the newest of these devices. They can impart energies of several billion electron volts to the protons which they accelerate.

9. Uranium has some unusual properties. The element uranium, atomic number 92, exists in nature in three isotopic forms, U–238, U–235, and U–234. By far, the most abundant is U–238, which forms 99.3% of naturally occurring uranium. U–235 exists to the extent of 0.7%, while only traces of U–234 have been found. These types of uranium atoms all have the same chemical properties, but have different nuclear properties.

When U–238 is bombarded with slow neutrons, these neutrons are captured by the U–238 nucleus. An unstable U–239 isotope is formed which emits a beta particle and forms a new radioactive element, neptunium, number 93. Neptunium also is unstable. It gives out a beta particle, forming another man-made element, number 94, plutonium. These two artificial elements, neptunium and plutonium, are

trans-uranium elements; that is, elements of higher atomic number than uranium.

U–235 also captures slow neutrons when bombarded with them, and the resulting nucleus is highly unstable. However, instead of emitting alpha or beta particles or gamma rays, the nucleus splits into two fairly equal parts. *This break-up of the nucleus of an atom into two nuclei of more or less equal mass is called* **fission.** During this fission neutrons are given out. There is a small loss of mass which appears as a tremendous burst of energy.

It later was discovered that plutonium, made from U–238, acts the same way as U–235 when bombarded with slow neutrons; it undergoes fission and produces more neutrons.

10. What is a chain reaction? We learned that the fission of both U–235 and plutonium is caused by bombardment with slow neutrons. Neutrons are given out during fission. *A reaction in which the material or energy*

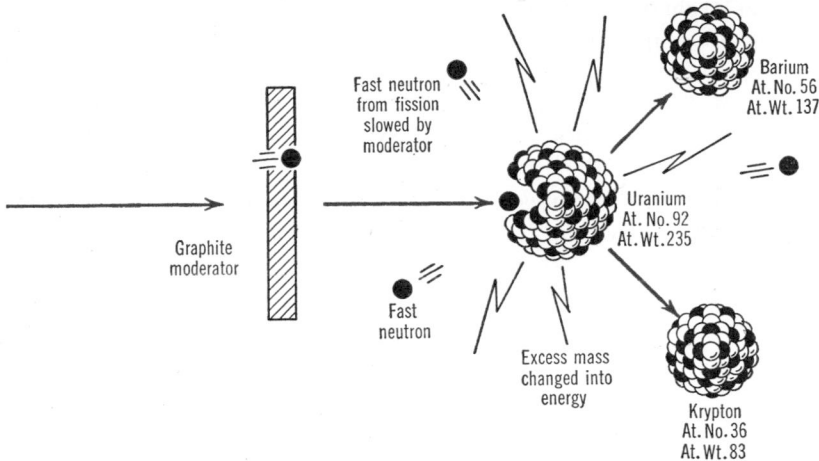

Fast neutron from fission slowed by moderator

Graphite moderator

Fast neutron

Excess mass changed into energy

Uranium
At. No. 92
At. Wt. 235

Barium
At. No. 56
At. Wt. 137

Krypton
At. No. 36
At. Wt. 83

moderator, can cause fission in a second U–235 atom. This process makes a chain

which starts a reaction is also one of the products is a chain reaction. The fission of plutonium and U–235 are such reactions. Neutrons initiate these reactions and also are one of the products. One neutron causes one atom of U–235 to undergo fission, as shown in Fig. 35-14. Suppose that two neutrons are produced. Each of them can now strike a U–235 nucleus, produce fission, and liberate four neutrons. These four can strike four more U–235 nuclei, causing them to undergo fission. In an extremely small fraction of a second billions of neutrons can be produced to act as bullets. This is what happens in an uncontrolled chain reaction. The explosion of an atomic bomb is an uncontrolled chain reaction.

11. Nuclear reactors contain controlled chain reactions. Some *nuclear reactors* are used in the production of plutonium. Here the chain reaction is controlled by rods of neutron-absorbing materials, Fig. 35-15. Large blocks of graphite slow up the fast

neutrons liberated by the radioactive materials so that they will be more easily captured by U–238 nuclei. Large amounts of heat are liberated, so that the reactor must be continually cooled by running water. Other reactors which are being operated by the United States Atomic Energy Commission are a breeder reactor and a materials-testing reactor. The breeder reactor is used to investigate the possibility of producing a greater amount of fissionable material than it consumes. The materials-testing reactor is used for testing structural materials to be used in other types of reactors. Reactors for electric power production are under construction at present.

12. The atomic submarine. The first practical use of a reactor for power production is in the atomic submarine. The heat generated by this reactor, shown in Fig. 35-16, is used to increase the temperature of water which is kept under pressure to prevent it from changing into steam. This superheated, pressurized water is pumped to a heat exchanger. In the heat exchanger, it gives up some of its heat to other water, which is thereby converted into steam. The pressurized water returns to the reactor for reheating. The steam produced in the outer jacket of the heat exchanger drives a steam turbine. The turbine then runs the propellers. The spent steam from the turbine is condensed and pumped back to the heat exchanger.

A second type of submarine power plant, using molten sodium as the circulating fluid in the reactor is also under construction. Using atomic power, a submarine may cruise rapidly for long distances without coming to the surface.

13. The atomic battery. The atomic battery is a device which converts nuclear energy directly into an electric current. The radioactive material used in the battery is strontium-90, a by-product of nuclear reactors. Strontium-90 emits high speed beta particles (electrons). These electrons collide with silicon atoms in the battery, and release 200,000 low-speed electrons for each high-speed electron. The low-speed electrons which are produced create a potential difference of one-fifth of a volt. The current produced by this battery is about five microamperes, and is strong enough to produce an audible tone in an earphone. Since strontium-90 is an isotope with a long life, such a battery will continue to deliver its current for about 20 years. It may be used in small, pocket-sized radio receivers or in hearing aids.

14. The uses of radioactive isotopes. One of the important developments resulting from the discovery of nuclear energy is the use of radioactive isotopes in medicine and in other fields of research. Radioactive isotopes can be readily produced in the heart of nuclear reactors, and then are available for the treatment of disease. Radioactive phosphorus is being used to combat diseases of the blood. Thyroid disorders can be helped by the use of radioactive iodine. Cancer patients are being treated with radioactive calcium.

Research has demonstrated the remarkable bacteria-killing power of the radiations from radioactive materials. These radiations have been used experimentally in the processing of food. The food is prepared and packed in sealed cartons. The radiation penetrates the package, killing all bacteria present. No heat treatment is required, and foods so processed may be kept at room temperature.

15. The hydrogen bomb. Atomic bombs owe their destructive force to

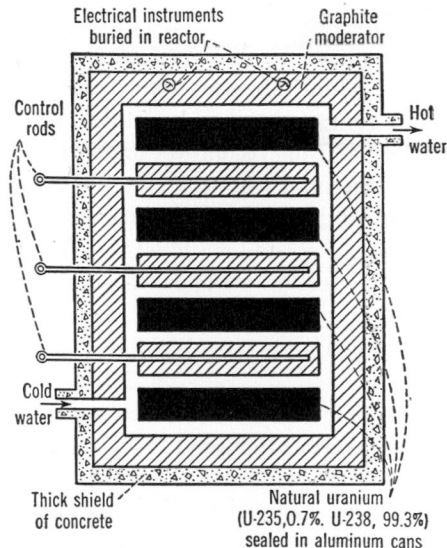

Fig. 35-15. A diagram of a nuclear reactor.

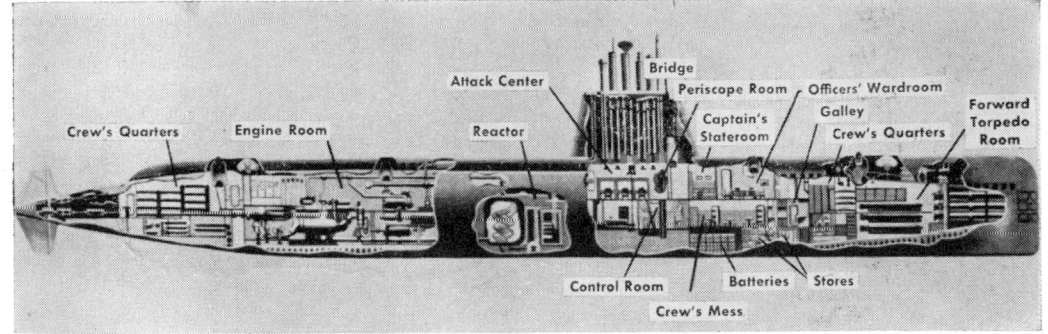

Fig. 35-16. An artist's drawing of the possible arrangement of equipment in the first atomic submarine, the **Nautilus**.

the great amount of energy liberated when large atoms split into smaller parts. A *thermonuclear* bomb, popularly called a hydrogen bomb, or H-bomb, produces energy when atoms of low atomic weight combine to form atoms of higher atomic weight. *This process of building up more complex atoms from simple ones is called **fusion**.* When fusion takes place there is a loss of mass, just as there is in the case of fission. This difference of mass appears as energy. A hydrogen bomb can be made much more destructive than an atomic bomb because more energy is liberated in a fusion reaction, and the quantities of reacting materials may be made much larger.

One probable reaction in a hydrogen bomb is the formation of alpha particles and tremendous energy from a compound of lithium and hydrogen. This compound may be formed of the particular isotopes lithium-6 and hydrogen-2. Such a fusion reaction can be started only by subjecting Li^6H^2 to extremely high temperature and pressure. These conditions are met by using an atomic bomb as the necessary detonator.

4. COSMIC RAYS

16. What are cosmic rays? An electroscope, if left out in the air, will slowly discharge. A Geiger counter will continue to click at an infrequent, yet definite rate even though no radioactive material is present. These observations indicate that there is some slight ionization in the air. Extensive experiments have shown that this ionization is caused by the reaction of particles coming into our atmosphere from outer space. These particles are nuclei of elements of low atomic weight. Protons, hydrogen nuclei, are the most abundant type. But other nuclei, ranging up to those of elements as heavy as iron, have also been detected in the upper atmosphere. Their source is not definitely known. *These high energy particles apparently come from beyond our solar system.* Hence they have been given the name **cosmic**

rays. Very few of these cosmic rays from outer space ever reach the surface of the earth. In collisions with the particles making up our atmosphere, they produce mesons. These do reach the surface of the earth as very penetrating particles, where they may be detected by trails of mist in cloud chambers or by clicks in Geiger counters.

Cosmic rays from outer space may also produce electrons and neutrons whenever they enter the atmosphere of the earth.

Summary

Atoms are composed of several types of particles — protons, electrons, and neutrons — arranged in a central nucleus and outer orbits. Positrons and mesons are particles of short life produced when atoms disintegrate.

Radioactivity is the spontaneous disintegration of the nuclei of atoms. Radioactive elements give off three different types of radiation — alpha particles, which are the same as the nuclei of helium atoms; beta particles, which are the same as electrons; and gamma rays, which are X rays.

Uranium exists in three forms, U–238, U–235, and U–234. U–238 when bombarded with slow neutrons ultimately produces plutonium, a transuranium element. U–235 when bombarded similarly undergoes fission, producing more neutrons and great amounts of energy. Plutonium acts in a manner similar to U–235.

Controlled chain reactions are carried out in nuclear reactors. These reactors are used to produce plutonium, to breed more fissionable material, and to test structural materials.

Terms to Define...

Alpha particle	Electroscope	Orbit
Artificial radioactive materials	Fission	Plutonium
	Fusion	Positron
Atomic battery	Gamma ray	Properties of radium
Atomic number	Geiger counter	Proton
Atomic submarine	Isotope	Radioactivity
Atomic weight	Meson	Synchro-cyclotron
Beta particle	Moderator	Synchrotron
Chain reaction	Neptunium	Uses of radioactive isotopes
Cosmic rays	Neutron	U–235
Cyclotron	Nuclear reactor	Van de Graaf generator
Electron	Nucleus	Wilson cloud chamber

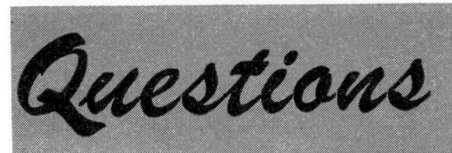

GROUP A

1. List the three main types of particles of which atoms are composed, and give the properties of each.

2. How are these particles arranged within the atom?

3. What is meant by radioactivity? Describe the types of radiations given off by radioactive elements.

4. What are some of the properties of radium?

5. Explain how radiation is detected by an electroscope. By a Geiger counter.

6. What is nuclear fission?

7. Van de Graaff generators and cyclotrons are called "atom smashers." Explain why.

8. What is necessary for a chain reaction? Give an example of a possible chain reaction.

9. How is nuclear energy used to propel the atomic submarine?

10. How is electricity produced in the atomic battery?

11. How are radioactive isotopes used?

12. What is the source of the destructive energy of a hydrogen bomb?

GROUP B

13. What are atomic weights? Are they actual weights? If not, what are they? What are atomic numbers?

14. Give some examples of isotopes of an element.

15. For what is a Wilson cloud chamber used? How does it operate?

16. Explain how radioactive disintegration causes elements to be transmuted from one to the other. How can this be done artificially?

17. How do synchro-cyclotrons and synchrotrons differ from a cyclotron?

18. How do the isotopes of uranium differ in their properties?

19. What is the difference between a nuclear reactor and an atomic bomb?

20. What are some of the properties of cosmic rays?

Things to Do

1. Read the account of the Curies' discovery of radium in any one of the several biographies written about them.

2. If you live near a college, university, or industrial laboratory which has a cyclotron, your teacher may make arrangements for several members of your class to see it.

3. Look up the story of the development of the atomic submarine and report on your findings to the class.

Mathematics Refresher

1. Introduction. The topics selected for this Mathematics Refresher are those which often are troublesome for physics students. You must frequently review these topics before you can solve certain types of physics problems. The method of presentation here is not so extensive as that given in mathematics textbooks. However, we have given you sufficient information to help you remember how to perform certain types of mathematical operations. You need these skills when solving elementary physics problems.

2. Square root. In some physics problems it is necessary to be able to extract the square root. The square root of a number is that number which when multiplied by itself produces the original number.

SAMPLE PROBLEM

Find the square root of 1108.89

SOLUTION

Separate the number into groups or periods, of two digits each, to the left and right of the decimal point. The decimal point in the answer is placed directly above the decimal point in the original number. The largest perfect square which is numerically less than 11, the number in the first group, is 9; and its square root is 3. Place these as shown, and subtract. Bring down the next period of two digits, the 08. Double the already obtained answer, 3, getting 6. *Mentally* multiply this 6 by 10, getting 60; and use this as a trial divisor. Dividing 60 into 208, we obtain the next digit of the square root, 3. Use this 3 also as the permanent second digit of the complete divisor, making it 63. Multiply 3 × 63 = 189; and subtract, 208 − 189 = 19. Bring down the next period of two digits, and repeat the process until the required number of decimal places is obtained. This means bring down the 89. Double the already obtained answer, 33, getting 66. Multiply this *mentally* by 10. Using 660 as the trial divisor into 1989, we obtain 3, the third digit of the answer, and the permanent third digit of the divisor. Multiply 3 by 663, obtaining 1989. Since there is no remainder, our problem came out even, and 33.3 is the exact square root of 1108.89.

```
              3  3. 3
          1 1 08.89
            9
    63       2 08
             1 89
   663         19 89
               19 89
```

Most of the physics problems in which you extract a square root will not come out even. In such cases your instructor may tell you the number of decimal places to which the answer is to be calculated. To assure the accuracy of the last decimal place required, you should calculate the answer to one additional decimal place and round off the answer. If the digit in the additional decimal place is 0 to 4, the preceding digit should remain as it is. If the digit in the additional decimal place is 5 to 9, the preceding digit should be increased by one.

SAMPLE PROBLEM

Extract the square root of 154.9, carrying the answer to the nearest second decimal place.

SOLUTION

Separate the number into groups or periods, of two digits each, to the left and right of the decimal point. Since the answer is required to the nearest second decimal place, we must add enough zeros to provide for three decimal places in the answer. Using the usual method for extracting square root, determine the answer to three decimal places. Since the third decimal place in our example is 5, the second decimal place is increased by one, and the answer, correct to the nearest second decimal place, is 12.45.

$$
\begin{array}{r|l}
 & 1\ \ 2.4\ \ 4\ \ 5 \\
 & 1\ 54.90\ 00\ 00 \\
 & 1 \\ \hline
22 & 54 \\
 & 44 \\ \hline
244 & 10\ 90 \\
 & 9\ 76 \\ \hline
2484 & 1\ 14\ 00 \\
 & 99\ 36 \\ \hline
24885 & 14\ 64\ 00 \\
 & 12\ 44\ 25 \\
\end{array}
$$

3. Conversion of a fraction to a decimal. Divide the numerator by the denominator, carrying the answer to the required number of decimal places.

SAMPLE PROBLEM

Convert $\frac{3}{8}$ to a decimal.

SOLUTION

Dividing 8 into 3, the equivalent decimal is found to be 0.375.

$$
\begin{array}{r}
0.375 \\
8\overline{)3.000}
\end{array}
$$

4. Calculation of percentage. The deviation of measurements or of other experimentally-obtained data from the accepted values is usually expressed as percentage error. Hence, we must know how to calculate percentage and percentage error; to convert fractions to percentages and percentages to decimals.

SAMPLE PROBLEM

What percentage of 19 is 11?

SOLUTION

We divide 11 by 19, and multiply the quotient by 100%. A multiplication by 100% does not change the value of the quotient, since 100% actually has a value of 1. When we multiply by 100%, we multiply the number by 100, and affix the % sign to the product. $\frac{11}{19} \times 100\% = 57.89\%$, rounded to two decimal places.

5. Calculation of percentage error. Percentage error is calculated thus:

$$\text{Per cent Error} = \frac{\text{Difference between Experimental Value and Correct Value}}{\text{Correct Value}} \times 100\%$$

SAMPLE PROBLEM

The accepted value for the speed of sound in air is 1120 ft/sec at 20° C. In a laboratory experiment, a student found the speed of sound to be 1118 ft/sec at 20° C. What was his percentage error?

SOLUTION

Substituting in the formula, $\frac{1120-1118}{1120} \times 100\% = 0.18\%$, rounded to two decimal places.

---

6. Conversion of fractions to percentages. To convert a fraction to a percentage, divide the numerator by the denominator, and multiply the quotient by 100%.

SAMPLE PROBLEM

Express $\frac{1}{13}$ as a percentage, rounding to two decimal places.

SOLUTION

$\frac{1}{13} \times 100\% = 7.69\%$.

---

7. Conversion of percentages to decimals. To convert a percentage to a decimal, move the decimal point two places to the left, remove the per cent sign.

SAMPLE PROBLEM

Convert 37.5% to a decimal.

SOLUTION

If we express 37.5% as a fraction, it becomes $\frac{37.5}{100}$. If we actually perform the indicated division, we obtain 0.375 as the decimal equivalent. You notice that the only change has been to move the decimal point over two places to the left, and remove the per cent sign.

---

8. Proportions. Many physics problems involving the temperature, pressure, and volume relationships of gases may be solved by proportion.

SAMPLE PROBLEM

Solve the proportion $\dfrac{x}{10} = \dfrac{50}{8}$, for x.

SOLUTION

Cross multiply the numerator on each side of the equation with the denominator on the other side, giving $8x = 10 \times 50$. Combining terms, $8x = 500$. Dividing by 8, $x = 62.5$, the required answer.

---

9. Fractional equations. The formulas for certain problems involving lenses, mirrors, and electrical resistances, produce fractional equations where the unknown is in the denominator. In solving such equations, clear of fractions by multiplying each term by the lowest common denominator. Then isolate the unknown, and complete the solution.

SAMPLE PROBLEM

Solve $\dfrac{1}{3} + \dfrac{1}{2} = \dfrac{1}{f}$ for f.

SOLUTION

The lowest common denominator of 3, 2, and f, is 6f. Multiplying the fractional equation by 6f, we obtain, $(6f)\overset{2}{\left(\dfrac{1}{3}\right)} + (6f)\overset{3}{\left(\dfrac{1}{2}\right)} = (6f)\left(\dfrac{1}{f}\right)$, or

$2f + 3f = 6$. Combining terms, $5f = 6$, and $f = 1.2$.

---

10. Formulas. In solving formula problems where the unknown is not the one usually isolated, it is helpful to rearrange the formula and isolate the actual unknown of the particular problem. Then you substitute the known values and solve the problem quickly.

SAMPLE PROBLEM

In the formula for liquid pressure, $p = hD$, we are to calculate h. How can we rearrange the formula to isolate h to make our calculations easier?

SOLUTION

First solve for h in the formula, $p = hD$. We do this by dividing both sides of the equation by D. The result is $p/D = h$, or $h = p/D$. Then we can substitute the numerical values for p and D, and complete our calculations.

---

11. Right triangles. In physics we use some of the facts about triangles that we learned in geometry in order to solve problems about forces and velocities.

1. 30°–60°–90° right triangle. In such a triangle it is convenient to remember that the hypotenuse is twice as long as the side opposite the 30° angle. The length of the side opposite the 60° angle is $s\sqrt{3}$, where s is the length of the side opposite the 30° angle.

2. 45°–45°–90° right triangle. The sides opposite the 45° angles are equal. The length of the hypotenuse is $s\sqrt{2}$, where s is the length of a side.

3. Any right triangle. The lengths of the sides and hypotenuse of any right triangle is given by Pythagoras' theorem. If a and b are the sides and c is the hypotenuse of a right triangle, then $a^2 + b^2 = c^2$.

SAMPLE PROBLEM

In a right triangle, side a is 4 in and side b is 5 in. Calculate the length of the hypotenuse.

SOLUTION

Substituting in the formula for a right triangle, $(4)^2 + (5)^2 = c^2$. Expanding the squared terms, $16 + 25 = c^2$. Combining terms, $c^2 = 41$. Extracting the square root, $c = 6.40$ in, rounded to two decimal places.

---

12. Circles. The formula for calculating the circumference of a circle is $c = \pi d$, where c is the circumference, and d is the diameter. A sufficiently accurate value of π for most physics problems is 3.14. The formula for the area of a circle is $A = \pi r^2$, where A is the area and r is the radius.

13. Cylinders. The formula for finding the volume of a right circular cylinder is $V = \pi r^2 h$, where V is the volume, r is the radius of the base, and h is the height.

14. Spheres. The formula for finding the surface area of a sphere is $A = 4\pi r^2$, where A is the surface area and r is the radius of the sphere. For finding the volume of a sphere: $V = \frac{4}{3}\pi r^3$, where V is the volume and r is the radius.

15. Numbers written in exponential form. *1. Very large numbers.* An exponential system of notation is used to write very large numbers when only the first few digits are accurately known. Instead of writing 27,000,000,000,000,-000,000,000 (27 sextillion), we may more conveniently write 2.7×10^{22}.

SAMPLE PROBLEM

Write 27,000,000,000,000,000,000,000 in exponential form.

SOLUTION

Take the known digits, 27, and write them with a decimal point after the first digit, 2.7. Count the number of *digits* to the *left* of the decimal point in the original number. In this case there are 23 digits. Since the exponent indicating the power of 10 is always one *less* than the total number of digits, the exponent is 22. Thus in exponential form the number is 2.7×10^{22}.

2. Very small numbers. A similar system may be followed for very small numbers. Instead of writing 0.001119, we may write 1.119×10^{-3}.

SAMPLE PROBLEM

Write 0.001119 in exponential form.

SOLUTION

Take the known digits, in this case the 1119, and write them with a decimal point after the first digit, as 1.119. Count the number of zeros to the *right* of the decimal point before the known digits start. In this case there are two zeros. The exponent which indicates the power of 10 is *one more* than the number of zeros to the right of the decimal point. As these small numbers are all less than 10, the exponent has a negative sign. Our answer is 1.119×10^{-3}.

---

16. Use of units in computation. In solving statement problems where units are used, the units can always be treated as algebraic quantities. They may be added, subtracted, multiplied, and divided. Many common units, such as foot-pounds, and grams per cubic centimeter, really tell us how they are calculated by their name. Foot-pounds, the unit of work in the English system of measurement, is calculated by multiplying the weight of the object in pounds by the height in feet through which it is lifted. The unit is abbreviated ft-lb. Grams per cubic centimeter, a unit of density, is obtained by dividing the mass of the object in grams by its volume in cubic centimeters. The word *per* always indicates a division, hence the unit may be abbreviated g/cm^3.

When solving a problem, if the algebraic manipulation of the units produces the correct type of unit for the answer, then the problem is set up properly. If you do the arithmetic accurately, you will get the right answer. This pre-calculation, with units only, serves as a check on the way the problem is set up. It avoids wasting time on calculations which later prove to be wrong.

A simple illustration of the usefulness of this technique is the conversion of a metric system unit to an English system unit, or vice versa. Suppose we wish to change 12.0 inches into its equivalent length in centimeters. We know that there are 2.54 centimeters to an inch, or expressed more briefly, 2.54 cm/in. To make the conversion, we must perform a multiplication or a division. But which? An examination of the units tells us that if we multiply in by cm/in, the answer will be cm, which we want. So, to complete the problem, 12.0 in $\times$ 2.54 cm/in = 30.48 cm.

If we wish to make the reverse conversion, and change 50.0 centimeters to inches, you notice that we must divide cm by cm/in in order to obtain the answer in inches. So the calculation is 50.0 cm $\div$ 2.54 cm/in = 19.69 in.

In physics, each problem will have units, and they are important. In solving each problem, all the units must be included as part of the solution.

Glossary...

ABSCISSA (ab-*sis*-uh). The horizontal line on a graph; the X axis.

Absolute humidity. The amount of water vapor in one cubic foot of air at any given time.

Absolute zero. That temperature attained by matter when it has given up all the thermal energy it can; −273.16° C or −459.69° F.

Absorption spectrum. A continuous spectrum interrupted by dark lines.

Abstract number. A number representing a measurement, but having no units associated with it.

Acceleration (ak-sel-uh-*ray*-shun). Rate of change of velocity.

Achromatic. Corrected both for spherical and chromatic aberration.

Adhesion. The force of attraction between different kinds of molecules.

Adsorption. Condensation of a gas on the surface of a solid.

Agonic line. A line drawn through places on the earth's surface that have zero declination.

Alpha particle. A charged particle composed of two protons and two neutrons.

Alternating current. A current in which the movement of the electrons is to-and-fro in the conductor.

Altimeter (al-*tim*-uh-ter). An aneroid barometer graduated to read altitude directly.

Ammeter. The instrument used for measuring the rate of flow of electricity.

Ampere. Unit of current strength. One ampere of current flowing through each of two long parallel wires one meter apart causes a magnetic force of 2×10^{-7} newtons on each meter of each wire.

Amplifier. A thermionic tube circuit used to increase the strength of an electric current.

Amplitude modulation, AM. The method of broadcasting in which the strength or amplitude of the carrier signal is changed by combining it with an audio signal.

Aneroid (*an*-er-oid). Without liquid.

Angle of incidence. The angle between the incident ray and the normal drawn to the point of reflection.

Angle of reflection. The angle between the reflected ray and the normal drawn to the point of reflection.

Angle of refraction. The angle between the refracted ray and the normal drawn to the point of refraction.

Anode. The positive terminal of an electrolytic cell.

Antenna. A device which changes a radio wave into an alternating electric current.

Archimedes' principle. The principle that the buoyant force which a fluid exerts upon a body placed in the fluid is equal to the weight of the fluid the body displaces.

Armature. A coil of wire formed around an iron or steel core which rotates in the magnetic field of a generator or motor.

Astigmatism (uh-*stig*-muh-tizm). A defect of vision caused by an irregularly curved cornea or lens.

Atmosphere. The layer of gases surrounding the earth.

Atom. The smallest particle of a chemical element.

Atomic battery. A device which directly converts nuclear energy into electrical energy.

Atomic number. A number identifying an element, equal to the number of protons in the nuclei of its atoms.

Atomic weight. The average relative weight of the atoms of an element compared with those of oxygen taken as a standard and given a value of 16.

BAROGRAPH (*bair*-uh-graf). A self-recording aneroid barometer.

Barometer (buh-*rom*-uh-ter). A device used to measure the pressure of the atmosphere.

Beam. Several parallel rays of light.

Beat. An outburst of sound followed by an interval of comparative silence.

Bernoulli's (Ber-*noo*-lees) **principle.** For the horizontal flow of a fluid through a tube, the sum of the pressure and the kinetic energy per unit volume of the fluid is a constant.

Beta (*bay*-tuh) **particle.** An electron.

Bevatron. An atom-smashing machine used to bombard the nuclei of atoms.

Bimetallic strip. Two strips of different metals which have been riveted or welded together.

Boiling point. The temperature at which a liquid boils when the atmospheric pressure is 76 centimeters of mercury.

Boyle's law. The volume of a dry gas varies inversely with the pressure exerted on it, provided the temperature remains constant.

Bright-line spectrum. Spectrum consisting of bright lines.

British thermal unit. The quantity of heat which raises the temperature of one pound of water one Fahrenheit degree.

Brittle. Easily broken.

Brownian movement. A movement caused by the ceaseless bombardment of particles by the molecules of the liquid in which they are suspended.

Brush. That part of an electric generator or motor which transfers current to or from an armature or a rotor.

Buoyant (*boy*-unt) **force.** The upward force which a fluid exerts on a body placed in it.

CALORIE. The quantity of heat which raises the temperature of one gram of water one Centigrade degree.

Camber. The amount of the curve of the surface of a wing.

Candle. The unit for measuring the intensity of a light source.

Capacitive reactance. The opposition of a capacitor to the flow of alternating current.

Capacitor. A combination of conducting plates separated by insulators.

Capillarity (kap-ul-*air*-ih-tee). The elevation or depression of liquids in small diameter tubes.

Carrier signal. The radio-frequency signal needed to carry an audio signal through space.

Carrying capacity. The amount of current in amperes which a conductor may safely carry.

Cathode. The negative electrode in an electronic tube, or the negative terminal of an electrolytic cell.

Center of curvature. The center of the sphere of which a curved mirror forms a part.

Center of gravity. That point at which all the weight of an object appears to be concentrated.

Centigrade scale. The temperature scale using the ice-point as zero and the steam-point as 100, with 100 equal divisions between called degrees.

Centrifugal (sen-*trih*-fyuh-gul). Acting away from a center.

Centripetal (sen-*trip*-uh-tul). Acting toward a center.

Chain reaction. A reaction in which the material or energy which starts the reaction is also a product.

Charles' law. If the pressure is constant, then the volume of a dry gas is directly proportional to the Kelvin temperature.

Chemical change. A change which alters the composition of the molecules of a substance. New substances with new properties are produced.

Chemosphere (*kem*-uh-sfihr). The region of the atmosphere from 20 to 50 miles above the earth where ultra violet rays are filtered out.

Chromatic aberration (kroh-*mat*-ik ab-er-*ay*-shun). The non-focusing of light of different colors.

Chromatic scale. The diatonic scale with five additional half tones added.

Coefficient of area expansion. The increase in a unit area of a solid when its temperature is increased one degree.

Coefficient of friction. The ratio of the force of friction to the normal force pressing the surfaces together.

Coefficient of linear expansion. The increase in a unit length of a solid when its temperature is increased one degree.

Coefficient of volume expansion. The increase in unit volume of a solid when its temperature is increased one degree.

Cohesion. The force of attraction between the same kind of molecules.

Color. A property of light waves which depends upon their wave length or frequency.

Complementary colors. Two colors which combine to form white light.

Compound machine. A combination of two or more simple machines.

Concave. Curved inward away from the observer.

Concave lens. A lens with concave surfaces which diverges parallel rays.

Concave mirror. One with a concave surface which converges parallel rays.

Concrete number. A number together with a unit of measurement.

Conductance. The reciprocal of resistance.

Conduction. The transmission of thermal energy from molecule to molecule.

Conductor. A material along which an electric charge can readily travel.

Continuous spectrum. An unbroken band of colors.

Convection (kun-*vek*-shun). The transmission of thermal energy by moving currents of molecules.

Convex. Curved outward toward the observer.

Convex lens. A lens with convex surfaces which converges parallel rays.

Convex mirror. A mirror with a convex surface which diverges parallel rays.

Cosmic rays. High energy particles coming from outer space.

Cosmotron. An atom-smashing machine used to bombard nuclei of atoms.

Coulomb. Unit of electric charge. One coulomb of electricity passes a given section of a conductor in one second when the conductor carries a constant current of one ampere.

Crest. The highest point of a wave.

Critical angle. That angle of incidence at which the refracted ray makes an angle of 90° with the normal.

Critical pressure. The pressure needed to liquefy a gas at its critical temperature.

Critical temperature. The temperature to which any gas must be cooled before it can be liquefied by pressure.

Cyclotron (*sy*-kloh-tron). An electromagnetic and electrostatic device for accelerating charged particles.

DENSITY. Weight per unit volume.

Detector. A tube or crystal which separates the audio signal from an amplitude-modulated carrier signal.

Deuteron. The nucleus of a deuterium (heavy hydrogen) atom. It consists of a proton and a neutron.

Dew point. Temperature at which the moisture in the air begins to condense.

Diamagnetic. Material that is feebly repelled by a magnet.

Diatonic (dy-uh-*ton*-ik) **scale.** A musical scale built up from three major chords.

Dielectric. The insulating material between the plates of a capacitor.

Diffraction. The bending or spreading of a light wave after passing through a very narrow opening.

Diffusion. Mixing of molecules of gases, liquids, or solids without regard to weight.

Diode (*dy*-ohd). An electronic tube containing a cathode and a plate.

Direct current. A current in which the movement of the electrons is in one direction only.

Direct proportion. The relation that exists between two quantities when an increase or decrease in one of them produces a corresponding increase or decrease in the other.

Discriminator. A tube which separates the audio signal from a frequency-modulated carrier signal.

Domain. A group of atoms which have their magnetic fields more or less permanently aligned.

Doppler effect. The principle according to which the frequency of sound or light waves depends on the relative velocity of the observer and the source.

Drag. The horizontal component of the forces on an airplane wing that retards its forward motion.

Ductile (*duk*-tul). Capable of being drawn into wire.

Duration of vision. The retention of an image on the retina for a short time after the removal of the object causing the image.

Dyne. In the CGS system, the force required to accelerate one gram of mass at the rate of one centimeter per second per second.

ECHO. A repetition of a sound due to the reflection of the sound wave from some surface.

Efficiency. The ratio of useful work to total work.

Elasticity. The ability of a solid to resume its original shape after being distorted.

Elastic limit. That limit beyond which a body subjected to a force can not go without becoming permanently distorted.

Electric current. The flow of electrons along a conductor.

Electrical density. The quantity of electrical charge per unit area.

Electrochemical equivalent. The number of grams of a material which will be deposited by the passage of one coulomb of charge.

Electrodes. Metal or carbon plates in an electric cell.

Electrolysis (eh-lek-*trol*-uh-sis). The conduction of electricity through a solution or through a molten compound together with the resulting chemical changes.

Electrolyte (eh-*lek*-truh-lyte). The solution or liquid through which current flows in an electrolytic cell.

Electromagnet. An iron bar or core wrapped with a large number of turns of insulated wire.

Electromagnetic spectrum. The complete array of known electromagnetic radiations.

Electron. A negatively charged particle which revolves about the nucleus of an atom.

Electron gun. An assembly of electrodes which produces an electron beam.

Electron microscope. A microscope which uses a beam of electrons to produce an image.

Electrophorus (eh-lek-*trof*-er-us). A device for producing electric charges by induction.

Electroplating. The process of depositing metal by using an electric current.

Electroscope. A device for detecting the presence of an electric charge, determining its sign, or measuring its intensity.

Energy. The capacity or ability for doing work.

Equilibrant force. The force which produces equilibrium. It is equal in magnitude but opposite in direction to a resultant force.

Equilibrium. The condition of a body when no unbalanced forces act upon it.

Erg. In the CGS system, the force of one dyne acting through a distance of one centimeter.

Evaporation. The process of changing from a solid or liquid into a gas.

Exosphere (*eks*-uh-sfihr). The region of the atmosphere from about 250 miles above the earth to the outer edge of the atmosphere.

External combustion engine. An engine in which the heat of the burning fuel is used to vaporize a liquid under pressure. The vaporized liquid is then permitted to expand in the cylinder or turbine chamber of the engine.

FADING. The periodic weakening of radio signals.

Fahrenheit scale. The temperature scale using the ice-point as 32 and the steam-point as 212, with 180 equal divisions between called degrees.

Farad. The unit of electrical capacity.

Farsightedness. Vision defect caused by too short an eyeball or too flat a lens.

Fission. The disintegration of an atom into two nuclei of more or less equal mass.

Fluid. A liquid or a gas.

Fluorescent (floo-o-*res*-ent) **lamp.** A lamp in which light is produced by radiation from ultraviolet rays.

Focus. A point at which light rays meet, or from which rays of light diverge.

Foot-pound. In the English system, the force of one pound acting through a distance of one foot.

Force. That which produces or prevents motion, or has a tendency to do so.

Fractional distillation. A method of separating the components of a liquid in a still.

Fraunhofer (*frown*-hohf-er) **lines.** Dark lines in the spectrum of sunlight.

Freezing point. The temperature at which a liquid changes to a solid.

Frequency. The number of cycles per second of the vibrating body which produces the sound.

Frequency modulation, FM. The

method of broadcasting in which the frequency of the carrier signal is changed by combining it with an audio signal.

Friction. The force which opposes motion.

Front. The boundary between two different air masses.

Fulcrum (*ful*-krum). The fixed point about which a lever turns.

Fundamental tone. The tone produced by an object which is vibrating as a whole.

Fusion. The change of phase from a solid to a liquid, also the process of building up more complex atoms from simple ones.

GALVANOMETER. (gal-vuh-*nom*-iter). An instrument for measuring the strength of a weak electric current.

Galvanoscope (gal-*van*-uh-skohp). A device used to detect the presence of an electric current or to determine its direction.

Gamma rays. High energy X rays.

Gas. The phase of matter which has neither a definite shape nor a definite volume.

Generator. A device for converting mechanical energy into electrical energy.

Grade. The ratio of the height of an incline to its length.

Gram. A metric unit of mass.

Gravitation. The mutual force of attraction between bodies.

Grid. A wire coil whose charge controls the passage of electrons from the cathode to the plate.

Ground wave. A radio wave which travels close to the ground.

Gyroscope (*jy*-rah-skohp). A heavy wheel mounted so that it is free to rotate on its axis within a light-weight frame.

HARD. Not easily scratched.

Heat. Thermal energy which is being transferred from one body to another.

Heat capacity. The quantity of heat needed to raise the temperature of a body one Centigrade degree.

Heat of fusion. The number of calories needed to melt one gram of a substance without increasing its temperature; or the number of British thermal units needed to melt one pound of a substance without increasing its temperature.

Heat of vaporization. The number of calories needed to vaporize one gram of a liquid without increasing its temperature; or the number of British thermal units needed to vaporize one pound of substance without increasing its temperature.

Helix. A conductor which has been wound into a spiral coil.

Henry. The unit of inductance.

Henry's law. For slightly soluble gases, the amount of gas that can be dissolved in a liquid is directly proportional to the pressure.

Hooke's law. Within the limits of perfect elasticity, strain is directly proportional to stress.

Horsepower. In the English system, the unit of power that is 550 foot-pounds per second.

Humidity. The amount of water vapor in the air.

ICE-POINT. The freezing point of water, and used as one of two fixed points on a thermometer.

Illuminated. Visible because of reflected light.

Image orthicon. A television camera tube.

Impedance. The total opposition of a load circuit to the flow of alternating current.

Impenetrability. The property of matter by virtue of which two objects can not occupy the same space at the same time.

Impulse. The product of a force times the length of time it acts.

Inclined plane. A slanted surface.

Index of refraction. The ratio of the speed of light in a vacuum to its speed in the given substance; the ratio of the sine of the angle of incidence to the sine of the angle of refraction.

Induced magnetism. Magnetism produced in a magnetic material by the presence of a magnet.

Induction. Producing an emf in a conductor by moving the conductor with respect to a magnetic field.

Inductive reactance. The opposition of a coil to the flow of alternating current.

Inertia (in-*er*-shuh). The property of matter which makes it necessary for a force to be exerted on the matter in order to accelerate it.

Infrared rays. Waves longer than visible light waves but shorter than radio waves.

Infrasonic. Below the range of human hearing.

Input. The product of the acting force by the distance it moves.

Insulator. A material along which an electric charge does not readily pass.

Intensity. A property of sound waves which depends on their energy. It is increased by increasing the amplitude and the area of the vibrating body.

Interference. The effect produced by the superimposing of two beams of light on one another.

Internal combustion engine. An engine in which the fuel is burned directly in the cylinder or turbine chamber.

Inverse proportion. The relation that exists between two quantities when an increase in one of them produces a corresponding decrease in the other.

Ion. An atom or group of atoms that has an excess or deficiency of electrons.

Ionosphere (eye-*on*-uh-sfihr). The region of the atmosphere from 50 to about 250 miles above the earth from which radio waves are reflected.

Isobar (*eye*-suh-bar). A line drawn on a weather map through places of equal barometric pressure.

Isoclinic lines. Lines drawn through places on the earth's surface having the same magnetic inclination.

Isogonic lines. Lines drawn through places on the earth's surface having the same magnetic declination.

Isotopes. Forms of the same element whose atoms differ only in weight.

JET STREAM. A narrow stream of air at a high altitude which moves at speeds 200 to 300 miles per hour.

Joule (*jowl*). In the MKS system, the force of one newton acting through a distance of one meter.

KELVIN SCALE. The temperature scale using absolute zero as the zero point and divisions that are the same size as Centigrade degrees.

Kilocalorie. 1000 calories.

Kilowatt-hour. 1000 watt-hours.

Kinetic (kih-*net*-ik) **energy.** Energy of motion.

Kinetic theory. A theory of matter which assumes that the molecules of matter are in constant motion.

LENS. A portion of a transparent substance bounded by two polished nonparallel curved surfaces or by one polished plane and one polished curved surface.

Lenz's law. A current induced in a moving conductor always flows in such a direction that it forms a magnetic field which opposes the motion of the conductor.

Lever (*lev*-er). A rigid bar which is free to turn about a fixed point.

Leyden jar. A glass jar coated on its inner and outer surfaces with a conducting material to be used for storing electric charges.

Light. Electromagnetic radiation which is visible to the human eye. Also applied to radiation having frequencies somewhat above and below the range of human sight.

Light-year. The astronomical unit of distance, which is the distance light can travel in one year.

Line spectrum. A spectrum consisting of distinct and separate colored lines.

Liquid. The phase of matter which has a definite volume but takes the shape of its container.

Liter. A metric unit of volume.

Local action. An effect produced in an electric cell by impurities.

Longitudinal (lon-jih-*too*-dih-nul) **wave.** A wave motion in which the particles vibrate to and fro along the path which the wave travels.

Loudness. The effect which sounds of varying intensity have on the ear.

Loudspeaker. A device for changing variations in an electric current into sound waves.

Lumen. Unit for measuring the illumination on a surface.

Luminous. Visible because of emitted light.

MAGNETIC DECLINATION. The deviation between true north and north as indicated by a compass needle.

Magnetic equator. The line drawn

through places on the earth's surface having zero inclination.

Magnetic field. The space permeated by magnetic lines.

Magnetic inclination. The deviation between the equilibrium position of a compass needle mounted on a horizontal axis and true horizontal.

Magnetic line. The path an independent north-seeking pole would take in moving from the N-pole to the S-pole of a magnet.

Magnetic material. Material that is attracted by a magnet.

Magnetic permeability. That property of materials which gathers in magnetic lines and affords an excellent path for their transmission.

Magnetic pole. The region of a magnet where the magnetic force appears to be concentrated.

Magnetic transparency. That property of a material which permits magnetic lines to pass readily through it as though the material were not present.

Magneto. A generator having a permanent magnetic field.

Major chord. Three tones having the frequency ratio of 4:5:6.

Malleable (*mal*-ee-uh-bul). Capable of being hammered out or rolled.

Mass. The measure of the quantity of matter.

Matter. Anything which occupies space and has weight.

Mechanical advantage. The ratio of the resisting weight to the acting force; or, the ratio of the distance through which the force is exerted divided by the distance the weight is raised.

Melting point. The temperature at which a solid changes to a liquid.

Meniscus (meh-*niss*-kus). The crescent-shaped surface of a liquid column.

Meson (*mee*-son). Charged particles with a mass about 200 times that of an electron.

Meter. A metric unit of length.

Microfarad. One-millionth of a farad.

Micron (*my*-kron). $\frac{1}{1,000,000}$ meter.

Microphone. A device for changing sound waves into variations in an electric current.

Mil. 0.001 inch.

Mirage (mer-*ahzh*). An optical illusion caused by refraction of light through air layers of different densities.

Mirror. A highly polished surface which can be used to form images by regular reflection of light.

Molecule. The smallest particle into which matter may be divided without destroying its characteristic properties.

Moment of a force. The effectiveness of a force in producing rotation.

Momentum. The product of the mass of an object times its velocity.

Monochromatic light. Light consisting of only one color.

Motion. A continuous change of place or position.

Motor. A device for converting electrical energy into mechanical energy.

NEARSIGHTEDNESS. A defect of vision caused by too long an eyeball or too convex a lens.

Neutron. A neutral particle found in the nucleus of an atom.

Newton. In the MKS system, the force required to accelerate 1 kilogram of mass at the rate of 1 meter per second per second.

Newton's law of cooling. The rate of cooling or warming of a body is proportional to the difference between the temperature of the body and the temperature of the surrounding medium.

Newton's law of universal gravitation. Every body in the universe attracts every other body with a force that is directly proportional to the product of their masses and inversely proportional to the square of the distance between their centers.

Noise. A sound produced by an object which vibrates in irregular fashion.

Normal. A line drawn perpendicular to a line or a plane.

North-seeking pole. The pole of a magnet which is attracted toward the North Magnetic Pole of the earth.

Nuclear change. A change which alters the identity of atoms.

Nuclear reactor. A lattice arrangement of fissionable material, radioactive isotopes, and energy; sometimes called an atomic pile.

Nucleus. The central part of an atom.

OHM. The unit for measuring electrical resistance.

Ohm's law. The current flowing in a circuit, in amperes, is directly proportional to the potential difference, in volts, and inversely proportional to the resistance of the circuit, in ohms.

Opaque (oh-*payk*). Does not transmit light.

Optical density. A property of a transparent substance which is a measure of the speed of light through the substance. Light travels more slowly through media of higher optical density.

Ordinate. The vertical line on a graph; the Y axis.

Oscillation. That process in which the circuit of an electrical device will produce alternating current at a frequency determined primarily by the sizes of the coils and condensers in the circuit.

Osmosis (oz-*moh*-sis). The diffusion of a liquid through a membrane.

Output. The product of the resisting weight by the distance it moves.

Overload. Forcing a conductor to carry a current greater than its carrying capacity.

Overtone. A tone whose vibration rate is a whole number multiple of that of the fundamental.

PARALLEL. That method of connecting electrical equipment so that there are several paths for the current through the various devices.

Parallel forces. Forces acting in the same or opposite directions.

Paramagnetic. Materials that are only very slightly attracted by a magnet.

Pascal's principle. Pressure applied anywhere on a confined fluid is transmitted undiminished in every direction.

Pendulum. A body suspended in such a manner that it can swing to-and-fro about a horizontal axis.

Penumbra. That part of a shadow which receives part of the rays of light from a luminous source.

Period of a pendulum. The time required for a complete vibration or cycle.

Permanent magnet. A magnet which retains its magnetism.

Permeable. Readily gathers in magnetic lines.

Photoelectric effect. The emission of electrons caused by the application of light.

Photometer (foh-*tom*-eh-ter). An instrument for comparing the intensities of two light sources.

Phototube. An electronic tube based on the photoelectric effect.

Physical change. A change which does not alter the composition of the molecules of a substance.

Pitch. The property of sound which depends on the frequency of the sound waves received by the ear.

Pitch of a screw. The distance between the threads.

Plate. The positive electrode in an electronic tube.

Polarization of an electric cell. A defect in cells caused by an accumulation of hydrogen bubbles on the positive plate.

Polarized light. Light whose waves vibrate in only one plane.

Polychromatic light. Light which is composed of several colors.

Porosity. The property of having small openings or spaces between particles of matter.

Positron. A particle with the mass of an electron but having a positive charge.

Potential energy. Energy of position, or stored energy.

Pound. The English system unit of force. It equals the weight of the standard pound at sea level and at 45° latitude.

Power. The rate of doing work.

Power factor. The ratio between the actual wattage and apparent wattage of an alternating current circuit.

Power of accommodation. The ability to change the curvature of the lenses of the eyes.

Pressure. Force per unit area.

Primary coil. The coil of wire through which current from an external source passes.

Primary colors. Red, green, and bluish-violet.

Principal focus. The point where parallel rays of light meet after being refracted by converging lenses.

Proton. A positively charged particle found in the nucleus of an atom.

Pulley. A wheel which turns readily on an axle mounted in a frame.

QUALITY. A property of sound waves which depends on the number and prominence of the overtones.

RADAR. A device used to detect distant objects by means of radio waves and their echoes.

Radiation. The transmission of thermal energy by electromagnetic waves.

Radioactivity. The spontaneous, uncontrollable breakdown of the nucleus of an atom with the emission of particles and rays.

Rarefaction. The region in wave motion where the medium is rarefied.

Ray. A single line of light coming from a luminous point.

Real image. An image which is actually formed by rays of light.

Rectifier. A device which changes alternating current to direct current.

Rectilinear (rek-tih-*lin*-ee-er). In a straight line.

Reflection. The turning back of light waves from a surface.

Refraction. The bending of light rays as they pass from one medium into another of different optical density.

Regelation (reh-jel-*ay*-shun). The process in which a solid melts under pressure and freezes after the pressure is released.

Relative humidity. The ratio of the amount of moisture which the air does contain to what it could contain.

Residual magnetism. Retained magnetism after a temporary magnet loses most of its magnetism.

Resistance. The opposition of a conductor to the flow of electrons.

Resistivity. The resistance of one mil-foot of wire.

Resolution of forces. The separation of a single force into two forces acting in definite directions upon the same point.

Resonance (*rez*-uh-nenss). The inducing of vibrations of a natural rate in matter by a vibrating source having the same or a simple multiple frequency.

Resultant force. The single force which has the same effect as two or more forces acting together.

Retina. The inner coat of the eye which contains the light-sensitive endings of the optic nerve.

Rheostat (*ree*-oh-stat). A device used to vary the flow of electric current by means of a variable resistance.

Rotary motion. Motion about a point which acts as a pivot.

SCALER (*skay*-ler) **QUANTITY.** A quantity which has only magnitude.

Screw. An inclined plane wound on a cylinder.

Secondary coil. The coil in which an emf is induced by current variations in the primary coil.

Secondary emission. The electrons knocked out of a positive plate by other electrons traveling at high speed.

Self-induction. A phenomenon in coiled conductors whereby the magnetic field of one turn induces an emf in an adjacent turn.

Series. A method of connecting electrical equipment so that all current must flow through each device in turn.

Shadow. The space from which light is excluded by an opaque object.

Short circuit. A circuit through a small resistance.

Siphon (*sy*-fun). A bent tube with arms of unequal length used to transfer liquids over an elevation.

Skip distance. The distance between points of good radio reception.

Sky wave. A radio wave which travels upward into the sky.

Slug. In the English system, the mass of a body which will be accelerated at the rate of 1 foot per second when 1 pound of force acts upon it.

Solar spectrum. The band of colors produced when sunlight is dispersed by a prism.

Solenoid (*soh*-luh-noyd). A coil of wire; a long helix.

Solid. The phase of matter which has a definite shape and a definite volume.

Solute. The substance which is dissolved.

Solution. The mixture of a solvent and a solute.

Solvent. The substance in which the solute is dissolved.

Sonar. A method of using sound wave echoes to aid in the navigation of ships.

Sound. Vibrations in matter which can be detected by our ears. Also applied to similar vibrations above and below the normal range of human hearing.

Source of electromotive force. A device which furnishes electrons of increased potential energy.

South-seeking pole. The pole of a magnet which is attracted toward the South Magnetic Pole of the earth.

Specific gravity. The ratio of the density of a substance to the density of a standard substance such as water.

Specific heat. The number of calories needed to raise the temperature of one gram of a substance one Centigrade degree; or the number of British thermal units needed to raise the temperature of one pound of a substance one Fahrenheit degree.

Spectroscope. An optical instrument used for examining spectra.

Speed. Rate of motion.

Spherical aberration. The non-focusing of rays from a single point to form a single point image.

Standard pressure. The pressure of a column of mercury 760 mm high.

Standard temperature. The temperature of melting ice, 0° C.

Static electricity. Stationary electric charges.

Station model. A system of recording on a weather map by symbols the observations made at the various weather stations.

Steam-point. The boiling point of water, and used as one of two fixed points on a thermometer.

Stefan's law. The amount of energy emitted by an ideal radiator is directly proportional to the fourth power of its Kelvin temperature.

Storage cell. An electric cell which can be recharged after being discharged.

Strain. The distortion produced by a stress.

Stratosphere (*strat*-uh-sfihr). The region of the atmosphere from 10 to 20 miles above the earth characterized by almost uniform temperature.

Streamline flow. The smooth flow of a fluid.

Stress. The force which tends to distort an object.

Sublimation. The evaporation of a solid to a gas directly without passing through a liquid phase.

Supercooled water. Water that is cooled below its normal freezing point.

Superheterodyne receiver. A receiver in which two waves of different frequencies combine to produce a third.

Surface tension. The tendency of a liquid surface to contract.

Synchrotron. An atom-smashing machine used to bombard the nuclei of atoms.

TEMPERATURE. The hotness or coldness of a body as determined by the thermal energy it possesses.

Tempered scale. A twelve-note scale with a constant frequency change between successive notes.

Temporary magnet. A magnet which loses nearly all its magnetism in a very short time.

Tensile strength. The force required to break a wire or rod of unit cross-sectional area.

Theory. A scientific explanation, tested by observations and experiments.

Thermal energy. The total potential and kinetic energy of the atoms of a body.

Thermionic (therm-eye-*on*-ik) **emission.** The emission of electrons from hot objects.

Thermocouple. Two dissimilar metallic conductors joined at their ends and used for measuring temperature.

Thermometer. A device for measuring temperature.

Thermostat. A device containing a bimetallic strip which is used for regulating temperatures.

Thrust. The forward reaction force.

Tone. A sound produced by an object which vibrates in regular fashion.

Torque (*tork*). The product of a force times the length of the arm on which it acts.

Total force. The force acting against the entire area of a surface.

Transformer. A device for changing the voltage of an alternating current.

Transistor. A device containing germanium which can be used in place of an electronic tube for controlling an electric current.

Translatory (*trans*-luh-tor-ee) **motion.** Motion along a line.

Translucent. Transmits light waves but scatters them so that objects can not be distinguished.

Transparent. Transmits light waves so that objects can be distinguished.

Trans-uranium elements. Elements of higher atomic number than uranium.

Transverse wave. A wave motion in which the particles vibrate at right angles to the path along which the wave travels.

Triode (*try*-ohd). An electronic tube containing a cathode, a plate, and a grid.

Tropopause (*troh*-puh-pawz). The upper edge of the troposphere.

Troposphere (*troh*-puh-sfihr). The lowest layer of the atmosphere.

Trough (*trawf*). The lowest point of a wave.

Tungar rectifier. A gas-filled diode used for charging storage batteries from an alternating current line.

Turbulent flow. The unsmooth flow of a fluid.

ULTRASONIC. Above the range of human hearing.

Ultraviolet rays. Rays shorter than visible light rays but longer than X rays.

Umbra. That part of a shadow from which all the rays of light are excluded.

VAPORIZATION. The change of phase from a liquid to a vapor.

Vector. An arrow used to represent a vector quantity.

Vector quantity. A quantity which has magnitude and direction.

Velocity (vuh-*loss*-ih-tee). Rate of motion in a particular direction.

Video detector. The detector in a television receiver which separates the picture, or video signal from the picture carrier.

Virtual image. An image which only appears to the eye to be formed by rays of light.

Viscosity. The internal resistance of a fluid which tends to prevent it from flowing.

Volt. The unit of potential difference. The difference in potential between two points is one volt if one joule of work is done by electrical forces in moving one coulomb of charge between the two points.

Voltaic cell. A device which transforms chemical energy into electrical energy. It consists of two dissimilar conducting materials immersed in a fluid which is also a conductor.

Voltmeter. The instrument used for measuring difference of potential.

Volume. Space taken up by matter.

WATER HEAD. The pressure caused by a difference in the level of the water in connecting pipes.

Water turbine. A device for changing the potential energy of water into the kinetic energy of a rotating shaft.

Watt. A unit of power. One watt is the power supplied when a current of one ampere is driven by a potential difference of one volt.

Watt-hour. A unit of energy. If the potential difference in a part of a circuit is one volt, a current of one ampere flowing continuously through it for one hour will furnish one watt-hour of electrical energy.

Wave length. The distance between any one particle in a wave and the particle in the next wave which is moving in a corresponding fashion.

Wedge. A double inclined plane.

Weight. The measure of the earth's attraction for a body.

Weld. To join metal parts by melting them together.

Wheatstone bridge. An electrical device used for precise measurements of resistance.

Wheel and axle. A wheel or crank rigidly attached to an axle.

Wimshurst machine. A machine that generates static charges by induction.

Work. The product of force times distance.

X RAY. Invisible electromagnetic radiation of great penetrating power.

YOUNG—HELMHOLTZ COLOR VISION THEORY. The theory that the retina of the eye is provided with three sets of nerves, each of which is sensitive to one of the three primary colors.

Appendix A...

FORMULAS

1. Weight Density

$$D = \frac{w}{V}$$

D is density; w is weight; V is volume.

2. Liquid Pressure

$$p = hD$$

p is pressure; h is depth; D is density.

3. Total Force

(1) *Horizontal Surfaces*

$$F = AhD$$

F is total force; A is area; h is depth; D is density.

(2) *Vertical Surfaces*

$$F = \frac{AhD}{2}$$

F is total force; A is area; h is depth; D is density.

4. Mechanical Advantage of Any Machine

$$\text{Mechanical Advantage} = \frac{w}{F}$$

w is weight supported; F is force applied.

5. Mechanical Advantage of Hydraulic Press

$$\text{Mechanical Advantage} = \frac{w}{F} = \frac{A}{a} = \frac{D}{d}$$

w is weight supported; F is force applied; A is area of large piston; a is area of small piston; D is diameter of large piston; d is diameter of small piston.

6. Specific Gravity of a Solid or Liquid

$$\text{Sp. gr.} = \frac{\text{density of substance}}{\text{density of water}}$$

7. Specific Gravity of a Solid

(1) *Denser than Water*

$$\text{Sp. gr.} = \frac{\text{weight in air}}{\text{buoyant force of water}}$$

(2) *Less Dense than Water*

$$\text{Sp. gr.} = \frac{w}{w' - w''}$$

w is weight of solid in air; w' is combined weight of solid in air and sinker in water; w'' is combined weight of both solid and sinker in water.

8. Specific Gravity of a Liquid

(1) *Bottle Method*

$$\text{Sp. gr.} = \frac{\text{weight of liquid}}{\text{weight of water}}$$

(2) *Loss-of-Weight Method*

$$\text{Sp. gr.} = \frac{\text{buoyant force of liquid}}{\text{buoyant force of water}}$$

(3) *Hydrometer Method*

$$\text{Sp. gr.} = \frac{\text{depth rod sinks in water}}{\text{depth rod sinks in liquid}}$$

9. Boyle's Law

$$pV = p'V'$$

p is original pressure; V is original volume; p' is new pressure; V' is new volume.

10. Hooke's Law

$$\text{Elastic Modulus} = \frac{\text{stress}}{\text{strain}}$$

11. Factor of Safety

$$\text{Factor of Safety} = \frac{\text{maximum load}}{\text{rated load}}$$

12. Composition of Forces

The resultant of two forces acting at an angle upon a given point is equal to the diagonal of a parallelogram of which the two force vectors are sides. The equilibrant equals the magnitude of the resultant, but acts in the opposite direction.

13. Resolution of Force of Gravity

Object Resting on Inclined Plane

$$W : W_p = l : h$$

W is weight of object; W_p is force tending to pull object down plane; l is length of plane; h is height of plane.

14. Coefficient of Friction

$$\mu = \frac{f}{N}$$

μ is coefficient of friction; f is force of friction; N is force normal to surface.

15. Speed

$$\text{Average Speed} = \frac{\text{distance traveled}}{\text{elapsed time}}$$

16. Accelerated Motion

$$v = at, \text{ or } v = gt$$

v is final velocity; a is acceleration, or g is acceleration due to gravity; t is time.

17. Accelerated Motion

$$s = \tfrac{1}{2}at^2, \text{ or } s = \tfrac{1}{2}gt^2$$

s is total distance; a is acceleration, or g is acceleration due to gravity; t is time.

18. Accelerated Motion

$$v = \sqrt{2as}, \text{ or } v = \sqrt{2gs}$$

v is final velocity; a is acceleration, or g is acceleration due to gravity; s is total distance.

19. Accelerated Motion

$$s = \tfrac{1}{2}a(2t - 1), \text{ or } s = \tfrac{1}{2}g(2t - 1)$$

s is distance traversed in a given second; a is acceleration, or g is acceleration due to gravity; t is the number of the given second.

20. Newton's Second Law of Motion

$$F = ma$$

F is force; m is mass; a is acceleration.

21. Force and Acceleration on Bodies of Known Weight

$$F : w = a : g$$

F is force; w is weight; a is acceleration; g is acceleration due to gravity.

22. Impulse and Momentum

$$Ft = mv$$

F is force; t is time; the product Ft is impulse; m is mass; v is velocity; the product mv is momentum.

23. Centrifugal Force

$$\text{Centrifugal Force} = \frac{mv^2}{r}$$

m is mass; v is velocity; r is radius of path.

24. Pendulum

$$t : t' = \sqrt{l} : \sqrt{l'}$$

t is period of first pendulum; t' is period of second pendulum; l is length of first pendulum; l' is length of second pendulum.

25. Pendulum

$$t = 2\pi \sqrt{\frac{l}{g}}$$

t is period; l is length; g is acceleration due to gravity.

26. Work

$$W = Fs$$

W is work; F is force; s is distance.

27. Power

$$P = \frac{W}{t}$$

P is power; W is work; t is time.

28. Horsepower

$$\text{hp} = \frac{Fs}{550t}$$

hp is horsepower; F is force in pounds; s is distance in feet; t is time in seconds.

29. Potential Energy

$$\text{P.E.} = mgh$$

P.E. is potential energy; m is mass; g is acceleration due to gravity; h is vertical distance.

30. Kinetic Energy

$$\text{K.E.} = \tfrac{1}{2}mv^2$$

K.E. is kinetic energy; m is mass; v is velocity.

31. Variation of Mass with Velocity

$$m = \frac{m_0}{\sqrt{1 - \dfrac{v^2}{c^2}}}$$

m is mass at velocity, v; m_0 is mass at zero velocity; c is speed of light.

32. Machines

$$F \times s_F = w \times s_w$$

F is acting force; s_F is distance acting force moves; w is resisting weight; s_w is distance resisting weight moves.

33. Machines

$$\text{Efficiency} = \frac{\text{useful work}}{\text{total work}}$$

34. Lever

$$\text{Mechanical Advantage} = \frac{EF}{RF}$$

EF is length of effort arm; RF is length of resistance arm.

35. Pulley

$$nF = w$$

n is number of strands supporting movable block; F is acting force; w is resisting weight.

36. Wheel and Axle

$$\text{Mechanical Advantage} = \frac{C}{c} = \frac{D}{d} = \frac{R}{r}$$

C, D, and R are circumference, diameter, and radius, respectively, of wheel; c, d, and r are circumference, diameter, and radius, respectively, of axle.

37. Inclined Plane

(1) *When Force Acts Parallel to Plane*

$$\text{Mechanical Advantage} = \frac{l}{h}$$

l is length of plane; h is height of plane.

(2) *When Force Acts Parallel to Base of Plane*

$$\text{Mechanical Advantage} = \frac{b}{h}$$

b is base of plane; h is height of plane.

38. Screw

$$\text{Mechanical Advantage} = \frac{2\pi r}{d}$$

r is length of arm on which force acts; d is pitch of screw.

39. Compound Machine

Total Mechanical Advantage = mechanical advantage (machine 1) $\times$ mechanical advantage (machine 2) $\times$ mechanical advantage (machine 3), etc.

40. Worm Wheel

$$\text{Mechanical Advantage} = \frac{nl}{r}$$

n is number of teeth in gear wheel; l is radius of wheel on which force acts; r is radius of axle on which weight acts.

41. Differential Pulley

$$\text{Mechanical Advantage} = \frac{2C}{C - c}$$

C is circumference of large wheel; c is circumference of small wheel.

42. Temperature Conversion

(1) *Centigrade to Fahrenheit*

$$t_F = \tfrac{9}{5}t_C + 32$$

t_F is Fahrenheit temperature; t_C is Centigrade temperature.

(2) *Fahrenheit to Centigrade*

$$t_C = \tfrac{5}{9}(t_F - 32)$$

t_C is Centigrade temperature; t_F is Fahrenheit temperature.

43. Linear Expansion

$$\Delta l = \alpha l(t - t_o)$$

Δl is increase in length; α is coefficient of linear expansion; l is original length; t is final temperature; t_o is original temperature.

44. Kelvin Temperature

$$T = t_C + 273$$

T is Kelvin temperature; t_C is Centigrade temperature.

45. Charles' Law

$$\frac{V}{V'} = \frac{T}{T'}$$

V is original volume; V' is new volume; T is original Kelvin temperature; T' is final Kelvin temperature.

46. Boyle's and Charles' Laws Combined

$$\frac{pV}{T} = \frac{p'V'}{T'}$$

p is original pressure; V is original volume; T is original Kelvin temperature; p' is final pressure; V' is final volume; T' is final Kelvin temperature.

47. Heat Exchange

$$Q = mc\Delta t$$

Q is amount of heat required; m is mass of substance; c is specific heat of substance; Δt is change in temperature.

48. Sound Wave Formula

$$v = f\lambda$$

v is velocity of wave; f is frequency; λ is wave length.

49. Intensity of Sound

$$\beta = 10 \log \frac{I}{I_o}$$

β is intensity of sound wave; I is energy of sound wave; I_o is energy of threshold of hearing, 10^{-16} watt/cm^2.

50. Resonance in Tubes

(1) *Closed Tube*

$$\lambda = 4(l + 0.4d)$$

λ is wave length; l is length of closed tube; d is diameter of tube.

(2) *Open Tube*

$$\lambda = 2(l + 0.8d)$$

λ is wave length; l is length of open tube; d is diameter of tube.

51. Illumination

$$E = \frac{I}{R^2}$$

E is illumination; I is intensity; R is distance from source to illuminated surface.

52. Images in Mirrors and Lenses

$$S_o : S_i = D_o : D_i$$

S_o is object size; S_i is image size; D_o is object distance; D_i is image distance.

53. Images in Mirrors and Lenses

$$\frac{1}{D_o} + \frac{1}{D_i} = \frac{1}{f}$$

D_o is object distance; D_i is image distance; f is focal length.

54. Index of Refraction

$$\mu = \frac{\sin \theta_i}{\sin \theta_r}$$

μ is index of refraction; θ_i is angle of incidence; θ_r is angle of refraction.

55. Light Wave Formula

$$c = f\lambda$$

c is velocity of light; f is frequency; λ is wave length.

56. Simple Magnifier

$$\text{Magnifying Power} = \frac{25 \text{ cm}}{f \text{ cm}} = \frac{10 \text{ in}}{f \text{ in}}$$

f is focal length of lens in units indicated.

57. Compound Microscope

$$\text{Magnifying Power} = \frac{25L}{f_e f_o}$$

L is length of tube in centimeters; f_e is focal length of eyepiece in centimeters; f_o is focal length of objective in centimeters.

58. Refracting Telescope

$$\text{Magnifying Power} = \frac{f_o}{f_e}$$

f_o is focal length of objective; f_e is focal length of eyepiece.

59. Ohm's Law

$$I = \frac{V}{R}$$

I is current; V is potential difference; R is resistance.

60. Laws of Resistance

$$R = \frac{\rho l}{d^2}$$

R is resistance; ρ is resistivity; l is length in feet; d is diameter in mils.

61. Resistances in Series

$$R = R_1 + R_2 + R_3 \cdots$$

R is total resistance; R_1, R_2, R_3, etc., are individual resistances.

62. Resistances in Parallel

$$\frac{1}{R} = \frac{1}{R_1} + \frac{1}{R_2} + \frac{1}{R_3} \cdots$$

R is joint resistance; R_1, R_2, R_3, etc., are individual resistances.

63. Quantity of Electric Charge

$$Q = It$$

Q is amount of charge; I is current; t is time.

64. Electric Power

$$P = IV$$

P is power; I is current; V is potential difference.

65. Electric Power

$$P = I^2 R$$

P is power; I is current; R is resistance.

66. Laws of Electrolysis

$$m = zIt$$

m is mass; z is electrochemical equivalent; I is current; t is time.

67. Cell Formula

$$I = \frac{\mathcal{E}}{R_e + R_i}$$

I is current; $\mathcal{E}$ is emf of cell; R_e is external resistance; R_i is internal resistance.

68. Cells in Series

$$I = \frac{n\mathcal{E}}{R_e + nR_i}$$

I is current; n is number of cells; $\mathcal{E}$ is emf of one cell; R_e is external resistance; R_i is internal resistance.

69. Cells in Parallel

$$I = \frac{\mathcal{E}}{R_e + \dfrac{R_i}{n}}$$

I is current; $\mathcal{E}$ is emf of one cell; R_e is external resistance; R_i is internal resistance, n is number of cells.

70. Joule's Laws

$$W = I^2 R t$$

W is energy; I is current strength; R is resistance; t is time.

71. Capacitive Reactance

$$X_C = \frac{159{,}000}{fc}$$

X_C is capacitive reactance in ohms; f is frequency in cycles; c is capacitance in microfarads.

72. Inductive Reactance

$$X_L = 2\pi f L$$

X_L is inductive reactance in ohms; f is frequency in cycles; L is inductance in henrys.

73. Impedance

$$Z = \sqrt{R^2 + (X_L - X_C)^2}$$

Z is impedance; R is resistance; X_L is inductive reactance; X_C is capacitive reactance.

74. Ohm's Law for A.C. Circuits

$$I = \frac{V}{Z}$$

I is current; V is voltage; Z is impedance.

75. Range of Television Station

$$D = 1.23\sqrt{H}$$

D is range in miles; H is height of antenna in feet.

Appendix B...

TABLE 1. — USEFUL NUMBERS — ENGLISH SYSTEM

12 in	= 1 ft	27 ft³	= 1 yd³
3 ft	= 1 yd	231 in³	= 1 gal
5280 ft	= 1 mi	60 mi/hr	= 88 ft/sec
1760 yd	= 1 mi	7000 grains	= 1 lb avoirdupois
144 in²	= 1 ft²	16 oz	= 1 lb
9 ft²	= 1 yd²	2000 lb	= 1 short ton
1728 in³	= 1 ft³		1 ft³ of water weighs 62.4 lb

TABLE 2. — METRIC-ENGLISH EQUIVALENTS

1 in	=	2.5400 cm	1 cm²	=	0.1550 in²
1 ft	=	30.480 cm	1 in³	=	16.3872 cm³
1 yd	=	91.440 cm	1 cm³	=	0.0610 in³
1 mi	=	1609.4 m	1 grain	=	0.06480 g
1 mi	=	1.6094 km	1 oz	=	28.3495 g
1 mm	=	0.03937 in	1 lb	=	453.592 g
1 cm	=	0.3937 in	1 lb	=	0.4536 kg
1 m	=	39.37 in	1 g	=	15.4324 grains
1 m	=	3.2808 ft	1 g	=	0.03527 oz
1 m	=	1.0936 yd	1 g	=	0.002205 lb
1 in²	=	6.4516 cm²	1 kg	=	2.2046 lb

TABLE 3. — SPECIFIC GRAVITY OF SOLIDS

Aluminum	2.7	Iron, steel	7.6–7.8
Bakelite	1.25–2.09	Iron, wrought	7.8–7.9
Brass	8.2–8.7	Lead	11.34
Brick	1.4–2.2	Limestone	2.7
Bronze	8.8	Lucite	1.16–1.20
Butter	0.87	Magnesium	1.74
Carbon	1.9–3.5	Maple	0.51–0.75
Chestnut	0.45	Marble	2.6–2.8
Coal, anthracite	1.4–1.8	Nylon	1.09–1.14
Coal, bituminous	1.2–1.5	Oak	0.60–0.98
Copper	8.9	Paraffin	0.87–0.91
Cork	0.24	Pine	0.37–0.64
Diamond	3.53	Platinum	21.37
Glass, crown	2.5	Porcelain	2.38
Glass, flint	2.9–5.9	Silver	10.5
Gold	19.3	Silver, sterling	10.38
Gold, 18k	14.88	Sulfur	2.0
Granite	2.65	Tin	7.3
Graphite	2.25	Tungsten	19.3
Human body	1.07	Velon	1.68–1.75
Ice	0.917	Vinylite	1.2–1.7
Iron, cast	7.1–7.7	Zinc	7.1

TABLE 4. — SPECIFIC GRAVITY OF LIQUIDS

(Room Temperature)

Alcohol, ethyl	0.789	Mercury	13.56
Alcohol, methyl	0.793	Milk	1.029
Carbon disulfide	1.29	Nitric acid, 68%	1.42
Carbon tetrachloride	1.60	Oil, castor	0.969
Chloroform	1.50	Oil, cottonseed	0.926
Ether	0.74	Oil, linseed	0.942
Gasoline	0.66–0.69	Oil, olive	0.918
Glycerin	1.26	Sulfuric acid	1.84
Hydrochloric acid	1.20	Turpentine	0.87
Kerosene	0.82	Water, sea	1.025

TABLE 5. — SPECIFIC GRAVITY OF GASES

(Air Standard, at 0° C and 760 mm of mercury)

Acetylene	0.907	Helium	0.138
Air	1.000	Hydrogen	0.0695
Ammonia	0.596	Hydrogen chloride	1.268
Argon	1.380	Methane	0.554
Carbon dioxide	1.529	Neon	0.696
Carbon monoxide	0.967	Nitrogen	0.967
Chlorine	2.486	Oxygen	1.105
Ethane	1.049	Sulfur dioxide	2.264

TABLE 6. — TENSILE STRENGTH OF METALS

MATERIAL	TENSILE STRENGTH IN POUNDS PER SQUARE INCH
Aluminum wire	30,000–40,000
Brass wire	50,000–150,000
Bronze wire, phosphor, hard drawn	110,000–140,000
Copper wire, hard drawn	60,000–70,000
Iron wire, annealed	50,000–60,000
Iron wire, hard drawn	80,000–120,000
Lead, cast or drawn	2600–3300
Magnesium, hard drawn	33,000
Platinum wire	50,000
Silver wire	42,000
Steel	40,000–330,000
Steel wire, maximum	460,000
Steel, piano wire, 0.033 inch, diameter	357,000–390,000
Tungsten, hard drawn	590,000

TABLE 7. — COEFFICIENT OF LINEAR EXPANSION

(Increase in Unit Length per Centigrade Degree)

Aluminum 0.000023	Invar 0.0000009	Quartz 0.0000005
Brass 0.000019	Iron 0.000011	Silver 0.000019
Copper............ 0.000017	Lead 0.000029	Steel........... 0 000013
Glass 0.000009	Platinum 0.000009	Tin 0.000027
Gold............. 0.000014	Pyrex 0.000004	Zinc 0.000026

TABLE 8. — COEFFICIENT OF VOLUME EXPANSION

(Increase in Unit Volume per Centigrade Degree)

Acetone............ 0.00149	Ether 0.00166
Alcohol, ethyl 0.00112	Glycerin 0.00051
Benzene............ 0.00124	Mercury 0.00018
Carbon disulfide 0.00122	Petroleum 0.00096
Carbon tetrachloride.. 0.00124	Turpentine 0.00097
Chloroform 0.00127	Water............... 0.00021

TABLE 9. — DENSITY OF WATER AT VARYING TEMPERATURES

°C	g/cm³	°C	g/cm³	°C	g/cm³
0	0.99987	15	0.99913	60	0.98324
1	0.99993	20	0.99823	65	0.98059
2	0.99997	25	0.99707	70	0.97781
3	0.99999	30	0.99567	75	0.97489
4	1.00000	35	0.99406	80	0.97183
5	0.99999	40	0.99224	85	0.96865
6	0.99997	45	0.99025	90	0.96534
8	0.99988	50	0.98807	95	0.96192
10	0.99973	55	0.98573	100	0.95838

TABLE 10. — HEAT CONSTANTS

MATERIAL	SPECIFIC HEAT	MELTING POINT	BOILING POINT	HEAT OF FUSION	HEAT OF VAPORIZATION
Alcohol, ethyl	0.581	−115° C	78.5° C	24.9	204
Aluminum...	0.214	659.7	2450	76.8	
Ammonia ...	1.125 (liq.)	−77.7	−33.35	83.9	327.1
Brass	0.09	940			
Copper......	0.0921	1083	2336	42	
Glass	0.1988				
Ice	0.5	0		79.71	
Iron	0.107	1535	3000	7.89	
Lead........	0.0306	327.4	1620	5.86	
Mercury.....	0.0333	−38.87	356.58	2.82	70.6
Platinum	0.0324	1773.5	4300	27.2	
Silver	0.0558	960.8	1950	21.07	
Steam.......	0.48				
Tungsten	0.0336	3370	5900		
Water.......	1.00		100		539.55
Zinc	0.0925	419.47	907	28.13	

TABLE 11. — VAPOR PRESSURE OF WATER

TEMP. ° C	PRESSURE mm of Hg	TEMP. ° C	PRESSURE mm of Hg	TEMP. ° C	PRESSURE mm of Hg
0	4.6	25	23.8	90	525.8
5	6.5	26	25.2	95	633.9
10	9.2	27	26.7	96	657.6
15	12.8	28	28.3	97	682.1
16	13.6	29	30.0	98	707.3
17	14.5	30	31.8	99	733.2
18	15.5	35	42.2	100	760.0
19	16.5	40	55.3	101	787.5
20	17.5	50	92.5	103	845.1
21	18.7	60	149.4	105	906.1
22	19.8	70	233.7	110	1074.6
23	21.1	80	355.1	120	1489.1
24	22.4	85	433.6	150	3570.5

TABLE 12. — WATER VAPOR CAPACITY OF AIR

Temp. °F	Grains per Cubic Foot	Temp. °F	Grains per Cubic Foot	Temp. °F	Grains per Cubic Foot	Temp. °F	Grains per Cubic Foot
0	0.479	40	2.863	66	7.082	86	13.272
5	0.613	45	3.436	68	7.560	88	14.090
10	0.780	50	4.108	70	8.066	90	14.951
15	0.988	52	4.407	72	8.600	92	15.858
20	1.244	54	4.725	74	9.165	94	16.810
25	1.558	56	5.062	76	9.761	96	17.812
30	1.942	58	5.420	78	10.392	98	18.863
32	2.118	60	5.800	80	11.056	100	19.966
35	2.375	62	6.203	82	11.756	102	21.123
38	2.658	64	6.630	84	12.494	104	22.337

TABLE 13. — RELATIVE HUMIDITY

Dry Thermometer °F	Difference between Dry-bulb and Wet-bulb Thermometers														
	1°	2°	3°	4°	5°	6°	7°	8°	9°	10°	11°	12°	13°	14°	15°
50	93	87	81	74	68	62	56	50	44	39	33	28	22	17	12
52	94	88	81	75	69	63	58	52	46	41	36	30	25	20	15
54	94	88	82	76	70	65	59	54	48	43	38	33	28	23	18
56	94	88	82	77	71	66	61	55	50	45	40	35	31	26	21
58	94	89	83	77	72	67	62	57	52	47	42	38	33	28	24
60	94	89	84	78	73	68	63	58	53	49	44	40	35	31	27
62	94	89	84	79	74	69	64	60	55	50	46	41	37	33	29
64	95	90	85	79	75	70	66	61	56	52	48	43	39	35	31
66	95	90	85	80	76	71	66	62	58	53	49	45	41	37	33
68	95	90	85	81	76	72	67	63	59	55	51	47	43	39	35
70	95	90	86	81	77	72	68	64	60	56	52	48	44	40	37
72	95	91	86	82	78	73	69	65	61	57	53	49	46	42	39
74	95	91	86	82	78	74	70	66	62	58	54	51	47	44	40
76	96	91	87	83	78	74	70	67	63	59	55	52	48	45	42
78	96	91	87	83	79	75	71	67	64	60	57	53	50	46	43
80	96	91	87	83	79	76	72	68	64	61	57	54	51	47	44
84	96	92	88	84	80	77	73	70	66	63	59	56	53	50	47
88	96	92	88	85	81	78	74	71	67	64	61	58	55	52	49
90	96	92	89	85	82	78	75	72	68	64	62	58	56	53	50

TABLE 14. — RELATIVE CONDUCTIVITY OF HEAT

(Based on Silver = 100)

Air................ 0.0057	German silver........ 7	Platinum.......... 17
Aluminum.......... 48	Glass........... 0.10–0.25	Sand, white......... 0.09
Asbestos........... 0.04	Gold.............. 70	Sawdust............ 0.012
Brass............. 26	Iron.............. 16	Silk............... 0.0095
Brick, common....... 0.15	Lead.............. 8	Silver............ 100
Concrete........... 0.22	Linen.............. 0.021	Steel............. 11
Copper........... 92	Magnesia............ 0.016	Water............. 0.14
Cork.............. 0.01	Mercury............ 2	Wool............. 0.010
Felt.............. 0.0087	Paper.............. 0.03	Zinc.............. 27

TABLE 15. — VELOCITY OF SOUND IN VARIOUS MEDIA

(Approximate)

Material	Ft/sec	Material	Ft/sec
Air..................	1,087	Hydrogen	4,165
Alcohol..............	3,890	Iron	16,500
Aluminum	16,740	Maple, along grain	13,470
Brass	11,480	Pine, along grain	10,900
Copper	11,670	Steel.................	16,500
Glass	16,500	Water	4,794

TABLE 16. — INDEX OF REFRACTION

($\lambda = 590$ mμ; Temperature, 20° C except as noted)

Air, dry, 0° C. 1.00029	Carbon tetrachloride.... 1.46	Glass, flint............ 1.61
Alcohol, ethyl....... 1.36	Diamond.............. 2.42	Quartz, fused.......... 1.46
Carbon disulfide 1.63	Glass, crown........... 1.52	Water................. 1.33

TABLE 17. — ELECTROCHEMICAL EQUIVALENTS

(Gram per coulomb)

Aluminum 0.0000932	Oxygen 0.0000829
Chlorine 0.0003674	Potassium 0.0004051
Copper 0.0003294	Silver 0.0011179
Hydrogen 0.0000104	Sodium 0.0002383
Magnesium 0.0001260	Zinc 0.0003388

TABLE 18. — NATURAL SINES AND TANGENTS

Angle	Sine	Tangent	Angle	Sine	Tangent	Angle	Sine	Tangent
0	0.000	0.000	31	0.515	0.601	62	0.883	1.881
1	0.017	0.017	32	0.530	0.625	63	0.891	1.963
2	0.035	0.035	33	0.545	0.649	64	0.899	2.050
3	0.052	0.052	34	0.559	0.675	65	0.906	2.145
4	0.070	0.070	35	0.574	0.700	66	0.914	2.246
5	0.087	0.087	36	0.588	0.727	67	0.921	2.356
6	0.105	0.105	37	0.602	0.754	68	0.927	2.475
7	0.122	0.123	38	0.616	0.781	69	0.934	2.605
8	0.139	0.141	39	0.629	0.810	70	0.940	2.747
9	0.156	0.158	40	0.643	0.839	71	0.946	2.904
10	0.174	0.176	41	0.656	0.869	72	0.951	3.078
11	0.191	0.194	42	0.669	0.900	73	0.956	3.271
12	0.208	0.213	43	0.682	0.933	74	0.961	3.487
13	0.225	0.231	44	0.695	0.966	75	0.966	3.732
14	0.242	0.249	45	0.707	1.000	76	0.970	4.011
15	0.259	0.268	46	0.719	1.036	77	0.974	4.331
16	0.276	0.287	47	0.731	1.072	78	0.978	4.705
17	0.292	0.306	48	0.743	1.111	79	0.982	5.145
18	0.309	0.325	49	0.755	1.150	80	0.985	5.671
19	0.326	0.344	50	0.766	1.192	81	0.988	6.314
20	0.342	0.364	51	0.777	1.235	82	0.990	7.115
21	0.358	0.384	52	0.788	1.280	83	0.993	8.144
22	0.375	0.404	53	0.799	1.327	84	0.995	9.514
23	0.391	0.424	54	0.809	1.376	85	0.996	11.43
24	0.407	0.445	55	0.819	1.428	86	0.998	14.30
25	0.423	0.466	56	0.829	1.483	87	0.999	19.08
26	0.438	0.488	57	0.839	1.540	88	0.999	28.64
27	0.454	0.510	58	0.848	1.600	89	1.000	57.29
28	0.469	0.532	59	0.857	1.664	90	1.000	Infinity
29	0.485	0.554	60	0.866	1.732			
30	0.500	0.577	61	0.875	1.804			

TABLE 19. — RESISTIVITY

(Ohms/mil-ft at 20° C)

Aluminum 17.01	Iron 60.2	Nichrome 602
Copper 10.37	Manganin 265	Platinum 60.2
German silver 198	Mercury 576	Silver 9.80

TABLE 20. — PROPERTIES OF COPPER WIRE

Gauge Number	Diameter, Mils	Ohms per 1000 Feet at 0° C	Ohms per 1000 Feet at 20° C	Feet per Ohm 20° C
0000	460.0	0.04516	0.04901	20,400
000	409.6	0.05695	0.06180	16,180
00	364.8	0.07181	0.07793	12,830
0	324.9	0.09055	0.09827	10,180
1	289.3	0.1142	0.1239	8,070
2	257.6	0.1440	0.1563	6,400
3	229.4	0.1816	0.1970	5,075
4	204.3	0.2289	0.2485	4,025
5	181.9	0.2887	0.3133	3,192
6	162.0	0.3640	0.3951	2,531
7	144.3	0.4590	0.4982	2,007
8	128.5	0.5788	0.6282	1,592
9	114.4	0.7299	0.7921	1,262
10	101.9	0.9203	0.9989	1,001
11	90.74	1.161	1.260	794.0
12	80.81	1.463	1.588	629.6
13	71.96	1.845	2.003	499.3
14	64.08	2.327	2.525	396.0
15	57.07	2.934	3.184	314.0
16	50.82	3.700	4.016	249.0
17	45.26	4.666	5.064	197.5
18	40.30	5.883	6.385	156.6
19	35.89	7.418	8.051	124.2
20	31.96	9.355	10.15	98.5
21	28.45	11.80	12.80	78.11
22	25.35	14.87	16.14	61.95
23	22.57	18.76	20.36	49.13
24	20.10	23.65	25.67	38.96
25	17.90	29.82	32.37	30.90
26	15.94	37.61	40.81	24.50
27	14.20	47.42	51.47	19.43
28	12.64	59.80	64.90	15.41
29	11.26	75.40	81.83	12.22
30	10.03	95.08	103.2	9.691
31	8.928	119.9	130.1	7.685
32	7.950	151.2	164.1	6.095
33	7.080	190.6	206.9	4.833
34	6.305	240.4	260.9	3.833
35	5.615	303.1	329.0	3.040
36	5.000	382.2	414.8	2.411
37	4.453	482.0	523.1	1.912
38	3.965	607.8	659.6	1.516
39	3.531	766.4	831.8	1.202
40	3.145	966.5	1049	0.9534

Acknowledgments...

Felix Cooper, Frank Decker, Christie McFall, and Thomas Morgan prepared the line drawings. John Marshall drew the cover illustration and the title page. The design for the entire book was done by Jack Donnelly, Jr.

Aeolian-Skinner Organ Co., Fig. 18-14

Airguide Instr. Co., Fig. 14-28

Allis-Chalmers Mfg. Co., Fig. 7-30

Aluminum Cooking Utensils Co., Fig. 14-14

American Iron & Steel Inst., Figs. 6-12, 6-13, 6-19, 14-10, 27-9

American Optical Co., Fig. 21-6

American Standard, Fig. 15-17

American Telephone & Telegraph Co., Figs. 27-18, 27-19, 27-23; Preview Unit 9

Anaconda Copper Mining Co., Fig. 29-8

Armstrong-Roberts, H., Fig. 9-1

Atlantic Aviation Co., Fig. 9-10 (redrawn with permission)

Avco Mfg. Corp., Fig. 34-18

Bausch & Lomb Optical Co., Figs. 23-7, 23-8, 23-12, 23-13, 23-20, 23-29

Bell & Howell Co., Figs. 23-22, 23-23

Bell Telephone Labs., Fig. 6-27

Bettman Archive, Figs. 3-28, 4-10, 8-8, 8-15, 27-1, 27-13

Blanchard Co., Wm. L., Preview Unit 5

Borg-Warner Corp., Fig. 11-39

Brookhaven National Lab., Fig. 35-13

Bucyrus-Erie Co., Preview Unit 6

Central Scientific Co., Figs. 4-11, 8-34

Chicago Apparatus Co., Fig. 28-8

Chrysler Corp., Fig. 16-13

Consumers Ice Co., Fig. 14-25

Culver Service, Figs. 4-2, 24-17, 25-3, 30-9, 31-6, 35-4

DeLaval Separator Co., Fig. 8-31

Douglas Aircraft Co., Fig. 9-6

DuMont Labs., Fig. 33-30

du Pont de Nemours Co., E. I., Figs. 1-5, 14-5, 21-14

Dutton Co., E. P., Fig. 4-1

Edison Inc., Thomas A., Figs. 18-18, 29-23

Electra Protection Co., Fig. 24-18

Electric Auto-Lite Co., Fig. 20-24

Eriez Mfg. Co., Fig. 26-6

Fairbanks-Morse Co., Fig. 16-14

Fasco Industries Inc., Fig. 15-14

Ford Motor Co., Figs. 3-25, 11-49, 33-44

Gendreau, Philip, Figs. 3-16, 10-6, 13-4, 18-12; Preview Unit 1, Preview Unit 10

General Electric Co., Figs. 8-32, 11-1, 15-10, 16-9, 19-11, 19-13, 26-5, 28-9, 30-6, 31-23, 31-28, 33-2, 33-36, 33-43, 33-45, 34-14; Preview Unit 8

General Foods Corp., Fig. 5-13

General Motors Corp., Figs. 5-18, 11-38, 11-41, 29-21, 29-22; Preview Unit 7

Greyhound Bus Lines, Fig. 5-19 (redrawn with permission)

Gulf Oil Corp., Fig. 30-14

Hevi Duty Electric Co., Fig. 30-14

Hunter Fan & Ventilation Co., Fig. 5-14

Ingersoll-Rand Co., Figs. 5-16, 5-17

International Harvester Co., Fig. 15-21

International News Photos, Fig. 6-17

Jersey Central Lines, Fig. 8-19

Johns-Manville Corp., Fig. 15-24

Libby-Owens-Ford Glass Co., Figs. 15-13, 15-25, 20-7

Lineback, Hugh, Figs. 18-9, 18-10

Martin Co., Glenn L., Preview Unit 4

Minneapolis-Honeywell Regulator, Fig. 13-11

Mt. Wilson Observatory, Fig. 19-8

National Bureau of Standards, Fig. 2-1

National Rifle Assoc., Fig. 8-13

Niagara Alkali Co., Fig. 29-7

N.J. Turnpike Auth., Fig. 24-28

Norfolk & Western Ry., Figs. 7-32, 16-5

Pennsylvania R.R., Fig. 11-17

Pennsylvania Turnpike Commission, Fig. 8-29

Pepsi-Cola Bottling Co., Fig. 6-29

Philharmonic Symphony Society of N.Y., Fig. 18-11

Pittsburgh Corning Corp., Fig. 20-4

Pratt & Whitney Aircraft Co., Fig. 15-4

Radio Condenser Co., Fig. 24-23

Randolph Labs., Fig. 8-33

R. C. A., Figs. 5-12, 18-16, 18-17, 34-16

Roberson Co., L. N., Fig. 15-19

San Francisco Chamber of Commerce, Fig. 6-10

Schwerdt, Dr. C. E., & Williams, Dr. R. C., Fig. 1-2

Science Service Inc., Fig. 35-7

Servel Inc., Fig. 14-27 (redrawn with permission)

Simplex Ceiling Corp., Fig. 17-10

Sinclair Refining Co., Figs. 3-39, 14-17

Smith Co., A. O., Fig. 15-22

Sperry Gyroscope Co., Fig. 33-49

Stansi Scientific Co., Fig. 24-25

Steelways Magazine, Figs. 16-10, 23-18

Studebaker-Packard Corp., Fig. 11-37

Supplex Corp., Fig. 3-20

Taylor Instr. Co., Figs. 4-14, 4-17, 12-11, 12-12, 12-13, 26-4

Texas Gulf Sulphur Co., Fig. 13-3

The Texas Co., Figs. 14-8, 17-9

Timken Roller Bearing Co., Fig. 7-33

Trane Co., Fig. 17-11

Triboro Bridge & Tunnel Auth., Fig. 5-25

Union Carbide & Carbon Corp., Figs. 13-7, 30-13

United Press, Preview Unit 2

United States
Air Force, Fig. 16-18
Army, Fig. 14-29
Bureau of Reclamation, Fig. 3-19
Coast & Geodetic Survey, Fig. 26-19
Coast Guard, Fig. 3-32
Navy, Figs. 1-1, 4-3, 5-33, 8-24

Weather Bureau, Fig. 4-20

U.S. Lines, Fig. 3-34

U.S. Steel Corp., Fig. 12-10; Preview Unit 3

Univ. of Calif. Radiation Lab., Preview Unit 11

Warner Bros. Pictures, Figs. 23-26, 23-27

Welch Mfg. Co., Figs. 5-6, 18-19, 24-4

Westinghouse Electric Corp., Figs. 11-32, 15-20, 24-16, 24-27, 30-2, 30-3, 30-4, 30-10, 31-14, 33-32, 33-33, 33-38, 35-11, 35-17

Weston Elec. Instr. Co., Fig. 19-14

Wide World Photos, Figs. 1-6, 3-17, 5-23

Index...

Page references for definitions or meanings of words and terms are cited first and in **boldface type.** *Italics* indicate an illustration. In many cases the topic, too, is to be found within the text on that page.

Kilogram, standard, 11, 137; unit of mass, 179
Kilogram-weight, 15
Kilowatt, 211
Kilowatt-hour, 535, 536–537
Kinetic energy, 208; measurement of, 213–214
Kinetic theory, 109; of gases, 109 110; of liquids and solids, 110–111

Lactometer, 55
Lamps, arc, 571–572; fluorescent, 402, 607–608; incandescent, 402, 569–571; infrared, 571; neon, 605, 607; photoflash, 571; photoflood, 570, 571; sun, 608
Land breezes, cause of, 322
Latent heat, 292
Lawrence, E. O., 655
Laws, Boyle's, 81, 82–83; Charles', 276–278; conservation of energy, 7; conservation of matter, 7; of cooling, 233; of electrolysis, 548–549; Henry's, 130; Joule's, 566; Lenz's, 579; of motion, 176–187; Newton's, 323; Ohm's, 492–493, 598; Pascal's, 39–42; of reflection of light, 408–409; of refraction, 427; of resistance, 493–494; Stefan's, 325–326; of strings, 382–384; of universal gravitation, 188
Lead, elastic modulus of, 121
Left-hand rule, 523, 525; and induced currents, 579
Length, units of, 13–14
Lenses, 423; achromatic, 447; anastigmat, 458–459; of cameras, 434, 435–436; center of curvature of, 432; converging, 431; convex, 433–435; determination of focal length of, 433; differ from mirrors, 433; diverging, 431; of eye, 452; focal length of, 436; in glasses, 455; images formed by, 432–435, 436; meniscus, 431, 456; optical center of, 432; plano-convex, 495; principal axis of, 432; rectilinear, 459; refraction of light by, 431–436; spherical aberration in, 435–436; of telescope, 434; uses of, 433–435
Lenz's law, 579
Lever, 223–228; classes of, 224–226; fulcrum of, 223; a simple machine, 221; mechanical advantage of, 223–224
Leyden jar, a capacitor, 483
Lift, 199
Lift pump, 98, 99
Light, 394, 396–470; absorption of, 397; amount needed, 403; atmospheric refraction of, 428–429; color of, 440–441; diffused reflection, 409; dispersion by prism, 439, 440; intensity of, 401–402, 404–405; measurement of, 401–402; monochromatic, 439; multiple reflection of, 413–414; nature of, 394–395; polarized, 448–

449, 468; polychromatic, 439; reflection of, 397, 408–422; refraction of, 423–437; sources of, 396; speed of, 399–400, 425; transmission of, 397; wave theory of, 447–448
Light bulbs, frosted, 410
Light meter, 405
Light rays, focus of, 414–415; critical angle of, 429–430; infrared, 440; path through glass, 427–428; ultraviolet, 440
Light valve, 465
Light waves, 324; differ from sound waves, 395–396; diffraction of, 448; interference of, 447–448
Lighting effects, of electricity, 565–573
Lightning, artificial, 480; cause of, 480–481
Lightning rods, 481
Limiter, of FM receivers, 638
Line spectrum, 439, 445
Liquefaction, of gases, 306–307
Liquid air, manufacture of, 306
Liquid films, elasticity of, 124
Liquid quart, 14, 16
Liquid surfaces, shape of, 124–125
Liquids, 10; buoyant force of, 43; capillarity of, 125–127; compressibility of, 36; density of, 24–25; diffusion of, 114–115; evaporation of, 114; expansion of, 273–275; heat conduction in, 318–319; kinetic theory of, 110–111; mechanics of, 22–58; molecular forces in, 122–123; pressure of, 22–58; properties of, 11; shape of free, 125; specific gravity of, 52–54; surface tension of, 123–124; total force of, 27–30; transmit pressure, 36–43; transmit sounds, 357
Liter, 14
Locomotive, 341
Lodestones, 508
Longitudinal wave, 355, 360
Loudness, 355, 365
Loudspeakers, 640; electrodynamic, 636; types of, 635
Lubricants, reduce friction, 160
Lucite, total reflection of, 430, 431
Lumen, 394, 401–402
Luminous objects, 394, 396

Machines, 220–250; compound, 238–250; efficiency, 222–223, 236; general principles, 220–223; input and output of, 222; mechanical advantage of, 221–222; simple, 221–237; uses of, 220–221
Magdeburg hemispheres, 68
Magnetic compass, uses of, 509
Magnetic declination, 507, 518; map of, 519
Magnetic dip, 518
Magnetic effects, of electricity, 522–533
Magnetic equator, 518